TH   LYNCH

MW00563646

MEDICAL MICROBIOLOGY

MEDICAL MICROBIOLOGY

Edited by

Felix Milgrom, M.D.

Distinguished Professor of Microbiology and Chairman
Department of Microbiology
Schools of Medicine and Dentistry
State University of New York at Buffalo

and

Thomas D. Flanagan, Ph.D.

Professor of Microbiology
Schools of Medicine and Dentistry
State University of New York at Buffalo

With 27 Contributors

CHURCHILL LIVINGSTONE
NEW YORK, EDINBURGH, LONDON, AND MELBOURNE   1982

© **Churchill Livingstone Inc. 1982**

All rights reserved. No part of this publication may be
reproduced, stored in a retrieval system, or transmitted in
any form or by any means, electronic, mechanical,
photocopying, recording or otherwise, without prior permission
of the publishers (Churchill Livingstone Inc., 1560 Broadway,
New York, N.Y. 10036).

Distributed in the United Kingdom by Churchill Livingstone,
Robert Stevenson House, 1–3 Baxter's Place, Leith Walk,
Edinburgh EH1 3AF and associated companies, branches
and representatives throughout the world.

First published 1982

Printed in U.S.A.

ISBN 0-443-08066-6

9 8 7 6 5 4 3 2 1

Library of Congress Cataloging in Publication Data
Main entry under title:
Medical microbiology.
   Bibliography: p.
   Includes index.
   1. Medical microbiology. I. Milgrom,
Felix. II. Flanagan, Thomas D. [DNLM:
1. Microbiology QW 4 M4861]
QR46.M468   616′.01   82–1261
ISBN 0-443-08066-6   AACR2

Manufactured in the United States of America

CONTRIBUTORS

C. John Abeyounis, Ph.D.   Professor of Microbiology, Schools of Medicine and Dentistry, State University of New York at Buffalo

Boris Albini, M.D.   Associate Professor of Microbiology, Schools of Medicine and Dentistry, State University of New York at Buffalo

Daniel Amsterdam, Ph.D.   Professor of Microbiology, Schools of Medicine and Dentistry, and Associate Professor of Medicine, School of Medicine, State University of New York at Buffalo; Director, Division of Clinical Microbiology and Immunology, Erie County Laboratory, Buffalo

Giuseppe A. Andres, M.D.   Professor of Microbiology and Pathology, Schools of Medicine and Dentistry, and Professor of Medicine, School of Medicine, State University of New York at Buffalo; Director, Renal Immunopathology Laboratory, The Buffalo General Hospital; Consultant in Clinical Immunology, Children's Hospital, Buffalo

Ernst H. Beutner, Ph.D.   Professor of Microbiology, Schools of Medicine and Dentistry, and Research Professor of Dermatology, School of Medicine, State University of New York at Buffalo

Arlene R. Collins, Ph.D.   Associate Professor of Microbiology, Schools of Medicine and Dentistry, State University of New York at Buffalo

Roger K. Cunningham, Ph.D.   Associate Professor of Microbiology, Schools of Medicine and Dentistry, and Associate Director, The Ernest Witebsky Center for Immunology, State University of New York at Buffalo

Thomas D. Flanagan, Ph.D.   Professor of Microbiology, Schools of Medicine and Dentistry, State University of New York at Buffalo

Eugene A. Gorzynski, Ph.D.   Professor of Microbiology, Schools of Medicine and Dentistry, State University of New York at Buffalo; Chief, Microbiology Section, Veterans Administration Medical Center, Buffalo

Diane M. Jacobs, Ph.D.   Professor of Microbiology, Schools of Medicine and Dentistry, State University of New York at Buffalo

Kyoichi Kano, M.D. Professor of Microbiology, Schools of Medicine and Dentistry, State University of New York at Buffalo; Consultant in Clinical Immunology, Erie County Medical Center, Buffalo

Joseph H. Kite, Jr., Ph.D. Professor of Microbiology, Schools of Medicine and Dentistry, State University of New York at Buffalo

Reginald M. Lambert, Ph.D. Professor of Microbiology, Schools of Medicine and Dentistry, State University of New York at Buffalo; Director, American Red Cross Blood Services, Buffalo Region

Kenneth F. Manly, Ph.D. Associate Research Professor of Microbiology, Roswell Park Graduate Division, State University of New York at Buffalo; Cancer Research Scientist V, Roswell Park Memorial Institute, Buffalo

Joseph M. Merrick, Ph.D. Professor of Microbiology, Schools of Medicine and Dentistry, State University of New York at Buffalo

Felix Milgrom, M.D. Distinguished Professor of Microbiology and Chairman, Department of Microbiology, Schools of Medicine and Dentistry, State University of New York at Buffalo

Richard L. Miner, M.D. Clinical Associate Professor of Medicine, School of Medicine, State University of New York at Buffalo

James F. Mohn, M.D. Professor of Microbiology, Schools of Medicine and Dentistry, and Director, The Ernest Witebsky Center for Immunology, State University of New York at Buffalo; Immunohematologist and Director, Blood Bank, The Buffalo General Hospital

David T. Mount, M.S. Clinical Assistant Professor of Microbiology, Schools of Medicine and Dentistry, State University of New York at Buffalo

Robert A. Nelson, Jr., M.D. Research Professor of Microbiology, Schools of Medicine and Dentistry, State University of New York at Buffalo; Scientific Director of Research and Development, ImmunoGenetics, Inc., North Berwick, New Hampshire

Erwin Neter, M.D. Professor Emeritus of Microbiology, Schools of Medicine and Dentistry, and Professor Emeritus of Pediatrics, School of Medicine, State University of New York at Buffalo; Former Director, Bacteriology and Serology, Children's Hospital, Buffalo; Consultant to Clinical Staff, Roswell Park Memorial Institute, Buffalo

Russell J. Nisengard, D.D.S., Ph.D.   Professor of Periodontics and Endodontics, School of Dentistry, and Professor of Microbiology, Schools of Medicine and Dentistry, State University of New York at Buffalo

Bernice K. Noble, Ph.D.   Assistant Professor of Microbiology, Schools of Medicine and Dentistry, State University of New York at Buffalo

Cornelius J. O'Connell, M.D.   Clinical Associate Professor of Medicine, School of Medicine, and Clinical Associate Professor of Microbiology, Schools of Medicine and Dentistry, State University of New York at Buffalo; Consulting Physician, The Buffalo General Hospital, St. Joseph's Intercommunity Hospital, and Roswell Park Memorial Institute, Buffalo; Attending Physician, Sisters of Charity Hospital and Erie County Medical Center, Buffalo

Carel J. van Oss, Ph.D.   Professor of Microbiology, Schools of Medicine and Dentistry, and Adjunct Professor of Chemical Engineering, Faculty of Engineering and Applied Sciences, State University of New York at Buffalo

Murray W. Stinson, Ph.D.   Associate Professor of Microbiology, Schools of Medicine and Dentistry, State University of New York at Buffalo

Harshad R. Thacore, Ph.D.   Associate Professor of Microbiology, Schools of Medicine and Dentistry, State University of New York at Buffalo

Konrad Wicher, D.M.Sc.   Professor of Microbiology, Schools of Medicine and Dentistry, State University of New York at Buffalo; Director, Clinical Microbiology and Immunology Laboratories, Division of Laboratory and Research, New York State Department of Health, Albany

Marek Zaleski, M.D., Ph.D.   Professor of Microbiology, Schools of Medicine and Dentistry, State University of New York at Buffalo

PREFACE

This book has been written for the use of medical students and medical practitioners. It may also be of interest to students and professionals in other health-related fields. It provides basic information about microbiology as it pertains to the practice of medicine. Therefore the emphasis has been placed on pathogenic microorganisms. All major pathogens are discussed from the point of view of their disease-producing mechanisms. Specific treatment and prevention of infectious diseases are also discussed at some length. The last chapter is meant as a recapitulation of the most important microbiological procedures as they are used and requested by the physician. Pathological and clinical aspects of diseases are not treated in any detail, since a textbook of microbiology should not intrude into the fields of pathology and infectious diseases.

The text could not remain indifferent to the unprecedented progress that microbiology has experienced in the last quarter of a century. Significantly, a great part of the progress in molecular biology has been made in studies of microbial physiology and genetics. These areas of general microbiology are discussed in this textbook; however, they are not given all the attention that they deserve, and the information provided is limited to that most useful for students of medicine.

The field of immunology, which originally emerged from medical microbiology, has become a part of practically each branch of medicine and biology. Here again, our purpose was to present briefly the vistas of immunology and to concentrate on those aspects of this science that have immediate bearing on recovery from and resistance to infectious diseases.

For many years the authors of this book have taught medical microbiology as a team. They are aware of the fact that with dozens of excellent textbooks of microbiology available on the market, it takes courage to produce one more. They believe, however, that through many years of teaching experience they have developed the skills of communicating with students of medicine and other health-related professions. They also trust that they have learned to select the microbiological material that is essential for students.

F.M.
T.D.F.
State University of New York at Buffalo

CONTENTS

Contents xiii

xiv Contents

The History of Microbiology

James F. Mohn

The farther backward you can look, the farther forward you are likely to see. (Sir Winston Churchill)

In the study of any branch of science, an acquaintance with the historical development of knowledge is an important element in a clear understanding of our present conceptions. To the student of bacteriology such a basis is essential. (Sir Graham S. Wilson and Sir Ashley A. Miles, Topley and Wilson's Principles of Bacteriology and Immunity)

The history of many concepts, such as the origin of life, putrefaction of dead organic materials, and the nature of communicable changes in the bodies of living men and animals, is incorporated in bacteriologic doctrines. At the time of Moses, the Jews believed that leprosy was contagious and could be spread through contact with the patient or his clothes or by living in the house of a former leper. These beliefs led to the Mosaic regulations that are set forth in the Old Testament (Leviticus 13 and 14).

Hippocrates (ca. 460 to 377 B.C.), a Greek physician now known as the Father of Medicine, elaborated a theory of disease that had two components: an intrinsic fac-

tor, a pathologic "constitution" of the individual, and an extrinsic factor, air infected with "miasms." He considered miasms to be a modification of air itself to such a degree that it became deleterious. This did not involve any idea of independent, active agents nor did he consider the possibility of contagion. His doctrine of miasms grew and thrived during the Middle Ages and has survived in modern times in certain medical terms, such as malaria (Italian, *mala aria* — bad air) and influenza (Latin, *influere* — to flow in).

Girolamo Fracastoro (ca. 1478 to 1553, Italy), commonly known by the latinized form of his name, Hieronymus Fracastorius, was a scholar, poet, and thinker, who was born in Verona and attended the University of Padua like other Veronese youths. His famous poem, *Syphilis sive morbus Gallicus* (Syphilis or the French Disease), written in Latin as was the custom of the times, was published in Verona in 1530. The disease is named after the youth Syphilis, the main character in his poem.

In 1546 he published a book in Venice on contagion and contagious diseases that is his chief work, entitled *De Sympathia et*

1

Antipathia Rerum. De Contagione (Liber Primus), De Contagiosis Morbis (Liber Secundus), De Curatione (Liber Tertius). This is a rare, small quarto book written in Latin in a condensed style. His work on contagion is actually written in three books bound together. The first and most important contains his theory of contagion, in which he expounds on a concept of infectious, communicable diseases, each caused by a living agent, *contagium vivum*; this theory was influenced by his knowledge of the natural history of syphilis. He was the first to indicate that "infection itself is composed of minute and insensible particles and proceeds from them," and he described the transmission of disease by direct contact, by intermediary, inanimate fomites, and through the air (*ad distans*). He noted that "the infection is the same for him who has received or has given the infection; also we speak of infection when the same virus has touched one or the other." In essence this was a true germ theory of disease, but the essentially true statements were unconvincing because they were not based upon the demonstration of the existence of his hypothetical, invisible organisms. Further progress was dependent upon invention of the microscope and the resolution of the problem of spontaneous generation. An account of different contagious diseases is given in the second book, which clearly describes the history of many contagions and makes valuable observations. As examples, the following can be cited: variola (smallpox) and morbilli (measles) affect children by preference and everyone is attacked once, but "it is rare for people who have had these diseases to have them again"; in regard to phthisis (tuberculosis), he believed in the infectivity of consumption, thought the "virus" was very tenacious, persisting in clothing for as long as 2 years, and considered the "germs" infective only for the lungs; rabies he stated was propagated only by the bite of a rabid dog and had an incubation period of about 30 days;

his views of syphilis were lucid and accurate, and he gave the first description of gummata, a lesion of tertiary syphilis, his term being "gumositates." The third book deals with his recipes for the cure of various contagious diseases. This all resulted from his practical and broad study of epidemics of syphilis, plague, typhus, and foot-and-mouth disease occurring in northern Italy in his time coupled with deep contemplation and reasoning on what he had observed and how he could interpret it.

Antoni van Leeuwenhoek (1632 to 1723, Holland) has been called the Father of Bacteriology and Protozoology because of his discovery of bacteria and protozoa. He was born in the town of Delft, where he spent his entire life at various occupations beginning as a draper and haberdasher (ca. 1654) and later receiving a series of minor municipal appointments — Chamberlain of the Council-Chamber of the Worshipful Sheriffs of Delft, surveyor, because he was qualified in mathematics, especially geometry, and wine-gauger of Delft. Strangely and with no known explanation, he was an amateur micrographer without any scientific training. He spent his spare time making lenses and mounting them to form a microscope of simple pattern. Nevertheless, he acquired much skill in their manufacture; he taught himself how to grind, polish, and mount lenses of considerable magnifying power, although his method of grinding lenses is unknown. During his life, he made a total of about 550 of these instruments. At the time of his death he left 247 completely finished microscopes and another 172 mounted lenses. The microscopes consisted of a simple, single biconvex lens of short focal length clamped between two metal plates in a fixed position, with the object under examination being moved into focus by means of screws. Of the nine still in existence, the magnification of the best is only 200 times. He left no description of the apparatus used for making his observations on protozoa and bacteria and of his particular manner of observing very small creatures and kept for himself his best microscopes, which probably had a magnification power of 300. Thus, he never divulged what his method was for using his homemade microscope that enabled him to outstrip all other microscopists for at least a century. His micrometry was astonishingly good, although the method of obtaining the illumination he required is unknown. His biographer, Dobell, deduced from his letters that he probably discovered a simple method of dark-field illumination.

Although the only language he knew was Dutch, he reported all of his experimental observations to the Royal Society of London in the form of letters that were translated into English and published in Philosophical Transactions. The first of these arrived in April 1673, curiously enough the very month and year he was elected a Fellow of the Royal Society. He discovered protozoa in 1674 with his observations on free-living protozoa seen in freshwater (Letter 6, September 7, 1674); bacteria in 1676 — the first account ever written on them being his celebrated Letter 18 (October 9, 1676) — from his examinations of rainwater, wellwater, seawater, and melted snow and strange and exotic watery extracts of pepper, ginger, clove, and nutmeg; anaerobic bacteria in 1680 (Letter 32, June 14, 1680); intestinal protozoa and bacteria of man in 1681, reported in his letter of great historic interest and importance (Letter 34, November 4, 1681) as "living animalcules in excrements"; and bacteria of the human mouth in 1683 in a letter as famous as any ever written to the Royal Society (Letter 39, September 17, 1683). Among all his observations of bacteria, the most fundamental that is scientifically accurate and the basis of all bacteriologic morphology to this date was his discovery of the three basic forms of bacteria: coccus (pl. cocci) — sphere, like a tennis ball; bacillus (pl. bacilli) — rod, similar to a piece of chalk or a cigar; and spirillum (pl. spirilla) — spiral,

a rigid form analogous to a comma, the letter S, or a corkscrew.

In a report published in 1762, Marcus Antonius von Plenciz (1705 to 1786, Austria), connected the speculations of Fracastorius with the observations of van Leeuwenhoek. He presented an advanced view on the specificity of disease based on a belief in specific microbes as agents of infectious diseases. The first infectious disease shown to be caused by a specific microorganism was the disease of silkworms called *mal segno* in Italy and *muscardine* in France. In 1835 in a remarkable series of investigations, Agostino Bassi (1773 to 1856, Italy) proved that a fungus, now named in his honor as *Botrytis bassiana*, was the causative agent of this disease. From his study he prophesied that microscopic organisms would be found as the causes of human disease.

In theoretical discussions of miasmatic and contagious diseases, Jacob Henle (1809 to 1885, Germany) affirmed his belief in the animate nature and specific action of agents of contagion and made the same prediction as Bassi. The early investigators of his time obtained pure cultures of bacteria only by accident and never knew when contaminants were present. This led to much speculation and loose thinking resulting in considerable equivocal work that hindered the development of the discipline. Henle's logical and critical point of view was a firm corrective. In 1840 he published a statement of the conditions that would have to be satisfied to prove the causal relationship between a particular organism and disease, anticipating Koch's postulates by 36 years. They were (1) demonstration of the constant presence of morphologically identical microorganisms in typical lesions, (2) isolation of these microorganisms *in vitro* in pure culture, and (3) reproduction of the same disease in experimental animals by inoculation of the pure culture.

The real development of bacteriology as

a science was the direct outcome of the research of Louis Pasteur (1822 to 1895, France). His work overshadowed all of his predecessors, and it can be unequivocally stated that he not only founded bacteriology but revolutionized medicine as well. Trained as a chemist, he was led to the study of microscopic organisms by his earlier studies on stereoisomerism and by observations on the phenomena of fermentation. In 1857 and 1858 he reported the results of his investigation on the basis of the formation of amyl alcohol during the course of lactic fermentation. It was his conclusion that such substances were synthesized by living organisms that caused the fermentative process. At this time he also turned his attention to alcoholic fermentation. His classic memoir, published in 1860, staunchly upheld the theories of Caignard-Latour (1836, France) and Schwann (1837, Germany) on the living, plantlike nature of "yeast globules." His findings that yeast cells increased in amount when transferred from one sugar to another and had decided preferences as regards the acidity or alkalinity of the media in which they grew disproved the theories of Leibig, Berzelius, and Wöhler that yeast cells were dead. His research was the first foundation of our knowledge of the conditions to be fulfilled for the cultivation of bacteria. In these investigations that spanned some 20 years, he proved that the fermentations of various organic fluids were always accompanied by the presence of living cells. He further showed that organisms that had different morphologic and cultural characteristics occurred in different types of fermentations. Thus the concept of the specificity of microorganisms was originated.

In these and other studies of this period, Pasteur made major advances in the technology required to further the progress of the study of microorganisms, such as introducing the extraordinary sterilizing effect of superheated steam that led to the development of the autoclave, the practice of sterilizing glassware with dry heat at 170°C, the cotton plug, and specific media.

In 1861 he turned to the examination of butyric fermentation and made the important discovery that it proceeds in the absence of oxygen. He showed that this fermentation was caused by certain microorganisms that could live without oxygen; he proved this by inhibiting the fermentative process by passing a stream of oxygen through an active butyric-fermenting liquid. This led him to find other organisms that lived in the absence of air, and in 1863 he introduced the terms aerobes (*aérobies*) and anaerobes (*anaérobies*) to indicate those microorganisms that live with and without free oxgyen.

In 1862 Pasteur was called upon by the government to determine the cause of the widespread spoilage of wine that was almost paralyzing this important French industry. His investigations, published in 1866 as his famous *Études sur le Vin*, proved that the damaging effect on the palatability and actual potability of wine was caused by wild fermentation produced by contaminating bacteria, which altered the wine's chemical and physical properties. This led him to introduce in 1863 the process known today in his honor as pasteurization, whereby heat-labile products such as wine and milk are subjected to heat sufficient to kill certain types of microorganisms and to decrease the viable population of many other types but insufficient to damage the material. In a similar vein, in 1865 he began research culminating in 1870 with the institution of procedures that saved the silk industry from being destroyed by a parasitic infection of silkworms, a disease called *pébrine*. This led him to espouse the principle of controlling the spread of an infection by detecting and isolating the infected individuals.

Robert Koch (1843 to 1910, Germany), an investigator previously unknown among bacteriologists, made his first outstanding contribution to the rapidly developing field of microbiology at the time he was a country practitioner and district physician at Wollstein. Under primitive conditions in his own home, with a microscope given by his wife but with all his other apparatus entirely homemade, he undertook an investigation of anthrax, which he had had the opportunity to observe in animals in the course of his medical duties. He showed that the disease was transmissible from mouse to mouse over 20 generations and that the lesions in each animal of the series were identical; he cultured the anthrax bacilli in drops of sterile blood serum or aqueous humor in slide cultures on a primitive warm, microscopic stage. He described the appearance of oval granular bodies in the filaments that he recognized were spores, which had not been seen before; he determined accurately the optimal thermal conditions for spore formation; and he reproduced the disease in mice by injection of his cultures. From these observations Koch concluded that only one kind of bacillus could induce the specific morbid process of anthrax, clearly enunciating the doctrine of a specific agent for a specific disease. The enormously significant report of his findings was published in 1876, and at once he was recognized as a great investigator in the field of bacteriologic research. This study of anthrax clearly established the criteria that had to be met in determining that a given microorganism was the specific etiologic agent of a disease. Thus he confirmed the doctrine promulgated previously by Jacob Henle, one of his teachers at the University of Göttingen. The conditions that he emphatically stated must be met are usually referred to as Koch's postulates but more correctly should preferably be called Henle-Koch postulates.

One of the major hindrances impeding the progress of these early microbiologists was the almost total lack of pure cultures of any human disease-producing bacteria. The notion of the existence of bacterial species as proposed by several of Koch's distinguished predecessors had led to the idea that it might be possible to obtain pure cultures in vitro of a particular variety of microorganism. This was supported by Pasteur's observations on specific fermentations. When Koch began his experiments in this area, almost all bacteria were being cultured in liquids that usually allowed the free intermingling and growth of all the different kinds of bacteria present in the original inoculum. Several attempts were made by different researchers to obtain pure cultures from fluid growths by dilution. One of these researchers was Lord Lister (see below), who in 1878 had published the results of his dilution studies in which he employed a specially constructed syringe to deliver a precise volume of bacteria countable under the microscope. It became increasingly apparent, however, that solid media would be required to effect proper separation and isolation of bacteria from mixtures.

Koch first employed the cut surface of raw potato, a method that had been used to considerable advantage previously by Joseph Schroeter (1872) in his classic work on pigment-producing bacteria. In 1881 Koch reported on his improved technique that included soaking the raw potato in a solution of corrosive sublimate followed by sterilizing it in steam and finally splitting it into two parts with a sterile knife. The two halves were allowed to separate in a sterile, covered glass vessel, and the cut surfaces were then inoculated with starting material. This was not very satisfactory because most of the disease-producing bacteria simply would not grow on raw potato; Koch therefore abandoned this approach.

Koch had foreseen the fundamental importance of pure bacterial cultures very early, and thus, he concentrated all of his energies on developing a simple and consistently successful procedure. His goal was to obtain a good, supportive medium that was simultaneously sterile, transparent, and solid. He first solidified proven nutrient fluid media by the addition of 2.5 to 5 percent gelatin to a 1 percent meat extract broth, referring to this product as *nutrient gelatin*. He introduced inoculating the surface of this gelatin by means of a sterilized needle or platinum wire, drawing a minimum quantity of inoculum in several crosslines rapidly and lightly over its surface. When different colonies of bacteria did make their appearance, each was transferred to a test tube plugged with cotton that contained sterile nutrient gelatin set in a slanted position. In this way he was able to achieve isolation and pure cultures and solve a problem that 3 years before he thought to be incapable of solution. Bulloch states concerning this achievement, "By this means he opened the door for one of the greatest advances ever made in the history of medicine."

He soon learned, however, that nutrient gelatin had one distinct and insurmountable disadvantage. It melted at 37°C, the temperature felt to be optimal for the cultivation of most disease-producing bacteria.

In 1882 Frau Hesse, wife of an early co-worker of Koch, first suggested the use of agar-agar as a solidifying base for culture media. Through some Dutch friends she had obtained samples from Batavia, where this material was well known and widely used for cooking, especially as a substitute for gelatin in the making of jams, fruit preserves, and jelled desserts. Agar, as it is now called, is a mixture of polysaccharides extracted from agar-bearing marine algae. The principal algae from which it is obtained live in the seas of eastern Asia from Sri Lanka (Ceylon) to Japan. Its distinctive virtue that rapidly established its dominance in bacteriologic culture technique is its peculiar property of liquefying if brought to 100°C, but once melted it will resolidify as a relatively stiff, transparent solid mass when it is cooled to 40 to 42°C. Thus any medium in which it serves as a solidifying base will remain solid on 37°C incubation.

In 1882 Koch wrote his classic paper describing the etiologic agent of tuberculosis that he had discovered, and in 1883 he wrote of his identification of the causative agent of Asiatic cholera. Koch was awarded the Nobel prize in 1905.

Sir Joseph Lister (1827 to 1912, England), a famous surgeon and scientist, was an early student of bacteriology and, in 1878, was the first investigator to obtain a pure culture of a bacterium by his dilution technique. In 1865 Lord Lister had his attention drawn to an article concerning Pasteur's report that air was full of living microorganisms that were carried on particles of dust floating in the atmosphere. He immediately related this to the possibility of preventing wound suppuration by applying in the dressing some material capable of destroying the life on these airborne, floating particles. He introduced lint soaked in carbolic acid (phenol) as a dressing for compound fractures. His early clinical studies soon indicated that pure carbolic acid was injurious to tissues. Nevertheless, having proved that this method prevented infection and was beneficial for the treatment of already contaminated wounds, he carried this idea into the operating room by introducing 1:20 diluted carbolic acid for soaking all surgical instruments and 1:40 diluted carbolic acid as a skin preparation prior to any surgical incision. This system of antiseptic surgery was announced in 1868. He augmented it in 1870 by the addition of carbolic acid sprays in the operating theater. His antiseptic treatment revolutionized surgery, and this was acknowledged in 1897 when he was raised to the peerage as Baron Lister.

The greatest scientific worker in medicine of his era, Paul Ehrlich (1854 to 1915, Germany), the founder and leading exponent of the science of hematology, turned his attention to the new field of immunology, becoming principally responsible for the direction that it would take and still follows. With respect to microbiology, he created the field of chemotherapy. After his extensive midperiod studies on immunity, for which he received the Nobel prize in 1908, Ehrlich focused his research efforts on the treatment of syphilis. He developed the concept of a therapeutic key, a synthetically created chemical that would kill the microorganism but not harm the patient, thus fitting like a key in a lock. With his Japanese coworker Hata he investigated arsenical compounds as a fruitful source. They succeeded in achieving the goal according to the criteria he laid down when they came to arsphenamine (salvarsan) in 1910, the 606th arsenical compound they tested, which was thus known as "606" for a long time. This was the beginning of the era of modern chemotherapy of infectious diseases of man.

As the direct consummation of Ehrlich's concepts on the development of chemotherapeutic agents and employing methods directly founded on those of Ehrlich, Gerhard Domagk (1895 to 1964, Germany), Director of the Institute of Experimental Pathology of I.G. Farbenindustrie, published in 1935 the results of his discovery that the compound Prontosil when given orally prevented the development of otherwise fatal β-hemolytic streptococcal infections in mice, cured chronic streptococcal infections also in mice, and favorably influenced staphylococcal infections in rabbits. This water insoluble basic azo dye, chemically known as sulfamido-chrysoidine (4'-sulfonamido-2,4-diaminoazobenzene), had been synthesized in 1932 by two chemists, Mietzsch and Klarer, and Domagk's experiments actually had begun in that year. Also in 1935 he reported that Neoprontosil, a more soluble compound, was as effective as Prontosil. In view of several clinical reports from Germany attesting to the therapeutic value of Prontosil in human streptococcal diseases, the Therapeutic Trials Committee of England, seeking to verify these reports, brought forth conclusive evidence in June 1936 that

Prontosil was of undoubted value in the treatment of puerperal sepsis caused by β-hemolytic streptococci. An important development then was announced by investigators at the Pasteur Institute in France; they postulated that Prontosil and Neoprontosil were reduced in the human body to form free sulfanilamide, which actually possessed the antibacterial activity attributed to the parent compounds. This tremendous breakthrough initiated many investigations to improve and modify sulfanilamide, leading to other sulfonamide compounds such as sulfapyridine, sulfathiazole, and sulfaguanidine. For this remarkable achievement in the therapy of certain bacterial infections, Domagk was awarded the Nobel prize in 1939.

Prior to the discovery of the antibacterial action of sulfonamides, Sir Alexander Fleming (1881 to 1955, England), a bacteriologist interested in improving the isolation of *Haemophilus influenzae*, had reported in 1929 a most significant observation that he considered of importance at the time primarily as a potential tool in diagnostic bacteriologic technique and that was treated for a decade as almost a curiosity. It can best be described in his own words:

> While working with staphylococcus variants a number of culture-plates were set aside on the laboratory bench and examined from time to time. In the examinations these plates were necessarily exposed to the air and they became contaminated with various micro-organisms. It was noticed that around a large colony of a contaminating mould the staphylococcus colonies became transparent and were obviously undergoing lysis. Subcultures of this mould were made and experiments conducted with a view to ascertaining something of the properties of the bacteriolytic substance which had evidently been formed in the mould culture and which had diffused into the surrounding medium. It was found that broth in which the mould had been grown at room tem-

perature for one or two weeks had acquired marked inhibitory, bactericidal and bacteriolytic properties to many of the more common pathogenic bacteria.

This mold was later identified by Charles Thom, the principal mycologist in the United States Department of Agriculture, as being *Penicillium notatum*.

In 1938 two investigators at the Sir William Dunn School of Pathology at Oxford University, England, Sir Howard W. Florey (1898 to 1968), pathologist, and Ernst B. Chain (born 1906), a German-born biochemist, decided to make an intensive survey of naturally produced antibacterial substances from both chemical and biologic viewpoints to determine if any one would be very effective against pathogenic microorganisms. By good fortune they decided in 1939 to examine penicillin, the soluble product of Fleming's mold, in spite of the fact that it was said to be very unstable. The results of these researchers, with the investigation they initiated having been extended through the close collaboration of a large number of scientists as a cooperative study on penicillin, were published in 1940, a monumental contribution to human medicine that was accomplished under the enormous difficulties imposed by the war in which the British were involved at that time. Their studies on penicillin included its methods of purification, its bacteriostatic properties *in vitro* and its chemotherapeutic action in animals. After months of labor, in 1941 they obtained enough of a fairly purified product to test it in human beings. Thus the great era of antibiotic therapy was born.

Fleming, Florey and Chain jointly received the Nobel prize in 1945 for the discovery of penicillin and its curative powers in infections, a milestone in man's quest for relief from the various ills to which the species is heir.

Immunology, now the copartner of microbiology, developed originally as an offshoot of bacteriology in the first attempts to protect man from infectious diseases, and in that early stage of its development concerned itself almost exclusively with infectious agents. The name of this branch of science quite appropriately comes from the Latin *immunis*, free of burden.

Smallpox was one of the truly dreaded scourges of mankind. Epidemics of great severity occurred in Europe in the Middle Ages, and two-thirds of the population of Greenland succumbed as the consequence of one case of the disease in a Danish sailor who stopped there with his ship. The disease from ancient times has been called *variola*, and it had been recognized especially by Fracastorius that survival from the disease produced resistance to ensuing attacks. Variolation, a rather drastic preventive measure, had been practiced in the East for centuries, reportedly in China from the mid-17th century, the end of the Ming dynasty. It consisted of the inoculation, either intravenously or into several small wounds in the arms or legs, of very small amounts of the contents of fresh smallpox pustules, which usually produced only a mild form of smallpox that was sufficient to induce immunity to the disease. This method seems to have been independently discovered by the Armenians, probably before the end of the 17th century, from whom it spread to Turkey.

An Italian physician, Emanuel Timoni, practicing in Constantinople (now Istanbul), introduced variolation, which already had been successfully used in Turkey for 40 years, into England through a letter to the Royal Society in December 1713. Adoption of this practice by the English was greatly encouraged by the efforts of Lady Mary Wortley Montagu, whose husband had been sent to Constantinople as the Ambassador Extraordinary on a mission of reconcilement between Turkey and Austria, then on the brink of war. She was particularly interested in preventing the disease as a result of her own childhood affliction with smallpox, which had marred her complexion. After having her son inoculated on March 18, 1717 by the surgeon of the British Embassy in Turkey, Charles Maitland, she wrote a very important letter on April 1, 1717 to Miss Sara Chiswell describing this practice. After returning to England, she became very alarmed for the safety of her daughter and others when a smallpox epidemic with a high fatality rate broke out in London in the early spring of 1721. She sent for Maitland to inoculate her little girl, which he did in the presence of three physicians of the College as witnesses. On her recommendation this led to the variolation of two of the daughters of Princess Caroline of Wales in April 1722, with such royal sanction lending credence to the general introduction of the practice.

Edward Jenner (1749 to 1823, England), a country physician of Gloucestershire, became concerned with the disease as a result of an epidemic that occurred in 1778. This brought to his notice something he had remembered from the time of his apprenticeship under the surgeon Ludlow in Sodbury as part of his training to be a physician. A dairymaid had remarked confidently that a skin infection of a pustular nature, for which she was being treated by the surgeon, could not possibly be smallpox, for she had already had the cowpox and nobody ever caught smallpox after that. Jenner wrote in reference to cowpox, "My attention to this singular disease was first excited by observing, that among those whom in the country I was frequently called upon to inoculate, many resisted every effort to give them the smallpox. These patients I found had undergone a disease they called the cow-pox, contracted by milking cows affected with a peculiar eruption on their teats. On inquiry it appeared that it had been known among the dairies from time immemorial, and that a vague opinion prevailed that it was a preventive

of the smallpox." Three years later he stated, "During the investigation of the causal cow-pox I was struck by the idea that it might be practicable to propagate the disease by inoculation, after the manner of the smallpox, first from the cow; and finally from one human being to another."

The opportunity to test his hypothesis came when he saw as a patient Sarah Nelmes, a dairymaid whose hand, previously injured by a scratch from a thorn, had become infected at that lesion with cowpox from her master's cows. Jenner took material from the sore on the hand of this dairymaid and inserted it on May 14, 1796 into the arm of an 8-year-old-boy, James Phipps, "by means of two superficial incisions, barely penetrating the cutis, each about half an inch long... Having never seen the disease but in its casual way before, that is, when communicated from the cow to the hand of the milker, I was astonished at the close resemblance of the pustules in some of their stages, to the variolous pustules. But now listen to the most delightful part of my story. The boy has since been inoculated for the smallpox which, as I ventured to predict, produced no effect. I shall now pursue my experiments with redoubled ardour."

Thus began active immunization for the prevention of infectious disease in this courageous human experiment of Jenner. In June 1798 he published a small book entitled *An Inquiry Into Cause and Effects of the Variolae Vaccinae*, a milestone in the history of medicine.

Passing from research on fermentation and specific infections of man with searches for the etiologic agents, Louis Pasteur turned to a study of what was described in France at that time as virus diseases typified by smallpox. That one attack conferred lasting immunity was to him remarkable. He was greatly impressed by this from a study of the literature of variolation and especially by Jenner's work on vaccination. His reasoning and instinct led him to believe that a process akin to vaccination might hold for other diseases, a fact he soon disclosed in his investigation of chicken cholera, the lightning disease that sometimes killed as many as 90 percent in a flock.

The bacterial cause had been recognized by a veterinarian, Perroncito, in Italy in 1879 and was confirmed by a French veterinarian, Touissant, in the same year, who sent the head of an infected animal to Pasteur. Pasteur first turned to improving the culture medium and determined that chicken boullion was the best medium. He found that his broth cultures of this organism had an extraordinary degree of pathogenicity (capacity to produce disease) — the smallest drop of a recent culture was sufficient to kill a chicken. This capacity to infect chickens could be maintained if the organisms were grown in series in cultures. As long as the culture flasks were inoculated with the chicken cholera organism without interruption at 24-hour intervals, the virulence (degree of pathogenicity) remained the same. Some hens inoculated with an old culture that had been put away and forgotten a few weeks before became ill but to Pasteur's surprise recovered. These unexpectedly refractory hens were then inoculated with a new, fresh culture and found to be highly resistant.

In 1880 Pasteur reported on his chicken cholera experiments, which constitute a fundamental discovery of immunology and preventive medicine. He introduced the term attenuation (reduction in virulence) for the enfeeblement of the "virus." Chickens first inoculated with living, attenuated organisms withstood subsequent injection with fully virulent cultures that acutely killed unprotected chickens. These observations led to his establishment of the principle of prophylaxis following inoculation with a specific attenuated organism. In honor of Jenner, he coined the term vaccine for such attenuated materials and vaccina-

tion, from the Latin word *vacca* for cow, for the process. At once he turned his attention to anthrax, swine erysipelas, and rabies, which investigations occupied him exclusively to the end of his scientific life.

In 1876 Robert Koch demonstrated the extraordinary resistance of the spores of anthrax bacilli. Pasteur in 1879 further emphasized this spore resistance when he found anthrax spores in soil above the carcasses of animals that had died of anthrax and had been buried 10 months previously. It was known that the optimum temperature for *in vitro* cultivation of anthrax bacilli was 30 to 35°C. In attempts to use a higher temperature of incubation for a possible attenuating effect, his experiments showed that anthrax bacilli could not be cultured at a temperature of 45°C but yielded abundant growth at temperatures of 42 to 43°C, at which temperature no spores developed. Following the principle he had discovered in chicken cholera, he kept virulent cultures at 42 to 43°C for 6, 8, 10, and 15 days. He challenged sheep, guinea pigs, and rabbits with these cultures and determined that there was a gradual loss of virulence — for example, 4 or 5 of 10 sheep were killed with a culture kept for 8 days and none of 10 with a culture kept for 10 to 12 days, when the control culture of the same strain at 24 hours of incubation killed 10 of 10 sheep. When he recultured those cultures held 10 to 12 days at 42 to 43°C at the optimum temperature of 30 to 35°C, they became fully virulent.

The practical usefulness of this information was tested in May 1882 at the farm of Pouilly le Fort, near Melun. In 1881, with his coworkers Chamberland and Roux, Pasteur had produced two vaccines of anthrax cultures of varying degrees of attenuation. The first (*premier vaccin*) consisted of organisms grown for 15 to 20 days at 42 to 43°C and that had become avirulent for guinea pigs and rabbits but remained potently virulent for mice. The second (*deuxième vaccin*) was made from cultures at 42 to 43°C for 10 to 12 days that had become avirulent for rabbits while retaining virulence for mice and guinea pigs. Following the program Pasteur had prepared, the Melun Agricultural Society put 60 sheep at Pasteur's disposal; 25 were to be vaccinated by one inoculation of each of these attenuated vaccines at 12 or 15 day intervals. Some days later these 25 supposedly protected sheep, along with 25 others as controls that had not been vaccinated, would be inoculated with some very virulent anthrax culture. Pasteur wrote, "The twenty-five unvaccinated sheep will all perish, the twenty-five vaccinated ones will survive." All these 50 animals would be compared with the 10 remaining sheep that had undergone no treatment at all. An even greater test of his hypothesis arose at the last moment when he was prevailed upon to include 10 cows, 6 to be vaccinated and 4 to remain unvaccinated as controls, although his tests on the vaccine for cows were not as advanced as those for sheep.

Inoculations with the first vaccine took place on May 5, followed by the second vaccine 12 days later on May 17. On May 31, all 50 sheep and 10 cows were challenged with a fully virulent culture. On June 2, 48 hours after the challenge inoculation, Pasteur found the carcasses of 22 unvaccinated sheep with two others breathing their last and all the vaccinated sheep in perfect health. With this tremendous success it was decided that the farm of Pouilly le Fort would henceforth bear the name Clos Pasteur. These experiments caused a tremendous sensation in the whole of France. Pasteur's son-in-law Vallery-Radot wrote, "Pasteur now knew fame

under its rarest and purest form; the loving veneration, the almost worship with which he inspired those who lived near him or worked with him, had become the feeling of a whole nation."

In a short chapter it is not possible to cover every discovery of importance in the history of this discipline. This review has been limited to very specific events of major importance in developing the principles of this science as they pertain to this day.

> The search for truth is in one way hard and in another easy. For it is evident that no one can master it fully nor miss it wholly. But each adds a little to our knowledge of nature, and from all the facts assembled there arises a certain grandeur. (Aristotle, 384 to 322 B.C.)

REFERENCES

Brock, T.D.: Milestones in Microbiology. Prentice-Hall, Englewood Cliffs, N.J., 1961.

Bulloch, W.: The History of Bacteriology. Oxford University Press, London, 1938.

Dobell, C.: Antony van Leeuwenhoek and His "Little Animals." John Bale, Sons and Danielsson Ltd., London, 1932.

Fisk, D.: Dr. Jenner of Berkeley. William Heinemann Ltd., London, 1959.

Fracastorius, H.: De Sympathia & Antipathia Rerum. Gulielmus Gazcius, Lugdunum (Lyon), 1550.

Vallery-Radot, R.: The Life of Pasteur. Translated from the French by Devonshire, R.L. Doubleday, Doran & Company, Inc., New York, 1928.

Wilson, G.S. and Miles, A.A.: Topley and Wilson's Principles of Bacteriology and Immunity. 5th Ed. Edward Arnold Ltd., London, 1964.

2

Bacterial Morphology and Physiology

Joseph M. Merrick

After the discovery of microorganisms, the early biologists began to classify them into the traditional plant or animal kingdoms. The distinction between plants and animals is relatively clear; that is, plants are principally nonmotile and photosynthetic, whereas animals are motile and nonphotosynthetic. However, it soon became apparent that the microbes could not be easily categorized into either of the kingdoms, since some were clearly plantlike, some animal-like, and some had properties common to both kingdoms. To avoid taxonomic problems, in 1866 a third kingdom, the protists, was suggested for the microorganisms. The protists include both eukaryotic (algae, protozoa, and fungi) and prokaryotic (bacteria and blue-green bacteria) cells and are distinguished from plants and animals by their relatively simple biologic organization. Generally they are unicellular, and those that are multicellular do not show extensive differentiation.

The cell structure of eukaryotic protists is similar to that of plants and animals and is characterized by a high degree of internal complexity. For example, the nucleus is surrounded by a membrane and there are cytoplasmic membranous structures, such as mitochondria, chloroplasts, Golgi apparatus, lysosomes, and endoplasmic reticulum. The structure of the prokaryotic cell is of a simple type. These cells contain a nucleus that is a single chromosome not bounded by a membrane, and they lack the membrane bound organelles found in eukaryotic cells.

BACTERIAL CLASSIFICATION

In the United States, the system of classification of bacteria generally used is found in Bergey's Manual of Determinative Bacteriology. Bergey's Manual represents an extensive effort to organize bacteria into related groups. The manual does not represent a phylogenetic classification of bacteria but is nevertheless a useful guide in the nomenclature of bacteria. Based on morphological and physiologic characteristics, the bacteria are divided into 19 parts. Each part is a descriptive group that is distinguishable from other groups by only a few easily discerned criteria. Some of these criteria include the Gram stain reaction, spore formation, morphology, and phys-

13

Table 2.1.   Classification of Bacteria

Part 1   Phototrophic bacteria

Part 2   Gliding bacteria

Part 3   Sheathed bacteria

Part 4   Budding and/or appendaged bacteria

Part 5   Spirochetes

Part 6   Spiral and curved bacteria

Part 7   Gram-negative aerobic rods and cocci

Part 8   Gram-negative facultative anaerobic rods

Part 9   Gram-negative anaerobic bacteria

Part 10   Gram-negative cocci and coccobacilli

Part 11   Gram-negative anaerobic cocci

Part 12   Gram-negative, chemolithotrophic bacteria

Part 13   Methane-producing bacteria

Part 14   Gram-positive cocci

Part 15   Endospore-forming rods and cocci

Part 16   Gram-positive, asporogenous rod-shaped bacteria

Part 17   Actinomycetes and related organisms

Part 18   Rickettsias

Part 19   Mycoplasmas

iologic and biochemical characteristics. The 19 parts are listed in Table 2.1.

In recent years there have been attempts to determine relatedness between various groups of bacteria that is based on the degree of homology of DNA. DNA homology can be determined by comparing the percentage of guanine and cytosine present and also by determining the amount of base pairing when DNA extracted from two different cells is permitted to undergo hybridization. Bacterial species can be defined as strains that exhibit the same or closely similar phenotypic properties and differ from other related strains by a number of independent characteristics. Bacteria, like other living organisms, follow the binomial system of nomenclature; that is, the name consists of two words. The first word refers to the genus and the second to the species

belonging to the genus; for example, *Escherichia coli*, which is often abbreviated to *E. coli*. In some bacteria it is possible to recognize a common evolutionary origin; for example, the enteric bacteria. The genera in this group are united into the family *Enterobacteriaceae.*

PROKARYOTIC CELL STRUCTURE

Size

Bacteria exhibit great variations in shapes and sizes. There are spherical, curved, spiral, and rod shaped forms. Generally, rod shaped cells are about 1 μm wide and 2 μm long. Because of the great diversity in shape, the only satisfactory basis for defining size is cellular volume. Sizes vary from a 0.1 μm^3 to 500 μm^3. Thus the smaller bacteria fall into the size range of the larger viral forms, and the larger bacteria into the size range of the smaller eukaryotic protists. The size of bacteria has certain fixed limits, which depend on the species. Nevertheless, there can be a great variation within these limits, depending on the age of the cell and cultural conditions.

Membrane

The cell membrane of prokaryotic cells, as seen in electron micrographs of thin sections, is a typical unit membrane, approximately 10 nm wide (Fig. 2.1). It represents about 10 percent of the dry weight of the cell and is composed of lipids (20 to 30 percent; mostly phospholipids) and proteins (60 to 70 percent). Sterols are absent from prokaryotic plasma membranes, except in the case of mycoplasmas, which will incorporate sterols in their membrane when grown on a medium containing sterols. The plasma membrane of bacteria and eukaryotic cells possesses a similar molecular organization. A schematic representation of the unit

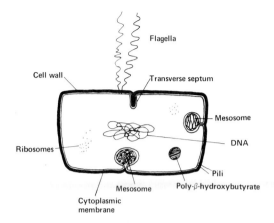

Fig. 2.1. Schematic representation of an electron micrograph of a thin section of a typical bacterium.

membrane is seen in Figure 2.2. Current models suggest that some proteins penetrate the lipid bilayer (integral proteins), whereas others appear to be associated with hydrophilic groups in the membrane and are more easily dissociated (peripheral proteins).

The bacterial cell membrane has many important metabolic functions: (1) It provides an osmotic barrier that is essentially impermeable to organic and inorganic mole-

cules, except for those substances that are carried into or out of the cell by *specific transport systems*. The transport of nutrients is catalyzed by specific proteins that are localized in the membrane. (2) It contains the *electron transport system*. Bacteria are devoid of mitochondria and ATP generation is carried out by components of the membrane. (3) Enzymes involved in biosynthesis of membrane lipids and macromolecules of the bacterial cell wall are localized in the membrane. (4) The bacterial chromosome and plasmids are connected to specific membrane attachment sites, and the membrane plays a role in their replication and subsequent segregation. (5) Bacteria secrete hydrolytic enzymes that break down macromolecular substances, such as proteins, nucleic acids, lipids, and polysaccharides to nutrients that can be utilized by the cell. These enzymes are synthesized and secreted at membrane sites. (6) Many bacteria possess complex membranous infoldings known as *mesosomes*. Mesosomal membranes are continuous with the external plasma membrane. They may appear as sacs containing clusters of vesicles or as sacs containing membranous whorls. These structures may

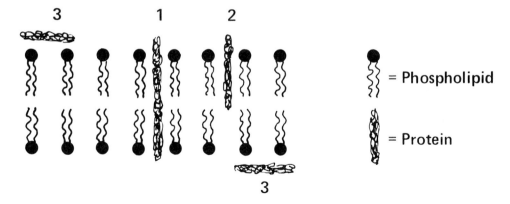

Fig. 2.2. Schematic representation of a membrane structure. The phospholipid bilayer forms the matrix; integral proteins are embedded within the bilayer. Some span the entire bilayer with hydrophilic ends protruding from both surfaces (1), whereas others project from only one of the surfaces (2). Peripheral proteins are associated with hydrophilic groups of phospholipids (3).

be involved in the formation of the transverse septum. It has also been suggested that they may function as attachment sites for DNA molecules.

Nucleus

When seen through the electron microscope, the nuclear region of the bacterial cell appears as a fibrillar area that is not bounded by a membrane to separate it from the cytoplasm and does not contain any substructures. This area is composed of closely packed, fine fibrils of DNA, which represent one continuous circular structure and is considered to be a single chromosome. The DNA of the bacterial nucleus has been isolated as long threads of approximately 1 mm in length in the unfolded state. These threads are contained in cells with an average length of about 2 μm. In *Escherichia coli* the bacterial chromosome contains approximately 5×10^6 base pairs, with a molecular mass of about 3×10^9 daltons.

Ribosomes

In electron micrographs ribosomes of the bacterial cell are seen as fine, regular, granular units. These are the sites of protein synthesis. Their abundance varies with the physiological state and age of the bacterial cell. Growing cells have a considerably higher ribosomal content than old or stationary phase cells. Prokaryotic ribosomes have a sedimentation velocity constant of 70 S and can be reversibly dissociated into 30 S and 50 S subunits.

Cytoplasmic Inclusions

Many bacteria accumulate nonnitrogenous reserve materials in the form of granular cytoplasmic inclusions that can, under appropriate circumstances, serve as an intracellular storage of carbon or energy.

Glycogenlike polysaccharides and a polyester β-hydroxybutyric acid, poly-β-hydroxybutyrate, are found in many prokaryotic organisms. Glycogen also occurs in eukaryotic cells, but poly-β-hydroxybutyrate is unique to the prokaryotes and may be considered to be an alternative to the deposition of neutral fat. Neutral fat is not found among prokaryotic cells. Usually, only one type of stored substance is formed by a given species; however, some can form both types. There are also bacteria that do not store any type of nonnitrogenous reserve substance. Reserve materials generally accumulate when a nitrogen source becomes limiting, but carbon is still available. Since these substances are neutral and osmotically inert, relatively large amounts can be stored. Many bacteria store polyphosphates, which are linear polymers of orthophosphate and are called *volutin* or *metachromatic granules*, since they appear red when stained with a blue dye. Some bacteria that oxidize H_2S may accumulate inclusions of elemental sulfur.

Cell Wall Structure

Based on the type of outer-bounding layer, one can distinguish three major groups of prokaryotes: (1) Cells that lack a cell wall, for example, mycoplasmas. (2) Cells that have a monolayered cell wall. In electron micrographs the walls of these organisms appear as a single, thick, continuous layer (Fig. 2.3). (3) Cells that have a multi-

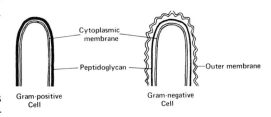

Fig. 2.3. Schematic representation of the cell wall of a gram-positive and a gram-negative cell.

layered cell wall. In electron micrographs the wall of these cells appears to be composed of at least two structurally distinct layers (Fig. 2.3).

Organisms that fall into groups (2) and (3) are distinguished by their differential staining properties when subjected to the Gram stain. Organisms in group (2) are gram-positive, whereas those of group (3) are gram-negative.

In Gram staining the bacterial cells are first stained with crystal violet, then treated with a dilute solution of I_2, which fixes the stain. The cells are washed with acetone or alcohol and then counterstained with a dye of a different color. Gram-positive cells retain the crystal violet and are stained blue-black. Gram-negative cells are decolorized by the solvent and are stained pink or red by the counterstain. The differences in the staining properties appear to be due to the differences in certain components of the cell wall of these two groups of organisms.

The *Mycoplasma* is the only group of

bacteria lacking a cell wall. These cells do not have a fixed shape and are readily deformed. In contrast, the cell walls of gram-positive or gram-negative cells confer on the cell its particular shape. The cell wall is a rigid structure that plays a vital role in protecting the cell from osmotic lysis. Bacterial cells can exist in a hypotonic environment because the tensile strength of the cell walls withstands the high internal hydrostatic pressures that are generated within the bacterial cell. If one removes the wall with specific enzymes that hydrolyze cell wall components, the cell will lyse because of the high osmotic pressure inside the cell. From a practical standpoint the cell wall is of particular interest, since it contains the major antigenic determinants of the cell surface. These determinants are easily detected in the diagnostic laboratory and can thus be used for identification purposes. Also, many antibiotics are effective against bacteria because they are able to prevent the synthesis of bacterial cell walls.

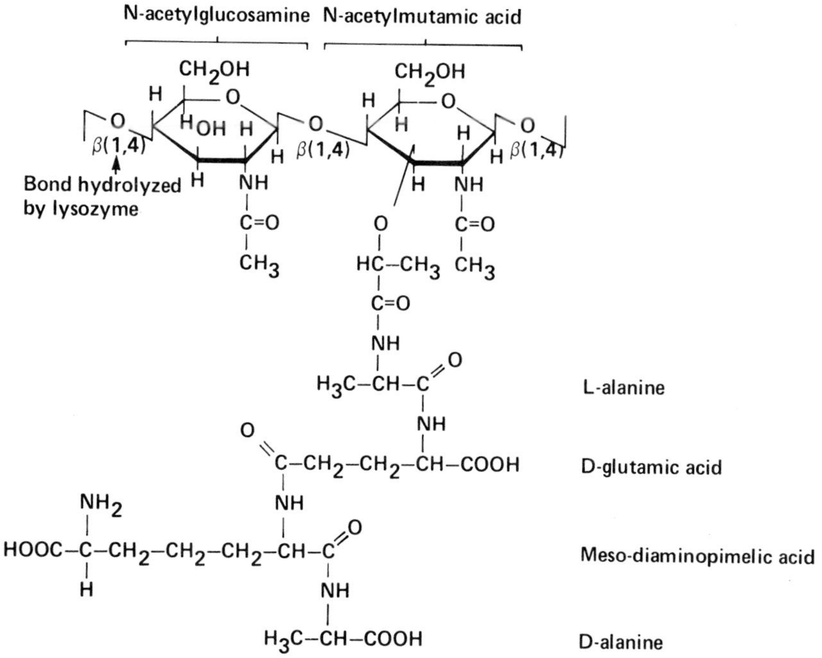

Fig. 2.4. Structure of a repeating unit of a peptidoglycan in *E. coli*.

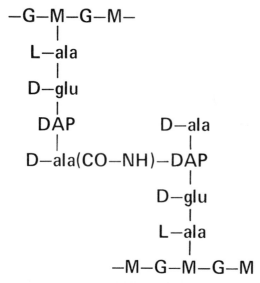

Fig. 2.5. Peptide bridges between the polysaccharide backbone are crosslinked. In the case of *E. coli*, the peptides are joined directly. G, *N*-acetylglucosamine; M, *N*-acetylmuramic acid; L-ala, L-alanine; D-ala, D-alanine; DAP *meso*-diaminopimelic acid; D-glu, D-glutamic acid.

Chemistry of Cell Wall Components.
Cell walls of both gram-positive and gram-negative bacteria contain a heteropolymer called peptidoglycan. This structure, found only in prokaryotes, forms a three-dimensional molecular mesh that surrounds the cell like a sack. It consists of a polysaccharide backbone composed of alternating residues of *N*-acetylglucosamine and *N*-acetylmuramic acid (Fig. 2.4). Identical tetrapeptides are attached to *N*-acetylmuramic acid (Fig. 2.4). These tetrapeptides crosslink the polysaccharides to one another by peptide bonding between the tetrapeptide of one chain and the tetrapeptide of another (Fig. 2.5). The amino acid sequence of the tetrapeptide is L-alanine (bound through the carboxyl group of muramic acid), D-glutamic acid, L-diamino acid, D-alanine. The diamino acid may be diaminopimelic acid or lysine. In some cases peptides between adjacent glycans are joined through the free amino group of

the diamino acid and the carboxyl group of D-alanine; for example, *E. coli* (Figs. 2.5 and 2.7A). There is some variation in the composition of the interpeptide bridges; for example, in *Staphylococcus aureus* cell wall tetrapeptides are linked through pentaglycine bridges (Figs. 2.6 and 2.7B).

Biosynthesis of Peptidoglycan. The biosynthesis of a repeating unit of peptidoglycan is seen in Figures 2.8, 2.9, and 2.10. Precursors of peptidoglycan, uridine diphosphate (UDP)-*N*-acetylmuramic acid (UDP-MurNAc)-pentapeptide and UDP-*N*-acetylglucosamine (UDP-GlcNAc), are synthesized in the cytoplasm. The synthesis of UDP-MurNAc-pentapeptide is shown in Figure 2.8. Amino acids are added sequentially to UDP-MurNAc by reactions that require ATP. If bacterial cells are exposed to cycloserine, the synthesis of UDP-MurNAc-pentapeptide is prevented. Cycloserine is a structural analog of D-alanine and is a competitive inhibitor of both ala-

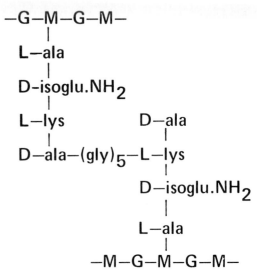

Fig. 2.6. Crosslinking of tetrapeptide through pentaglycine bridges. Example shown is found in the peptidoglycan of *S. aureus*. G, *N*-acetylglucosamine; M, *N*-acetylmuramic acid; L-ala, L-alanine; D-ala, D-alanine; gly, glycine; D-isoglu.NH$_2$, D-isoglutamine; L-lys, L-lysine.

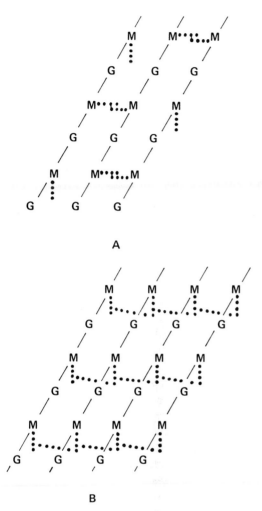

Fig. 2.7. Schematic representation of *E. coli* peptidoglycan in (A) *E. coli* and (B) *S. aureus*. In *E. coli*, not all of the peptides are crosslinked. *E. coli* is a "loose" peptidoglycan with about 50 percent of the peptide units present as noncrosslinked monomers. *S. aureus* peptidoglycan is highly crosslinked. Dots represent amino acids; G, *N*-acetylglucosamine; M, *N*-acetylmuramic acid.

The disaccharide pentapeptide is subsequently transferred to an acceptor molecule, that is, a growing peptidogylcan chain, to form a linear peptidoglycan. Bactoprenol pyrophosphate is released and dephosphorylated. The resulting bactoprenol-P can again accept MurNAc-pentapeptide and the cycle is repeated. The antibiotic bacitracin blocks cell wall synthesis by inhibiting the dephosphorylation reaction, thus preventing the regeneration of the carrier lipid.

The final step in peptidogylcan synthesis is to crosslink the linear polymers. The crosslinking step is carried out by transpeptidation, using the energy of the peptide bond, and thus does not require ATP (Fig. 2.10). The terminal D-alanine that did not participate in the transpeptidation reaction is removed by a D-alanine carboxypeptidase. The peptidoglycan is responsible for the structural strength of the outer envelope and prevents lysis of the bacterial cell in

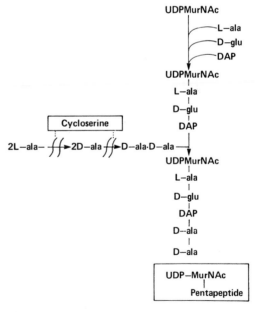

Fig. 2.8. The synthesis of UDP-*N*-acetylmuramic acid pentapeptide. L-ala, L-alanine; D-ala, D-alanine; D-glu, D-glutamic acid; DAP, *meso*-diaminopimelic acid; MurNAc, *N*-acetylmuramic acid.

nine racemase and D-alanine synthetase.

In the next stage of peptidogylcan synthesis, MurNac-pentapeptide is linked to a membrane lipid carrier — bactoprenol or undecaprenyl phosphate. GlcNAc from UDP-GlcNA is then added to form disaccharide-(pentapeptide) PP-bactoprenol.

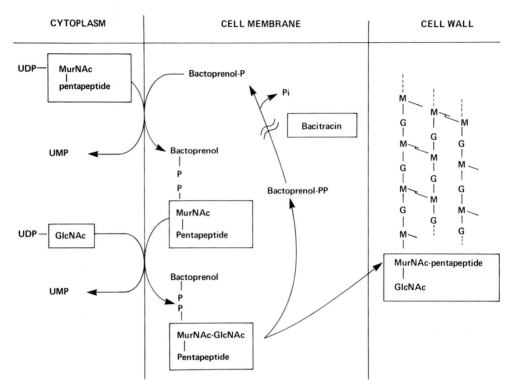

Fig. 2.9. The synthesis of a linear peptidoglycan. The reactions shown above are involved in the elongation of a peptidoglycan chain by a disaccharide pentapeptide. GlcNAc or G, *N*-acetylglucosamine; MurNAc or M, *N*-acetylmuramic acid.

most environments. Penicillin (Ch. 4) interferes with the terminal crosslinking step in biosynthesis of the peptidoglycan and leads to the formation of walls that lack tensile strength, and as a result the growing cells will lyse. Thus penicillin is a very effective against bacterial cells and does not interfere with normal mammalian cell metabolism, since peptidoglycan is only found in prokaryotes.

Other Cell Wall Constituents. In gram-positive cells, the peptidoglycan accounts for 40 to 90 percent of the dry weight of the cell. The cell walls of most gram-positive organisms also contain teichoic acids, which may form up to 50 percent of the dry weight of the cell. These substances are the major surface antigenic constituents of gram-positive cells. They are water-soluble polymers containing ribi-tol or glycerol residues joined by phosphodiester bonds (Fig. 2.11). Most of the cell wall teichoic acid is covalently linked to peptidoglycan by phosphodiester bonds to *N*-acetylmuramic acid. Some glycerol teichoic acid is covalently linked to glycolipid and is associated with the membrane. This material is called membrane teichoic acid or lipoteichoic acid (Fig. 2.11). Most teichoic acids are substituted on the free hydroxyl groups with D-alanine or D-lysine by ester linkages. Sugar substituents, such as glucose, galactose, or *N*-acetylhexosamines may also be present in O-glycosidic linkages.

The cell wall of gram-negative cells is multilayered (Fig. 2.3); the peptidoglycan is the innermost layer and constitutes from 5 to 10 percent of the dry weight of the cell wall. The outermost layer, referred to as

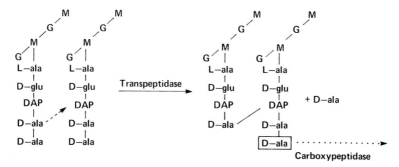

Fig. 2.10. Crosslinking of linear peptidoglycan chains by transpeptidation. A peptide bond is formed between D-alanine of one peptide unit and diaminopimelate of an adjacent peptide unit with the concomitant release of a terminal D-alanine residue. The remaining terminal D-alanine is removed by a D-alanine carboxypeptidase. For an explanation of abbreviations, see Figure 2.5.

the outer membrane, is a typical unit membrane and is composed of phospholipids, proteins, and lipopolysaccharides. The outer membrane is a barrier to the passage of molecules greater than the molecular weight of 700, but permeable to smaller molecules. Permeability is conferred by some of the proteins of the outer mem-

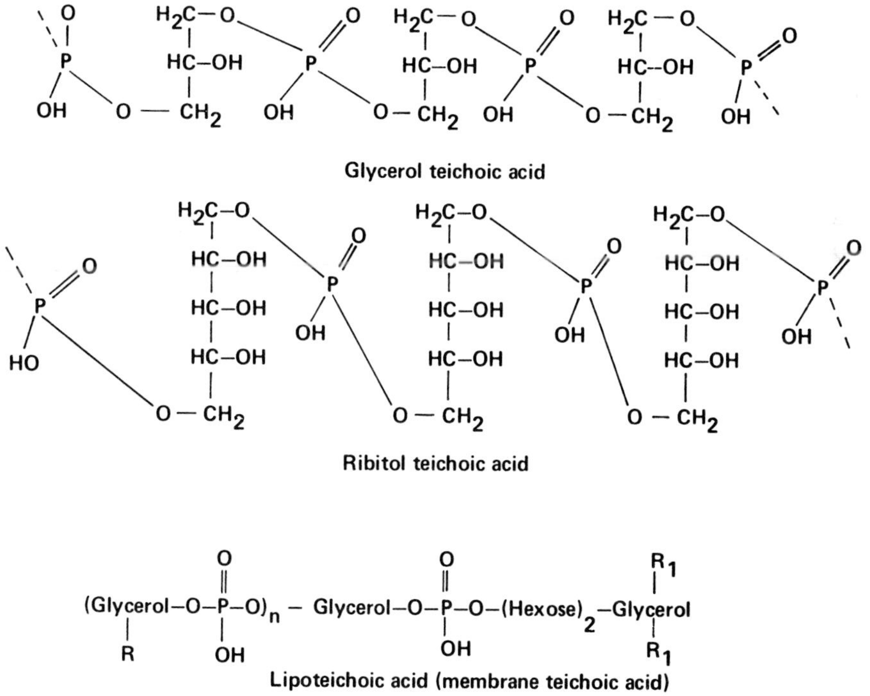

Glycerol teichoic acid

Ribitol teichoic acid

$$(\text{Glycerol}-\text{O}-\overset{\overset{\text{O}}{\|}}{\underset{R}{P}}-\text{O})_n - \text{Glycerol}-\text{O}-\overset{\overset{\text{O}}{\|}}{\underset{\text{OH}}{P}}-\text{O}-(\text{Hexose})_2-\underset{R_1}{\overset{R_1}{\text{Glycerol}}}$$

Lipoteichoic acid (membrane teichoic acid)

Fig. 2.11. Teichoic acids. Repeat units may vary from 10 to 30 carbons or more in length. Repeat units of glycerol are joined by 1,3 or 1,2 linkages; repeat units of ribitol are joined by 1,5 linkages. Most teichoic acids are substituted at the free hydroxyl groups in ester linkage with D-alanine or D-lysine; in glycosidic linkage with glucose, galactose, N-acetylglucosamine, or N-acetylgalactosamine.

Lipid A — polysaccharide core — O-specific side chains

Fig. 2.12. The unit structure of lipopolysaccharide is composed of lipid A linked to the core polysaccharide, which in turn is linked to the O-specific side chains.

brane, called porins, which form transmembrane channels or pores that nonspecifically permit the passive diffusion of solutes across the outer membrane. The outer membrane prevents the penetration of certain detergents and antibiotics and blocks the escape of secreted hydrolytic enzymes from the cell that accumulate between the cell membrane and outer membrane (periplasmic space).

The *lipopolysaccharides* (LPS) of the outer membrane carry the major antigenic determinants of gram-negative cells and are referred to as somatic O antigens. They are also called endotoxins (heat stable toxins associated with gram-negative cells; exotoxins are extracellular toxins) because they are responsible for the toxic activities that occur when gram-negative bacteria are introduced into the bloodstream of an animal. Lipopolysaccharides also play a role in the infection of bacteria by certain viruses by providing specific receptors for the attachment of viruses to the cell.

Lipopolysaccharides are complex molecules that can be divided into three distinct regions, as shown in Figure 2.12. The lipid A region is the hydrophobic region of the molecule and is responsible for the toxic

properties of lipopolysaccharides. It consists of a glucosamine disaccharide that is substituted with phosphate and long-chain fatty acids in ester and amide linkage (Fig. 2.13). The polysaccharide core is attached to lipid A by glycosidic linkage of an eight carbon sugar (2-keto-3-deoxymannooctulosonic acid, ketodeoxyoctonoate, KDO) to a free hydroxyl group of glucosamine. The core consists of KDO, heptose (L-glycero-D-mannoheptose, Hep), glucose, galactose, and N-acetylglucosamine (Fig. 2.14). KDO and Hep are unusual sugars that are apparently found only in lipopolysaccharides. The O-specific side chains attached to the polysaccharide core consist of repeating oligosaccharide units (e.g., repeating tri-, tetra-, or pentasaccharides). Some of the types of repeating units found in lipopolysaccharides are seen in Figure 2.15. Some repeating units contain a dideoxyhexose (abequose, colitose, tyvelose, and paratose). These sugars are relatively rare in nature but are frequently found as components of the O antigen. The antigenic determinants of the lipopolysaccharide molecule resides in the O-specific side chains. These chains may vary for different species, but most importantly

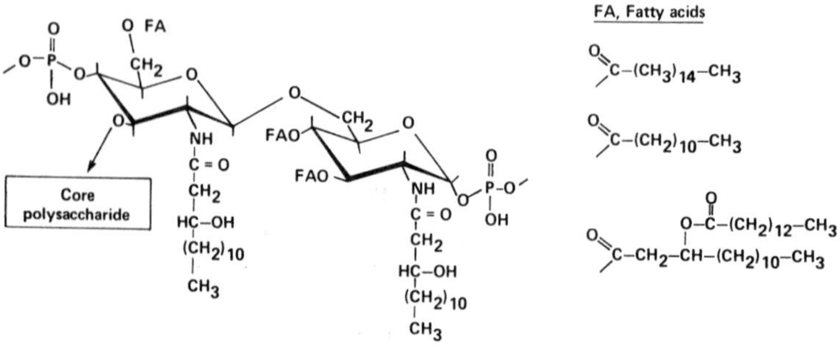

Fig. 2.13 Proposed structure of lipid A.

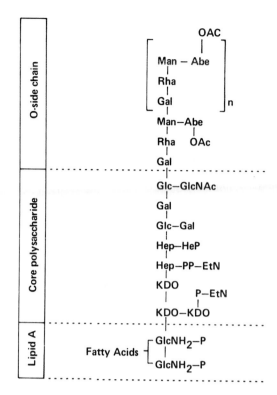

Fig. 2.14. Structure of the *Salmonella typhimurium* lipopolysaccharide. Abe, abequose; EtN, ethanolamine; Gal, D-galactose; Glc, D-glucose; GlcNH₂, glucosamine; GlcNAc, *N*-acetylglucosamine; Hep, L-glycero-D-mannoheptose; KDO, ketodeoxyoctonoate; Man, D-mannose; OAc, O-acetyl; P, phosphate; PP, pyrophosphate; Rha, L-rhamnose.

which suggests that there may be a selective advantage for these organisms. However, mutants lacking O-specific side chains (R or rough forms) are perfectly viable. R forms lacking most of the sugars of the core polysaccharide can also be isolated, but the lipid A region and the three residues of KDO appear to be essential for bacterial survival, since mutants defective in synthesis of these components have never been isolated. In the case of pathogenic gram-negative bacteria, cells that possess O polysaccharides may have a selective advantage because of their relative resistance to engulfment by the phagocytes of the animal host.

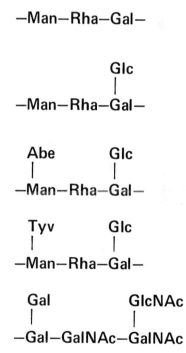

Fig. 2.15. Some lipopolysaccharide O-specific polysaccharide repeating oligosaccharide units. Abe, abequose; Gal, D-galactose; GalNAc, *N*-acetylgalactosamine; Glc, D-glucose; GlcNac, *N*-acetylglucosamine; Rha, L-rhamnose; Tyv, Tyvelose.

they can vary among different strains of the same species. There are many variations possible and the antigenic types depend on sugar composition, sequence, linkage, and whether additional substituents such as acetyl groups are present. The lipid A region appears to be relatively constant in most gram-negative organisms. In the case of *Salmonella*, the polysaccharide core is similar for any given species, but it differs from that of *Shigella* or *Escherichia*. At least three different core structures have been detected in *E. coli*.

Gram-negative bacteria isolated from nature usually possess O-specific side chains,

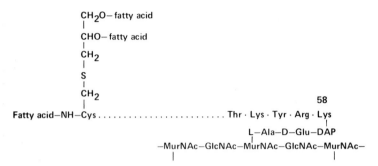

$$CH_2O-\text{fatty acid}$$
$$CHO-\text{fatty acid}$$
$$CH_2$$
$$S$$
$$CH_2$$

58

Fatty acid—NH—Cys . . . . Thr · Lys · Tyr · Arg · Lys
L—Ala—D—Glu—DAP
—MurNAc—GlcNAc—MurNAc—GlcNAc—MurNAc—

Fig. 2.16.   Structure of an *E. coli* lipoprotein.

The outer membrane of *E. coli* has been studied extensively. It is anchored to the peptidoglycan by *lipoprotein* molecules. This lipoprotein consists of 58 amino acids, has a molecular weight of 7200, and may be the most abundant protein in *E. coli* (750,000 copies per cell). The amino terminal end, which is embedded in the outer membrane, contains an unusual amino acid, glycerylcysteine, to which three fatty acids are covalently attached. The carboxy terminal lysine is covalently linked to every 10th to 12th diaminopimelate residue of the peptidoglycan (Fig. 2.16). A schematic model of the gram-negative cell wall is seen in Figure 2.17.

Lysozyme, a ubiquitous enzyme found in tears, saliva, egg white, nasal secretions, and extracts of various organs including skin, attacks the peptoglycan at the β-1,4 linkage between *N*-acetylmuramic acid and *N*-acetylglucosamine residues (Fig. 2.4). In a hypotonic medium the cell undergoes rapid osmotic lysis. Treatment of gram-positive cells with lysozyme in a hypertonic solution of sucrose or salts results in the formation of *protoplasts* or wall-free cells. Similar treatment of gram-negative cells gives rise to *spheroplasts* — cells in which the outer membrane is still attached. The wall can also be removed by growing cells in the presence of the antibiotic penicillin in an appropriate osmotically buffered medium. Removal of penicillin results in a reversion to normal cell structure. In some cases, after continued growth with penicillin, it may be possible to grow these cells in the absence of penicillin. In such cases the cells are known as *L forms*. L forms lack peptidoglycan but are stable and capable of growing in an appropriate medium. Only rarely do they revert to their normal form.

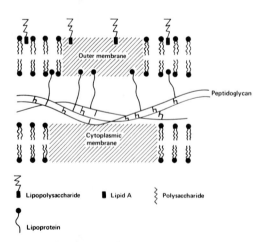

Lipopolysaccharide   Lipid A   Polysaccharide

Lipoprotein

Fig. 2.17.   Schemtic model of a gram-negative cell wall.

Capsules

Many bacteria secrete extracellular polymers that encapsulate the bacterial cell. These polymers are generally polysaccharides. *Bacillus anthracis*, however, possesses a capsule of poly-D-glutamate. The presence of capsules or slime is variable and may be dependent on nutrients available to the cell. For example, *Streptococcus mutans* produces a polyglucose polymer called dextran when grown on sucrose but not when grown on glucose. Most organisms can lose their capsule without affecting viability. The presence or absence of a capsule can sometimes be associated with the degree of virulence of an organism. *Streptococcus pneumoniae*, an encapsulated pathogen involved in diseases of the respiratory tract, is avirulent in the absence of a capsule because of the increased ease of destruction of the capsule-free cells by phagocytes.

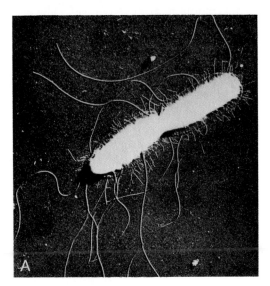

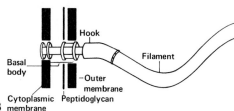

Fig. 2.18. (A) An electron micrograph of *S. typhi* showing flagella and pili (× 20,000) (Gillies, R.R., and Dodds, T.D.: Bacteriology Illustrated. 4th Ed. Churchill Livingstone, Edinburgh, 1976.) (B) A schematic model of the basal body and flagellum of a bacterial cell. (Adapted from Moat A.G.: Microbial Physiology. John Wiley & Sons, Inc. New York, 1979.)

Flagella

The movement of certain bacteria is accomplished by the use of flagella. These thin, long, wavy filaments (3 to 20 μm long; 12 to 18 nm in diameter) are constructed from a single type of protein called flagellin. The flagellar filament is attached to the bacterial cell through a hook-like structure and which serves to anchor the flagellum to the cell wall and membrane (Fig. 2.18B). The basal body contains two pairs of rings in gram-negative cells and one pair in gram-positive cells. The arrangement of flagella on a cell is relatively constant for a given bacterial species and can be used to separate flagellated bacteria into three groups: (1) *peritrichous flagellation* — flagella randomly distributed over cell surface; (2) *monotrichous flagellation*— single polar flagellum; and (3) *lophotrichous flagellation* — tuft or polar flagella.

Mobility can be mediated by other types of organelles; for example, the axial filament found in the spirochetes. Another type of locomotion is carried out by the myxobacteria. These organisms are capable of moving on a solid surface by a gliding movement, but the mechanism is unknown and no organelles of locomotion have thus far been detected.

Pili (Frimbiae)

Pili are filamentous surface appendages found only in gram-negative bacteria. These appendages are shorter, straighter, and thinner than flagella (Fig. 2.18A) and are composed of a single protein, pilin. There is recent evidence that suggests that pili may be involved in the colonization of specific host cells. One type of pili, known as sex pili or F pili, function in bacterial conjugation.

Bacterial Spores

The medically important gram-positive bacteria that are capable of forming spores be-

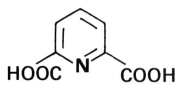

Fig. 2.19. Dipicolinic acid.

long to the genus *Bacillus* (aerobes or facultative anaerobes) and the genus *Clostridium* (strict anaerobes). These organisms have the capacity, under conditions where nutrients are limited (e.g., shifting from an exponential to a stationary phase of growth), to undergo a complex process of diffferentiation that leads to the formation, within the vegetative cells, of a new type of cell called an *endospore*. After lysis of the vegetative cell, the spore is liberated into the environment, where it can remain dormant but viable for many years. Mature spores are highly dehydrated and extremely stable structures. They exhibit little metabolic activity and show a marked resistance to heat, drying, freezing, and toxic chemicals. The ability of spores to resist heat may be due to their dehydrated state and their content of calcium dipicolinate (Fig. 2.19). As the spore matures, the uptake of Ca^{2+} ions by the sporulating cell and the synthesis of dipicolinic acid is correlated with the development of refractility and heat resistance. Dipicolinic acid accounts for 10 to

15 percent of the spore dry weight and is only found in the spore, not in the vegetative cell. The morphological events leading up to sporulation is shown in the Figure 2.20. As the growth phase shifts from an exponential to a stationary phase, an axial filament of chromatin is seen (Stage 1). The next event is the formation of a transverse septum near one pole of the cell (Stage 2), which separates the DNA and cytoplasm of the smaller cell from the rest of the cell. The membrane of the larger cell continues to grow around the smaller cell (Stage 3) and encloses the forespore protoplast within the cytoplasm of the larger cell. The cortex layer and spore wall are synthesized between the two unit membranes (Stage 4). The spore wall that surrounds the inner membrane is a typical cellular peptidoglycan, which will become the cell wall of the germinating cell. The cortex is composed of a unique peptidoglycan with very little cross-linking between tetrapeptide chains. Spore-coat formation occurs outside the outer unit membrane surrounding the cortex and represents 30 to 60 percent of the dry weight of the spore (Stage 5). It is a keratinlike protein that contains a high content of cysteine and hydrophobic amino acids and accounts for approximately 80 percent of the total spore protein. Spore maturation occurs during Stage 6 — refractility develops, Ca^{2+} ions and dipicolinic acid are accumulated, and the mature spore becomes heat resistant. In some cases an additional outer envelope called the *exosporium* is formed. In Stage 7 the mature endospore is liberated from the mother cell.

GROWTH

Growth is defined as the orderly increase in the amount of all components of the bacterial cell. A bacterial cell placed in a suitable environment grows until it almost doubles in size, and then divides by binary fission into two daughter cells. Under ideal condi-

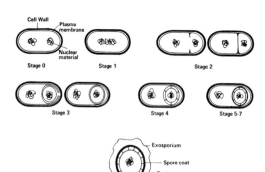

Fig. 2.20. Morphologic events associated with sporulation. See text for explanation.

tions the daughter cells will also continue to grow at the same rate as their parent and again, when the cells attain the critical size, will undergo binary fission to produce four cells. Under optimal conditions this process could go on indefinitely but, of course, does not for reasons that will be discussed shortly.

There are a number of ways to measure the growth of a bacterial population, among them are the determination of cell mass and cell numbers. Cell mass can be determined directly by measuring dry weight per unit volume of culture, but this method is not done routinely because it is time consuming and relatively insensitive. It can be determined indirectly by measuring nitrogen or protein content or by determining the amount of light scattered by a suspension of cells using a spectrophotometer. The transmission is related to the dry weight of cells per unit volume of culture by means of a standard curve. The standard curve can then be used to convert absorbancy readings to that of cell mass.

The total number of cells per unit volume of culture can be determined microscopically by counting the cells in a special counting chamber. This count represents both viable and nonviable cells, and requires 10^7 bacterial cells per ml or more before counts can be made with any degree of accuracy. The most sensitive method of determining the number of bacterial cells is the viable cell count. Suitable dilutions of a bacterial suspension are plated in an agar medium that will permit growth of the organism. Each cell deposited on the medium will grow to a macroscopic colony that can be counted.

The Growth Curve

Under ideal conditions bacteria, like other living organisms, grow according to a geometric progression. Each cell gives rise to two daughter cells, each daughter cell in turn gives rise to two more cells (a total of four

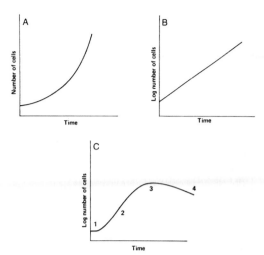

Fig. 2.21. (A) A plot of number of cells vs. time results in an exponential curve. (B) A plot of logarithm of cell numbers vs. time gives rise to a straight line. (C) Growth curve showing the various phases of growth — (1) lag phase; (2) exponential phase; (3) stationary phase; and (4) death phase.

cells), and so forth. If the number of cells per unit volume of culture is plotted directly as a function of time (Fig. 2.21A), an exponential curve is obtained — plotting the logarithm of the number of cells as a function of time (Fig. 2.21B) gives a straight line. This phase of bacterial growth is known as the exponential or logarithmic phase. The exponential phase of growth is a constant rate of growth that is maximal for the organism in a specific environment. It is an inherent property of the species and may differ from species to species.

The straight-line relationship between the logarithm of the cell number versus time is given by the following equation:

$$\log_{10}N = \frac{\mu}{2.303}\ (t - t_0) + \log_{10}N_0 \qquad (1)$$

where N_0 and N are the number of cells at times t_0 and t, respectively, and μ is the growth-rate constant. The slope of the line is $\mu/2.303$. The rate of growth of a culture can be defined by μ or g, which is the generation time or mean doubling time. This value expresses the growth rate as the period of time required for a growing population to double. When $N = 2N_0$, $t-t_0 = g$. Substituting in equation (1), one obtains

$$g = \frac{0.693}{\mu}$$

The value of g varies depending on the organism and the growth medium. In some bacteria g is rapid (e.g., 0.3 hours for *E. coli*) or very slow (e.g., 20 hours for *Nitrobacter agilis*).

The exponential phase of growth continues until the environment becomes less favorable for growth, and the growth rate declines until it enters the stationary phase of growth (Fig. 2.21C). In this phase no further increase in growth takes place, and the total number of viable cells remains constant. A declining growth rate is usually due to nutrient exhaustion or the accumulation of toxic metabolic products. If cells remain in the stationary phase for a period of time, they will begin to die. The death rate exhibits exponential kinetics and is dependent on the type of organism (some die slowly, others rapidly) in the environment.

When bacterial cells are transferred from an exponentially growing culture into a fresh medium of the same composition, the new culture will continue to grow at the same exponential rate. If, however, the inoculum is transferred to a fresh medium of a different composition (e.g., different carbon or nitrogen source), the number of viable cells may not increase immediately and a lag phase is observed (Fig. 2.21C). During the lag phase, the cells are adjusting to the new environment by synthesizing the necessary enzymes and metabolic intermediates that are required for growth. When sufficiently high levels of the necessary components are present, the cells can then resume growth at a maximal rate. Lag phases are often observed when bacterial cells obtained from a stationary culture are inoculated into fresh medium. In this case

the lag phase may be due to the low level of ribosome content. Ribosome content declines during the stationary phase, and sufficiently high levels must be restored to permit rapid protein synthesis. Bacterial cells grown in a rich medium are larger than cells grown in a poor medium. Cells growing at the faster rate have higher levels of ribosomes than cells growing more slowly. It is the ribosome content that accounts for the increase in size in the more rapidly growing cells.

Factors Influencing Bacterial Growth

The growth of bacteria is influenced by both the physical and nutritional environments.

Physical Factors. Physical factors include temperature and pH. Generally, most bacteria, including pathogens, have optimal growth at temperatures between 30 and 44°C. Bacteria in this group are called *mesophiles*. *Psychrophiles* grow best at temperatures between 15 and 20°C, but members of this group may grow at temperatures as low as 2 or 3°C. *Thermophiles* grow best between 50 and 60°C, although some forms have even been found growing at temperatures above 95°C.

Most bacteria grow optimally between pH 6.0 and 8.0. Some forms have pH optima as low as 2.0, whereas others may have optima as high as 8.5.

Nutritional Factors. Nutrients in the environment must provide the bacteria with a source of energy and carbon for synthesis of cellular components. Bacteria that are *heterotrophic* utilize organic carbon as a source of energy and as a precursor to synthesis of cell materials. *Autotrophic* (*lithotrophic*) organisms utilize carbon dioxide as the sole source of carbon. These organisms either use sunlight (photoautotrophs) or oxidize inorganic compounds (chemoautotrophs) as a source of energy. Nitrogen must be provided in a form that can be utilized by the bacteria. Some bacteria can reduce atmospheric nitrogen, others can use nitrates or nitrites, and some require nitrogen in the form of ammonium salts or in an organic form. In addition to carbon and nitrogen, bacteria require other elements, such as sulfur, phosphorous, potassium, magnesium, calcium, and iron.

ENERGY METABOLISM

In order to grow, bacterial cells must utilize nutrients from the environment as a source of energy and as a source of raw materials for synthesis. The sum total of these chemical processes is designated as the metabolism of the cell. The mechanisms used by microorganisms to generate energy in the form of ATP include fermentation, respiration, and photosynthesis.

Fermentation

Fermentation is defined as an energy-yielding oxidation-reduction process, in which organic compounds serve as electron donors and electron acceptors. In the ox-

idation of the metabolite, two electrons and two protons are removed (this is equivalent to removal of two hydrogen atoms), and the metabolite that becomes oxidized is referred to as the electron or H donor. The substance that accepts the two electrons and two protons and becomes reduced is referred to as the electron or H acceptor.

Many bacteria, including those of clinical importance, ferment carbohydrates to pyruvate by glycolysis (Fig. 2.22). The fermentation of glucose to pyruvate yields two molecules of ATP and two molecules of $NADH_2$ per molecule of glucose fermented. ATP and $NADH_2$ are generated by the oxidation of glyceraldehyde 3-phosphate to 3-phosphoglyceric acid. The conversion of 3-phosphoglyceric acid to pyruvic acid also results in the formation of ATP. This process of ATP formation is known as *substrate level phosphorylation*. In order for fermentation to continue, $NADH_2$ must be reoxidized to NAD, which can then pick up more electrons. Thus the coenzyme can function in a catalytic manner. Pyruvate or some metabolite derived from pyruvate, functions as the

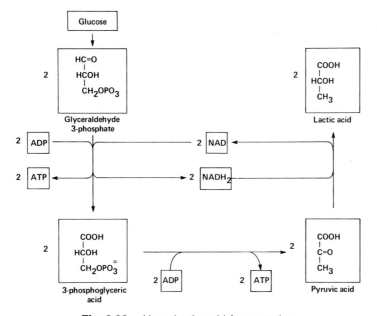

Fig. 2.22.   Homolactic acid fermentation.

electron acceptor, accepting electrons from NADH$_2$, which becomes reoxidized to NAD. The reduced substance accumulates as the characteristic end product of the fermentation.

The end products of fermentation are characteristic for specific groups of organisms. Members of the genus *Streptococcus*, which include important pathogens, ferment glucose almost quantitatively to lactic acid (Fig. 2.22). This is called *homolactic fermentation*.

The *alcoholic fermentation* characteristic of yeasts utilizes glycolysis to ferment glucose to ethanol and CO$_2$. As a consequence of the reduction of acetaldehyde, NAD is regenerated (Fig. 2.23). The intermediate pyruvate can give rise to various end products — the major products and the fermentation type is shown in Figure 2.24.

The energy obtained from a sugar molecule by fermentation is only a small fraction of the energy available. In order to liberate the remaining energy, pyruvic acid must be further oxidized to CO$_2$ and H$_2$O. This occurs in respiration and is discussed in the next section. It should be noted that some

bacteria use mechanisms other than glycolysis for the fermentation of sugar (e.g., reactions of the pentose phosphate pathway). Also, substances other than carbohydrates can be fermented (e.g., amino acids, organic acids, purines, and pyrimidines).

Respiration

Respiration can be defined as an energy-yielding process in which either organic or inorganic compounds are electron donors and inorganic compounds are electron acceptors. If the final electron acceptor is O$_2$, the process is called *aerobic respiration*. If the final electron acceptors are carbonates, nitrates, or sulfates, the process is called *anaerobic respiration*.

Respiratory processes are characterized by the presence of an electron transport chain. Electrons removed from the substrate are accepted by NAD, which becomes reduced to NADH$_2$. NADH$_2$ is then reoxidized by donation of electrons through a system of carriers that become reduced and then reoxidized as the electrons are transferred to the next component of the chain.

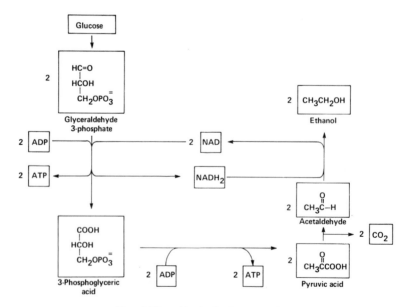

Fig. 2.23. Alcoholic fermentation.

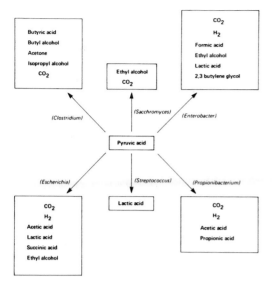

Fig. 2.24. Fermentation end products derived from pyruvic acid.

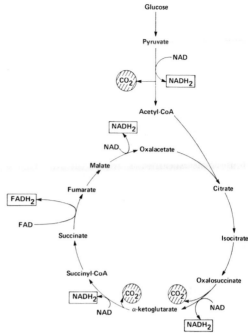

Fig. 2.26. The tricarboxylic acid cycle.

(Fig. 2.25). As electrons move down the chain, energy is released and trapped as ATP. The generation of ATP by this process is referred to as *oxidative phosphorylation*.

The oxidation of glucose to CO_2 and H_2O utilizes the glycolytic (or alternative pathways) to pyruvate. Pyruvate is oxidized to acetyl coenzyme A (CoA) and CO_2, and acetyl-CoA enters the tricaboxylic acid cycle (Krebs cycle) and is oxidized to CO_2 and H_2O. Electrons that are removed are passed along the electron transport chains to the terminal electron acceptor, and ATP is produced (Fig. 2.26).

Microorganisms are capable of oxidizing many substrates other than glucose, for example, amino acids, lipids, and a variety of other carbohydrates. In fact, for each naturally occurring substance, there is a microorganism capable of oxidizing it.

If oxygen is unavailable, some organisms are able to utilize nitrate instead of O_2 as the terminal electron acceptor. Bacteria capable of using nitrate, however, prefer to use O_2 as the electron acceptor if it is available. Nitrate is reduced to nitrite (e.g., *E. coli*), and nitrite is excreted. Certain bacteria, such as *Pseudomonas aeruginosa*, are able to reduce nitrate to N_2 gas, which is released into the atmosphere. These are the denitrifying bacteria, and the process is called denitrification. Anaerobic respiration using nitrate as the terminal electron acceptor permits the complete oxidation of the substrate to CO_2. For example, *Bacillus licheniformis* growing in glucose and nitrate under anaerobic conditions will oxidize glucose to CO_2 and H_2O via glycolysis and the tricarboxylic acid cycle. The $NADH_2$ formed will donate electrons to the respiratory chain, which are then transferred through the chain to the nitrate.

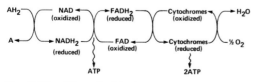

Fig. 2.25. The electric transport system. The transport of a pair of electrons from NAD to O_2 produces 3 molecules of ATP.

32   Medical Microbiology

Some bacteria can use CO_2 and sulfate as terminal electron acceptors. The reduction of CO_2 to methane and sulfate to sulfide is carried out by strict anaerobes; O_2 is not an alternative electron acceptor. The methanogenic bacteria are responsible for the biological formation of methane in anaerobic environments where there is decomposing organic matter. The sulfate-reducing bacteria (desulfovibrios) occur in anaerobic sediments that contain organic matter and sulfate.

A unique group of aerobic chemoautotrophic bacteria are capable of obtaining energy from the oxidation of inorganic compounds and can utilize CO_2 as a carbon source. Inorganic electron donors include H_2, NH_4^+, NO_0^-, Fe^{2+}, H_2S, S, and S_2O_3. The oxidation of the inorganic substance provides ATP and reducing power for the synthesis of cellular material from CO_2. The nitrifying bacteria oxidize NH_4^+ to NO_2^- (*Nitrosomonas*) and NO_2^- to NO_3^- (*Nitrobacter*). The sulfur oxidizers oxidize H_2S, S, or $S_2O_3^{2-}$ to SO_4^{2-}, the iron bacteria oxidize Fe^{2+} to Fe^{3+}, and the hydrogen bacteria oxidize H_2 to H_2O. The latter group of bacteria are also chemoheterotrophs (can utilize organic substances as sources of carbon and energy).

Microorganisms that have an absolute requirement for O_2 as the terminal electron acceptor are *obligate aerobes*. These organisms are strictly dependent on respiration as their ultimate source of energy. *Obligate anaerobes*, on the other hand, grow only in the absence of O_2. Some organisms are inhibited or may even be killed by exposure to O_2. These organisms obtain their energy by fermentation or by anaerobic respiration. *Facultative anaerobes* can grow in the absence of O_2; for example, by fermentation. However, if O_2 is available, these organisms can shift to a respiratory metabolism. *Aerotolerant anaerobes* do not use O_2 but can grow in its presence. These organisms use a fermentation type of metabolism and are not sensitive to the presence of air.

Obligate anaerobes are sensitive to O_2 because they lack the ability to remove toxic by-products that result from O_2 consumption; for example, hydrogen peroxide (H_2O_2) and the highly reactive free radical, superoxide (O_2^-). Obligate anaerobes lack the enzyme superoxide dismutase, which catalyzes the reaction

$$2O_2^- + 2H^+ \rightarrow O_2 + H_2O_2$$

and the enzyme catalase, which catalyzes the reaction

$$2H_2O_2 \rightarrow 2H_2O + O_2$$

Some microorganisms lack catalase (e.g., lactic acid bacteria) but utilize peroxidases (enzymes that catalyze the oxidation of organic compounds by H_2O_2; H_2O_2 becomes reduced to $2H_2O$). According to present evidence, the presence of superoxide dismutase is indispensable for an organism to survive in the presence of air. Mutants of *E. coli*, a facultative anaerobe, that lack the enzyme become obligate anaerobes.

Photosynthesis

Some bacteria, like green plants and blue-green bacteria, are capable of generating ATP by using light as a source of energy. In the case of green plants and the blue-green bacteria, photosynthesis also produces $NADPH_2$ and O_2 as a result of the oxidation of water. $NADPH_2$ is subsequently utilized as a source of reducing power for the assimilation of CO_2, the principal carbon source. Unlike green plants or the blue-green bacteria, phototrophic bacteria do not utilize water as the ultimate reductant, and O_2 is never evolved. In bacterial photosynthesis the principal photochemical event results in ATP formation. Some photoautotrophic bacteria oxidize inorganic substances, such as H_2S or H_2, in order to obtain the necessary reducing power for CO_2 assimilation. Photoheterotrophic bacteria are able to oxidize organic compounds as the principal carbon source and do not require inorganic compounds as reductants.

REFERENCES

Davis, B.D., Dulbecco, R., Eisen, H.N., et al: Microbiology. 3rd Ed. Harper & Row, New York, 1980.

Gottschalk, G: Bacterial Metabolism. Springer-Verlag, New York, 1979.

Jawetz, E., Melnick, J.L., and Adelberg, E.A.: Review of Medical Microbiology. 13th Ed. Lange Medical Publications, Los Altos, 1976.

Joklick, W.K., Willett, H.P., and Amos, D.B., Eds.: Zinsser Microbiology. 17th Ed. Appleton-Century-Crofts, New York, 1980.

Moat, A.G.: Microbial Physiology. John Wiley & Sons, Inc., New York, 1979.

Stanier, R.Y., Adelberg, E.A., and Ingraham, J.L.: The Microbial World. 4th Ed. Prentice-Hall, Englewood Cliffs, 1976.

3

Bacterial Genetics

Murray W. Stinson

Heredity in bacteria is governed by genes located in the single DNA molecule or chromosome comprising the nuclear body. In many bacteria additional genetic information is carried on small extrachromosomal DNA elements known as *plasmids*. Both DNA structures are duplicated and transmitted linearly to the succeeding generation during transverse binary fission.

CHROMOSOMAL REPLICATION AND SEGREGATION

The physical properties of the bacterial chromosome have been previously described (Ch. 2). A schematic representation of the semiconservative replication of the *Escherichia coli* chromosome is shown in Figure 3.1. In the initial step, a region of the double-stranded chromosome (replicator site) separates into single strands. This is followed by synthesis of a short complementary segment of RNA by an RNA polymerase on each of the strands. The RNA serves as an initial primer for DNA polymerase III, which then moves along the single-stranded DNA templates. Two growing points of DNA polymerization, known as *replication forks*, proceed in opposite directions from the initiation site until they meet 180 degrees away on the circular chromosome. The supercoiled DNA helix unwinds ahead of the replicating fork. The torque exerted on the fragile molecule by the unwinding mechanism is relieved by the action of certain enzymes (swivelase) that break one strand from time to time, creating a swivel. The break is resealed immediately after unwinding. Polymerization occurs only in a 5' to 3' direction on each of the template strands. Since the template strands are antiparallel, their replication occurs simultaneously in opposite directions. Short segments of about 1000 nucleotides (connected to the RNA primer) are polymerized on the DNA template by DNA polymerase III. These short DNA–RNA hybrid strands, named Okazaki segments after their discoverer, are further processed by ribonuclease H and DNA polymerase I. The former enzyme degrades the RNA primer segment, and the latter replaces it with DNA. A continuous DNA strand is then produced by the action of DNA ligase, which joins the 5' phosphoryl and 3'-OH ends of the newly synthesized segments.

Separation of the replicating chromosome occurs gradually during growth of the bacterial cell. Movement of the chromosomes is mediated by the cytoplasmic membrane, rather than the microtubules characteristic of the mitotic apparatus of eukaryo-

35

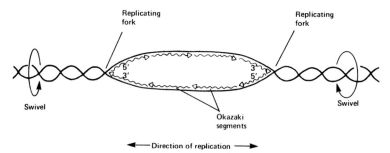

Fig. 3.1. Schematic representation of chromosome replication. DNA synthesis proceeds in opposite directions from the point of initiation, creating two replication forks. The newly synthesized DNA strands (Okazaki fragments) are polymerized in the 5' to 3' direction using the single-stranded regions of the original molecules as templates. These fragments are subsequently joined together by DNA ligases. Endonucleases periodically make cuts in one DNA strand to permit the localized unwinding of the DNA duplex.

tic cells. A diagramatic model for DNA segregation in bacteria is shown in Figure 3.2. A specific region of the bacterial chromosome is attached to a component (presumably a protein) on the internal surface of the cytoplasmic membrane. The replicator site and the membrane attachment site are in close proximity on the chromosome. After duplication of this DNA region, both attachment sites are bound to distinct points on the membrane surface. Growth of the membrane spreads these attachment sites farther and farther apart as DNA replication proceeds. During logarithmic growth, the separation of daughter chromosomes occurs well ahead of cell division.

PLASMIDS

Plasmids confer important characteristics on the host bacterium, such as drug resistance (R plasmids), the ability to transfer DNA through cell to cell contact (conjugative plasmids), toxin production (toxogenic plasmids), antibiotic production (bacteriocin plasmids), and metabolic activity (degradative plasmids). Also, some bacteria contain plasmids whose properties have not yet been identified (cryptic plasmids). Under most environmental conditions, plasmids are not essential to cell viability; that is, they may be lost without any ill effects.

Plasmids are circular, double-stranded

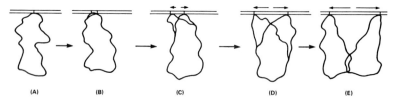

(A)   (B)   (C)   (D)   (E)

Fig. 3.2. A hypothetical model showing the segregation of membrane-attached bacterial chromosomes during replication. (A) The chromosome is attached to the membrane at or near the replication site. (B) After replication of this DNA region, both attachment sites are membrane bound. (C, D, E) As DNA replication proceeds, the membrane attachment sites are separated by localized membrane synthesis and the DNA molecules are drawn toward the cell poles.

DNA molecules with a size range of 5 to 140 megadaltons, corresponding to about 7 to 200 genes. Plasmids associate with specific sites on the internal surface of the cytoplasmic membrane and undergo autonomous replication, usually in synchrony with the bacterial chromosome. The mechanism of replication appears to be similar to the one previously described for the bacterial chromosome, although in some plasmids replication may be unidirectional. Some plasmids contain regions that have base sequence homology with sites on the host chromosome and can combine (integrate) with the chromosome, forming a single replicon. Therefore, in these bacteria the plasmid can replicate either autonomously on the cell membrane or as an integral part of the chromosome. Plasmids with the ability to shift between these two modes of replication are called *episomes*. This term is used to describe the behavior of a plasmid rather than as a synonym, since it is a variable characteristic. For example, plasmids capable of inhabiting more than one bacterial genus may exist as an episome in one host and strictly as a plasmid in the other.

Some plasmids are transmitted from cell to cell by direct contact, a process known as bacterial *conjugation*. The physiologic mechanisms that mediate the mating process and DNA transfer are governed exclusively by plasmid genes. Plasmids that do not mediate self-transfer can be transmitted to other bacteria by temperate bacteriophages in a process known as *transduction*.

PHENOTYPIC VARIATION

The full complement of genes carried by a cell is called its genotype, whereas the characteristics conferred upon the cell by the products of these genes are its phenotype. In bacteria, phenotype is highly variable, since the expression (transcription) of most genes is stringently regulated. Under any set of environmental conditions, some genes are transcribed whereas many are not. This regulation enables the bacterial cell to adapt to the everchanging environmental conditions. Signals are received from the environment in the form of low molecular weight nutrients, temperature, hydrogen ion concentration, or oxygen pressure. Some act as inducers of gene transcription, resulting in a marked increase in the rate of synthesis of one or more enzymes. For example, *E. coli* has genetic information for the metabolism of lactose, but the necessary enzymes are not synthesized unless lactose is present in the environment. Other environmental factors act as corepressors of gene transcription, causing a marked reduction in the rate of synthesis of one or more enzymes. This type of regulation is commonly encountered with biosynthetic systems. For example, the set of genes involved in the biosynthesis of tryptophan in *E. coli* are not expressed when large quantities of the amino acid are present in the environment. It is more efficient for the cell to obtain the preformed tryptophan from the environment than to synthesize it from other nutrient precursors.

A simplified scheme for genetic regulation is shown in Figure 3.3. In inducible systems a regulator gene codes for an active repressor protein which binds to the operator locus on the chromosome (when the inducer is absent) and prevents transcription of the adjacent genes. The inducer, usually the substrate, binds to and inactivates the repressor protein, preventing its binding to the operator locus and thereby permitting transcription to occur. In repressible systems the regulator genes code for an inactive repressor protein. Since this repressor cannot bind to the operator, transcription of the adjacent genes occurs freely. The repressor protein becomes activated after combining with a corepressor, such as the end product of a biosynthetic pathway. The resulting complex then binds

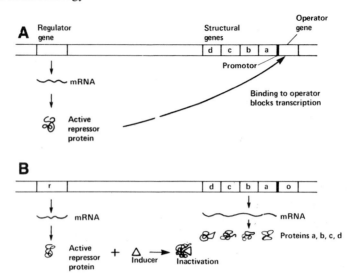

Fig. 3.3 Operon model for the regulation of inducible enzyme synthesis. The horizontal bar represents a region of a chromosome. Genes are indicated by segments. (A) In the absence of an inducer, an active repressor protein is produced by a regulator gene. This protein then binds to its specific operator gene and blocks transcription of the adjacent genes *a* through *d*. (B) When the inducer is present, it combines with the repressor protein preventing it from binding to the operator gene. Genes *a* through *d* are then transcribed.

to the operator to block transcription of the genes coding for the enzymes of the biosynthetic pathway.

GENOTYPIC VARIATION

In addition to the acquisition of extrachromosomal DNA, bacteria obtain new characteristics through mutations in chromosomal genes. These changes in the nucleotide sequence of a gene result in a polypeptide with an altered structure and function. Mutations may appear spontaneously or by induction with chemical agents (mutagens). As a consequence of mutation, a given gene can exist in a number of different forms called *alleles*. Native genes, as they are found in organisms when first isolated from nature, are designated *wild-type alleles*, whereas modified forms of these genes are termed *mutant alleles*.

The most frequent mutations are the re-sult of base-pair substitutions, frame-shift alterations, and large deletions. Base-pair substitutions, also called point mutations, are characterized by the modification of a single codon within the gene. This occurs when one base pair, such as TA, is replaced by a different base pair, such as GC, during replication. Frame-shift mutations are characterized by breaks in the sugar-phosphate backbone of DNA and a deletion or insertion of one or a few base pairs, causing a shift in the reading frame for translation. In this shift an entirely new set of codons is produced. For example, if a segment of the wild-type gene reads –/CAA/GAG/ACT/CAG/TTA/–, deletion of the third base shifts the reading frame to –/CAG/AGA/CTC/AGT/TA–. Large deletions, as the name implies, are mutations in which a long segment of the gene is removed.

The probability that a bacterium will experience a spontaneous mutation is 10^{-6} to

10^{-8} per generation, about the same as in higher organisms. Although mutation is a rare event, a small number of mutant cells are always present in bacterial cultures due to their short generation times (some divide every 30 minutes) and the extremely large numbers of cells in most populations; for example, a milliliter of a broth culture or a single colony on an agar medium often contains 10^9 cells. In nature most mutant cells do not survive very long after their initial appearance in the population. This is because most mutations result in some impairment of gene function. For example, the cell may lose an enzyme necessary for the synthesis of the amino acid tryptophan, creating a nutritional requirement. Under conditions of tryptophan limitation, the mutants gradually die out, whereas the wild-type cells proliferate. If a mutation does not cause a serious defect, the mutant cell may continue to grow at the same rate as the wild-type cell, so that the proportion of mutants in the population remains constant. A mutant cell is unlikely to become the predominant strain in the population unless the environment provides them with a selective advantage. When they occur these selective pressures can be very strong. For example, a mutation that alters the structure of the ribosomal protein S12, so that it no longer has a binding affinity for streptomycin, renders the cell antibiotic resistant. In the absence of the drug, the mutant cells remain at a low frequency in the population. However, when streptomycin is present in the environment, the mutant strain overgrows the streptomycin-sensitive parental strain with astonishing speed. After only a few hours incubation, the entire population is composed of the mutant strain.

GENETIC RECOMBINATION

In procaryotic cells new genes arising from mutation and selection are subsequently distributed among taxonomically related microorganisms by genetic recombination. In this process a recombinant chromosome is derived from the DNA of two parental cells. The mechanism of gene transfer in prokaryotic cells differs considerably from the sexual process of eukaryotic cells, in which two haploid gametes fuse to form a diploid zygote. Instead, only a fragment of the chromosome of the donor bacterium is transferred to the recipient cell. The recipient cell becomes a partial zygote or *merozygote*, since it is diploid in only a portion of its chromosome. The fragment of donor cell DNA introduced into the recipient cell is termed the *exogenote*, and the chromosome of the recipient cell is designated the *endogenote*. Transfer of the exogenote is accomplished by three distinct mechanisms: the uptake of naked DNA from the environment (transformation), direct cell to cell contact (conjugation), or bacteriophage infection (transduction).

Fates of the Exogenote

Host Restriction. The persistence of the exogenote in the recipient cell following transfer depends upon the DNA restriction –modification systems of both the donor and recipient cells. Bacteria contain endonucleases (restricting enzymes) that degrade foreign DNA that has penetrated the cell. The endogenote is protected from this fate by methylation of the bases at the same sites recognized by the endonuclease. The DNA base sequences recognized by restricting and modifying enzymes vary widely in bacteria, and complex patterns of compatibilities exist between genera, species, and strains. If the exogenote is derived from a cell with a restriction–modification system dissimilar to that of the recipient cell, in most instances it is rapidly degraded. Rarely does it persist long enough for methylation and recombination to occur. Conversely, an exogenote from an organism with a restriction–modification system compatible with the recipient survives for extended periods following transfer.

Recombination. Three types of recombination occur in bacteria and bacteriophages; generalized, site-specific, and illegitimate recombination. These mechanisms are distinguished from one another by their requirements for base-sequence homology between the parental DNA strands, the source of the protein mediators, and the extent of DNA degradation and synthesis. *Generalized recombination* requires extensive base-sequence homology between the parental DNA molecules. After hydrogen bonding between the complementary strands, a recombinant chromosome is formed by crossing-over, a process involving breakage and reunion of the parental strands. In *E. coli* the mechanism is mediated by endonuclease, exonuclease, DNA polymerase, and polynucleotide ligase — enzymes that also function in DNA repair. Chromosomal genes *recA, recB,* and *recC* control the production and action of the nucleases. Although a number of models have been proposed to explain generalized recombination, the exact sequence of

events is unknown. Recombination between two DNA duplexes is believed to be initiated by an endonuclease that makes a nick at appropriate sites on the DNA strands. Subsequent events lead to an asymmetric strand integration (Fig. 3.4) or a double strand integration (Fig. 3.5). Recombination between an endogenote and a single-stranded exogenote, such as that acquired by transformation, is depicted in Figure 3.6.

Site-specific recombination does not require extensive homology between the DNA molecules and is independent of the *rec* gene system. This mechanism mediates the integration of the bacteriophage λ genome into the *E. coli* chromosome. Integration comprises a single reciprocal cross-over event within a 15-base-pair sequence of the circular viral DNA and an identical seqence in the host replicon. The process requires the presence of a viral gene product, λ integrase. No DNA degradation or synthesis occurs. Excision of the prophage from the chromosome (Fig. 3.12)

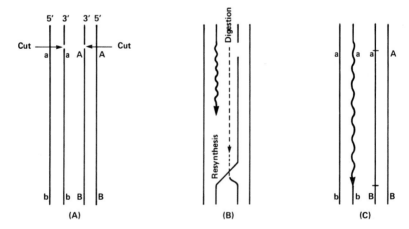

Fig. 3.4 Genetic recombination by asymmetric strand integration. (A) One parental molecule carries the markers AB, the other ab. Each parental molecule has a single-strand cut. (B) The parental duplexes have partially unwound and a strand from one molecule has paired with the complementary strand of the second molecule. The free strand is digested by exonuclease, and resynthesis occurs along the single-strand regions. Resynthesis and rejoining produce a heteroduplex on only one of the parental molecules.

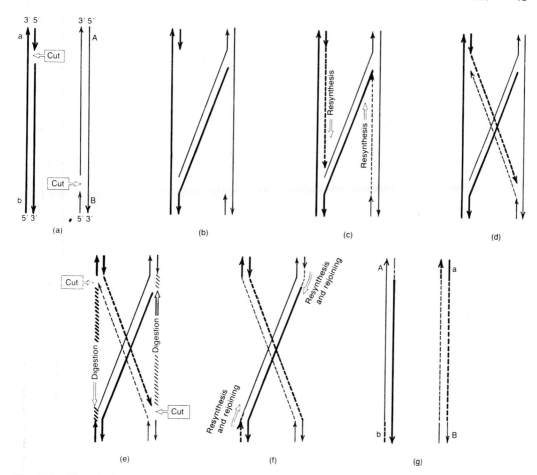

Fig. 3.5. Hypothetical mechanism of recombination between DNA molecules. (a) One parental molecule carries the markers AB, the other ab. Each parental molecule has a single strand cut at a different position, between markers A and B. (b) The parental duplexes have partially unwound, and a strand from one molecule has paired with a strand from the other molecule. (c) Resynthesis occurs along the single-stranded region of each parental molecule (dashed lines). (d) The newly synthesized strands pair with each other. (e) An endonuclease makes a single-strand cut in each parental duplex, and the cut 3' ends are sequentially digested by an exonuclease. (f and g) Resynthesis and rejoining produce two recombinant molecules, Ab and aB. (After H. White-house. From Stanier, R.Y., Adelberg, E.A., and Ingraham, J.L.: The Microbial World. 4th Ed. Prentice-Hall, Englewood Cliffs, N.J., 1976.)

reverses this process and is dependent on another viral protein, excisionase.

Illegitimate recombination is independent of the *rec* gene system and does not exhibit site specificity. This mechanism is responsible for the transposition of DNA segments within replicons. Bacterial chromosomes and plasmids may have several segments, containing 800 to 1400 base pairs, that can be translocated to another region of the same or to another replicon. These *insertion sequences (IS)* can integrate at any site on the DNA duplex. When inserted next to a gene, an IS may influence that gene's function or may occasionally carry the gene along when it undergoes transposition. Several stable transposable elements containing genes that specify drug resistance

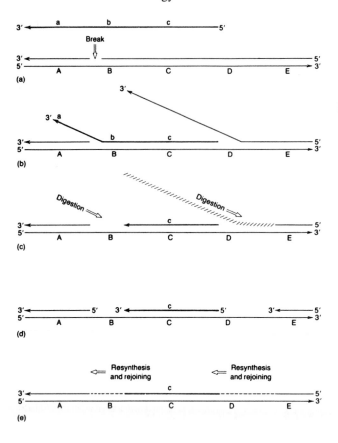

Fig. 3.6. Integration of a single-stranded exogenote with a double-stranded endogenote. (a) A single-stranded fragment carrying the markers abc lies near a double-stranded molecule carrying the markers ABCDE. There is a single-strand break between markers A and B. (b) Partial unwinding of the duplex permits pairing between exogenote and endogenote. (c and d) An exonuclease digests the free 3' ends. (e) Resynthesis by polymerase and rejoining by polynucleotide ligase produce a recombinant molecule, in which one of the strands carries the markers ABcDE. (Stanier, R.Y., Adelberg, E.A., and Ingraham, J.L.: The Microbial World. 4th Ed. Prentice-Hall, Englewood Cliffs, N.J.; 1976.)

mechanisms have been detected in bacteria. In these *transposons* (*Tn*) the drug resistance gene is flanked by identical IS segments. The mechanism by which the IS and Tn elements undergo recombination is obscure. The IS segments may serve as recognition sites for specialized recombination enzymes. IS and Tn elements are replicated at the time of transposition; one copy is inserted at the new site and the other copy remains at the old site. Illegitimate recombination also occurs during generation of F' genotes (Fig. 3.11C) and λdg genote (Fig. 3.12B) and is believed to be mediated by IS segments.

Abortive Transduction. If host restrictions and chromosome recombination do not occur, the exogenote may persist and function without replication. This situation occurs frequently in transduction and is known as *abortive transduction*. At the time of cell division, the transducing DNA is passed to only one of the daughter cells. As growth and cell division proceed, only one cell in the entire clone is a partial diploid.

Autonomous Replication. When the exogenote contains genes governing autonomous replication, such as a segment of a prophage or plasmid, the DNA element may persist, function, and replicate as an independent unit.

Transformation

A number of bacterial genera (*Streptococcus*, *Bacillus*, *Neisseria*, and *Haemophilus*) readily take up soluble DNA released into the environment by the lysis of other bacteria. Other bacteria, such as *E. coli* and *Pseudomonas aeruginosa*, can be induced to take up extraneous DNA by suspending them in high concentrations of divalent cations (calcium or magnesium). This treatment apparently increases DNA penetration by dissociating lipopolysaccharide and proteins from the cell surface and unmasking DNA binding sites on the cytoplasmic membrane. The phenomenon of transformation has been intensively studied in *Streptococcus pneumoniae* and *Bacillus subtilis.* Although a general model can be proposed on the basis of these studies, the biochemical and physical properties of bacteria responsible for the transport of high molecular weight DNA through the cytoplasmic membrane and its recombination with the endogenote have yet to be identified.

The initial event in transformation is the binding of DNA fragments to the surface of the recipient cell. This attachment is mediated by specific receptors located on the ex-

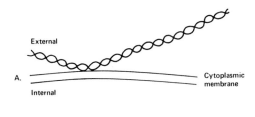

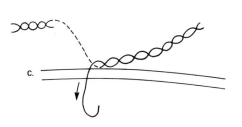

Fig. 3.7. Schematic representation for the uptake of soluble DNA by bacteria. A. A double-stranded DNA segment is bound to the external surface of the cytoplasmic membrane. B. Endonucleases cut the DNA strands. C. One strand is translocated across the membrane while the second is degraded by exonuclease.

ternal surface of the cytoplasmic membrane (Fig. 3.7). Binding is accompanied by a single-strand scission by an endonuclease. Entry of DNA does not commence until a second endonuclease cuts the remaining parental DNA strand opposite the original nick, causing a double-strand break. One DNA strand is then translocated across the membrane, while the complementary strand is enzymatically digested. Only one strand of the original duplex is taken into the cell. Uptake is by active transport, that is, it requires the expenditure of metabolic energy.

The ability of a bacterium to take up DNA is termed *competence.* This physiologic state fluctuates greatly during growth of the culture, with maximum activity occurring during the logarithmic phase. Moreover, competence varies regularly during the cell division cycle. Synchronized cultures in logarithmic growth demonstrate maximum DNA uptake activity during the brief period of transverse septum formation.

The nature of competence is not fully understood, but current evidence suggests that it reflects the presence of a certain surface protein responsible for DNA binding, processing, and transport. For example, a membrane localized exonuclease is produced by competent *B. subtilis* cells, and competent *S. pneumoniae* cells possess an endonuclease in the membrane that is essential for DNA uptake. *S. pneumoniae* also secretes a protein (competence factor) into the culture medium that can confer competence to other *S. pneumoniae* cells. The mechanism of action of this 5000 to 10,000-dalton protein is not known, but it is suspected of functioning in membrane transport or as an autolytic enzyme that alters the cell surface, exposing DNA receptors.

Competent bacteria do not take up DNA molecules smaller than 300,000 to 500,000 daltons, and double-stranded DNA (linear and cyclic) is bound to the cell surface and transported more efficiently than single-stranded DNA. The length of the internalized DNA varies among bacteria. In *S. pneumoniae* the strands found after entry are uniform in size (2 to 3 × 10⁶ daltons), regardless of the size of the initial donor DNA. In the divalent cation-facilitated transformation of *E. coli* and *P. aeruginosa*, it appears that the entering DNA remains unbroken. These bacteria can take up intact strands of plasmid and bacteriophage DNA.

Conjugation

Conjugation is the process by which bacteria transfer genetic material by direct cell to cell contact. The ability to undergo conjugation is determined by the presence of a conjugative plasmid (fertility factor) in the donor cell. This class of extrachromosomal DNA elements occurs in many genera of gram-negative bacteria, including *Escherichia, Proteus, Pseudomonas, Salmonella, Serratia, Shigella, Vibrio,* and *Yersinia.*

Two types of conjugative plasmids exist — those that replicate autonomously and those that replicate either autonomously or as part of the bacterial chromosome after integration. The autonomous conjugative plasmid facilitates its own transfer during conjugation, whereas the integrated plasmid can also mediate the transfer of bacterial genes. Most of our knowledge concerning the phenomenon of conjugation has come from studies of the *E. coli* system.

The conjugative plasmid initially detected in *E. coli* was designated the F (fertility) factor (now F1 plasmid). This double-stranded, circular DNA molecule has a mass of 45 megadaltons, about 1/50 the size of the *E. coli* chromosome. Although the F1 plasmid contains 40 to 60 genes, very few gene products have been identified. It is known that the plasmid codes for proteins necessary for autonomous replication and for a hollow surface appendage called the *sex (donor) pilus*. The pilus mediates the coherence of donor and recipient cells during conjugation and may participate in

DNA transfer (see below). Plasmid gene products also mediate the transfer of a molecule of plasmid DNA into the recipient cell. Bacteria bearing this plasmid in the autonomous state are termed F⁺ (males), and those cells not containing the plasmid are designated F⁻ (females).

Segments of the F1 plasmid share base-sequence homology with regions of the *E. coli* chromosome, permitting recombination. During this event the plasmid is integrated intact into the host genome by a double-strand crossover (Fig. 3.5). Bacteria carrying the plasmid in this state are termed *Hfr cells* (see below). In these cells the plasmid may dissociate itself from the host chromosome, reentering the autonomous state. Occasionally these excised plasmids contain small segments of DNA derived from the chromosome. These cells are called *F-prime (F')*, and the plasmid with the attached bacterial genes is known as an *F' genote* or simply *F genotes.*

F⁺ × F⁻ Crosses. The F⁺ × F⁻ con-

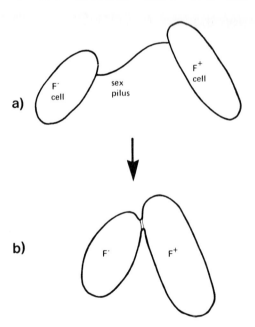

Fig. 3.8. Conjugation bridges in bacteria. a) A male and female cell connected by a conjugative pilus. b) A mating pair joined by a cell wall bridge.

jugation has been intensively studied in *E. coli*. Following a chance encounter between F⁺ and F⁻ cells, coherence is established via the sex pilus. The tip of this surface appendage on the F⁺ cell binds to a specific receptor site on the surface of the recipient cell (Fig. 3.8), an event analogous to the attachment of a bacteriophage tail. This cellular coherence phenomenon may result in mating aggregates containing between 2 and 20 cells. Although the pilus is essential for conjugation, its exact function is still open to speculation. Some experimental evidence indicates that DNA transfer can occur between cells separated by a significant distance. Therefore it has been proposed that the tubular sex pilus may act as a DNA transfer bridge during conjugation; however, conclusive evidence, such as isolation of pili containing DNA, is lacking. Studies with male-specific bacteriophages,

viruses that infect bacteria by attaching to the pilus, also implicate these structures as DNA transfer bridges. It has also been proposed that sex pili can retract, drawing the conjugation cells into tight wall-to-wall contact (Fig. 3.8). DNA transfer may then proceed through the retracted pilus or through a newly formed surface connection; that is, partial digestion of cell walls followed by fusion of cytoplasmic membranes. Electron microscopic examination of mating pairs has revealed both pilus linkage and cytoplasmic bridges. Although sex pili do retract into the male cell following the attachment of male-specific bacteriophages or incubation at 50°C, they have not as yet been observed to do so during conjugation.

Contact between the sex pilus and the recipient cell elicits a cycle of asymmetric replication of the plasmid DNA (Fig. 3.9).

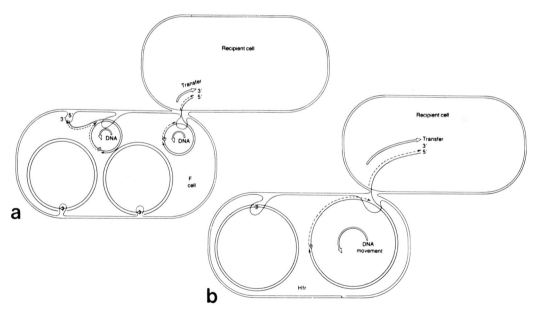

Fig. 3.9. A hypothetical mechanism of DNA transfer as a consequence of F replication. (a) An F⁺ cell, containing two autonomous F replicons and two chromosomes, is shown conjugating with a recipient cell. The F at the left is replicating within the host cell; the F at the right is being driven into the recipient by replication. (b) The same process takes place when an Hfr cell conjugates. Now, however, chromosomal DNA is also transferred as a result of its integration with F. (Stanier, R.Y., Adelberg, E.A., and Ingraham, J.L.; The Microbial World. 4th Ed. Prentice Hall, Englewood Cliffs, N.J., 1976)

One of the DNA strands is nicked by an endonuclease at a specific site, and the duplex unwinds. Replication of the intact DNA strand occurs as the plasmid rotates past the transfer bridge. The 5′ end of the broken strand enters the transfer bridge and is forced into the recipient cell, where synthesis of the complementary strand and circularization of the resulting duplex promptly ensue. Acquisition of the conjugative plasmid renders the recipient cell male; and since the donor cell retains a copy of the plasmid, it does not lose its ability to conjugate.

Although the plasmid is readily transmitted among *E. coli* cells, F⁺ strains are less prevalent in nature than F⁻ strains. The plasmid is lost spontaneously from many cells during growth of the culture. This is due to the failure of the plasmid to replicate synchronously with the host-cell genome. Experimentally, bacteria may be freed (cured) of conjugative plasmids and other plasmids by prolonged incubation in the stationary phase of growth, addition of low concentrations of chemicals that inhibit DNA replication (e.g., mitomycin C, actinomycin D, and acridine dyes), or growth at an elevated temperature (42°C).

F-Mediated Chromosome Transfer. Matings between F⁺ and F⁻ cells occasionally result in the transfer of bacterial genes; cells with recombinant chromosomes appear at a frequency of 10^{-4} to 10^{-5}. This mobilization of host cell DNA is due to the integration of the F plasmid into the chromosome, forming a single replicon. This cell and its progeny are called *Hfr strains* for the high frequency of recombination (10^{-2} to 10^{-3}) that occurs in the recipient cell population following conjugation.

The F1 plasmid can be reversibly integrated into eight or ten different sites on the *E. coli* chromosome. The chromosomal genes that are transferred during conjugation depend upon the site of integration. In a population of F⁺ cells, integration between the F1 plasmid and the chromosome

occurs approximately once per 10^{5} cells at each generation. Similarly, in a population of Hfr cells, detachment of the plasmid by a second double-strand crossover event occurs within one cell in 10^{5} per genera-

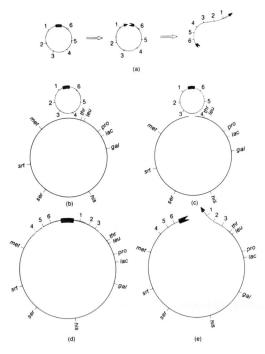

Fig. 3.10 The breakage and transfer of the Hfr chromosome as a consequence of its integration with F. (a) F is shown as a circle, which has a special site of breakage between markers 1 and 6. Breakage is followed by transfer (during conjugation), such that F markers penetrate the recipient in the order 1-2-3-4-5-6. (b) F has paired with a chromosomal site between *met* and *thr*. (c) A crossover in the region of pairing integrates the two circles. (d) Same as (c) but redrawn as a single circle. (e) Breakage at the special F site leads to transfer causing F markers 1-2-3 to enter the recipient first, followed by chromosomal markers *thr, leu, pro, lac*, and so on; F markers 4-5-6 enter last. Recombinants will be males if they receive all six F markers; thus, the terminal end of the chromosome must be transferred to produce an Hfr recombinant. (Stanier, R.Y., Adelberg, E.A. and Ingraham, J.L.: The Microbial World. 4th Ed. Prentice-Hall, Englewood Cliffs, N.J., 1976.)

tion. Consequently, every F⁺ culture contains a few Hfr cells, and every Hfr culture contains a few F⁺ cells.

Conjugation between Hfr and F⁻ cells proceeds in a manner similar to that previously described for F⁺ and F⁻ matings. A nick is made by an endonuclease at a specific site on one strand of the integrated plasmid. The 5′ end of the broken strand crosses the transfer bridge as the intact strand is replicated (Fig. 3.9). An interval of 90 minutes at 37°C is required for the complete transfer of the donor chromosome. The recipient cell thus becomes a true diploid cell. If recombination does not occur, the two chromosomes are segregated by cell division producing two homozygotic cells.

Complete transfer of the donor chromosome is a rare event and has been observed only under special experimental conditions. The slow linear transfer of bacterial genes is usually interrupted by spontaneous breaks in the delicate DNA strand or in the transfer bridge. The time at which the break occurs is random. Therefore, the probability of transfer for a given bacterial gene depends upon its proximity to the leading end of the strand; those close to the origin will be transferred with a probability close to 1.0, whereas the terminal genes will be transferred with a probability of less than 0.01. Since the sequence of genes on the donor chromosome is revealed by its relative time of transfer, experimental interruption of mating pairs and characterization of resulting recombinant chromosomes has been used to construct an accurate genetic map of the *E. coli* chromosome.

The integration of the F1 plasmid into the *E. coli* chromosome has another striking consequence — the plasmid becomes essentially nontransmissible. Since the initial DNA scission occurs in the plasmid, the resulting two plasmid segments are separated by the entire length of the bacterial chromosome (Fig. 3.10). When DNA transfer is interrupted, the segment at the

trailing end of the strand is left behind. The recipient cell becomes Hfr only when the entire chromosome is transferred.

Formation and Transfer of F′ Genotes. The integration of F plasmids into host chromosomes is a reversible event. Excision occurs by a reciprocal cross-

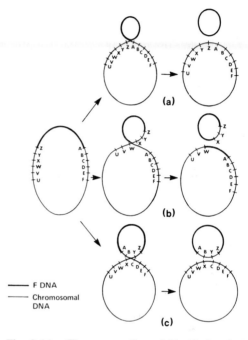

Fig. 3.11. The generation of F genotes in primary F′ cells. At the left is an Hfr chromosome with the integrated F DNA at the top. Letters A to F and U to Z represent chromosomal markers. (a) Crossing over within the original region of pairing between F and chromosome regenerates a normal F. (b) Pairing in an exceptional region followed by crossing over generates an F genote carrying the chromosomal markers XYZ. The chromosome of the primary F′ contains a segment of F DNA and has a deletion of the XYZ segment. (c) Exceptional pairing in a different region has generated an F genote containing a full complement of F DNA plus chromosomal genes from both sides of the former attachment site. (Stanier, R.Y., Adelberg, E.A., and Ingraham, J.L.: The Microbial World. 4th Ed. Prentice Hall, Englewood Cliffs, N.J., 1976.)

over at the same location as the initial integration, thereby regenerating intact circular plasmid and chromosome replicons (Fig. 3.11). On rare occasions (10^{-6} to 10^{-8} per generation), crossovers occur at different DNA sites in an abnormal region, resulting in a circular plasmid containing a short segment of bacterial DNA. Cells containing this DNA element (F' genote) exhibit characteristics of both F+ and Hfr. F' cells transfer the plasmid and the conjoined bacterial genes at a high frequency. The recipient cell almost always becomes male, since the shorter distance between the leading and trailing ends of the plasmid decreases the probably of DNA breakage during transfer. Transfer of bacterial genes in this manner is also known as *sexduction*. Acquisition of an F' genote by sexduction results in a cell that is diploid for a portion of its chromosome. This diploid state is relatively stable, since both alleles are situated on two autonomous replicons. Crossing over occurs frequently in F' cells in which the entire F' genote is integrated, producing an Hfr cell.

Conjugative Transfer of Antibiotic Resistance. Plasmids carrying both conjugative genes and antibiotic resistance genes (conjugative R plasmids) have been detected in many gram-negative bacteria (Ch. 4). These DNA elements are readily transmitted to other bacterial cells by conjugation, resulting in what is commonly referred to as *infectious drug resistance*. This mechanism of transfer accounts for the rapid increase in the incidence of drug resistance in gram-negative bacteria. The antimicrobial drugs for which resistance may be mediated by conjugative R plasmids include ampicillin, chloramphenicol, kanamycin, neomycin, penicillin, streptomycin, the sulfonamides, and the tetracyclines. The number of resistance genes on a plasmid varies from one to as many as eight or nine. The genes confer resistance by coding for enzymes that specifically denature the antibiotic molecules (Ch. 4).

Conjugative R plasmids resemble F genotes in that they contain two distinct segments of DNA. Some have actually been shown to reversibly dissociate into two autonomously replicating plasmids, a conjugative plasmid (previously known as resistance transfer factor), and a nonconjugative resistance plasmid. The stability of the composite plasmid (cointegrate) varies widely with both the host cell and the plasmid. Some conjugative R plasmids readily dissociate in one bacterial host but not at all in another genus or species. Cells containing these autonomous DNA units may transfer one or the other or both. If only the nonconjugative R plasmid is transferred, the recipient cell will exhibit drug resistance but will be unable to transfer it by conjugation. Nonconjugative R plasmids (lacking conjugation genes) can be transmitted to other cells by the process of transduction.

Conjugation in Gram-Positive Bacteria. The phenomenon of conjugation has only recently been demonstrated in gram-positive bacteria. In *Streptococcus faecalis* a number of plasmids are capable of self-transfer and mobilization of other plasmids and chromosomal genes. Plasmid-linked characteristics transmitted in this manner include bacteriocin and toxin (hemolysin) production and resistance to erythromycin, lincomycin, kanamycin, neomycin, streptomycin, and tetracycline. Preliminary reports indicate that conjugal transfer of plasmid DNA may also occur among oral streptococci.

The mechanism of DNA transfer may be analogous to that of gram-negative bacteria, except for the nature of the conjugation bridge. Since pili have not been detected in gram-positive bacteria, it is assumed that a direct cell-surface bridge is involved.

Transduction

The third means by which DNA is transmitted from one bacterium to another is transduction by bacteriophage. This mechanism occurs in both gram-positive and gram-negative cells and may well be the most common mechanism of DNA transfer in bacteria. In this process a small segment of bacterial chromosome or an intact plasmid is incorporated into the head of a maturing bacteriophage. When this virus particle infects a new bacterium, it injects the chromosomal DNA from the previous host, thus making the recipient a partial zygote. Some bacteriophage particles pick up host genes in a random manner so that any chromosomal marker has roughly an equal chance of being transferred. This is called *generalized transduction*. Other types of bacteriophages transfer only a few selected chromosomal genes — a process known as *specialized* or *restricted transduction*.

Only temperate bacteriophages are capable of mediating transduction. In contrast to virulent bacteriophages that always kill their hosts, temperate viruses have two alternative host-parasite interactions. One option is to enter a lytic (virulent) cycle of infection in which a crop of progeny virus particles are produced and then liberated by host cell lysis. This sequence of events is designated *vegetative virus replication*. The second option is to enter a state of lysogeny in which the virus genome produces a protein that specifically represses virus maturation. In this situation the host cell remains viable. Although structural proteins are not synthesized, the virus genome, now known as *prophage*, replicates in synchrony with the bacterial chromosome, and copies are passed to each daughter cell during division. The prophage behaves as a plasmid in this infected cell progeny. Occasionally, a prophage within this population of cells spontaneously becomes derepressed and enters a cycle of vegetative replication, resulting in cell lysis and liberation of mature virions. Since prophage-containing cells have a latent ability to produce mature virions, they are said to be *lysogenic*.

Generalized transducing phages, such as

phage P1 of *E. coli*, enter the prophage state as autonomously replicating elements, presumably attached to cytoplasmic membrane sites. Upon release from lysogeny, viral genes that code for enzymes necessary for the synthesis of viral DNA and structural proteins and for the degradation and modification of host cell components are transcribed. During the maturation phase of vegetative virus production, a specific viral protein (condensing factor) binds to viral DNA molecules, causing them to condense to a compact unit. Structural proteins, also synthesized during this phase, assemble around the condensed genome forming the virus head. Infrequently, these proteins condense and package segments of host DNA; about one virus particle in 10^5 or 10^6 is a transducing particle. The amount of genetic information transferred by the particle is limited by the capacity of the

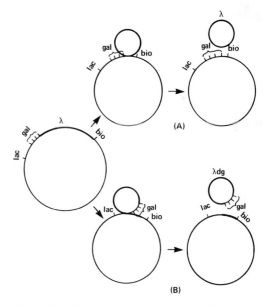

Fig. 3.12. The formation of λ*dg*. (A) Normal pairing followed by a single crossover event regenerates the wild-type λ genome. (B) Abnormal pairing followed by a single crossover event generates the λ*dg* genetic element. (Stanier, R.Y., Adelberg, E.A., and Ingraham, J.L.: The Microbial World. 4th Ed. Prentice-Hall, Englewood Cliffs, N.J., 1976.)

phage head. This corresponds to a linear DNA piece of about 6×10^7 daltons, which is about 2 percent of the *E. coli* chromosome, or the size of an average plasmid.

For specialized transduction to occur, the prophage must be integrated into the host chromosome, where it replicates and is inherited as an episome. This mechanism is typified by bacteriophage lambda (λ), which inserts itself into the *E. coli* chromosome between the galactose and biotin loci (Fig. 3.12). Release from lysogeny (derepression) involves excision of the virus genome from the bacterial chromosome, followed by viral DNA replication, particle assembly, and host cell lysis. In a lysogenic cell population, this occurs at a rate of one cell in 10^4. On rare occasions an error is made in the excision of the viral genome so that a segment of host DNA, either the *gal* or *bio* locus, is taken into the circular loop of DNA that separates from the chromosome. The mechanism is analogous to the formation of F' genotes; only those genes adjacent to the integrated prophage are involved. The transducing DNA is replicated and encased in the protein heads of the virion particles. Since the amount of DNA that can be carried in the phage head is fixed, a segment of λ DNA corresponding in size to that of the acquired host DNA segment must be deleted. As a result the transducing particles are always defective in some virus functions. However, since recipient bacteria are usually infected simultaneously with normal virus particles, they can experience either lysogenic or virulent virus replication. If the recipient cell enters the lysogenic state, the transferred bacterial genes will have an opportunity to undergo recombination with the endogenote and to be expressed. In a population of lysogenic bacteria, the frequency of transducing particles is about one in 10^6.

Lysogenic Conversion

Other than the ability to donate DNA by transduction, most bacteria that are infected with temperate bacteriophages exhibit the same characteristics as uninfected cells. A few lysogenic bacteria, however, have been found to acquire new properties from the viral genome. For example, *Corynebacterium diphtheriae* produces diphtheria toxin only when infected by phage β; *Clostridium botulinum* type C becomes toxigenic when infected with phage CEβ; erythrogenic toxin of scarlet fever is produced by lysogenic *Streptococcus pyogenes*; and the antigenic properties of somatic O antigen of *Salmonella* spp. are modified by the presence of a prophage in the cell. This acquisition of new properties by the expression of prophage genes is known as *phage* or *lysogenic conversion*.

RECOMBINANT DNA TECHNOLOGY

In recent years it has become possible to experimentally splice short segments of DNA from many sources (containing several genes) onto bacterial plasmid or viral DNA molecules. The resulting recombinant DNA can then be introduced into a bacterial cell, such as *Escherichia coli*, by the process of transformation. The plasmid or viral DNA molecules serve as vehicles for the transfer of the foreign DNA and ensure its survival, replication, and transcription once inside the host cell. This technique permits the study of mammalian gene regulation in the simplified background of a bacterial cell; bacteria contain only 1/1000 as much DNA as mammalian cells. Also, since these host cells can be rapidly and inexpensively grown in enormous numbers, the mammalian genes and their products can be produced in almost unlimited quantities.

The potential benefits of recombinant DNA technology are enormous. For example, knowledge of mammalian gene activation and repression is central to understanding cancer, a disease in which abnormalities occur in the genetic mechanism regulating cell growth. Practical applica-

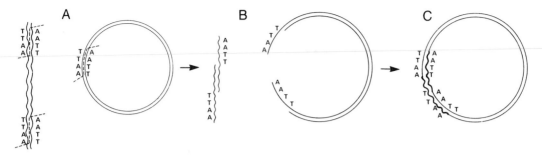

Fig. 3.13. Diagram of *in vitro* DNA recombination. A. A segment of mammalian DNA (wavy line) and a bacterial plasmid (circular structure) contain one or more base-pair sequences that are cleaved by a particular restriction enzyme. B. The resulting DNA fragments contain single-stranded termini (sticky ends) at the 5′ ends. C. Under annealing conditions, the open plasmid will sometimes take in a segment of foreign DNA. DNA ligase then seals the broken strands.

tions include the production of medically useful human proteins, such as hormones, clotting factors, interferon, and immunoglobulins. However, recombinant DNA research is accompanied with some risk. The introduction of foreign DNA into bacteria might prove hazardous to man and his environment should these microorganisms escape from the laboratory. To minimize these risks, recombinant DNA research should be subject to stringent guidelines and to extensive laboratory safeguards.

The most commonly used procedure for the joining of DNA fragments employs restriction endonucleases of bacteria. These enzymes make cuts on plasmid and eukaryotic cell DNA leaving extended single-stranded termini, two to five nucleotides long, at the 5′ ends of both strands of the DNA fragments. Since the enzyme recognizes the same base-pair sequences on both the plasmid and foreign DNA molecules, the resulting unpaired ends of the fragments are complementary. Under appropriate annealing conditions, these complementary strands (sticky ends), on the same or different molecules, can transiently form hydrogen bonds with each other. The joined strands are then covalently sealed by the action of DNA ligase. The recombinant DNA is introduced into a bacterial host by transformation, where it is replicated and transcribed.

REFERENCES

Clowes, R.C.: Molecular structure of bacterial plasmids. Bacteriol. Rev., *36:* 361, 1972.

Cold Spring Harbor Symposia on Quantitative Biology. Vol. XLV. Movable Genetic Elements. Cold Spring Harbor, 1981.

Fox, M.S.: Some features of genetic recombination in procaryotes. Annu. Rev. Genet. *12:* 47, 1978.

Geftner, M.L.: DNA replication. Annu. Rev. Biochem. *45:* 55, 1975.

Joklik, W.K., Willett, H.P., and Amos, D.B., Eds.: Zinsser Microbiology. 17th Ed. Appleton-Century-Crofts, New York, 1980.

Low, K.B. and Porter, D.D.: Modes of gene transfer and recombination in bacteria. Annu. Rev. Genet. *12:* 249, 1978.

Sherratt, D.J.: Bacterial plasmids. Cell *3:* 189, 1974.

Sinsheimer, R.L.: Recombinant DNA. Annu. Rev. Biochem. *46:* 415, 1977.

Stainer, R.Y., Adelberg, E.A., and Ingraham, J.L.: The Microbial World. 4th Ed. Prentice-Hall, Englewood Cliffs, 1976.

Willets, N.: The genetics of transmissible plasmids. Annu. Rev. Genet. *6:* 257, 1972.

4

Chemotherapeutics and Antibiotics

Murray W. Stinson

Antimicrobial drugs (chemotherapeutic agents) are chemicals that inhibit the growth of parasitic microorganisms while being tolerated by the host. The drugs exert this selective toxicity by interrupting metabolic or synthetic processes that are unique to the microorganism. They interfere with cell wall synthesis, membrane function, protein synthesis, nucleic acid synthesis, and intermediary metabolism. The inhibitory effect of some antimicrobial drugs is irreversible and lethal for the infectious microorganism (bactericidal, fungicidal). Others exert a reversible effect (bacteriostatic; fungistatic) in which the microorganism revives after the drug is removed. In infections treated with these "static" drugs, the killing of the microorganism is achieved primarily by the host's cellular defense mechanisms. Although these traditional terms are still used to describe the action of antimicrobial drugs, the distinction between them is unclear in some instances. For example, some bactericidal drugs at low dose concentrations are bacteriostatic and conversely, prolonged exposure to bacteriostatic drugs can result in the loss of bacterial viability.

Antibiotics are antimicrobial substances produced by certain soil bacteria and fungi; for example, members of the genera *Bacillus, Streptomyces*, and *Penicillium*. Commercially, most of these substances are isolated and purified from liquid cultures of these microorganisms; however, several are now more efficiently synthesized chemically. In recent years chemical modification of naturally occurring antibiotics has been used to increase the effectiveness and stability of these substances. In addition to antibiotics, a variety of antimetabolic drugs have been chemically synthesized. Of the several hundred antimicrobial drugs presently available, only a few dozen have sufficient selective toxicity to be useful in the treatment of infectious diseases. This does not mean that medically useful drugs are nontoxic to man. Antimicrobial drugs may exert adverse effects on the patient, ranging from mild side-effects (dizziness, headache, intestinal cramps, and diarrhea) and allergy (rash, fever, and hives) to severe toxicity (renal damage, hemolytic and aplastic anemia) and allergic reactions (anaphylaxis). Descriptions of these undesirable drug effects are not included in this chapter, since this area is discussed extensively in pharmacology textbooks. The emphasis of this chapter will be on the mechanisms by which the drugs affect the

53

microorganisms and how the microorganisms resist the action of the drugs.

INHIBITORS OF CELL WALL SYNTHESIS

Antibiotics that interfere with the synthesis of bacterial cell walls include bacitracin, the cephalosporins, the penicillins and vancomycin. These drugs vary widely in chemical composition and the mechanisms by which they inhibit the biosynthesis of peptidoglycan. The biosynthetic pathway for this cell wall polymer is described in Chapter 2 and summarized in Figures 2.8 and 2.9. It should be noted that since these antibiotics prevent cell wall formation, they are effective only on growing cells.

The rigid cell wall is responsible for maintaining the shape and integrity of the bacterial cell. Interference with its synthesis leaves the fragile cytoplasmic membrane unsupported, and because of the high osmotic pressures normally present in bacteria, lysis usually ensues. In a hypertonic environment (e.g., 20 percent sucrose), inhibition of cell wall synthesis can lead to the formation of spherical protoplasts, bacteria bounded only by the cytoplasmic membrane.

The Penicillins

The group of antibiotics known as the penicillins include the naturally occurring substances and their semisynthetic derivatives. The original drugs were obtained from penicillium molds (*P. notatum* and *P. chrysogenum*) as a mixture of active compounds. All have the same basic structure, 6-aminopenicillanic acid, which consists of a thiazolidine ring joined to a β-lactam ring containing a free amino group (Fig. 4.1). Differences occur in the composition of the acyl side chains that are attached to the amino group. The integrity of the 4-membered β-lactam ring is essential for the

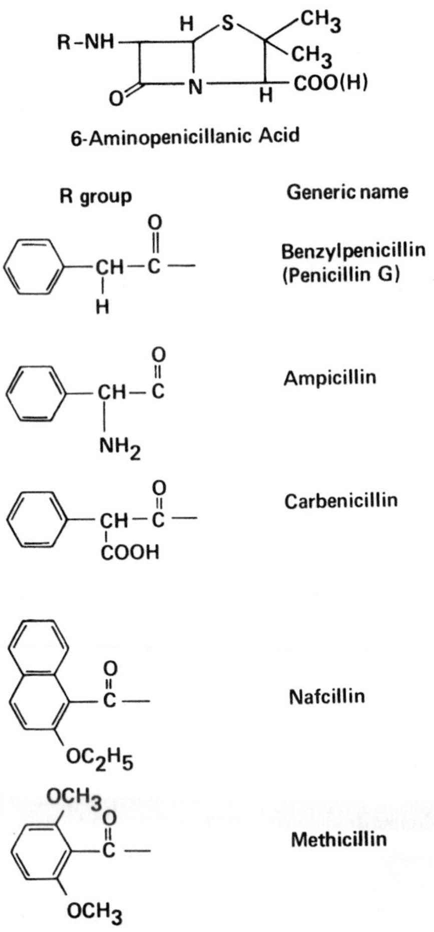

Fig. 4.1. Structures of selected penicillins.

antibacterial activity of the drug. The CO–N bond is susceptible to hydrolysis by acid and β-lactamases (penicillinases), yielding inactive penicilloic acid. The stability of the β-lactam ring and the antibacterial properties of the antibiotic are influenced by the nature of the acyl side chain.

Benzylpenicillin (penicillin G) is the most widely used and inexpensive of the natural drugs. It is nontoxic and highly effective against gram-positive bacteria. Of the gram-negative bacteria, only *Neisseria* are sufficiently sensitive to make treatment with penicillin G feasible. It is rapidly destroyed by stomach acid, making oral administration of limited value. Penicillin

G is also inactivated by the action of penicillinase. The natural derivative phenoxymethyl penicillin (penicillin V) is highly resistant to gastric acidity.

Approximately 30 semisynthetic penicillins have been designed and are now in clinical use. The pharmacologic advantages obtained by substitution of the prosthetic groups at the 6-amino position, however, are generally at the expense of antimicrobial activity. Most derivatives are less potent for gram-positive bacteria than the natural penicillin G. Therefore considerably larger doses are necessary to achieve the same levels of inhibition. The spectrum of antimicrobial action, however, can be increased by chemical modification. Ampicillin and carbenicillin are effective against many gram-negative bacteria, but remain sensitive to penicillinase inactivation. Semisynthetic derivatives with resistance to penicillinase include methicillin, nafcillin, oxacillin, and dicloxacillin. The bulky side groups sterically hinder their binding by penicillinase. With the exception of methicillin, these antibiotics also demonstrate acid stability.

The primary site of penicillin action is at the final crosslinking step in peptidoglycan biosynthesis. The antibiotic is a structural analogue of the D-alanyl-D-alanine terminus of the peptide moiety of peptidoglycan and appears to prevent peptide bond formation by competitive inhibition of transpeptidase. Since crosslinking of the linear peptidoglycan strands is necessary for the tensile strength of the cell wall, the resulting structure cannot contain the internal osmotic pressure, and the cell lyses.

Many bacteria (staphylococci, coliforms, pseudomonads) become resistant to the action of penicillin by production of β-lactamases (penicillinases), which cleave the molecule to inactive penicilloic acid. The enzyme is associated with the cell membrane of these bacteria and can in some cases be secreted into the environment. In most cases the biosynthesis of

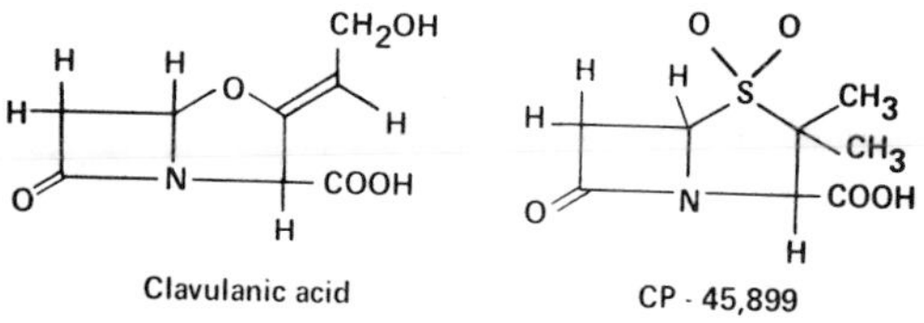

Fig. 4.2. Structures of penicillinase inhibitors.

these enzymes is under the genetic control of plasmids residing in the cytoplasm of the bacterium (Ch. 3). Some bacteria (*Neisseria*) may develop penicillin resistance through chromosome mutations that result in altered transpeptidase with lower affinities for the antibiotic. Consequently, larger drug doses are required to inhibit cell wall synthesis in these bacteria.

Recently, naturally occurring and semisynthetic derivatives of penicillin have been developed for their ability to inhibit bacterial β-lactamase (Fig. 4.2). Although these agents (clavulanic acid and CP-48,899) have weak antibacterial activity, they bind irreversibly to the β-lactamase, causing the bacterium to lose its main line of defense. Simultaneous administration of ampicillin or penicillin G is now much more effective against these bacteria. Combined therapy with penicillin and β-lactamase inhibitors has been successful in the treatment of experimental animal infections by penicillinase-producing bacteria. Human studies are currently in progress.

Penicillins may induce either immediate or delayed hypersensitivity in some individuals (1 to 5 percent of American adults). These antibiotics and their degradation products (e.g., penicilloic acid) bind to serum and tissue proteins and act as haptens. Immunologically, the drugs are crosssensitizing and crossreacting. Sensitization may occur through previous drug administration and by ingestion of penicillin-containing foods (milk). Skin tests with the antibiotics or peptide-coupled penicilloic acid may be used to detect hypersensitized individuals.

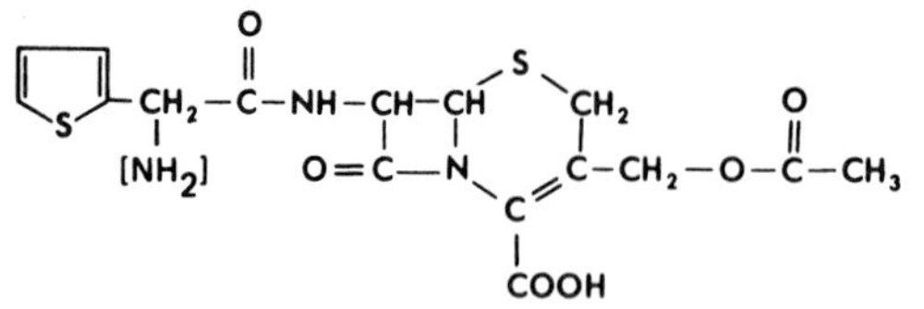

Fig. 4.3. Cephalothin.

Cephalosporins

Cephalosporins are a group of antibiotics that are produced by species of the soil mold *Cephalosporium*. They are similar to the penicillins in that they possess a fused β-lactam ring and inhibit the transpeptidation reaction in peptidoglycan biosynthesis (Fig. 4.3).

Several useful semisynthetic derivatives have been developed, including cephalothin, cefazolin, cephaprin, and cephalexin. They possess a moderate spectrum of activity against gram-positive and gram-negative bacteria and are resistant to degradation by staphylococcal β-lactamase, although some β-lactamases of gram-negative bacteria are capable of hydrolyzing these antibiotics. These drugs are often used to treat staphylococcal and streptococcal (other than enterococci) infections in patients with a history of mild penicillin allergy (rash and febrile reactions) but not in patients who have experienced an anaphylactic response. The administration of the cephalosporins does not cause serious hypersensitivity reactions in these patients. This practice is somewhat controversial because serologic crossreactions do occur between the penicillins and the cephalosporins. In recent years these drugs have been widely used in the prevention of infection during and after a surgical procedure.

Bacitracin

Bacitracin is a polypeptide antibiotic produced by several species of *Bacillus*, for example, *B. subtilis* and *B. licheniformis*

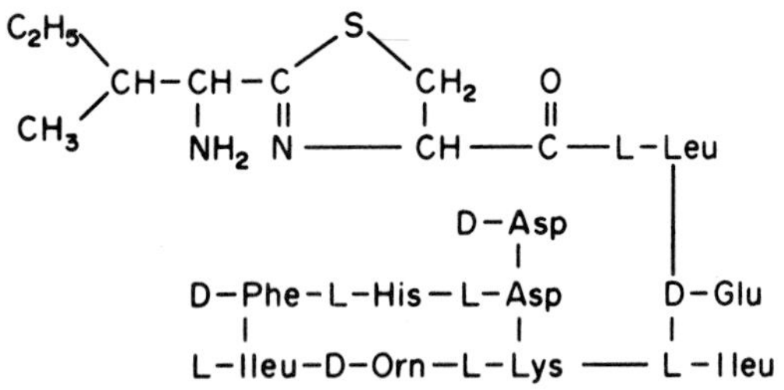

Fig. 4.4. Bacitracin A.

(Fig. 4.4). It is bactericidal for gram-positive bacteria but has little effect on gram-negative organisms. It inhibits cell wall synthesis by penetrating the cytoplasmic membrane and binding to the undecaprenylpyrophosphate (glycosyl-carrier lipid). This membrane phospholipid is essential for the biosynthesis of peptidoglycan subunits and their subsequent transport to the external surface of the membrane. The pyrophosphorylated form of the glycosyl-carrier lipid is generated when the GlcNAc-MurNAc-pentapeptide is released to the growing peptidoglycan chain. To re-enter the synthetic cycle, the lipid must be dephosphorylated to undecaprenylmonophosphate (the active form) and inorganic phosphate. Bacitracin blocks this reaction. The kidney toxicity of bacitracin prohibits its use in systemic chemotherapy; however, it is useful in the treatment of skin and wound infections as a component in topical ointments.

Vancomycin

Vancomycin is an antibiotic produced by several species of *Streptomyces* (e.g., *S. orientalis*). It inhibits peptidoglycan biosynthesis at the external surface of the cytoplasmic membrane. The drug forms complexes with the acyl-D-alanyl-D-alanine terminus of the linear peptidoglycan, thus blocking the transfer (transglycosylation) of the disaccharide-pentapeptide unit from the carrier lipid to the growing end of the peptidoglycan chain and transpeptidation reactions. Development of penicillin resistance by bacteria does not diminish the effective-ness of vancomycin. This antibiotic is used in the treatment of staphylococcal infec-tions and bacterial endocarditis caused by enterococci.

INHIBITORS OF MEMBRANE FUNCTION

A number of antibiotics have been discov-ered that exert their lethal action by in-creasing the permeability of the cytoplas-mic membrane. This effect causes the mi-croorganism to leak essential metabolites (nucleotides and cofactors) and proteins in-to the environment. A few of these antibio-tics can distinguish between microbial and mammalian cell membranes and are useful in chemotherapy. These include the polymyxins and the polyenes (nystatin and amphotericin B).

Polymyxin

Polymyxin B (Fig. 4.5) and polymyxin E (colistin) are polypeptide antibiotics pro-duced by *Bacillus polymyxa* and are active only against gram-negative bacteria. The antibiotic molecule has amphipathic prop-erties in which both lipophilic and hy-drophilic regions are present. In solution the antibiotics behave as cationic detergents. The lipophilic portion of the molecule

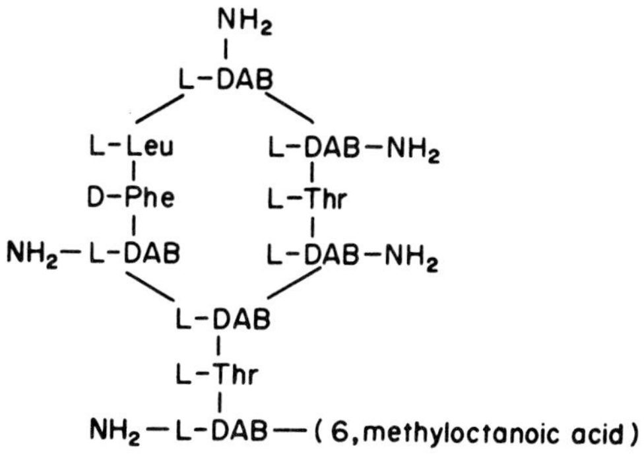

Fig. 4.5. Polymyxin B.

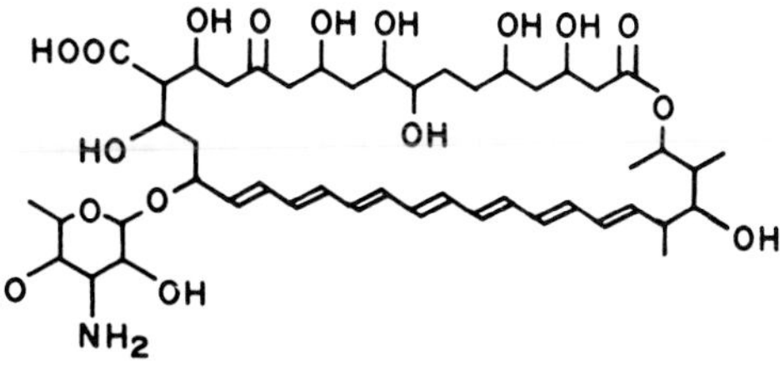

Fig. 4.6. Amphotericin B.

appears to be selectively bound to phospha-tidylethanolamine of the bacterial mem-brane. Its insertion into the membrane dis-rupts the osmotic barrier, killing the cell. These antibiotics are particularly useful in the treatment of infections caused by *Pseudomonas aeruginosa*, a bacterium notoriously resistant to many antibiotics. A combination of polymyxin, bacitracin, and neomycin is also used in topical ointments.

Polyenes

Nystatin and amphotericin B are produced by *Streptomyces noursei* and *S. nodosus*, re-spectively. These antibiotics are composed of a large ring structure containing a hy-drophobic region of unsubstituted, conju-gated double bonds and a hydrophilic, hy-droxylated region with an attached amino sugar (Fig. 4.6). Both antibiotics are spe-cific for sterol-containing membranes, which are found in fungi and mycoplasma but not in other bacteria. Unfortunately, these drugs possess considerable toxicity for mammalian cells, since sterols are also pres-ent in their membranes. Selective toxicity may reside in the chemical nature of the membrane sterol. It has been suggested that amphotericin B has a greater affinity for ergosterol of fungal membranes than for cholesterol of animal cell membranes.

INHIBITORS OF NUCLEIC ACID BIOSYNTHESIS

A variety of antimicrobial drugs have been discovered that interfere with the biosyn-

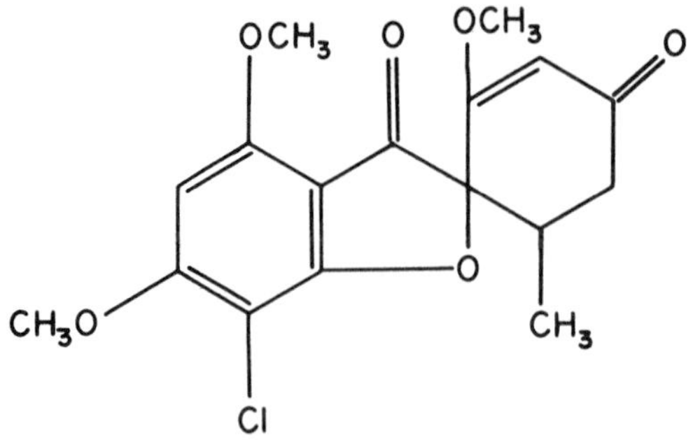

Fig. 4.7. Griseofulvin.

thesis of DNA or RNA. Unfortunately, most of these substances also show considerable toxicity to host cells making them unsuitable for chemotherapeutic purposes. Antimicrobial drugs that possess adequate selective toxicity for microorganisms are griseofulvin and rifampin.

Griseofulvin

Griseofulvin (grifulvin) is a fungistatic antibiotic produced by certain *Penicillium* spp. (Fig. 4.7). Its activity is limited to the dermatotrophic fungi (e.g., *Microsporum audouini* and *Trichophyton rubrum*) that infect keratinized structures — skin, hair, and nails. It does not inhibit the growth of fungi (yeasts) that cause systemic mycoses. To be effective the antibiotic must be administered orally for an extended period (weeks or months) so that the drug is incorporated into newly synthesized keratin. Whereas topically applied griseofulvin penetrates into the keratinized skin layer (stratum corneum) where the dermatophytic fungi are located, it does not inhibit their growth. The mode of action of griseofulvin appears to be inhibition of fungal mitosis by interaction with the proteins that form the mitotic spindle.

Rifampin

Rifampin (rifampicin) (Fig. 4.8) is a semisynthetic derivative of rifamycin, an anti-biotic obtained from *Streptomyces mediterranei*. It is effective against pyogenic cocci, mycobacteria, and chlamydiae. The antibiotic selectively inhibits DNA transcription by binding to the β-subunit of DNA-dependent RNA polymerase. The rifampin-enzyme complex can still attach to the promotor region of DNA but cannot initiate RNA synthesis. Mutations affecting the ability of the RNA polymerase subunits to bind rifampin often appear in bacterial populations, and prolonged administration of the antibiotic permits the proliferation of these highly resistant strains. To prevent the growth of these mutants during the treatment of tuberculosis, rifampin is administered in combination with isoniazid or ethambutol.

INHIBITORS OF PROTEIN SYNTHESIS

A number of antibiotics are inhibitors of RNA translation. These include the aminoglycosides, the macrolides, the tetracyclines, chloramphenicol, and lincomycin. The selective toxicity of these antibiotics resides in their high binding affinities for structural components (protein or rRNA) of bacterial ribosomes or for bacterial enzymes. They do not readily bind to the ribosomes of eukaryotic cells because of structural dissimilarities.

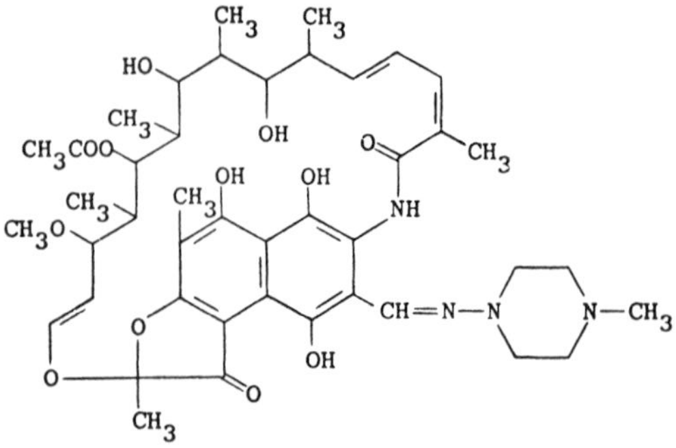

Fig. 4.8. Rifampin.

Aminoglycosides

Aminoglycosides are a large group of chemically and pharmacologically related antibiotics produced by *Streptomyces* spp. They contain an inositol ring substituted with one or two amino or guanidino groups and with various sugars and aminosugars (Fig. 4.9). Therapeutically useful aminoglycosides include streptomycin, kanamycin, neomycin, gentamicin, amikacin, and tobramycin. These antibiotics have a common mechanism of action but differ from one another in potency, antimicrobial spectrum, and crossresistance. The mode of action of streptomycin has been the most intensively studied.

Streptomycin binds irreversibly to structural protein S12 (formerly P10) of the 30 S ribosomal subunit. This region of the ribosome contains the attachment sites for both mRNA and the amino-acyl-tRNAs. The binding of streptomycin blocks the movement of the initiation complex of peptide synthesis (mRNA + formyl methionine + tRNA) from the A site to the P site of the ribosome. As a result "streptomycin monosomes", consisting of 30 S and 50 S ribosome particles, mRNA, and streptomycin, accumulate in the bacteria. Recent studies indicate that the ribosome-streptomycin complexes slowly dissociate from the mRNA as 70 S ribosomes, which may then bind to other mRNA. Thus, the binding of streptomycin to the 30 S ribosomal subunit results in a cycle of initiation, blockade of chain extension, gradual release of the ribosomes, and reinitiation. Nucleases degrade the distal regions of the streptomycin monosomes. The interaction of streptomycin and ribosomes after initiation has taken place often results in the production of faulty proteins. For example, during *in vitro* protein synthesis, using synthetic mRNA, aminoglycoside binding to the ribosome causes the mRNA to be misread, leading to the insertion of incorrect amino acids into the growing

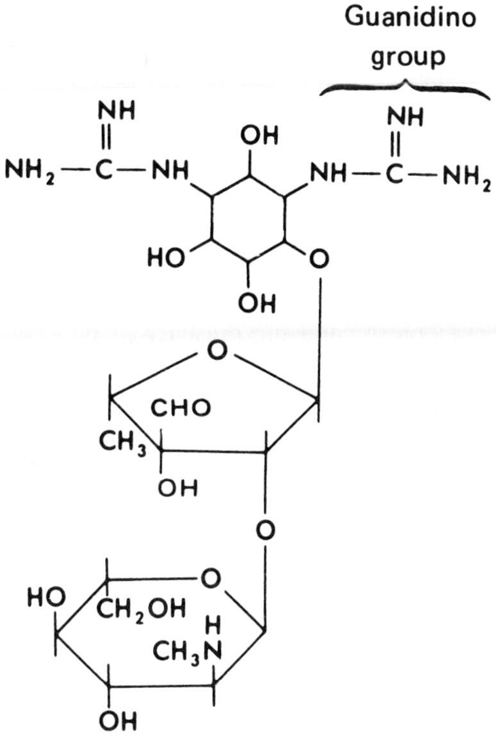

Fig. 4.9.   Streptomycin.

polypeptide chain. This indicates that streptomycin distorts codon-anticodon interactions on the ribosome surface; however, the *in vivo* significance of this effect is unclear.

Chromosomal mutations resulting in altered S12 proteins with reduced affinity for streptomycin are frequently recovered from *in vitro* cultures. These bacteria become resistant to very high concentrations of antibiotic. Mutant bacteria that demonstrate a dependence on streptomycin, that is, they require the antibiotic for growth, have also been isolated. It is believed that the mutation results in an altered S12 protein in the 30 S ribosomal subunit that causes misreading of mRNA. In this mutant the subsequent binding of streptomycin corrects the configuration of the ribosome and restores proper mRNA translation. Aminoglycoside-resistant strains of bacteria may also arise from chromosomal mutations that alter the permeability of the cell or from the acquisition of a plasmid carrying genes for enzymes (streptomycin phosphotransferase, gentamicin acetyltransferase) that degrade the antibiotic. Plasmid-mediated resistance is the most common mechanism found among clinically isolated bacteria.

The bacteriocidal activity of aminoglycoside antibiotics is depressed by acidity, anaerobiosis, and the presence of divalent cations, such as Mg^{2+} and Ca^{2+}. These conditions reduce the rate of drug uptake by bacteria. These antibiotics are less effective against intracellular bacteria (mycobacteria) than free organisms, apparently due to poor uptake by host cells and the presence of antagonistic ions in the host cytoplasm.

The spectrum of antimicrobial activity varies among the aminoglycosides. Kanamycin is active against gram-negative enteric bacteria but ineffective against pseudomonads and serratiae. Since it is poorly absorbed from the intestinal tract, it is valuable in the treatment of infantile gastroenteritis and for reducing the intestinal flora prior to bowel surgery. Neomycin is closely related to kanamycin in most characteristics but has a high systemic toxicity. Consequently, neomycin is used almost exclusively in topical ointments, often in combination with polymyxin and bacitracin. Gentamicin is active against most gram-negative bacteria, including *Proteus*, *Pseudomonas*, and *Serratia*, which are frequently resistant to other drugs. It is often the drug of choice for the treatment of urinary tract infections caused by gram-negative bacteria. Gentamicin is also used in combination with carbenicillin for the treatment of systemic infections caused by *Pseudomonas* spp. Tobramycin has an antibacterial spectrum similar to gentamicin but is more effective against *Pseudomonas*. Streptomycin is bacteriocidal for a large number of gram-positive and gram-negative bacteria. It is effective against *Mycobacte-*

Fig. 4.10.   Spectinomycin.

rium tuberculosis and is administered in combination with one or two other antituberculosis drugs (isoniazid, rifampin, *para*-aminosalicylic acid). It is also used in combination with a penicillin in the treatment of enterococcal endocarditis.

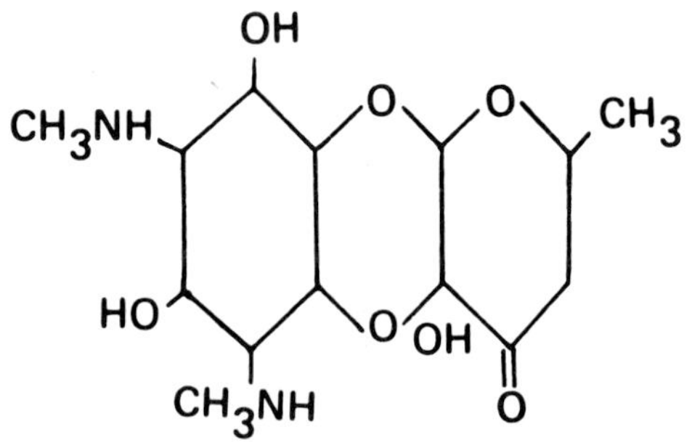

Spectinomycin

Spectinomycin is a bacteriostatic antibiotic that resembles the aminoglycoside structure but lacks the amino sugar moiety (Fig. 4.10). The antibiotic binds reversibly to the 30 S subunit of the ribosome but does not cause misreading of the mRNA. Spectinomycin is used for the treatment of gonorrhea caused by penicillin-resistant bacteria.

The Tetracyclines

The tetracyclines are a group of closely related antibiotics produced by several *Streptomyces* spp. These antibiotics possess a common structure (Fig. 4.11) of four fused rings (tetracycline) but differ from

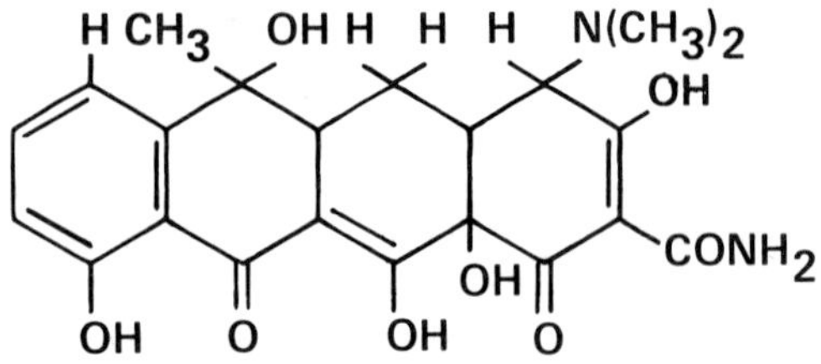

Fig. 4.11.   Tetracycline.

one another in the nature of several side groups. Important derivatives include tetracycline, chlortetracycline (Aureomycin), demeclocyclin (Declomycin), oxytetracycline (Terramycin), minocycline, and doxycycline. All are broad-spectrum antibiotics that exert a bacteriostatic effect against most gram-positive and gram-negative bacteria. Tetracyclines are drugs of choice in infections caused by mycoplasmas, rickettsiae, and chlamydiae. They bind reversibly to the 30 S ribosomal subunit, blocking the attachment of aminoacyl-tRNAs, particularly formly-methionyl-tRNA, to the A site. As a result formation of the initiation complex is blocked, and peptide chain elongation is interrupted. Bacterial resistance to tetracyclines is usually the result of an alteration in membrane permeability, a characteristic under the genetic control of a transmissible plasmid. Tetracycline susceptible bacteria accumulate internal drug concentrations many times higher than that of the environment, whereas resistant bacteria do not exceed environmental levels. Bacteria that acquire resistance to one tetracycline are also resistant to the other derivatives.

Because of its broad spectrum of action, the administration of tetracyclines has an undesirable bacteriostatic effect on the normal microbial flora of the gastrointestinal and upper respiratory tracts. Under these conditions tetracycline-resistant, indigenous microorganisms (*Proteus*, *Pseudomonas*, *Candida*, and some strains of staphylococci) are capable of unrestricted growth, resulting in "superinfections." The growth of these microorganisms is normally held in check by the antagonistic action of other members of the normal flora.

Chloramphenicol

Chloramphenicol (Fig. 4.12) is a broad-spectrum antibiotic that was originally isolated from cultures of *Streptomyces venezuelae* but is currently synthesized chem-

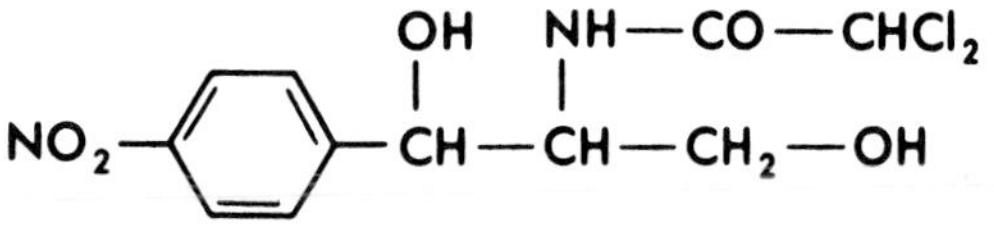

Fig. 4.12. Chloramphenicol.

ically. Chloramphenicol is bacteriostatic for most gram-positive and gram-negative bacteria, rickettsiae, chlamydiae, and mycoplasmas. It is used in the treatment of enteric fevers caused by salmonellae, bacteroides infections, and meningococcal infections in patients hypersensitive to penicillin. Since the drug also has considerable toxicity for mammalian cells, its usefulness is severely limited.

Chloramphenicol blocks protein synthesis by binding to the 50 S ribosomal subunit in the vicinity of the peptidyl transferase site. Only one molecule of chloramphenicol is bound per ribosome. Inhibition of peptidyl transferase blocks peptide bond formation between the growing peptide chain (peptidyl-tRNA) on the P site and the amino acid (aminoacyl-tRNA) on the A site of the ribosome. The ribosomes, however, are not forced to dissociate from the mRNA.

Bacterial resistance to chloramphenicol may appear as a result of chromosome mutations that produce an altered ribosome receptor with a decreased affinity for the drug. These mutant bacteria may also demonstrate resistance to the macrolides and to lincomycin, since these drugs bind to the same region of the ribosome. Chloramphenicol resistance may also arise from the acquisition of a plasmid that carries genes for chloramphenicol-inactivating enzymes (chloramphenicol acetyltransferase) or for altered membrane permeability.

Macrolides

The macrolides are a family of antibiotics produced by *Streptomyces*, having a common structure consisting of a lactone ring of 12 to 22 carbon atoms with one or more

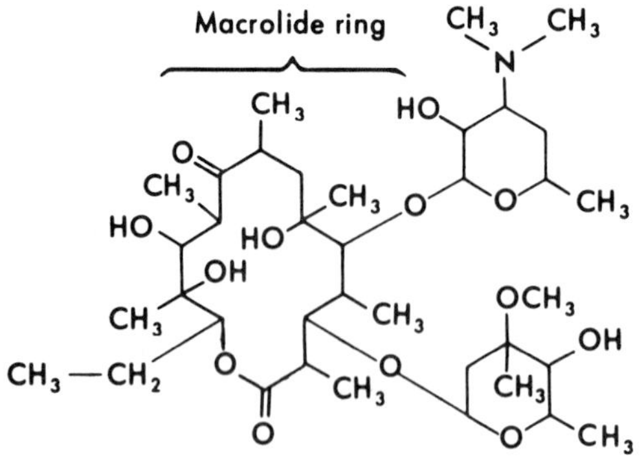

Fig. 4.13. Erythromycin A.

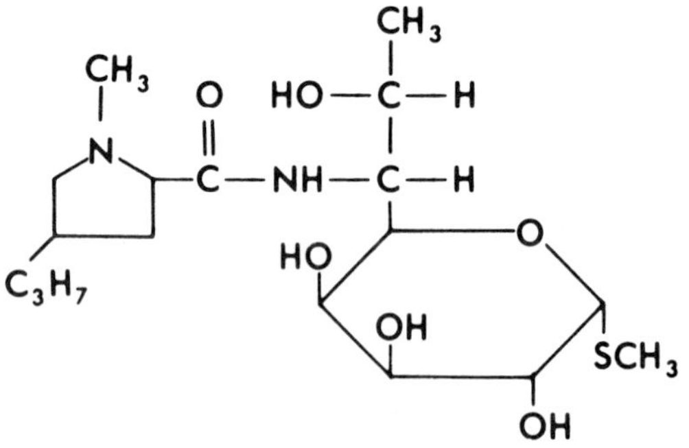

Fig. 4.14. Lincomycin.

sugar residues attached (Fig. 4.13). Clinically important drugs include erythromycin, oleandomycin, carbomycin, and spiramycin. These antibiotics are active against most gram-positive bacteria, mycoplasmas, and chlamydiae. Erythromycin is the most potent member of the macrolide group and is frequently used to treat streptococcal infections in individuals hypersensitive to penicillin. The macrolide antibiotics are among the least toxic of the antibiotics and may be administered orally or parenterally.

The mode of action of erythromycin is similar to that of chloramphenicol. It binds reversibly to a protein component of the 50 S ribosomal subunit, blocking peptide bond formation between the aminoacyl-tRNA and the peptidyl-tRNA. Should peptidyl transfer occur, erythromycin also appears to inhibit the subsequent translocation reaction, during which t-RNA is released, peptidyl-tRNA is shifted from the A site to the P site, and the ribosome moves along the mRNA to the next codon. Resistance to erythromycin results from alteration of the ribosomal receptor site by plasmid-controlled enzymes (methylation of rRNA) and by chromosomal mutations, which alter adjacent ribosomal proteins.

Lincomycin

Lincomycin (Fig. 4.14) is a bacteriostatic antibiotic produced by *Streptomyces lincoln-*ensis. The antimicrobial spectrum and mode of action resembles that of erythromycin; however, its structure is dissimilar. Clindamycin, a chlorine substituted derivative, is particularly effective against *Bacteroides* spp. and is used in the treatment of a variety of anaerobic infections. Lincomycin and clindamycin selectively bind to the region of the 50 S ribosomal subunit, as do chloramphenicol and the macrolide antibiotics, thereby inhibiting peptidyl transfer. Unlike chloramphenicol and erythromycin, lincomycin also appears to inhibit the initiation complex, since it causes the dissociation of pre-existing polysomes. It should be apparent that since these antibiotics compete with each other for the single ribosomal binding site, combined therapy with two or more of these agents is of no value.

METABOLIC ANTAGONISTS

Among the first antimicrobial substances to be discovered and used successfully in the treatment of infectious diseases were synthetic antimetabolites. This approach to chemotherapy is based upon the inhibition of metabolic enzymes with compounds that structurally resemble their natural substrates. These metabolic analogues bind to the enzyme at its catalytic site (competitive and noncompetitive inhibitors) or to a second site (noncompetitive inhibitors). In both instances the catalytic function of the

enzyme is blocked. With competitive inhibitors the extent of inhibition is a function of the ratio of inhibitor to natural substrate, rather than a strict function of inhibitor concentration. Therefore, inhibition can
be reversed by increasing the concentration
of the natural substrate. In noncompetitive
inhibition the effect depends solely on the
concentration of inhibitor. Although
thousands of synthetic analogues of essential
metabolites (vitamins, purines, pyrimidines) have been designed, only a few possess the selective toxicity necessary for clinical application.

The Sulfonamides

The sulfonamides are a group of antimetabolites that include sulfanilamide, sul-

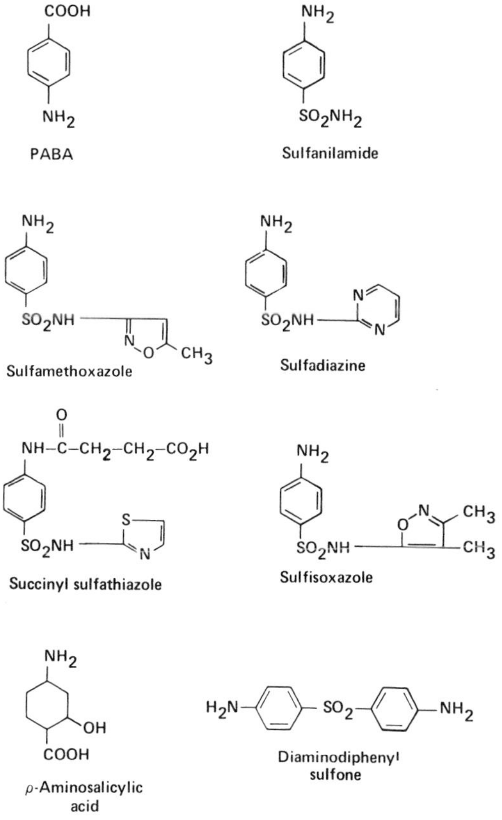

Fig. 4.15. p-Aminobenzoic acid and selected
analogues.

fadiazine, sulfisoxazole, sulfamethoxazole,
sulfamethoxypridazine, succinylsulfathiazole, and phthalylsulfathiazole (Fig. 4.15).
These compounds have bacteriostatic activity against a variety of gram-negative and
gram-positive bacteria, nocardiae, and
chlamydiae. Their mechanism of action is
the inhibition of folic acid biosynthesis, an
essential coenzyme in amino acid metabolism and purine nucleotide synthesis. The
sulfonamides are structural analogues of
the folic acid precursor *para*-aminobenzoic
acid (PABA) and compete for the catalytic
site on the enzyme (dihydropteroic acid
synthetase) that incorporates PABA into
folic acid. Only microorganisms that
synthesize their own folic acid are affected.
Many resistant microorganisms, like man,
require preformed folic acid and cannot
synthesize it from PABA.

The clinical application of the various derivatives takes advantage of their respective
solubilities and rates of absorption from the
gastrointestinal tract and subsequent excretion in the urine. The more soluble
drugs (sulfadiazine, sulfisoxazole, and sulfamethoxazole) are readily absorbed, distributed throughout tissues and body fluids,
and excreted, making them particularly useful in the treatment of urinary tract infections caused by coliform bacteria. Sul-
famethoxypyridazine and sulfadimethoxine
are excreted very slowly, resulting in high
tissue levels that are more effective against
meningitis and respiratory infections.
Others, such as succinylsulfathiazole and
phthalylsulfathiazole, are poorly absorbed
from the gastrointestinal tract and are used
in the treatment of carriers of salmonellae
and shigellae and for the suppression of intestinal flora prior to bowel surgery. Combined administration of a sulfonamide with
trimethoprim results in marked enhancement of antimicrobial activity.

Resistance to sulfonamides occurs frequently among neisseriae, shigellae, streptococci, and *Escherichia coli*. In many
organisms resistance is mediated by plas-

mids that code for a dihydropteroic acid synthetase that does not bind sulfonamides. Resistance may also arise by chromosomal mutations affecting the specificity of the target enzyme or membrane transport of the drug.

Para-Aminosalicylic Acid (PAS)

Para-aminosalicylic acid is also an analogue of *para*-aminobenzoic acid (Fig. 4.15); however, its antimicrobial activity is limited to *Mycobacterium tuberculosis*. It is administered in combination with isoniazid, streptomycin, ethambutol, or rifampin in the treatment of tuberculosis. Multiple drug therapy reduces the incidence of drug resistance in these bacteria. The use of this drug in tuberculosis therapy has declined in recent years with the advent of more effective and less toxic drugs.

Isoniazid (Isonicotinic Acid Hydrazide, INH)

Isoniazid is also used exclusively in the treatment of infections caused by mycobacteria. It is structurally similar to the B vitamins pyridoxine and nicotinamide (Fig. 4.16); however, its mechanism of action is uncertain. Although competitive inhibition by isoniazid of metabolic enzymes involving these vitamins has long been hypothesized, it has not been convincingly demonstrated. The drug is bactericidal only against actively growing cells and is slow acting; at least one cell generation occurs before loss of viability. Prolonged exposure

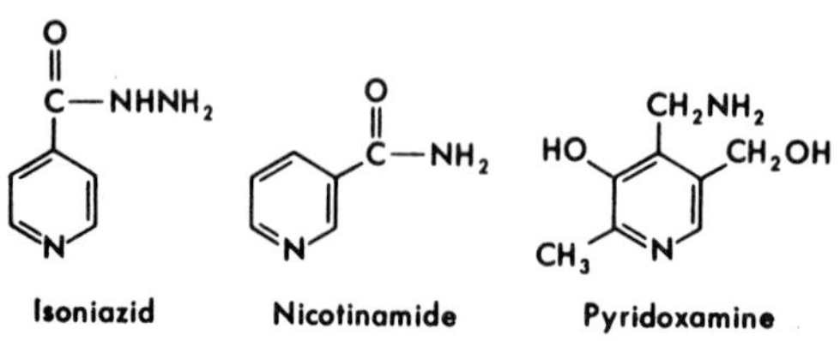

Fig. 4.16. Isoniazid, nicotinamide, and pyridoxamine.

to isoniazid causes the bacteria to become pleomorphic and to lose acid-fastness, indicating an inhibition of cell wall biosynthesis. Recent studies have shown that isoniazid inhibits the biosynthesis of mycolic acids by mycobacteria. These α-alkyl β-hydroxy fatty acids, containing up to 90 carbon atoms, are major components of the cell wall, wax D, and cord factor. Specific inhibition of the desaturation of long-chain (C24 and C26) fatty acids has also been demonstrated. It is not known whether the unsaturated fatty acids are precursors of mycolic acids. Isoniazid has also been found to bind to a component of the electron transport chain, interrupting the normal regulation of NADH dehydrogenase activity. This drug effect does not appear to be the result of competitive inhibition, since distinct NAD and isoniazid binding sites have been detected.

Isoniazid-resistant mutants rapidly emerge during drug therapy. This is prevented by the simultaneous administration of a second antituberculosis drug, such as rifampin or ethambutol.

Sulfones

Diaminodiphenylsulfone (Fig. 4.15) and several of its derivatives have been used successfully in the treatment of leprosy. The sulfones block folic acid synthesis by competitive inhibition. The appearance of sulfone resistance in *M. leprae* has been recently reported.

Ethambutol

Ethambutol is another synthetic drug (Fig. 4.17) used in the treatment of tuberculosis. Its mode of action is uncertain but is suspected of inhibiting RNA synthesis. Since drug resistance emerges quickly in mycobacteria when any chemotherapeutic agent is used alone, ethambutol is administered together with isoniazid or rifampin.

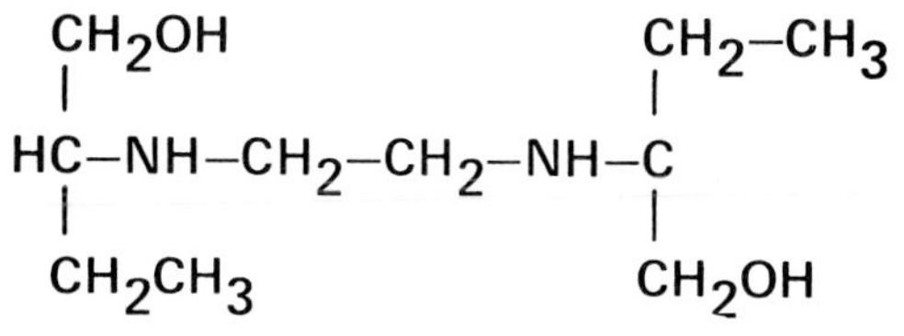
CH2OH
CH2–CH3
HC–NH–CH2–CH2–NH–C
CH2CH3
CH2OH

Fig. 4.17. Ethambutol.

Trimethoprim

Trimethoprim blocks DNA biosynthesis in many gram-positive and gram-negative bacteria. Trimethoprim (Fig. 4.18) is a metabolic antagonist for folic acid and specifically inhibits dihydrofolic acid reductase. This enzyme generates tetrahydrofolic acid, an essential cofactor in purine nucleotide biosynthesis. A combination of sulfonamides and trimethoprim (5:1 ratio) is more effective than either drug alone (synergism). This mixture is known as cotrimoxazole and is used in the treatment of enteric fevers, urinary tract infections, meningitis caused by *Hemophilus influenzae,* and pneumonia caused by *Pneumocystis carnii.*

Nalidixic Acid

Nalidixic acid is a synthetic derivative of 1,8-naphthyridine (Fig. 4.19). It is primarily effective against gram-negative enteric bacteria and is used in the treatment of chronic urinary tract infections by these microorganisms. Nalidixic acid is excreted in the urine and prevents bacterial growth by inhibiting DNA synthesis and damaging cell membranes.

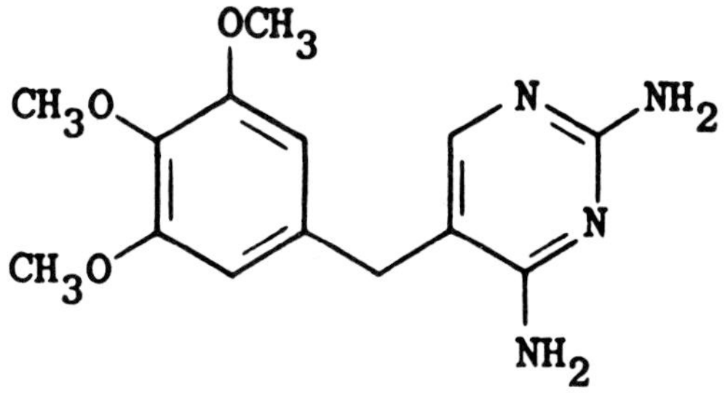
OCH3
CH3O
CH3O
N
NH2
N
NH2

Fig. 4.18. Trimethoprim.

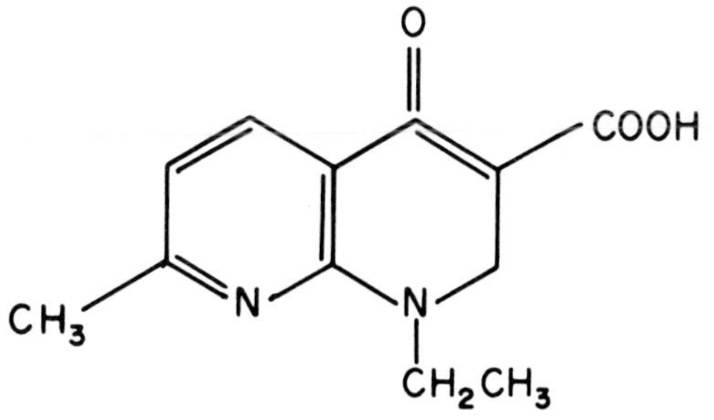
O
COOH
CH3
N
N
CH2CH3

Fig. 4.19. Nalidixic acid.

Nitrofurantoin

Nitrofurantoin (Fig. 4.20) is a synthetic compound that is bacteriocidal for many gram-positive and gram-negative bacteria. Its principal application is in the treatment of urinary tract infections, since it is readily absorbed from the gastrointestinal tract and excreted in the urine. It is not useful for the treatment of systemic infections, because its activity is antagonized by serum proteins. The mechanism of action of nitrofurantoin is not known.

Flucytosine (5-Fluorocytosine)

Flucytosine is a potent fungicide that is used in the treatment of candidiasis, cryptococcosis, blastomycosis, and coccidioidomycosis. Flucytosine is administered orally and is rapidly absorbed and distributed in tissues and body fluids. The drug is taken up by fungal cells, where it is deaminated by cytosine deaminase to 5-fluorouracil. It is 5-fluorouracil that is toxic to fungi. Although the exact mechanism of

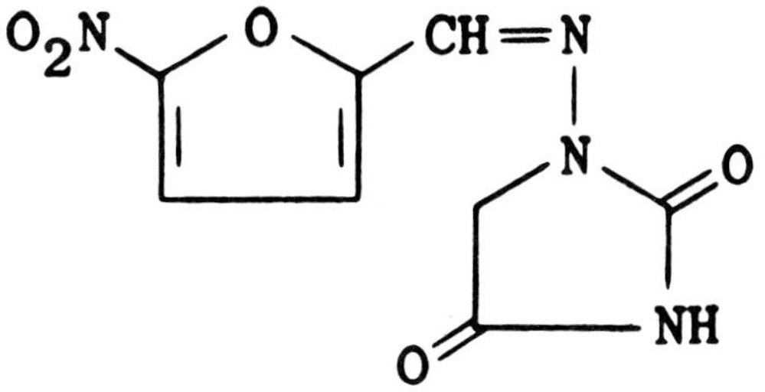
O2N
O
CH=N
N
O
NH
O

Fig. 4.20. Nitrofurantoin.

action is not well defined, current evidence suggests that 5-fluorouracil is incorporated into RNA, causing it to malfunction. The chemical alteration of flucytosine by the fungal cells determines its selective toxicity. In man the drug is not metabolized to the highly toxic derivative, 5-fluorouracil. Prolonged chemotherapy often results in the outgrowth of flucytosine-resistant mutants, unless amphotericin B is used concurrently to inhibit these organisms.

DRUG RESISTANCE

Although the application of antimicrobial drugs for the treatment of infectious diseases has revolutionized modern medicine, the optimistic predictions made during the early 1950s of "complete irradication of bacterial infections within 25 years" have fallen far short. Many infectious diseases continue to pose serious health problems. This is due to natural drug resistance of some bacteria and to the ability of susceptible bacteria to acquire resistance to antimicrobial drugs *in vivo*, through either mutation or gene transfer mechanisms.

Mutation and Selection

Antimicrobial drugs demonstrate binding specificity for components (receptors, target sites) of susceptible microorganisms, such as enzymes, ribosomal proteins, and undecaprenol-pyrophosphate. Spontaneous chromosomal mutations, occurring at a frequency of 10^{-7} to 10^{-12}, can result in a structurally altered bacterial component with a reduced binding affinity for a certain drug. Subsequent exposure of the microbial population to this drug inhibits the growth of the parental drug-sensitive organisms and permits the emergence of the resistant mutant as the predominant strain. Selection of mutant strains resistant to aminoglycosides, lincomycin, rifampin, isoniazid, and *p*-aminosalicylic acid may occur *in vivo*.

This is particularly true with *M. tuberculosis* infections, in which patients are subjected to prolonged chemotherapy. The outgrowth of drug-resistant mutants during long-term treatment can be repressed by the administration of two drugs with different sites of action. Each drug serves to inhibit both the wild-type bacteria and spontaneous mutants resistant to the second drug.

Gene Transfer

Bacteria can acquire drug resistance from other bacteria by the transfer of DNA segments containing resistance genes. This DNA may be either chromosomal (mutant genes) or extrachromosomal (resistance plasmids). The mechanisms of DNA transfer (transformation, transduction, conjugation) are discussed in Chapter 3.

Resistance plasmids (R plasmids) may code for one to several different drug-resistance mechanisms. For example, a plasmid discovered during an outbreak of shigellosis in Japan in 1957 conferred resistance to streptomycin, sulfonamide, tetracycline, and chloramphenicol. Subsequent studies on this and other R plasmids have defined many resistance mechanisms. The resistance genes may code for enzymes that inactivate the inhibitor, modify the drug receptor site, decrease membrane permeability (active transport) to the drug, or mediate metabolic reactions blocked by antimetabolites. Examples of these mechanisms are shown in Table 4.1.

Natural Resistance

Many bacteria escape the toxicity of antimicrobial drugs through what is known as *natural resistance*. This is due to the impermeability of the cell to the drug, lack of the appropriate drug receptor or target site, or the absence of the metabolic activity specified by an antimetabolite. For example,

Table 4.1.   Resistance Mechanisms Mediated by R Factors

Antibiotic	Resistance Mechanism
Chloramphenicol	Inactivation by acetylation (chloramphenicol acetyltransferase)
Erythromycin/lincomycin	Modification of drug receptor (RNA methylase)
Kanamycin/neomycin	Inactivation by phosphorylation (phosphotransferase)
Penicillin	Inactivation by hydrolysis (β-lactamase)
Tetracyclines	Decreased membrane transport
Sulfonamides	Folic acid biosynthesis by plasmid-coded dihydropteroic acid synthetase; reduced membrane transport

mycoplasma are resistant to penicillin because they do not possess cell walls; *Pseudomonas aeruginosa* and *Serratia marcescens* are insensitive to many antibiotics because the drugs do not readily penetrate the cell surface structures; and bacteria that obtain folic acid from the environment rather than synthesize it themselves are unaffected by sulfonamides.

DRUG SUSCEPTIBILITY TESTS

The ability of antimicrobial drugs to inhibit the growth of pathogenic bacteria may be determined *in vitro* using either the agar dilution or disk diffusion methods.

Agar Dilution Test

The agar dilution test employs a series of petri dishes containing a suitable solid culture medium and various concentrations of a selected antibiotic. Standardized amounts of the microorganisms to be tested are spotted onto the surface of each agar plate. Reference strains of *S. aureus*, *E. coli*, and *P. aeruginosa* are also spotted on three separate areas of the plate medium to serve as a comparison, since their susceptibility to the antibiotic is well documented. After 18 to 24 hours incubation, the minimal inhibitory concentration (MIC) for each bacterium is taken as that dilution of antibiotic that prevents visible growth.

Disk Diffusion Test

In the disk diffusion test, a suspension of the test organism is seeded uniformly over the surface of an agar plate medium. Paper disks impregnated with known amounts of antibiotic are then placed on the agar surface. Diffusion of the drug into the medium produces a concentration gradient around the paper disk. The plate is examined for bacterial growth after a suitable incubation period. Bacteria that are resistant to the drug are able to grow in close proximity to the paper disk, whereas susceptible bacteria, inhibited by relatively low drug concentrations, produce a zone of no growth around the paper disk. The diameter of the zone of growth inhibition can be correlated to the drug sensitivity of the microorganism.

REFERENCES

Blumberg, P.M. and Strominger, J.L.: Interaction of penicillin with the bacterial cell: Penicillin-binding proteins and penicillin-sensitive enzymes. Bacteriol. Rev., *38*: 291, 1974.

Corcoran, J.W. and Hahn, F.E., Eds.: Antibiotics. Mechanism of Action of Antimicrobial and Antitumor Agents. Vol. 3. Springer-Verlag, New York, 1975.

Franklin, T.J. and Snow, G.A.: Biochemistry of Antimicrobial Action. John Wiley and Sons, New York, 1975.

Garrod, L.P., Lambert, H.P., and O'Grady, F.: Antibiotics and Chemotherapy. Churchill Livingstone, London, 1973.

Hahn, F.E.: Acquired resistance of microbes to antimicrobial agents. Antibiot. Chemother. *20*: 1, 1976.

Joklik, W.K., Willett, H.P., and Amos, D.B., Eds.: Zinsser Microbiology. 17th Ed. Appleton-Century-Crofts, New York, 1980.

Meynell, G.G.: Bacterial Plasmids. MIT Press, Cambridge, 1973.

Peska, S.: Inhibitors of ribosome function. Annu. Rev. Microbiol. *25*: 487, 1971.

Pratt, W.B.: Chemotherapy of Infection. Oxford University Press, New York, 1977.

Salton, M.R.J. and Tomasz, A.: Mode of action of antibiotics on microbial walls and membranes. Ann. N.Y. Acad. Sci. *235*: 5, 1974.

5

Action of Physical and Chemical Agents on Microorganisms

Carel J. van Oss

Techniques of inactivation and/or elimination of viable microorganisms are of crucial importance in the prevention of the dissemination of contagious diseases, the eradication of microbial contamination and spoilage of materials and foodstuffs, and the practice of virtually all aspects of medicine and surgery. A number of definitions pertinent to the subject are given in Table 5.1. Also stressed in this section is the unique role of water as the most important medium for microorganisms and as a chemical participating in the basic functions of microorganisms and of their constituent biopolymers.

The genera *Bacillus* and *Clostridium* of the family *Bacillaceae* (gram-positive rods) comprise species that produce spores, or endospores, that form inside the vegetative cells. Bacterial endospores contain very little water; therefore they easily survive further dehydration and are extremely resistant to various denaturing and coagulating agents, especially heat. Bacterial spores are completely differentiated cells that can lie dormant for long periods of time under the most inhospitable conditions and may afterwards be induced to germinate when returned to a more favorable environment. The capacity of certain bacterial species to sporulate is one of the factors that necessitates the use of more drastic physical or chemical measures than would otherwise be required.

INFLUENCE OF WATER

The denaturation of biopolymers, especially proteins, is a chemical reaction in which water is one of the principal reagents and plays a crucial role (Table 5.2). When water is removed from a medium, by either physical or chemical means, denaturation becomes much more difficult. For example, ethanol has much stronger antiseptic properties when mixed with 20 to 50 percent water than when applied 96 or 100 percent pure; or "wet" heat can be used at much lower temperatures to achieve sterility than "dry" heat.

PHYSICAL AGENTS

The various actions principal physical agents have on microorganisms are summa-

69

Table 5.1. Terms Applicable to Sterilization and Disinfection

Viability
The degree to which microorganisms are able to propagate when placed in a suitable environment compared to their initial capacity to propagate in the same environment (before having undergone a given treatment).

Sterilization
The use of physical and/or chemical methods to eliminate **all** viable microorganisms.

Disinfection
The application of chemical methods (generally) to eliminate all potentially **infective** microorganisms without necessarily destroying all other viable microbes.

Antisepsis
The local application of chemical agents to a body surface to kill, or at least to inhibit, infective microorganisms. Antisepsis may be likened to disinfection of a body surface.

Sanitizing
The application of measures to lower the content of microorganisms of various materials and objects (e.g., those used in the preparation of food) to a less drastic extent than is required for complete sterilization.

rized in Table 5.3. It is important to realize that the presence of non-microbial organic matter, such as food, blood, or fecal material, may modify the influence of various physical agents on microorganisms. With high organic content, longer exposure times may be needed (to given conditions) in order to achieve microbial inactivation.

Heat

Of the physical agents used to eliminate microorganisms, the application of heat by various means is one of the earliest recognized and most widely used methods.

Wet Heat. Wet heat is heat applied by means of steam or heat applied to aqueous solutions or suspensions. Complete sterility can be obtained by steam autoclaving at 121°C for 20 minutes. At sea level this

temperature is attained with steam at a pressure of 15 pounds per square inch (≈ 1 atmosphere ≈ 100 kilo-pascal), whereas at higher elevations greater steam pressures are needed to attain this temperature. Different bacteria are destroyed at different temperatures. A useful criterion for the susceptibility of bacteria to heat is called the *thermal death point*. This is defined as the lowest temperature at which an exposure of 10 minutes results in complete destruction of a bacterial culture in broth. For *Escherichia coli* this temperature is 55°C and for *Mycobacterium tuberculosis*, 60°C; for most bacterial endospores the thermal death point is 121°C. Wet heat applied for 5 to 10 minutes at 55 to 60°C results in the death of most microorganisms in solutions or suspensions at pH of less than 3.5.

Pasteurization. The same treatment at a pH between 3.5 and 4.5 results in *pasteurization*. Pasteurization may be likened to sanitization; that is, it eliminates all potentially infective microorganisms, as well as most microorganisms likely to cause spoilage, without destroying all viable microbes. Liquids of pH 4.5 can be pasteurized at 62°C for 30 minutes. If changes in taste concomitant to that pasteurization method are objectionable (e.g., with milk or cream), *flash pasteurization* may be applied by heating the liquid to 72 to 85°C for 1 minute or less. Boiling at 100°C for 10 minutes results in microbial death only a low (≈ 3.5) or at high (≈ 10.0) pH, and will not destroy spores. To be certain all spores are

Table 5.2. Denaturation of Ovalbumin

Percentage H_2O Present in Ovalbumin	Temperature Required for Coagulation in 30 Minutes
50	56°C
25	74–80°C
6	145°C
0	160–170°C

Table 5.3.   Physical Methods of Decontamination

Agent or Process	Conditions		Effective On	Acts On	Remarks

Heat (with water)	5 to 10 min at
	  pH < 3.5
	30 min
	1 min
		55 to 60°C
		62°C
		72 to 85°C
			Vegetative
			  bacterial cells
				Enzymes	Pasteurization

	20 min	121°C	Spores, fungi,
			  vegetative
			  bacterial cells,
			  viruses
				Enzymes,
				  membranes,
				  nucleic acids
					Sterilization by
					  autoclaving

Heat (without
  water)
	1 to 2 hr	160°C	Spores, fungi,
			  vegetative
			  bacterial cells,
			  viruses
				Enzymes,
				  membranes,
				  nucleic acids	

Radiation	Infrared	>7600 Å	Spores, fungi,
			  vegetative
			  bacterial cells,
			  viruses
				Enzymes,
				  membranes,
				  nucleic acids
					Actually sterilizes
					  by heat

	Visible	3600 to
		  4500 Å
					No antimicrobial
					  activity;
					  photo-
					  reactivation

	Ultraviolet	2600 to
		  3100 Å
			Spores, fungi,
			  vegetative
			  bacterial cells,
			  viruses
				Nucleic acids	Dimer formation
					  between
					  adjacent
					  thyidine and
					  uracil bases

	X-rays, gamma
	  rays
			Spores, fungi,
			  vegetative
			  bacterial cells,
			  viruses
				Enzymes,
				  nucleic acids
					Oxidation by free
					  radicals;
					  denaturation of
					  DNA

Filtration
  Membrane filters
	0.8 μm pore
	  diameter
			Yeasts, some large
			  bacterial cells		

	0.45 μm pore
	  diameter
			Most vegetative
			  cells		

	0.2 μm pore
	  diameter
			All bacterial cells
			  and spores, some
			  viruses		

	0.02 μm pore
	  diameter
			All microbial forms
			  including viruses		

destroyed, complete sterilization at 121°C for 20 minutes (see section on wet heat) should be effected. Another method consists of boiling at 100°C for 10 minutes, incubating the liquid at 37°C for 24 hours to allow the spores to germinate, and then reboiling the liquid to kill the vegetative cells that have grown from the spores. The process, called *Tyndallization*, may have to be repeated several times to achieve sterility.

The mechanism of sterilization by wet heat at 121°C is mainly the irreversible denaturation of the microorganisms' proteins.

Dry Heat.   To sterilize with dry heat, a

temperature of 160°C should be maintained for 1 or 2 hours. Under these conditions, pyrogens, which resist wet heat, are destroyed. The mechanism of sterilization by dry heat is the oxidative destruction of the protoplasm and the irreversible denaturation of the proteins of the microorganisms. At the temperature of a hot flame, less than 1 second may suffice to obtain complete sterility. Flaming of the tools used by microbiologists before and after use has become standard practice in laboratories of microbiology.

Cooling. Cooling microorganisms does not destroy them. Even freezing does not destroy most microorganisms, although a few may be damaged from being pierced by ice crystals. Cooling at 4°C in a refrigerator severely slows down the metabolism and virtually suspends the multiplication of most microorganisms, and is thus an extremely useful method for conserving food for several days longer than would be possible at room temperature.

Freezing. Freezing at −20°C allows food to be conserved for several months; it must be kept in mind that, upon thawing, virtually the same number of viable microorganisms present before freezing will still be found. Freezing at very low temperatures (−85°C or colder) allows food to be conserved for many years, and also permits the virtually unlimited conservation of many strains of microorganisms.

Drying. Drying also does not destroy microorganisms, although thorough drying, like cooling or freezing, severely slows down the metabolism and suspends the multiplication of microorganisms. Since the earliest times, drying of foodstuffs has been a method for conserving food (e.g., for long sea voyages). The addition of large amounts of sugar in fruit confitures, or salt in meat or fish preserves, has been practiced for centuries. Neither sugar nor common salt are disinfectants, strictly speaking; they simply serve as dehydrating agents.

Freeze-drying is an even better method for preserving microorganisms than conventional drying methods. As the dehydration takes place by sublimation from the frozen state, most untoward effects of the local excesses of concentration of salts and other solutes that prevail during the ordinary drying process are entirely circumvented. Most materials, tissues, or microorganisms that have been freeze-dried can then be stored at room temperature, although lower temperatures in some cases may be advantageous when very long-term conservation is necessary.

Radiation

Nonionizing radiation from 30 cm to 200 nm wavelength (comprising microwaves and infrared, visible, and ultraviolet light) and ionizing radiation especially at wavelengths from 1 to 4×10^{-4} nm (comprising x-rays, gamma rays, and cosmic rays) have various degrees and types of influence on microorganisms.

Microwaves and Infrared Light. Microwaves and infrared irradiation are used for sterilization of various objects. For example, syringes can be sterilized within their sealed containers by exposing them to infrared radiation for 10 minutes, causing them to reach 190°C.

Visible Light. Light in the visible region of the spectrum has no special denaturing or sterilizing influence on microorganisms, but it does have a cancelling influence on the denaturing effects of ultraviolet light. Irradiation with visible light tends to counteract the damage done by ultraviolet light by repairing the damaged DNA (see below). This is accomplished by replacing stretches of DNA by new synthesis and ligation in a process called *photoreactivation*.

Ultraviolet Light. Ultraviolet light at wavelengths between 200 and 300 nm (and especially at 265 nm) affects microbial protein as well as DNA. Protein damage is effected by rupturing the disulfide and hydrogen bonds of the peptide chains, whereas DNA is affected by dimerization of adjacent thymidines on the same strand. Mercury vapor lamps, emitting ultraviolet light in the 240 to 280 nm range, and other ultraviolet light sources are frequently used to keep rooms, cabinets, or hoods sterile, especially during periods when people are not exposed to the light. The lethal dose for most bacteria is $\approx$ 10 to 20 mWsec/cm^2, and for spores $\approx$ 40 mWsec/cm^2 up to $\approx$ 1 Wsec/cm^2. People, however, must not be exposed for more than a minute or so to an ultraviolet intensity required to inactivate *E. coli.*

Ionizing Radiation. Ionizing radiation — irradiation by x-rays (0.1 to 1 nm), gamma rays ($\approx$ 0.001 nm), and cosmic rays ($\approx$ 0.0004 nm) — acts by eliminating electrons in its path, which in turn can produce further ionization in other atoms. The presence of oxygen strongly enhances the damage inflicted by ionizing radiation. The irreversible denaturation of nucleic acids is one of the principal mechanisms of effecting sterilization by these forms of radiation. The unit of measure for the amount of absorbed ionizing radiation is the rad (r), which corresponds to the energy absorption of 200 erg/g of material. Irradiation of cultured mammalian cells with $\approx$ 200 r kills 50 percent of them; 50 percent of people or animals die within 21 days after whole body irradiation with $\approx$ 500 r. Bacteria, spores, and small viruses are killed upon irradiation with $\approx$ 10^5 r, 2 $\times$ 10^6 r, 4 $\times$ 10^6 r, respectively. Ionizing radiation has an exceedingly strong penetrating power; when it is used for sterilizing purposes, elaborate screening is necessary for the protection of personnel. Although quite effective, the sterilization of food by this method has not as yet found any general application because of the fear for the possible dangerous changes that may take place in the molecules of the food itself.

Mechanical Destruction Methods

Grinding and Blending. Grinding and blending are fairly inefficient methods for killing bacterial cells, because the cells are so small that any purely mechanical device liable to impair them by shearing or deformation would simultaneously engender so much heat through friction as to inactivate irreversibly most intracellular enzymes and other proteins by thermal denaturation.

Pressure Release Methods. Sudden release of pressure will cause dissolved gases to reassume the gaseous phase and thus to expand considerably. When this expansion is made to take place intracellularly in bacteria, it causes them to explode and to release their cytoplasmic enzymes and other solutes and organelles into the medium. Pressure bombs, in which bacteria suspended in an aqueous medium are temporarily subjected to a high pressure by means of an inert compressed gas (170 to 680 kg/cm^2), which is then suddenly released, are quite efficient for disintegrating bacteria without concomitant protein denaturation. One hundred percent bacterial disintegration cannot, however, be obtained after only one cycle of pressure and release.

Disruption of cells by ultrasonic waves is based on the same principle and is actually just another pressure release method. Sonication is only effective when dissolved gas is present; the repeated cavitation caused by the ultrasonic waves alternatively causes points of high and low pressure. At the low pressure points, dissolved intracellular gas is released in the gaseous form, causing the cells to explode. At high pressure points, temporary implosions can also occur, which may play an additional role in cellular disintegration. It is likely that violent oscillations in suspended gas bubbles caused by sonication also play a role in cell destruction by this method.

Other Pressure Methods. Bacteria

and other cells can also be disintegrated by squeezing them, in the frozen stage, under very high hydraulic pressures (10 to 25 metric tons) through two tiny openings. The mechanism of disruption in this case is mainly mechanical shear.

High pressures of the order of ≈ 500 atm are detrimental to most physiologic functions of bacteria, but only very high pressures (several thousand atm) will inactivate bacteria completely.

Low Pressure. Many aerobic bacteria can grow at pressures as low as 0.01 atm, whereas anaerobic species are only slightly inhibited at pressures as low as 10^{-3} atm and can survive at even lower pressures. In an ultrahigh vacuum, such as is found on the surface of the moon, many microbial species can remain viable for considerable lengths of time.

Mechanical Separation Methods

Filtration. For the better part of a century, various filters have been in use for the sterilization of liquids. With the earlier filters, adsorption of bacteria onto the filter material played as important a role as the retention of bacteria due to the smallness of the pores. Many of the filters were made in the form of candles. These filters are made of diatomaceous earth, and adsorption plays a strong role in their sterilizing action. Candle filters made of unglazed porcelain, as well as the flat filters made of fritted glass, depend mainly on filtration and only slightly on adsorption. With all of these filters, pore sizes of ≈ 0.45 μm diameter are required for removing most bacteria and pore sizes of ≈ 0.2 μm for the elimination of all bacteria. Flat asbestos pads depend principally on adsorption and thus have to be used at a slow flow rate and low pressures; the densest asbestos pads can even be used for the removal of pyrogens (medium to high molecular weight, soluble bacterial lipopolysaccharides that induce fever upon parenteral in-

jection). Pyrogens can also be removed by adsorption onto activated charcoal but they cannot be destroyed by wet heat.

Membranes made of cellulose acetate or other synthetic polymeric materials are frequently used for sterilization. Most membranes have a fine random-pored, sponge-like structure. Another membrane variety consists of very thin, solid sheets of a polymer, such as polycarbonate, perforated by many identically sized cylindrical pores, which are induced by collimated bombardment with charged particles in a nuclear reactor, followed by controlled etching of uniform cylindrical pores along the ionized paths. With all of the above membranes, pore diameters of ≈ 0.45 μm will assure the removal of most bacteria, and pore diameters of ≈ 0.2 μm of all bacteria. Viruses, however, are not retained by these membranes. Membranes with pore sizes of $\approx$ 0.8 μm remove all yeast cells and many other microorganisms. Membranes of this type make it possible to conserve filtered beer in containers, thus lending the taste of "draft beer" to bottled beer. Before this became possible, prior to bottling all beer except that which was to be consumed shortly after brewing had to be pasteurized, which somewhat altered its taste.

To retain all viruses, membranes with pore diameters <20 nm are necessary; their flow rate is very low, and they retain many other compounds as well. Thus for the purpose of sterilization virus-retaining membranes are not commonly used.

Centrifugation. Although large-scale centrifugation is seldom used to remove bacteria from liquids, on a laboratory scale it is entirely feasible to sediment bacteria into a pellet by 1 hour centrifugation at 10,000 g. The supernatant, if carefully removed, is then devoid of bacteria. Viruses can be sedimented by the same techniques but at higher gravitational forces. Zonal centrifuge rotors, with the help of sucrose density gradients, are used for the continuous separation and purification of various viruses (e.g., influenza virus), allowing the preparation of antiinfluenza vaccines with much reduced side effects.

Microorganisms Capable of Existing Under Extreme Physical Conditions

There are various microorganisms that have found a niche in some of the more extreme physical conditions that can be encountered on our planet. Microorganisms that thrive under high pressures are called *barophilic*, those living at high temperatures *thermophilic*, and those at low temperatures *psychrophilic* or *cryophilic*. None of the bacteria that thrive under extreme conditions grow well under more normal ambient circumstances and therefore none of them shows the least tendency of pathogenicity toward man.

Barophilic Bacteria. In deep sea samples taken at depths from 7000 to 12,000 meters below sea level, barophilic species have been isolated that still grow at 700 to 1000 atm and actually thrive at 200 to 400 atm. There are various *Pseudomonas* spp. in this class, along with *Flavobacterium marinotypicum* and *Bacillus abysseus*.

Thermorphilic Bacteria. There are thermophilic bacteria that thrive in a neutral and alkaline pH, at temperatures around the boiling point of water at ambient pressures (90 to 101°C). In the acid pH range, the maximum temperatures at which bacteria may be encountered are around 75 to 80°C. For example, *Bacillus stearothermophilus* will survive autoclaving for 30 minutes at 121°C but can be killed at 125°C.

Psychrophilic Bacteria. Many of the psychrophiles are gram-negative rods, but gram-positive rods also occur. They thrive at −5 to −10°C; most of them are inactivated, although not killed, at 25 to 30°C.

CHEMICAL AGENTS

The various actions the principal chemical agents have on microorganisms are summarized in Table 5.4. The presence of nonmicrobial organic matter may strongly influence the action of various chemical agents on microorganisms. With high organic content, higher concentrations of a given chemical and/or longer exposure times may be needed to achieve microbial inactivation. The action of various classes of chemicals on microorganisms outside of the human host is discussed in this section, regardless of the possible action these chemicals might have on the human host. The special class of chemicals designated as antibiotics are discussed separately (Ch. 4).

Acids and Alkalis

Microorganisms in general are more readily inactivated under acid conditions than under neutral or moderately alkaline conditions. Inorganic acids kill most microorganisms, as will organic acids and strong alkalis. Mycobacteria are more resistant to the action of both acids and alkalis.

Alkaloids and Dyes

Alkaloids. Alkaloids do not play an especially important role in sterilization or disinfection. A noteworthy exception, mainly used analytically, is represented by optochin, which specifically inhibits *Streptococcus pneumoniae* in concentrations ≈ 2 to 200 ppm.

Dyes. Various organic dyes are mildly bactericidal in fairly low concentrations (0.1 to 1000 ppm), but they do not affect spores. They are more active against gram-positive than gram-negative bacteria. Some examples are brilliant green, crystal violet, methylene blue, and acridine dyes.

Salts

Neutral salts in fairly high concentrations are mildly bacteriostatic, mainly owing to their dehydrating action (see Drying,

Table 5.4.   Action of Chemical Agents on Microorganisms

Agent	Concentration	Effective Against	Acts On	Remarks
Acids				
Mineral (HCl and others)	0.01N to >1N	Spores, vegetative cells, viruses	Cell membrane, enzymes	Mycobacteria are relatively resistant
Organic (lactic and others)	1000 ppm	Vegetative cells	Cell membrane, enzymes	Mycobacteria are relatively resistant
Alkalis				
NaOH and others	0.01N to >1N	Spores, vegetative cells, viruses	Cell membrane, enzymes	Mycobacteria are relatively resistant
Alkylating agents				
Ethylene oxide and formaldehyde	100 to 1000 ppm in solution	Spores, vegetative cells, viruses	Cell membrane, enzymes, nucleic acids	Can be used as a gas
Detergents				
Anionic	1000 ppm	Vegetative cells		Effect principally due to washing action
Cationic	1 to 1000 ppm	Vegetative cells	Cell membrane, enzymes	Some effect on spores
Dyes				
Crystal violet and others	0.1 to 100 ppm	Vegetative cells	Nucleic acids	Used in selective media, principally active on gram-positive organisms
Organic solvents				
Ethanol and other alcohols	50 to 70%	Spores, vegetative cells, some viruses	Cell membrane, enzymes	Not active against nonenveloped viruses
Oxidants				
Halogens				
I_2	2 to 7%	Spores, vegetative cells, viruses	Cell membrane, enzymes	Spores more resistant to Cl_2, O_3, and $KMnO_4$
Cl_2	200 ppm			
O_3	6 to 7%			
$KMnO_4$	1000 ppm			
Sulfhydryl poisons				
Hg and other heavy metals	>1.0 ppm	Spores, vegetative cells, viruses	Enzymes	Very toxic

above). Borax ($Na_2B_4O_7 \cdot 10H_2O$) is a mild antiseptic in concentrations of 1 or 2 percent, as is sodium fluoride (NaF). Potassium tellurite (K_2TeO_3) inhibits gram-negative bacteria; corynebacteria are particularly resistant to tellurite. This is the basis of its use in selective media. Salts of heavy metals have a different mode of action as described in the section on sulfhydryl poisons.

Complexing Agents

Salts that bind multivalent cations, especially those forming a strong bond such as (ethylene dinitrilo) tetraacetic acid, or its sodium salt, Na_2EDTA, act upon cell membranes in concentrations ≈ 0.1 percent. The bactericidal action of complexing agents is much enhanced by and synergic with the action of cationic detergents.

Oxidants

Oxidants are widely used as sterilizing agents or as disinfectants. Iodine is used as a topical disinfectant in solution (2 to 7 percent) in ethanol, or dissolved in a 10 percent aqueous KI solution. These preparations tend, however, to leave a strong yellow stain. To obviate that, I_2 can be solubilized by the admixture of nonionic detergents ("iodophors") and thus be rendered virtually stainless and odorless. A solution of ≈ 3 percent H_2O_2 is also used as a topical disinfectant. Chlorine is commonly used as a water disinfectant in drinking water (0.5 to 1.0 ppm) and swimming pools ($\approx$ 200 ppm). In many cities Cl_2 is being replaced by ozone (O_3), which is much less irritating and almost tasteless and odorless. Other oxidants frequently used are potassium permanganate ($KMnO_4$) at ≈ 0.1 percent and perchloric acid ($HClO_4$) at ≈ 100 ppm.

Reducing Agents

One of the longest used disinfecting agents is sulfur dioxide (SO_2); its mode of action is primarily due to its strong reducing capacity. For centuries, and up to less than a century ago, it has been used in the fumigation and disinfection of ship holds, barrels, warehouses, and so on. Sulfur dioxide is strongly irritating to the eyes and respiratory tract and for that reason has now been largely replaced by other agents.

Phenols

Phenol was first used by Joseph Lister as a disinfectant in surgery. Since then, many phenol and *bis*-phenol derivatives with significantly stronger disinfectant properties have been developed and put to various bactericidal uses. An even older application of phenolic derivatives can be found in the use of smoke in the preservation of meat, sausage, and fish. In the disinfecting activity of smoke, its phenolic content is of major importance. The degree of activity of a given phenolic derivative is expressed as its *phenol coefficient*, which is the ratio of the minimal sterilizing concentration of phenol with respect to a given microorganism to the minimal sterilizing concentration of the phenolic derivative in question. Phenol and phenolics act primarily on the cell wall and cell membranes and, to a lesser extent, on the proteins of microorganisms. Phenolics can be germicidal in concentrations from 10,000 down to 1 ppm; they are somewhat more effective against gram-positive than gram-negative bacteria. For example, 4-N-hexylphenol has phenol coefficients of 33, 313, and 389 with regard to *Salmonella typhi, Staphylococcus aureus*, and *M. tuberculosis*, respectively. Cresols, or alkyl phenols, which are not very soluble in water, are solubilized by mixing them with soap; such mixtures are frequently used as disinfectants for bacteriologically contaminated matter. Chlorinated *bis*-phenols, such as hexachlorophene-2,2'-methylene-*bis*-(3,4,6-trichlorophenol), are bactericidal in high dilutions and are used in deodorant soaps. However, they are known to be toxic when absorbed through the skin. Chlorhexidine, or 1,1'-hexamethylene-*bis*-(*p*-chlorophenyl-5-biguanide), is bacteriostatic at concentrations as low as 1 ppm. The bacteriostatic action of many phenolics is reversible; removal of the compounds by leaching out, dilution, or dialysis may restore some degree of microbial viability. The addition of a crystal of thymol, which is fairly insoluble in water, to biologic preparations can often prevent or delay bacterial and fungal growth. A compound related to phenol, benzoic acid, is used in preserving foods, fruit juices, wine, and fats.

Detergents

Detergents or surfactants comprise compounds endowed with a hydrophilic as well as a hydrophobic moiety, which makes them soluble in water and causes them to form micelles when dissolved. This enables them to solubilize or disperse hydrophobic materials in water. There are anionic, nonionic, ampholytic, and cationic detergents. The anionic detergents include ordinary soaps and salts of fatty acids. The nonionic detergents have virtually no germicidal effect and may, indeed, actually serve as a nutrient medium to various microorganisms. The ampholytic detergents, although mildly bacteristatic, are not extensively used for sterilizing or sanitizing purposes.

Anionic Detergents. The most common anionic detergents comprise the ordinary soaps and sodium dodecyl or lauryl sulfate. Anionic detergents with saturated fatty acid chains are more effective against gram-negative bacilli, whereas those with unsaturated fatty acid chains are more active against gram-positive bacteria, as well as against *Neisseria* spp. The main activity of the various natural and synthetic anionic soaps, however, is based more on their washing and dirt removal activity than on their actual bactericidal properties, which are, compared to other agents, mild at best.

Cationic Detergents. Cationic detergents, especially quaternary ammonium bases such as cetyltrimethyl ammonium bromide and benzalkonium chloride, are bactericidal at relatively low concentrations (1 to 1000 ppm), acting mainly on the cell membrane but also forming complexes with nucleic acids and cytoplasmic proteins. They are most active against gram-positive bacteria but are inactive against spores, mycobacteria, and most viruses. Cationic detergents are most active at neutral and alkaline pH. They are inactive under acid conditions and must never be used in the presence of anionic detergents, which combine with and neutralize them. Quaternary ammonium bases enhance the bactericidal activity of complexing agents. Even when covalently bonded to solid surfaces (e.g., of catheters), totally insolubilized quaternary ammonium bases retain their antimicrobial capacity.

Sulfhydryl Poisons (Heavy Metals)

Agents that can block the sulfhydryl groups of proteins to yield insoluble sulfides and thus to denature proteins, including bacterial enzymes, tend to be strongly germicidal. They comprise salts of heavy metals such as Hg, Ag, As, Sb, Cu, Cd, and Pb. They are quite toxic. Certain organic Hg salts are active at concentrations of less than 1 ppm, such as sodium merthiolate. At these low concentrations they are much less toxic, but they also have a decreased bactericidal effect and have little action on spores.

Alkylating Agents, Gases

Alkylating agents act as sulfhydryl poisons but also denature proteins by crosslinking carboxy, amino, and hydroxy groups. Iodoacetate and mustard gas are in this class, but of greater importance are ethylene oxide, formaldehyde, and, to a certain extent, glutaraldehyde. Ethylene oxide and formaldehyde are important because they can be applied as gases for the sterilization of dry surfaces of materials that cannot be heat-treated; also they are both virucidal. Formalin is the designation for a solution of formaldehyde in water.

Formalin ($\approx$ 0.1 percent formaldehyde) is also used for inactivating various toxins and viruses, while leaving their antigenic properties relatively unimpaired. Alkylation effectively blocks all enzymatic activity but leaves most antigenic determinants unchanged; it acts more on the amino terminal end than on the carboxy terminal end of most peptides. Thus treatment with formalin is effective for transforming toxins into toxoids and viruses into "killed" vaccines. The action of formalin is to some extent reversible. Whereas formalin leaves antigens relatively unaltered, it inactivates antibodies.

Organic Solvents

Various organic solvents have a certain degree of germicidal power; the most important are the water-soluble alcohols and, to a lesser extent, some lipid solvents.

Alcohols. The most important bacteriostatic alcohols are ethanol and isopropyl alcohol applied in aqueous solution at an optimal concentration of 50 to 70 percent (v/v). These alcohols are not active at concentrations below 25 percent. Most viruses tend to be resistant to the action of alcohols. Phenylethyl alcohol is active against gram-negative bacilli at $\approx$ 2500 ppm; it may also, of course, partly be considered a phenolic. Glycerol and glycol are mildly bacteristatic; they are used especially as aerosols.

Lipid Solvents. Toluene or chloroform will, when added in small quantities to biological preparations, have bacteristatic and fungistatic effects. Other solvents such as ether, chloroform, benzene, and acetone, are also mildly bacteristatic. Ether inactivates enveloped but not naked viruses, and may be used to distinguish between these two varieties.

Enzymes

Lysozyme, found in tears, saliva, and eggs, causes lysis of gram-positive bacteria. Various proteolytic enzymes, especially pronase, inactivate enveloped viruses. Phospholipase A inactivates some arboviruses, and phospholipase C renders influenza virus susceptible to attack by proteolytic enzymes.

REFERENCES

Bernarde, M.A., Ed.: Disinfection. Marcel Dekker, New York, 1970.

Borick, P.M., Ed.: Chemical Sterilization. Dowden, Hutchinson & Ross, Stroudsburg, Pa., 1973.

Breach, M.R.: Sterilization: Methods and Control. Appleton-Century-Crofts, New York, 1968.

Hugo, W.B., Ed.: Inhibition and Destruction of the Microbial Cell. Academic Press, New York, 1971.

6

Microbial Pathogenicity and Host-Parasite Relationships

*Boris Albini and
Carel J. van Oss*

The initiation, course, and outcome of infectious diseases are determined by the properties of the infectious agents (i.e., the parasites) and of the infected macroorganisms (i.e., the hosts). The majority of clinical symptoms and the natural history of infectious diseases result from the interaction and interrelation of these two biologic entities, which are both involved in establishing optimal conditions for their survival and reproduction. The overall effect of mechanisms employed by the host to fend off infection is summarized as *host defense*. The impact of the mechanisms employed by the parasites that cause disease in the host is termed *virulence* or *pathogenicity*. *Communicability*, the ability of the infectious agent to spread from host to host, also obviously determines the parasite's fate and its relationship to the host. These concepts and terms are useful in the discussion of infectious diseases. Virulence and pathogenicity, however, should not be confused with the parasite's capability to colonize a host. Many parasites survive and re-

produce in a host without inducing any or only very mild clinically detectable damage. Minimizing the tissue lesions and damage inflicted on a host optimizes the chance for survival and proliferation of parasites. The longer the host survives after infection and the better the host tissues are supplied with nutrients, the greater the chance for the majority of parasites to multiply and infect another host. Indeed, parasites best adapted to a host seem to cause only minimal disease or none at all. Sometimes harmless parasites colonizing a host may be of great benefit to the host. Their survival will therefore be enhanced in a macroorganism "eager" to host them.

Human *parasites* are viruses, chlamydiae, rickettsiae, bacteria, fungi, protozoa, and helminths. Most of these may be classified as microorganisms, that is, living matter of a size requiring a microscope to become visible to our eyes. Many microorganisms, however, are not parasitic in the strict sense, that is, they do not depend on feeding on living matter. Such microorganisms

81

not requiring a living host are termed *sap-rophytes* because they live on rotten, dead organic matter. They do not concern us in this chapter but are of the utmost importance in processing decayed matter. On the other hand, some parasites are not microorganisms. For example, most helminths are readily visible to the unaided eye. Parasites are not by definition harmful to a host. Some of the parasites just use the host as an environment but do not interfere with the host's well-being. Some even add to the host's prosperity. These nonpathogenic parasites are discussed in detail later in this chapter. Some parasites cannot complete their life cycle outside the host; they are *obligate* parasites. Others can live in both living hosts and on decaying organic matter; these are *facultative* parasites.

Virulence and pathogenicity of a parasite define its ability to cause disease in a healthy, normal host of a defined species, sex, and age. Parasites that are able to infect normal hosts are called *pathogens*. Parasites not able to cause disease in healthy hosts but only in those with impaired defense mechanisms ("compromised hosts") are termed *opportunistic*. It should be mentioned here that the term parasite often is used in a more restricted way to denote parasitic protozoa and helminths. However, we do not use the term parasite in this way in this chapter.

Communicability is not always involved in the development of a disease. Botulism and staphylococcal food poisoning follow ingestion of toxins elaborated outside the host's body. Thus microbial products cause disease without colonization or infection of the host. These diseases, although ultimately related to microorganisms, are not infectious diseases but toxicoses.

Another aspect of host–parasite interactions is the pattern of microbial diseases in human populations. Although these considerations are properly the province of epidemiology, a number of characteristics of disease occurrence and impact are perti-

nent to discussions of infections. Measurement of these parameters employs statements of frequency or severity. Among the more commonly employed measures are the *mortality rate*, which expresses the number of deaths (due to a disease) in a whole population over a defined period of time. The *morbidity rate* is the number of new cases of a disease recognized in the population over a defined period. The *fatality rate* is the number of deaths from a disease compared to the number of cases.

A number of other descriptive terms are also used. The *attack rate* is the number of cases that occur in a specifically defined population as opposed to a general population. *Incidence* refers to the number of new cases in a population over a defined period and is equivalent to the morbidity rate, whereas *prevalence* is the total number of cases, new or old, in a population at any given time.

In this chapter an attempt will be made to familiarize the reader with the main factors involved in the individual host's defense and in the parasite's abilities to colonize or infect and to damage the host. Then, the path taken by parasites in their quest for optimal breeding grounds in the host will be outlined. Finally, opportunistic infections will be reviewed.

A CATALOGUE OF HOST DEFENSE MECHANISMS

Mechanisms of host defense are often characterized as either *specific* or *nonspecific*. The specificity referred to most often is *immunological specificity*. This is the restriction of an effector's ability to react with only one distinct molecular structure (i.e., antigenic determinant; Ch. 8). Therefore immunologic reactions and phagocytosis enhanced by immunologic reactants are considered specific host defense mechanisms. Mechanical, physical, chemical, and biochemical factors, as well as phagocytosis without participation of immunologic effectors, are called nonspecific. As useful as this subdivision may be, it should be kept in mind that host defense mechanisms show a continuous spectrum of specificities: an antibody is assumed to be specific for the one epitope to which it was elicited; lysozyme reacts almost exclusively with gram-positive bacteria; and the skin represents a barrier to the majority of potential parasites.

Physical Barriers

Mechanical barriers preventing parasites from invading host tissues are of utmost importance. Most of the host is covered by skin. Its epidermal portion consists of many layers of specialized cells. Keratinized dead cells form the outermost portion. Intact skin is practically impermeable to all but a few parasites (Table 6.1). Not all of the host body, however, is covered by skin. Other covering is required at sites of in-

tense communication and exchange with the host's environment. Such exchange is necessary through the gastrointestinal, respiratory, and urogenital tracts, all of which participate in intense exchange between host and environment. The mucosal epithelium shows no stratum corneum, which would impair this exchange. The surface of epithelial cells is covered by mucus, a viscous gel. Many parasites can penetrate mucosal epithelium. Additional defense mechanisms, however, are abundant along mucosae.

Skin is covered by more or less dense lawns of hair. Hairs form a palisade, impairing the parasite's progress toward the skin. In addition, hair also helps to preserve the microenvironment created by the products of sweat and sebaceous glands, enhancing its inhospitable nature for parasites. At portals to the host's body, hairs may perform the role of primary filters, excluding large particles from reaching the

Table 6.1.   Microorganisms That Infect Skin or Enter the Body via Skin

Microorganisms	Disease	Comments
Arthropod-borne viruses	Various fevers, encephalitides	150 distinct viruses, transmitted by infected arthropod bites.
Rabies virus	Rabies	Bites from infected animals
Vaccinia virus	Skin lesion	Vaccination against smallpox
Rickettsiae	Typhus, spotted fevers	Infestation with infected arthropods
Leptospira	Leptospirosis	Contact with water containing infected animal urine
Staphylococci	Boils, impetigo	Most common skin invaders
Streptococci	Impetigo, erysipelas	
Bacillus anthracis	Cutaneous anthrax	Systemic disease following local lesion at inoculation site
Treponema pallidum and *pertenue*	Syphilis, yaws	Warm, moist skin is more susceptible
Pasteurella pestis	Plague	Bite from infected rat flea
Plasmodium	Malaria	Bite from infected mosquito
Tinea spp. and other fungi	Ringworm, athlete's foot	Infection restricted to skin, nails, and hair

(With permission from Mims, C.A.: The Pathogenesis of Infectious Disease. Academic Press, 1976.)

mucosae. Thus specialized hairs in the nares guard the entrance to the respiratory tract. In general, particles larger than 10 μm in diameter are prevented from passing. Similarly, eyelashes protect the conjunctiva.

Cleansing Mechanisms

Keratinized squames forming the outer layer of the skin are shed continuously. One billion squames are lost and replaced daily. Parasites managing to colonize the skin are disposed of continuously with the squames. Even so, the number of bacteria present on the intact skin of humans is in the range of 10^{12}.

The ciliated epithelial cells of the respiratory tract create a steady motion, transporting mucus and particles embedded in it toward the pharynx mucociliary escalator. Coughing and sneezing increase this transport efficiently. Peristalsis of the bowels sweeps the gastrointestinal tract, moving its contents towards the anus and preventing parasites from attaching to the epithelium. Vomiting is an additional cleansing mechanism for the upper gastrointestinal tract; diarrhea accomplishes the same goal with regard to the lower intestines. Saliva flushes the mouth cavity (up to 1.5 litres are produced daily). Tears, moved by the eyelids, wash over the conjuctiva. Finally, body hygiene and washing are important behavioral complements of biological cleansing mechanisms.

Physicochemical Characteristics of the Microenvironment

Host defenses rely heavily on the preservation of an acidic environment in some areas on the body. Products of skin glands keep the pH of the skin moderately acid. Properly functioning stomach mucosa ensures a very low pH of the stomach contents. This is fatal to most ingested parasites. In patients with decreased acidity of stomach juices, infection with *Vibrio cholerae* may be effected by 10,000 times fewer microorganisms than required in healthy individuals.

Other small molecules, such as ammonia, have inhibitory effects on microorganisms. Zinc, found in semen, also has a protective role for the host. There is also a basic peptide found in semen called spermin, which is bactericidal.

Loss of Cell Receptors

Parasites have to react with receptors on the cells of the host in order to colonize or infect them; for example, poliovirus interacts with receptors on human intestinal and nerve cells before infection occurs. Other parasites have to establish firm contact with epithelial cells of the mucosa to avoid being swept away. The presence and distribution of such receptors on distinct cell types may determine the site and character of the ensuing pathological processes. Absence of receptors, on the other hand, may make the host refractory to infection with a particular parasite. The importance of the loss or lack of cell receptors for host defense has been best documented for some plant parasites.

Denial of Nutrients to the Parasite

Changes in the host that prevent the parasite from satisfying its nutritional requirements occur in the course of some infectious diseases. The relation between erythrocyte abnormalities and incidence of malaria is an example of such mechanisms. Sickle-cell anemia is accompanied by serious disease in homozygotes. However, it renders heterozygous hosts relatively resistant to malaria (Ch. 51). The malarial plasmodia cannot utilize the abnormal hemoglobin as efficiently as the normal molecule. Furthermore, the erythrocytes are removed more rapidly from circulation, and more parasites are thus taken up by phagocytic cells. Consequently, the number of parasites is kept lower in hosts with sickle-cell anemia than in healthy individuals. Sickle-cell anemia decreases fertility and the rate of reproduction less than malaria does. Heterozygotes with sickle-cell anemia therefore have a significantly better chance to survive and reproduce in geographical regions with endemic malaria than do populations with normal hemoglobins. Some other defects of erythrocyte metabolism convey also a survival advantage to the host with malaria. Genes coding for deficient erythrocyte enzymes accumulate in populations abiding in regions with endemic malaria.

Immunologically Nonspecific Antibacterial Factors

Molecules that interact with surface structures of parasites, degrade integral components of the surface membrane or the cell wall, and ultimately lyse parasites are widespread in hosts. Small molecular components of the bile are lytic for many microorganisms. Bile salts activate enzymes of the host and may activate autolytic enzymes of microorganisms. For example, they activate an amidase of *Streptococcus pneumoniae* causing the bacteria to undergo lysis. Lysozyme, a low molecular weight basic protein, degrades certain acetylaminopolysaccharides of peptidoglycans found in bacterial cell walls (Ch. 2). Lysozyme is present in serum, in tears, and in lysosomes. Its serum concentration is 6 to 15 μg/ml. It usually acts on gram-positive bacteria during their logarithmic phase of growth. Modifications of peptidoglycans as seen in *Staphylococcus aureus* or deletion of *N*-acetyl groups as seen in members of the genus *Bacillus* make these bacteria resistant to lysozyme. Lysozyme may contribute to lysis of resistant organisms in the presence of other lysosomal components, serum, or complement. Nonspecific opsonins (i.e., molecules enhancing pha-

gocytosis) are α_2H glycoprotein and fibronectin. Enzymes of the host, such as trypsin and chymotrypsin, degrade nonpeptidoglycan protein components of the bacterial envelope. These and other enzymes participate in the digestion of damaged or dead parasites. Iron-binding proteins, such as transferrin of the serum, milk, and mucus, deprive parasites, e.g., *Escherichia coli*, of this metal essential for their survival.

Interferon

Viral proliferation in cells is inhibited by a mechanism mediated by a small glycoprotein called *interferon*. The properties and activities of interferon are described in Chapter 49. In the present discussion, it should be noted that interferon is a potent nonspecific factor in host defense and control of viral infections. Its antiviral activity, although the best studied of its properties, is only one of its effects. Apparently it also has antitumor activity and is a potent modulator of immune mechanisms.

Fever

Body temperatures above the normal values are seen in many infectious diseases in humans. Fever is not usually induced directly by products or components of the parasites but via mediators produced by phagocytic cells, i.e., macrophages and neutrophilic granulocytes. These mediators are called *endogenous pyrogens*. They are small proteins that act on the hypothalamic temperature regulation center. The thermoregulatory set point is increased, and a temperature increase of the body follows.

The survival of fever in the course of human evolution and that of some other animals makes it probable that it is of some benefit to the host. There is suggestive evidence that fever indeed is in many instances of advantage to host defense. The beneficial effect of fever seems to depend on the relative increase of temperature and not on its absolute value. In contrast to some other laboratory animals, which respond to infection without change in temperature or with hypothermia, rabbits are comparable to humans in manifesting fever in the course of infections. Rabbits show increased resistance to *S. pneumoniae* at higher than normal temperatures. In the wake of infections with *Pasteurella multocida*, rabbits with mild fever are less "protected" against death than rabbits developing high fever; rabbits developing extremely high fever, however, have a decreased survival rate. Thus there seems to be an optimal temperature range for host defense.

In humans, hyperthermia and artificially induced fever have been used in the therapy of some infectious diseases. Malaria therapy was used in neurosyphilis, gonococcal arthritis and endocarditis, and meningitis caused by *S. pneumoniae*. However, with the arrival of antibiotics, fever therapy was practically abandoned. Reports on superior results obtained in some diseases by a combination of chemotherapy and hyperthermia over the approach of using either of the two separately are of interest. Thus better results were obtained by combination therapy than by treatment with penicillin or fever alone in human neurosyphilis. However, cycloserine seems unaffected by fever, and tetracycline and vancomycin have higher efficiency at lower than normal temperatures.

Mycobacterium leprae is widely disseminated throughout the host's body, but lesions occur predominantly at sites with low temperature. It seems possible that, in addition to a low optimal growth temperature of the microorganism, cellular immunity and phagocytosis by macrophages may be enhanced at higher temperatures. Supporting this notion are reports that febrile crises transiently ameliorate the symptoms of leprosy and lead to a regression of the lesions. Moderate fever may induce relative and absolute neutrophilic granulocytosis, and the motility of granulocytes may be enhanced. Recent studies demonstrated enhanced chemotaxis, engulfment of *S. aureus*, digestion of *Candida albicans*, and oxygen consumption by human neutrophilic granulocytes at moderately elevated temperatures. Some reports claim that high temperature increases the mitogenic response of lymphocytes and the cytotoxicity of T cells. Lymphokine production may also be enhanced.

On the other hand, endotoxin-induced damage is enhanced in hyperthermic rabbits. Fever often reactivates latent viral infections (fever blisters caused by herpesvirus). Killing of *Escherichia coli* by human leukocytes is decreased at high temperatures.

Prolonged high fever may be associated with adverse reactions in the host. The heart rate may be increased, convulsions may ensue (almost exclusively in pediatric patients), and the increased metabolic rate may lead to negative nitrogen balance. Very high fever leads to increased permeability of the vasculature, hemorrhages, parenchymatous swelling, and necrosis of cells. The thermoregulatory center becomes disregulated at temperatures higher than 106°F. Heat shock may ensue in a short time.

Phagocytosis

Many cells ingest particles. Epidermal cells of the skin and intestines, and endothelial cells of the vessels can internalize carbon or other particles. This activity, however, is very limited in extent. In contrast, there are some cell lines specialized in internalization and degradation of particulate matter. These are the polymorphonuclear leukocytes, especially the neutrophilic granulocytes, and cells of the macrophage-monocyte series.

Somewhat artificially, the process of phagocytosis may be divided into several stages. First, the particle to be ingested has to attach to the cell membrane of the phagocyte. Then, it is wrapped up in the cell membrane. The cell membrane segment containing the particle becomes detached from the cell membrane and forms a membrane-delineated vesicle in the cytoplasm, the *phagosome*. Thus the ingested particle is kept separated from direct contact with the cytoplasm. Next, a lysosome and a phagosome approach each other and their membranes establish contact and fuse. Lysosomes contain enzymes and other moieties necessary for the killing and digestion of parasites. The contents of the lysosome pour into the phagosome. At this stage the membranes of the two primary vesicles (lysosomes and phagosomes) wall off a single, secondary vesicle, the *phagolysosome*. In this vesicle the digestion of the ingested particle takes place. Undigested residues of the particle, still demarcated from the rest of the cytoplasm, form *residual bodies*. This general outline of phagocytosis is depicted in Figure 6.1.

Recruitment. Neutrophilic granulocytes move rapidly. They travel at rates of up to 40 μm per minute. They leave the circulation by attaching first to the endothelium of venules and then passing through the vessel wall. In tissue they exhibit a random motion, which may contribute to their location of the infectious agents. More importantly, their directional motion is governed by chemotaxis. Products of parasites themselves and substances generated in the course of inflammation and immune response, as well as compounds produced by other phagocytic cells, may attract the phagocyte along a concentration gradient towards the site of infection or inflammation. The slower cells of the monocyte-macrophage line follow similar mechanisms. Among the important chemotactic factors are complement components C3a, C5a, the complex C567, and a number of lymphokines (Ch. 13). After phagocytic

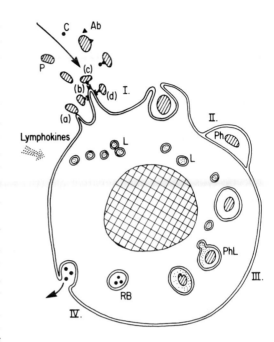

Fig. 6.1. A schematic representation of phagocytosis (clockwise, from the upper left corner). I. (a) Particles (P) may come in close contact with processes of the phagocyte without involvement of immunological reactants; (c) antibodies (Ab, ▲) opsonizing such moieties may facilitate such interactions by binding to Fc receptors (◣) on the phagocyte; (b) some particles (e.g., viruses, bacteria) may activate complement (C, ●) components, which bind to complement receptors (◣); finally, (d) particles may be opsonized by both antibodies and complement. After close contact between particle and cell membrane has been established, a portion of the latter begins to enwrap the former entity. II. The particle becomes completely enveloped by cell membrane. This newly formed phagosome (Ph) consisting of the particle and cell membrane, becomes internalized into the cell; it has been ingested. III. In the cytoplasm, lysosomes (L) merge with phagosomes. In the emerging phagolysosomes (PhL), the catabolic enzymes of the lysosome degrade components of the ingested particle. IV. Some undigested remnants of the particles may remain in membrane-bound residual bodies (RB). Ultimately, the undigested vestiges of the ingested particles are shed into the environment of the phagocyte.

cells have arrived at the site of infection, they are induced to stay by migration inhibition factor (MIF) (Ch. 13) or complement component C3b.

Attachment. Establishment of close contact between two cells depends on the surface properties of the two reactants: cellular surface potential, interfacial free energy, cell shape, and surface viscosity. Usually, both the parasites and the phagocytic cells have a high negative electrical surface potential (zeta potential) which keeps the distance between them at more than 50 to 60 Å. This property of cell surfaces does not seem to be involved directly in enhancement of intercellular contacts in phagocytosis. Interfacial free energy and the shape of the cell seem to be the determining parameters.

The difference in interfacial free energy between the particle and the phagocytic cell seems to be the major factor in attachment and engulfment. Phagocytic cells are hydrophilic; the particles to be engulfed are relatively hydrophobic. Hydrophilic cells establish close contact with hydrophobic parasites following thermodynamic drive. Hydrophobicity of parasites can be increased by interaction with antibodies, since the Fc portion of IgG is highly hydrophobic. The complement component C3b further increases the hydrophobicity. Opsonized microorganisms not only attach more readily to phagocytic cells but are killed and digested more efficiently. Interaction of Fc portions of an antigen–antibody complex, as well as of the attached C3b molecule, with the phagocytic cell takes place via Fc and C3b receptors on the leukocyte's surface.

The shape of the phagocytic cell also seems crucial for attachment to occur. The capability of the cell to form protrusions of a diameter of less than 500 Å makes it possible to circumvent the repulsive forces of the zeta potentials. If cells cannot form thin, fingerlike protrusions, their capability to phagocytize is markedly reduced. The shape of cells depends on environmental and intrinsic factors, such as viscosity of the cell membrane. The presence of divalent cations modulates the phagocytic activity of cells. Finally, phagocytic cells that attach to surfaces display increased phagocytic capability compared to cells suspended in fluids.

Constituents of Lysosomes and the Process of Intracellular Digestion. The breakdown and killing of phagocytosed parasites is accomplished by lysosomal enzymes and other lysosomal compounds after the fusion of lysosomes and phagosomes has occurred. Lysosomes have a low pH, and when they fuse with phagosomes, the ingested particles or cells are confronted with a pH of 3.5 to 4.0. This acid environment by itself has deleterious effects on many parasites and may kill some.

Bacterial killing may occur a few minutes after engulfment, whereas the digestion of the parasite may be accomplished much later. Morphological changes of the cell wall of *E. coli* have been reported 15 minutes after ingestion by neutrophilic granulocytes, which have the most potent arsenal of lysosomal agents. Constituents of neutrophilic lysosomes are summarized in Table 6.2.

After engulfment occurs, there is an increased metabolism, which results in increased production of enzymes, especially of myeloperoxidase. This enzyme, with peroxide and Cl⁻, forms a potent antimicrobial system (the halide-peroxide-myeloperoxidase system) found in neutrophilic granulocytes. This system seems to be effective against bacteria, mycoplasmas, and a number of viruses. Lysozyme is also present in lysosomes. Cationic proteins are important agents in killing parasites, but the mechanism of their reactivity is not known. Lysosomes also contain neutral and acid proteases and nucleases which degrade the components of the cytoplasm and nucleus of the ingested parasites.

The contents of lysosomes may be voided into the phagocyte's surroundings. This

Table 6.2 Lysosomal Constituents of
Neutrophilic Granulocytes

Hydrolases
  α-And β-glucosidases
  α-And β-galactosidases
  α-Mannosidase
  Alkaline phosphatase
  Lysozyme
  Acid ribonuclease
  Acid deoxyribonuclease
  Acid phosphatase
  γ-Glucuronidase
  Naphthylamidase
  N-acetyl-β-glucosaminidase
  Arylsulfatase
  Phosphodiesterase
  5'-nucleotidase
  Proteases (several)
  Peptidases (several)
  Esterases (several)
  Lipase
  Phospholipase A, B
  Lecithinase A
  Lysolecithinase
  α-Amylase
  Dextranase
  Prolidase
  Elastase
  Collagenase

Oxygenases
  Myeloperoxidase
  Cationic proteins

(Cline, M.D.: The White Cell. Harvard University Press, Cambridge, Mass., 1975. Reprinted by permission.)

occurs particularly when phagocytosis of a particle is impossible or hampered. It is often seen in pathologic processes associated with immune complexes (Ch. 15), but may also be important in damaging and killing parasites outside of the phagocyte.

Macrophages do not contain cationic proteins and the myeloperoxidase-peroxide-halide system found in neutrophilic granulocytes. They are therefore in some aspects less efficient in killing and degrading parasites. Most other lysosomal constituents are present in both cell types. Macro-

phages, however, are better equipped to resynthesize lysosomal reactants over a prolonged period of time.

Phagocytic cells differ in their lifespan. The neutrophilic leukocyte, which acts as the "acute" phagocyte, lives for 2 or 3 days after its release from the bone marrow. Roughly 2.5×10^{10} neutrophilic granulocytes are present in the circulation of an adult human — a formidable number. But even more impressive is the number of readily available neutrophilic granulocytes stored in the bone marrow. Up to a hundred times the number of circulating neutrophils is available for immediate deployment to endangered areas throughout the host's body. Neutrophils die rapidly at the site of infection, either as a consequence of their intrinsic activity (e.g., by accumulation of superoxide radicals), as victims of activities of the parasite (see below), or simply of old age. When their number at a site of infection is low, the simultaneously present macrophages ingest the remains of the short-lived neutrophils. Upon the accumulation of a large number of neutrophilic granulocytes, pus is formed by dead phagocytes, remnants of parasites, and tissue constituents liberated by lytic and necrotizing enzymes. Macrophages survive much longer and actively proliferate in tissues. They may be held at infection sites for several weeks and are essential in organizing a barrier to prevent further dissemination of parasites. Macrophages participate as essential reactants in the formation of granulomas (Ch. 15).

Phagocytosis in the first-line of defense may be specific or nonspecific. It may be enhanced by inflammatory mediators, such as activation of complement by endotoxins of gram-negative bacteria. Alternatively, opsonizing antibodies may combine with the parasites, decreasing the hydrophilicity of the parasite's surface. Additional enhancement of phagocytosis is seen after immune complex-mediated activation of complement. Phagocytes may also be activated by reactants generated in the framework of cell-mediated immunity or delayed hypersensitivity (Chs. 12 and 13).

Neutrophilic granulocytes are the cells of acute and rapid reactions to invaders; macrophages are the somewhat slower, initially less effective but longer lived and more insistent phagocytes, characteristically found in lesions of chronic infections.

Immune Responses

Parasites are complex organisms and each one of them displays a number of distinct antigens, mostly polysaccharides or proteins. Polysaccharides induce predominantly humoral immune responses. They are T cell independent antigens in mammals. Proteins elicit both humoral and cell-mediated immunity. Only a few antigens of a parasite elicit protective immune responses. For example, antibody against protein M of streptococci is protective, whereas there is no evidence for such activity of many antibodies against other streptococcal antigens. The efficiency of the immune response also depends on the site of infection. In noninvasive infections of the mucosae, secretory immunoglobulins play the predominant role. In parasitemia both IgM and IgG antibodies are effective. In infected tissues IgM is somewhat disadvantaged, since it does not leave the vasculature as readily as the much smaller IgG molecule. Immune responses to particular organisms have been reviewed in other chapters of this volume.

Antibody-mediated mechanisms contribute predominantly to defense against extracellular parasites. They interact with parasites in body secretions (predominantly as secretory IgA), in circulation during parasitemias, and in tissue fluids. They may contribute significantly to containment of viral infections, especially in the primed host who has had contact with the infecting virus in the past. This is true of epithelial infections in which secretory IgA is impor-

tant and of systemic infections in which IgM and IgG play a role in controlling diseases with a viremic phase. IgA and sIgA, which are quite hydrophilic, do not attach to cell surfaces and thus are especially efficient in the prevention of viral attachment to and penetration into cells in the upper respiratory and lower digestive tracts (see Ch. 10).

Intracellular parasites are protected from antibodies by the surface membrane of the host cell in which they abide. Lymphocytes may support the struggle of host cells against intracellular parasites by production of interferon. Most importantly, T cells constitute the major force in host defense against such intruders. They accomplish their protective functions by two mechanisms: lymphokine production and direct cytotoxicity. Lymphokines are produced by both B and T cells; their production and effects have been most widely studied in the latter cells (Ch. 13). Suffice it here to point out their role in chemotaxis and activation of granulocytes and cells of the monocyte-macrophage line. Alternatively, T cells may interact directly with cells containing parasites. Cytotoxic T cells interact with surface determinants on the cells harboring the parasites and ultimately induce lysis of the cells without participation of complement. It was convincingly demonstrated by Doherty and Zinkernagel that sensitized T cells not only recognize the parasite-specific antigen on the cell surface but also histocompatibility antigens (Ch. 14). These histocompatibility antigens are encoded by genes of the A and B loci of the major histocompatibility complex (MHC) in man. Thus T cell-mediated cytotoxicity seems to be not only specific for foreign parasite antigens but also restricted to reaction with the host's own cells. This mechanism seems effective in many viral infections and in some bacterial infections, e.g., with *Listeria monocytogenes*.

Cell-mediated immunity is decisive in viral infection of cells when the virus is propagated by cell to cell passage or by vertical transmission to progeny cells, and in bacterial infection in which the bacteria cannot be disabled by nonactivated macrophages. Often parasites are engulfed by phagocytic cells but cannot be digested without support provided by T cell lymphokines.

Immune effectors, upon reaction with the antigen, amplify their impact on parasites by activating the mediators of inflammation. Interactions with inflammatory cells are discussed briefly in this chapter and in Chapter 15.

Humoral Mediators of Inflammation

Immune effectors (i.e., antibodies, lymphokines, and sensitized lymphocytes) may recruit mediators of inflammation to enhance incapacitation and elimination of parasites. The mediators of inflammation, however, may be activated directly by parasites or by components of tissue exposed by injury. Thus endotoxin may initiate the complement system, and denuded collagen fibers of the tissue may activate the Hageman

system. Complement is discussed in Chapter 11. The central role of Hageman factor in inflammation has to be recalled here (Fig. 6.2); it may influence blood coagulation, fibrinolysis, complement, and the kinin system.

Normal Flora of the Host

Nonpathogenic microorganisms compete with pathogens for food and space and thereby diminish the prospects for the pathogen to become established in the host. A number of microorganisms populating the normal, healthy host produce compounds inhibiting the growth of other microorganisms. For example, some bacteria produce bacteriocidins. A well studied example of such a substance is colicin, produced by *E. coli*. Nonpathogenic microorganisms are present in varying numbers at sites of the normal host's body that are in contact with the environment. These organisms are called *commensals*. In addition to competing with pathogens, a number of nonpathogenic microorganisms contribute

Interrelationship
between inflammatory mediator systems

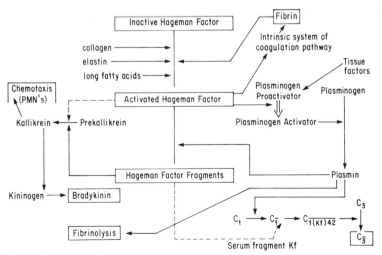

Fig. 6.2. Role of Hageman factor in inflammation. (With permission, from Albini, B., Brentjens, J.R., and Andres, G.A.: The Immunology of the Kidney. Edward Arnold, London, 1979, and Year Book Publishers, Chicago, 1979.)

more actively to the well-being of the host. Lactobacilli colonize the female genital tract during the reproductive age of the host. The high concentration of glycogen present in the vaginal epithelium provides conditions conducive to the growth of these bacteria. The bacteria thrive on glycogen, the concentration of which is regulated by estrogen in the circulation. The lactobacilli produce acids and thus ensure an environment hostile to many potential pathogens. Intestinal bacteria, forming part of the normal flora, may produce compounds essential for the host's nutritional needs. This is well documented in rabbits, which derive some of their vitamins from intestinal bacteria. In humans, microorganisms that synthesize vitamins and other essential nutrients may be of importance in combating malnutrition. Such microorganisms are termed *symbionts* in an effort to convey the notion of mutual benefit for host and parasite.

Considering these beneficial aspects of colonization by a number of parasites, it is easy to understand that measures to fight infectious agents should be well balanced and specific. The physician has to aim at eliminating the one specific parasite causing the disease but, at the same time, has to be careful to minimize any disturbance of the normal flora. A total attack against microorganisms in general may be as deleterious to the host as reluctance to initiate efforts to stop the invasion and multiplication of pathogens.

THE PARASITE'S WEAPONRY: FACTORS DETERMINING PATHOGENICITY, VIRULENCE, AND COMMUNICABILITY

However sophisticated and varied the host defense mechanisms may seem, the parasites are able to adapt to them. The very short generation time of most of the parasites makes such an adaption feasible in very short time intervals.

Adhesins

Parasites have to attach to the host's surface structures to gain access to its cells and tissues, their ultimate breeding grounds. Many viruses and bacteria display protrusions on their surface facilitating adhesion to other cells and produce molecules that react with structures of the host's cells or tissues and guarantee establishment of close contact between parasites and host. Such products are called *adhesins*. The structures in the host with which the adhesins react are termed *receptors*. The presence or absence of receptors and adhesins determine to some degree species and tissue specificity seen with many infectious agents. Myxoviruses possess hemagglutinins on their surfaces. These not only agglutinate erythrocytes but also react with neuraminic acid residues on ciliated epithelia of the respiratory tract. *Mycoplasma pneumoniae* attaches to the same structures, whereas rhinoviruses and *Bordetella pertussis* interact with other cell surface structures. Poliovirus capsids interact with components of gastrointestinal epithelium as does *V. cholerae*. Chlamydiae attach to cells of the conjunctiva. *Streptococcus salivarius* and *Streptococcus mutans* secrete dextrans, which allow them to form densely populated plaques on the enamel of teeth. Helminths attach via hooks and sucking devices. Blood group determinants may be of importance in the attachment of plasmodia to erythrocytes.

Overcoming Mechanical Barriers and Cleansing Mechanisms

Although the intact skin is almost impenetrable for most parasites, the cercariae of *Schistosoma* spp. can digest their way through the skin. Amebas gain access to host tissue by actively moving between epithelial cells, penetrating the less forbidding barrier of mucosa. *Haemophilus influenzae* and *M. pneumoniae* neutralize the cleansing mechanism provided by the mucociliary escalator via a reactant that inhibits ciliary movements.

Penetration of Host Cells

Whereas many parasites enter host cells during phagocytosis, some actively penetrate the cell surface membrane. Shigellae and salmonellae, among other bacteria, induce a local breakdown of cell membrane structures and thus enter intestinal epithelial cells. The discontinuity in the cell membrane is quickly repaired. Some protozoa, such as trypanosomes, *Toxoplasma gondii*, and *Entamoeba histolytica*, have their own

Table 6.3.   Exotoxins

Microorganism	Toxin	Action	Significance *in Vivo*
Clostridium perfringens	α-Toxin	Phospholipase (action on cell membrane)	Cell necrosis, hemolysis, toxemia
Clostridium tetani	Toxin	Blocks action of inhibitory neurons	Overaction of motor neurons, muscle spasm, lockjaw
Corynebacterium diphtheriae	Toxin	Inhibits cell protein synthesis	Heart damage, nerve paralysis.
Shigella dysenteriae	Enterotoxin (neurotoxin)	Induces fluid loss from intestine, and vascular endothelial damage in brain	Diarrhea, neurologic disturbances
Vibrio cholerae	*Toxin (choleragen)*	Activates adenyl cyclase, and raises cAMP level in cells	Acts on intestinal epithelial cell, water and electrolyte loss into intestine
Bacillus anthracis	Toxic complex	Three factors form a toxic complex and cause increased vascular permeability	Edema and hemorrhage (primary lesion); circulatory failure (systemic disease)
Clostridium botulinum	Toxin	Blocks release of acetylcholine	Neurotoxic signs, paralysis
Bordetella pertussis	Toxin	Ciliary damage	?
Streptococcus pyogenes	Erythrogenic toxin	Vasodilation	Causes scarlet fever rash
	Leukocidin Streptolysin	Kills phagocytes	Antiphagocytic
	Streptokinase	Lyses fibrin	Promote spread of bacteria in tissues?
	Hyaluronidase	Liquefies connective tissue matrix	
Staphylococcus aureus	α-Toxin	Cytotoxic; action on cell membranes	Necrosis at site of infection; systemic toxicity
	Leukocidin	Kills phagocytes	Antiphagocytic
	Enterotoxin	Action on vomiting center in brain	Nausea, vomiting, diarrhea (food poisoning)

(With permission from Mims, C.A.: The Pathogenesis of Infectious Disease. Academic Press, London, 1976.)

complement of lysosomal enzymes that break down membranes of host cells. Since most viruses are susceptible to killing by lysosomal components, direct infection of the cytoplasm, avoiding phagocytosis, gives the parasite the chance to initiate reproduction before it comes under the influence of lysosomal enzymes; lysosomal components are not restricted to specialized phagocytic cells but occur, even though in much lower quantities, in many other cell types. The envelope of viruses may fuse with the cell membrane, and the core may thus be internalized (Ch. 39). Other viruses are able to pass through the membranes of phagosomes in the time interval prior to lysosomal fusion. Malarial plasmodia induce their internalization into the host's red blood cells by establishing contact between their conoid and the erythrocyte membrane; subsequently, they are engulfed by the host cell.

Toxins

Parasites contain or secrete compounds that are harmful to cells and tissue components of the host or induce derangements of cell and organ functions. The most extensively studied toxins are those produced by bacteria. *Exotoxins* are secreted by proliferating bacteria. *Endotoxins* are liberated upon disintegration of the microorganisms. Table 6.3 gives a list of exotoxins.

Exotoxins are produced predominantly by gram-positive microorganisms. The most potent exotoxin is synthesized by *Clostridium botulinum*; 1 g of this toxin would suffice to kill 2×10^{11} mice.

Toxins may act locally. Toxins of *Clostridium perfringens*, the most common organism isolated in gas gangrene, facilitate the spread of the organism by breaking down connective tissue and inducing necrosis of cells. Among them is the α-toxin, a lecithinase acting on cell membranes. After reaching circulation, this enzyme induces massive intravascular hemolysis. It acts at the site of

infection. The exfoliating toxin of *S. aureus* causes the rare scalded-skin syndrome in children; it cleaves the skin at the stratum granulosum and thereby induces formation of bullae.

Other toxins have systemic action. The most important parasite-induced diseases with systemic toxicoses are botulism, tetanus, diphtheria, and scarlet fever. *Corynebacterium diphtheriae* multiplies in the epithelium but does not penetrate deep into the tissue. Still, the diphtheria toxin reaches the circulation and causes damage to kidney, heart, and nerve tissue. It also acts locally, inducing necrosis of epithelial cells and incapacitation of phagocytic cells. Tetanus toxin binds to synaptosomes in the spinal cord. Botulinum toxins are absorbed by the intestines and interfere with the release of acetylcholine at cholinergic interneuronal junctions and motor end plates. The erythrogenic toxin of some temperate phage-infected strains of *Streptococcus pyogenes* causes the rash of scarlet fever. In some infections, toxins acting only over a short distance from the microorganism have systemic effects, because the microorganisms involved spread throughout the body. This is the case in infections with *Bacillus anthracis*.

Two other groups of exotoxins merit brief discussion here. One is the group of bacterial enterotoxins. Enterotoxins act on the gastrointestinal tract. The mechanisms of their actions vary widely. The toxin of *V. cholerae* combines with a ganglioside of epithelial cell membranes and activates adenyl cyclase, which results in an increased concentration of cellular cyclic AMP. Consequently, electrolytes and water are lost. Similar mechanisms occur with toxins from *E. coli*. The enterotoxin of *Shigella dysenteriae* penetrates epithelial cells and leads to their degeneration; it also interacts with blood vessels.

The other group of exotoxins to be mentioned here are fungal toxins. *Claviceps purpurea*, a fungus infecting wheat and rye, produces ergotamine, which causes ergot poisoning in humans upon consumption of contaminated grain. A number of species of mushrooms produce substances that are highly toxic for humans and other animals. Exotoxins may be altered to lose their toxicity, usually by treatment with formaldehyde, and retain their antigenicity. Such preparations are called toxoids.

Endotoxins found in a variety of gram-negative bacteria all have the same basic structure; they are lipopolysaccharides (LPS) (Ch. 2). Endotoxins, in contrast to exotoxins, are heat stable and cannot be converted into a nontoxic form (Ch. 8). LPS induces the release of endogenous pyrogens and thereby produces fever. It activates the complement system via both the classical and the alternate pathways. In sufficient quantities it has a profound effect on the circulation. It is one of the factors that, upon massive release into the circulation, may lead to severe shock. LPS-induced shock occurs most often during gram-negative sepsis. This shock syndrome is characterized by a drastic fall of blood pressure caused by peripheral pooling of blood, collapse, and sometimes death. LPS has been shown to be a mitogen for lymphocytes and a polyclonal activator of B cells. It directly affects lysosomes and mitochondrial metabolism. The latter effect leads to accumulation of NADH in the cytoplasm, favoring conversion of pyruvate to lactate. Since small amounts of LPS are constantly absorbed from the normal flora of the gastrointestinal tract, it is possible that it plays some role in the physiology of the immune response. The reactivity of LPS differs among species of gram-negative bacteria. Endotoxins other than LPS are found in some bacteria, e.g., *Yersinia pestis*, *B. pertussis*, and streptococci.

Protective Cell Coats

Viral DNA is covered by protein that is arranged in the form of capsomers, which form capsids (Ch. 39). In addition to enhancing absorption of the virion to cell membranes, these capsids also protect the nucleic acid of the virus from enzymes of the host. Many animal viruses also have an envelope consisting of lipid bilayer membranes and proteins. These proteins are virus-specific. The envelope provides an additional protective coat for the genetic material of the virion.

In gram-positive bacteria a thick peptidoglycan layer (Ch. 2) protects the cytoplasm from the more common proteolytic enzymes. Nevertheless, man has a number of enzyme systems that are effective in digesting peptidoglycans, the most prominent of which is lysozyme. Gram-negative bacteria, although having a much thinner peptidoglycan layer than their gram-positive analogs, possess an outer membrane that prevents contact of lysozyme and similar enzymes with peptidoglycans. Acid-fast bacteria, with their unusual cell wall composition, are resistant to most chemical disinfectants and survive for more than a week in droplets and in dust, provided direct sunlight is excluded.

Some bacteria can produce endospores specialized for prolonged survival in a dormant stage. These specialized forms give *Clostridium* and *Bacillus* spp. an advantage for survival in an adverse environment.

Many bacteria and fungi are able to produce mucopolysaccharide capsules or slimes. These structures decrease the threat of being phagocyticized, as they increase hydrophilicity of the cell. In addition, capsules may prevent the interaction of parasites and the host's immune reactants. Strains forming capsules produce smooth colonies (S); microorganisms without capsules produce rough colonies (R). The shift from smooth to rough colonies (S to R) is usually accompanied by loss of virulence.

Motility and Recruitment of Transport

The advantage of motility for spreading through the host's body is obvious. Many bacteria, protozoa, and helminths have developed various means of locomotion. Another behavioral adaptation achieving the goal of dissemination is the capability of parasites to survive in blood and to use the host's circulatory system to be carried throughout the body. The parasite may become adapted for survival in mobile host cells. Survival in phagocytic cells ensures a "free ride" in these relatively rapidly moving host cells. This mechanism seems to be used by influenza viruses, mycobacteria, and some protozoa.

Genetic Factors Enhancing Parasite Survival

Microorganisms, especially viruses, rickettsiae, and some bacteria, have a tremendous advantage in their adaptability to the host and the changes in the host's defense mechanisms. Their generation time is much shorter than that of the human host (e.g., 20 minutes for many bacteria, 15 to 30 years for man). Microorganisms, it should be expected, have an advantage in natural selection when competing with defense mechanisms of the host.

Some microorganisms have developed specialized mechanisms to allow for frequent genetic changes or transmission of genetic information from one individual to the other of the same species. The appearance of new antigenic properties is enhanced in the influenza virus by the presence of eight segments of RNA in the virion. Thus in cells infected by two strains of influenza virus, recombination may easily occur, giving rise to new antigenic variants (Ch. 40).

Some strains of bacteria may exhibit a rudimentary form of genetic exchange by conjugation (Ch. 3). This type of exchange of information is crucial in the development and spreading of resistance to antibiotics and chemotherapeutic agents.

Microbial Strategies Concerning Host Phagocytes

In response to the host's deployment of phagocytic cells throughout the body, parasites have evolved a variety of mechanisms to circumvent or destroy these cells. It should be kept in mind that phagocytic cells are involved in first-line defense as well as throughout the course of the infection, being integrated in the immune response and inflammation. The parasites produce a number of substances that decrease the likelihood of being engulfed by phagocytes. Some of these substances damage the phagocytic cell. These are toxins and may be called *aggresins*. Other factors impede phagocytosis without inducing damage to the phagocytic cells. It has been proposed that they be called *impedins*.

Certain bacteria produce aggressins, and phagocytic cells attracted to the site of infection are killed. *S. pyogenes* produces streptolysin O, which causes the release of lysosomal constituents into the phagocytotic cell's own cytoplasm, causing the cell to digest itself. Similarly, staphylococcal hemolysins and leukocidin induce bursting of lysosomes with subsequent autolysis of the phagocytic cell. This toxin-induced discharge of lysosomes into the cytoplasm is more readily induced in neutrophilic granulocytes than in macrophages. It does not require direct cellular interaction between the phagocytic cells and the parasite.

A number of parasites kill phagocytic cells after engulfment has taken place. Chlamydiae are engulfed by macrophages; after internalization they too induce the release of lysosomal enzymes into the cytoplasm. In contrast, virulent shigellae, upon being phagocytized, release a cytotoxin that diffuses through the membrane of the phagosomes. Many of the microorganisms surviving and proliferating in macrophages ultimately lead to the destruction of the phagocytic cell. This may be due to cell disruption by the proliferating parasites or caused by their toxic products.

Parasites may inhibit chemotaxis of phagocytic cells. It has been claimed that some bacterial products interfere with chemotaxis of neutrophilic granulocytes when present at low concentrations.

Some speculations have been made on a possible role for the inhibition of the colony-stimulating factor(s). Neutralizing this factor would impair mobilization and proliferation of phagocytic stem cells in the bone marrow. A lack of this factor may indeed occur in infections with *Salmonella typhi* and brucellae.

Absorption of parasites to phagocytic cells and their engulfment is a prerequisite for their destruction. Mycoplasmas, which are very hydrophilic, are not engulfed by human neutrophilic granulocytes. They probably influence the metabolism of the phagocytic cell; there is an increased glucose oxidation and defective killing of unrelated microorganisms. On the other hand, neutrophilic granulocytes "run away" from live *T. gondii*.

Many surface components of microorganisms (e.g., capsules and cell walls of bacteria) give antiphagocytic protection. The surface of the parasites covered with such components becomes less hydrophobic in relation to the phagocytic cell. The M protein of streptococci and the polysaccharide capsule of *S. pneumoniae* have this property. Polysaccharide capsules are also seen in *H. influenzae* and *Klebsiella pneumoniae* and in the fungus *Cryptycoccus neoformans*. Pathogenic strains of *E. coli* and *S. typhi* possess a thin layer of acidic polysaccharides, the K antigen. The K antigen may also have antiphagocytic effects. O antigens of gram-negative bacteria, which reside in the polysaccharide side chains of LPS, also may have a protective role. Some O antigen specificities are associated with smooth colony formation. Polysaccharide capsules are also seen in some saprophytic

microorganisms. They probably did not develop as a response to defense mechanisms of the host but as a device in the microorganism's own defense system against bacteriophages and bacteriocidins. Capsules consisting of proteins and lipoproteins are seen in *B. anthracis* and *Y. pestis*, and they too have antiphagocytic effects. A carbohydrate layer on the trypanosomes that cause African sleeping sickness prevents phagocytosis of the parasite by cells of the reticuloendothelial system.

Mobility of microorganisms obviously makes phagocytosis more difficult. Also, excessive size of parasites may prevent effective engulfment. Thus growing fungal hyphae push macrophages along and are not ingested.

Prevention of the fusion of lysosomes with phagosomes is a mechanism that efficiently counteracts the digestion and killing of parasites by phagocytes. However, examples of parasites having this "nonfusion" mechanism are as yet few: chlamydia in tissue cultures, *S. aureus* in Kupffer cells of *in vivo* perfused livers, *M. tuberculosis* in mice, and *T. gondii* in human macrophages.

Resistance to killing by phagocytes is essential to many viruses and intracellular bacteria. These mechanisms are still not well understood. Many parasites multiply in phagocytic cells, especially in macrophages.

Parasites may even use lysosomal enzymes to their own advantage. Reovirus has to be engulfed and must come in contact with lysosomal enzymes to loose the outer capsid in order to replicate.

A number of intracellular protozoan parasites produce capsules or cystic membranes around themselves and their progeny. The host's attempt to destroy the invaders are ineffective because the effector cells or molecules cannot reach their target. For example, *T. gondii* forms cysts in macrophages present in the central nervous system, muscles, or lungs. In addition to avoiding destruction by intracellular mechanisms, the antigens of this cyst-producing parasite are kept secluded from immune effectors.

Evasion of Immune Response

Parasites use a variety of means to evade, divert, or at least delay the consequences of immune reactivity of the host. Certain parasites have established mechanisms by which immune effectors are rendered harmless at the site of the parasite's proliferation. *Neisseria gonorrhoeae, Neisseria meningitidis*, and other bacteria produce a protease that cleaves one subclass of human IgA, thus rendering it harmless. Virulent staphylococci elaborate protein A, which combines with Fc fragments of some immunoglobulins. No opsonization occurs because no free, hydrophobic Fc portions are available for interaction with phagocytic cells. The dog tapeworm produces huge cysts containing its larvae. Despite vigorous immune response, no damage to the parasite occurs because immunologic reactants cannot reach the larvae.

Intracellular parasitism has the advantage of seclusion, especially when only a few antigenic determinants of the parasite are expressed on the host cell surface. Circulating lymphocytes infected with Epstein-Barr virus (EBV), macrophages in leprosy and leishmaniasis, and hepatocytes containing malarial plasmodia illustrate the advantage of intracellular parasitism. In fetal rubella infection, the virus survives in the progeny of the originally infected cells despite the presence of a neutralizing antibody.

Microorganisms abiding in bodily sites inaccessible to immune reactants may not induce or be affected by the immune response. Such advantage for survival is enjoyed by cytomegalovirus, which infects salivary or mammary glands, by the wart viruses, and by some bacteria. In carriers of *S. typhi*, microorganisms are restricted to

fibrotic sections of the biliary and urinary tracts. They may reach the environment but are shielded from the host's immune system.

Antigens are frequently released from parasites or parasite-infected host cells. Viral surface antigen is released into the circulation in the course of hepatitis B virus infections. Capsular polysaccharides are present in the serum during infections with *S. pneumoniae* and *N. meningitidis*. These soluble, circulating antigens may react with available immune effectors and thus prevent interaction with the intact and viable parasites.

Infectious agents may impair the host's immune responsiveness to an unrelated antigen. Measles, mumps, EBV, and cytomegalovirus induce immunosuppression of cell-mediated immunity. Leishmanial trypanosomes and malarial plasmodia depress immune responses to unrelated antigens. Most of these microorganisms proliferate in macrophages or lymphocytes. This and antigenic competition may explain the depressed immune response, which obviously increases the chances for secondary infections.

In many instances depression of the immune reactivity is specific for the inducing antigen. Parental infection may be of importance in the induction of tolerance. Although tolerance is only partial and the fetus is capable of producing IgM antibodies, fetal rubella infection is associated with deficient cell-mediated immunity. Circulating antigen in massive quantities may not only neutralize immune reactants by occupation of antigen binding sites but may also depress the immune response. Patients with visceral leishmaniasis or disseminated coccidiomycosis show depressed T cell reactivity.

The parasite's antigens may be crossreactive with host's cell or tissue antigens. Immune reactivity to such antigens may not occur because the antigens are not recognized as foreign. Alternatively, cross-reactivity of antigens may induce autoimmunity

(Ch. 15). Schistosomes have an efficient mechanism of adaptive mimicry — upon entering the host, they cover themselves with host antigens. In consequence, they are not treated by the immune system as foreign.

Diversion of the immune response is another efficient means of parasite survival. Antibodies predominantly reacting with internal components of the parasite are not protective. Their production may exhaust the host's resources by competition. Similarly, antibodies reactive with surface structures of the parasite but unable to cause serious damage (e.g., to induce lysis because of inability to fix complement) may enhance the parasite's chances of survival rather than protect the host. Infectious organisms that are effectively destroyed by cell-mediated immunity may benefit from a host's profuse antibody production (*enhancing antibodies*). Gram-negative bacteria may induce production of nonprotective antibodies due to polyclonal activation of B cells by endotoxin.

Antigenic drifts and shifts in parasites help to render the host's immune response less than optimally effective. The antigenically changing patterns of microorganisms encounter naive, unsensitized populations of hosts. Therefore the parasite may spread widely in a short period of time. After a great enough proportion of the population has become sensitized, the spread stops until the microorganism undergoes a new change or reassembly of the genetically determined antigens. This occurs with influenza virus, which causes epidemics and pandemics (worldwide epidemics) at relatively fixed time intervals marking the occurrence of major genetic changes.

Inhibition of Soluble Mediators of Inflammation

A number of parasites produce toxins influencing the coagulation and fibrinolytic systems of the host (e.g., streptokinase). The K antigen of *E. coli* has an inhibitory action on complement. O antigens are located on the side chains of LPS relatively distant from the cell membrane; this may interfere with an effective lysis mediated by antibody and complement.

THE PARASITE'S ITINERARY IN THE HOST

Infectious diseases depend on the entry of parasites into host tissue. Penetration of su-

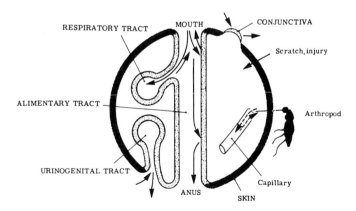

Fig. 6.3. "Invaginations" of the environment. Schematic representation of body surfaces as sites of microbial infection and shedding. (With permission from Mims C.A.: The Pathogenesis of Infectious Disease. Academic Press, London, 1976.)

perficial layers may suffice. *Corynebacterium diphtheriae* proliferates locally in the mucosa and causes systemic disease by dissemination of its powerful toxins. In other infections deep tissue layers have to be reached and access gained to visceral organs. Many parasites residing and proliferating in deep tissues and visceral organs ultimately have to reach the surface of the host in order to be transmitted to a new host.

The surface of the host is covered mostly

Table 6.4. Major Defense Mechanisms at Portal of Entry to the Host

Portal of Entry	Major Defense Mechanisms
Gastrointestinal tract	Mucus-covered epithelium Peristalsis (vomitus, diarrhea) Gastric acid Bile Secretory IgA Commensals (symbionts) Kupffer cells
Oropharynx	Stratified epithelium Saliva (flushing effect) Lysozyme and other enzymes Secretory IgA
Urogenital tract	Stratified epithelium Urine flow Spermin Zinc Secretory IgA Commensals (symbionts)
Conjunctiva	Stratified epithelium Lid movement Tears (flushing effect) Lysozyme Secretory IgA
Respiratory tract	Mucus-covered epithelium Ciliary movement Secretory IgA Alveolar macrophages

by skin. There are weak points, however, where this layer does not exist — these are the mucosa-covered invaginations of the environment into the host (Fig. 6.3). Parasites may also use carriers or vectors, such as mosquitos, to reach directly the deep tissue or the circulation of the host. The portal of entry may influence the character of the ensuing infectious disease. Table 6.4 reviews the host defense mechanisms important at portals of entry to the hosts.

By overcoming the surface defense, the parasite establishes itself in the epithelium. From this bridgehead it may penetrate further into the subepithelial layers of the host. A list of parasites restricted to epithelia is given in Table 6.5. These organisms spread only along the epithelium and do not cross the epithelial basement membrane.

Other parasites, however, penetrate the subepithelial tissues. Here, antimicrobial efforts rely predominantly on cellular and soluble mediators of inflammation. Phagocytosis, first nonspecific and then aided by immune reactants, is of paramount importance. The vasculature ensures transport of antigens to immunologically reactive tissue, the supply of inflammatory mediators to the site of infection, and the transport of parasites to strategically located organs (the lymph nodes) specialized in clearing the lymph of particles and initiating the immune response.

Many parasites established in subepithelial tissues spread locally. This spread is enhanced by bacterial enzymes, which digest and degrade host tissue. Thus proteinases, lipases, nucleases, hyaluronidase, and streptokinase are efficient enzymes in this respect and contribute to the fulminant skin infection known as erysipelas.

Lymph and blood flow are essential for the host's defense, but they also may become the media for the spread of the parasite through the host's body. The total daily lymph flow in humans is estimated at 1.3 liters. The filter function of lymph nodes

Table 6.5. Microbial Infections That are Generally Confined to Epithelial Surfaces of the Body

Microorganisms	Respiratory Tract and Conjunctiva	Urogenital Tract	Skin	Intestinal Tract
Viruses	Influenza Parainfluenza 1–4 Rhinoviruses Coronaviruses	Human papilloma virus	Human papilloma virus Molluscum contagiosum virus	Diarrhea viruses of man (Norwalk agent, rotaviruses, enteroviruses)
Chlamydiae	*Chlamydia trachomatis*	*C. trachomatis* (nonspecific urethritis)	—	—
Mycoplasmas	*Mycoplasma pneumoniae* (atypical pneumonia)	T strains (nonspecific urethritis)	—	—
Bacteria	*Bordetella pertussis* *Corynebacterium diphtheriae* Streptococci	*Neisseria gonorrhoeae*	Staphylococci	Most salmonellae, shigellae
Fungi	*Candida albicans* (thrush)	*C. albicans*	*Trichophyton* spp. (athlete's foot, ringworm, etc.)	—
Protozoa	—	*Trichomonas vaginalis*	—	*Entamoeba histolytica*

(Adapted with permission from Mims, C.A., The Pathogenesis of Infectious Disease. Academic Press, London, 1976.)

may be impaired by the parasite's mechanisms counteracting phagocytosis. Furthermore, exercise and inflammation diminish lymph flow. Excessive numbers of parasites reaching the lymph nodes may simply overpower its phagocytotic capabilities. Certain microorganisms are capable of surviving and proliferating in lymphatic vessels and lymph nodes. *M. leprae* multiplies in the endothelium of lymphatic vessels, and *Y. pestis*, brucellae, rickettsiae, and some viruses survive and proliferate in lymph nodes. Some parasites eventually reach the bloodstream via the thoracic duct.

Spread via the bloodstream seems most effective. Distant parts of the body are reached in 1 or 2 minutes. In addition to the thoracic duct, the parasites may enter the blood by direct invasion through capillaries or post-capillary venules. by direct introduction into blood vessels using insects as vectors, or in the wake of traumatization. Viruses and rickettsiae are most frequently spread by hematogenous routes. Bacteria and fungi reach the blood relatively less frequently. Viremias and rickettsemias are asymptomatic in most cases. Blood-borne bacteria and fungi, often producing toxins, may cause severe clinical symptoms (e.g., the systemic toxemia during the parasitemia by *B. anthracis*). Parasites may produce two consecutive parasitemias. During the primary parasitemia, the parasite reaches a visceral organ, where it proliferates. The secondary parasitemia reflects a second entry into the blood and often results in the

reappearance at the host's body surface. In
some diseases there is continuous parasitemia. For example, in lepromatous leprosy,
M. leprae is located inside macrophages
and does not produce toxins; therefore the
bacteremia remains asymptomatic. Parasites may be carried in various blood compartments (Table 6.6). Arthropod-borne
viruses and rickettsiae may colonize endothelial cells of capillaries.

Spread of microorganisms may also occur
along serosal mesothelia or nerves or in the
cerebral spinal fluid. Infectious agents may
pass the placenta and infect the fetus
(Table 6.7).

The ultimate goal of most parasites is to
proliferate in a host and then reach a new
one. Only a few microorganisms remain in
the dead host, survive in the soil, and infect
new hosts via water, soil, or contaminated
objects (fomites).

CONTAGION

Spread from host to host is as important to
the survival of parasites as their capability
to multiply in the host's environment.
Spread may be horizontal, with subsequent
infection of hosts belonging to roughly the
same generation, or it may be vertical, with
transmission occurring from parents to
offspring. Horizontal spread is accomplished via infected air, water, food, fomites, animal vectors, or direct contact.
The parasite's capability to reach a new
host depends also on its stability in the environment. Parasites resistant to heat, light,
dessication, and cold have a better chance
to contact a new host than parasites rapidly
destroyed outside the host.

Transmission may occur using a number
of distinct routes. Airborne particles containing parasites preferentially originate

Table 6.6. Transport of Microorganisms in Different Compartments of Blood

| | Free in Plasma | Leukocyte Associated | | Erythrocyte-Associated | Platelet-Associated |
		Mononuclear Cells	Polymorpho-nuclear Cells		
Viruses	Poliovirus Yellow fever virus	Measles Epstein-Barr virus Herpes simplex virus Cytomegalovirus Variola virus		Colorado tick fever virus	LCM virus
Rickettsiae	All types				
Bacteria	Pneumococci Leptospira *Bacillus anthracis* *Borrelia recurrentis*	*Mycobacterium leprae* *Listeria monocytogenes* *Brucella* spp.	Pyogenic bacteria		
Protozoa	Trypanosomes	*Leishmania donovani* *Toxoplasma gondii*		*Plasmodium* spp. Babesia	

(With permission from Mims, C.A.: The Pathogenesis of Infectious Disease. Academic Press, London, 1976.)

Table 6.7. Principal Microorganisms Infecting the Fetus

Microorganisms	Effect
Viruses	
Rubella virus	Abortion
	Stillbirth
	Malformations
Smallpox virus	Abortion
Cytomegalovirus	Malformations
Bacteria	
Treponema pallidum	Stillbirth
	Malformations
Listeria monocytogenes	Meningoencephalitis
Protozoa	
Toxoplasma gondii	Stillbirth
	CNS disease

(With permission from Mims, C.A.: The Pathogenesis of Infectious Disease. Academic Press, London, 1976.)

from the respiratory tract. Coughing and sneezing increase the shedding significantly. Small particles (1 to 4 μm) have a good chance to reach the lower respiratory tract of new hosts. Particles of this size also stay almost indefinitely suspended in the air. Some hardy parasites remain contagious outside the body for a long period of time (for example, *Mycobacterium tuberculosis* or smallpox virus). In contrast, influenza and rhinoviruses survive for only very short periods of time in sunlight and dry environments; therefore, close contact is necessary for their transmission. Transmission modes are summarized in Table 6.8. The role of insects as vectors and of other animals as intermediary hosts for human infectious diseases will be discussed for individual microorganisms later in this volume.

Contagion is often best counteracted by measures of general hygiene, such as efficient waste disposal, water purification and decontamination, general cleanliness, control of animal diseases, and eradication of insect vectors, as well as isolation of in-

fectious patients. Such measures have probably contributed as much to containment and control of many infectious diseases as direct medical intervention.

Table 6.8. Modes of Transmission of Infection

Direct contact
Venereal infections — syphilis, gonorrhea
Inoculation of wounds — tetanus, rabies, sporotrichosis
Penetration of intact skin — schistosomiasis, hookworm
Skin to skin contact — staphylococcal infections, ectoparasites

Contamination of food and water
Fecal-oral spread from other humans — poliomyelitis, dysentery, amebiasis, ascariasis
Naturally occurring contamination of food by parasites that can infect man — salmonellosis, trichinosis, tapeworm infection
Milk-borne diseases — brucellosis, tuberculosis

Respiratory spread
By droplet infection only — bacterial and viral pneumonias, influenza
By inhalation of dried material containing spores or resistant forms — tuberculosis, pulmonary mycoses, anthrax

Arthropod vectors
From man to man — yellow fever, relapsing fever, malaria, filariasis
From animal to man — plague, most rickettsioses

Transmission by medical procedures
Blood transfusion — viral hepatitis
Wound infections — infection with staphylococci, *Klebsiella*
Associated with urologic instrumentation — infection with various gram-negative rods
Associated with respirators and ancillary equipment — infection with various gram-negative rods
Associated with intravenous therapy (infected catheters, infected fluids) — candidiasis, infection with gram-negative bacteria

Congenital infections
Transplacental — syphilis, rubella, toxoplasmosis
From the birth canal — herpes simplex, group B streptococcal infection

Communicability and virulence, along with the efficacy of host defense, determine the frequency and character of infectious diseases in a population. Parasite-induced maladies may occur as epidemics or pandemics when parasites are highly contagious and the hosts are not immune. Infectious diseases may also occur at a constant frequency in a host population over an indefinite time period. This mode of appearance of contagious diseases is termed *endemic.*

OPPORTUNISTIC INFECTIONS

Certain parasites infect hosts and cause disease only if the host's defense mechanisms are impaired. Parasites infecting compromised hosts may be termed *opportunists.* Most of them form part of the pool of symbionts and commensals normally inhabiting various parts of the body. Otherwise, the parasite may be latent in a clinically silent state in host tissue until reactivation, or may be recruited from the vast pool of free-living saprophytic organisms. In addition, deficiency of the host defense may potentiate infections with otherwise only mildly pathogenic microorganisms.

Two groups of genetically determined deficiencies in host defense will be discussed briefly. Chronic granulomatous disease is an X-linked recessive trait in which phagocytosis is impaired by defective intracellular killing of bacteria. The defect is in the myeloperoxidase-peroxide-halide system and in the generation of superoxide radicals. Staphylococci and gram-negative bacteria, which under normal circumstances have a low degree of pathogenicity, are the main culprits in producing severe and recurrent suppurative infections in these patients. Neutrophilic granulocytes accumulate at the site of infections but are unable to eliminate the parasites, and granulomatous lesions ensue. Streptococci, which possess their own catalase activity and generate peroxide by themselves, are

lysed readily by the patient's defective phagocytes. In the rare Chediak-Higashi syndrome, defective lysosomal fusion accounts for increased susceptibility to infection. In this disease neutrophilic granulocytes contain characteristic giant lysosomes with normal enzyme content. In patients with chronic mucocutanous candidiasis and in some children with eczema and raised IgE serum concentrations, the chemotaxis of phagocytes is impaired.

Defective development of humoral and cell-mediated immunity is well documented. Infants with congenital X-linked agammaglobulinemia remain healthy as long as antibodies from the mother are available. Usually, during their first 6 to 18 months, these infants become infected with a series of pyogenic microorganisms (staphylococci, streptococci, *H. influenzae*). With recurrent infection many of the children develop chronic bronchiectases and may die from pulmonary complications. Selective IgA deficiencies are frequent and have rather mild effects on the host's defense. Infants with thymic aplasia (DiGeorges' syndrome) have no cell-mediated immunity and are susceptible to viral, fungal and bacterial infections. Combined B and T cell deficiencies have been reported in a number of patients.

Environmental factors may reduce host defense mechanisms significantly. X-irradiation or acute leukemia lead to a shortage of neutrophilic granulocytes and predispose the host to infection with gram-negative and pyogenic gram-positive bacteria. Malnutrition is another important contributor to acquired deficiencies. Patients with severe disease, extensive burns, severe infections, or malignancies have a decreased capability to effectively combat parasites.

Health care itself may pose serious threats to mechanisms of host defense. Hospital-acquired or *nosocomial* infections comprise up to 50 percent of all infections treated in hospitals. They are of special concern to physicians because they arise as a direct consequence of health care. Among nosocomial infections, "hospitalism" is especially difficult to counter. In the specific environment of the hospital, the normal flora of the host changes radically. The host rapidly acquires a flora that resembles that of other persons in the hospital. This flora consists of many species of bacteria that are resistant to antibiotics. Also, in hospitals there is a community of patients with a generally reduced status of resistance. Infections are enhanced by the close contact among patients and between patients and staff members. Infected fomites, like bedcovers, aerosol apparatuses, appliances in bathrooms and toilets, and chronic dialysis equipment, contribute to the creation of an unhealthy environment.

Iatrogenic infections are a group of diseases induced directly by manipulation by the physician or medical personnel. For example, ophthalmologists may transmit adenovirus infections of the eye via their instruments.

The main causes contributing to the surge in nosocomial infections may be summarized as (1) indwelling tubes (intravenous tubes, urinary catheters); (2) foreign bodies (e.g., artificial heart valves); (3) increased use of potent immunosuppressive drugs (e.g., cortisone, cyclophosphamide, nitrogen mustard); (4) increased use of aggressive diagnostic procedures (e.g., organ biopsies, mediastinoscopy); (5) increased resource to extensive surgical procedures; (6) increased use of blood transfusion even during minor surgery (entailing a great risk of hepatitis virus infection); and (7) the transfer of patients from their normal home environment to a hospital (this may have both psychological and biologic consequences detrimental to the host defenses).

Common parasites involved in opportunistic infections are listed in Table 6.9. Any measure to be taken in the health care of an individual patient has to be considered

Table 6.9. Common Opportunistic Microorganisms

Foreign body implantation (indwelling i.v. catheters; prosthetic heart valves; ventriculoatrial shunt) — *S. aureus* and *epidermidis, Propionibacterium acnes, Aspergillus* spp., *C. albicans*

Indwelling urinary catheters — *S. marcescens, P. aeruginosa*

Splenectomy — *S. pneumoniae*

Hematoproliferative disorders — *C. neoformans*, varicella-zoster virus, *L. monocytogenes*

Diabetes — *S. aureus, C. albicans, P. aeruginosa*, phycomycetes

Alcoholism — *S. pneumoniae, K. pneumoniae*

Burns — *P. aeruginosa*

Cortisone — *S. aureus* and *epidermidis, M. tuberculosis*, fungi

Immunosuppression — *N. asteroides*, mycobacteria, *Aspergillus* spp., *C. albicans, T. gondii, Pneumocystis carinii*, herpes simplex virus, varicella-zoster virus, cytomegalovirus, diphtheroids

---

meticulously by the physician. Now more than ever before, with all the formidable but potentially harmful tools at our disposal, it is unforgivable to forget the rule of *primum non nocere* ("most importantly, do no harm").

SUMMARY

The 500 or so microorganisms infecting humans have been described, and it has been estimated that each of us is infected 100 to 150 times during life. Many of these infections go by unnoticed, but a number of them become clinically manifested. Infectious diseases have contributed to much of human misery and have often shaped history. The unique achievements of medicine in the development of efficient antiparasitic drugs and the implementation of sanitary codes have greatly diminished the parasite's menace to mankind and changed the spectrum of infectious diseases. On the other hand, availability of more and more effective tools for medical diagnosis and treatment have led to an upsurge of nosocomial and other opportunistic infections. This and the parasite's amazing ability to adapt to all defense efforts of the host make the host-parasite relationship in everlasting and everchanging struggle. In this struggle continuous research and improvement of medical care are the only ways to secure the upper hand for the human host.

REFERENCES

Burnet, F.M. and White, D.O.: The Natural History of Infectious Disease. 4th Ed. Cambridge University Press, London, 1972.

Ciba Foundation Symposium. Parasites in the Immunized Host: Mechanisms of Survival. ASP, Amsterdam, 1974.

Cline, M.D.: The White Cell. Harvard University Press, Cambridge, Mass., 1975.

D'Arcy, P.F. and Griffin, J.P.: Iatrogenic Diseases. 2nd Ed. Oxford University Press, New York, 1979.

Fauci, A.S.: Host Defense Mechanisms Against Infection. Upjohn, Kalamazoo, 1978.

Mims, C.A.: The Pathogenesis of Infectious Disease. Academic Press, London, 1976.

Oss, C.J. van, Gillman, C.F., and Neumann, A.W.: Phagocytic Engulfment and Cell Adhesiveness. Marcel Dekker, New York, 1975.

Peterson, P.K. and Quie, P.G.: Bacterial surface components and the pathogenesis of infectious diseases. Annu. Rev. Med. *32*: 29, 1981.

Roberts, N.J., Jr.: Temperature and host defense, Microbiol. Rev. *43*: 241 1979.

Verhoef, J. and Verbrugh, H.A.: Host determinants in staphylococcal disease. Annu. Rev. Med. *32*: 107, 1981.

Youmans, G.P., Paterson, P.Y., and Sommers, M.M.: The Biologic and Clinical Basis of Infectious Diseases. W.B. Saunders, Philadelphia, 1980.

7

Arthropod Vectors of Pathogenic Microorganisms

Marek Zaleski and
Roger K. Cunningham

GENERAL CHARACTERISTICS AND TAXONOMY

The vast majority of animal parasites of man are either protozoa or helminths and are described in Chapters 51 and 52. Nevertheless, some other animals, especially those belonging to the largest animal phylum, *Arthropoda*, are of a certain medical significance and are briefly discussed here. Only a few of these animals invade human tissues; the remaining affect the health of man without actually being parasites. In this chapter we will describe their role as vectors of infectious agents, and in Chapter 52 their significance as parasites will be discussed. A brief description of the basic morphology and biology of the arthropods should be helpful in better understanding their relationship with man and his health.

Arthropods are characterized by metameric segmentation, jointed appendages, and a hard, chitinous exoskeleton. All arthropods have three basic features in common:

1. The body is covered by an exoskeleton composed of a layer of the polysaccharide chitin, which sometimes be-comes impregnated with mineral salts. The dorsal part of the exoskeleton (tergum) is usually thicker and harder than its ventral (sternum) or lateral (pleuron or pleurites) portions. The segments of the exoskeleton corresponding to different parts of the body in many species have merged, forming a single plate covering almost the entire body. The entire exoskeleton is shed and replaced by a new one during the periods of growth.

2. All arthropods have a series of paired appendages arising from the ventrolateral part of the body. Each appendage consists of several parts attached to each other by flexible joints (arthros). In primitive arthropods the appendages in each segment of the body were relatively simple and served multiple purposes. In the course of evolution, the various appendages have transformed into specialized structures. The paired appendages are modified into walking legs in terrestrial species and swimming organs in the aquatic. The appendages of the head have specialized into structures, such as sensory antennae, components of mouth parts, or piercing organs.

3. The circulatory system of all arthro-pods consists of two communicating por-

Table 7.1. Simplified Classification of Medically Important Members of the Phylum *Arthropoda*

Class	Order	Genus (Common Name)	Vector or Intermediate Host of:[a]
Crustacea	*Eucopepoda*	*Cyclops* (water flea)	*Dracunculus medinensis* *Diphyllobothrium latum* *Gnathostoma spinigerum*
		Diaptomus	*Diphyllobothrium latum*
	Decapoda	*Procambarus*	*Paragonimus westermani*
		Cambroides	and *kellicotti*
		Cambarus (freshwater crayfish)	
		Potamon	
		Eliocheir (land crabs, prawns)	*Angiostrongylus cantonensis*
Diplopoda		*Julus*	*Hymenolepis diminuta*
Arachnida	*Acari*	*Trombicula* (Japanese red bug)	*Rickettsia tsutsugamushi*
		Dermanyssus (chicken mite)	Viruses of encephalitis
		Liponyssus (rat mite)	*Rickettsia typhi*
		Bdellonyssus (rat mite)	
		Allodermanyssus (mouse mite)	*Rickettsia akari*
		Dermacentor (hard tick)	*Rickettsia rickettsii* *Coxiella burnetii* *Francisella tularensis* Viruses
		Ixodes	
		Haemaphysalis	Viruses
		Rhipicephalus	*Coxiella burnetii*
		Ambylama (hard tick)	*Rickettsia rickettsii*
		Ornithodoros (soft tick)	*Borrelia duttoni*
Insecta (Hexapoda)	*Mallophaga*	*Trichodectes* (dog louse)	*Dipylidium caninum*
	Anoplura	*Pediculus* (human louse)	*Rickettsia prowazekii* *Rickettsia quintana* *Borrelia recurrentis*
	Blattaria (*Orthoptera*)	*Periplaneta* (cockroach)	*Hymenolepis diminuta* *Gongylonema pulchrum* *Moniliformis moniliformis* *Entamoeba histolytica*
	Heteroptera (*Hemiptera*)	*Triatoma* (triatomid bug)	*Trypanosoma cruzi*
		Panstrongylus (cone-nosed bug)	
	Coleoptera	(beetle)	*Hymenolepis nana* *Hymenolepis diminuta*
	Diptera	*Anopheles* (mosquito)	*Plasmodium* spp. *Brugia malayi* *Wuchereria bancrofti*
		Culex (mosquito)	*Wuchereria bancrofti* Encephalitis viruses

Table 7.1 Cont'd

Class	Order	Genus (Common Name)	Vector or Intermediate Host of:[a]
		Aedes (mosquito)	*Wuchereria bancrofti*
			Yellow fever virus
			Dengue virus
			Encephalitis virus
		Culicoides (gnat)	*Dipetalonema perstans*
			Mansonella ozzardi
			Acanthocheilonema
		Simulium (black fly, black gnat, or coffee fly)	*Onchocerca volvulus*
		Chrysops (mango and deer fly)	*Loa loa*
			Francisella tularensis
		Phlebotomus (sand fly)	*Leishmania* spp.
			Bartonella bacilliformis
			Charon spp.
		Lutzomyia	*Leishmania* spp.
		Glossina (tsetse fly)	*Trypanosoma* spp.
	Siphonaptera	*Xenopsylla* (rat flea)	*Yersinia pestis*
			Rickettsia typhi
			Hymenolepis diminuta
		Ctenocephalides (dog flea)	*Dyphilidium caninum*
	Hymenoptera	*Formica* (ant)	*Dicroccelium dendriticum*[b]

[a]Vector or intermediate host for the pathogens listed. For the description of parasites and diseases caused by them, see other chapters of this book.

[b]Cosmopoliton sheep liver fluke that may be acquired by man ingesting ants (about 100 reported cases).

tions — a closed portion composed of a heart and paired vessels and an open portion called a hemocele. The latter corresponds to the body cavity of higher animals.

In addition to these three features, other common characteristics are more or less distinctly seen in various members of the phylum *Arthropoda*. The most important of them are (1) a central nervous system composed of a cephalic brain and paired nerve trunks with several ganglia; (2) an intestinal tract consisting of three distinct portions — anterior, median, and posterior; (3) striated musculature; and (4) secretion of a specific growth hormone called ecdysone. Respiration occurs by gills in aquatic forms and by tracheae (tubular extensions of the outer covering) in terrestrial forms.

All arthropods are sexually dimorphic with separable sexes, although in some instances parthenogenesis, development of an embryo from the unfertilized egg, may occur. As part of their life history, most arthropods go through a series of developmental changes (metamorphosis), which includes larval, pupal (resting), nymphal, and adult stages. The extent of metamorphosis varies, being relatively limited in primitive species and highly complex in more evolved species.

The evolutionary diversification of arthropods has resulted in the largest number of genera and species among animals; these are adapted to a variety of living environments. The different respiratory and locomotory organs found in arthropods reflect their adaptation to different environments and life histories.

The taxonomy of the arthropods is extremely complex and still open to debate. Table 7.1 summarizes in a simplified form the classification of arthropods, indicating the taxonomic position of only those species that are of medical importance.

ARTHROPODS AS INTERMEDIATE HOSTS AND VECTORS OF PARASITES

Representatives of all major groups of parasites, that is, viruses, bacteria, spirochetes, rickettsiae, protozoa, and helminths, may be transmitted by arthropods. The transmission occurs in two distinct ways — biologic and mechanical.

In biologic transmission the arthropod serves as a host for the agent. Such a relationship may involve multiplication and/or transformation of the parasite. A particular form of biologic transmission is represented by those cases in which a pathogenic organism invades the ovaries or eggs of the arthropod and subsequently is transmitted to its offspring. Such vertical transmission, commonly observed in ticks, is called *transovarian* and plays an important role in maintaining human pathogens in nature without a human host.

Mechanical transmission, on the other hand, does not involve a biologic relationship, and the arthropod serves merely as a vehicle in transporting the agent from one location to another, such as flies that act as mechanical vectors for enteric pathogens.

Either biologic or mechanical transmission may be involved in the transport of a parasite and its corresponding disease from one geographic area to another. This process of dissemination becomes of even greater importance in these times of increased and rapid contacts between different areas.

The specific relationships between parasitic organisms and arthropods are discussed in connection with the particular pathogenic organisms described in this book, and there is no need to repeat them here. However, a brief discussion of the biology of arthropods as vectors of disease-causing organisms is necessary. The transmitting arthropods constitute the largest portion of all medically important members of this phylum and belong to several distinct groups.

Crustaceans living in fresh and usually still water participate in the transmission of several parasitic helminths (Table 7.1). These arthropods vary from the almost microscopic copepods to larger animals, such as crayfish, shrimp, and crabs. Usually they constitute an intermediate host for the larval stages of the helminths. Transmission of the parasite to humans occurs because the arthropod enters man's food chain, and man either ingests the infected and uncooked arthropod or ingests fish that feed on the infected arthropods.

Mites are small (up to 1 mm), cosmopolitan organisms living either in water or on land. Typically they go through several developmental stages — egg, larva, nymph, and adult. The adult has four pairs of legs, and its head, thorax, and abdomen are fused together into a single structure, often covered with hairs. They live on the skin of various wild or domestic animals, for example, *Liponyssus bacoti* in rats or *Dermanyssus gallinae* in chickens.

The mites of rodents harbor several species of rickettsiae — *Rickettsia tsutsugamushi*, *R. typhi* (*mooseri*), and *R. akari* — that cause disease in animals or humans. The mites of birds harbor and transfer the viruses that cause western equine and St. Louis encephalitis.

Land living, cosmopolitan ticks, which have four pairs of legs are larger than mites. In their development they undergo metamorphosis, consisting of egg, larval, nymphal, and adult stages. The adult animals are covered with a leathery cuticle and rigid shield (scutum) in the hard-bodied ticks, the *Ixodidae*, or with a cuticle alone in the soft-bodied ticks, the *Argasidae*. The first group transmits such parasites as *Coxiella burnetii*, *Rickettsia rickettsii*, *Francisella tularensis*, and various viruses, whereas the second group transfers *Borrelia duttoni*.

Insects, the largest class of arthropods, are characterized by a distinct division of the body into a head, thorax, and abdomen; the possession of six legs; a respiratory system composed of branching tubules called tracheae; and the possession of wings by some species. The class is subdivided into several subclasses and families on the basis of (1) the presence or absence of wings and, when present, their structure; (2) the extent and completeness of metamorphosis; and (3) the structure of mouthparts. Of over 30 distinct orders, only eight contain members that are of medical importance, which will be briefly discussed in this chapter.

Mallophaga are wingless insects, developing without metamorphosis (ametabolous) with only a nymphal stage. Their mouthparts are adapted for chewing. The most important representative is the dog louse, *Trichodectes canis*, which is an ectoparasite of dogs and serves as an intermediate host for the canine tapeworm, *Diphylidium caninum*. Although this helminth is essentially a parasite of dogs, occasionally children become infected by accidental swallowing of the infected insect.

Anoplura are also wingless, ametabolous insects with piercing and sucking mouthparts. The major representatives are the human louse, *Pediculus humanus*, and the crab or pubic louse, *Phthirus pubis*. Though morphologically quite different, both species undoubtedly originated from a common ancestor that adapted itself into various living conditions and gave rise to the subspecies *Pediculus humanus corporis*, the body louse that resides in clothing, and *P. humanus capitis*, the head louse that resides in the hairs of the head. *Phthirus pubis*

lives in pubic and underarm hairs. Only *Pediculus* is known to transmit pathogens, such as *Rickettsia prowazekii*, *R. quintana*, and *Borrelia recurrentis*. The transmission of pathogens does not take place by the saliva during biting but by contamination of the skin with the feces (rickettsiae) or crushed bodies (borreliae) of infected lice. With poor socioeconomic conditions, large gatherings, and the unavailability of hygienic facilities, louse-borne disease can assume cataclysmic dimensions, killing thousands of human beings.

Blattaria (*Orthoptera*) are usually two-winged, nocturnal insects with chewing mouthparts. A typical representative is the common cockroach, *Periplaneta americana*. Because of their living habits and feeding on man's food and feces, they can mechanically transfer a variety of pathogens, including enteric bacteria and cysts of *Entamoeba histolytica*; in addition, they may be an intermediate host for the rat tapeworm, *Hymenolepis diminuta*.

Heteroptera (*Hemiptera*), or true bugs, typically have two pairs of wings, with the front pair often leathery, but sometimes they are wingless. They undergo gradual metamorphosis without a pupal state, and the adult individuals have piercing and sucking mouths. The most important representatives are various genera of triatomid bugs, for example, *Triatoma*, *Rhodnius*, and *Panstrongylus*. They are quite large, often brightly colored, predominantly nocturnal insects living in the tropics and the subtropics, including the southern United States. During the day they hide in crevices of bark, wood, walls, and so on. Although their bites are painless, they are very dangerous, since during biting the insects defecate, passing *Trypanosoma cruzi*, the etiologic agent of Chagas' disease.

Flour beetles are intermediate hosts for larval stages of the tapeworm *Hymenolepis*. Transmission to humans is effected by the accidental eating of the infected arthropod.

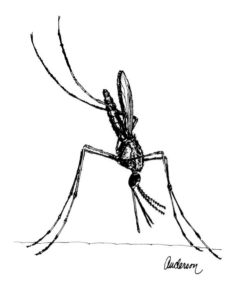

Fig. 7.1. Female mosquito (*Anopheles* sp.) in resting position. (Beck, J.W. and Davies, J.E.: Medical Parasitology, 2nd Ed. C.V. Mosby, St. Louis, 1976).

Diptera, or true flies, undergo full metamorphosis. Adult insects have one pair of membranous wings and piercing and sucking mouths. The hind pair of wings is vestigial and serves as a balancing organ (halteres). The medically most important members of this order are three genera of mosquitoes, *Anopheles, Culex,* and *Aedes*; two genera of gnats, *Culicoides* and *Simulium*; and three genera of flies, *Chrysops, Phlebotomus,* and *Glossina.*

It is quite easy to recognize the mosquito (Fig. 7.1) by the typical appearance of membranous wings, long, thin legs, and a proboscis. Although both the male and the female have a piercing and sucking proboscis, only the latter feeds on human blood. Mosquitoes are daylight insects, but their habitats and behavior vary significantly from species to species. Since all have a requirement for still water during the larval stage, the most effective control measures are directed at the removal of breeding environments, that is, standing water. Mosquitoes serve as hosts and vectors for para-

sites of malaria (*Anopheles*), filariasis (*Anopheles, Aedes, Culex*), and various viral diseases (*Aedes, Culex*).

Gnats (punkies, biting midges) are small insects, often capable of passing through protective netting. Those living in the United States are more pests than transmitters of diseases. However, in other areas the members of the genera *Culicoides* and *Simulium* are intermediate hosts for various filariae (*Dipetalonema perstans, Mansonella ozzardi,* and *Onchocerca volvulus*).

Flies are usually larger than gnats and are diurnal insects with piercing and sucking mouths. The most important representatives are those belonging to the many species of the genus *Phlebotomus* (sand flies) (Fig. 7.2), which serve as intermediate hosts of leishmania, viruses, and bacteria, and the genus *Glossina* (tsetse flies) (Fig. 7.3), which transmit trypanosomes.

The stable fly, *Stomoyxs calcitrans,* mechanically transmits some trypanosome species, and the house fly, *Musca domestica,* is a mechanical vector for various enteric pathogens.

Siphonaptera, or fleas, are holometabolous, wingless, small insects with piercing and sucking mouths. They live among hairs and move very quickly by jumping with the help of their long strong legs. The move-

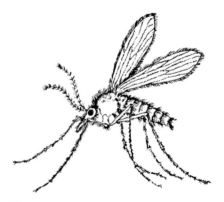

Fig. 7.2. Sand fly (*Phlebotomus* sp.). (Beck, J.W. and Davies, J.E.: Medical Parasitology. 2nd Ed. C.V. Mosby, St. Louis, 1976.)

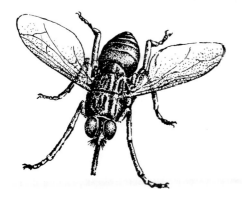

Fig. 7.3. Tsetse fly (*Glossina* sp.). (Beck, J.W. and Davies, J.E.: Medical Parasitology, 2nd Ed. C.V. Mosby, St. Louis, 1976.)

ments are facilitated by lateral compression of their bodies, thus allowing passage between hairs of the host. Two genera, *Xenopsylla* and *Ctenocephalides*, are im-

portant vectors of other parasites. Fleas of rodents, *Xenopsylla*, and the related genera *Nosopsyllus* and *Leptopsylla* transmit *Yersinia pestis* and *R. typhi* and occasionally *H. diminuta*, whereas *Ctenocephalides*, an ectoparasite of dogs and cats, may transfer a tapeworm of those two animals, *D. caninum*, to children.

REFERENCES

Beck, J.W. and Davies, J.E.: Medical Parasitology, 2nd Ed. C.V. Mosby, St. Louis, 1976.

Chandler, A.C.: Introduction to Parasitology. 9th Ed. John Wiley & Sons, New York, 1955.

Faust, E.C., Russell, P.F., and Jung, R.C.: Craig & Faust's Clinical Parasitology, VIIIth Ed. Lea & Febiger, Philadelphia, 1970.

Marcial-Rojas, R.A., Ed.: Pathology of Protozoal and Helminthic Diseases with Clinical Correlation, Williams & Wilkins, Baltimore, 1971.

8

Basic Concepts of Immunology

Felix Milgrom

In Chapter 6 invasion of the human body by pathogenic microorganisms, that is, infection, was discussed. Also described were the many defense mechanisms available to the host for prevention of microbial penetration. Such mechanisms include mechanical and chemical barriers by which the deeper layers of tissues are separated from the outside world. Organisms that succeed in passing these barriers encounter another defense line offered by phagocytic cells. All of these defense mechanisms are referred to as nonspecific, since they do not show any selectivity towards a particular microorganism.

From these nonspecific mechanisms of resistance are distinguished defense mechanisms that emerge as the result of a previous contact with a particular microorganism and are specifically directed against this organism. These specific defense mechanisms are discussed under the broad term of *specific protection* or *immunity*, a word derived from the Latin adjective *immunis*, which means free from duty or protected. In antiquity doctors and laymen alike observed the selectivity of immunity. In the Middle Ages people who survived an epidemic of plague were used to care for the patients during the next epidemic because it was recognized that they were resistant to this disease.

ANTIBODIES AND ANTIGENS

The mechanisms underlying the specific protection against infectious diseases remained obscure until the very last of the nineteenth century. It was then demonstrated that the blood serum of man and animals who have had contact with a microorganism combines specifically with the given microbe or its products.

In 1890 von Behring and Kitasato noticed that sera of animals injected with sublethal doses of tetanus or diphtheria toxin neutralized the corresponding toxin. The essential characteristic of immunologic specificity was established in these experiments — they showed that serum from animals infected with diphtheria toxin neutralized only diphtheria toxin and not tetanus toxin, and vice versa. Serum components involved in the neutralization of toxins were called *antitoxins*.

From 1893 to 1895 Pfeiffer and his associates studied the dissolution of bacterial cells, which is called *lysis* or more specifically, *bacteriolysis*. They showed that blood serum and other body fluids of guinea pigs previously injected with killed cultures of cholera vibrios would dissolve these organisms in a test tube. Furthermore, they described an interesting experiment, referred to as Pfeiffer's phenomenon, in which living cholera vibrios were injected into the peritoneal cavity of a guinea pig pretreated with killed vibrios. In sequential samples of peritoneal fluid taken from such an animal, immobilization, granular degeneration, and dissolution of vibrios were observed. Substances responsible for the dissolution (lysis) of bacteria were called *lysins* or, more specifically, *bacteriolysins.*

In 1896 Gruber and Durham described clumping of typhoid bacilli by sera of animals previously injected with these organisms, and a few months later Widal reported similar clumping of typhoid bacilli by sera of patients recovering from typhoid fever. This phenomenon was called *agglutination* and substances producing it were called *agglutinins*. In 1897 Kraus studied the reaction between sera of rabbits injected with killed plague bacilli or cholera vibrios and cell-free filtrates from cultures of these organisms. He noticed that upon reaction with the serum, the soluble bacterial components present in the filtrate produced turbidity and sedimented. This phenomenon was called *precipitation*, and the serum substances responsible for it were named *precipitins.*

The serum components discussed above — antitoxins, lysins, agglutinins, and precipitins — were all called *antibodies*. Antibody-containing serum has been referred to as *antiserum* or *immune serum*. Circumstances leading to antibody formation, such as injection of bacteria or their components, were called *immunization* or, if immunization has been performed with the specific aim of eliciting protection, *vaccination.*

It was soon realized that not only bacteria and their products elicit formation of antibodies. In 1898 Bordet showed that sera of rabbits injected with blood from animals of other species formed antibodies reacting with erythrocytes, producing lysis (or more specifically, *hemolysis*) and agglutination (or more specifically, *hemagglu-*

tination). Here again the specificity of these reactions was clearly recognized in that they were limited to the erythrocytes from an animal of the same or related species as the animal that donated the blood used for immunization.

The term *antigen* was introduced to name all substances capable of stimulating antibody formation. This term was coined in 1899 by Deutsch, who created a Greek-Latin expression, antisomatogen, meaning "antibody former." After shortening, the term antigen emerged, which now has been used for more than 80 years.

Antigens are presently defined as macromolecular substances, primarily proteins and polysaccharides, which upon proper administration to a vertebrate host stimulate formation of antibodies and combine with their corresponding antibodies in a recognizable way. It is clear that two properties are required to call a substance an antigen: (1) stimulation of antibody formation and (2) reaction with the antibody formed. The first attribute of antigen is now frequently called *immunogenicity*, and substances possessing this attribute are referred to as *immunogens*. (This is certainly not very logical, since the term "antigen" etymologically means the same thing). Substances that are not capable of eliciting antibody formation but are capable of combining with antibodies are called *haptens*. These are usually micromolecular substances. Finally, the smallest moiety of an antigenic molecule that can be recognized by an antibody is called an *antigenic determinant* or *epitope*. Many antigens exert the immunizing stimulus only if administered by a parenteral route, since they are degraded by enzymes of the digestive tract. Still, under natural conditions a great deal of antibody formation is stimulated by ingested or inhaled antigens.

Antibodies are defined as serum globulins that are formed as a result of a stimulus exerted by an antigen and that combine specifically with the antigen responsible for their production. The globulins carrying antibody specificity are called *immunoglobulins*, and we now recognize five classes of immunoglobulins — IgG, IgM, IgA, IgE, and IgD (Ch. 10). Of the previously discussed antigen-antibody reactions, neutralization of toxins, agglutination, and precipitation do not require for their manifestation any factors in addition to the antigen and antibody. On the other hand, lysis is accomplished by the action of antibody and complement. *Complement* is a normal serum component consisting of at least 12 proteins that interact with antibody-sensitized cells in a cascadelike reaction leading to cell lysis. This and many other functions of complement will be discussed in Chapter 11.

We discussed previously four kinds of antibodies — antitoxins, lysins, agglutinins, and precipitins; later in this text, other types of antibodies will be discussed. At the beginning of the immunologic era, it was believed that distinct properties of antibodies were responsible for the various forms of reactions with the antigen. It was, however, soon realized that the same antibody molecule, combining with its corresponding antigen, may elicit various manifestations of this reaction, depending on the form of antigen and conditions of the reaction. It was shown that an antibody that neutralizes toxin can also precipitate it, an antibody that lyses erythrocytes can also agglutinate them, and an antibody that agglutinates cells can precipitate their soluble components. In such a way, a unitarian hypothesis was advanced, primarily by Zinsser, according to which each antibody can participate in various reactions with its antigen, depending on the conditions of the test performed. Whereas this theory is basically correct, we know today that there are some antibodies incapable of participating in all of the reactions mentioned; for example, antibodies of the IgA or IgE class cannot participate in complement-mediated lysis (Ch. 10).

Since the very beginning of immunologic research, investigators have been fascinated with a phenomenon referred to as immunologic memory. This is best illustrated by the comparison of a "primary" with a "secondary" immune response. An animal that has never had contact with a particular antigen* responds to injection of this antigen with relatively slow antibody formation. It takes usually 3 to 4 days before antibodies are detectable. The titer of antibodies increases slowly and reaches its maximum after 1 to 2 weeks. Thereafter, the titer of antibodies remains unchanged for a few weeks; then it slowly declines over a period of several weeks or months to an undetectable level. In contrast, an animal that has had previous contact with the particular antigen (frequently referred to as a primed animal) responds promptly to the injection of this antigen. Antibodies are detectable within the first day of antigen injection and they very quickly, in 2 to 3 days, reach the highest titer.

The immunity mediated by serum antibodies is frequently referred to as *humoral* immunity. One of the major characteristics of antibody-mediated immunity is the fact that it may be passively transferred to a normal individual of the same or different species by means of injection of the antiserum. This is the principle of passive immunity that was employed for the first time in human medicine on Christmas 1891 in Berlin when a child suffering from diphtheria was injected with a sheep antiserum to diphtheria toxin. Passive immunity as a therapeutic measure is now rather seldom employed; however, antisera to some bacterial toxins and snake venoms are still used as the only efficient therapeutic agents. Antiserum produced in horses or other animals by injections of human lymph-

---

*There is no good or consistent term to denote such a "virgin soil" animal; some investigators call it simply a normal animal, whereas others use the term naive animal.

ocytes or thymocytes is used as an immunosuppressant in organ transplantation.

Passive immunity is of short duration; it fades away with the disappearance of the transferred antibodies. In the case of immunity transferred with a serum of the same species as the recipient, the duration of this immunity depends almost exclusively on the normal rate of catabolism of immunoglobulins (e.g., the half-life of human IgG is 3 weeks). In the case of foreign species antiserum, the elimination is markedly precipitated by formation of antibodies to the foreign immunoglobulins.

Under natural conditions, passive immunity is established in the fetus by transfer of maternal antibodies through the placenta. In man only IgG antibodies cross the placenta. These antibodies equip the newborn with immunity to several diseases, including diphtheria, scarlet fever, and measles. Obviously, within a few months after birth, this immunity disappears, but at that time the baby is already involved in active production of antibodies.

SEROLOGIC REACTIONS AND THEIR APPLICATIONS

All antigen-antibody reactions taking place *in vitro* are called *serologic reactions*. The outstanding feature of serologic reactions, their specificity, depends on the fit of the antibody molecule to its corresponding antigen, frequently compared to the fit of a key to its lock. Significantly, only a very small portion of the antibody molecule, referred to as its combining site, mirrors the surface structure of the antigen. Most antibodies have two combining sites, but some of them have up to ten sites. This will be discussed in Chapter 10.

The specificity of serologic reactions has been the basis for the development of serodiagnostic tests that found applications in most areas of biology and medicine. Two major principles of serodiagnostic procedures should be distinguished: (1) procedures in which a known antibody-containing serum serves as a reagent to identify an unknown antigen, and (2) procedures in which a known antigenic preparation serves to identify an unknown antibody in the serum tested.

The first principle has been broadly applied in microbiology, in which antisera serve as reagents to identify microorganisms of various species and serotypes. Furthermore, these procedures may be used for demonstration and for identification of blood groups, tissue groups and serum protein allotypes (Ch. 14). Diagnosis of an infectious disease may occasionally be made on the basis of detection of a microbial antigen in tissue extracts or body fluids by means of a reaction with the proper immune serum (e.g., Ascoli test for anthrax, tests for pneumococcal polysaccharides in pleural effusion and in cerebrospinal fluid). Procedures of this type are finding more and more applications. Furthermore, immunofluorescence staining procedures help in the identification of microorganisms (e.g., treponemes, gonococci, or meningococci) in smears from pathologic material. In more recent years immune sera have been used as diagnostic reagents to detect and quantitate various tissue antigens. Pregnancy tests have been based on detection of chorionic gonadotropin in urine by means of a corresponding immune serum.

Serologic tests are also used for detection and quantitation of various hormones in the blood. Detection and quantitation of carcinoembryonic antigen and α-fetoprotein in the blood plays a role in the diagnosis and prognosis of malignancies. For detection and quantitation of antigens, very sensitive radioimmunoassays have been developed. Increased attention is being devoted to tests in which purified antibody is attached to particles that then undergo agglutination if suspended in a medium containing the corresponding antigen. However, such tests have not yet been broadly used as routine diagnostic procedures.

Serodiagnostic tests have also found application in forensic medicine. Cells, tissues, and body fluids are strongly impregnated with species specificity. Therefore a proper antiserum, for example, of rabbit origin, can readily serve to distinguish the blood serum of various species, for example, human serum from bovine serum. The antigenic differences between species reflect biologic proximity. Therefore it is much less difficult to distinguish human serum from bovine serum than human serum from chimpanzee serum or bovine serum from goat serum. Tests based on identification of the species origin of blood stains or tissue debris have been successfully employed in criminal cases. Similar tests can also be used for detection of adulteration of food products. Application of serodiagnostic tests in medicolegal cases of disputed parenthood will be discussed in Chapter 14.

The second principle of serodiagnostic tests has served for the diagnosis of many infectious diseases since the original observation by Widal in 1896 of agglutination of typhoid bacilli by sera of patients suffering or recovering from typhoid fever. Many other infectious diseases have been successfully diagnosed by tests based on a similar principle. Since the antibodies in a patient's serum may originate from a previous patent or subclinical infection or from vaccination, a serodiagnostic test performed only once may be difficult to interpret and is sometimes deceiving. On the other hand, comparison of the titer of the reaction in the serum obtained at the beginning of the disease and, then, 1 to 2 weeks later, is most valuable diagnostically if a significant increase of the titer is noted. In viral diseases, hospital vernacular refers to the comparison of reactions in "acute sera" and "convalescent sera."

Serodiagnostic tests based on the detection of antibodies have also been employed for the diagnosis of noninfectious diseases. Demonstration of rheumatoid factor, that is, antibodies to denatured IgG, is helpful for the diagnosis of rheumatoid arthritis. Thyroglobulin antibodies are characteristic for some forms of thyroiditis, and antinuclear antibodies for systemic lupus erythematosus.

In all serodiagnostic tests two important characteristics of the tests may be distinguished — *sensitivity* and *specificity*. These terms are used here with clinical connotations. The sensitivity of a test is measured by the proportion of patients suffering from the disease for which the test was designed who give positive results upon examination. All serologic tests approach the sensitivity of 100 percent, but they do so only in some phase of the disease. For example, the Widal test approaches this sensitivity 4 to 5 weeks after infection. At the beginning of the disease the sensitivity of the serologic test is usually low, and positive results are obtained only in a small proportion of patients. Also, with recovery from an infectious disease, the amount of the antibody may decrease and, accordingly, also the proportion of patients in whom the test is positive. Specificity of a test, or, more correctly, its nonspecificity, is measured by the frequency of positive results in normal subjects and patients suffering from diseases other than the one for which the given test was designed. No serologic test is ideally specific, and "false" tests are observed primarily in those patients who have had previous experience with a given disease or who previously suffered or currently suffer from a disease elicited by biologically related microorganisms.

In developing each serodiagnostic test, the investigator has to keep in mind that higher sensitivity is usually acquired at the price of lower specificity, and vice versa.

An interesting and important area of serology was initiated at the beginning of the century with the demonstration that various tissues differ in their antigenic structure. Here again, immune sera most frequently raised in a rabbit serve as reagents to detect antigens characteristic of, for example, the brain, thyroid, kidney, and testicle. Tissue-specific antigens may, under proper experimental conditions, elicit autoantibody formation, which may lead to experimental autoimmune diseases, such as allergic encephalomyelitis, experimental thyroiditis, and aspermatogenesis. Autoimmune responses may also lead to pathologic lesions in humans (Ch. 15).

In recent years antibodies produced in the test tube have been used with increasing frequency as serodiagnostic reagents. To this end lymphoid cells of an immunized animal are fused with malignant cells, in most instances murine myeloma cells. The resulting hybrid cells, referred to as hybridomas, are selected for production of the desired antibody. Antibodies formed by hybridoma cells are all identical, since they are formed by the same clone of cells (monoclonal antibodies). The advantage of using antibodies produced in this way is obvious.

CELL-MEDIATED IMMUNITY

As discussed above, antibodies serve as effectors for humoral immunity. Besides humoral immunity, man and animals respond to antigens with cell-mediated immunity (CMI). This immunity cannot be demonstrated in blood serum by serologic techniques or transferred passively with serum. In CMI, T cells, that is, lymphoid cells that have matured in the thymus, serve as effectors. The effector T cell has on its surface receptors specifically combining with the antigen. These receptors closely resemble antibody combining sites in many respects; however, its immunoglobulin nature has never been demonstrated.

CMI will be discussed at some length in Chapter 13. It may be stated here that the basic phenomenon of CMI is the interaction of sensitized T lymphocytes with their corresponding antigens; among other important events, this interaction may lead to the destruction and elimination of pathogenic microorganisms and probably also of malignant cells.

For many decades CMI could be detected only by means of *in vivo* reactions, principally skin tests. These reactions depended not only on the interaction between T cell and antigen but on mobilization of many cells, predominantly mononuclear cells, in the site of reaction. For diagnostic purposes the tests measuring CMI have usually been performed by means of intracutaneous injection of the antigen. Characteristically, an inflammatory reaction would appear in several hours and reach its peak about 24 hours after injection of antigen. Therefore the term *delayed hypersensitivity reactions* has been used to distinguish these reactions from those of the immediate type, appearing in 15 to 30 minutes. The prototype of the delayed hypersensitivity reaction is the tuberculin reaction. The test for tuberculin hypersensitivity, as well as many other delayed hypersensitivity tests, has been used for diagnostic purposes since the beginning of the twentieth century.

In recent years *in vitro* tests for CMI have been developed that are based on blastogenic transformation of T lymphocytes in the presence of their specific antigen. In addition stimulated T cells release a number of substances called *lymphokines*, which can be detected by proper procedures. The methods of detecting lymphokines and their role in CMI is discussed in Chapter 13.

SALIENT FEATURES OF IMMUNE RESPONSES

Cells of the Immune Response

The immune system interacts with components of its environment by means of specific structures on its effectors, that is, antibody molecules or lymphocytes that are capable of recognizing surface properties of antigenic moieties. Such structures are termed *combining sites* when they occur on antibodies and *receptors* when they are present on cells. Receptors for antigens on lymphocytes are essential in the initiation of any response of the immune system. Antigen recognition and the interaction of cells with specific antigens are properties of B cells as well as T cells. B cells mature in the bursa of Fabricius of birds and in an undefined counterpart of this organ in mammals. T cells mature in the thymus.

Stimulation of B cells by the majority of antigens requires cooperation of T cells. Such antigens are called *T cell dependent*. Following stimulation with the antigen, B cells transform to lymphoblasts and eventually to plasma cells, the latter being the major source of antibodies. For further discussion see Chapter 9.

In vitro production of antibodies has been studied for a few decades. In recent years a great deal of work was devoted to the production of monoclonal antibodies by hybridoma cells (see above).

Specific Unresponsiveness

The concept of specific immunologic unresponsiveness was advanced in 1900 by Ehrlich and Morgenroth in their famous *horror autotoxicus* rule. In working on immunization of goats with blood of other goats, Ehrlich and Morgenroth noted frequent formation of antibodies combining with foreign erythrocytes (alloantibodies), but they never noted formation of antibodies to the animals' own erythrocytes (autoantibodies). They concluded that a healthy animal refuses to form antibodies against autologous antigens, since such antibodies could lead to disease and death. The horror autotoxicus rule has been broadly accepted as a general biologic phenomenon. Many investigators had believed that unresponsiveness to autologous antigens is under genetic control. An alternative explanation was proposed by Burnet that recognition of autologous antigens (*self-recognition*) is acquired in ontogenesis as a result of contact of immune apparatus with overwhelming amounts of autologous antigens.

The concept of Burnet and Fenner was consistent with Owen's observations on cattle chimerism, in which dizygotic cattle twins exchange the cells through placental anastomoses and subsequently fail to respond to each other's antigens.

Experimental induction of immunologic unresponsiveness has been studied since the 1920s. Several investigators showed that overloading an animal with antigen leads to unresponsiveness. The best known of these experiments were those conducted on mice with pneumococcal polysaccharides.

Experiments stimulated by observation of cattle chimerism and the self-recognition concept were conducted in the 1950s by Medawar and his associates. They showed that intrauterine injection of embryos of mouse strain CBA with a suspension of cells from another mouse strain A resulted in "acquired immunologic tolerance" of A cells by CBA mice, which would accept A skin in adulthood. Experiments on acquired immunologic tolerance have been confirmed by many investigators. Most of these experiments were performed by injecting embryonal or neonatal animals with foreign cells, but in several instances tolerance was elicited in adult animals. This was especially the case when the two experimental strains differed only in weak antigens.

The original explanation of the mechanism of acquired tolerance was clonal abrogation, that is, the destruction of all lymphoid cells destined to produce an immune response to the injected antigen. This explanation is still tenable in many instances, but today we know that other mechanisms also play an important role in immunologic unresponsiveness. Of these, we may briefly discuss humoral antibodies and suppressor cells.

It has been known for several decades that passive administration of IgG antibodies interferes with active immune response to the antigen against which these antibodies are directed. Fascinating achievements using this principle were made in the prevention of sensitization of Rh-negative mothers delivering Rh-positive babies (Ch. 14). Injection of IgG anti-Rh antibodies right after the delivery was shown to prevent sensitization in most instances. The mechanism of this phenomenon is not well understood. The possibility exists that the erythrocytes sensitized by antibodies are eliminated by the liver rather than by the spleen, or otherwise that the antibodies wall off the antigenic determinants on the red cells and prevent their expression. Obviously and significantly, the described procedure does not result in a lasting suppression and therefore has to be repeated after each incompatible pregnancy.

The suppressive effect of T lymphocytes has been studied in the last decade. This type of unresponsiveness is sometimes referred to as "infectious" tolerance because the state of unresponsiveness may be transferred by lymphocytes from the tolerant to the normal animal. Long-lasting, strain-specific unresponsiveness to H-2-incompatible skin allografts could be achieved by proper experimental manipulation, resulting in stimulation of suppressor cells.

THEORIES OF ANTIBODY FORMATION

As stressed repeatedly, the specificity of immunologic reactions is their outstanding feature. The way by which the specificity of an antibody for its corresponding antigen is established has intrigued immunologists for

the last 90 years, and this basic dilemma is still not settled. Attempts to explain antibody formation have been presented in numerous theories that have had a most important impact on the development of immunologic research.

The theories of antibody formation may be divided into two major groups: (1) instructive theories postulate that antigen by itself participates in antibody formation by

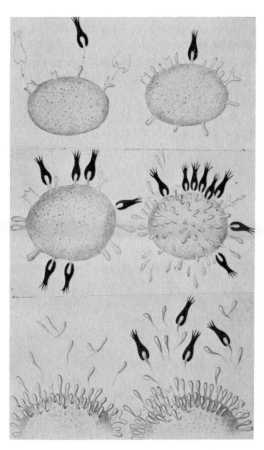

Fig. 8.1. Ehrlich's theory of antibody formation. The side chains combine with their corresponding antigens and are detached from the cell. They regenerate in excess and can no longer be accomodated on the cell. (Reprinted with permission according to Ehrlich, in Himmelweit, F.: The Collected Papers of Paul Ehrlich. Vol. II. Immunology and Cancer Research. Copyright 1957, The Royal Society.)

"instructing" the cells as to what kind of antibody they should synthesize; (2) selective theories propose the preexistence of all possible antibody patterns; according to these theories, antigen selects its corresponding pattern and engenders its replication.

The first theory of scientific interest was the famous side-chain theory of antibody formation proposed by Ehrlich in 1900. According to this theory, cells have side chains or receptors that serve to bind nutrients important in cell physiology. Even though antigen is not necessarily a nutrient, it finds its corresponding receptor, combines with it, and causes its detachment from the cell. The ensuing regeneration produces a great excess of receptors of the same structure, which can no longer be accommodated on the cell and are shed off into the circulation (Fig. 8.1). These receptors are antibodies. Ehrlich's theory is clearly a selective theory, since it postulates the preexistence of all antibody patterns.

At Ehrlich's time the number of known antigens was rather limited; therefore a selective theory did not elicit any significant opposition. In the subsequent decades, however, the number of known antigens steadily increased, and finally it was demonstrated that chemical compounds synthesized at the will of an investigator may have a distinct antigenic specificity. At that time it appeared that the number of possible antigens and, accordingly, the number of their corresponding antibodies was infinite. Any selective theory therefore seemed naive. We will discuss later the fallacy of this reasoning. Starting in the 1930s, a number of instructive theories were advanced, and they dominated the field for over a quarter of a century.

The first instructive theories were advanced at the time when very little was known about the mechanism of protein synthesis, and the role of nucleic acids in this synthesis was not appreciated. Therefore in a way rather naive for a student of contemporary biology these theories postulated that antigen by itself directs the synthesis of antibodies in a way similar to a stamper making its imprint on coins. These theories are frequently called direct template theories. The most popular direct template theory was proposed in 1930 by Breinl and Haurowitz, who postulated that the cell involved in the formation of globulins possesses some normal template, directing the synthesis of normal globulins. Upon entering such a cell the antigen becomes incorporated into the normal template and thereafter has its imprint on the globulin synthesis; it was known at that time that antibodies are globulins. Wherever an antigen would have a strong polar group, the corresponding site on the antibody would have a polar group with an opposite charge. In such a way, the sequence of amino acids in the newly synthesized polypeptide chain would be influ-

Fig. 8.2. Pauling's theory of antibody formation. Diagrammatic representation of the sequence of events assumed to occur if antibody activity results from a directed folding of the peptide chain after synthesis. (Burrows, F.M.: Textbook of Microbiology, 19th Ed. W.A. Saunders, Philadelphia, 1968.)

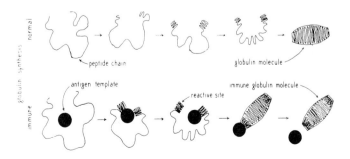

enced by the antigen itself. The completed chain dissociates from the antigen-containing template, and the accomplished antibody is shed off into the circulation. Obviously, the immunized animal would maintain the production of normal globulins and, as a matter of fact, antibodies would constitute only a relatively small fraction of all globulins produced. Theories similar to that proposed by Breinl and Haurowitz were also advanced by Alexander (1931) and Mudd (1932).

In 1940 Pauling proposed another direct template theory that was popular for several years. According to Pauling, antigen also directly influences the structure of antibody; but rather than directing the sequence of the amino acids in the polypeptide chain, the antigen exerts its imprint on the folding of the chain into a three-dimensional protein molecule (Fig. 8.2).

Thus Pauling's theory proposed that antigen influences the tertiary structure of the globulin molecule. A somewhat similar theory was advanced by Karush, who postulated that the precursor polypeptide chains are formed in a labile form and are capable of folding in many ways; they are stablized by disulfide bonds. Since the bridging of the chains by disulfide bonds occurs in the presence of the antigen, the chains acquire a configuration complementary to the antigen. It should be stressed, however, that according to our present knowledge, the structure of the combining site of an immunoglobulin is determined by the sequence of amino acids rather than the folding of the molecule.

Modern instructive theories take cognizance of the role of nucleic acids in the synthesis of proteins. Accordingly, these theories postulate that the antigen has its imprint on the DNA, mRNA, or tRNA involved in antibody synthesis. These theories are frequently called indirect template theories.

In the 1950s Schweet and Owen proposed that antigen modifies DNA in the antibody-forming cell, and Haurowitz proposed that antigen introduces itself into the translation phase by interfering with the function of tRNA. In the early 1960s great interest was elicited by the theory of Fishman. He proposed that antigen ingested by macrophages has its imprint on mRNA. This RNA would then be incorporated into antibody-forming cells and would direct the synthesis of antibodies. Later, a similar mechanism of antibody formation was advocated by Jacherts and by Pilch. *In vitro* experiments on antibody formation have indeed showed that RNA extracted from macrophages that ingested the antigen is very powerful in provoking an immune response of B or T cells. It remains to be clarified what this immunogenic RNA or I-RNA is. As mentioned, some investigators propose that it is an RNA modified by an antigen. Others, however, believe that I-RNA is simply RNA which is complexed with an antigenic fragment and which acts as a "superantigen".

In general, instructive theories account very adequately for the multiplicity of antibodies, the main reason for which they were created. On the other hand, these theories fail to explain the differences between primary and secondary immune responses, and they do not account for immunologic memory. In addition, self-recognition (see below) cannot be readily explained by most of these theories. The majority of instructive theories postulate that antigen enters the antibody-forming cell. Significantly, meticulous experiments with radiolabelled antigens have failed to support this contention.

A revival of selective theories was initiated in 1955 when Jerne proposed that the formation of antibodies in response to immunization depends on multiplication of preexisting natural antibodies. Natural antibodies can be demonstrated in any mature man or animal. The immunizing stimulus that engendered formation of these antibodies is unknown. Most contemporary investigators believe that natural antibodies are formed in response to "hidden" immunizing stimuli provided by inhaled and ingested antigens as well as by subclinical infections with a variety of microorganisms. In contrast, Hirszfeld (1928) and some other investigators expressed the views that natural antibodies develop spontaneously without any antigenic stimulation. Jerne accepted a similar view and proposed that man and animals have natural antibodies for any potential antigenic determinant, except for autologous determinants. Whereas some natural antibodies attain detectable levels, others fail to do so. The antigen introduced into the animal's body combines with its corresponding natural antibody. The resulting antigen-antibody complex is taken up by the antibody-forming cell in which this particular antibody pattern is replicated. The theory did not explain how this occurs. The great merit of the theory, however, was to stimulate the revival of interest in selective theories.

Hardly any biologic theory had more influence on the experimentation in its field than the famous clonal selection theory of antibody formation advanced in 1959 by Burnet. The term *clone* is used for the progeny population derived from a single cell through repeated cell divisions. According to Burnet, the lymphoid cell population of man and animals is composed of numerous clones. The cells within one clone produce antibodies of one specificity (unipotential cells). The ancestor cell of each clone acquired the genetic information for the synthesis of one particular antibody pattern through random somatic mutation, which had occurred early in ontogenesis. Accordingly, this ancestral cell and later all of its descendants have formed this one particular antibody. Significantly, Burnet believes that the somatic mutations of lymphoid cells occur spontaneously without any contact with antigen.

According to Burnet, the effect of exposure of a clone to its corresponding antigen is different in the embryonal stage than in the mature life of the animal. In the embryo, the clone is composed of just a few cells and is overwhelmed and destroyed by the excess of antigen. This phenomenon accounts for the "self-recognition" resulting from the destruction of the clones of cells forming antibodies to autologous antigens. Accordingly, under normal conditions there is no autoantibody formation in the animal's adult life. Those clones that escaped destruction by contact with autologous antigen in the early stages of development could sometimes remain as "forbidden" clones that would be able to form autoantibodies. This could result in an autoimmune disease.

Studies on acquired immunologic tolerance performed in the 1950s, primarily by Medawar and his associates, were apparently consistent with Burnet's theory. These studies showed that an embryonal or neonatal animal may be "deceived" by confronting it with artificially introduced foreign antigen. The corresponding clone was destroyed, and the animal showed unresponsiveness or tolerance to this particular antigen. Under natural conditions, cells of nonidentical twins may be exchanged *in utero*, resulting in mutual tolerance. This phenomenon has been described in cattle, man, and other mammals.

When contact of the clone with its corresponding antigen occurs in a mature individual, the cells are stimulated to proliferate. The number of cells belonging to this particular clone increases most significantly. Therefore clones that formed undetectable levels of antibodies before antigenic stimulation would produce readily detectable amounts of antibodies after stimulation.

The crucial postulate of clonal selection theory — the unipotentiality of the antibody-forming cells — has been proved in elegant experiments that showed that upon stimulation with two antigens a single lymphoid cell from the draining lymph node was involved in the formation of antibodies against one or another antigen. Only very few cells produced antibodies against both antigens.

Similar to other discussed theories, the clonal selection theory addressed itself to the formation of humoral antibodies. Burnet postulated, however, that the cells responsible for cell-mediated immunity emerge also from random mutations.

Several other selective theories were proposed in the 1960s and 1970s. All of them resemble the clonal selection theory in that they postulate selection of antibody-forming cells by the antigen. In contrast to the original theory of Burnet, some theories reject somatic mutation and propose that the fertilized ovum contains genetic information for production of all possible antibodies. These theories are referred to as germ line theories. They are based on the well established fact that the process of differentiation results in repression of some and augmentation of other genetic information carried by the fertilized ovum. Accordingly, each immunoglobulin-producing cell would contain genetic information for formation of all possible antibodies. In an individual cell, however, all this information is repressed except for the information pertaining to one antibody pattern.

There are also interesting theories that postulate the existence of two "half-genes" that fuse into one gene before coding for the synthesis of the immunoglobulin polypeptide chain. Genetic material in the half-gene coding for a constant polypeptide region of immunoglobulin would stem from germ cells, whereas the material contained in the half-gene coding for the variable portion of the polypeptide chain (i.e., this portion that contains the antibody combining site) would emerge through somatic mutation.

For the last 20 years, selective theories have been generally accepted. Still, as mentioned before, from the beginning of the 1930s to the mid-1950s the field was dominated by instructive theories. This was so because investigators were impressed with the number of possible antibodies, which seemed to be infinite. The revival of selective theories occurred undoubtedly under the influence of studies on bacterial genetics and the demonstration that bacterial selection rather than adaptation is responsible for resistance to antibiotics, chemotherapeutics, and bacteriophages. With the increasing evidence for the correctness of selective theories, the thesis of infinite numbers of antibody patterns has been questioned.

The classic and most suggestive experiments on "ideal" specificity of antibodies to chemically defined antigens were conducted by Landsteiner. He showed that antibodies to *ortho*-aminobenzene sulfonic acid not only combined with their corresponding antigen but also acted upon the analogous

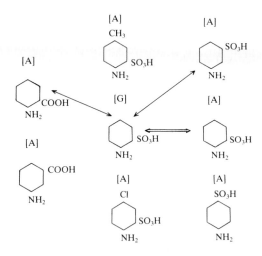

Fig. 8.3. Crossreactivity of haptens. (G) indicates the active group in the azo protein used as an antigen in precipitation test. (A) indicates antibodies against given compounds. A double arrow indicates a strong reaction and a single arrow a weak reaction. Lack of arrow indicates no reaction. (Wilson, G.S. and Miles, A.A., Eds.: Topley and Wilson's Principles of Bacteriology, Virology and Immunity. 6th Ed., Vol. I. Edward Arnold Ltd., London, 1975.)

meta compound, even though they did so more weakly. However, the antibodies gave no reaction with the analogous *para* compound. Replacement of the sulfonic group by a carboxylic group at the *ortho* position resulted in a crossreacting epitope, and only when the carboxylic group was shifted to a *meta* position did the reaction cease (Fig. 8.3). It may be readily concluded that these experiments can be more properly used to argue for imperfect specificity of antibodies than for an exquisite specificity. As a matter of fact, crossreactions noted by Landsteiner seem to indicate that a finite number of antibody structures may account for reactions with all possible epitopes. The same conclusion can be derived from the simple consideration that the combining site of antibody is composed of just a few amino acid residues. Since there are only 20 amino acids and certainly not all of them participate in the building of combining sites, at least not with equal frequency, the number of possible antibody patterns has to be finite. Most investigators would agree that about 10^6 antibody patterns could account for all antibody variability.

THEORIES OF IMMUNE REGULATION

Several investigators have addressed their theories to the regulatory mechanisms that prevent antibody or T lymphocytes with one specificity from achieving an exceedingly high concentration, which would preclude any further immune response to other antigens. Among recently advanced hypotheses, those presented by Jerne (1974 to 1979) are of special interest. The basis for these theories are the regulatory activities of antiidiotypic antibodies. Idiotypes were described in the 1960s as specificities carried by variable domains of immunoglobulins. Idiotypic specificity is an antigenic determinant very closely related to the antibody combining site but not identical with it.

Idiotypes elicit the formation of antibodies in an animal of another species, in an animal of the same species, and even in the antibody-forming animal itself. Jerne uses Ab-1 to refer to the antibody against a given antigen and Ab-2 to refer to the antibody against the idiotype of Ab-1. The important observation was that Ab-2 injected into a nontreated animal would frequently suppress the formation of Ab-1 expected upon antigenic stimulation. In some other instances, it was noted that Ab-2 would favor rather than suppress the formation of Ab-1. At any rate, convincing evidence was presented showing that Ab-2 exerts a regulatory influence on Ab-1 formation.

As mentioned previously, the idiotype and the antibody combining site are not identical but are only related structures. Antibodies of the same specificity, even if they originate from the same animal, may frequently have different idiotypes; conversely, antibodies of different specificities may have the same idiotype. From this information it can be concluded that each Ab-1 would have a number of "connected" Ab-2 and each Ab-2 would have a number of connected Ab-1. Jerne postulates that this "connection" results in a network or a web of structures engaged in regulatory activities against each other.

Other investigators go further in their hypotheses by postulating the existence of Ab-3 that suppresses (or stimulates) Ab-2. It should be stressed that Ab may stand for humoral antibodies or for lymphocytes carrying specific receptors. According to this concept, specific T suppressor cells are cells with antiidiotypic reactivity.

More details about regulatory mechanisms of immune responses are discussed in Chapter 9.

REFERENCES

Doerr, R.: Die Immunitätsforschung. Ergebnisse und Probleme in Einzeldarstellungen. Vols. 1–4. Springer-Verlag, Vienna, 1947–1949.

Fudenberg, H.H., Stites, D.P., Caldwell, J.L., and Wells, J.V., Eds.: Basic and Clinical Immunology. 2nd Ed. Lange Medical Publications, Los Altos, 1978.

Hirszfeld, L.: Konstitutionsserologie und Blutgruppenforschung. Springer, Berlin, 1928.

Humphrey, J.H. and White, R.G.: Immunology for Students of Medicine. 3rd Ed. F.A. Davis, Philadelphia, 1970.

Kolle, W., Kraus, R. and Uhlenhuth, P., Eds.: Handbuch der pathogenen Mikroorganismen. Vol. II, Parts 1 & 2. Gustav Fischer, Jena; Urban & Schwarzenberg, Berlin & Vienna; 1929.

Rose, N.R., Milgrom, F., and van Oss, C.J., Eds.: Principles of Immunology. 2nd Ed. Macmillan, New York, 1979.

9

Structural and Functional Aspects of the Immune Response

Boris Albini

Antigen introduced into human or other vertebrate organisms elicits an immune response. The protagonists of the immune response are lymphocytes. They recognize the antigen, become sensitized, and ultimately either produce effectors of immunologic reactions capable of interacting with the antigen in attempts aimed at its removal or turn off the production of these effectors, thereby inducing immunologic unresponsiveness or tolerance. Lymphocytes are responsible for the development of immunologic memory (Ch. 8). They and some of their products convey specificity to immune reactions. Lymphocytes may interact with each other and with immunologically nonspecific cells during antigen recognition. Later in the immune response, effectors of immunologic reactions may recruit a vast array of immunologically nonspecific cells and soluble mediators of inflammation.

At a basic level, the immune response may be subdivided into three stages: the afferent stage, comprising antigen recognition; a central stage, comprising production of effectors, which is governed by regulatory mechanisms; and an efferent stage, comprising the effector mechanisms.

The immune response is the function of a specialized tissue — the lymphoid tissue. This tissue may be distributed in organs more or less diffusely. Large amounts of diffuse lymphoid tissue are seen in the gastrointestinal and respiratory tracts, bone marrow, and blood. Sometimes, lymphoid tissue may define whole organs, such as lymph nodes, spleen, thymus, Peyer's patches, and tonsils.

In this chapter a brief description of morphological and functional principles governing the immune response will be attempted. For more detailed accounts, the reader is referred to the publications given in the list of references.

THE LYMPHOCYTE

Lymphocytes appear in a blood smear as inconspicuous cells with a large nucleus and a thin rim of clear cytoplasm. They convey the impression of inactive cells. Until a few decades ago they were of little interest to students of histology, cytology, or hematology, even though Ehrlich had suggested a role for these cells in immune reactions as early as the turn of the century. It was almost 50 years later that Chase, Harris, Fagraeus, and others provided substantial evidence for the involvement of lymphoid cells in immunologic reactions. A real breakthrough in the understanding of lymphocyte function came with Nowell's demonstration that these cells, rather than being inactive, do indeed respond eagerly to appropriate stimuli with profound changes in metabolism and morphology. The pivotal role of lymphocytes as the protagonists of the immune response was established in elegant experiments conducted by Gowans. Finally, the previously unsuspected heterogeneity of lymphocyte populations became obvious through the work of Glick, Good, Miller, and, more recently, Boyse and Cantor and many others.

Origins

Cells with the characteristics of lymphocytes are found in all vertebrates. Some invertebrates have white blood cells performing functions similar to those of lymphocytes; such cells have been called *protolymphocytes*. All lymphocytes arise from pluripotent hemopoietic stem cells and thus are relatives of the cells of the monocyte-macrophage, myeloid, erythroid, and megakaryocyte-platelet series. In ontogeny, which has been studied most extensively in lambs, mice, and chickens, hemopoietic stem cells arise from the areae vasculosae of the yolk sac. Later in fetal life, the hemopoietic stem cells lodge in the liver and ultimately in the bone marrow. The bone marrow remains the source of hemopoietic stem cells during the entire life. In ontogeny and in maturation of lymphoid cells in the adult, the pluripotent stem cell gives rise to "precommitted" stem cells, which carry some characteristics of mature lymphocytes. To mature, the lymphoid stem cells have to reach a central (or "primary") lymphoid organ, which provides the necessary microenvironment for maturation. In mammals the central lymphoid organ is the thymus. Lymphocytes maturing in the thymus become *T cells*. In birds, in addition to the thymus another central lymphoid organ — the bursa of Fabricius — is present during some time of fetal development and early life. Lymphocytes leaving the bursa are called *B cells*. An equivalent for the bursa has not yet been found in mammals; B cells, however, do occur in mammals; the function of the bursa in mammals may be performed by more diffuse lymphoid tissue. The differentiation and maturation of lymphocytes in central lymphoid organs seem to be independent of contact with antigens. Further maturation of lymphocytes also occurs in peripheral lymphoid organs (e.g., in lymph nodes and the spleen). This process, however, seems dependent on the presence of antigen.

Morphology

Lymphocytes measure 5 to 15 μm in diameter. Histologists have attempted to categorize lymphocytes according to their size — 5 to 8 μm, small; 8 to 12 μm, intermediate; and 12 to 15 μm, large lymphocytes — but these are not really three discernible populations of lymphocytes, and the spectrum of sizes is continuous. The nucleus of the lymphocyte is round or oval, with densely aggregated chromatin. This prominence of heterochromatin is most impressive in the smallest cells of this series. Lymphocytes have only a thin rim of clear cytoplasm (Fig. 9.1). In electron microscopy only a few mitochondria and vesicles can be seen. Ribosomes occur most often as isolated granules. Lymphocytes are motile cells, but their movements are slower than those of granulocytes.

Activated lymphocytes (lymphoblasts) are seen infrequently in blood but are prominent in lymphoid organs during sensitization. They are seen after interaction of

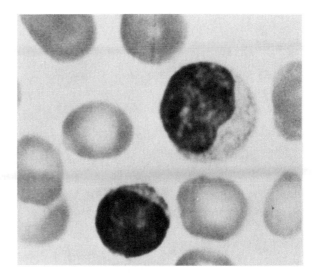

Fig. 9.1. Small and medium-sized lymphocytes from the peripheral blood of a normal subject; Wright stain (× 2000). (Cline, M.J.: The White Cell. Harvard University Press, Cambridge, 1975. Reprinted by permission.)

lymphocytes with antigens and in the wake of antigen-independent induction of mitosis, for example, by lectins (Ch. 13). They are large cells, 12 μm or more in diameter. Their nuclei contain loosely packed chromatin. Compared to small lymphocytes, lymphoblasts have a broad cytoplasm. Electron microscopy reveals groups of polyribosomes, a fully developed Golgi area, centrioles, and an increased number of mitochondria and vesicles. Some lymphoblasts derived from B cells produce antibodies, which may be demonstrated by immunohistologic techniques (Fig. 9.2).

A cell considered to represent the end stage of B cell maturation is the plasma cell (Fig. 9.3). It is somewhat larger than the lymphocyte (9 to 20 μm). The nucleus, located eccentrically in the abundant cytoplasm, shows a typical "wheel-spoke" arrangement of heterochromatin. The cytoplasm has a clear perinuclear zone containing the Golgi apparatus. Mitochondria are numerous. The most impressive feature in plasma cells is the rough endoplasmic reticulum, with its parallel membranes beaded with ribosomes forming tightly packed stacks, indicating avid protein synthesis.

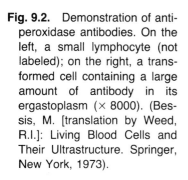
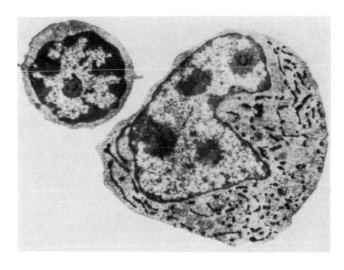

Fig. 9.2. Demonstration of anti-peroxidase antibodies. On the left, a small lymphocyte (not labeled); on the right, a transformed cell containing a large amount of antibody in its ergastoplasm (× 8000). (Bessis, M. [translation by Weed, R.I.]: Living Blood Cells and Their Ultrastructure. Springer, New York, 1973).

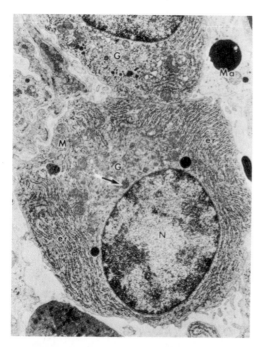

Fig. 9.3. Normal mature plasma cells from bone marrow (× 8000). The large cell with an eccentrically located nucleus (N) has extensive areas of endoplasmic reticulum (er), a large Golgi zone (G), several mitochondria (M), and multivesicular structure (arrow). Vesicles of variable size contain material of differing density in the Golgi area, some of which may correspond to the azurophilic granules seen by light microscopy. This is evident in the upper cell. The nucleus has some chromatin concentrated around its periphery, a characteristic of the maturing cell. Electron-dense particles and part of a macrophage (Ma) are in the right upper corner, as well as a blood vessel in the left upper corner. (Tanaka, Y. and Goodman, J.R.: Electron Microscopy of Human Blood Cells. Harper & Row, New York, 1972.)

Subpopulations

The diversity of lymphocyte subpopulations became obvious with the demonstration of distinct functions being carried out by certain lymphocytes and with the discovery of surface markers on distinct lymphocyte subpopulations. The majority of lymphocytes belong either to the B cell or the T cell pools. B cells, eventually developing into plasma cells, have been shown to be responsible for production of antibodies. T cells provide the effector cells in the classical cell-mediated immunity of the tuberculin type (Ch. 13). Furthermore, T cells may interact with B cells or other T cells in the process of antigen recognition, in regulatory mechanisms, and possibly also in the effector phase of the immune response.

Morphological aspects of lymphocytes do not usually permit distinction of B from T cells. A number of surface markers, however, make the distinction feasible (Table 9.1). Some lymphocytes have neither B nor T cell markers. They were originally called "null" cells. More recently, it has been established that at least some of the cells lacking B or T cell markers are involved in antibody-dependent cell-mediated cytotoxicity reactions (ADCC; see Ch. 13). They have receptors for the Fc portion of immunoglobulins (Ch. 10) and have been named K (killer) cells. Another cell probably belonging to the lymphoid cell line but lacking B and T cell markers is involved in destruction of tumor cells and is called the NK (natural killer) cell. B and T cells themselves are not homogeneous cell populations. According to their state of maturation and their function, their surface markers vary. The most comprehensive attempt to identify lymphocyte subpopulations has been made in mice (Table 9.2). Also, early T cells are less resistant to corticosteroids than mature T cells. Recently, promising results have also been obtained in humans.

LYMPHOID TISSUES AND ORGANS

Diffuse Lymphoid Tissue

Diffuse accumulations of lymphoid cells occur at many sites of the body, especially in mucosae, submucosae, and the bone marrow; they are associated with glomerulus-like vascular structures of the omentum. In

Table 9.1   B and T Cell Markers in Mice

	B cells	T cells
Surface markers		
Immunoglobulins	+	−
Thy.1[a]	−	+
Lyt1,2,3[a]	−	+
Complement receptors	+	−
Receptor for Fc of immunoglobulins	+	±
Cell transformation induced by nonspecific mitogens		
Phytohemagglutinin	−	+
Lipopolysaccharide (Ch. 13)	+	−

[a]Alloantigens (Ch. 14).

addition to lymphocytes scattered throughout the tissue, lymph follicles may form.

In pathologic conditions lymphoid cells may be seen in many organs that normally do not contain them. They first appear around vessels and then migrate further into the tissue. In some conditions — for example, pyelonephritis and autoimmune thyroiditis — much of the organ involved may be transformed into lymphoid tissue. Plasma cells may be prominent, and lymph follicles may appear.

Table 9.2   Subpopulations of B and T Cells in Mice

		Immunoglobulins on Surface		Complement Receptor	Alloantigens[a]	
		IgM	Other Ig		Ia	PCI
B cell maturation	B cell precursor	±?	−	−	−	−
	Early B cell	+	+	−	−	−
	Mature B cell	+	+	+	+	−
	Plasma cell	−	−	−	−	+

		Alloantigens[a]					
		H-2	TL	Thy.1	Lyt1	Lyt2	Lyt3
T cell maturation	Prethymic stem cell	+	−	−	−	−	−
	Thymic T cell	+	+	+++	+	+	+
	Mature T cell						
	Helper T cell	+	−	+	+	−	−
	Regulatory T cell	+	−	+	+	+	+
	Suppressor T cell	+	−	+	−	+	+
	Cytotoxic T cell	+	−	+	−	+	+
	T cells involved in delayed hypersensitivity	+	−	+	+	−	−

[a]H-2, major histocompatibility antigens in mice; TL, Thy.1, Lyt1, 2, 3, alloantigens of mouse lymphocytes (Ch. 14); Ia, antigens coded for by the *I* region of the major histocompatibility complex (Ch. 14); PCI, alloantigen specific for plasma cells in mice.

Lymphoid Organs

Lymphoid organs show a characteristic architecture. There is a basic structure provided by a network of epithelial or reticular cells and their products. A vascular network is superimposed. Ultimately, lymphoid and phagocytic cells occupy the spaces defined by the two networks.

Central Lymphoid Organs

The central lymphoid organs have a basic structure provided by mats of epithelial cells. The bursa of Fabricius of birds develops from an epithelial outpouching of the proctodeal plate located dorsally in the cloaca, near the posterior end of the intestinal tract. The thymus anlage arises from the third and fourth branchial cleft. Precommitted stem cells (*pre-B* and *pre-T* cells) migrate into the thymus or bursa anlage. The microenvironment provided by the epithelial thymus seems essential for the maturation of lymphoid cells.

The thymus consists of a cortex and a medulla. The cortex is subdivided into lobules by connective tissue, forming septa. These septa are contiguous with the connective tissue enveloping the thymus as its capsule. In light microscopy the cortex is discernible as an area densely populated by small lymphocytes. A few macrophages may also be seen. The medulla consists of more loosely assembled lymphocytes, and special structures — Hassall's corpuscles — are seen. They consist of several layers of flattened cells, presenting an onion-peel pattern. Most lymphocytes of the thymus die in it and thus never leave this organ. Other lymphocytes mature in the cortex, pass through the medulla, and reach the lymph vessels and blood; the major efferent pathway for thymus lymphocyte is the ductus thoracicus. In addition to its function as the primary lymphoid organ providing the site for maturation of lymphocytes, the thymus is also an endocrine organ, secreting hormonelike factors essential for the extrathymic maturation of thymocytes. Various preparations of these factors have been characterized — thymosin, thymic humoral factor, thymopoietin, and serum thymic factor. Their relationship to each other is not yet fully understood.

Peripheral Lymphoid Organs

Peripheral or secondary lymphoid organs have a basic network of reticular cells and fibers. A reticular network, the vasculature, and lymphoid cells are the architectural elements of the lymph node (Fig. 9.4). B cells populate the lymph follicles and the medullary cords. T cells lodge predominantly in the deep cortex (formerly called the "paracortical" areas). Thus B and T cells preferentially home to distinct, well defined areas of the peripheral lymphoid organs.

Tonsils contain accumulations of lymphocytes and lymphoid follicles. They are located between the columns of the soft palate, at the back of the ventral tongue next to the eustachian tubes and on the posterior wall of the pharynx. All ingested food and inhaled air has to make contact with the tonsils. Peyer's patches, localized in the ileum, are rich in lymphoid follicles, most of which contain germinal centers (see below).

The spleen is enveloped in a capsule, consisting, in man, mainly of connective tissue. The connective tissue continues into the organ as trabecules. Again, a reticular network of cells and fibers forms the basis of this organ's architecture. The vasculature shows a complex arrangement: blood enters the spleen via the splenic artery, trabecular arteries, and medullary arteries, and it passes through the white pulp in "central" and "penicilliary" arteries. The white pulp consists of follicles rich in B cells and of periarteriolar sheaths abounding in T cells. The blood then passes into the sinuses of the red pulp. These sinuses have

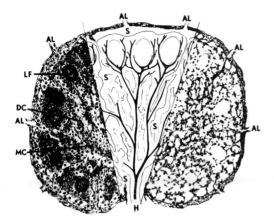

Fig. 9.4. Three views of a lymph node. AL, afferent lymph vessel; DC, deep cortical, region; LF, lymph follicles; MC, medullary cord; S, sinus. On the right the reticulum of the node is depicted — the reticular cells in nucleated outline and the fibers in stipple. Afferent lymphatics penetrate the capsule emptying into the subcapsular sinus. This sinus is virtually coextensive with the capsule and is crisscrossed by reticular fibers. Trabeculae interrupt it at several places. Radial sinuses, also crisscrossed, run from the subcapsular sinus irregularly toward the hilus, where they converge into large efferent vessels. The reticular meshwork is specialized to form the follicles and perifollicular zones of the cortex, the deep cortical zone, and the medullary cords. In the central panel, the distribution of veins is shown, closely drawn after the work and illustrations of Guy Sainte-Marie. Note how postcapillary venules, the terminal twigs, originate about the cortical follicles as well as deep in the follicles. In the left panel, the arrangement of the reticulum together with the lymphocytes and other free cells is presented. The reticulum becomes masked by the crowds of lymphocytes. Nodules are present in the cortex, many of them containing germinal centers. Note that where sinuses become crowded with lymphocytes, the line of demarcation between the sinus and contiguous tissue is not clear. The endothelium of the sinuses is incomplete on that aspect of the vessels that abut lymphatic masses. (Weiss, L.: The Cells and Tissues of the Immune System. Structure, Functions, Interactions. Reprinted by permission of Prentice-Hall, Englewood Cliffs, N.J., 1972.)

an interrupted basement membrane and are surrounded by Billroth's cords. Finally, the blood passes through the veins of the spleen and leaves the organ via the splenic vein. The complex architecture of the vasculature allows for fine regulation of the amount of blood present at a given time in the various structures of the spleen. The broad sinuses, with a sluggish blood flow, make intensive interaction among various blood elements and cells of Billroth's cords possible. The spleen is a peripheral lymphoid organ but also performs other functions, for example, elimination of effete erythrocytes.

Lymphoid Follicles and Germinal Centers

Lymphoid follicles are sites of antigen recognition. The marginal zone of the follicles is highly vascularized, ensuring optimal distribution of circulating antigen and blood cells. In the follicle, cells with long, reticular pseudopods seem to enrich the antigen on their surface membranes. The preponderant lymphocyte of lymphoid follicles is the B cell. After sensitization of lymphoid cells by antigens, the cells in the center of the follicle are transformed into lymphoblasts and the lymphoid follicle develops into a *germinal center*.

Circulation and Recirculation of Lymphocytes

The lymphoid cells migrate from primary lymphoid organs into the periphery, lodge in various secondary lymphoid organs, and then may resume their wanderings, reaching other secondary lymphoid organs, remaining for some time in the lymph or bloodstream, and possibly returning to the primary lymphoid organ. The exchange of lymphoid cells between the vasculature and tissues occurs most intensely across the walls of postcapillary venules.

Distribution of Lymphoid Tissue in the Body

Secondary lymphoid organs and diffuse lymphoid tissue are placed strategically at points of maximum danger for the host. They are found along potential routes of microbial invasion throughout the body. In the oropharynx, they are present in the tonsils. As mentioned above, diffuse lymphoid tissue occurs along the whole gastrointestinal tract, accentuated in the ileum. The respiratory tract, especially in its upper portion, is richly endowed with lymphoid tissue. Lymph nodes are placed at convenient sites along the drainage path of lymph in such a way that the draining lymph has to pass through a number of hierarchically organized lymph nodes, ensuring optimal filtration. Antigens introduced into the blood are brought in contact with lymphoid cells in the spleen. In lymphoid tissue, lymphocytes are provided with the optimal conditions to engage in immune response.

FUNCTIONAL ORGANIZATION OF THE IMMUNE RESPONSE

As mentioned before and with some oversimplification, the immune response may be envisaged as functioning in three phases. There is an afferent phase, a central regulatory phase leading to production of effectors of immunologic reactivity, and an efferent phase.

Histocompatibility antigens (see Ch. 14) predominantly on lymphocytes and macrophages and their recognition by other lymphocytes greatly influence cell interactions occurring in the course of the afferent, regulatory, and efferent phases of the immune response (*major histocompatibility complex [MHC] restriction*).

Afferent Phase: Antigen Recognition

The immune system interacts with components of its environment by means of specific structures on its effectors, that is, on antibody molecules or lymphocytes, which are capable of recognizing surface properties of antigenic moieties. Such structures are termed *combining sites* when they occur on antibodies (Ch. 10) and *receptors* when they are present on cells. Antigen receptors on lymphocytes are essential in the initiation of any response of the immune system, be it in the induction of enhanced production of immune effectors or in the shut down of its activities (induction of specific unresponsiveness or tolerance). Antigen recognition, that is, the interaction of cells with specific antigens, is a property of both B and T cells.

Interaction of antigen with a specific receptor on B or T cells leads to changes in the cell membrane. Secondary messengers transmit the stimuli to the cytoplasm and nucleus. In the sensitized cell, DNA, RNA, and protein synthesis increase, and the activated cell shows increased euchromatin in the nucleus and the presence of more cell organelles in the cytoplasms. This transformed cell, frequently called an *immunoblast*, may undergo proliferation. Out of one cell triggered by an interaction with antigen, a *clone* of many cells producing identical immune effectors emerges.

Stimulation of B cells by the majority of antigens requires cooperation with T cells (helper T cells). Such antigens are called *T cell dependent*. Only a few antigens, predominantly molecules with many repetitive epitopes (e.g., polymerized flagellin but not monomeric flagellin), may trigger B cells without the help of T cells. The teamwork among lymphocytes during the phase of antigen recognition (called *cell cooperation*) also involves cells from the monocyte-macrophage series. The latter cells, however, do not recognize specific antigens and thus lack the immunologic specificity characterizing lymphocytes. They may function in cell cooperation either by cell membrane-associated phenomena or by processing antigens in their cytoplasm. Pure T cell responses as well as most B cell responses appear to depend on interaction with cells from the monocyte-macrophage series. The antigen-presenting monocyte-macrophage is a radiation-resistant cell with no surface immunoglobulins or T cell-associated markers. However, it has Ia antigens on its membrane (Ch. 14). It seems that in mice, cells collaborating in antigen recognition have to share the same histocompatibility antigens coded for by the *I* genes. The T cell can enter collaboration only if it recognizes the self Ia on the cells simultaneously with the specific antigen to which it is being sensitized (MHC restriction).

Antigen receptors on B cells are immunoglobulins. T cell receptors seem to contain antigen binding sites similar to those found on B cells. Their structure, however, is still not defined. T cells may cooperate with B cells by presenting the antigen to B cells in optimum density and form. They may shed antigen-receptor complexes, which may accumulate on macrophages and then may interact with B cells. Alternatively, they may produce antigen-specific substances or nonspecific lymphokines, which may be required for efficient stimulation of B cells (Fig. 9.5).

Regulatory Events

The extent and scope of immune responsiveness to a specific antigen is constantly controlled and adjusted to the needs of the organism. Regulation occurs in the framework of cell to cell interactions or reactions of cells with soluble factors. Best understood is the influence of helper (or amplifier), suppressor, and regulatory cells of the T cell series on B cell-mediated responses. T cells, characterized by distinct surface properties, perform helper (or amplifier), suppressor, and regulatory functions (Table 9.2). Recently, complex T cell activities regulating antibody production in the mouse have been described. These cells form a *T cell network*, which consists of

feedback mechanisms and amplification and suppression loops.

Antibodies themselves may have a regulatory role. Thus antibodies combined with antigen may interact with B cells and lead to a shutdown of antibody production. Furthermore, idiotype — antiidiotype networks (Ch. 8) may modulate production of antibodies and of effector lymphocytes.

Efferent Limb: Effector Mechanisms

There are two categories of immune effectors — immunoglobulins (i.e., soluble proteins) (Ch. 10) or sensitized lymphocytes. The immunoglobulins mediate reactions of humoral immunity, for example, direct neutralization or lysis of antigenic targets by antibodies with or without the participation of complement. Once sensitization of the organism has been accomplished and antibody is available, antibody-mediated reactions occur immediately upon reinjection of antigen. Humoral immunity therefore is also responsible for immediate-type hypersensitivity (Ch. 12).

Sensitized lymphocytes interact with antigens and may directly induce damage to structures containing the antigen (e.g., lysis of virus-infected cells) or may produce antigen-nonspecific soluble moieties — the lymphokines (Ch. 13), which act on other lymphoid, inflammatory, or tissue cells. These cell-mediated immune mechanisms are discussed in Chapter 13.

It is now well established for some infections with viruses and intracellular bacteria that the immune effectors, T cells, have to recognize antigens of self present on the surface of the infected cell. These antigens are encoded by genes of the MHC. In the mouse these antigens are encoded by the *D* and *K* regions of the MHC (Ch. 14). It was by this phenomenon that the term MHC restriction was first used.

The immune effectors may recruit a number of inflammatory mediators. These mediators contribute to the degradation of

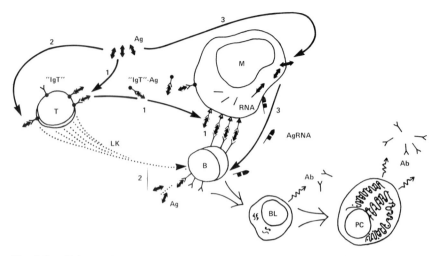

Fig. 9.5. Schematic representation of three hypotheses advanced to describe cell cooperation. Ab, antibody; Ag, antigen; "IgT", T cell receptor for antigen; L, lymphokines; BL, B lymphoblast; PC, plasma cell; T, T cells; B, B cells; M, macrophages. 1. Antigen interacts with antigen receptors on a T cell [this receptor has sometimes been named immunoglobulin T (IgT)]. Complexes of antigen and antigen receptor are liberated from the surface of the T cell and accumulate on the surface of macrophages. This high local density of antigenic determinants enables B cells to recognize the antigen and to become sensitized. 2. Antigen interacts with antigen receptors on the surface of a T cell. This interaction stimulates the T cell to produce lymphokines. Stimulation of a B cell by both lymphokines and the antigen leads to sensitization. 3. Antigen is ingested by a macrophage. It is modified in the cytoplasm of macrophages, possibly coupled to RNA (formation of "immune RNA"), and this complex containing antigen is set free into the cell's environment. Upon interaction of the processed antigen with B cell membrane, sensitization occurs. Ultimately, the B cell transforms into a lymphoblast and eventually into a plasma cell. Both lymphoblast and plasma cell secrete antibody.

antigen or antigenic particles. It should be stressed that inflammatory mechanisms, even though contributing to the destruction of foreign substances invading the body, often cause tissue damage. This damage may be envisaged as a spillover effect. Thus, for example, granulocytes liberate lysosomal contents into their surroundings, degrading antigenic material of microorganisms; at the same time, however, tissue elements undergo the same enzymatic catabolic processes as the antigenic material (Ch. 15). Similarly, T cells involved in immunologic reactions against viruses destroy the cells of the tissue in which the virus resides.

COMMENT

The immune response, leading to enhanced production of immune effectors or to unresponsiveness, is a function of lymphocytes. It occurs in the compartmentalized microenvironments provided by lymphoid organs and diffuse lymphoid tissue deployed along the most likely invasion routes of the body. Complex networks of cells and soluble mediators regulate the extent and character of the immune response. Genetic determinants control many cell interactions and possibly preset the amplitude of responsiveness or unresponsiveness. This may be controlled by *immune re-*

Table 9.3. Phylogenetic Development of the Lymphoid Tissue and the Immune Response

	Invertebrates	Hagfish	Lamprey	Fishes Lower	Fishes Higher	Amphibians	Reptiles	Birds	Mammals
Lymphocytes	–	+	+	+	+	+	+	+	+
Thymus anlage	–	–	+	+	+	+	+	+	+
Rejection of transplants	?	?	+	+	+	+	+	+	+
Plasma cells	–	–	–	–	+	+	+	+	+
Bursa of Fabricius	–	–	–	–	–	–	+[a]	+	–
Antibody production:									
IgM (or analog)	–	?	+	+	+	+	+	+	+
Other	–	–	–	–	+	+	+	+	+
Spleen	–	–	+	+	+	+	+	+	+
Lymph nodes	–	–	–	–	–	–	–	–	+
Lymph follicles with germinal centers	–	–	–	–	–	–	–	+	+

[a]Only in some species.

sponse (*Ir*) genes and their products (Ch. 14). The immune system and lymphoid tissue have developed steadily during phylogenesis, allowing for more selective and effective host defense against invading microbes, prevention of acceptance of foreign cell structures, and, possibly, elimination of neoplastic cells. The steady development of the immune system (Table 9.3) suggests that immunity indeed confers biologically significant advantages for survival.

REFERENCES

Bach, J.-F., Ed.: Immunology. John Wiley & Sons, New York, 1978.

Bessis, M.: Living Blood Cells and Their Ultrastructure. Springer, New York, 1973.

Cantor, H. and Boyse, E.A.: Regulation of cellular and humoral immune responses by T cell subclasses. Cold Spring Harb. Symp. Quant. Biol. *41*: 119, 1976.

Fagraeus, A.: Antibody production in relation to the development of plasma cells. *In vivo* and *in vitro* experiments. Acta Med. Scand. *130*: 1, 1948.

Greaves, M.F., Owen, J.J.T., and Raff, M.C.: T and B Lymphocytes; Origin, Properties and Roles in Immune Response. Elsevier, Amsterdam, 1973.

Gowans, J.L.: Lymphocytes. The Harvey Lectures. *64*: 87, 1970.

Herberman, R.B. and Holden, H.T.: Natural cell-mediated immunity. Adv. Cancer Res. *27*: 305, 1977.

Jerne, N.K.: Towards a network theory of the immune system. Ann. Immunol. *125*: 373, 1974.

Klinman, N., Mosier, D.E., Scher, I., and Vitetta, E.S., Eds.: B Lymphocytes in the Immune Response. Developments in Immunology. Vol. 15. Pergamon Press, Elmsford, N.Y., 1981.

Loor, F. and Roelants, G.: B and T cells in immune recognition, John Wiley & Sons, London, 1977.

Marchalonis, J.J.: The Lymphocyte. Parts I and II. Marcel Dekker, Inc., New York, 1977.

Nowell, P.C.: Phytohemagglutinins: An initiator of mitosis in cultures of normal human leucocytes. Cancer Res. *20*: 462, 1960.

Park, B.H. and Good, R.A.: Principles of Modern Immunology. Lea & Febiger, Philadelphia, 1973.

Rodkey, L.S.: Autoregulation of the Immune Response. In Waters, H., Ed.: Handbook of Cancer Immunology. Vol. 9. Garland STPM Press, New York, 1981.

Weiss, L.: The Cells and Tissues of the Immune System. Prentice Hall, Englewood Cliffs, N.J., 1972.

10

Antigens and Antibodies

Carel J. van Oss

ANTIGENS

Antigens are compounds that, when injected or otherwise introduced into a host, elicit the formation of antibodies that react specifically with them.

In general, for a compound to be an antigen it has to be foreign to the host into which it is introduced. Antigens are generally rather high molecular weight compounds with a molecular weight of at least 1000 and generally more than 10,000. Proteins, polysaccharides, glycoproteins, lipoproteins, nucleoproteins, lipopolysaccharides, and teichoic acids can all be antigens. Antigens can also be part of the surfaces of particles or cells. Cells may carry many different antigenic aspects on their surfaces; they can also carry the same antigenic aspects many times repeated on their surfaces. These different antigenic aspects are referred to as *antigenic determinants.* When they are polypeptides, antigenic determinants are generally the size of penta-hexa-, or heptapeptides; if they are polysaccharides, they are in the size range of penta-, hexa-, or heptasaccharides. The total surface area of one antigenic determinant varies between 300 to 500 $Å^2$.

The three-dimensional configuration of an antigen is of great importance for the general antigenicity of the molecule or antigenic determinant. The most immunodominant antigenic determinants are those that contribute principally to the binding between antigen and antibody. Those parts of an antigenic molecule that find themselves most exterior and most easily accessible to interaction with antibody molecules are the most immunodominant ones. Within antigenic determinants the presence of aromatic amino acids, such as tyrosine and tryptophane, is especially likely to make them immunodominant, and polypeptides of mixed composition tend to be more immunodominant than polypeptides that contain repeating polymers of the same amino acids. In branched and linear polysaccharides, the terminal nonreducing sugar is immunodominant, as are the peptide groups from prominent bends and corners in the tertiary structure of polypeptide chains, and also the carboxy terminal ends. Strongly negatively charged antigens tend to give rise to positively charged antibodies, and strongly positively charged antigens tend to give rise to negatively charged antibodies.

There is also a class of low molecular weight compounds that, although unable to elicit formation of specific antibodies, nevertheless can bind specifically with anti-bodies once such antibodies are formed against them by an artifice. Such small molecules, called *haptens*, may elicit antibody formation when attached to a carrier molecule of large molecular weight, or to a particle. Not only isolated antigenic groups that occur naturally on various biopolymers can be haptens; so can many low molecular weight synthetic organic chemicals, especially aromatic organic compounds.

ANTIBODIES

All antibodies are immunoglobulins, which are serum globulins of slow electrophoretic mobilities; that is, they are in the range of the β- and especially the γ-globulins.

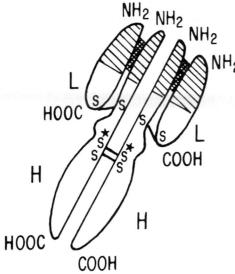

Fig. 10.1. Diagram of human IgG. Two H chains are connected to one another with two disulfide bonds. Each L chain is connected to an H chain with one disulfide bond. The amino and carboxy terminal ends are indicated. The variable (V) parts are drawn hatched. The two antibody active sites are situated near the amino terminal ends and are drawn cross hatched. * indicates the site of the hinge region. (Milgrom, F., Abeyounis, C.J., and Kano, K. Eds.: Principles of Immunologic-al Diagnosis in Medicine. Lea & Febiger, Philadelphia, 1981.)

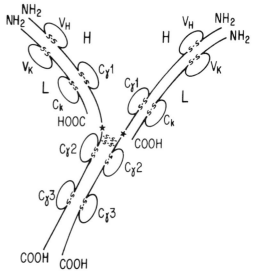

Fig. 10.2. Diagram of the domains of the tetrapolypeptide IgG1, with L chains. The interchain and the intrachain disulfide bonds are shown; the loops formed by the latter are the domains. * indicates the site of the hinge region. IgG and IgA H chains each have four domains; IgM, IgD, and IgE H chains have five domains. (Milgrom, F., Abeyounis, C.J., and Kano, K., Eds.: Principles of Immunological Diagnosis in Medicine. Lea & Febiger, Philadelphia, 1981.)

All immunoglobulins have basically the same fundamental structure or are polymers of this fundamental structure. They consist of four polypeptide chains — two identical heavy chains each with a molecular weight ranging between 50,000 to 70,000, and two light chains each with a molecular weight of 23,000 (Fig. 10.1).

The four chains are arranged in such a manner that their amino terminal ends are all at the same end of the complete molecule. That is the end where the two identical antibody active sites are situated. That is also the end of each of the four chains where the amino acid composition is extremely variable. The carboxy terminal ends of the four immunoglobulin chains have a more constant amino acid composition. Each polypeptide chain consists of a

Table 10.1. Various Properties of Human Immunoglobulins

	IgG	IgA	IgM	IgD	IgE
Normal adult serum concentration (per dl)	1.0–1.4	0.2–0.3	0.4–0.15	0.003	10^{-3}–10^{-4} (average ≈ 10^{-4})
Distribution	Intravascular and extracellular fluid	Intravascular and internal secretions	Mainly intravascular	Mainly intravascular	Intravascular and skin, respiratory and GI tracts
Molecular weight	150,000	155,000 (395,000 for sIgA)	900,000	185,000	187,000
Molecular weight of the H chains (MW of the L chains ≈ 23,000)	53,000	55,000	65,000	70,000	71,000
Nomenclature of H chains	γ	α	μ	δ	ε
Molecular formula	$\gamma_2\kappa_2$, $\gamma_2\lambda_2$	$\alpha_2\kappa_2$, $\alpha_2\lambda_2$	$\mu_{10}\kappa_{10}J$, $\mu_{10}\lambda_{10}J$	$\delta_2\kappa_2$, $\delta_2\lambda_2$	$\varepsilon_2\kappa_2$, $\varepsilon_2\lambda_2$
Valency	2	2 (monomer)	10	2	2
Normal κ/λ chain ratio	2/1	5/4	3/1	1/6	—
H chain subclasses	IgG1, IgG2, IgG3, IgG4	IgA1, IgA2,	IgM1, IgM2	Ja, La	—
Approximate occurrence of the H chain subclasses (%)	75, 15, 7, 3	93, 7	—	85, 15	—
Number of domains per H chain	4	4	5	5	5
Allotypes (all immunoglobulins with κL chains have InV = Km allotypes)	Gm	Am	Mm	—	—
Carbohydrate (%)	2.9	5–10	12	13	12
Synthetic rate (g/day/70 kg)	2.3	1.7	0.1	0.03	2×10^{-4}
Half-life (days)	23	6	5	3	
Complement binding (via the classical pathway)	+	–	+	–	–
Involvement in opsonization	+	–	+[a]	–	–
Placental transport	+	–	–	–	–
Other important biological properties	Major Ig in antimicrobial defense; Ig with strongest precipitating capacity	Major Ig (in secretions) in antiviral defense	Major Ig produced in the primary response; Ig with strongest agglutinating capacity	Present on the surface of B lymphocytes of the newborn	Involved in atopic allergy; increased in parasitic infections

[a]In the presence of complement only.

(Reprinted with permission from van Oss, C.J.: General physical and chemical and biological properties of the human immunoglobulin. In Greenwalt, T.J. and Steane, E.A., Eds.: Blood Banking, Vol. II CRC Handbook Series in Clinical Laboratory Science, Cleveland, CRC Press, 1980, Copyright, The Chemical Rubber Co., CRC Press, Inc.

number of globular domains, or homology units, each comprising 100 to 120 amino acids. These domains are loops that are held together by a disulfide bond, and when single domains are isolated only homologous domains tend to interact with one another.

The heavy chains of two of the major immunoglobulins, IgG and IgA, consist of one variable and three constant domains. In IgG the complement binding site is on $C\gamma2$, as is the carbohydrate component. The $C\gamma3$ domain comprises the site that attaches to phagocytic cells (Fig 10.2); IgM, IgD, and IgE have four constant domains. In each individual Ig molecule, the two heavy chains are completely identical to one another; the two light chains are also identical to each other.

There are five human immunoglobulin classes, the salient properties of which can be found in Table 10.1. Human immunoglobulins of all five classes (IgG, IgA, IgM, IgD, and IgE) have the same light chains in common, which can be of only two possible types — κ or λ light chains. Any given individual immunoglobulin molecule of any of these classes must have light chains that are either of the κ or the λ variety. The difference between the immunoglobulin classes is reposed entirely in the heavy chains. They are named by the Greek letter corresponding to the Roman letter of the immunoglobulin class: the heavy chains of IgG are γ chains; of IgA, α chains; of IgM, μ chains; of IgD, δ chains; and of IgE, ε chains. Most immunoglobulin classes have known subclasses; IgG has four subclasses, named IgG1, IgG2, IgG3, and IgG4. IgA, IgM, and IgD each have two subclasses. The heavy chains carry the allotypic determinants called, in the case of IgG, Gm markers, in the case of IgA, Am markers, and in the case of IgM, Mm markers. The allotypes or κ light chains are termed Km (Ch. 14). No allotypes of λ chains are known.

IgG is the most abundant human immunoglobulin; it is also the only immuno-globulin that can pass the placental barrier. Together with IgM it is one of the two immunoglobulins that fix complement according to the classical pathway, and it is the major immunoglobulin that, in the aggregated form or following the alteration suffered in reaction with its antigen, can bind rheumatoid factor. IgG is the only immunoglobulin that can by itself, in the absence of complement, facilitate phagocytosis. It plays a major role in the defense against bacterial infection. IgG-type antibodies tend to be formed particularly in the secondary immune or anamnestic response. IgG antibodies are the most effective immunoglobulins in precipitation. IgG1, IgG2, and IgG3 fix complement. (IgG3 fixes complement with particular strength.) Different allotypes (Gm markers) are associated with the different IgG heavy chain subclasses (Ch. 14).

In serum IgA occurs mainly in the divalent monomeric form. It does not fix complement by the classical pathway, and it has no opsonizing power. IgA is the principal

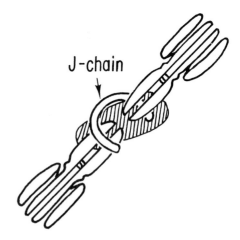

J-chain

Fig. 10.3. Diagram of sIgA; the J chain is indicated, and the T component is drawn hatched. (Milgrom, F., Abeyounis, C.J., and Kano, K. Eds.: Principles of Immunological Diagnosis in Medicine. Lea & Febiger, Philadelphia, 1981.)

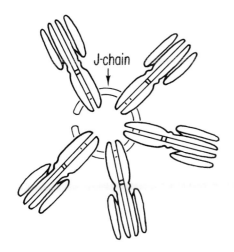

J-chain

Fig. 10.4 Diagram of IgM; the J chain is indicated; the pentameric form and dekavalency are clearly shown. (Milgrom, F., Abeyounis, C.J., and Kano, K., Eds.: Principles of Immunological Diagnosis in Medicine. Lea & Febiger, Philadelphia, 1981.)

secretory immunoglobulin, and in that guise it occurs in saliva, colostrum, and tears, as well as in nasal, intestinal, bronchial, and other secretions. As secretory IgA (sIgA) it occurs in the dimeric form and is then tetravalent. The two monomeric units are joined together via disulfide bonds with the help of a polypeptide called a J chain. Secretory IgA also has a secretory piece or transport component, which seems to serve the purpose of helping it to be secreted (Fig. 10.3). In a small proportion IgA also occurs as a dimer in the blood circulation. In this case it does not contain the secretory component, but the two monomers in the dimer are bound together by a J chain. IgA, in the guise of sIgA, plays a major role in the defense against viral infections in the upper respiratory and lower digestive tracts.

IgM is a pentamer of the fundamental immunoglobulin tetrapeptide depicted in Figure 10.1. It is basically shaped like a starfish (Fig. 10.4). The five monomers, exactly as is the case with dimeric IgA and

with sIgA, are linked covalently, aided by a J chain. IgM fixes complement via the classical pathway and in that manner is capable of opsonizing, thereby facilitating phagocytosis. IgM tends to be the first major antibody formed after each normal antigenic stimulus, that is, it is the principal antibody of the primary immune response. Significant IgM levels in the newborn are an important indication of congenital or perinatal infection. IgM is the most effective type of antibody in agglutination.

IgD is divalent and occurs in rather low concentration in serum. It occurs on the surface in a high proportion of B lymphocytes in the blood of newborn babies. IgD appears to play a special role in the primary antibody response; no role has as yet been found for it in the anamnestic antibody response.

IgE is the immunoglobulin that occurs in the lowest concentration in human serum; serum IgE mainly encompasses the "reaginic" antibodies and plays a role in atopic allergies, such as asthma and hayfever. IgE antibodies are homocytotropic, that is, they bind to the host's own cells, such as mast cells and basophilic granulocytes. When IgE is bound to such cells, the reaction of allergens with it induces the cells to release mediators, such as histamine, that trigger the allergic symptoms. In allergic individuals IgE levels may be increased to ten or more times the level found in normal subjects; those levels nevertheless are still extremely low. It is likely that the original biologic function of IgE is the defense against parasitic infections. IgE is divalent; its capacity to bind to mast cells and basophils disappears upon heating to 56°C.

Low molecular weight immunoglobulin fragments usually occur in very low concentrations in normal serum and also find their way into normal urine. In about 16 percent of monoclonal hypergammaglobulinemias, immunoglobulin fragments may be produced in fairly large quantities. Since their molecular weight is rather low, they are found in the urine. Particularly common in such cases are dimers of L chains, called *Bence Jones protein*. Much less common are the fragments of γ, α, or μ chains, which may be excreted in cases of heavy chain disease.

ANTIGEN–ANTIBODY BONDS

The bonds resulting from the specific interaction between antigens and antibodies are noncovalent bonds. They belong to the class of the weak or physical bonds and consist essentially of two different types: dispersion or van der Waals–London forces, and electrostatic or coulombic forces. Of the other weak physical interactions, hydrogen bonds play a fairly small role, if any, in antigen–antibody interactions. Van der Waals–London interactions occur between all atoms, molecules, and particles when they are brought closely enough together. They are caused by the universally occurring fluctuations of charge due to the never-ceasing movement of the electrons in opposing atoms or molecules; temporary dipoles in one atom induce dipoles in opposing atoms and these then attract each other. Van der Waals–London forces are, to a significant degree, additive, that is, the attractive forces increase up to a point, with increasing size of the molecules or particles that are brought close together. Antigenic determinants and antibody active sites, when reacting together, generally can come to within only a few Angströms of one another. Thus van der Waals–London interactions occur when the attraction is solely of the van der Waals–London type, as well as when antigenic determinants and antibody active sites are brought together by means of a pattern of electrostatically oppositely charged sites, in which case there often is a van der Waals–London attraction in addition to the electrostatic attraction.

Electrostatic or coulombic bonds are caused by the attraction between opposed

negatively and positively charged groups on an antigenic determinant and an antibody active site. In most cases electrostatic bonds occur when the antigen is a protein; the antibody, of course, is always a protein. As in the case of van der Waals–London forces, electrostatic interactions are also strongest when the oppositely charged sites are brought close together.

In aqueous media hydrophobic aspects of the antigenic determinant, as well as of the antibody active site, tend to be attracted to one another owing to a mutual van der Waals–London interaction. Upon such an interaction, fairly organized water of hydration that before the interaction covered both the antigenic determinant and the antibody active site is now repelled as randomly oriented water molecules in the bulk liquid. This *hydrophobic effect* is not a special type of weak chemical bond. The main effect of the randomization of water molecules after completion of binding between the two hydrophobic aspects is a major cause of the increase in entropy that often accompanies antigen–antibody interactions.

The strength of antigen–antibody interactions can be measured by determination of the equilibrium constant K. This is done by evaluating the amounts of free and bound antigen and antibody after equilibrium has been reached. In different antigen–antibody systems K can vary rather widely, from 10^3 to 10^{10} liters per mole. The standard free energy change $\triangle F^0$, can also be derived from K through the equation

$$\triangle F^0 = -RT \ \ln K$$

(where R is the gas constant and T the absolute temperature in degrees Kelvin). $\triangle F^0$ varies from -4 to about -12 kCal/mole.

For the dissociation of antigen–antibody bonds, first the van der Waals–London interaction, which is always present, has to be neutralized. This can be done by lowering the surface tension of the aqueous medium by means of the addition of ethylene glycol, dimethylsulfoxide, or propanol. The electrostatic bonds, if any, can then be dissociated by increasing the pH to about 9.5 or 10, by decreasing it to about 3.5 or 4, or by adding salts with, for example, divalent cations. Decreasing the pH to about 4 with an organic acid such as propionic acid is particularly effective because propionic acid at the same time both lowers the pH of the medium and decreases its surface tension. Antigen–antibody interactions are generally exothermal, so that heating, for instance, to about 56°C also helps to dissociate antigen–antibody bonds. Some antigen–antibody complexes may also be dissociated by the addition of an excess of hapten.

ANTIGEN–ANTIBODY INTERACTIONS IN VITRO

Precipitation

Precipitation of soluble antigen molecules with soluble antibodies is caused by the formation of large, insoluble antigen–antibody complexes. Both antigens and antibodies are plurivalent, and their combination can give rise to complexes of very widely varying antigen–antibody ratios. The composition of such complexes is dependent mainly on the starting concentrations of the antigens and antibodies taking part in the reaction. With excess antigen, as well as with excess antibody, only small and generally soluble complexes tend to form. It is only when the reaction takes place close to the optimal antigen–antibody ratio that large insoluble complexes are formed. The insolubility of these complexes is due mainly to their large size. Close to the optimal antigen–antibody ratio precipitate tends to form at the most rapid rate.

The oldest method for determining the optimal antigen–antibody ratio is by pre-

cipitation in an aqueous medium in test tubes. Nowadays, however, most antigen–antibody precipitation tests are done by various gel precipitation procedures. In double diffusion in gels, soluble antigen and antibody molecules are deposited in separate wells some distance from each other. They diffuse toward one another and, upon meeting, form a precipitate band or line that is specifically impermeable to just the antigen and antibody molecules that constitute it. The property of specific impermeability to the forming specific antibody and antigen molecules is the basis for the

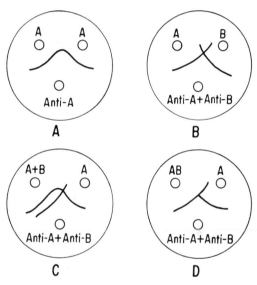

Fig. 10.5. Double diffusion precipitation in gels. A. Fusing of precipitate bands both formed by an A–anti-A system: reaction of identity. B. Crossing of precipitate bands formed by, respectively, A–anti-A and B–anti-B: reaction of nonidentity. C. Fusing of precipitate bands formed by an A–anti-A system with, in addition, crossing of the fusing bands by a band formed by a B–anti-B system. D. Same as part C, but the A and B antigenic determinants are in this case part of the same antigen molecule. The combination of fusing and crossing bands take the shape of a spur: reaction of "partial identity." (Milgrom, F., Abeyounis, C.J., and Kano, K., Eds.: Principles of Immunological Diagnosis in Medicine. Lea & Febiger, Philadelphia, 1981.)

use of these systems in distinguishing between identical and nonidentical antigen–antibody systems. When two identical antigens that diffuse from different wells interact with a specific antiserum, the two resulting precipitate bands must necessarily fuse (Fig. 10.5). However, two completely unrelated antigens that diffuse from different wells against a mixture of antisera deposited in another well form two precipitate bands that cross one another. A combination of fusing and crossing bands can also be obtained when various antigens have certain antigenic determinants in common and when one of the antigens has an additional antigenic determinant that is lacking in the other one. Situations such as that will give rise to spur-shaped precipitate bands (Fig. 10.5).

Gel double diffusion is a fairly slow process, but it can be speeded up and also made more efficient when methods are utilized to bring antigen and antibody molecules together from their different wells by force. This can be done by electrophoresis in cases in which the antigen and antibody molecules have different isoelectric points. At a pH value between the isoelectric points of the two reagents, electrophoresis will bring the two reagents together, which speeds up the precipitation process considerably. Antigen and antibody molecules can also be brought together by forced evaporation of water immediately above the space between the two, so that by capillary flow the water from the extremities of the gel forces antigen and antibody molecules to form together a precipitate band. The electrophoretic method is called *counterimmunoelectrophoresis*, and the hydrodynamic evaporation method is called *immunorheophoresis*. The latter can be used even in those cases in which there is no appreciable difference in isoelectric point between antigen and antibody molecules (as in IgG–anti-IgG systems).

Precipitate bands formed in gels by antigen and antibody molecules remain specifically impermeable only about as long as equivalent concentrations of freely dissolved antigen and antibody molecules remain present on both sides of the precipitate band. As long as that is the case, the precipitate band remains thin and stationary. However, when one of the reagents is present at a much higher than optimal concentration, it will subsequently break down the initially impermeable band and pass through it. This causes the band to become thicker or to form several bands, or it may dissolve and form again farther away from the well with the reagent that was present in the higher concentration, which gives the impression that the band has moved away in that direction. Observation of these phenomena makes it possible to determine at which concentrations optimal antigen and antibody ratios were initially present because it is at those concentrations that the band formed will remain thin and stationary. Optimal ratio determinations and quantitative titrations of antigens and antibodies are thus made possible by gel double diffusion.

Concentrations of antigens can be readily ascertained by single diffusion of the antigen into a gel incorporating a dilute solution of antibody. Upon diffusing out, the antigen forms a precipitate ring around the well, and, according to the amount of antigen still present in the starting well, this precipitate ring will grow concentrically until all the antigen has been spent. When the precipitate ring has reached its maximum size, its surface area is directly proportional to the initial antigen concentration. Thus when one plots the squares of the diameters of the precipitate rings versus the concentrations of the antigens that were initially put into the various wells, straight lines are obtained. The radial single diffusion method is widely used in clinical diagnosis of, for example, the levels of the various serum proteins (Fig. 10.6). If time is of the essence, for instance in a clinical setting, the ending of the single diffusion process,

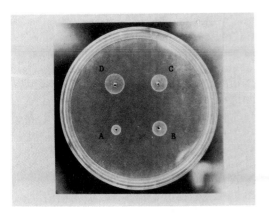

Fig. 10.6. Radial single diffusion titration (Mancini plate). The agarose in the plate contains a uniform solution of rabbit anti–human IgG (diluted 1/10). The wells contain human IgG: A. 1.25; B. 2.50; C. 3.75; and D. 5.00 mg/ml. The diffusion was allowed to continue until the precipitate discs attained their maximum size; a plot of their surface areas versus the initial concentrations yields a straight line. (Milgrom, F., Abeyounis, C.J., and Kano, K., Eds.: Principles of Immunological Diagnosis in Medicine. Lea & Febiger, Philadelphia, 1981.)

When zone electrophoresis in gels is followed by double diffusion precipitation in a direction perpendicular to the direction of electrophoresis, the result is the extremely powerful technique called *immunoelectrophoresis*. With this method antigen mixtures, such as the proteins of whole serum, are first separated by zone electrophoresis in a gel. Upon completion of the electrophoretic separation an antiserum to the antigens of the first serum is allowed to diffuse from a trough parallel to the original path of electrophoresis. Different antigens that are overlapping in zone electrophoresis give rise to crossing precipitation lines (Fig. 10.5), so that they become distinguishable from one another (Fig. 10.8). Immunoelectrophoresis is of great importance in research as well as in clinical diagnosis, especially in the diagnosis of serum protein and particularly of immunoglobulin abnor-

which normally may take 1 day or more to reach completion, may be anticipated by taking readings after exactly 16 hours (overnight) and by plotting the diameters of the antigen–antibody precipitate rings versus the logarithms of the antigen concentrations. The single diffusion process may also be speeded up by depositing the antigen, as mentioned previously, in wells in antibody-containing gel and by then electrophoresing the antigen into the gel, which produces rocket-shaped precipitates. When this process has been allowed to come to full completion, the surface area under the precipitate rocket will also be proportional to the amount of antigen initially deposited in the well; or, as a rough first approximation, instead of the surface area, the height of the rocket may be taken to be proportional to the amount of antigen (Fig. 10.7).

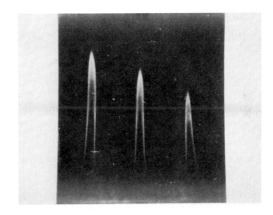

Fig. 10.7. Unidimensional electrophoresis of serum albumin into an agarose gel containing a uniform solution of rabbit anti–serum albumin (diluted 1/25). The wells contain albumin from left to right in concentrations of 2.0, 1.5, and 1.0 mg/ml. After the "rockets" reached their maximum size, the electrophoresis was stopped. The surface areas of the rockets are proportional to the initial concentrations of albumin. (Milgrom, F., Abeyounis, C.J., and Kano, K., Eds.: Principles of Immunological Diagnosis in Medicine. Lea & Febiger, Philadelphia, 1981.)

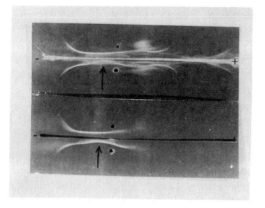

Fig. 10.8. Photograph of an immunoelectropherogram of a normal human serum (top well) and of a serum from a patient with a monoclonal (IgG-type) "spike" (bottom well), developed with rabbit anti–whole human serum (top slide) and with rabbit anti–human IgG (bottom slide). The sharp dip (see arrow) in the precipitate line formed with the patients' IgG is typical for such monoclonal abnormalities. (Milgrom, F., Abeyounis, C.J., and Kano, K., Eds.: Principles of Immunological Diagnosis in Medicine. Lea & Febiger, Philadelphia, 1981.)

malties. Monoclonal immunoglobulin components are clearly distinguishable in immunoelectrophorograms because of the sharpness of the curvature of the precipitate bands that are formed with monoclonal homogeneous immunoglobulin. Polyclonal immunoglobulins (particularly IgG) form long, only slightly curved precipitate bands (Fig. 10.8).

Agglutination

In contradistinction to precipitation, which is the formation of insoluble particles due to the reaction of dissolved antigen with dissolved antibody molecules, agglutination is caused by the crosslinking of preexisting antigenic particles by means of the interaction with dissolved antibody molecules to form networks of much larger particles, or agglutinates. Agglutinated clumps can be visualized on glass slides either with the naked eye or with the microscope. When suspended in tubes, agglutinates can be easily discerned by their increased sedimentation velocity or by the pattern formed by the sedimented clumps on the bottom of test tubes, which in the case of agglutinates take up a large surface area and frequently form rings, whereas nonagglutinated particles or cells form small buttons at the bottom of the tubes. Erythrocytes and bacteria are often studied by means of agglutination. Inert particles such as bentonite or polystyrene latex particles, to which various antigens may be attached, are frequently used in agglutination tests.

Hemagglutination is the agglutination of erythrocytes by means of antibodies directed to various antigenic determinants on the erythrocytic surface. Blood group determinations are done mainly in this manner. The IgM antibodies are most suited for hemagglutination. They have ten antibody active sites, which are always positioned in such a manner that some of the sites are diametrically opposed to each other at a distance of about 350 Å. The total distance between the two antibody active sites on IgG class antibodies is no more than about 150 Å. With only two valencies and with a much smaller total reach distance, in many cases IgG class antibodies are incapable of crosslinking erythrocytes without further assistance. By various means, however, all of which temporarily tend to bring erythrocytes more closely together, hemagglutination with IgG class antibodies can be achieved. Among the various methods used for bringing erythrocytes closer together so that IgG molecules can crosslink them are adding high concentrations of macromolecules, treatment of the erythrocytes with proteolytic enzymes, centrifugation, lowering of the ionic strength, addition of basic polymers, and extending the size and doubling the valency of IgG by means of anti-IgG or *Coombs antibodies*.

Certain viruses can agglutinate erythrocytes of various species. One can demonstrate the presence of antibodies against such viruses by inhibition of agglutination. Erythrocytes can be agglutinated not only by antibodies specific for antigens that are part of the erythrocytic surface but also by antibodies to soluble and unrelated antigens that have been artificially attached onto the surface of erythrocytes. When this takes place, the method is called *passive hemagglutination*. Polysaccharide antigens easily adsorb spontaneously onto erythrocytes. For the adsorption of protein antigens, however, erythrocytes must first undergo some treatment, for example, with tannic acid.

Bacterial agglutination is one of the oldest methods for demonstrating the presence of antibacterial antibodies in the serum of patients. Some bacterial agglutination tests are still important for the demonstration of bacterial disease. An example of this is the Widal test for antibodies to typhoid bacilli.

Various inert particles, such as polystyrene latex particles, are often used in passive agglutination. The latex test with particles coated with human IgG is used to demonstrate the presence of rheumatoid factor. Inhibition of latex particle agglutination is used in pregnancy tests; latex particles that are coated with chorionic gonadotropin are normally agglutinated by antiserum to gonadotropic hormone but become nonagglutinatable if the antiserum has first been inhibited by pregnancy urine. Agglutination tests are also used to determine the presence of, for example, C-reactive protein, antithyroglobulin antibodies, and antistreptolysin antibodies.

The presence of antigens on various cell types may be demonstrated with the help of erythrocytes that are themselves also coated with antibody molecules and antiimmunoglobulin antibodies that can crosslink both sensitized cell types. Visual or microscopic inspection is generally sufficient to determine whether or not *mixed agglutination*, as this technique is called, has occurred. The technique is also frequently used with monolayer cell cultures. Also increasingly used are erythrocytes and other particles coupled to specific antibody molecules directed to antigenic determinants on various cells. The presence of such antigenic determinants is visualized by rosette formation.

Soluble Antigen–Antibody Complexes

Under a variety of conditions and especially when either antigen or antibody is present in considerable excess as compared to the optimal proportions, antigens and antibodies will not precipitate upon interaction, but instead will form soluble complexes. Such soluble complexes can be characterized in the dissolved state by techniques such as analytical ultracentrifugation, electrophoresis, or gel filtration. Antigen–antibody complexes can also be precipitated by the addition of, for example, ammonium sulfate or polyethylene glycol (MW $\approx$ 6000) solutions at concentrations in which the complexes will precipitate while unreacted antigen and/or antibody molecules remain in solution.

Use of Labeled Antibodies or Antigens

There are diverse methods for visualizing and/or qualitatively or quantitatively characterizing antigen–antibody interactions with the help of labeled antibody or antigen molecules. Such methods include tagging with fluorescent molecules (for immunofluorescence microscopy), enzymes (for immunoenzyme microscopy or electronmicroscopy, immunoenzyme electrophoresis, or enzyme-linked immunosorbent assay), and radioisotopes (for various radioimmunoassays).

Immunofluorescence is used in many diagnostic tests, such as the characterization of pathogenic microorganisms in samples, the detection of antinuclear antibodies in lupus erythematosus, and the demonstration of immune complexes in kidney tissue. Generally, the IgG antibodies used are conjugated to fluorescein isothiocyanate;

when illuminated with ultraviolet or with blue light, such conjugated antibodies will emit green light, thus visually revealing the antigen or cell to which they are bound.

Enzymes bound to antibody molecules are used in many ways to reveal antigen–antibody interactions. Specific color reactions (brought about, for example, by the substrate diaminobenzidine, which turns brown after reacting with peroxidase) allow the visualization of antigen–antibody complexes by light and electron microscopy and even by immunoelectrophoresis. Enzyme-linked antibodies can also be used to characterize antigens that have been adsorbed to solid carriers, such as plastic or glass beads, plastic plates, or test tubes. This technique, called *enzyme-linked immunosorbent assay* (ELISA), is used for the detection of antigens of many kinds of microorganisms, for the determination of various hormones, for the characterization of tumor-associated antigens, and for the demonstration of autoantibodies.

Radioimmunoassay has become an extremely versatile method for detecting antigens. In this method antigens labeled with radioactive isotopes are used most often. Addition of given amounts of unlabeled antigen to an antigen–antibody complex (containing radioactive antigen) will replace radioactive antigen with nonradioactive antigen in the complex, which can be precipitated. The decrease in the radioactivity of the precipitate is thus a function of the amount of nonlabeled antigen added. Radioimmunoassay is used in the quantitative analysis of most hormones and vitamins, many drugs, and other compounds that normally are present in samples (such as serum) at very low concentration, such as IgE and viral antigens.

Antigen–Antibody Reactions Causing Cell Lysis or Cytotoxicity

Cell lysis (most often the lysis of sensitized erythrocytes) is frequently used as an indicator system for the occurrence of antigen–

antibody reactions. In the presence of complement (Ch. 11), sheep erythrocytes sensitized with antisheep erythrocyte antibodies will lyse. When an antigen–antibody reaction is allowed to take place in a complement-containing medium, the antigen–antibody complexes bind or "fix" the complement, so that it is then no longer available to lyse the sensitized sheep red blood cells. This complement fixation test is one of the oldest methods for revealing antigen–antibody interactions (e.g., in the Wassermann test for syphilis) and is still often used in various qualitative and quantitative tests. All the components of the classical complement pathway are required for complement-mediated hemolysis.

Some bacteria (especially gram-negative bacteria), after sensitization with specific antibodies, can also be lysed in the presence of complement, if lysozyme is also present.

In the presence of complement, antibodies to cellular surface antigens are cytotoxic to tissue culture cells bearing these antigens. Cytotoxicity is visible within minutes by the swelling of the cells; within an hour the cell membranes rupture, ghosts are formed, and the cells or their remnants detach from the wall of the culture dish or bottle.

There is also one mechanism of antibody-dependent cell-mediated cytotoxicity (ADCC) that does not involve complement. The mediator cells in this case are "killer" or K lymphocytes.

IN VIVO ANTIGEN–ANTIBODY INTERACTIONS

The same types of reactions between antigens and antibodies that occur *in vitro* can, of course, also occur *in vivo*; however, their role and importance in the defense against invading microorganisms or other foreign material is often entirely different from the *in vitro* considerations discussed above.

The formation of complexes or precipitates is important in allowing the recognition of circulating foreign antigen molecules and thus causing their subsequent phagocytosis through the opsonizing activity (see below). Toxins, viruses, and so on can thus be speedily eliminatd. Complexing with antibody may also counteract the toxic activity of toxins and, especially with sIgA, may neutralize the cell-penetrating power of viruses and thus diminish their pathogenicity.

Agglutinating bacteria into large clumps, particularly by means of IgM antibodies, does not directly lead to their destruction, but to some extent it facilitates their phagocytosis because the ingestion of large clumps of bacteria is not significantly more burdensome for phagocytes than the ingestion of single cells. It also facilitates the disposal of many more microorganisms per ingestion.

Motile microorganisms can be immobilized with specific antibodies by crosslinking their flagella. Some microorganisms — spirochetes, for example — are immobilized by reaction with antibodies, followed by binding of complement.

IgGl and IgG3 antibodies can induce phagocytic ingestion without complement by means of Fc receptors on the surface of phagocytic cells. They also can induce phagocytosis after binding complement; this process is mediated by complement (C3b) receptors on phagocytic cells. IgG2 and IgM induce phagocytosis only after binding of complement (C3b). This phenomenon is called *opsonization*; it makes microorganisms more "palatable" to phagocytes (for further information see Ch. 6).

Antigens and antibodies of the IgG and IgM classes that bind complement upon interacting cause lysis of erythrocytes, bacteria, and other cells. The lysis of gram-negative bacteria, as well as the destruction of other foreign invading cells, is of importance in the defense of the organism against them.

Of more importance, however, are in all probability the two functions complement has in promoting phagocytosis, that is, opsonization (in which $C\overline{1423}$, in the shape of C3b, is involved) and chemotaxis (principally by means of C5 or, more precisely, C5a). Chemotaxis is the induction of migration of (phagocytic) cells to the locus of antigen–antibody–complement interaction by locomotion in the direction of the highest concentration of the chemotactic agent (C5a) (Ch. 11). Complement also plays a role in a number of pathologic reactions, such as immune complex diseases and transfusion reactions.

IgE class antibodies can cause anaphylactic shock and the immediate-type atopic hypersensitivies or allergies (Chs. 12 and 15). Immune complex-induced allergies comprise the Arthus-type reaction — acute and chronic serum sickness syndromes in which IgG is the principal antibody and complement is involved. Antibodies as well as complement are also involved in transfusion reactions.

Hemolytic disease of the newborn involves placenta-crossing maternal antibodies that primarily compromise Rh-positive babies of Rh-negative mothers.

The protective and pathologic roles of humoral immunity are discussed at some length in Chapter 12.

REFERENCES

Glynn, L.E. and Steward, M.W.: Immunochemistry. John Wiley & Sons, New York, 1977.

Kabat, E.A.: Structural Concepts in Immunology and Immunochemistry. Holt, Rinehart & Winston, New York, 1976.

G.W. Litman and R.A. Good, Eds.: Immunoglobulins. Plenum, New York, 1978.

Nisonoff, A., Hopper, J.E., and Spring, S.B.: The Antibody Molecule. Academic Press, New York, 1975.

Rose, N.R., Milgrom, F. and van Oss, C.J., Eds.: Principles of Immunology. Macmillan, New York, 1979.

11

Complement

*Roger K. Cunningham and
Robert A. Nelson, Jr.*

The complement system is composed of a group of at least 12 proteins in normal serum that are involved in a wide range of immunologic events. Nine of these proteins are termed *complement components*; these combine and react in a distinctly specific sequence, following the activation of the first component after combination with an antigen-antibody complex. This antibody-dependent sequence reaction of C1 through C9 is called the *classical pathway*. Three other normal serum proteins are inhibitors or inactivators of specific components, namely, C1, C3, and C6. Some investigators believe that there may also be specific inhibitors of the remaining six components. It is possible that these proteins are an important biologic part of a *homeostatic system*, which serves to control complement activity so that potentially harmful effects of complement activation do not cause undue damage to the host.

In addition, there are four or possibly five other proteins in normal serum that become functional as a system following activation by specific stimuli that are independent of antibody. Because this system involves activation of complement components C3 and C5, without an effect on C1, C4, or C2, their sequential reactivity is currently called the *alternate pathway* (or *alternative pathway*) of complement activation.

Under ordinary biologic circumstances all nine components exist in normal plasma either as proenzymes or as inert substrates susceptible to other components following their activation to the enzymatic state. Most components migrate electrophoretically with the β proteins, except for C8, which is in the γ zone, and C9, which is in the α zone. Their concentration in serum is low, falling between 25 and 80 μg/ml, except for C9, at about 230 μg/ml; C4, about 400 μg/ml; and βlc (see below), about 1200 μg/ml. Most of the components have molecular weights ranging from 117,000 to 206,000, except for C9, with a molecular weight of about 79,000, and C1, about 900,000. Once the host responds immunologically to antigenic stimulation either naturally, due to ingestion or inhalation, or artificially, due to any immunization regimen, antibody is produced and the stage is set for the action of complement. It should be noted that relatively few important biologic events follow the combination of antibody along with antigen, either in the

155

soluble phase or when the antigen is in or on a cell membrane. One important exception, of course, is the fact that the combination of antibody with viruses abolishes the capacity of the viruses to infect a susceptible cell. In contrast to the seemingly ineffective results of antibody combination, the sequence of events following C1 combination and activation is so dramatic that the term complement was first coined to express the essential "complementary" role of these normal plasma proteins in the final expression of antibody-induced reactivity.

Originally, one important beneficial effect of complement was observed during the lysis of certain gram-negative bacteria by antibody and fresh normal serum. A convenient experimental model was then developed using sheep erythrocytes (E) that posssess specific sites (S), specific antibody (A), and fresh guinea pig serum (C). For almost 50 years the complement system was believed to consist of four components and one inactivator. The components were numbered C1 through C4, based on the order of their discovery and *not* on their order of reactivity, which later was shown to be C1, C4, C2, C3. Since all available experimental data during that time indicated that depletion of complement reactivity occurred only and specifically in the presence of antigen–antibody complexes, there was widespread clinical use of complement-fixation tests to detect infection, evaluate natural immunity, and follow the effectiveness of artificial immunization procedures. In the early 1960s investigators at the Howard Hughes Medical Institute proved conclusively that the original C3 was actually a mixture of six proteins. Thus there were in fact nine separate and distinct proteins in guinea pig and human serum that were essential for the lysis of sensitized sheep erythrocytes (EA) and for the cytotoxic effect of antibody on bacteria or tumor cells. In addition there were two new activators discovered for components C3

and C6. The era for advances in understanding the biochemistry of complement had thus begun.

In the classical pathway the initiation of activation of the complement system follows the combination of either naturally occurring or immune antibody with almost any antigen. The combination and activation of the first component to respond, C1, is in itself quite remarkable. This component exists in normal plasma as an 11 S macromolecule. Experimentally it may be dissociated by chelation into three molecular entities with distinct biologic characteristics. One of these subunits, C1q, has a molecular weight of about 400,000 and possesses a combining group that is uniquely specific for bound antibody. It will combine with a single IgM antibody molecule or with two IgG antibody molecules of classes 1, 2 and 3, provided that they are in close approximation. It will combine with IgM and IgG antibodies in an immune complex most efficiently when the ratio of antigen to antibody is at or near equivalence. It does not ordinarily combine with IgG antibody of class 4 nor with IgA or IgE antibodies. It will even combine with "normal" gamma globulin that has been artificially aggregated by heating, that is, without combining with antigen.

One observation of potentially important significance in tumor immunology is that certain highly malignant cell lines will produce, *in vitro*, a protein substance that inhibits the combination of C1 with IgG sites but not with IgM sites. It should be emphasized that it is this combining site on the C1 molecule that determines the specificity of complement; hence it is often referred to as the *recognition unit*.

The immediate consequence of combination of the macromolecule is a Ca^{2+}-dependent activation of a second portion of the molecule, C1r. Activated C1r has a molecular weight of approximately 170,000 and serves to convert the C1s portion of the molecule into an active protease. Activated

C1s has a molecular weight of approximately 86,000. It has two naturally occurring substrates in normal plasma, C4 and C2, and is sterically inhibited by a normally occurring protein with a molecular weight of approximately 90,000, known as C1 esterase inhibitor or, more commonly, as C1 inactivator (C1 INA).

The exact nature of the C4 and C2 reaction steps and the resultant complex is generally accepted as the conversion of two proenzymes, C4 and C2, by the C1s site to yield an activated enzymic complex that is capable of cleaving C3 into two fractions — a larger C3b, which attaches to the complex, and a smaller C3a, which is released into the fluid phase. Thus the site, S-A-C1, C4, C2 is ordinarily referred to as a *C3 convertase*. This concept is based on the assumption that a protein with βlc electrophoretic mobility and a molecular weight of about 180,000 represents complement component C3. This is disputed by one group of investigators, who believe that C3 and βlc are separate molecular entities and who in fact have evidence that βlc is a substrate for activated C3. According to their interpretation, the S-A-C1, C4, C2 complex is not enzymic but does accept the combining group of C3. This combination of C3, not unlike the combination of C1, results in conformational changes with at least two striking new properties. The C3 becomes activated enzymically so that it may now cleave its two naturally occurring substrates, C5 and βlc. The smaller cleavage products of both these molecules possess chemotactic and anaphylatoxic properties. It should be noted that the enzymatic activity of C3 is brief, that is, the site has a half-life of only 12 minutes at 30°C. In contrast, the conformational change results in a concurrent exposure of at least two new sites that are relatively stable. The first of these is the site that combines with the immune adherence or C3 receptor, which has been demonstrated on primate erythrocytes, nonprimate platelets, and on primate and nonprimate granulocytes and B lymphocytes. Thus there is a role of complement in enhanced phagocytosis (resulting from the combination of sensitized particulate antigens with granulocytes), in wound healing (owing to potential liberation of platelet-derived growth factor from platelets reacting in immune adherence with C3-sensitized antigens), and as an influence on antibody formation (resulting from attachment of sensitized soluble antigens with B lymphocytes). A second stable area of the C3 molecule is exposed after the conformational change. This is the site that is susceptible to cleavage by the C3 inactivator (C3 INA).

One of the more important effects of the activation of enzymatic C3 concerns its cleavage of C5. The larger fragment of C5, called C5b, remains attached to the site S-A-C1, C4, C2, C3. The union is also unstable until C6, or C6 and C7, combine with it. Even with the relatively stable C5b-C6 site and the even more stable C5b-C6-C7 site there is some dissociability. The complexes that are freed from the site may attach to other nonsensitized cells that possess the appropriate lipid membrane. Such cells are sometimes referred to as *bystander* cells, that is, they do not have antibody or the preceeding reacting complement components on their surface.

The exact mode of attachment of C5b and the events that follow have only recently been defined. From this knowledge has emerged the concept that the C5b-C6-C7-C8-C9 complex functions as a *membrane attack complex (MAC)* for certain bacteria, viruses, and tissue cells. Penetration of the lipid bilayer of specific cell membranes occurs by the C5b-C6-C7 complex, which is then highly susceptible to combination by C8 followed by C9. After combination of C9, hemoglobin is released from sensitized erythrocytes, and distinct and characteristic changes appear on the cell membrane. These may be easily visualized by electron microscopy. The "lesions" in the membrane resemble craters or holes, which have recently been defined immunochemically as 10 to 40 Å channels in the lipid bilayer. These channels consist of portions of the molecules of C5 through C9 and seem to penetrate as deep as the hydrocarbon interior of the lipid bilayer. It is through these channels that water enters the cell, causing an osmotic inbalance due to the Donnan effect, leading to rupture of certain cells. It is to be noted, however, that death of the cell due to the internal imbalance or to the escape of vital molecules may take place without the gross membrane damage usually referred to as lysis. In addition it is of considerable interest that some penetration of the erythrocyte membrane occurs even after cleavage and combination of C5 by activated C3. Two groups of investigators independently demonstrated these changes by electron microscopy on cells in the state EA-C1, C4, C2, C3, C5b. No such lesions were noted on EA-C1, C4, C2, C3 when the C3 used to form the complex was free of β1c.

Some of the results of activation of the nine component system in the classical pathway are beneficial to the host — for example, the cytocidal or cytolytic effect on pathogenic bacteria and viruses, the cytocidal effect on certain parasites and tumor cells, and the destructive effect on cellular mutants of the host that are potentially harmful. In addition, there are protective or healing-promoting phenomena that result from cleavage products of individual components — for example, both immune adherence and phagocytosis follow the combination of C3 to the sensitized site S-A-C1, C4, C2, and chemotaxis induced by a fragment of C5, which is generated into the fluid phase following the enzymatic activity of C3 on the site S-A-C1, C4, C2, C3. In contrast there are a variety of undesirable effects caused by activated components that possess enzymatic reactivity or by split products of individual components that have been generated by a component

with enzymatic reactivity. One example of the former is the disease syndrome known as hereditary angioneurotic edema. In these patients there is a deficiency of the C1 inactivator; during periodic episodes of the disease, activated C1 in the serum and tissues initiates the classical pathway and produces pathologic changes that may be fatal. In addition, there are inflammatory changes during the Arthus reaction and other allergic or hypersensitivity disorders that result chiefly from the release of pharmacologically active substances from cells that have been acted on by fragments of C5 or of the proteins known as β1c. For many years this effect was described as being caused by a substance termed "anaphylatoxin."

There is at least one other important immunopathologic sequence whereby cells may be killed or lysed that is independent of the classical pathway just described. This involves a series of reactions that do not require antibody and do not affect C1, C4, or C2 (Fig. 11.1). One of the earliest described "bypass" reactions was the presumed specific depletion of C3 of the then recognized four component system by cobra venom. In 1964 this reaction was shown by one of us (R.A.N.) to be initiated by a 6 S protein in cobra venom, following combination with a specific protein in normal

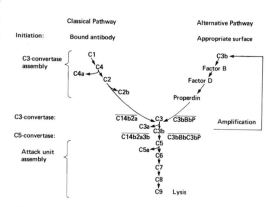

Fig. 11.1. The sequence of events in activation of complement by the classical and alternate pathways.

serum, called the venom cofactor or C3 proactivator, to activate and destroy C3 without appreciable depletion of C5 through C9. When experimental circumstances were adjusted in a certain fashion the activated C3 cleaved C5, and the remainder of the sequence was triggered so that all six components, C3 through C9, were depleted in normal serum. This *alternate pathway* has been found to be initiated by several different materials, most notably the polysaccharide constituent of yeast cell walls known as zymosan, the lipopolysaccharides of certain gram-negative bacteria, and other specific polymers, especially carbohydrates, that have the essential surface properties necessary to initiate a series of reactions resulting in important biologic consequences both in immunologic phenomena and, perhaps even more importantly in the inflammatory response.

There are at least two series of conflicting claims that must be included in an evaluation of data on the precise mechanisms and consequences of the alternate pathway. First, in a large series of investigations in the mid-1950s, certain basic experimental results were misinterpreted, leading to erroneous and confusing results as well as misleading nomenclature that have only recently been at least partially resolved. The early observation that yeast cell wall zymosan seemed to deplete only C3 led to the hypothesis that a then presumably new serum protein, termed properdin, was responsible. Actually, in 1958 this original properdin system was shown by one of us (R.A.N.) to be antibody dependent and involved a series of reactions identical to the classical pathway. Several years later a quite new and distinct series of reactions was described that was similar in effect on the complement system to the cobra venom "bypass" phenomenon except that substances with specific surface active properties served as the initiating reagent. An investigation of these materials led to the discovery that at least four new substances

were involved in an alternate pathway of complement activation and depletion. Unfortunately, one of these was named *properdin*, but this new 184,000 molecular weight protein has no relationship to the 11 S properdin described in the mid-1950s.

There is a second reservation that must be kept in mind when interpreting the mechanisms involved in both the classical pathway and the alternate pathway and that concerns the relationship of C3 and $\beta1c$. According to the majority of investigations, these two terms represent a single molecular entity. Thus the alternate. pathway is defined as the sequence that follows the activation of C3, by any of the substances described above, without an involvement of antibody, C1, C4, or C2. The activation of C3 is followed quickly by a cleavage of the molecule into two fragments. A smaller fragment, C3a, passes into the fluid phase, while the larger fragment, C3b, binds to the surface of the substance that was used to initiate the reaction. The C3b is then stated to combine with an enzyme unique to the alternate pathway, factor B (also referred to as Bf), yielding complexes either of C3b-B or C3b-B-C3b. Both of these complexes act as substances for yet another enzyme, called factor D. This magnesium-dependent reaction results in cleavage of the B portion of the complexes. A small fragment, Ba, is released into the fluid phase, while a larger fragment, Bb, remains associated with the C3b. The resulting complexes, C3b-Bb and C3b-Bb-C3b, are postulated to have four distinguishing characteristics:

1. Both will serve to cleave native C3; hence they are termed C3 *convertases*. In addition, the C3b-Bb-C3b complex will cleave native C5; hence it is termed *C5 convertase*.

2. The postulated fragment of C3 in both complexes, C3b, is resistant to degradation by the naturally occurring C3 inactivator of the classical pathway, C3 INA. Under ordi-

nary circumstances this enzyme will destroy the reactivity of any antigen–antibody–C3 complex in immune adherence, immune phagocytosis, or specific attachment to B lymphocytes, as well as in its classic ability to cleave C5.

3. The two complexes are said to be unstable under ordinary circumstances. However, their molecular structures and "convertase" activities are preserved following combination with another 6 S protein of normal plasma, unfortunately named properdin. This "new" properdin has no relationship to the now defunct definition of properdin used in the 1950s. Instead, it has a specific stabilizing effect when it combines with either C3b-Bb or C3b-Bb-C3b, thus preserving their enzymatic reaction on C3 and C5, respectively.

4. This phase of the alternate pathway, which may be beneficial (by chemotoxis) or harmful (by anaphylatoxins), seems to be under homeostatic control by an inactivator protein. β1H acts as an enzyme and slowly degrades the C3b-Bb-properdin and C3b-Bb-C3b–properdin complexes.

Thus the alternate pathway can be envisaged to have at least two important biologic functions. First, in cases of invasion of the host by certain pathogens against which there is neither strictly specific nor cross-reacting antibody, the activation of C3 by the alternate pathway may proceed directly to an enhancement of phagocytosis or to sequential complement component combination and reactivity, leading to lysis or death of the organism. Second, in cases of penetration of tissues by materials capable of initiating this pathway, a whole series of reactions characteristic of the inflammatory sequence is set up, resulting in chemotaxis

and invasion of the site by granulocytes, which are capable of ingesting and destroying the foreign substance.

From these observations on the classical pathway of sequential reactivity of nine serum proteins stimulated by antigen–antibody complexes and on related but independent mechanisms involved in the alternate pathway following changes in a single complement component (C3) there has resulted an understanding of specific mechanisms involved in a diverse array of biologic phenomena. Of equal interest there are new data being collected and analyzed that suggest quite different concepts of a role for complement components in human disease.

REFERENCES

Alper, C.A. and Rosen, F.S.: Clinical applications of complement assays. Adv. Int. Med. *20*: 61, 1975.

Fearon, T. and Austen, K.: The alternative pathway of complement — A system for host resistance to microbial infection. N. Eng. J. Med. *303*: 259, 1980.

Müller-Eberhard, J.: Complement. Ann. Rev. Bioch. *44*: 697, 1975.

Nelson, R.A., Jr.: An alternative mechanism for the properdin system. J. Exp. Med. *108*: 515, 1958.

Nelson, R.A., Jr., Jensen, J., Gigli, I., and Tamura, N.: Methods for the separation, purification and measurement of nine components of hemolytic complement in guinea pig serum. Immunochemistry *3*: 111, 1966.

Osler, G.: Complement: Mechanism and Function. Prentice-Hall, Inc., Englewood Cliffs, N.J., 1976.

Rapp, J. and Borsos, T.: Molecular Basis of Complement Action. Appleton-Century-Crofts, New York, 1970.

12

Humoral Immunity and Hypersensitivity

Felix Milgrom

SPECIFIC PROTECTION

In Chapters 8 and 10, *in vitro* serologic reactions — that is, antigen–antibody reactions — were discussed. It has been mentioned that serologic reactions have found practical applications in serodiagnostic tests. Diagnosis of an infectious disease may be made on the basis of detection of antibodies in the patient's serum that are directed against microorganisms or their products. Alternatively application of serodiagnostic tests can be based on detection and identification of antigens by means of antibody-containing sera used as reagents.

The role of humoral immunity in preventing and overcoming an infection has been obvious since the classical studies of Pfeiffer, which clearly showed destruction of cholera vibrios in the peritoneal cavity of preimmunized guinea pigs. From subsequent studies it became obvious that in order to play a protective role an antibody has to be directed against surface antigens of a microorganism. Alternatively, antibodies may neutralize some microbial product or activity that plays an important role in pathogenicity. Destruction of microorganisms may be accomplished *in vivo* in the simplest way by the action of antibody and complement. The above-mentioned Pfeiffer's phenomenon is an outstanding example of a complement-mediated dissolution of microorganisms *in vivo*.

Another mechanism by which humoral antibodies act is the promotion of phagocytosis. The humoral factors promoting phagocytosis were described under the name of *opsonins* by Wright and Douglas in the first decade of this century. These were thermolabile substances present in normal sera, resembling complement in that they were removed from the serum by antigen–antibody complexes. In his further experiments Wright noted that the phagocytosis-promoting power of serum increases with immunization and that large amounts of antibodies may by themselves mediate phagocytosis of bacteria. Otherwise, in the presence of small amounts of antibodies the addition of complement is necessary to increase phagocytosis. The phagocytosis-promoting action of antibodies has been studied on pneumococci by Wood and his associates, who showed that nonencapsulated pneumococci readily undergo phagocytosis even on smooth surfaces, such as glass. On the other hand, encapsulated

161

pneumococci, because of their "slippery" surface, escape a phagocytic cell by sliding away from pseudopods. Antibodies make pneumococci "sticky," and therefore the bacteria are engulfed by the pseudopods even on smooth surfaces.

Studies by van Oss that related phagocytosis to surface tension showed that encapsulated pneumococci are more hydrophilic and that nonencapsulated cells are more hydrophobic than leukocytes. Sensitization by antibodies and, still more so, binding of antibodies and complement decreases the hydrophilic properties of pneumococci. Recovery from pneumonia (especially without antibiotic treatment) depends on the formation and action of antibodies to capsular polysaccharides. Similarly, natural or artificially induced resistance to pneumococci depends on antibodies to capsules. The term *opsonization* has been retained to denote the phagocytosis-promoting effect; with more information available, distinction is being made among opsonization effected by antibodies, complement, or other factors.

The neutralization of toxins is an outstanding example of humoral immunity, which often leads to recovery from a disease elicited by toxin-producing bacteria and may prevent the recurrence of such a disease. Most data were accumulated in studies on diphtheria. Immunity to diphtheria may be measured by the Schick test. In this test a small amount of toxin (1/50 of the minimal lethal dose) is injected intracutaneously. If the tested subject is sensitive (i.e., has no antitoxin in the circulation), he or she develops a positive skin test. Erythema, edema, and tenderness start 24 hours after administration of toxin, and the reaction reaches its maximum extent of about 3 cm in diameter after 1 week. A negative test proves that the injected toxin was neutralized; that is, the tested individual had antitoxin in the circulation at a concentration of at least 100 antitoxic units/ml of blood.

It is obvious that after spontaneous recovery from diphtheria there is conversion of Schick positivity into Schick negativity. However, even before artificial immunization for diphtheria was instituted the majority of the population sometime in their lives would convert to Schick negativity without any patent disease. This conversion was due to subclinical infections in which small amounts of toxin were released from infecting organisms, not enough to establish disease but enough to elicit immunity.

The Schick test provided a great deal of

Table 12.1. Percentage of Schick-Negative Individuals in the Population of New York City and New Jersey

Age Group	Percentage Negative
(months)	
6–7	43.3
7–8	36.6
8–9	16.2
9–10	6.9
10–12	11.5
(years)	
1–3	16.8
4–6	41.4
6–7	49.6
7–8	56.5
8–9	63.4
9–10	67.8
10–11	70.7
11–12	71.8
12–13	73.4
13–14	76.9
14–15	80.3
15–16	82.2
16–17	81.4
20–30	88.3
30–40	89.4
40–50	91.8
50–60	93.6
60–70	94.6
Over 70	94.5

(With permission, data by Zingher, 1923, modified from Topley and Wilson's Principles of Bacteriology, Virology and Immunity, Vol 2. 6th Ed. Edward Arnold Ltd., London, 1975, p. 1420.)

interesting information about the epidemiology of diphtheria. A child is born with immunity acquired by passive transfer of antitoxic antibodies from the mother. This passively transferred immunity disappears a few months after birth. Without vaccination the immunity would be acquired as a result of subclinical infections or, occasionally, as a result of patent disease. Table 12.1 shows acquisition of Schick negativity by the population in New York City and New Jersey in the time prior to the introduction of vaccination. It is obvious that with increasing age there was an increase of Schick negativity; in adulthood about 90 percent of the population was resistant to diphtheria.

Upon infection of a Schick-negative person with toxigenic diphtheria bacilli, the toxin set free into the body elicits a quick secondary immune response that pevents manifestations of the disease. Death from diphtheria in untreated, sensitive individuals occurs in 10 to 40 percent of the patients, depending on the severity of the epidemic. The remaining patients develop enough antitoxin to neutralize all the toxin excreted by invading corynebacteria.

Fortunately, at the time when clinical manifestations of diphtheria are obvious, toxin usually has not yet been bound by tissues in a lethal dose, and free toxin can be neutralized by either passively introduced or actively formed antibodies. A very similar situation prevails in scarlet fever. On the other hand, toxigenic clostridia excrete large amounts of toxins quickly. At the time when clinical manifestations of tetanus become obvious, lethal amounts of toxin are usually already firmly bound to the tissues and the patient can hardly be helped by antitoxic serum therapy.

Preventive immunization against toxigenic infections depends on the administration of toxoids and the building up of active immunity. In many developed countries, immunizations against diphtheria and tetanus are compulsory.

The antibodies responsible for the antimicrobial activities discussed above are primarily of the IgM and the IgG classes. These constitute the major immunoglobulin classes found in the circulation. On the other hand, the major immunoglobulin in secretions (e.g., mucus of the respiratory and gastrointestinal tracts) is IgA — more accurately, secretory IgA (sIgA). Whereas IgM and IgG are synthesized primarily in lymph nodes, spleen, and bone marrow, synthesis of sIgA occurs primarily in salivary glands, mammary glands (especially early after delivery), the lamina propria of intestine, and the respiratory tract. These sIgA antibodies play an important role in resistance to viral diseases. Significant production of sIgA in the alimentary tract and nasopharynx is observed only after oral administration of the antigen. Once their production has been stimulated, elevated titer of IgA antibody is observed for several months. Prompt secondary response to local immunization is usually absent, indicating that there is no significant memory in sIgA production. High correlation between the titers of sIgA antibodies and resistance to polioviruses, influenza viruses, parainfluenza viruses, rhinoviruses, and rubella viruses has been demonstrated. These observations justify oral vaccinations against several viral diseases. Secretory IgA also plays a role in bacterial infections, preventing colonization of some bacteria in the gastrointestinal tract. The definite protective role of sIgA antibodies against *Vibrio cholerae* has been documented.

More detailed information about the protective role of humoral antibodies is to be found in the chapters dealing with individual microorganisms.

HYPERSENSITIVITY REACTIONS MEDIATED BY HUMORAL ANTIBODIES

The term allergy was originally introduced by von Pirquet to denote all altered immunologic reactivities. At present this term is usually employed as a synonym for hypersensitivity and refers to all exaggerated and frequently harmful immunologic responses, both humoral and cellular.

Anaphylaxis

As mentioned previously, the harmful role of humoral immunity has been clearly recognized since the beginning of this century. The most dramatic pathogenic effect of humoral antibodies was first observed in dogs by Portier and Richet in 1902. These investigators administered two inoculations of a toxin from a sea anemone to the dogs. A second dose of toxin was smaller than the minimal lethal dose, and still a fatal shock developed in animals that had already been inoculated with the toxin prior to the shock-inducing injection. Therefore the two investigators assumed that this phenomenon was an effect not of the toxin directly but of the animal's response that had been stimulated by the first injection of the toxin. The phenomenon was the opposite of the induction of protective immunity or prophylaxis. In this case the sensitization of the animal with toxin did not lead to immune reactions promoting the animal's survival. On the contrary, it apparently rendered the animal much more vulnerable to the toxin. This phenomenon was called *anaphylaxis* by Richet and Portier. In subsequent years anaphylaxis was most frequently studied in guinea pigs.

Active Systemic Anaphylaxis. Sensitization is elicited by the introduction of an antigen (but not of a hapten) by any parenteral route. It usually consists of one injection of a minute dose of antigen; for example, 1 ml of horse serum at 10^{-6} dilution suffices to sensitize a guinea pig. Anaphylactic shock is elicited by injection of the challenging dose of the same antigen. The challenging dose should be administered optimally 10 to 20 days after sensitization to allow for formation and fixation of antibodies. The challenging dose has to be considerably larger than the sensitizing dose and is most efficient when administered intravenously.

Within 1 minute after the challenging injection the guinea pig becomes restless, raises to its hind legs, and rubs its nose with its front legs. It frequently jumps and has convulsions. It falls on its side and has severe breathing difficulties, making violent respiratory efforts through an open mouth. Breathing ceases within a few minutes, but the heart continues to beat for several minutes more. At autopsy the most striking finding is that of distended lungs (Fig. 12.1). Histologically striking is the contraction of the smooth muscles of the bronchioli. The emphysema is caused by the retention of inspired air in the alveoli

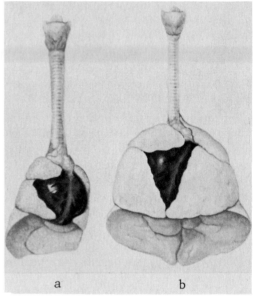

a   b

Fig. 12.1.a. Organs of the chest of a normal guinea pig. **b.** Organs of a guinea pig immediately after death from anaphylactic shock. (Doerr, R.: Allergie und Anaphylaxie. In Kolle, W., Kraus, R., and Uhlenhuth, P., Eds.: Handbuch der pathogenen Mikroorganismen, Vol. I, Part 2. Gustav Fischer, Jena; Urban & Schwarzenberg, Berlin & Vienna, 1929.)

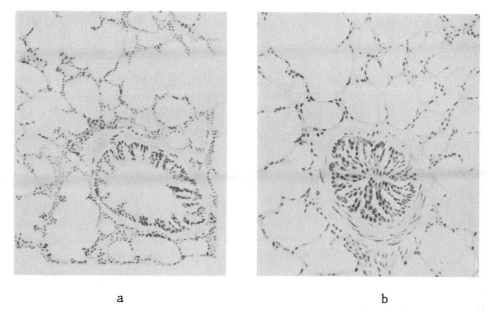

Fig. 12.2.a. Section of a normal guinea pig lung (× 100). **b.** Section of the lung of a guinea pig that died in acute anaphylactic shock (× 100). (Doerr, R.: Allergie und Anaphylaxie. In Kolle, W., Krause, R., and Uhlenhuth, P., Eds: Handbuch der pathogenen Mikroorganismen, Vol. I, Part 2. Gustav Fischer, Jena; Urban & Schwarzenberg, Berlin & Vienna, 1929.)

(Fig. 12.2). Death is clearly caused by suffocation.

In other animal species, anaphylactic shock may have other clinical manifestations. In all instances, however, contraction of the smooth muscles is an outstanding characteristic. The phenomenon of anaphylaxis shows the specificity characteristic for all immunologic reactions, that is, only the antigen used for sensitization or a closely related antigen can induce the shock. The challenging substance does not have to be a whole antigen; it may be a hapten. However, a univalent hapten (i.e., a molecule containing only one antigenic determinant) is incapable of eliciting anaphylactic shock; as a matter of fact, it prevents induction of a shock by a polyvalent hapten or antigen.

If the challenging dose is too small to elicit shock, then abortive symptoms may ensue. An animal exposed to repeated small doses of the antigen eventually becomes desensitized in that there is no shock produced upon injection of an otherwise "shocking" dose of the antigen. Such states of desensitization are of short duration, and sensitivity returns as soon as fresh antibodies are produced and fixed to the tissues.

Active Local Anaphylaxis. Intracutaneous injection of the antigen into a sensitized animal causes a reaction in the form of a wheal and a flare appearing within 15 minutes (hence, immediate hypersensitivity). The increased vascular permeability that accounts for this reaction can also be conveniently demonstrated by leakage of an intravenously injected dye such as Evans blue. Extravasation of the dye results in a blue spot around the site of the injection of the antigen.

In Vitro Anaphylaxis. In 1910 Schultz and Dale showed that a portion of the ileum or uterine horn excised from an actively sensitized guinea pig would contract if exposed to the specific antigen. This

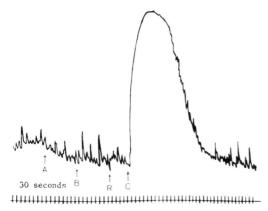

30 seconds

Fig. 12.3. Kymograph tracing of a Schultz-Dale reaction with a uterine horn from a virgin guinea pig sensitized with horse serum. At A, 0.5 ml of sheep serum and at B, 0.5 ml of cat serum were added. At R, Ringer's solution in the bath was changed. At C, 0.1 ml of horse serum was added. (Doerr, R.: Allergie und Anaphylaxie. In Kolle, W., Krause, R., and Uhlenhuth, P., Eds.: Handbuch der pathogenen Mikroorganismen, Vol. I, Part 2. Gustav Fischer, Jena; Urban & Schwarzenberg, Berlin & Vienna, 1929.)

test, referred to as the Schultz-Dale reaction, is usually performed on an organ strip suspended in Ringer's solution. The contraction of the muscle is recorded on a rotating cylinder (Fig. 12.3). This is a very sensitive procedure that may detect antigen in nanogram concentrations.

Passive Systemic Anaphylaxis. The state of sensitization may be passively transferred by injection of serum from a sensitized guinea pig into a normal guinea pig, which rather clearly demonstrates that humoral antibodies mediate anaphylaxis. For systemic transfer of anaphylaxis, a few ml of serum are injected intravenously or intraperitoneally into the recipient. In order to allow time for fixation of antibodies to the cells of the recipient, the challenging injection has to be administered 1 to 2 days later. The anaphylactic shock in passive anaphylaxis is indistinguishable from that in active anaphylaxis and obviously can be produced only with the antigen to which the donor of the serum was sensitized.

Passive Local Anaphylaxis. An animal with passively induced systemic anaphylaxis responds also to a local intracutaneous injection of small amounts of antigen by producing the usual wheal and flare reaction.

The state of anaphylaxis may also be transferred locally by intracutaneous injection of the antibody-containing serum. Such a procedure introduces a small amount of antibodies; therefore only the local area around the injection site is sensitized. Antigen has to be administered in the immediate proximity of the injection site of the serum. Here again, a wheal and flare reaction is noticed. In man such a procedure has been used for many years to demonstrate the presence of sensitizing antibodies in the serum of patients with various hypersensitivities. The test, called the Prausnitz-Küstner test, performed on human volunteers, used to be employed quite frequently but is now rarely used. The sensitizing serum is usually injected at various dilutions; such a titration procedure permits evaluation of the strength of antibodies by noticing the highest serum dilution at which the reaction occurs after introduction of antigen. In animal experiments the antigen may also be administered intravenously (obviously in considerably larger amounts than at local administration), and the reaction appears at the skin site, passively sensitized with antibodies. This type of experiment is called *passive cutaneous anaphylaxis (PCA)*. The antigen is usually injected intravenously along with a dye, such as Evans blue, 3 to 6 hours after injection of the antibody-containing serum. This results in the appearance of a blue spot in the sensitized area, which is caused by increased vascular permeability (Fig. 12.4). The procedure of passive cutaneous anaphylaxis has been studied extensively by Ovary. By means of this procedure as little as 0.01 μg of antibody nitrogen may be detected.

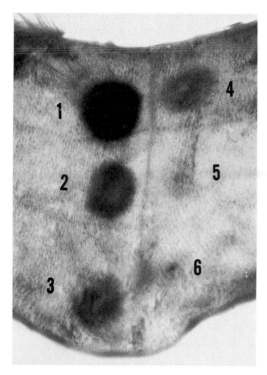

Fig. 12.4. Passive cutaneous anaphylaxis. Sites 1–4 were injected with various rabbit antisera to bovine adrenal. Site 5 was injected with rabbit antiserum to bovine spleen and site 6 with normal rabbit serum. All rabbit sera were applied at 1:10 dilutions. Four hours later the guinea pig was challenged intravenously with thermostable ethanol-insoluble preparation of bovine adrenal and 1 percent solution of Evans blue. (Milgrom, F. and Witebsky, E.: Immunological studies on adrenal glands. I. Immunization with adrenals of foreign species. Immunology, *5*, 46, 1962.)

Passive Anaphylaxis in Vitro. For this procedure a strip of ileum or uterine horn is soaked in antibody-containing serum. After a few hours the excess of serum is washed off and contraction of muscles may be elicited by the addition of the corresponding antigen to the bath.

Antibodies Involved in Anaphylactic Reactions. The model of passive anaphylaxis offers the possibility of studying antibodies responsible for anaphylactic reactions. The latent period between injection of antibody-containing serum and the establishment of the state of anaphylaxis reflects the time needed for antibodies to become bound to cells. These antibodies are called *cytotropic antibodies*. Passive transfer of anaphylaxis, either local or systemic, can be achieved with antibodies from a donor belonging to the recipient's species (*homocytotropic antibodies*) or to another species (*heterocytotropic antibodies*).

In man the major homocytotropic antibodies belong to the IgE class. These antibodies may elicit passive sensitization, systemically or locally, of a man. Cases of systemic sensitization have been observed as the result of inadvertent transfer of antibodies with transfused blood. Local sensitization may be achieved by intracutaneous injection of an antibody-containing serum into a normal subject, as done in the Prausnitz-Küstner reaction. In guinea pigs homocytotropic antibodies were shown to be fast-moving immunoglobulins, designated γ_1. Most homocytotropic antibodies are thermolabile, that is, they are destroyed at 56°C.

Heterocytotropic antibodies have been extensively studied in guinea pigs. Passive sensitization of guinea pigs can be achieved by antibodies of rabbit, man, and monkey but not of horse or cattle. Heterocytotropic antibodies are of the IgG class. It should be noted that human IgG antibodies sensitize guinea pigs as heterocytotropic antibodies, but they do not sensitize man or other primates. On the other hand, IgE antibodies, as homocytotropic antibodies, sensitize man and other primates but they fail to sensitize guinea pigs.

The sensitizing antibody becomes attached to the cell through the mediation of the carboxy terminal portion of the Fc fragment; accordingly, the sensitization depends on the presence of this fragment. $F(ab')_2$ fragments of antibodies are incapable of inducing sensitization. The most important cells in anaphylactic reactions are mast cells and basophilic leukocytes. There are about 40,000 to 100,000 receptors per cell for IgE on human basophilic granulocytes. The equilibrium constant for the reaction of IgE and its receptor is very high. This is in agreement with the finding that minute amounts of IgE suffice to sensitize these cells. Upon reintroduction of the antigen into the organism, IgE molecules bound to the cells react with antigen via their Fab portion. It is suggested by the available evidence that antigen "bridges" IgE molecules, thereby inducing clustering of membrane receptors. Bridging results in degranulation and the liberation of inflammatory mediators. During this process the basophilic granulocytes or mast cells remain intact and viable. Reaction of antigen with antibodies bound to the cells results in the discharge of pharmacologically active substances that cause symptoms of anaphylaxis. For human anaphylactic reactions, histamine is by far the most important substance.

The major inflammatory mediators released from these cells upon interaction of the antigen with IgE are summarized in Table 12.2. Products of basophils and mast cells act on the endothelium of the vasculature and lead to increased vascular permeability. Furthermore, they may induce

Table 12.2.   Mediators Released from Basophilic Granulocytes and Mast Cells in Anaphylaxis

Mediator	Molecular Weight	Effect	Inactivation
Histamine	111	Contraction of smooth muscle; increased vascular permeability; elevation of cAMP; enhanced migration of eosinophilic granulocytes	Histaminase
Serotonin	220	Increases vascular permeability	5-Hydroxytryptamine
Eosinophil chemotactic factor of anaphylaxis (ECF-A)	360–390	Chemotaxis of eosinophils; deactivation of eosinophils	Aminopeptidase
Neutrophil chemotactic factor	750,000	Chemotaxis of neutrophils	?
Heparin	750,000	Anticoagulant; anticomplementary activity	?
Chymase	27,000	Proteolysis	?
Platelet-activating factor (PAF)	300–500	Release of mediators from platelets	Phospholipase D
Platelet lytic factor (PLF)	?	Release of mediators from platelets	Phospholipase D
Slow-reacting substance of anaphylaxis (SRS-A)[a]	400	Contraction of smooth muscle; increased vascular permeability	Arylsulfatases A and B

[a] Elaborated in cooperation with another not yet identified cell.

contraction of the smooth muscles of the vessels, bronchi, intestines, and uterus. Histamine also has positive inotropic and chronotropic effects on the heart. The eosinophilic chemotactic factor of anaphylaxis attracts eosinophils to the sites of degranulation of basophils or mast cells (the role of eosinophils in anaphylaxis is described below). More recently, a factor from basophils and mast cells has been shown to be chemotactic for neutrophilic granulocytes. The latter cells may contribute lysosomal constituents to the anaphylactic reaction. The platelet aggregating factor (PAF) and the platelet lytic factor (PLF) induce release of additional inflammatory mediators from platelets and provide a means for activation of the blood coagulation system. Basophil kallikrein (BK) cleaves bradykinin from kininogen, adding another pathway to kinin involvement in anaphylaxis (kinins may also be recruited via the Hageman factor system, which may be activated by the injured tissue itself). Enzymes from basophilic granulocytes and mast cells have lytic activities for collagen and for connective tissue polysaccharides. Basophils and mast cells probably interact with some other as yet unidentified cells to produce the slow reactive substance of anaphylaxis (SRS-A). Heparin may activate the fibrinolytic system and play a role as an anticomplementary agent. Lysolecithin is also liberated during degranulation; it may damage cell membranes.

Atopic Diseases. Immediate hypersensitivity reactions, referred to in man as atopic diseases, constitute very frequent human disorders, with which about 10 percent of the population is afflicted. Full-blown anaphylactic shock is very rarely observed in man. Most fatal anaphylactic shocks have been observed after injection of penicillin into sensitized individuals. Edema of the upper respiratory segments and bronchial spasms are the most characteristic symptoms that are elicited predominantly by histamine.

Asthma, rhinitis, and skin eruptions are common manifestations of atopic reactions in man. As mentioned previously, these reactions are caused by the IgE class of antibodies. Sensitization resulting in IgE formation is induced by antigens frequently referred to as allergens. This includes inhaled antigens, such as pollens, dander, and dust; ingested antigens, such as various food products and drugs; and injected antigens, such as bee venom and various drugs. It appears likely that the original, protective role of the IgE class of antibodies was in response to parasitic infections.

Before antibodies responsible for atopic diseases were identified as IgE antibodies, they were considered unusual types of antibodies and were referred to as "reagins". This term and the term "reaginic antibody" are still used today.

As mentioned in Chapter 10, IgE immunoglobulins appear in normal individuals at a concentration of a few hundred ng per ml. Detection of the level of IgE, important for diagnostic purposes, may be achieved by means of simple radial immunodiffusion in those instances in which the concentration of IgE considerably exceeds its average concentration. Otherwise the concentration of IgE may be established by radioimmunoassay, a convenient technique that is based on diffusion of a test serum into agar, into which ^{125}I labeled antibodies to IgE, raised in a foreign species, were incorporated. The concentration of IgE is established on the basis of the size of the rings visualized by autoradiography.

In many instances identification of the allergen to which the patient is sensitized is of great importance, since avoiding this antigen may prevent disease manifestations. The antigen may be conveniently identified by skin tests in which highly diluted antigens are injected intracutaneously and the injection sites are inspected for wheal and flare reactions. Passive transfer into human volunteers may be performed as local anaphylaxis in the Prausnitz-

Küstner test, which permits titration of IgE antibodies. The same principle of a passive local transfer of hypersensitivity may be employed using nonhuman primates, such as rhesus monkeys, as recipients of the tested sera. Passive local anaphylaxis tests (Schultz-Dale tests) may be performed using a piece of human or primate intestine.

Recently, a convenient test for *in vitro* identification of the allergen has been described under the name of *radioallergosorbent test* (RAST). In this test the examined allergen, for example, ragweed, is coupled to cellulose beads and mixed with the patient's serum. Following washing, the preparation is incubated with ^{125}I labeled, anti-IgE antibodies, and, again following washing, the radioactivity is measured. The test is positive only if the patient's serum contained IgE antibodies to the antigen under examination.

Antibodies to Tissue and Cell Constituents

The pathogenic role of antibodies directed against cell surface components was clearly realized in experiments performed at the beginning of the twentieth century. Several investigators noted that intravenous injection of minute volumes of serum with Forssman antibodies into a Forssman-positive animal, such as a guinea pig, results in the immediate death of the animal with symptoms resembling anaphylaxis. In a similar way, injection of rabbit antisera against guinea pig erythrocytes resulted in anemia and death of the injected guinea pig. More recently, dramatic pathogenic action of humoral antibodies was observed in hyperacute graft rejection when a kidney was placed into a recipient containing humoral antibodies directed against transplantation antigens of the donor. In contrast, antibodies to intracellular antigens usually do not result in any dramatic untoward manifestations. Significantly, autoantibodies to surface antigens of cells such

as erythrocytes are formed only under exceptional pathologic conditions, whereas autoantibodies to intracellular antigens, such as Wassermann antibody, occur relatively frequently and may be produced quite readily under experimental conditions. These matters will be discussed in some detail in Chapter 15.

Immune Complexes

The pathogenic role of antigen–antibody complexes has been recognized since the very beginning of this century. The most pathogenic immune complexes are those formed in slight or moderate antigen excess. They have a lattice structure, which accounts for the molecular transformation of antibody molecules and which is important for binding of complement and consequent pathogenicity. Activation of complement results in liberation of anaphylatoxins, which in turn causes the release of pharmacologic mediators of anaphylaxis from mast cells, leukocytes, and platelets. Activation of the complement system also liberates chemotactic factors, which attract polymorphonuclear leukocytes. On the other hand, very small complexes formed in excess of antigen do not show lattice structure. Consequently, they do not bind complement and are virtually non-pathogenic. Large complexes formed in the equivalence zone or in moderate antibody excess are readily phagocytosed and removed.

The first pathogenic effect of immune complexes to be described was the Arthus reaction, which is produced when a soluble antigen is administered subcutaneously into an animal, producing antibodies directed against this antigen. Local formation of antigen–antibody complexes, which results in the accumulation of polymorphonuclear leukocytes and the occurrence of necrotizing vasculitis, are the hallmarks of this reaction. Pathologic lesions resembling those of the Arthus reaction are found in several infectious diseases and also in autoimmune diseases.

Another form of pathogenicity of immune complexes is serum sickness, which was observed frequently in human beings at the time when antitoxic sera originating from a foreign species were used for treatment of diphtheria and for prophylaxis of tetanus. Serum sickness is a disease characterized by fever, lymphadenopathy, arthralgia, skin eruptions, and edema, which are observed within 2 weeks after injection of the foreign serum. In most instances the disease subsides without any sequelae, but occasionally it takes a severe form with neurologic and cardiac manifestations. Von Pirquet described clinical manifestations of serum sickness and recognized that they are associated with the immune response to foreign proteins (Ch. 15).

Animal experiments on acute serum sickness were helpful in explaining the pathogenicity of this condition (Ch. 15). Animal experiments also brought a description of pathologic conditions, primarily renal lesions resulting from repeated injections of a foreign antigen. These typical lesions, produced by the deposition of immune complexes, have usually been referred to as chronic serum sickness. The human counterparts of experimental chronic serum sickness are various forms of glomerulonephritides with deposits in which the presence of immunoglobulins and complement can be demonstrated by immunofluorescence procedures. The outstanding example is the glomerulonephritis accompanying systemic lupus erythematosus. In this disease DNA was shown to be the antigenic material forming the complexes. In some other diseases, such as poststreptococcal nephritis or malarial nephritis, the microbial antigen could also be demonstrated in glomerular deposits, though with some difficulty. In many other forms of human "immune complex glomerulonephritis," the antigens producing the complexes remain unknown.

In vitro demonstration of immune complexes in the patient's serum and other body fluids has attracted considerable interest in recent years. Several procedures, such as analytical ultracentrifugation, gradient centrifugation, gel filtration, and selective ultrafiltration, depend on the physical properties of immune complexes, as does precipitation of immune complexes with polyethylene glycol.

Other procedures are based on biologic properties of immune complexes. Of these procedures, binding of Clq and measurement of this binding by several methods, primarily radioimmunoassay, seems to be quite popular. Absorption of rheumatoid factors and other antiglobulin factors has been quite extensively used. A very popular test involves binding of immune complexes by Raji cells, which are cultured lymphoid cells. In most instances this test is based on binding of immune complexes (that had combined with complement) to the complement receptors on the Raji cells. Detection of complexes bound to the cells is achieved by staining the components of complexes (antigen, antibody, complement) with proper fluorescein labeled antisera or by means of radioimmunoassays.

Detection of immune complexes in pathologic tissues is achieved by immunofluorescence or immunoelectron microscopy.

REFERENCES

Humphrey, J.H. and White, R.G.: Immunology for Students of Medicine. 3rd Ed. F.A. Davis, Philadelphia, 1970.

Kolle, W., Kraus, R., and Uhlenhuth, P., Eds.: Handbuch der pathogenen Mikroorganismen. Vol. I, Part 2; Vol. II, Parts 1 & 2. Gustav Fischer, Jena; Urban & Schwarzeberg, Berlin & Vienna, 1929.

Middleton, E., Jr., Reed, C.E., and Ellis, E.F., Eds.: Allergy. Principles and Practice. Vol. 1 & 2. C.V. Mosby, St. Louis, 1978.

Neter, E. and Milgrom, F., Eds.: The Immune System and Infectious Diseases. S. Karger, Basel, 1975.

Rose, N.R., Milgrom, F., and van Oss, C.J., Eds.: Principles of Immunology. 2nd Ed. Macmillan, New York, 1979.

Samter, M., Ed.: Immunological Diseases. 3rd Ed. Little, Brown, Boston, 1978.

Wilson, G.S. and Miles, A.A., Eds.: Topley & Wilson's Principles of Bacteriology, Virology and Immunity. 6th Ed. Williams & Wilkins, Baltimore, 1975.

13

Cell-Mediated Immunity and Hypersensitivity

*Diane M. Jacobs and
Bernice K. Noble*

CHARACTERISTICS OF CELL-MEDIATED IMMUNITY

A normal host exposed to antigen may respond by developing a state of immunity characterized by the presence of antigen-reactive lymphocytes. The central role of specifically sensitized lymphocytes, which act both to recognize antigen and as the effector arm of the immune response, distinguishes cell-mediated immunity (CMI) from humoral immunity (discussed in the preceding chapter), in which effectors are antibody molecules. Historically, a number of individual immunologic phenomena that are now all attributed to CMI were described and given various names, presented at the end of this chapter.

Tuberculin-type hypersensitivity, contact sensitivity, and cutaneous basophil hypersensitivity take their names from characteristics of the skin reactions that occur when antigen is applied to or injected into the skin of an immune host. Antigens inducing CMI under natural (rather than experimental) conditions are most often infectious agents or chemicals that have reacted with the host's own proteins.

Transplantation immunity and tumor immunity refer to responses directed toward antigens on foreign cells and tumor cells, respectively. Work with experimental models of these immune responses has demonstrated that immunity can be passively transferred from immune to normal or immunologically incompetent hosts with lymphoid cells but not with serum. For that reason the term *cell-mediated immunity (CMI)* has been applied to all of these immune responses.

In this chapter we will be concerned primarily with forms of CMI in which the antigenic stimulus comes from natural infection, from exposure to a reactive chemical, or from immunization with purified proteins or microbial extracts.

DELAYED HYPERSENSITIVITY

CMI develops naturally as a consequence of infection with microorganisms that grow as intracellular parasites. Some bacteria, viruses, many fungi, and a number of animal parasites, whose growth and multiplication are not inhibited by phagocytosis or by specific antibodies, stimulate CMI in most

Table 13.1.   Infectious Agents Giving Rise to Cell-Mediated Immunity

Bacteria	Viruses
Mycobacterium tuberculosis	Herpes simplex virus
Listeria spp.	Vaccinia virus
Brucella spp.	Cytomegalovirus
Treponema pallidum	Variola virus
Salmonella typhi	Varicella zoster virus
Norcadia spp.	Mumps
Francisella tularensis	Measles virus
Fungi	
Cryptococcus neoformans	Protozoa
Coccidioides immitis	*Toxoplasma gondii*
Histoplasma capsulatum	*Trypanosoma cruzi*
Candida albicurs	*Leishmania* spp.
Aspergillus spp.	Helminths
	Schistosoma mansoni
	Trichinella spiralis
	Wuchereria bancrofti

infected animals (Table 13.1). The host response to antigens of such infectious agents most commonly results in an inflammatory process, which can be seen as an attempt to destroy the infectious agent. If this primary exposure results in more efficient resistance or recovery after secondary exposure, CMI is responsible for protective immunity. If tissue damage occurs, the process may be referred to as *hypersensitivity* and *bacterial allergy*.

Following the subcutaneous or intradermal injection of specific antigen in an appropriately sensitized animal, a slowly evolving inflammatory response develops at the skin test site. The response of a previously infected guinea pig to a subcutaneous injection of virulent tubercle bacilli was first described by Robert Koch in 1891. He observed that although the original injection produced a persistent ulcer at the inoculation site and spread of bacilli to regional lymph nodes, subsequent superinfection by introduction of the tubercle bacilli at another skin site led to rapid ulcer formation, followed by healing without involvement of draining lymph nodes. The altered response to living tubercle bacilli and to antigenic material extracted from these organisms, which characterizes exposure of a previously infected animal, has been called the *Koch phenomenon*.

To test for previous infection of man with *Mycobacterium tuberculosis*, an intradermal skin test with a standard amount of a purified protein derivative (PPD) prepared by extraction from cultures of *M. tuberculosis* is often used (Ch. 34). Since the delayed skin response resulting from infection with *M. tuberculosis* has been most thoroughly studied, that skin reaction to tuberculin protein is considered the prototype *delayed hypersensitivity* (*DH*) reaction. Delayed reactions that histologically resemble the reaction to *M. tuberculosis* may be called tuberculin-type reactions. Although it was once thought that DH was an immune response unique to exposure to antigens of microbial agents, we now know that immunization with proteins and with simple chemicals (haptens) conjugated to proteins may also produce CMI detectable by delayed reactions. The use of purified proteins to elicit CMI detectable by skin reactions has been very valuable in studying and analyzing DH in the laboratory.

Artificial immunization to produce DH

of the tuberculin type is best achieved by the intradermal introduction of antigen. An intravenous route of antigen administration usually favors antibody formation. The response is enhanced when the antigen is injected in a stable emulsion with a suitable adjuvant. The most commonly used adjuvant, complete Freund's adjuvant (CFA), is a suspension of killed mycobacteria in paraffin oil. A water-in-oil emulsion of CFA and the antigen is used for immunization. A typical delayed skin reaction can be elicited within a week of immunization. Amounts of antigen many times smaller than those required for effective immunization are sufficient to elicit substantial skin reactions. Specific skin reactivity may persist for many years without further boosting.

Within 6 to 8 hours after injection of antigen into the skin, erythema and induration can be observed at the skin test site. The reaction reaches a maximum in size and intensity in 24 to 48 hours and then usually subsides. Very strong reactions may show central necrosis. The magnitude of the skin reaction can be assessed by measuring the diameter of the area of erythema, the increase in skin thickness, and the intensity of redness at fixed times after skin testing. The major histologic feature of the classic tuberculin-type DH skin reaction is a diffuse cellular infiltration of the dermis. The infiltration begins as a perivascular accumulation of cells. Later the cellular infiltrate becomes diffuse throughout the dermis. Because it is difficult to distinguish cell types in tissue sections stained by conventional methods, the cellular composition of the infiltrate is usually described as "mononuclear". Both lymphocytes and macrophages are present. The composition of the cellular infiltrate is somewhat different in different species. For example, in guinea pigs, the animal that most closely resembles man in cutaneous manifestations of DH, polymorphonuclear leukocytes constitute a larger fraction of the cells in the infiltrate than is commonly seen in man.

The indurated nature of the DH reaction has long been attributed to the influx of large numbers of cells from the circulation into the local site of antigen deposition. With modern techniques, fibrin deposits have been demonstrated in DH inflammations. It appears that fibrin deposition and not cellular infiltration is responsible for the characteristic induration.

DH skin reactions reflecting CMI may be distinguished in several ways from skin reactions caused by antibodies. First, antibody-mediated inflammatory reactions in the skin occur more rapidly. For example, the wheal and flare reaction, which is produced by homocytotropic antibodies (IgE in man), is visible at the injection site within minutes and is therefore referred to as *im-*

Table 13.2. Comparison of Humoral and Cell-Mediated Skin Reactions

	Immediate	Arthus	Delayed
Time for maximum response in sensitized individuals	Minutes	4 to 8 hours	24 to 48 hours
Macroscopic appearance	Wheal (urticaria), flare (erythema)	Soft, ill defined edema, erythema	Well defined induration, erythema
Histologic hallmark	Eosinophils	Polymorphonuclear leukocytes	Lymphocytes and macrophages
Passive sensitization	Serum	Serum	Sensitized lymphocytes
Mediator/effector	IgE antibodies	IgG antibodies	T cells

mediate hypersensitivity. Skin reactions of the Arthus type, mediated by IgG antibodies, may resemble delayed hypersensitivity reactions in the first few hours after the introduction of antigen, but a maximum is attained in 6 to 8 hours. Arthus reactions usually subside in 24 hours, although severe reactions may still be quite strong after 24 hours. Eosinophils are the striking feature of the cellular infiltration that accompanies the immediate hypersensitivity skin reaction; the inflammation associated with IgG-mediated reactions in the skin has a preponderance of neutrophils. Arthus reactions are further distinguishable from DH reactions by their edematous nature (Table 13.2).

It should be realized that the delayed period required for full expression of CMI in skin testing is the function of the skin assay as well as the immunological reactions that produce the inflammation. In other *in vivo* models of DH the time course of the reaction may be different. DH can be studied by the intraperitoneal administration of antigen into experimental animals. In that case the maximum intensity of the reaction in the peritoneal cavity is seen within a few hours.

In addition to DH reactions of the tuberculin type, two other major classes of delayed skin reactions are attributable to CMI. Contact sensitivity and cutaneous basophil hypersensitivity also result from the interaction of specifically sensitized lymphocytes with local deposits of antigen. Furthermore, the time course of the skin inflammation is similar to that of the classic tuberculin-type DH. Differences from tuberculin-type reactions are significant, however, and serve to illustrate the possible range of expression of CMI when conditions of induction or elicitation of the response in sensitized individuals differ from the tuberculin-type DH model.

The antigens that produce contact sensitivity are characteristically highly reactive chemicals that can combine with proteins of

the host. Textile and hair dyes are often responsible for contact sensitivity. Some highly reactive plant products, such as those found in poison ivy, are also potent immunogens. Metals such as mercury, nickel, and chromium may produce hypersensitivity, which manifests as a delayed skin reaction. It appears that most antigens that stimulate contact sensitivity are haptens. They must combine with a protein constituent of the epidermis to form hapten-protein conjugates in order to become complete antigens. Sensitization may be measured in a delayed skin reaction within a week of initial exposure of skin to the antigen. Similar to tuberculin-type DH reactions, contact sensitivity reactions can be elicited with skin-test doses of antigen many times lower than those required for immunization. To elicit a contact reaction, a patch test can be used. Alternatively, the reactive hapten may be dropped directly on the skin in a carefully measured volume of an appropriate solvent. The inflammation usually reaches a maximum intensity within 24 to 48 hours. However, the maximum may be delayed as long as 96 hours because of the key requirement that the antigen first interact chemically with the skin. Severe reactions may last a week. The test site becomes erythematous and indurated. Blister formation is common. Histologic changes associated with contact sensitivity include a perivenous accumulation of mononuclear cells in the dermis. The invasion of the epidermis by mononuclear cells results in intraepidermal edema (spongiosis), vesiculation, and death of epidermal cells.

Guinea pigs immunized without mycobacterial adjuvants may develop CMI that gives rise to a delayed skin reaction somewhat different from the tuberculin-type reaction. The modified delayed skin reaction has been called Jones-Mote hypersensitivity to distinguish it from the classical tuberculin reaction. With the application of modern techniques to fix, stain, and study tissues, it has been possible to identify a large percentage (up to 50 percent) of cells in the Jones-Mote skin reaction as basophils. For that reason the name *cutaneous basophil hypersensitivity* (*CBH*) has come into general use to replace the original designation. Infiltration of the skin-test site with large numbers of basophils has been found to be a feature of delayed skin reactions following immunization with soluble protein antigens, in many contact allergies, and in reactions to insect bites. Although the time course and the gross appearance of CBH skin reactions are very similar to those of tuberculin-type DH reactions, fibrin deposition and induration are much less pronounced. Neutrophils and macrophages are rare cellular constituents of CBH inflammation.

CELLULAR BASIS OF CMI

The gross appearance, cellular composition, and time course of DH skin reactions are usually sufficiently different from those mediated by antibodies to permit an unequivocal indentification to be made. However, it is possible for considerable overlapping of any or all of these criteria to be encountered in gross or microscopic examination. CMI can be formally and rigorously distinguished from antibody-mediated immunity by the demonstration of a requirement for living cells in passive transfer experiments. Skin reactivity of the delayed type may be conferred on a nonimmune animal by the injection of sufficient numbers of lymphoid cells from an appropriately sensitized donor. Spleen cells, lymph node cells, or peritoneal exudate cells taken from an immunized animal, in which cell-mediated skin reactions can be elicited, will transfer specific sensitivity to an animal that has not had previous exposure to the antigen in question. A positive skin reaction to the specific antigen in the recipient demonstrates a successful cell transfer. Transfer of serum from the same donor to a nonimmune recipient does not have the same effect. In contrast, antibody-mediated skin reactions of the immediate hypersensitivity or Arthus type will be positive in a normal animal that has received injections of serum containing specific antibody. Therefore the combination of both cell and serum transfer experiments provides a very valuable criterion for distinguishing phenomena attributable to CMI from those dependent on the action of antibodies. Cell transfer experiments have been very useful to analyze cell interactions in CMI.

Several lines of evidence indicate that the lymphoid cells responsible for *in vivo* manifestations of CMI and for effective passive transfer of CMI are thymus-dependent or thymus-derived, T cells. The T cell is a lymphocyte whose ability to develop immunocompetence in the host is dependent on the presence of an intact thymus. This requirement distinguishes T cells from B cells, which are lymphocytes that develop into antibody-forming cells. Adult animals whose thymuses have been removed surgically during the neonatal period have greatly reduced levels of functional T cells. Depletion of T cells in young adults is accomplished by the combination of thymectomy and total body irradiation to kill peripheral T cells. The hemopoietic system is restored by transfer of immature bone marrow cells. Animals without T cells are immunologically deficient and cannot be immunized for CMI. Their capacity to be immunized for CMI can be restored by either a thymus graft or transfer of purified populations of T cells, spleen, or lymph node cells. Lymphoid cell populations depleted of active T cells are ineffective in restoring CMI to immunologically deficient animals.

Clinical observations are consistent with such laboratory experiments. Patients with the congenital immunologic deficiency disease, Di George's syndrome, have normal levels of serum immunoglobulin but do not have active T cells in the peripheral blood. They are extremely susceptible to viral and fungal diseases. Another type of immunodeficiency disease is characterized by a high incidence of infections with pyogenic bacteria but normal resistance to viral infections. Those patients have low levels of circulating immunoglobulin and normal levels of active T cells in the peripheral blood.

Experiments with *in vivo* models of DH have established the immunologic basis of the skin reactions and described the cells taking part in such reactions. From such studies the reaction has been shown to be immunologically specific; the test antigen must be the same as, or closely related to, that used to immunize the host. In addition, it has been learned that most of the mononuclear cells accumulating at the skin test site are not specific. When sensitized lymphoid cells taken from immunized donors are "tagged" with a radioactive label and subsequently injected into a nonimmune recipient, only a small fraction (less than 10 percent) of the mononuclear cells present in the specific delayed skin reaction of the recipient are found to contain the radioisotope. Since most of the cells in the infiltrate are not radioactive, they must come from the recipient. Therefore it can be concluded that the large majority of the cells present in a cell-mediated skin reaction have not had a previous exposure to specific antigen. A skin-test reaction of the recipient to an antigen to which the recipient but not the donor has been previously sensitized also contains a small fraction of radiolabeled cells derived from the donor. Furthermore, in similar experiments it has been shown that a nonimmunologic skin inflammation induced in the same recipient contains as many radiolabeled cells as an antigen-specific reaction, suggesting that the accumulation of lymphoid cells in an inflammatory response need not be an immunologically directed process. In addition, macrophages and granulocytes do not

possess any immunologic specificity, yet they clearly participate in the various stages of the inflammatory response. These observations strongly suggest that immunologically nonspecific cells of various types are recruited, possibly by soluble factors, to participate in the inflammatory response initiated by an immune reaction. The time required for such secondary effects could explain the delay in the development of the skin reaction. Necrosis and tissue destruction seen in some DH skin reactions and in graft rejections raise the possibility that cells mediating these responses are directly cytotoxic.

From experiments with models of CMI in living animals (DH, transplantation immunity) it has been possible to draw certain conclusions and to make some inferences about the mechanisms responsible for the observable phenomena. Extension of the study of CMI to *in vitro* models has permitted experiments to be performed under carefully controlled conditions using purified populations of cells. Those experiments have confirmed ideas of CMI that emerged from work performed *in vivo*. *In vitro* experiments have also considerably extended our view of CMI, with the result that a complex picture of the possible range of cellular interactions in CMI has emerged.

The incubation of sensitized T cells with antigen *in vitro* for several days results first in blastogenesis. Small lymphocytes with a dense nucleus and scanty cytoplasm are activated and become blast cells, which have a less dense nucleus and more cytoplasm. This is followed by DNA synthesis and mitosis. It appears that two different effector mechanisms can result from this process of T cell activation: the production of lymphokines and the development of cytotoxic cells. The major portion of our knowledge of lymphokines comes from experiments with models of DH. Cytotoxic lymphocytes have been most widely studied in transplantation immunity.

EFFECTOR MECHANISMS: SOLUBLE FACTORS ACTING ON CELLS (LYMPHOKINES)

Lymphokines are soluble factors produced by lymphocytes that in an immunologically nonspecific fashion may affect lymphocytes and/or other inflammatory cells. Their function is to recruit, immobilize, and activate those cells that produce the inflammatory response at the site of antigen deposition in an immune host. A number of lymphokine activities have been detected in supernatant fluids of cultures of lymphoid cells from immune hosts after incubation of those cells with antigen. Lymphokines may also be found in supernatants of normal lymphoid cells cultured *in vitro* in the presence of mitogens such as phytohemagglutinin (PHA) or concanavalin A (Con A). They have been given descriptive names according to their activities on target cells. Only a few of these soluble factors have been purified to homogeneity. It is not yet clear whether each separate lymphokine activity is mediated by a chemically distinct molecule or whether some molecules have several different activities.

Factors Acting on Macrophages

Migration Inhibitory Factor (MIF). Normal macrophages, packed into a capillary tube and placed horizontally in tissue culture medium in tissue culture vessels, migrate from the opening of the capillary tube in 24 hours. However, if the tissue culture medium also contains MIF, the macrophages do not migrate, but remain inside the capillary. Supernatant fluids obtained from lymphocytes incubated with the specific antigen are said to contain MIF if they inhibit migration. Culture fluids taken from cells incubated without antigen possess no MIF activity, leaving macrophages to migrate freely as with

medium alone. MIF is one of the few mediators that has been chemically purified. Guinea pig MIF is a glycoprotein of 35,000 to 55,000 daltons that interacts with fucose residues on target cell surfaces. It appears to act by first causing macrophages to become sticky and clump together.

Macrophage Activation Factor (MAF). Other changes that occur when macrophages are exposed to supernatant fluids from cultures of sensitized lymphocytes incubated with specific antigen have been attributed to a lymphokine called *macrophage activation factor*. It has not yet been possible to separate MAF from MIF, and the activities may be due to the same molecule. When normal macrophages are incubated with MAF for several days, a number of alterations are observed, including increases in adherence to the culture vessel, ruffled membrane activity, phagocytosis, pinocytosis, glucose oxidation, and bactericidal activity. Eventually, macrophages may show increased motility.

The apparent inconsistency of observing both MIF-mediated inhibition of motility and MAF-mediated enhancement of motility may be explained by differences in the time at which each characteristically occurs. It is likely that initial changes in cell surface charge result in stickiness, which causes inhibition of motility. Metabolic changes that occur later lead to increased motility. Macrophages activated by MAF may also become cytotoxic for syngeneic tumor cells.

Macrophage Chemotactic Factor (MCF). MIF/MAF activities can explain *in vivo* observations of macrophage activation in delayed skin reactions, but they do not adequately account for the large accumulation of macrophages at the skin-test site. The attraction of macrophages can be attributed to macrophage (monocyte) chemotactic factor. Chemotactic activity for macrophages and other cells can be measured in a *Boyden chamber*. The Boyden chamber has two compartments separated by a membrane with pores large enough to allow passage of migrating cells. The fluid to be assayed is placed on one side of the filter and cells in tissue culture medium on the other. When a fluid with MCF is present on one side of the test chamber, cells migrate actively through the membrane and adhere to its opposite surface. If the test medium is a supernatant fluid from sensitized cells incubated in the absence of antigen, cells do not migrate through the membrane. Absence of such movement indicates the absence of MCF. MCF can be separated physically from MIF. Furthermore, MCF activity is not altered by the addition of MIF.

Factors Affecting Granulocytes

The normal mobility of polymorphonuclear leukocytes can be measured in a capillary tube system in the same way that macrophage movement is measured. Leukocyte mobility is inhibited by *leukocyte inhibitory factor* (*LIF*), which is produced by lymphocytes following stimulation by specific antigen or mitogen. Some characteristics of LIF indicate that it is different from MIF. It has a higher molecular weight than MIF and is a protein rather than a glycoprotein.

Antigen- or mitogen-stimulated lymphocytes may also produce soluble factors that are chemotactic for neutrophils, basophils, or eosinophils. *Neutrophil chemotactic factor* (*NCF*) has been separated from macrophage chemotactic activity. These factors could explain the accumulation of large numbers of one cell type in some skin reactions, as for example, basophils in CBH.

Factors Affecting Lymphocytes

Experiments in animals have demonstrated that only a fraction of the lymphocytes present in a delayed skin inflammation can be considered "specific." It was therefore postulated that a mechanism existed to acti-

vate or recruit nonsensitized lymphocytes to the skin-test site. A soluble factor that causes lymphocytes to divide, called *lymphocyte mitogenic factor* (*LMF*), has been found in supernatant fluids of lymphocyte cultures exposed to antigen. LMF induces blastogenesis and DNA synthesis in normal lymphocytes. Stimulation of normal lymphocyte activity may result in the production of additional lymphokines by newly recruited nonimmune cells. In this way a significant amplification of the inflammatory response can occur.

***Transfer Factor* (*TF*)** is produced by sensitized cells that have been stimulated by antigen or by extraction of sensitized lymphoid cells. It has been reproducibly demonstrated only in man and not in laboratory animals. When prepared from cells of an immune host, transfer factor has the property of conferring CMI on a nonimmune recipient. It also enables nonimmune lymphocytes to respond to specific antigen *in vitro*. TF is a low molecular weight material. Though resistant to nucleases, it does appear to contain a polynucleotide portion. Although its activity is not well understood, human TF has been used successfully for clinical therapy against opportunistic infections in some cases of severe immunodeficiency.

Factors Acting on Other Cells

The supernatant fluids of cultures of sensitized lymphocytes in the presence of the corresponding antigen contain factors cytotoxic or cytostatic to special target cells. These lymphokines are *lymphotoxin* (*LT*), *proliferation inhibition factor* (*PIF*), and *cloning inhibition factor* (*CIF*).

Osteoclast-activating factor (*OAF*), which promotes bone resorption, may be of importance in pathologic disease of the oral cavity, osteomyelitis, and rheumatoid arthritis.

Supernatant fluids from cultures of antigen- or mitogen-stimulated lymphocytes inhibit growth of viruses *in vitro*. The factors responsible for inhibition belong to the class of proteins called *interferons*, which are also produced by fibroblasts and leukocytes in response to a variety of nonimmunologic stimuli. Interferons differ from each other in antigenic and chemical characteristics, which provide the basis for a new system of nomenclature (Ch. 49).

Interferons induce a number of changes in cells in addition to inhibition of virus growth. These include inhibition of cell multiplication, changes in cell surfaces, regulation of interferon synthesis, and immunomodulation. CMI and antibody formation may be either inhibited or enhanced by interferon, and the activity of natural killer cells (see below) is increased.

Biologic Significance of Lymphokines

The preceding section has shown that a large number of biologic activities can be detected in cultures of properly stimulated lymphocytes. It is now time to ask what relevance lymphokine activity measured *in vitro* may have for the expression of CMI in a sensitized animal. The demonstration of lymphokines and the attribution of particular phenomena to lymphokine activity *in vivo* is difficult. It has not yet been possible to show that lymphokines are present in every reaction in which they are suspected to play a role. However, there is considerable evidence that some lymphokines behave in animals as they do in model systems *in vitro*.

Three main approaches have been used to show that lymphokines may play a role in CMI. First, a lymphokine-rich supernatant fluid, or purified lymphokine, may be injected into an animal and the biologic activity of the cell-free extract may be measured. In this way it can be demonstrated that lymphokines alone produce a skin inflammation that resembles a delayed skin reaction in many features. The maximum intensity of lymphokine-induced skin reac-

tions occurs much earlier (12 hours) than a conventional DH skin reaction. The later appearance of a delayed skin reaction could well reflect the time required for sensitized lymphocytes to elaborate sufficient quantities of lymphokines and recruit nonspecific cells. Intravenous injections of MIF-rich supernatants into normal guinea pigs have also been shown to result in a great reduction of monocytes in peripheral blood.

A second way to show the importance of lymphokines in CMI is to isolate lymphokine activity from body fluids and, in particular, from tissue sites where an immunologically mediated inflammatory reaction is taking place. In a large number of such experiments lymphokine activity, mostly MIF activity, has been demonstrated in serum, lymph, peritoneal exudates, DH skin sites, effusions of otitis media, joint fluids, and schistosome egg granulomas.

Finally, antibodies raised against lymphokines are able to suppress DH skin reactions when injected into the skin test site.

EFFECTOR MECHANISMS: DIRECT CELLULAR CYTOTOXICITY (CYTOTOXIC CELLS)

Cytotoxic Lymphocytes

Specific T cell responses can be elicited to histocompatibility antigens, tumor-associated transplantation antigens, and virus-associated antigens present on the surface of cells infected with nonlytic viruses. The predominant effector cells in some cases are antigen-specific cytotoxic lymphocytes. Cytotoxic lymphocytes belong to a subclass of T lymphocytes, distinguished from the T cells that produce lymphokines by a characteristic cell surface antigen. Cytotoxicity occurs by the direct interaction of T lymphocytes with target cells. Metabolic changes in the target cell result in damage to the target cell membrane. Even when the killer T cell is not specifically directed against histocompatibility antigens, cytotoxicity requires interaction with histocompatibility antigens on the target cell. This phenomenon is called associative recognition or MHC restriction (see Ch.14).

Cytotoxic Macrophages

As has been explained previously, macrophages may be activated by lymphokines that have been released as a result of the interaction of T lymphocytes with specific antigen or mitogens. Activation of macrophages may also be achieved by nonimmunological means, such as exposure to bacterial lipopolysaccharide. One property of activated macrophages is the ability to kill or inhibit growth of syngeneic or allogeneic tumor cells. The cytotoxic activity of macrophages does not show immunologic specificity, since a variety of tumor cells are susceptible to such killing. However, there is some evidence that an immunologically specific macrophage-arming factor (SMAF) can render macrophages cytotoxic for the tumor that induced the factor

Other Cell-Mediated Cytotoxicity

From studies on T cell-mediated cytotoxicity and macrophage cytotoxicity, two additional types of cytotoxicity have been discovered. These cytotoxic phenomena are dependent on cells (and therefore are referred to as "cell mediated"), but the effectors have characteristics that distinguish them from cytotoxic T cells and macrophages.

Natural Killer(NK) Cells.   Natural killer cells are found in normal hosts, both man and animals. In the absence of deliberate exposure to antigen, they are capable of effectively killing a variety of lymphoid tumor cells. NK cells are found in lymphoid tissue but do not possess the surface antigens that characterize either T cells or B cells. Because of this they are often referred to as *null cells.* Their activity is increased by interferon. The biologic function of NK cells is unknown, but one current hypothesis suggests they may act as a surveillance system for cells that have escaped from other homeostatic controls.

Antibody Dependent Cell-Mediated Cytotoxicity (ADCC).   This type of cytotoxicity is mediated by several types of cells that can bind specific antibody via cell surface receptors for the Fc region of immunoglobulins. Such cells include macrophages, immature monocytes, immature polymorphs, eosinophils, and null cells (so-called killer or K cells). When the attached antibody possesses specificity for a cell surface antigen, cells bearing the antigen can be killed by interaction with the "armed" effector cells. ADCC is involved in the defense against some viruses, such as measles; for example, K cells plus IgG kill measles-infected target cells. ADCC is also a major component of defense against parasites such as *Schistosoma mansoni* (eosinophils plus IgG, macrophages plus IgE).

IN VITRO TESTS OF CLINICAL VALUE FOR ASSESSMENT OF CMI

Skin tests have been used for many years to evaluate the state of immunity to a number of bacterial antigens. However, useful skin tests are limited to those for which antigen is available in at least partially purified form. Furthermore, such tests may be carried out only when the administration of even a small amount of antigen is not harmful to the patient. Finally, patients with a variety of infections or states of immunologic deficiency do not respond to common skin test antigens, a condition of nonresponsiveness known as *anergy.*

Several *in vitro* tests originally developed for research purposes have proven useful in assessing CMI of patients. These tests are carried out with peripheral blood lymphocytes of patients to test their specific cellular reactivity to test antigens. To perform the test, the patient's lymphocytes must first be separated from granulocytes and erythrocytes under sterile conditions and then suspended in nutrient medium. The cell suspensions are incubated in tissue culture vessels for periods lasting as long as 1 week, depending on the particular assay.

Macrophage Migration Inhibition Assay

We have seen that lymphocytes from an individual with CMI produce MIF when incubated in culture with specific antigen. To test MIF production by cells of a patient, peripheral blood lymphocytes are incubated in the presence of test antigen and in medium alone, and the supernatant fluids are collected. These fluids are tested for MIF activity by adding each to a tissue culture vessel containing a capillary tube packed with guinea pig macrophages. The cultures are incubated for a further 24 hours and the behavior of the macrophages examined. Supernatant fluids from cells incubated with medium alone always permit normal macrophages to migrate. Supernatants obtained from sensitized cells incubated with antigen inhibit macrophage migration. The detection of MIF in culture supernatants is evidence that the patient's circulatory lymphocyte population contains T cells specifically sensitized and responsive to the test antigen.

Mitogenic Assay

When lymphocytes from a sensitized host are incubated *in vitro* with medium alone, there is little change in the cells. When they are incubated in the presence of an antigen to which the host has been sensitized, a gradual change in the population of the cells in the culture can be detected by conventional stains. In addition to the original small lymphocytes placed in culture, the first to appear are large cells, which have a larger nucleus and more cytoplasm, con-

taining substantial amounts of RNA. Subsequently, mitotic figures appear. The change that can be measured most simply is the synthesis of DNA. This is carried out by measuring the incorporation of a radioactive precursor of DNA into cells. A trace amount of ^{3}H-thymidine is added to the cultures. After 6 to 24 hours the cells are harvested and washed. The amount of radioactivity incorporated is measured with a scintillation counter. Similar "pulses" may be carried out daily in a series of cultures. With a soluble antigen, such as purified protein derivative (PPD, an antigen from culture filtrates of *M. tuberculosis*) or streptokinase/streptodornase, maximum DNA synthesis occurs only after 5 to 7 days of culture. Standardization of incubation time and antigen concentration is important in evaluating CMI accurately by this method.

A culture of cells with mitogen(s) instead of specific antigen may be used to evaluate the general level of T or B lymphocyte activity in a patient. Plant extracts such as PHA and Con A are mitogenic for T cells, whereas pokeweed mitogen (PWM) also stimulates mitogenesis in B cells. These materials stimulate most or all cells of the particular cell lineage, and responses appear earlier in the culture period (2 to 4 days) than responses of sensitized cells to specific antigen.

The culturing together of two sets of lymphocytes differing in histocompatibility antigens is called a *mixed lymphocyte culture (MLC)* or a *mixed lymphocyte reaction (MLR)*. If neither set of cells is treated in any way, the culture is referred to as a *two-way MLR* because cells from both sets proliferate. Most often the cells serving as antigen (stimulator cells) are irradiated or treated with mitomycin C (an inhibitor of DNA synthesis), so that DNA synthesis measured is due to responding cells only. This is referred to as a *one-way MLR*. Maximum responses occur in 5 to 6 days.

Cytotoxicity

Cells incubated with lymphocytes in an MLR or exposed *in vivo* or *in vitro* to cells with other surface antigens associated with CMI develop into cytotoxic T cells. The cytotoxic activity of lymphocytes as well as the cytotoxicity of macrophages, NK cells, or ADCC can be measured *in vitro*. Cells to be tested are incubated for several hours with target cells that have been labeled with a radioisotope. The incubation time is dependent on the isotope used and the nature of the target cell. The most common isotope used is ^{51}Cr, in which case the assay is called a *chromium release assay*. Target cells are prepared by incubation for 30 to 60 minutes with medium containing ^{51}Cr. After the excess radioisotope is removed, the radiolabeled target cells are added to suspensions of cells to be tested and the cell mixture incubated further for 4 hours. At the end of this period the cells are centrifuged, and the amount of radioactivity in an aliquot of supernatant fluid is determined. By comparing the amount of radioactivity released after incubation of effector and target cells to the total amount of radioactivity in a sample of target cells, the percentage of radioactivity released is calculated. Lymphoid cells with no cytotoxic activity have little effect on target cells, and only small amounts of radioactivity are released. Since the cytotoxicity is antigen specific, labeled target cells lacking the antigen in question will also lose only little radioactivity during the incubation period.

among immunoglobulin classes. T cells can be divided into classes on the basis of distinctive surface markers, and these classes have characteristic functions. Interaction of one kind of T cell with antigen results in production of lymphokines, which, by recruiting and activating lymphocytes, are able to amplify the recruitment and local activation of macrophages, which in turn kill intracellular bacteria or suppress their growth. When the lymphokine produced is interferon, virus growth in target host cells is inhibited. Interferon production also increases the activity of NK cells, which can participate in ADCC reactions against multicellular parasites. A different class of T cells with different surface markers develops into cytotoxic cells, which destroy virus-infected cells. Still other classes of T cells with regulatory functions are stimulated by exposure to antigen to amplify or suppress effector T and B cell function. The complex interrelationships among classes of T cells and effector inflammatory cells depend on the type and dose of antigen, genetic factors, the nutritional state of the host, and other physiologic factors. Thus resistance to and recovery from infectious disease varies from host to host, even under apparently identical conditions. Furthermore, destruction of the invading organism may result in temporary tissue damage, such as the exanthems associated with some bacterial and viral infections. In yet other circumstances, CMI responses may result in chronic inflammation and tissue destruction, as seen in infection with *M. tuberculosis*.

CONCLUSION

CMI, by which a host deals with many types of harmful invaders, may be seen to be mediated by several different mechanisms, each with an immunologically specific component. Among the T cells, there is a "division of labor" with regard to many effector functions comparable to that seen

TERMS IN COMMON USE

A number of terms are commonly used to denote the phenomena associated with CMI. These terms tend to be descriptive, focusing on one aspect of the biologic process we observe; as such they reflect our ignorance and prejudice. As our understanding of immunology has progressed, the meanings of these terms have changed, often resulting in some ambiguity. Explanations of each term are given below in order of the authors' preference, in an attempt to provide a useful guide to the literature and to this and other textbooks.

Bacterial allergy. Delayed hypersensitivity occurring as a result of bacterial infection.

Contact sensitivity. (1) Immunologic state in which delayed skin reaction may be elicited by topical application of antigen. Also called contact allergy and contact dermatitis. (2) Also refers to skin reaction evoked.

Cutaneous basophil hypersensitivity. (1) Immunologic state in which delayed skin reaction consists of a high proportion of basophils. Also called Jones-Mote hypersensitivity. (2) Term also used to refer to skin reaction evoked.

Delayed hypersensitivity. (1) Immunologic state detected by characteristic delayed reaction (see below) in response to administration of specific antigen in or on the skin. (2) Often used to mean any cell-mediated immune response. (3) Sometimes used as a synonym for tuberculin-type delayed hypersensitivity. (4) Skin reaction elicited in immune host.

Delayed (skin) reaction. Inflammatory response to intradermal or topical antigen administration. The term is derived from the delay in development (peak at 24 to 48 hours), in contrast to antibody mediated immediate reactions, occurring in minutes or a few hours. Can be elicited in host with CMI to given antigen.

Sensitized lymphocytes. A population of lymphoid cells after primary or initial exposure to antigen; implies that subsequent interaction with specific antigen will lead to some type of measurable response.

Transplantation immunity, allograft immunity. Immunologic state in which lymphoid cells interact with cell-bound, foreign histocompatibility antigens, detected by the nonphysiologic exposure of host to foreign cells, organs, or tissues.

Tuberculin-type delayed hypersensitivity. (1) Immunologic state detected by characteristic delayed reaction with mononuclear infiltration in response to intradermal administration of antigen; so called because response to infection with *M. tuberculosis* has been the prototype or classical system studied. Often referred to simply as delayed hypersensitivity. (2) Skin reaction elicited in immune host.

Tumor immunity. Immunity directed toward tumor-specific antigens, characterized by ability of host to delay or prevent growth of syngeneic or autochthonous tumor.

REFERENCES

Cohen, S., Pick, E. and Oppenheim, J.J.: Biology of the Lymphokines. Academic Press, New York, 1979.

Mishell, B.B. and Shiigi, S.M., Eds.: Selected Methods in Cellular Immunology. W.H. Freeman, San Francisco, 1980.

Turk, J.L.: Delayed Hypersensitivity. North Holland Publishing Company, Amsterdam, 1975.

Waksman, B.H.: Cellular hypersensitivity and immunity: Conceptual changes in the last decade. Cell. Immunol. *42*: 155, 1979.

14

Immunogenetics of Mammals

Marek Zaleski

Formal Genetics

An inheritable physical or functional *trait* is determined by a factor called a *gene*.* The variants of a particular trait are determined by the variants of its gene, summarily called *alleles*. A given gene or its allele is located in a particular *chromosome*, where it occupies a characteristic and constant place called a *locus*. Only one allele can be present at the locus in a given time.

Since the cells of sexually reproducing organisms possess two *homologous* sets of chromosomes, one contributed by the maternal and the other by the paternal germ cell, they always have a pair of alleles for a given trait. If both alleles in the pair determine the same variant of the trait, the cell (organism) is a *homozygote* for this particular gene; when the two alleles of the pair determine two discrete variants of the trait, the cell (organism) is a *heterozygote*. All alleles contributed by one of the parents form a *haplotype*, and two parental haplotypes form a *genotype* or *genome*. The genotype constitutes a pool from which

some, but not all, genes are expressed as detectable traits. The set of all traits composes a *phenotype*. The expression of different alleles by genotypically identical cells of a given individual results in a multitude of phenotypically different cells corresponding to the different types and subtypes of the tissue. The sum of all cellular phenotypes gives the phenotype of the whole organism.

Alleles of a given gene may differ in their ability to be expressed, i.e., in their *expressivity*. An allele that is not expressed even in the homozygote is called *silent* or amorphic. An allele that is expressed in the homozygote but not in the heterozygote is called *recessive*, and an allele that is expressed in both homozygote and heterozygote is called *dominant*. Two alleles expressed simultaneously in the heterozygote are termed *codominant*. The expressivity of any allele is relative, since an allele dominant over one allele may be either codominant or recessive in relation to another allele.

Neither a gene nor its alleles are invariable, and they may and do undergo changes, called *mutations*. The phenomenon of mutation results in genotype variability of individuals and may ultimate-

---

* All symbols referring to genes and genotypes are by convention written in italics, as opposed to traits and phenotypes, which are written in roman characters.

ly lead to a change in the whole population or even the species. The frequency of the particular phenotypic variant of a trait (f) reflects the frequency of the corresponding allele (p) in a given population. This relationship is expressed by the formula

$$p = 1 - \sqrt{1-f}$$

The value of p for any allele or the sum of values of p for all alleles at a given locus cannot exceed 1.0 (100 percent). The polymorphism of a gene is measured by the number of its alleles and by their frequencies in a given population. A gene is considered polymorphic if it has at least two alleles with frequencies higher than 0.01 (1 percent), whereas a gene even with several alleles with frequencies lower than 0.01 is for practical reasons nonpolymorphic.

If the mating in a population is random, the frequencies of all alleles at a given locus remain relatively constant, and such a population is believed to be in a state of *equilibrium*. However, under some circumstances equilibrium can be temporarily or permanently disturbed. For example, if mutations are extremely frequent, the constant appearance of new and disappearance of old alleles prevents the establishment of an equilibrium.

Cellular Genetics

The entire genotype of a *somatic* cell is transmitted from one to another cell generation, since during the *S-phase* that precedes cell division all chromosomes (and thus the entire set of genes) are replicated. A change in an allele due to its structural modification, either during replication or during any stage of the cell cycle, produces a new phenotypic trait and is called a *somatic mutation*. Such a mutation is transmitted from one cell to another but not to the offspring of the individual. Transmission of parental genes to the offspring is accomplished by the *germ* cells — *ova* and *spermatozoa*. During the development of germ

cells the number of chromosomes is reduced, so that each germ cell contains only one set representing a random combination of maternal and paternal chromosomes.

The independent segregation of chromosomes during *reductive division (meiosis)* is responsible for the independent transmission of genes located in two different chromosomes. In contrast, genes in the same chromosome have a tendency to be transmitted together, and they form a *linkage group*. However, *linked* genes may be separated from each other by the process of *crossing over* occurring in meiosis and leading to the mutual exchange — *recombination* — of fragments between chromosomes of the homologous pair. In this way alleles originally in the same chromosome, which otherwise would be transmitted together, appear in two different chromosomes and are transmitted separately. The recombination frequency (fr) between two linked genes is directly related to the distance between them. The value of fr cannot exceed 0.5 (50 percent), since by random chance two genes in separate chromosomes are transmitted together in 50 percent of cases. Two genes at the extreme ends of the same chromosome have almost the same (0.5) chance of being separated by crossing over. Conversely, two genes that are close to each other have a relatively small probability of separation and in most instances are transmitted together. In the extreme case, two genes next to each other become separated so rarely that they may be considered mistakenly as a single gene and their variants as the alleles *(pseudoalleles)* of such a fictive gene. When, ultimately, a recombination is demonstrated, they are recognized for what they are, two discrete genes.

Because of the relationship between fr and the relative position of two genes, fr is utilized to measure the distance between genes in units called centimorgans (cM), 1 cM being equal to the distance between two genes with $fr = 0.01$ (1 percent). The sequence of any three genes in a linkage group can be established (*genetic mapping*) by determining distances between these genes, since distances between two neighboring genes should add up to the distance between two distal genes.

Molecular Genetics

At a molecular level each gene represents a stretch of chromosomal DNA determining the primary structure of a single polypeptide, a primary *gene product*. The primary product may by itself constitute a phenotypic trait, or it may be involved in a synthesis of some nonprotein moiety (e.g., some blood group determinant) or may determine a functional trait (e.g., ability to metabolize certain substrate). Replication of chromosomal DNA should lead to production of exact copies of DNA and thus genes. However, spontaneous or induced errors in replication result in nonexact copies corresponding to alleles. Moreover, a segment of DNA may be replicated twice instead of once; thus the genes in this segment are *duplicated*. Duplicated genes are originally identical (*redundant*), but owing to independent mutations they diverge ultimately. The structural divergence of duplicated genes is accompanied by functional divergence, though some analogy can be often traced. If the duplicated genes remain in the same chromosome, they form a cluster of related genes (*complex* or *supergene*), but they may be separated by *translocation*, which leads to two related genes in two different chromosomes. More detailed data concerning the molecular aspects of genetics can be found in Chapter 3 or in specialized monographs.

Immunogenetics and Its Methods

There is not an officially approved definition of immunogenetics, and the scope of the field varies depending on the personal preferences and interest of the scientist. For the purpose of this chapter, it will be accepted that the primary object of immunogenetics is the study of the inheritance of moieties capable of inducing an immune response (*antigens*) or the factors determining the nature and magnitude of an immune response to a given antigen (*responsiveness*). In pursuit of these studies, genetic and immunologic methods are employed in a complementary manner.

An elementary genetic analysis consists of four steps leading to defining for a given trait genetic nature, mode of inheritance, association with other genes, and the position of a gene in a given chromosome. The basic method employed consists of controlled breeding or, in the case of human beings, family studies to determine polymorphism of the gene in question, the expressivity of different alleles, conformance of inheritance with Mendelian predictions, linkage with other genes, and, finally, genetic mapping on the basis of recombination frequency. In addition, for a randomly bred population of animals or for human beings the frequencies of alleles and phenotypes are determined. In parallel to genetic analysis, attempts are made, employing chemical or immunochemical techniques, to define a structural gene product.

A different situation arises when laboratory animals are studied, since in some species — e.g., mice, rats, and guinea pigs — *inbred strains* have been produced by many (at least 20) generations of sister-brother mating that results in homozygosity at virtually all loci. This means that all individuals of a given strain are both genotypically and phenotypically identical with the exclusion of genes in the male (Y) sex chromosome. From inbred strains *congenic* strains are derived by crossing members of two strains differing for an allele at a given locus and then mating the progeny to one of the strains (inbred strain) for 12 consecutive generations, always selecting for breeding those individuals that carry the particular allele from the other strain (donor strain). The strain produced in this way differs from the original inbred strain by one small segment of genotype (genome) containing the particular allele. In rare instances two strains will differ by precisely *one* allele; such strains are called *coisogenic*. Availability of a cogenic strain allows study of the effect of a given allele without interference from other genes.

HUMAN BLOOD GROUPS

There is a large array of substances found predominantly on the surface of erythrocytes but occurring in other cells as well. These substances are determined either directly or indirectly by independent polymorphic genes forming distinct blood group systems. Three of these systems are of great practical importance in medicine and will be discussed briefly.

Genes, Products, and Antigens of the ABO (H) System

The *ABO* (*H*) system discovered in 1900 by Landsteiner proved to be more complex than originally believed; it consists of two independent loci, *H* and *ABO*.

The gene at the *H* locus is practically monomorphic, since a dominant allele, *H*, is found in the vast majority of individuals. The primary product of the *H* allele is an enzyme, *fucosyl transferase*, that catalyzes the transfer of α-L-fucose from glycosylated guanosine diphosphate (GDP) to the terminal galactose of the glycolipid molecule of erythrocytes, thus forming the secondary product called *H substance*. The *ABO* locus has three common alleles; the primary products of the codominant *A* and *B* alleles are α-D-N-acetylgalactosamine transferase and α-D-galactose transferase, respectively, whereas the recessive *O* allele appears to be amorphic (silent).

The two enzymes catalyze the transfer of corresponding carbohydrates from glycosy-

lated uridine diphosphate (UDP) to the terminal galactose of the H substance, producing either A or B blood group substance. The primary and secondary products of the *H* allele are prerequisite for the expression of *A* and *B* alleles, since in rare cases of homozygosity for the recessive *h* allele no H substance is produced and thus the primary products of the *A* and *B* alleles (i.e., transferases), although present, have no substrate and subsequently no secondary products are formed (see Bombay phenotype in Table 14.1).

The secondary products, A and B substances, are antigenic for those individuals who do not possess them and thus are capable of eliciting a specific immune response resulting in formation of anti-A and anti-B hemagglutinins. Either substance or its analog can be found in various common bacteria, plants, and animals, and accidental encounters with them are most likely responsible for appearance of natural anti-A, anti-B, or both in sera of individuals with the phenotypes, B, A, or O, respectively. Thus the natural hemagglutinins are only incidentally related to the blood group genes and will not be discussed here.

The quantity of either substance in a single cell may vary over quite a wide range, especially in the case of A substance. These variations are the basis for distinction of subgroups, either common (A_1 and A_2) or rare (A_3, A_x, and A_m). Some of the subgroups appear to be determined genetically, but the molecular basis remains unclear. Two mechanisms, presently disputed, consider either differences in the activity of corresponding transferases or complementation between alleles at the *ABO* locus.

The expression of the *H* gene is influenced by alleles at still another locus, the *secretor*. The dominant allele *Se*, present in 80 percent of individuals, determines glycosyl transferase, which permits activity of a fucosyl transferase (product of the *H* allele) in various organs, resulting in the

Table 14.1. Relationship Between Genotypes and Phenotypes of ABO (H) and Lewis Blood Groups Among Whites in North America

Genotypes and Allele Frequencies				A	B	H	Le^a	Le^b	Blood Groups and Their Frequencies	
H/H or H/h	Se/Se or Se/se	Le/Le or Le/le	A/A or A/O	+		+	+	+	A	Le (a – b +)
			A/B	+	+	+	+	+	AB	
			B/B or B/O		+	+	+	+	B	
			O/O			+	+	+	O	
		le/le	A/A or A/O	+		+			A	Le (a – b –)
			A/B	+	+	+			AB	
			B/B or B/O		+	+			B	
			O/O			+			O	
	se/se	Le/Le or Le/le	A/A or A/O				+		A	Le (a + b –)
			A/B				+		AB	
			B/B or B/O				+		B	
			O/O				+		O	
		le/le	A/A or A/O						A	Le (a – b –)
			A/B						AB	
			B/B or B/O						B	
			O/O						O	
h/h	Se/Se or Se/se	Le/Le or Le/le	A/A or A/O				+		Oh^A	Le (a + b –)
			A/B				+		Oh^{AB}	
			B/B or B/O				+		Oh^B	
			O/O				+		Oh^O	
		le/le	A/A or A/O						Oh^A	Le (a – b –)
			A/B						Oh^{AB}	
			B/B or B/O						Oh^B	
			O/O						Oh^O	
	se/se	Le/Le or Le/le	A/A or A/O				+		Oh^A	Le (a + b –)
			A/B				+		Oh^{AB}	
			B/B or B/O				+		Oh^B	
			O/O				+		Oh^O	
		le/le	A/A or A/O						Oh^A	Le (a – b –)
			A/B						Oh^{AB}	
			B/B or B/O						Oh^B	
			O/O						Oh^O	

$H \sim 1.0$	Se 0.52	Le 0.82	A 0.28						A 0.44	Le(a+b–) 0.22
h very low	se 0.48	le 0.18	B 0.06						AB 0.04	Le(a–b+) 0.78
			O 0.65						B 0.12	Le(a–b–) very low
									O 0.40	

Oh in all cases refers to Bombay phenotype.

production and subsequent secretion of H, A, and B substances into serum and body fluids (saliva, gastric juice, tears, semen, and milk). Recessive *se* alleles inhibit conversion of precursor into H when the precursor is not cell bound. Thus homozygosity for the recessive *se* allele does not interfere with the appearance of H, A, and B substances on erythrocytes, but it prevents the secretion of these substances.

The biologic significance of the ABO system and its polymorphism is not fully understood. However, several phenomena of medical significance are associated with the ABO system. In extremely rare instances (0.1 percent of pregnancies in whites), ABO incompatibility may produce typical hemolytic disease of newborn (see below). Such a situation occurs almost exclusively when a mother with an O phenotype carries a fetus with an A phenotype. In contrast to Rh hemolytic disease of the newborn, this condition can occur even during the first pregnancy. However, it is usually mild and transient.

On the other hand, ABO incompatibility has significant protective effect against hemolytic disease caused by simultaneous Rh incompatibility. The protection is achieved by maternal antibodies to either A or B antigen. Apparently, these antibodies eliminate ABO-incompatible fetal erythrocytes before they can induce formation of anti-Rh antibodies that cause hemolytic disease. The immunogenicity of A and B antigens and their broad tissue distribution make them the histocompatibility antigens; the linkage between *ABO* and the minor *histocompatibility* genes cannot be ruled out.

The ABO phenotypes are thought to be positively associated with the incidence of various diseases (gastric and duodenal ulcer, gastric and pancreatic carcinoma, pernicious anemia, choriocarcinoma). The mechanisms of this association are not clear. It is interesting that no evidence of association between ABO phenotypes and

susceptibility to infections with bacteria carrying blood group substances (e.g., *Shigella*) has been proved, although one might expect that sharing the substances with bacteria should decrease the immune response to such bacteria. On the other hand, recent reports suggest an increased susceptibility of individuals with A or AB phenotypes to infections with *Escherichia coli* and some species of *Salmonella*.

Genes, Products, and Antigens of the Lewis (Le) System

The *Le system*, consisting of a gene with two alleles, is closely related to ABO (H) system, since it affects the common precursor substance(s) in a way that depends on alleles at the *secretor* locus.

The dominant *Le* allele determines a fucosyl transferase that transfers α-L-fucose from glycosylated GDP to glucosamine of the precursor glycolipid, producing Le^a substance regardless of the alleles at *H* and *secretor* loci. The same enzyme in the presence of the dominant *H* and *Se* alleles transfers fucose to glucosamine of H substance, producing Le^b substance. Either substance is originally released into serum, from which it is adsorbed on the surface of erythrocytes, imparting upon them the corresponding Le phenotype. The Le phenotype actually changes during life, since erythrocytes of the newborn may be at first Le$^{(a+b-)}$, then changing to Le$^{(a+b+)}$, to become ultimately Le$^{(a-b+)}$ at the age of 3 to 6 years. The recessive *le* allele is amorphic; thus in *le/le* homozygotes, regardless of *H* and *Se* alleles, neither Le^a or Le^b substances are formed and erythrocytes have le$^{(a-b-)}$ phenotype.

Genes and Antigens of the Rh System

Extreme antigenic complexity and only limited knowledge concerning the chemistry of the antigens are stumbling blocks to the understanding of the genetics of the Rh system. Two alternative concepts have been advanced, and three nomenclatures that are used interchangeably add to the confusion. Wiener proposed a single locus, *Rh*, with multiple alleles determining the antigens differing from each other by combination of specificities. On the other hand, Fisher and Race postulated three closely linked loci, *C*, *D*, and *E*, each with two alleles, forming 12 distinct haplotypes determining the molecules with various combinations of specificities. Further, studies demonstrated that genes at these loci may have more than two alleles — e.g., *D*, *D^u*, *d* (amorphic); *C*, *C^w*, *C^x*, *c*; *E*, *E^w*, *e*, *e^s* — and that some combinations of alleles in a given haplotype may determine a new specificity not determined by either allele alone — e.g., *ce* determines f or *ce^s* determines the V antigen. This phenomenon is called *intergenic complementation*.

Rosenfield proposed a uniform notation for all specificities regardless of whether they are determined directly or through intergenic complementation. Presently, 33 specificities are defined. Furthermore, haplotypes in which some or all alleles were deleted have been found, bringing the number of haplotypes and corresponding phenotypes to over 30, of which 5 are most common (Table 14.2). The remaining specificities and haplotypes are extremely rare and are of interest only to a small group of specialists.

Accepting Fisher's hypothesis, one may speculate about the evolutionary origin of the *Rh* complex. The prevailing view assumes that the ancestral complex consisted of the haplotype *cDe*. The basis of the assumption is the presence of the c and D determinants in many animals. The other haplotypes would have developed by mutations, resulting in *cDE*, *CDe*, and *cde* haplotypes, with the last being favored for unknown reason(s). The rare haplotypes *CDE*, *cdE* (0.01). *Cde* (0.01), and *CdE*

Table 14.2. Most Common Alleles (Haplotypes) of the Rh System and Their Specificities

Allele or Haplotype[a]	Allele (Haplotype) Frequency in Whites	Phenotypic Specificity[b]			
R^1	0.41	rh'	Rho	hr"	rhi
CDe		C	D	e	Ce
		Rh2	Rh1	Rh5	Rh7
R^2	0.14	hr'	Rho	rh"	—
cDE		c	D	E	cE
		Rh4	Rh1	Rh3	Rh27
R^0	0.03	hr'	Rho	hr"	hr
cDe		c	D	e	ce(f)
		Rh4	Rh1	Rh5	Rh6
R^z	0.002	rh'	Rho	rh"	—
CDE		C	D	E	CE
		Rh2	Rh1	Rh3	Rh22
r	0.39	hr'	—	hr"	hr
cde		c	—	e	ce(f)
		Rh4	—	Rh5	Rh6

[a]Allele and haplotype correspond to Wiener's concept of a single locus or to Fisher's concept of three loci.

[b]Designations correspond to Wiener's (first line), Fisher's (second line), and Rosenfield's (third line) nomenclatures.

(very rare) would be formed by recombination of those more frequent haplotypes; their rarity could reflect either their recent development or negative selection eliminating carriers of such haplotypes.

Very little is known about the chemistry of Rh antigens except that they appear to be phospholipids or proteophospholipids. It has been suggested that Rh molecules are formed from a precursor determined by a gene analogous to *H*. Furthermore, the conversion of the precursor seems to follow the sequence D, C, E. This concept is supported by the finding of phenotypes with total deletion of Rh antigens — Rh null (analogous to the Bombay phenotype) — and partial deletions — Cd– or –D– but not C–– or ––E, suggesting that neither C nor E can be present without D.

The Rh antigens are immunogenic, especially D, c, and C, and they usually elicit production of antibodies of the IgG class. These antibodies have characteristics of "incomplete" or "blocking" antibodies, since they do not cause hemagglutination under ordinary conditions and since they prevent hemagglutination by Rh-specific IgM antibodies. The antibodies to Rh antigens appear only upon immunization (transfusion, incompatible pregnancy, intentional or unintentional injection of Rh-incompatible erythrocytes). These antibodies are responsible for hemolytic disease of the newborn, occurring in about 1 percent of all pregnancies in whites. Usually, the first pregnancy of an D-negative woman with an D-positive child causes only priming without ill effects, but each subsequent pregnancy with an D-positive child boosts the production of IgG antibodies, which can pass the placenta and elicit the disease and even cause death of the fetus or newborn.

Since hemolytic disease affects *D/d* heterozygotes of *d/d* homozygous mothers, if not counterbalanced, it should lead to elimination of heterozygotes and ultimately to total elimination of the *d* allele from the population. However, the discovery of a preventive measure against hemolytic disease may eventually lead to a complete elimination of the selective pressure against heterozygotes. The preventive measure consists of administering to the mother a standard dose of anti-D antibodies within 72 hours of delivery. While there are several explanations for the effect of Rh prophylaxis most workers believe that this causes rapid removal of D-positive fetal cells from the mother's circulation, thus preventing the priming of the mother.

Practical Considerations

Blood transfusion, often a lifesaving procedure in a variety of diseases, became possible after discovery of blood groups. Practically, two blood group systems, ABO and Rh, must be determined prior to any transfusion. In the case of the ABO system, in which the antibodies occur naturally, the phenotype of the recipient is determined and blood of the donor with the same phenotype is selected for crossmatch (see below). Determination of the Rh phenotypes is essential in preventing the transfusion of D-positive erythrocytes into an D-negative recipient. Such a transfusion could result in the production of anti-D antibodies by the recipient, and during subsequent transfusion the antibodies could react with D-positive erythrocytes from other donors, causing posttransfusion reactions. In women anti-D antibodies could react with D-positive erythrocytes of the fetus, causing its hemolytic disease.

Although either natural or induced antibodies to other blood group antigens are very rare, they may, if present in the recipient's serum, cause a severe or even lethal reaction by combining with the donor erythrocytes if these carry the corresponding antigens. To avoid such a reaction, a pretransfusion crossmatch (major compatibility test) must always be carried out. This test consists of mixing the erythrocytes of the prospective donor with serum of the prospective recipient. The mixture is incubated under various conditions permitting the detection of antibodies belonging to different classes. One should remember that this test is capable of detecting the presence of antibodies in the recipient and of the corresponding antigens in the donor but does not identify the particular blood group system involved.

The minor compatibility test, which is occasionally performed, employs serum of the prospective donor and erythrocytes of the prospective recipient in search of donor antibodies capable of reacting with the recipient's erythrocytes. However, such antibodies, even if present, are usually of no importance since during transfusion they are rapidly diluted by recipient's plasma and therefore do not inflict significant damage to the recipient's erythrocytes.

Although under normal circumstances the donor and recipient should be identical with respect to ABO and Rh antigens, in an emergency or if donors of identical ABO groups are not available it may be necessary to use an ABO nonidentical combination, provided that the major histocompatibility test does not detect any reaction. Under such circumstances individuals of the O phenotype are considered universal donors, since their erythrocytes are not agglutinated by either anti-A or anti-B antibodies of other phenotypes. Such transfusions should be given in the form of packed red blood cells in order to avoid administration of anti-A and anti-B antibodies present in plasma of O phenotype donors. Conversely, individuals of AB phenotype, because of absence of either antibody specificity, are considered universal recipients.

Determination of blood groups plays an important role in forensic medicine, since some blood group substances can be detected serologically in blood stains. The ABO character of blood can always be detected if the blood is present in a sufficient quantity. In an examination utilizing secretions or body fluids such a determination is feasible only if an individual has an Se phenotype. The understanding of genotypes and inheritance of blood groups opened the possibility to determine — or more exactly to exclude — the relationship between two individuals by studying their blood groups. Such a problem most commonly arises in the cases of questionable paternity.

In attempts to exclude the fatherhood of an individual, two basic principles are invoked. First, a father must contribute one of the ABO alleles to his child. Second, the father cannot lack an allele present in the child but absent from the mother.

The first principle alone allows paternity exclusion in those instances when blood group phenotypes of only the putative father and the child are known. An individual with AB phenotype must contribute either A or B allele; hence a child with blood group O cannot have been fathered by him. Conversely, an individual with phenotype O must contribute an O allele; thus a child with blood group AB cannot be his.

The second principle is applicable when the blood groups of the putative father as well as those of the mother and child are known. Since neither A or O men have the B allele, such individuals cannot have children with B antigen from women of A or O phenotypes. Similarly, B or O individuals do not have the A allele; hence they cannot have children with A antigen if a mother has the blood group B or O. Presently, using a large number of different alloantigenic systems, in addition to blood groups, the exclusion of falsely claimed paternity is possible in practically all instances.

Studies of the frequency of blood groups and their geographic distribution provide clues to the ethnic origin and migratory events in the history of various human groups. Such studies and subsequent conclusions are feasible because of distinct differences in frequencies of various blood groups. One must remember, however, that in any such analysis a variety of factors, such as independent mutations, positive and negative selections, or epidemiologic catacylsms, must be taken into account before valid conclusions are drawn.

Blood Groups in Animals

The polymorphism of erythrocyte antigens is not limited to man. In all animal species thus far studied, alloantigens, more or less analogous to human blood groups, have been found. The genetic complexity of such systems varies from the extraordinarily complicated B system of cattle, with more than 300 alleles, to the several relatively simple murine Ea blood group systems. Interestingly, some animal blood groups bear a striking analogy to human blood groups — e.g., the cattle J system and Le

systems of man. Unless such similarity is incidental, it may suggest either common origin or similar biologic significance of certain blood groups.

GENETICS OF IMMUNOGLOBULINS

Two distinct polypeptide chains, *light* and *heavy*, forming the immunoglobulin molecule require at least two discrete genes L and H. However, demonstration of two distinct portions, *constant* and *variable*, in each chain necessitates the assumption that each postulated gene actually consists of a pair of genes, C and V, that determine corresponding portions. These two genes appear to be closely linked; in fact, they produce a single mRNA and therefore also a single immunoglobulin chain. Since each individual has several types and subtypes of

Table 14.3. Linkage Groups of Immunoglobulin Genes

Linkage Group	C Genes		Alleles	V Genes
λ	Type — $C\lambda$ Subtypes — $C\lambda$ (−,−) $C\lambda$ (+,−) $C\lambda$ (−,+) $C\lambda$ (Mcg)		1	Group — $V\lambda$ Subgroups — 6
κ	Type — $C\kappa$ Subtypes — none		3	Group — $V\kappa$ Subgroups — 4
H (heavy)	Class — $C\alpha$ Subclasses — $C\alpha1$ $C\alpha2$		 1 2	Group — V_H Subgroups — 5
	Class — $C\gamma$ Subclasses — $C\gamma1$ $C\gamma2$ $C\gamma3$ $C\gamma4$		 6 2 12 2	
	Class — $C\mu$ Subclasses — $C\mu1$ — $C\mu2$			
	Class — $C\delta$		1	
	Class — $C\varepsilon$		1	

light chains or classes and subclasses of heavy chains, the two genes, *L* and *H*, must be considered as two sets of genes. Presently available data strongly suggest that the two sets form three linkage groups, two for two light chain types, κ and λ, and one for all the heavy chain classes, α, γ, μ, δ, and ε (Table 14.3).

In the cell that actively produces immunoglobulin, only two genes, one for the light and one for the heavy chain, are expressed at a given time, while the others are suppressed. Such a selective expression is due to a still unknown regulatory mechanism that specifically activates only two genes at a time. Presumably, the same or a similar mechanism is involved in the switch from IgM to IgG production that occurs during an ordinary immune response.

C Genes Determining the Constant Region

C_L Genes. These genes, for light chain types λ and κ, are referred to as C_λ and C_κ, respectively. Either gene determines a segment of the chain consisting of about 100 amino acids and corresponding to a domain (see Ch. 10).

In man the C_λ gene appears to be monomorphic — i.e., all individuals carry the same allele. However, all individuals have four λ chains subtypes, called λ KERN⁻Oz⁻, λ KERN⁺Oz⁻, λ KERN⁻Oz⁺, and λ Mcg. Since the subtypes differ from each other by one or three amino acid substitutions, the C_λ gene must represent a family of four closely linked genes, $C_\lambda(-,-)$, $C_\lambda(+,-)$, $C_\lambda(-,+)$, and $C_\lambda(\text{Mcg})$. These four genes most likely developed from the ancestral gene, $C_\lambda(+,-)$, by duplications and mutations. Of these four C_λ genes only one is expressed at a given time in each individual antibody-producing cell.

The C_κ gene is polymorphic and has at least three — but possibly four — codominant alleles: *Km¹*, *Km¹·²*, and *Km³*. The alleles determine three polypeptide variants

differing from each other by a single amino acid substitution and are called *allotypes*, Km(1), Km(2), and Km(3), originally referred to as Inv factors. These variants can be identified by inhibition of hemagglutination* or occasionally by direct precipitation with monospecific antiserum. As opposed to the λ chain, no κ subtypes are known so that presumably a single locus for a C_κ gene exists. This gene is not linked to either C_λ or to C_H although in the latter case loose linkage cannot be totally ruled out.

C_H Genes. C genes for the different classes of heavy chain are designated C_α, C_γ, C_μ, C_δ, and C_ε. These genes are closely linked to each other, and each determines a polypeptide consisting of 350 to 450 amino acids. Three (in α and γ chains) or four (in μ, δ, and ε chains) segments called domains and consisting of 100 to 110 amino acids can be distinguished within each polypeptide chain on the basis of structural homology. Since within the α, γ, and μ classes of heavy chains distinct subclasses are identifiable (Ch. 10), the C_α, C_γ, and C_μ genes must represent families of closely linked genes determining corresponding subclasses. Accordingly, there must be at least 10 discrete C_H genes. While some genes (C_α, C_δ, and C_ε) appear to be monomorphic, the remaining genes ($C_{\alpha2}$, $C_{\gamma1}$, $C_{\gamma2}$, $C_{\gamma3}$, $C_{\gamma4}$, $C_{\mu1}$, and $C_{\mu2}$) are polymorphic, with their alleles determining allotypes of respective heavy chains.

There are two allleles of the $C_{\alpha2}$ gene — one determining A2m(2) specificity that is also found in all molecules of α1 subclass, and the other determining A2m(1) specificity found only in α2 subclass. The A2m(1) allotype is characterized by the lack of cysteine at position 131 in the first

---

*An antiserum directed to a Km specificity agglutinates erythrocytes coated with immunoglobulins of the corresponding Km variant. Addition of free immunoglobulins of the same Km variant binds the antibody and abolishes the agglutination.

domain resulting in the lack of a bisulfide bond between heavy and light chains. The frequencies of alleles determining the two allotypes vary in different racial and ethnic groups. In the heterozygous individual both allotypes are expressed, but any single cell is believed to express either one or the other allele, a phenomenon called *allelic exclusion*.

All four C_γ genes are polymorphic. $C_{\gamma2}$ has two alleles determining G2m(23) or G2m(23–) and $C_{\gamma4}$ has also two alleles and they determine 4a or 4b allotypic specificities. On the other hand, at least six $C_{\gamma1}$ alleles determining various combinations of five G1m are distinguishable. Similarly 12 $C_{\gamma3}$ alleles determining various combinations of 12 G3m are known. Each specificity represents a point mutation(s) leading to amino acid substitution in one or two domains. There are also seven Gm specificities for which the subclass is unknown.

All C_γ subclass genes are closely linked, though occasional recombinations have been reported. Accordingly, alleles of these genes appear in specific combinations called *haplotypes* (formerly *allogroups*). The frequencies of specific haplotypes differ in various racial and ethnic groups. Similar to $C_{\alpha2}$ alleles, the C_γ alleles (haplotypes) are codominant in an individual but are subject to allelic exclusion in the cell. The biologic significance of allotypic diversity is not yet fully realized. However, since allotypic specificities are predominantly located in the Fc portion of the heavy chain, they may affect the properties associated with this portion, e.g., complement or receptor binding, though an effect on antigen binding cannot be excluded. One well established but poorly understood effect of the allotypy is the influence of certain specificities on the serum concentration of a given subclass or even other subclasses or classes. Some allotypic specificities, while being allelic in one subclass, are present in all chains of another subclass in all individuals. Such specificities were formerly called non-

markers and presently are referred to as isoallotypes — e.g., G3m(5–) and G3m(11–), or 4a and 4b.

V Genes Determining the Variable Portion

The synthesis of the variable portion of either heavy or light chains is controlled by separate *V* genes. The *V* genes are closely linked to the corresponding *C* genes; thus three groups of *V* genes, V_κ, V_λ and V_H, can be distinguished (Table 14.3). In fact, each group consists of a family of genes determining four, six, and five subgroups, respectively.

The subgroups of variable portion are distinguished on the basis of similarities in amino acid sequence in four relatively constant segments forming the *framework*. Between the framework segments three or four *hypervariable* stretches, consisting of seven to ten amino acids, are inserted. The term hypervariable has been coined to indicate that the amino acid sequences of these regions vary widely from molecule to molecule and cannot be categorized into groups the way that those for framework segments of variable and constant parts of the polypeptide chain can be. Hypervariable regions of heavy and light chains complement each other in the formation of the antigen-combining site of the antibody molecule. Unique amino acid sequences of the hypervariable regions determine the specificity of this site. The uniqueness of each antibody combining site with respect to its amino acid composition and its structure is reflected in its unique specificity. Antigenic specificity related to the antibody combining site is called *idiotype* or *idiotypic specificity*. Antiidiotype antibodies raised by immunization with immunoglobulin molecules of a given antibody specificity and directed against the hypervariable region of these molecules react only with molecules that have identical hypervariable regions. Some antiidiotype antibodies compete with the antigen for the antibody combining site, some do not; but in all cases they are directed against structures closely associated with the antibody combining site. At least some of the idiotypic specificities have been shown to be determined by genes linked to those determining framework. The former are believed to be constantly generated by somatic mutations, whereas the latter appear to be relatively stable.

The existence of hypervariable regions calls for a mechanism by which the genes coding for these regions could be integrated with the framework V genes. Once those two genes are integrated into a single V gene this gene fuses with the corresponding C gene so that a single molecule of mRNA and a single polypeptide chain is produced. The mechanisms of this integration and fusion are still subjects of hypotheses.

It is believed that idiotypic determinants can elicit an immune response in an individual that produces immunoglobulins bearing these idiotypic determinants. This response against idiotypic determinants may play a crucial role in regulating the immune response to the antigen that induced the formation of this particular idiotype (Ch. 8).

Evolutionary Considerations

Structural inter- and intraspecies similarities between domains as well as between types and classes of different chains provide a valuable clue into the probable evolution of the immunoglobulin genes. It is believed that the primitive gene, presumably resulting from duplication of an archetypal gene common for both major histocompatibility complex (see below) and immunoglobulins, underwent duplications and translocations to give rise to the future three linkage groups, κ, λ, and heavy chain genes, as well as to the gene for β_2-microglobulin. This primitive gene determined a polypeptide

analogous to the domain and consisting of about 100 amino acids. Further duplication in each linkage group led to development of ancestral C and V genes.

While the ancestral C_λ gene duplicated and mutated to produce λ subtypes, the C_κ gene mutated only to give κ allotypes. An ancestral C_H gene corresponding to a single domain duplicated 2 or 3 times, and the resulting genes merged to form a single final C_H gene determining the entire constant portion of the heavy chain, consisting of 3 or 4 domains. This gene subsequently duplicated to produce first genes determining classes and then genes for subclasses of heavy chains. Mutations occurring before duplication were responsible for the isoallotypic specificities present in several subclasses, whereas mutations after duplication produced the allotypic specificities present in a single subclass.

The duplications and mutations of ancestral V genes determining framework segments led to the development of subgroups sometimes referred to as *germ line* genes inherited according to Mendelian principles. The mechanism of diversification of these subgroup genes, resulting in multitude of hypervariable regions and formation of idiotypes limited to a group (clone) of lymphocytes, derived from a single precursor cell, is still the subject of speculation (Ch. 12).

HISTOCOMPATIBILITY ANTIGENS

The name *histocompatibility* (*H*) *antigens* and the corresponding term *histocompatibility genes* were introduced in 1948 by Snell for the cell surface substances capable of eliciting an immune response that results in rejection of an *allogeneic graft* (see below). In mice, which have been most extensively used in studies of the H antigens, more than 50 distinct H genes have thus far been identified. Among these antigens, those that produce exceptionally rapid graft rejection are called major antigens whereas all others are classified as minor antigens.

Minor Histocompatibility Antigens

Genetically, each minor H antigen is determined by a discrete *H* gene, although some of the genes are closely linked and form gene clusters. The majority of *H* genes have at least two alleles, but in a few instances as many as five alleles have been identified. In mice, chromosomal localization was established by linkage analysis for 27 of 49 minor *H* genes, two of them being in sex chromosomes Y and X.

The chemical nature of the *H* gene products in most instances remains unknown, as do their physiologic functions. Histocompatibility antigens induce an immune response in an individual with an allelic variant of a given antigen, i.e., they are recognized as alloantigens by an individual who carries a different allele. The immune response is predominantly cell mediated, and only occasionally are antibodies produced. The intensity of the response is reflected by the time required to reject the graft, which varies from 25 to 400 days. In extreme cases the reactions may be so weak that even after several hundred days only some, but not all, grafts are rejected. Differences in the intensity of response are attributable to the immunogenicity of allelic variants of antigens and to the inherent responsiveness of the graft recipient. Characteristically, the responses to minor H antigens can be almost totally inhibited by an immunosuppressive regimen.

Little if anything is known about minor H antigens in man, since the only information available is derived from studies of selected patients receiving organ grafts. However, there are no reasons to assume that in regard to number and polymorphism of such antigens man differs significantly from the other species thus far studied (e.g., mouse, rat, and Syrian hamster).

Major Histocompatibility Complex

In all species studied the immune reaction elicited by some of the H antigens is exceptionally strong, leading to skin graft rejection within 3 weeks, and is usually accompanied by the appearance of cells and antibodies toxic for the cells of the graft donor. Antigens responsible for the rapid rejection are determined by a cluster of closely linked genes forming the *major histocompatibility complex* (MHC). The MHC is found in all species, including man, but only murine and human complexes will be discussed here at length. While the murine MHC serves as the model for theoretical considerations, the practical significance of the human MHC is self-evident for students of medicine.

Genes and Products of the H-2 Complex of Mice.
The murine MHC, the *H-2 complex*, is located on chromosome 17 and consists of four regions: *K, I, S,* and *D,* with the *I* region subdivided into five subregions: *A, B, J, E,* and *C* (Table 14.4). The regions and subregions of the *H-2* complex were defined by recombinations and hence could be considered as individual loci. However, sometimes more than one phenotypic trait appears to be associated with a given segment of the *H-2* complex. Different traits most likely reflect different properties of a single gene product, but it is also possible that a given region contains several genes so closely linked that no recombination between them has yet been found.

The *H-2* complex occupies a unique position among murine genes. Most mouse genes either are monomorphic (single allele) or are moderately polymorphic (usually 2 or 3 alleles) with one allele being distinctly more frequent than other(s); usually only 10 percent of individuals are heterozygous at a given locus. In contrast, polymorphism of the *H-2* genes, especially those at *K, D* and *I-A* regions, is strikingly high; for instance, at the *K* region 29

Table 14.4.   Regions, Loci, Alleles, and Products of the H-2 Complex

	K	A	B(?)	J	E^a	C^a	S	D	
Region	K	I					S	D	
Subregion		A	B(?)	J	E^a	C^a			
Loci (see text)	H-2K Lad Ir(?)	H-2A Lad Ia-1(A$_\alpha$,A$_\beta$) A$_e$ Ir-1A CI	Ia-2(?) Ir-1B	Ia-4(?)	Lad Ia-5(E$_\alpha$)	H-2C Ia-3(?) Ir-1C ECS	Ss Slp	H-2D Lad	H-2L Lad(?)
Number of alleles^b	56		9?	9	14		6^c	45	5
Class of molecule	I	II	?	II(?)	II		III	I	I
Localization of molecules	All cells	B and T cells, epithelial cells, macrophages	?	Some T cells	B and T cells, macrophages		Serum (C4 of complement)	All cells	All cells
Detected by	Ctx and MLR^d		Immune response	Inhibition of suppressor cells	Ctx and MLR		Immuno-precipitation	Ctx and MLR	Ctx and MLR

H-2 Haplotype

^{a}Possibly single locus.

^{b}Both laboratory and wild mice were considered.

^{c}Minimum number of alleles.

^{d}Ctx, complement-mediated toxicity by specific antisera; MLR, mixed lymphocyte reaction.

alleles, and at the *D* region 38 alleles, have so far been described. These alleles appear in more or less equal frequencies, and 90 percent of individuals in wild populations are *H-2* heterozygous.

The set of alleles at all regions and subregions forms the *H-2* haplotype. With the remarkable polymorphism at each region, thousands of *H-2* haplotypes are possible, but at the time of writing only some 127 distinct *H-2* haplotypes have been identified.

While it is generally taken for granted that all alleles of the *H-2* complex are strictly codominant, several observations suggest that this may be not always true; some alleles may be partially recessive, resulting in F_1 hybrids of two inbred strains lacking some parental allelic products.

Genes identified in the close vicinity of the *H-2* complex can be grouped into three broad categories: those determining cell surface antigens (*T, t, Qa, Tla, Ea*, minor *H*), those determining enzymes,* and those determining complement   factor (*C3–1*).

Genes at the *K* and *D* regions determine the glycoproteins (45,000 daltons) found in cell membranes of all cells and referred to as *class I molecules*. These molecules are noncovalently associated with β_2-microglobulin (12,000 daltons), a protein that is homologous with a domain of the Ig chain and that is determined by a gene *not* linked to the *H-2* complex. Products of the allelic genes within each of these regions may differ from each other by amino acid substitutions at about 10 percent of positions.

With use of monospecific alloantisera 75 discrete class I antigenic determinants (specificities) have been demonstrated in laboratory mice. In wild mice, which only

* *PGK-2*, phosphoglycerate kinase-2; *Glo*, glyoxylase; *Map-2*, α-mannosidase processing-2; *Apl*, liver acid phosphatase.

recently have become the subject of extensive studies, 42 specificities have been identified thus far. Each specificity represents a structural (primary, secondary, or tertiary) variant of the protein portion of the molecule determined by an allele at a given locus. Antigenic specificities of the class I molecules are classified into two categories, private and public.

A specificity found exclusively in the product of only one allele is called *private*. Thus there are as many distinct private specificities as there are alleles at the K region and at the D region. On the other hand, alleles at the L locus seem to have no private specificities. The presence of a given private specificity precludes the presence of any other private specificities. In this regard the private specificities appear to correspond to discrete mutational changes affecting the same point in different alleles at either the K or D region.

The specificity that is found in the products of more than one allele is called *public*. A given public specificity may be present in the molecules determined by alleles at either one region or by alleles at two regions; such a specificity is called uniregional or biregional, respectively. Furthermore, a given public specificity may be found in only a few or in almost all allelic molecules; hence, correspondingly, it may be called *short* or *long*. The allelic products of genes at the K and D regions differ from each other by the various combinations of about 10 (out of 75 known) specificities, one of them being private and the remaining public. The allelic products of genes at the L locus are characterized by a particular combination of 3 to 5 public specificities, but they do not have a private specificity.

Products of I region genes, called *Ia* (for I associated) or *class II molecules*, are glycoproteins found in cell membranes of some lymphoid cells (most B and some T cells), macrophages, spermatozoa, and some epithelial cells (thymus epithelium

and epidermis). The protein part of the molecule, not associated with β_2-microglobulin, is composed of two noncovalently bound polypeptides, α (35,000 daltons) and β (26,000 daltons). In fact, the Ia molecule associated with the IE region consists of an α polypeptide determined by the E_α gene at the IE region and a β polypeptide determined by the A_e gene at the IA region. Assembling two polypeptides leads to the formation of serologic specificities that are absent from either polypeptide. In other words, some specificities result from the complementation of the two polypeptides forming the Ia molecule.

Recent studies demonstrate that α and β polypeptides determined by some alleles at two regions, IA and IE/IC, of some H-2 haplotypes may complement each other in the H-2 heterozygote. As a result, the heterozygote may possess a unique Ia specificity that is not found in either homozygous parent. The new Ia specificity, sometimes referred to as the F_1 antigen, has all the properties of the orthodox Ia specificity — i.e., it elicits production of specific antibodies as well as induces the mixed lymphocyte reaction (see Ch. 13). There are also indications that it may be involved in the Ir phenomenon (see below). The amino acid compositions of these polypeptides do not show any sigificant homology either with each other or with class I molecules. Generally, β polypeptides show extensive allelic variability, while α polypeptides are less heterogeneous.

Serologic analysis has permitted identification of 50 specificities associated with the protein portion of the molecule. The association of some of them with a carbohydrate side chain cannot be ruled out. It seems probable that in analogy to class I molecules the specificities of class II molecules may also be classified as private or public. At present, however, the evidence is still incomplete.

Polymorphism of Ia-1 molecules determined by alleles of the $A\alpha$ and $A\beta$ genes of the *I-A* subregion consisting of 21 alleles, appears to be as extensive as that of class I molecules. With regard to the polymorphism at the *I* subregions *E* and *C*, it is still not clear whether these two subregions are indeed distinct entities and whether their products exist as two discrete molecules, Ia-3 and Ia-5. At any rate, the polymorphism of Ia-3/Ia-5 molecules with 6 allelic variants seems to be less extensive than that of Ia-1 molecules. The product of a gene at the *I-J* subregion, the Ia-4 molecule, is detectable serologically in T suppressor cells, but little is known about its chemistry or the extent of polymorphism. Since thus far no seriologically or biochemically indentifiable product of gene at the *I-B* subregion has been demonstrated, the Ia-2 molecule remains a hypothetical entity. The *I-B* subregion is defined only functionally on the basis of association with responsiveness to various antigens (see the discussion of *Ir* genes below).

The *S* region is associated with two *class III molecules*, Ss (serum substance) and Slp (sex limited protein), that presumably are the products of two closely linked genes, *Ss* and *Slp*; so far no recombination between these genes has been demonstrated. Ss and Slp molecules are synthesized by liver cells and macrophages and are released into the circulation. They are composed of three polypeptide chains, α (87,000 to 95,000 daltons), β (70,000 to 78,000 daltons) and γ (30,000 to 33,000 daltons), that are obtained by the cleavage of a single precursor molecule (180,000 daltons). The Ss and Slp molecules are distinguishable by their chemical, serologic, and biologic properties. The *Ss* gene appears to have at least two alleles, Ss^h and Ss^l, that determine different — high and low, respectively — serum concentrations of Ss molecules. It has been suggested that actually several alleles at the *Ss* subregion may exist, each allele determining different serum concentration of Ss molecules.

Recently, three electrophoretic variants of the γ chain were described, presumably determined by three codominant alleles. Furthermore, one of the variants (γ_2) appears to be distinguishable from the others by presence of the antigenic determinant (H-2.7) formerly believed to be controlled by gene at the distinct *G* region. The serum level of Ss is influenced by male hormones, as evidenced by significantly higher concentration in adult males than in females or young males. Biologically,

Table 14.5.   Loci, Alleles, and Products of the HLA System

Locus	C-2	DRW[a]	D[a] (Lad-1) ESC, Ir	B	Bf	C	Lad-2	A
			HLA Haplotype					
Number of alleles	3	10	12	32	4	8	?	17
Sum of frequencies in whites	1.0	0.79	0.70	0.98	1.0	0.70	?	0.98
Class of molecules	III	II(?)	II	I	III(?)	I	II	I
Localization of molecules	Serum (complement)	B cells	B and T cells	All cells	Serum (alternate pathway)	All cells	?	All cells
Detected by	Electrophoresis	Ctx[b]	MLR[b]	Ctx	Electrophoresis	Ctx	MLR	Ctx

[a]Possibly single locus.

[b]Ctx, complement-mediated toxicity by specific antisera. MLR, mixed lymphocyte reaction.

it is identical with complement factor 4 (C4).

The *Slp* gene has at least three alleles, *Slp*^{wr7}, *Slp*^{a}, and *Slp*^{o}. These alleles determine very high or moderate serum concentrations or the absence of Slp substances, respectively. The presence of more alleles that may control intermediate concentrations of Slp molecules has also been suggested. The expression of *Slp* alleles depends on the presence of male hormones. In females, Slp molecules can be detected only in the presence of the *Slp*^{wr7} allele. Slp molecules are serologically related to the Ss but also carry a unique determinant. It is interesting that Slp molecules, in spite of their chemical and serologic similarities to Ss molecules, have no C4 activity.

Genes and Products of the HLA System of Man.

The human leukocyte antigen (*HLA*) complex located on chromosome 6 consists of several discrete loci, *C-2, D, B, Bf, C, Lad-2,* and *A*, as well as a series of ill defined loci such as *DRW, ECS, Ir, C-4,* and *C3d* receptors (Table 14.5). The latter were found to be linked with *HLA*, but neither their identity nor their exact location have been established. While genes at some loci (e.g., *A* and *B*) appear to be highly polymorphic (having ≥ 17 and 32 alleles, respectively), polymorphism of some other loci (e.g., *Bf* and *C-2*) is limited to 3 or 4 alleles. It appears, although not demonstrated definitely, that all alleles are fully codominant. The set of alleles at all loci in a given chromosome forms the *HLA* haplotype, although in practice only alleles at *D, B, C,* and *A* loci are usually determined. Assuming that the alleles at the two linked loci *A* and *B* are independent of each other, the frequency of the haplotype *p(h)* containing these alleles should equal the product of frequencies of those alleles, *p(A)* and *p(B)*. However, in the case of some alleles, they appear in a particular combination either more or less frequently than expected. For example, combinations of *A1* and *B8* in Europeans and *A1* and *BW7* in East Indians are found more frequently than expected from frequencies of corresponding alleles. This phenomenon is called *linkage disequilibrium* and is measured by the value of △ calculated from the formula

$$\triangle = p(h) - [p(A) \times p(B)]$$

The cause of linkage disequilibrium is not totally clear but it has been suggested that under particular environmental conditions an association of some alleles may produce a selectional advantage or disadvantage.

The frequencies of alleles for each locus vary considerably among different racial or ethnic groups; in certain populations some alleles may be completely absent. While the frequencies of alleles at the *A* as well as at the *B* locus add to almost 1.0, suggesting that essentially all of them have been identified, the frequencies of alleles at the *C* locus add up to only 0.7, indicating that some of the *C* alleles remain undetected. Similar to the *H-2* complex, the *HLA* complex is associated with genes determining several enzymes.*

The alleles at the *B, C,* and *A* loci determine the products referred to as class I molecules and identifiable by biochemical and immunologic procedures. The molecules are glycoproteins (44,000 daltons) found in the membranes of all types of cells but at different concentrations. They are noncovalently bound to β$_2$-microglobulin which is determined by a gene not linked to the *HLA* complex. The carbohydrate portion contains, among other sugars, mannose and glucosamine and constitutes about 10 percent of the total weight of the HLA molecule. The amino acid sequence of some HLA class I molecules shows extensive homology between allelic products and also with class I molecules of other species.

PGM-3, phosphoglucomutase-3; *GLO-1*, glyoxalase-1; *ME-1*, malic enzyme-1; *SOD-2*, superoxide dismutase-2; *Pg*, pepsinogen.

Class I molecules were originally demonstrated serologically by a variety of methods. Presently, the most commonly used method is complement mediated toxicity for the cells that carry the molecules by monospecific antisera. The antisera are procured from multiparous women or from individuals receiving multiple blood transfusions. Intentional immunization of volunteers or even immunization of some animals is occasionally employed to produce antisera.

Presently the specificities identifying distinct class I allelic molecules are divided into three categories: (1) firmly established (designated by a capital letter indicating locus and an Arabic number), (2) requiring reconfirmation (designated by additional letter W (for workshop) and, (3) newly identified (designated by any arbitrary symbol). Two specificities, BW4 and BW6, appear to be shared by different allelic B molecules thus resembling public specificities of murine K or D molecules. It has not been established whether these two specificities are determined by alleles at the B locus or by alleles at a closely linked locus in linkage disequilibrium with some B alleles.

Products of two other loci, D ($Lad-1$), and $Lad-2$, presumably correspond to class II molecules and have not thus far been characterized chemically or serologically. Several allelic variants of these products are present on some but not on all lymphocytes and spermatozoa. Conventionally, they are detected on the basis of their ability to induce the mixed lymphocyte reaction (MLR) (Ch. 13). To identify these molecules, a panel of standard $HLA-D$ homozygous typing cells (HTC) is used. Recently, a test employing spermatozoa and called the spermlymphocyte reaction (SLR) was introduced. The SLR is claimed to be more sensitive and more discriminatory than the MLR.

The D molecules appear to be associated with serologically detectable determinants found predominantly on B cells. Originally, the assay for these determinants was based on the inhibition of the MLR by the specific immune sera, but subsequently a conventional cytotoxic assay was developed. While the specific allelic variants of these B cell determinants are associated with specific allelic variants of D molecules, there is no direct evidence of the identity of these two types of molecules. Therefore temporarily the terms DRW (D related) or Ia-like are used. Although it is possible that DRW molecules are determined by a gene distinct from the $HLA-D$ gene and that the observed association is due to linkage disequilibrium between $HLA-D$ and $HLA-DRW$ alleles, several observations suggest structural identity of D and DRW molecules.

The HLA system contains structural genes for C2 and C4 factors of the classic complement pathway and for the B factor (Bf) of the alternative pathway (Ch. 11). The association between HLA and genes controlling the sythesis of complement components was established by family studies of inheritance of either particular deficiencies or electrophoretic variants of the factors. The location of the $C2$ and Bf genes appears to be well established, but the position of $C4$ is still not clear. In fact the $C4$ "gene" actually consists of two genes, A, with six alleles, and B, with four alleles. Products of these two genes are adsorbed on erythrocytes mimicking blood groups; to designate these "blood groups" the names Rodgers (A) and Chiddo (B) were formerly used. In addition, HLA determines the cellular receptor for the C3 complement component; some investigators speculate that the previously mentioned BW4 and BW6 specificities represent allelic variants of the receptor for C3, since treatment of lymphocytes with antisera against these specificities blocks binding of erythrocytes, sensitized by antibodies and C3, to lymphocytes possessing the receptor (EAC rosettes).

MHC of Other Mammals.   The obvious

biologic significance of the MHC and its products prompted the extension of studies to various animal species. Presently, rat (*RTI*), guinea pig (*GPLA*), hamster (*Hm-1*), rabbit (*RLA*), dog (*DLA*), rhesus monkey (*RhLA*) and chimpanzee (*ChLA*) MHC are defined. In all instances the products can be divided into three distinct classes of molecules analogous to the class I, class II, and class III molecules found in mice and man. The extent of polymorphism of the MHC, so striking in mice and man, was at first found to be limited in some of the laboratory species. However, further studies involving wild populations of the respective species often revealed significant polymorphism. Therefore earlier findings must be partially attributed to the fact that some species of laboratory animals originated from relatively few individuals. For example, all laboratory hamsters are descendants of three litermates captured in Syria, and laboratory guinea pigs originate from a few individuals brought to Europe by the Spaniards after their conquest of South America. Available data indicate that in all animals thus far studied the MHC systems have similar genetic structure, consisting of a cluster of closely linked loci with high polymorphism. The products determined by the MHC systems show a considerable degree of interspecies homology from both the structural and functional points of view.

Evolutionary Remarks

A simple assumption that the MHC evolved by pure accident as a cluster of unrelated genes whose polymorphism is of no biologic significance can hardly be accepted. Conversely, one must consider the possibility that the MHC developed from an archetypal gene (see above) by a series of duplications, deletions, and possibly translocations. The duplicated genes diverged from the original one by continuous mutations leading to biologically favorable polymorphism. Indeed, the inter-

and intraspecies homologies between various classes of molecules and their allelic variants strongly support such a contention. The characteristic chromosomal position in the vicinity of particular genes (complement, enzymes) also suggests a common evolutionary pathway. Structural and functional similarities between class I and immunoglobulin molecules (glycoprotein nature, the presence of two chains, high polymorphism, association with immune responses) suggest that MHC and immunoglobulin systems might have had a common archetypal gene. This hypothetical relationship was recently extended by the concept that the phenotypic variability in both systems may result from similar mechanisms, i.e., in both instances each individual carries essentially all variants in the form of a family of closely linked genes but, owing to the action of specific regulatory genes, expresses only one of the variants.

While there is ample evidence for such a mechanism in the immunoglobulin system, in the case of the MHC the evidence is at best very weak and hardly convincing. Nevertheless, the concept should not be rejected outright if for no other reason than because it stimulates research in the genetics of the MHC. Assuming that indeed the MHC evolved from a single gene by duplication and differentiation via mutations, one must search for the functional relationship between products of various genes of the MHC.

Functional Considerations

The extraordinary *pleiotropism* of the MHC is exemplified by its association with over 60 phenotypic traits. At least some of these traits appear to reflect the basic biologic role of the MHC. The *immunogenicity* (i.e., the ability to induce an immune response) of MHC products has been very extensively studied mostly because the cellular alloimmune response results in graft rejection. *In vivo* incompatibility for either class I or class II molecules leads to a rapid graft rejection, and the murine H antigens determined by presumptive genes at various regions of the *H-2* complex have been designated H-2K, H-2A, H-2C, H-2D, and H-2L. Attempts to reproduce allograft-induced responses *in vitro* revealed that they are both qualitatively and quantitatively different for incompatibilities at various regions in spite of apparent similarity of the *in vivo* responses. Incompatibility of class I molecules alone elicited a weak MLR, while incompatibility of class II molecules caused a strong MLR. These differences have been attributed to either qualitative or quantitative differences in products of specific genes called lymphocyte-activating determinant (*Lad*) that are considered distinct from those determining the antigens responsible for graft rejection *in vivo*.

Incompatibility limited to only one class, either I or II, results in only negligible numbers of effector cells detectable by cell mediated lymphocytotoxicity (CML) (Ch. 13). On the other hand, simultaneous incompatibility of both classes results in a strong MLR and a strong CML, with the latter being directed to class I but not class II molecules. To account for this phenomenon it was recently postulated that in fact class II incompatibility is determined by hypothetical effector cell stimulator (*ECS*) genes with products presumably distinct from those of *Lad* genes. The ECS product would not generate effector cells either for itself or for class II molecules but would amplify the ultimate response to class I molecules. However, one should be aware that differences in immunogenicity of the two classes are not absolute, since under proper conditions a strong MLR can be induced by class I molecules just as a strong CML can be demonstrated against class II molecules. Thus the differences may reflect merely differences in sensitivity of corresponding assays.

It is interesting that the originally postulated differences between the two classes in their capabilities of inducing humoral or cellular responses leading to occasionally used distinction of serologically defined (SD) and lymphocyte defined (LD) antigens corresponding to class I and class II molecules, respectively, turned out to be entirely spurious, since presently both can be defined serologically and by MLR as well.

The role of MHC-determined molecules in allograft rejection prompted the MHC matching of donor and recipient in clinical transplantation of kidney. For the matching to be beneficial for graft survival one must be concerned with both classes of molecules, but in man class II molecules (products of *D* and *Lad-2* genes) thus far are not reliably detected by serologic methods, since the relationship between D and DRW antigens is still unresolved. With this in mind, two matching procedures are employed. Class I molecules of the donor and recipient are identified by a battery of appropriate monospecific antisera. The identity of class II molecules is determined by MLR or SLR (when applicable) tests among donor, recipient, and standard cells. Since *HLA* haplotypes are inherited within a family as blocks and since recombinations occur with low frequency (about 0.01), in the matching of siblings, demonstration of identity of one molecule of each haplotype should be sufficient. Matching of two unrelated individuals requires identification of all molecules, since the *HLA* haplotypes are randomly assembled.

The success of clinical grafting is conventionally measured by the percentage of grafts surviving for a given period of time. This percentage varies depending on the combination of donor and recipient employed. Highest values, approaching 100 percent, are observed if the donor and recipient are identical twins, since they share not only the HLA but also the entire set of minor transplantation antigens. Two siblings in a given family have a 25 percent probability of having identical *HLA* genotypes. When donor and recipient are HLA-identical siblings, a high percentage of renal grafts survive for many years. The percentage is consistently higher than that for the donor-recipient siblings carrying either one or both incompatible *HLA* haplotypes. Theoretically, matching *HLA* genotypes of donor and recipient from unrelated individuals should have a beneficial effect on graft survival. Indeed, some investigators provided evidence that complete HLA matching results in a significantly higher percentage of surviving renal grafts, but there are other reports that have failed to confirm these data.

Restriction of either the recognition or effector phases of immune responses to some cell associated antigens appears to be another basic function of the MHC. The precursors of effector cells, during their sojourn in the thymus (Ch. 9), learn to recognize efficiently certain antigens (minor H, some viruses) only if these antigens are presented in association with (or in the context of) class I molecules. Two alternative concepts are presently disputed: (1) each cell acquires two receptors, one for an antigen and one for class I molecule(s), or (2) each cell acquires a single receptor for the complex of an antigen and class I molecule(s). The hypothetical complex may be recognized as an altered-self class I molecule because under normal circumstances cells of an individual encounter an antigen in association with class I molecules of this individual. The emerging effector cells are capable of interacting with the antigen only if the antigen is presented in association with the same class I molecule with which it was originally recognized. Thus specificity and/or effectiveness of some cell-mediated and possibly some humoral immune responses to an antigen is restricted by class I molecules with which such an antigen is originally recognized (MHC restriction).

The restriction of T-B cell collaboration (Ch. 9) seems in many aspects similar to MHC restriction in the antigen-cell interaction. In this case the identity of class II molecules of collaborating cells appears to be a prerequisite for the effectiveness of such collaboration. The molecules involved appear to be associated with the *I-A* subregion or *HLA-D* locus, since identity of such molecules with Ia or D molecules, respectively, has not yet been proved, a hypothetical *CI* (cell interaction) gene has been postulated in mice.

The *Ir phenomenon* demonstrated in virtually all species studied refers to the association between the MHC of an individual and the magnitude of immune responses elicited by a variety of antigens such as synthetic polypeptides, native proteins (strictly speaking, their discrete antigenic determinants), or cell surface antigens. While generally the ability to respond is associated with the *I* region, the responses to different antigens are associated with different subregions; thus *Ir* (immune response) genes of these subregions have been designated *Ir-1A*, *Ir-1B*, and *Ir-1C*. The effect of *Ir* genes appears to be antigen specific, since an individual may be a good responder to one antigen but poor to another. In several instances alleles of two distinct *Ir* genes at two distinct subregions have been found to influence the response to the same antigen, apparently complementing each other. In other cases the response controlled by the MHC-linked *Ir* gene is further influenced by genes outside the MHC. The effect of *Ir* genes appears to be exerted mostly on T helper cells; the genes affect the switch from an early IgM to a subsequent IgG response. In man, at least two *Ir* genes, one affecting an IgE response to ragweed and another influencing the *in vitro* response to streptococci, have been identified in the vicinity of *D* locus. The hypothesis postulating that class II molecules are in fact products of *Ir* genes is discussed in the next section.

The association between *HLA* haplotypes and certain diseases may be closely

Table 14.6. Positive Association Between the *HLA* Alleles and Certain Diseases

Disease	Allele	Relative Risk	Significance[a] (*p*)	Remarks
Hodgkin's disease	*A1*	1.4	10^{-6}	*B8* associated with survival
	B5	1.6	10^{-6}	
	B18	1.9	10^{-6}	
Acute lymphocytic leukemia	*A2*	1.3	10^{-2}	*B8* associated with better survival
	B12	1.2	5×10^{-2}	
Chronic glomerulonephritis	*A2*	1.5	10^{-3}	
Acute uveitis	*B27*	10.4	10^{-6}	
	B13	5.0	ND	
Dermatitis herpetiformis	*B8*	4.3	10^{-6}	Also *DW3* (15.4) and *A10*
Psoriasis	*B13*	4.3	10^{-6}	Also *CW6* (13.3).
	B17	4.8	10^{-6}	*DW2, B13,* and *B37* (2.6);
	B37	8.4	10^{-4}	in Japanese, *A1* (21), *B13* (22), *B37* (26), and *CW6* (15)
Coeliac disease	*B8*	9.5	10^{-6}	
	DW3	10.8	ND	Also *DW7*
Autoimmune hepatitis	*B8*	3.6	10^{-6}	
Myasthenia gravis	*B8*	5.0	10^{-6}	Also *DR3* (2.5); in Japanese, *B12, AW19,* and *AW31*
		2.3	ND	
Sjögren's disease	*B8*	3.2	10^{-6}	
Diabetes	*B9*	1.9	10^{-4}	Also *DR2* (0.2), *DW3* (4.5), *DW4* and *DR4,* (6.4), *DW6* (3.7); negative association with *B7*
	B15	2.3	10^{-6}	
Graves' disease	*B8*	2.5	10^{-6}	
	BW35	13.7	10^{-4}	In Japanese
Addison's disease	*B8*	6.4	10^{-5}	Also *DW3* (10.5)
Multiple sclerosis	*B7*	1.5	10^{-4}	Also *DW2, DR2* (2.5); in Japanese *BW22, DR 5*; In Italians *A10, DW4, DR4,* and *DR5*
Ankylosing spondylitis	*B27*	87.4	10^{-6}	
Reiter's syndrome	*B27*	37.0	10^{-6}	
Psoriatic arthritis	*B27*	5.4	10^{-6}	Also B13, B17

[a]$p \leq 10^{-3}$ is highly significant. ND, not determined.

related to the Ir phenomenon; alternatively, it may reflect linkage disequilibrium between *HLA* and a yet unidentified gene(s) predisposing to disease. When determining actual association between any particular *HLA* gene and disease, one must remember the serious pitfalls of such determination. Differences in size and origin of populations, studies limited to one HLA antigen, and subjectivity in clinical diagnosis all may lead to contradictory or overtly false conclusions. The significance of an association is determined by χ^2 analysis from a 2 × 2 table,

		Antigen	
		Present	Absent
Disease	Present	a	b
	Absent	c	d

and then the relative risk (rR) of a disease in a person carrying a given *HLA* haplotype is calculated from the formula

$$rR = \frac{ad}{bc}$$

Table 14.6 summarizes well established associations recorded with the international registry in Copenhagen.

Antigen-specific suppression in which exposure to an antigen results in suppression of the response to this antigen has been shown to be associated with the *H-2* complex, and more specifically with the products of the *I-J* and probably *I-A* subregions. The mechanism of such a suppression is unknown except for the finding that molecules determined by the *I-J* subregion are expressed in T suppressor cells, where they may be associated with molecules bearing idiotypic specificities for the antigen in question. It may be of interest that during induction of tolerance (Ch. 8) to alloantigens they seem to be recognized in the context of I-J products — i.e., an alloantigen is tolerated if it is presented with I-J products of a "tolerized" individual. The phenomenon appears to be similar to previously discussed observations

that an alloantigen must be presented in context of self molecules of class I to induce an immune response.

Complement factors both from the classical (C4, C2, and C3) and from the alternate (Bf) pathways are determined by genes within or in proximity to the MHC. Interestingly, some complement receptors and the rate of their appearance in ontogenesis are also controlled by the MHC. Whether these associations are accidental or biologically significant has not been determined.

General Interpretation

Any coherent interpretation of the MHC, to be tenable, must account for its polymorphism and pleiotropism and must be compatible with experimental data concerning the basic function and evolution of MHC. Although it is still highly speculative because of scarcity and often inconsistency of available data, one hypothesis appears to fulfill most satisfactorily the above requirements. The central point of the hypothesis is that the immune system originally functioned to counteract either spontaneous or induced alterations of self molecules. In theory such alterations pose a serious threat to the integrity of an individual and a species. The property of counteracting alteration of self molecules served during evolution as a framework for developing reactivity to exogenous antigens. Accordingly, the repertoire of T cells of any individual consists of cells primarily recognizing alterations of class I or class II molecules. The alterations may be represented by mutations of corresponding genes or by association of the products of these genes with an exogenous antigen. In either instance the resulting alterations are recognized by T cells as *alloantigens* and thus trigger an immune response directed against the cell carrying the altered moiety. Altered class I molecules induce T cytotoxic effector cells, whereas altered class II molecules induce T helper cells, which in turn "assist" B cells in production of specific antibodies. One can see that the effectiveness of a response will depend on the capability of a given molecule to become altered by a given antigen.

This hypothesis accommodates the multiplicity and apparent specificity of *Ir* genes by postulating that various antigens create various alterations of class II molecules, each recognized by a specific clone of T cells. A given antigen forms different alterations in allelic molecules, hence different individuals may display different responsiveness to a given antigen. Thus *Ir* genes and their products would be identical with "*Ia*" genes and Ia molecules, respectively, and the specificity of *Ir* genes would be the result of a unique alteration of an allelic product, imparted by a given antigen. The specificity and magnitude of MHC restricted responses would reflect the unique alteration imparted by a given antigen upon class I allelic molecules. The hypothesis clearly implies close similarity, if not identity, of Ir phenomenon and MHC restriction, the notion propounded by many leading immunologists.

The repertoire of T cells in an individual capable of recognizing various alterations is limited by the total number of available cells, by the selection of cells recognizing relatively small alterations as they are most likely to occur, and by the extent of alterability of self molecules. These limitations, however, pose a serious danger to an individual confronted with a highly pathogenic factor causing an alteration for which there could be no (or very few) reactive cells. One can imagine that should all individuals of a species have the same alterable molecules the above situation could be catastrophic to the species, since none of the individuals would be able to mount an effective defense. Such a catastrophe is averted by the extraordinary polymorphism of the MHC, especially classes I and II, assuring that at least some individuals of a species

will have in their repertoires cells capable of recognizing an alteration caused by the pathogen. To put it differently, the limited variability of each individual is offset by the essentially unlimited variability of the species. The concept in which the MHC is assigned a central role in alloreactivity directed to altered cell surface self molecules and therefore primarily concerned with cell destruction permits considerations about the association between complement or its receptors and the MHC. Complement may be viewed as a "descendant" of molecules involved in focusing the cytotoxic reaction on the surface of altered cells.

The concept outlined above allows one to dispose of a multiplicity of genes (*Ir, Is, CI, Lad, ECS*, etc.) by postulating that most, if not all, phenomena attributed to such genes reflect an associative recognition event. Indeed, studies with MHC mutants are consistent with such a concept. The mutation altering a given molecule invariably results in simultaneous alteration of all phenomena associated with the region bearing the gene for such a molecule. Thus one is tempted to postulate that a single gene and its product determine several phenomena, rather than that each phenomenon is determined by a distinct gene.

Practical Considerations

Early attempts of correctional therapy by use of tissue or organ grafts often met serious obstacles. The application of grafts that are permanently accepted because the donor and recipient are either the same individual (*autogenic*) or two individuals genotypically identical (*syngeneic*) is limited by a variety of factors. The most important of these factors relate to technical difficulties of procuring the autogenic grafts and the relative rarity of syngenicity (identical twins) among human beings. In early attempts, the use of grafts secured from an individual genotypically different from the recipient (allogeneic) invariably resulted in a rapid rejection of the graft. Improvement in immunosuppression regimens, discovery of the major histocompatibility antigens, and progress in tissue-typing techniques opened the possibility of matching the donor and recipient for most or all HLA antigens, thus prolonging the survival of allogeneic grafts (see above). Since, as indicated earlier, the immune response against the minor histocompatibility antigens can be to a great extent controlled by chemical immunosuppression, HLA typing has become an important procedure in clinical grafting. Introduction of standard typing procedures for various HLA antigens made kidney grafts a common and highly successful therapeutic measure. In fact, during the last two decades over 30,000 patients have received allogeneic kidney grafts and survived months and years thereafter.

Thus far, only renal grafts have had a measurable degree of success. Although heart transplants are far from a routine procedure, recent years have brought progress warranting a certain degree of optimism. Skin grafts, even with total HLA matching and intensive immunosuppression, are rapidly rejected. Allogeneic grafts of liver, pancreas, or intestine are still in the sphere of experimentation; problems mostly are due to technical difficulties encountered in grafting. Finally, the grafting of hemopoietic or lymphatic tissue poses a peculiar problem of graft-versus-host reaction (Ch. 8). While HLA matching eliminates the reaction due to major antigens, the reaction directed to minor antigens is responsible for eventual failure of bone marrow grafts in a large number of cases.

In addition to pretransplantation matching, HLA typing has found another medical application in cases of disputed paternity. The principle of the procedure is essentially the same as that described for blood group determination. However, while HLA paternity testing is efficient at excluding falsely claimed paternity, its application remains restricted to highly competent laboratories.

REFERENCES

Altman, P.L. and Katz, D.D. (Eds.): Inbred and Genetically Defined Strains of Laboratory Animals. FASEB, Bethesda, Md., 1979.

Cavalli-Sforza, L.L. and Bodmer, W.F.: The Genetics of Human Populations. W.H. Freeman and Co., San Francisco, 1971.

Cinader, B. (Ed.): Regulation of the Antibody Response. Charles C Thomas, Springfield, Ill., 1968.

Festenstein, H. and Demant, P.: HLA and H-2 Basic Immunogenetics — Biology and Clinical Relevance. Edward Arnold Ltd., London, 1978.

Fudenberg, H.H., Pink, J.R.L., Wang, A.-C., and Douglas, S.D.: Basic Immunogenetics, 2nd Ed. Oxford University Press, New York, 1978.

Götze, D. (Ed): The Major Histocompatibility System in Man and Animals. Springer-Verlag, Berlin, 1977.

Grubb, R.: The Genetic Markers of Human Immunoglobulins. Springer, New York, 1970.

Hildemann, W.H., Clark, E.A., and Raison, R.L.: Comprehensive Immunogenetics. Elsevier North-Holland, Amsterdam, 1981.

Klein, J.: Biology of the Mouse Histocompatibility-2 Complex. Springer, New York, 1975.

Mollison, P.L.: Blood Transfusion in Clinical Medicine. F.A. Davis, Philadelphia, 1967.

Race, R.R., and Sanger, R.: Blood Groups in Man. F.A. Davis, Philadelphia, 1975.

Snell, G., Dausset, J., and Nathenson, S.: Histocompatibility. Academic Press, New York, 1976.

Zaleski, M.B., Abeyounis, C.J., and Kauo, K. (Eds.): Immunobiology of the Major Histocompatibility Complex. S. Karger, Basel, 1981.

15

Immunopathology

*Boris Albini and
Giuseppe A. Andres*

Immunopathology is a term defining the study of the pathogenic mechanisms and the structural and functional alterations induced in vertebrate tissues or cells by immune reactions. Immune reactions play a protective role, as shown by the frequent development of infectious diseases in subjects with immune deficiencies. Immune reactions, however, can also cause tissue injury, and the terms *allergy* or *hypersensitivity* are often used to characterize these noxious effects. Immunopathologic injury can result from a response either to foreign or autologous antigens. *Autoimmunity* is the term used to define a reaction of the host against autologous antigens. Crossreactivity among antigens of infectious agents and autoantigens of the host may induce autoimmune phenomena in the wake of infections. For instance, streptococcal antigens may crossreact with human tissues, such as myocardium and brain. In addition, alterations of autoantigens by disease processes or exposure of hitherto "hidden" antigens of the host's tissues may lead to autoreactivity. It seems, however, that autoreactivity per se is a normal expression in some immune responses. Only under certain circumstances does pathogenic autoreactivity develop.

Gell and Coombs have provided a classification of immunopathologic reactions (Table 15.1). These authors list four major types of immunologically mediated tissue injury: (1) immediate, reagin-dependent hypersensitivity; (2) antibody-mediated hypersensitivity to cell surface and other tissue antigens; (3) tissue injury mediated by antigen-antibody complexes; and (4) delayed hypersensitivity mediated directly by sensitized lymphocytes. Most immunologically mediated diseases, however, involve the combined effects of more than one of these pathogenetic mechanisms. The factors that determine the character and extent of these reactions are complex and not clearly understood. They involve the type of antigen, the route of inoculation, the tissue where the reaction occurs, and parameters intrinsic of the host.

REAGIN-MEDIATED HYPERSENSITIVITY

The protective role of reagin-dependent mechanisms is still not clearly established. The harmful effects they have in the framework of immediate hypersensitivity reactions, however, are well documented (Ch. 12). This "true" anaphylaxis involves

213

Table 15.1.   Histologic Characteristics of Immunopathologic Reactions

Immunologic Reaction[a]	Histological Findings	Immunohistology	
		Components of Deposits Detected by Immuno-fluorescence	Type of Cells in Infiltrate
Reaginic antibody-dependent reactions — anaphylaxis	Edema, cellular infiltrates, degranulated granulocytes	Sometimes IgE, IgG; usually negative	Basophil and eosinophil granulocytes
Other antibody-mediated reactions	Edema, necrosis, cell proliferation, cellular infiltrates	IgG, IgM, IgA, complement, sometimes fibrinogen (on cell surface or linear in basement membrane)	B cells, K cells, macrophages, epithelioid and giant cells, neutrophil granulocytes
Immune complex-mediated reactions — Arthus reaction, serum sickness	Edema, necrosis, hemorrhage, changes in vasculature, cell profiltration, cellular infiltrations, electron-dense deposits	IgG, IgM, IgA, IgE, complement, sometimes fibrinogen (granular to ribbonlike pattern)	Neutrophil granulocytes, macrophages, B cells, basophil and eosinophil granulocytes
Delayed hypersensitivity	Cellular infiltrates, granuloma formation, necrosis	Variable	T cells, macrophages, epithelioid and giant cells, sometimes basophil or eosinophil granulocytes

[a]According to Gell and Coombs.

a class of homocytotropic antibodies (*reagins*), interacting with basophil granulocytes and mast cells (Fig. 15.1). In man, most reagins belong to the IgE class of immunoglobulins (Ch. 12). Anaphylaxis must be distinguished from similar reactions induced by immune complexes or immune aggregates. These latter reactions are termed *anaphylactoid reactions* or *aggregate anaphylaxis*. True and aggregate anaphylaxis are characterized by release of the same inflammatory mediators. The immune effectors involved, however, are different (reagins versus immune complexes or aggregated immunoglobulins). Moreover, true anaphylaxis is complement independent, whereas in anaphylactoid reactions complement is activated.

The basophilic granulocyte originates from stem cells in the bone marrow. Analogous to the neutrophil and eosinophil cells of the same series, it contains characteristic granules. These granules react with basic dyes and contain inflammatory mediators, mainly histamine, eosinophil chemotactic factor of anaphylaxis (ECF-A), and heparin. Basophil leukocytes are blood cells but may migrate into the tissues. The larger mast cells, found exclusively in tissues, contain the same type of granules. Both cell types have receptors for the Fc portion of IgE on their cell membranes.

The eosinophil granulocytes have endocytotic and phagocytic abilities. In regard to phagocytosis of bacteria, however, they are significantly less active than neutrophil granulocytes. Eosinophils release granule-associated enzymes upon interaction with antigen–IgE complexes. Interestingly, histamine and ECF-A induce an increase in the density of eosinophil membrane receptors. The role of eosinophil granulocytes in anaphlyaxis can be conceived of as "modulators" in the release of inflammatory mediators by basophil granulocytes and mast cells. The eosinophils produce prostaglandins (PGE_1 and PGE_2), which inhibit the release of mediators from basophil leukocytes and mast cells by increasing the cyclic AMP concentration in

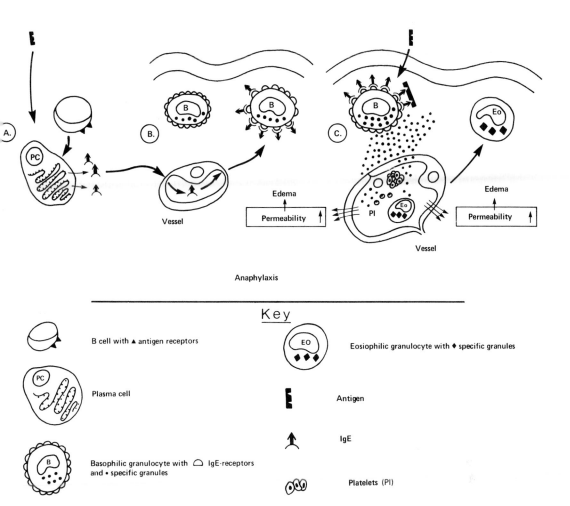

Anaphylaxis

Key

B cell with ▲ antigen receptors

Plasma cell

Basophilic granulocyte with ◯ IgE-receptors
and • specific granules

Eosiophilic granulocyte with ♦ specific granules

Antigen

IgE

Platelets (PI)

Fig. 15.1. Schematic representation (with key) of the reactions occurring in cutaneous anaphylaxis. A. Contact of an antigen with the immune system leads to sensitization of B cells. Plasma
cells develop that produce homocytotropic antibody (in man, predominantly IgE). The antibody is
secreted by the plasma cells and reaches circulation. B. Homocytotropic antibody leaves the
circulation and travels through the tissue. If contact with basophilic granulocytes or mast cells is
established, homocytotropic antibody interacts with receptors for its Fc portion, which are present
on the cell surfaces. The cells become covered or "armed" with homocytotropic antibodies. C.
Upon renewed introduction of antigen into the tissue, homocytotropic antibodies on the surface of
basophilic granulocytes or mast cells are bridged by the antigen molecules, inducing changes in
cell membrane distribution of proteins and possibly in characteristics of the membrane lipids. A
signal reaches the cytoplasm that ultimately leads to "degranulation" of the cells. This, in turn,
entails the liberation of inflammatory mediators, predominately of vasoactive amines, into the
tissue. They act upon vessel walls by increasing the permeability. Amounts of fluid much higher
than usual leave the vessel; the tissue becomes edematous. In addition, some mediators liberated upon degranulation affect the platelets. Platelets amplify the reaction by liberating additional
inflammatory reagents. Finally, factors chemotactic for eosinophilic granulocytes attract these
cells, which have a regulatory effect on the inflammation initiated by degranulation of basophilic
granulocytes and mast cells.

these latter cells. Basic proteins of eosinophil granulocytes interact with heparin
and inactivate it; this inactivation is not an
enzymatic process. On the other hand, enzymes liberated from eosinophil granulocytes are capable of degrading many of the
mediators released by mast cells and
basophil granulocytes. There is experimental evidence that eosinophil granulocytes are instrumental in the restoration
of the full function of mast cells and
basophil granulocytes after degranulation.
Eosinophil granulocytes may be seen in tissue not only immediately after degranulation of mast cells and basophil leukocytes
but also "in a second wave" several hours
later. A chemotactic factor responsible for
this second, "late" immigration of eosinophils has been defined. It is not clear
how and whence it is released.

Upon histologic examination a tissue in
which local anaphylaxis has occurred may
show degranulated mast cells and basophil
granulocytes. Usually, biopsies of tissues
from patients with anaphylaxis show one of
the two following pictures: In biopsies
taken from patients with urticaria (skin
eruptions caused by anaphylaxis), edema is
prominent; a few lymphocytes and eosinophil granulocytes may be present around
vessels. Alternatively, tissues may show impressive infiltration with eosinophils and
only a few neutrophil granulocytes or lymphocytes; this second histologic pattern can
be observed in the lungs of patients with
some forms of asthma.

It should not be forgotten that eosinophil granulocytes may constitute an important component of some delayed
hypersensitivity lesions and that some parasites, especially helminths, may produce
chemotactic factors specific for eosinophils
without involvement of the immune system.

Anaphylaxis has been studied extensively
in guinea pigs, and a number of experimental protocols have been developed
to elicit this reaction (see Ch. 12). Anaphy-

laxis is seen in some patients in response to
contact with fungi (e.g., *Aspergillus fumigatus*) and may contribute to host defense
against helminths. Of special clinical importance are anaphylactic reactions in patients with drug hypersensitivity.

Clinical tests useful for the diagnosis in
patients with anaphylactic manifestations
are the immediate skin reaction, reaching
its maximum 10 to 20 minutes after injection of antigen and disappearing 50 to 90
minutes later (Table 13.2), the Prausnitz-
Küstner reaction, and the RAST test for
specific antibodies of the IgE class
(Ch. 12).

ANTIBODY-MEDIATED LESIONS AFFECTING VERTEBRATE TISSUES OR CELLS

Cell Surface Antigens

Antibody reacting with cell surface determinants may by itself impair the normal
function of cells. More often, upon reaction
with the antigen, antibody recruits inflammatory mediators — blood clotting,
kinin, complement, and phagocytic cell systems. Histopathologically, lesions involving
these mechanisms are characterized by the
presence of immunoglobulins, with or without complement components on the surface
of the cells. The cells exhibiting the antigen
may show degenerative changes or necrosis. Alternatively, interaction of antibodies
with cell surface constituents may induce
cell proliferation. Inflammatory and lymphoid cells may infiltrate the tissues.

Diseases characterized by antibody- and
complement-mediated destruction of blood
cells include transfusion reactions, erythroblastosis fetalis, acquired hemolytic
diseases, and hemolytic reactions to drugs.
One example of the last type of blood cell
injury is "Sedormid" purpura. This drug
adheres to the surface of platelets and
stimulates antibody production, which ultimately brings about platelet destruction. A

variety of infectious diseases caused by salmonellae and mycobacteria are associated with hemolytic anemias. In the former, there is evidence that red blood cell lysis is due to an antibody- and complement-mediated reaction against the lipopolysaccharide endotoxins of the microorganisms, which bind to the patient's erythrocytes.

Endothelial cells are targets of both transplantation and Forssman antibodies. Renal allograft recipients who have been presensitized to histocompatibility antigens of the donor develop, in the allograft, pathologic changes hallmarked by endothelial degeneration. Forssman antibodies, when injected into an animal expressing Forssman antigen on its cells, lead to the same pattern of pathologic changes. Thus both of these unrelated types of antibodies induce swelling and necrosis of endothelial cells, exposure of the vascular basement membrane to the circulation, adherence of granulocytes and platelets to vessel walls, precipitation of fibrin, thrombosis, and ischemic necrosis.

Tissue Antigens

Sensitization to homologous or heterologous tissue frequently encompasses the production of antibodies that react with the respective tissues of the host (autoimmunization). A typical and intensively studied example of this type of autoimmune response is the glomerulonephritis induced by immunization of sheep with heterologous or homologous glomerular basement membranes (GBM) in adjuvants (i.e., reagents enhancing the immune response to simultaneously injected antigens). The primary role of antibody in the pathogenesis of this disease is shown by the outcome of passive transfer experiments. Circulating antibodies, which react with GBM, are capable of transferring the glomerulonephritis to normal sheep. The sequence of events following interaction of antibody with GBM

has been clarified. Complement is usually activated through the classical pathway; as the sequence of activation proceeds, its anaphylatoxic components (Ch. 11) may induce increased permeability of the GBM and contribute to inflammation. The chemotactic factors of the complement system attract polymorphonuclear leukocytes to the site of antigen–antibody reaction. C3b present in proximity to the surface of GBM provides a site for immune adherence of these cells. There the polymorphonuclear leukocytes release lysosomal enzymes, which further alter the permeability properties of the GBM. At the same time there is a marked accumulation of mononuclear cells. Other inflammatory mediators besides complement, such as kinins, may also contribute to the inflammatory process. The rapidity and the intensity of the injury is usually related to the amount of antibody involved. The final extent of tissue injury also depends on how long the antibody is present at the reaction site. In sheep the lesion is characterized by linear deposits of IgG and complement in the GBM, formation of "crescents," which obliterate Bowman's space, and disruption and collapse of glomerular capillary walls. The crescents are formed by accumulation of blood-borne macrophages that escape through the broken glomerular capillary walls. This antibody-mediated glomerulonephritis usually leads to fulminant renal failure.

Another example of pathology induced by antibody and complement is the autoimmune tubulointerstitial nephritis of guinea pigs immunized with rabbit tubular basement membranes (TBM) and Freund's adjuvant. The animals develop antibody that crossreacts with guinea pig TBM. Direct immunofluorescence reveals linear deposits of guinea pig IgG and complement in the TBM. In this disease polymorphonuclear leukocyte infiltration is usually lacking. Instead, mononuclear cells are found. The role of these cells in the pathogenesis of the disease is shown by experiments demon strating that tissue injury by passive transfer of antibody is prevented when the guinea pigs are depleted of radiosensitive bone marrow cells before the injection of antibody.

Anti-GBM and anti-TBM antibody-mediated diseases are rare but severe in man. The patients make antibodies to their own renal basement membranes. When the antibodies crossreact with the alveolar basement membranes, they can induce, in addition to kidney disease, hemorrhagic pneumonitis (Goodpasture's disease).

REACTIONS MEDIATED BY IMMUNE COMPLEXES

Immune complexes (IC) may result from the combination of antibody with antigens released in the circulation or antigens present in extracellular tissue. Localized antigens usually result in an inflammatory reaction comparable to local Arthus reaction. Immune complexes formed in the circulation induce lesions comparable to acute or chronic serum sickness.

The antigens responsible for IC formation may be exogenous (bacterial, viral, parasitic, etc.) or autologous (DNA, thyroglobulin, etc.).

Localized Immune Complex Disease: The Arthus Reaction

The Arthus reaction is a local inflammatory reaction in which antigen in the tissue combines with precipitating antibodies either formed locally or diffused from the blood. The classical Arthus reaction is induced by the injection of antigen into the skin of an individual with circulating antibody to the injected antigen. The reaction reaches a peak 6 to 10 hours after the injection and consists of an area of edema with hemorrhagic necrosis. The basic lesion is a vasculitis with infiltrating polymorphonuclear leukocytes, extravasation of proteins, and occasional thrombosis. To induce a macroscopically detectable reaction, the amount of antigen injected must be relatively large.

The pathogenesis of the lesion is well understood. Antibody reacts with the antigen, usually within the wall of the vessel. There is local formation of IC with the activation of complement by classical and alternate pathways. Chemotactic factors are generated. Neutrophilic granulocytes, which have surface C3 receptors, are attracted and bind to the IC. Neutrophil granulocytes phagocytize the IC, there is platelet aggregation, and during these processes, lysosomal components (among these, cathepsins D and E, elastase, collagenase, and a variety of cationic proteins) are released, causing tissue injury.

Administration of cobra venom, which almost completely depletes serum C3, suppresses the Arthus reaction. Likewise, depletion of neutrophils or platelets diminishes the intensity of inflammation.

In man, local IC pathology comparable to the Arthus reaction may occur in rheumatoid arthritis, hypersensitivity pneumonitis (e.g., eosinophil infiltrates in the lung of patients infected with *Aspergillus fumigatus*), and in several infectious diseases in which bacterial, fungal, parasitic, or viral antigens present in tissues react with antibodies diffusing from the circulation. Furthermore, there is some evidence that in certain autoimmune diseases, such as thyroiditis and systemic lupus erythematosus, antigens (thyroglobulin, DNA) released or accumulated in tissues (e.g., in basement membranes) may react locally with antibodies and elicit an Arthus-type inflammation. More recently, another mechanism for local, *in situ* formation of IC has been proposed. Antigen is trapped in tissue structures such as basement membranes, and circulating or locally produced antibody may react with these tissue-bound antigens and form IC. The trapping itself may be accomplished by physicochemical interactions, such as coulombic forces, or by immune reactions such as encountered in nephrotoxic glomerulonephritis. In this experimental condition a recipient animal is injected with heterologous antibody to its own GBM. The antibody binds in a linear pattern to the GBM (heterologous phase). A few weeks later the recipient animal produces antibody to the heterologous immunoglobulin implanted in the GBM (autologous phase). The ensuing immune reaction, representing *in situ* formation of IC, leads to a severe glomerulonephritis.

Systemic Immune Complex Disease: Serum Sickness-like Reactions

IC formed in the circulation are deposited in the vasculature of various tissues and induce an acute transient, or chronic progressive, inflammation called *serum sickness* (Ch. 12). In patients this disease was first described by Lublinski, Francioni, and von Pirquet. Sera raised in animals against diphtheria and tetanus toxins were intro-

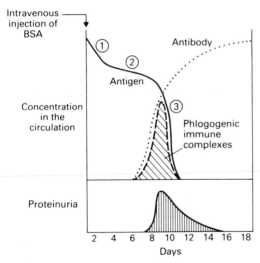

Fig. 15.2. The development of acute serum sickness in a rabbit injected intravenously with one large dose of bovine serum albumin (BSA). 1, equilibration phase; 2, catabolic phase; 3, immune elimination phase. (Albini, B., Brentjens, J.R., and Andres, G.A.: The Immunopathology of the Kidney. Edward Arnold, Ltd., London 1979.)

duced for treatment of patients during the last decade of the 19th century. Von Pirquet found antibody to horse serum in the blood of convalescent patients with serum sickness but not at the peak of the disease. He attributed the symptoms to the formation of "toxic products" arising in the wake of antigen–antibody reactions.

The rabbit model of experimental serum sickness has greatly contributed to clarifying our understanding of the pathogenesis of this condition. Both acute and chronic models of serum sickness have been developed.

Acute Serum Sickness. The basic model of acute serum sickness is illustrated in Figure 15.2. When a single, large dose of bovine serum albumin (BSA) is injected intravenously into a rabbit, it is eliminated from the circulation in three phases. First, there is equilibration between intra- and extravascular spaces; second, a slow catabolic phase comparable to that of autologous proteins is seen; third, there is a phase of rapid immune clearance that is caused by the combination of BSA with anti-BSA antibody and the formation of IC in the circulation, followed by vasculitis affecting kidneys, joints, lungs, and heart. Lesions are most prominent in renal glomeruli.

Acute IC glomerulonephritis is characterized by accumulation of neutrophils, mononuclear cells, and platelets, proliferation of mesangial cells, and alteration of endothelial cells and GBM. By immunofluorescence irregular granular deposits of BSA, rabbit IgG, and complement can be detected in the vasculature. In glomeruli the immune deposits can be visualized by electron microscopy as focal deposits of foreign material present along the subendothelial part of the GBM and in the mesangium. As the immune response progresses and more antibody is made, IC of larger size are formed. These larger IC are taken up by hepatic and splenic phagocytes and do not participate in tissue damage.

During the next 15 to 20 days the BSA is eliminated, and the IC disappear from the circulation. Likewise, the IC disappear from the tissues; as can be expected, the clinical symptoms progressively abate. It is at this time that free antibodies to BSA appear in the circulation.

Formation of IC in the circulation is not the sole event responsible for acute serum sickness. A host of additional factors cooperate in the pathogenesis of tissue injury. Anatomical and physiologic properties of the vasculature are important. IC preferentially localize and induce damage in capillaries (such as those of renal glomeruli) characterized by a fenestrated endothelium, high blood flow, and high hydrostatic pressure. Individuals capable of mounting a vigorous antibody response to highly immunogenic antigens are obvious candidates to develop acute serum sickness. The amount of antigen must be relatively large, and the antigen must circulate for a sufficient time in order to combine with antibody. Small-sized IC in slight antigen excess bind less avidly to phagocytic cells, circulate longer, and have a better opportunity to localize in the walls of the vessels. It seems that there must be increased vascular permeability to allow the IC to penetrate the vessel walls. This increased permeability is promoted by release of vasoactive amines discussed above (histamine or serotonin) from degranulated basophil granulocytes and platelets. Hemodynamic factors, such as manifested in areas of turbulence, favor IC localization. A depressed activity of the reticuloendothelial system, especially of the spleen, allows IC to circulate longer and may enhance the development of tissue damage.

There is convincing evidence that acute serum sickness mechanisms operate in man, especially in postinfectious glomerulonephritis, which is seen often after infections with streptococci or staphylococci and in certain forms of vasculitis. Several exogenous antigens have been demonstrated convincingly or tentatively in glomeruli or other vessels of patients with poststreptococcal glomerulonephritis or endocarditis, pneumococcal or staphylococcal otitis, ventriculoatrial shunts infected with staphylococci, or hepatitis B virus infection.

Chronic Serum Sickness. If an antigen is introduced or released continuously, regardless of the amount in the circulation, prolonged formation of IC may occur. This event usually results in renal pathology. The most important factors for the development of chronic serum sickness are the presence of the antigen in the circulation and the quantity and quality of the antibody response.

Again, important information has been obtained from a rabbit model of experimental serum sickness. Daily intravenous injections of BSA, in doses matching the amount of circulating antibody, may induce three patterns of response. The rabbits that are unresponsive to BSA do not develop disease, indicating that the antigen itself is harmless. The rabbits generating a high antibody response form IC in antibody excess. These large IC are rapidly phagocytized by the reticuloendothelial system. Only mild glomerulonephritis develops, at least until the antibody response ultimately subsides, with resulting formation of nephritogenic IC in antigen excess. Lastly, the rabbits that make an average antibody response, matching the dose of injected BSA, develop a severe proliferative, exudative, and/or membraneous glomerulonephritis. In these rabbits large amounts of IC in slight antigen excess persist in the circulation for prolonged periods of time. The morphology of the lesions covers a large spectrum of human pathology. Although the main changes are observed in the kidney, IC pathology can occur in several organs, for example, the choroid plexus, the lung, the spleen, and the ovary. Granular immune deposits, presumably representing IC, can be found by immunofluorescence and electron microscopy in the walls of the vessels, usually in the basement membranes. In rabbits the end result of chronic serum sickness is proteinuria, azotemia, and, eventually, death from renal failure.

The pathogenesis of chronic serum sickness, especially the role of mediators of the inflammatory reaction, has not been clarified. It is conceivable that some of the pathogenetic mechanisms characteristic of acute serum sickness may also be operative in chronic conditions. *Membranous lesions*, characterized by accumulation of IC in basement membranes without concomitant cellular infiltration or obvious tissue damage, seem to result from small IC acting over a long period of time, from the depletion of essential inflammatory mediators that may occur with a longstanding, ongoing immune reaction, or from a combination of factors, including the physicochemical properties of antibody and antigen and the role of the reticuloendothelial system.

In man IC circulating for a prolonged period of time seem to account for the majority of glomerulonephritides. In systemic lupus erythematosus, the role of nuclear antigens, their corresponding antibodies, and complement has been convincingly demonstrated. In most human "chronic IC diseases," however, the antigens responsible for the inflammatory reactions are unknown.

DELAYED HYPERSENSITIVITY

In the most common usage, *delayed hypersensitivity* (DH) denotes an immunologically mediated inflammatory reaction in which the immune effector is a T cell (Ch. 13). Available evidence indicates that in the mouse this effector T cell carries Lyt1 alloantigens (Ch. 9). This immunopathologic entity is associated with a delayed skin reaction (Table 13.2) and with a predominately mononuclear cell infiltrate in tissue lesions (at least in man and in some other species). In the remainder of this chapter the discussion will be limited to this DH of the tuberculin type in humans (Ch. 13).

Early in the course of sensitization for DH and after exposure to antigen, small lymphocytes present in the deep cortical areas of lymph nodes or the periarteriolar sheaths of the spleen transform into large pyroninophilic blast cells. In mice sensitized to bacillus Calmette-Guerin (BCG), reintroduction of the same microorganism induces accentuated proliferation of lymphocytes. After a short time the sensitized cells leave the lymphoid tissue via the afferent lymphatics and reach the circulation and the sites of injection. Here, blast cells may revert to small lymphocytes, morphologically indistinguishable from the original cells proliferating in the lymphoid organs. These small lymphocytes derived from blast cells can apparently perform the effector functions required in DH, but they are no longer able to migrate through vessel walls.

It seems that interactions of T cells developing into effector cells with other T cells and with B cells or B cell products (i.e., antibodies and antibody–antigen complexes) allow for regulatory mechanisms defining the ultimate type and extent of the DH reaction. These mechanisms may be analogous to those seen in the regulation of B cell activity via the T cell network or antigen receptor–antireceptor systems (Chs. 8 and 9).

Products of T cells in DH mobilize and activate macrophages and other cells. Also, some T cells may lyse cells by direct contact. The mechanism of action of T cells on target cells, however, is not yet completely understood. On the other hand, T cell products (lymphokines) mobilizing and activating macrophages or other inflammatory cells have been demonstrated and, to some extent, characterized (Ch. 13).

The histologic features of a delayed reaction induced in a sensitized host (Fig. 15.3)

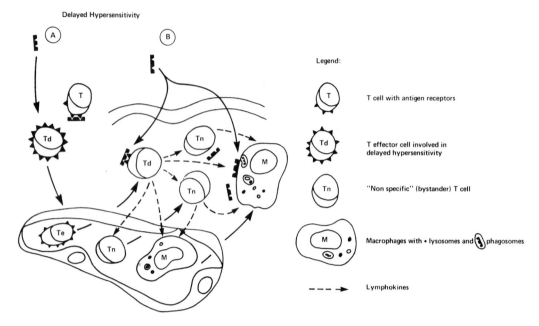

Fig. 15.3. Schematic representation of "classical" delayed hypersensitivity skin reaction of the tuberculin type. A. An antigen brought in contact with the cells of the immune system leads to sensitization of T cells. These cells reach the circulation. B. Upon renewed introduction of antigen into the tissue, sensitized T cells interact with it. This interaction induces the sensitized T cells to produce lymphokines. Subsequently, these soluble mediators recruit nonsensitized "bystander" T cells and macrophages and thus produce an accumulation of mononuclear cells at sites containing the antigen.

are characteristic enough to allow tentative identification. In contrast to reactions caused by immediate hypersensitivity, in which polymorphonuclear granulocytes and serous exudates determine most lesions, in DH the inflammatory infiltrates consist almost exclusively of mononuclear cells. In early infiltrates the cells are predominantly small lymphocytes and lymphoblasts. These cells form cuffs around venules and veins. Later, monocytes become the predominant cell type. Monocytes and macrophages may, upon activation, be transformed into epithelioid cells and, ultimately, into multinucleated giant cells. The cellular infiltrates may remain diffuse or may organize into granulomas. These immune granulomas are characterized by dense, focal accumulations of mononuclear phagocytes. Macrophages, epithelioid cells, and multinucleated giant

cells usually form many layers around the cells or tissue containing the microorganisms. The granulomas also contain a small population of lymphocytes, eosinophil and neutrophil granulocytes, and fibroblasts. Sometimes even plasma cells may be found. Soluble antigens usually cause diffuse reactions, whereas antigens on insoluble particles (microbes), which easily survive in macrophages, usually induce formation of granulomas.

Highly activated macrophages in granulomas have large amounts of cytoplasm which stains characteristically with eosin dyes. These cells are called *epithelioid* because they often form tight layers of cells somewhat similar to an epithelium. They contain increased amounts of lysosomal enzymes and are thus especially equipped to kill facultative intracellular organisms. Less activated macrophages are present at the periphery of granulomas, and the content of enzymes in phagocytes increases towards the center.

Multinucleated giant cells form by fusion of many macrophages. It is not completely clear what advantage the formation of giant cells confers on the host. It is possible that very large particles are phagocytized easier by these cells, or that enzymes synthesized in the cytoplasm of the giant cells may be effectively concentrated at one site of it.

Macrophages may divide actively within the granulomas; they may leave them or die in them. Granulomas and diffuse reactions can be transformed into each other by changing the mode of presentation of the antigen from particulate to soluble or vice versa in the same sensitized animals.

Despite the characteristic histologic appearance of DH, it should be kept in mind that other immunologically and nonimmunologically mediated mechanisms may induce histologic features resembling those described above. Thus, for example, lymphocytes, macrophages, and giant cells are found in the cellular infiltrates of interstitial nephritis mediated by antibodies to tubular basement membranes. All the available data, however, indicate that antibody-mediated mechanisms and not immunity mediated by effector T cells are involved in this condition. Similarly, in spontaneous autoimmune thyroiditis of chickens, cellular infiltrates consist of mononuclear cells, almost exclusively of lymphocytes. It seems, however, that the cells are predominantly K cells and B cells. On the other hand, granulomas may arise without participation of immune mechanisms, as is seen in the case of foreign body granulomas. There is no infallible histologic criterion to differentiate immune from nonimmune granulomas. Histologically, most of the constituents of inflammation in the delayed-type reaction represent immunologically nonspecific elements. It is obvious that many pathogenetic mechanisms may lead to the same or similar morphological pictures, since the same effector of inflammation may be triggered by very different agents and still produce the same inflammatory phenomenon.

DH as described here occurs in man and some other species. Mice, however, show a preponderance of polymorphonuclear leukocytes in DH lesions.

In infectious diseases DH is seen predominately as a defense mechanism against intracellular or facultative intracellular microorganisms (see Ch. 13). T cells may directly interact with cells infected by viruses or bacteria in cytotoxic reactions. In such reactions the effector T cells must recognize on the host cell surface not only antigens, which are encoded by the microorganisms's genome, but also histocompatibility antigens of "self" (for further discussion of this phenomenon, called *MHC restriction*, see Ch. 14). Viruses, such as herpesviruses, and chlamydiae such as *Chlamydia trachomatis*, may be able to survive even in macrophages. The activation of macrophages by T cell products in the course of DH may be crucial to counter the adaptation of these microorganisms to life inside phagocytic cells.

Microscopic observation of autopsy material is of relevance in the confirmation or establishment of the diagnosis of a disease mediated by DH. Obviously, retrospective diagnosis is only of epidemiologic and not of clinical interest. In rare cases biopsy material may be available, and its histologic and possibly immunohistologic analysis may contribute to diagnosis. In most patients, however, DH is assessed using skin tests or *in vitro* correlates. Skin tests, despite being often difficult to interpret, still are of primary importance because they are relatively easy to perform. Skin tests are usually executed with more or less crude antigenic preparations (Ch. 13). *In vitro* correlates of DH (Ch. 13) have the advantage of well controlled conditions and good understanding of the lymphocyte activity tested. Unfortunately, very little is known as to how much the specific aspects of T cell function evaluated *in vitro* contribute to the *in vivo* phenomena of DH.

Although T cell-mediated mechanisms underlying DH appear designed for protection of the host (cell-mediated immunity, see Ch. 13), they frequently contribute to tissue damage. This is understandable because they are directed toward intracellular parasites. Thus in elimination of the infectious agents the host cells must be destroyed too. In addition, many of the microorganisms eliciting DH cause chronic disease, and the protective effect therefore is achieved only after a long period of time. Cell-mediated immunity occasionally is inefficient and not able to achieve the ultimate goal of destroying the invading infectious agents. Under these circumstances the host defense may rely on "palliative" measures. For example, granulomas wall off and demarcate foci where microorganisms cannot immediately be destroyed. Granulomas may develop extensive central necrosis and induce fibrosis of tissue at their periphery. In addition to isolating the infectious agents, this process may lead to destruction of whole organs. In tuberculosis the cavity formation in the lung by caseous necrosis is the outcome of granuloma formation. For optimal therapy of infectious diseases involving DH, it seems indispensable to attempt to determine to what extent the immune response is beneficial or harmful to the host.

CONCLUSIONS: THE ROLE OF IMMUNOPATHOLOGY IN INFECTIOUS DISEASES

In the course of infectious diseases, tissue pathology may arise from various mechanisms, which may be grouped into three categories: (1) direct tissue damage caused by the microorganisms of their products; (2) indirect tissue damage caused by inflammatory processes without participation of immune mechanisms; and (3) immunopathology.

Of the direct effects of microorganisms on tissue, the cytopathic effects and the effects of microbial toxin should be mentioned. Cytopathic effects entail impairment of cell function and eventual death of the cell. These effects are seen not only in viral infections but also in some bacterial infections, such as tuberculosis or leprosy. Tissue damage by toxins occurs frequently in bacterial and fungal infections but may be seen in protozoan infections as well; for example, the eggs of schistosoma liberate substances damaging the surrounding tissue. Toxins act with a broad variety of mechanisms. Lecithinase of *Clostridium perfringens* has a cytotoxic effect by lysing cell membranes. Hyaluronidase of streptococci degrades connective tissue elements, leading to derangement of tissue structure (Ch. 6).

Without participation of specific immune reactants, bacterial endotoxin may activate inflammatory mediators, e.g., the complement cascade; endotoxin also may cause the Shwartzman reaction. (In this reaction, which may be either localized or generalized, activation of complement and release of thromboplastinlike material from leukocytes seem to contribute to the formation of thrombi and to hemorrhagic tissue lesions. In human infectious diseases, Shwartzman-like syndromes may be encountered in the course of sepsis caused by gram-negative bacteria.) Worms apparently secrete a chemotactic factor attracting eosinophils. Tissue damage (produced by toxins or trauma) may by itself recruit the Hageman system. These are some examples of inflammatory responses induced by microorganisms without participation of the immune system.

The immunologic mechanisms involved in tissue injury have been outlined in this chapter. Which type(s) of hypersensitivity is (are) elicited by a microorganism at a certain time of infection in a certain host obviously depends on the outcome of a complex of interrelated mechanisms taking place in the framework of the regulatory networks of the immune system such as idiotype–antiidiotype network (see Ch. 8) and T cell regulatory complex which has been best described in the mouse. These mechanisms ultimately determine the type and quantity of immune effectors that are produced (i.e., antibodies, lymphokines, and sensitized cells). On the other hand, the regulatory mechanisms of the immune system are influenced not only by the quality and quantity of the antigenic stimulus, the route of immunization, and the immune state of the host but also by the state of the nervous and the hormonal systems of the host and by general conditions, such as nutritional status, stress, age, and sex. Furthermore, tissue damage produced by immunological mechanisms depends on the interaction of immune effectors with inflammatory mediators and on interaction among these mediators themselves. Thus it is obvious that the final reaction is very complex and the elucidation of the individual mechanisms involved extremely difficult.

In almost all infectious diseases with tissue injury, the histopathologic mechanisms include more than one type of hypersensitivity in addition to direct microbial and inflammatory damage. Thus aspergillosis of the lung may involve both anaphylaxis and immune complex-mediated hypersensitivity mechanisms, and *Candida* infections may lead to immune complex and T-cell-mediated hypersensitivity. In infections with helminths, immune complex and cell-mediated hypersensitivity, direct tissue damage by trauma and helminthic products, and nonimmunologic inflammatory mechanisms may operate simultaneously. In some diseases — for example, leprosy — either immediate or delayed hypersensitivity mechanisms may determine the clinical manifestation in individual patients, or lack of

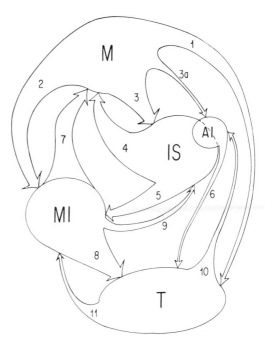

Fig. 15.4. Flowchart analysis of tissue damage in infectious diseases. M, microorganism (or parasite); IS, immune system; AI, autoimmune responses; MI, mediators of inflammation; T, tissue of the host. *1.* Components of M directly damage T (e.g., via toxins, enzymes). *2.* M induces inflammatory response without participation of IS (e.g., bacterial chemotactic factors). *3.* M stimulates IS to produce antibodies or effector cells reactive with antigens specific for M. *3a.* M stimulates IS to produce antibodies or effector cells reactive with autoantigens of the host (the sensitizing agents are cross-reactive antigens). *4.* IS produces effectors reacting with M. *5.* Immune effectors, upon reaction with M, recruit MI. *6.* Autoimmunization induces immune effectors reacting with components of T. *7.* MI react with M. *8.* MI induce changes (e.g., increased or decreased flow rate in the vasculature) and possibly damage (e.g., by spilling of lytic enzymes from lysosomes of granulocytes) in T. *9.* Recruitment of MI may influence the immune response (e.g., solubilization of immune complexes by complement components). *10.* Upon damage, T may liberate hitherto hidden antigens; alternatively, antigens of T may become altered in the course of tissue damage. Both processes may lead to autoimmunization. *11.* Upon damage, T may liberate components recruiting MI (e.g., tissue chemotactic factors).

immune response may be seen. DH granulomas may determine the manifestations
and outcome of some forms of leprosy. In
other patients erythema nodosum, possibly involving immune complex-mediated
hypersensitivity, may predominate. In some
infections hypersensitivity mechanisms may
be responsible for sequelae following the
original disease caused by the microorganisms. Thus there is suggestive evidence that
rheumatic fever may be caused by
hypersensitivity to microbial antigens or
antigens shared by the host and the microorganisms. These mechanisms may cause
tissue lesions without necessarily involving
the infectious agent in the effector phase.

The flowchart given in Figure 15.4
should provide a basis for the analysis of
tissue damage in specific infectious diseases. It is far from complete, but it out-
lines the main pathways of defense or injury. Thorough analysis of the pathogenic
mechanisms is obviously essential not only
for the academic purpose of enhancing our
understanding but also for a meaningful
therapeutic strategy devised to cope with
the often changing and interrelated protective or damaging events that characterize
the invasion of microorganisms into a host.

Obviously, the battery of immunodiagnos-
tic tests available, including skin tests
(Table 13.2) and biopsies, can be used
efficiently only after understanding the
basic mechanisms of immunopathology.

REFERENCES

Cohen, S., Ward, P.A., and McCluskey, R.T.,
Eds.: Mechanisms of Immunopathology.
John Wiley and Sons, New York, 1979.
Dvorak, H.R., Galli, S.J., and Dvorak, A.M.:
Expression of cell-mediated hypersensitivity
in vivo — recent advances. Int. Rev. Exp.
Pathol. *21*: 119, 1980.
Gell, P.G.H., Coombs, R.R.A., and Lach-
mann, P.J., Eds.: Clinical Aspects of Im-
munology. 3rd Ed. Blackwell Sci. Publ., Ox-
ford, 1975.
Milgrom, F. and Albini, B., Eds.: Immuno-
pathology. S. Karger, Basel, 1979.
Samter, M., Ed.: Immunological Diseases.
Vols. I and II. 3rd Ed. Little, Brown, Boston,
1978.
Talal, N., Ed.: Autoimmunity. Academic Press,
New York, 1977.
Turk, J.L.: Immunology in Clinical Medicine.
3rd Ed. Heineman, London, 1978.

16

Laboratory Diagnosis of Infectious Diseases

Eugene A. Gorzynski,
Konrad Wicher, and
Thomas D. Flanagan

The primary function of the clinical microbiology laboratory is to provide data that enable the diagnosis of infectious diseases and aid in the selection of appropriate therapy. In general this is achieved by isolation and identification of the etiologic agent or by demonstration of the antigenic properties of the agent. Finally, in those cases amenable to chemotherapy, the laboratory may test the causative organism for susceptibility to various antimicrobial drugs.

It should be realized that not all microbiologic diagnostic procedures are equally accessible or necessary. Some simple stains and culturing methods can be performed in the physician's office or clinic. Others require the more specialized materials, equipment, and personnel normally found in hospitals. Certain special tests are available only at medical centers or regional reference laboratories, such as the Center for Disease Control (CDC) of the United States Public Health Service in Atlanta. There are also national and international centers that deal with specific infectious diseases, such as the World Health Organization Center for Arboviruses in New Haven. A knowledge of the resources available for microbiologic diagnosis is necessary for the physician to deal properly with problems of infectious diseases.

Exhaustive identification of bacteria to the subspecies level is seldom justifiable to the physician who wishes to know only the nature of a microorganism in the broadest sense and its susceptibility to antimicrobial agents. Yet to other specialists, subspeciation has epidemiologic implications related to both identifying the source of infection and starting appropriate control measures. In this regard biochemical data, which determine the biotype, and serologic data, which determine serotype or serogroup, should be accumulated and stored for use in the future.

A major reason for routinely determining the species of an isolate is to provide a data base for rational selection of therapeutic agents. For example, knowledge of species alone, even in the absence of antibiotic patterns of sensitivity, is usually sufficient for the clinician to start treatment of infections caused by *Streptococcus pneumoniae*, *Streptococcus pyogenes* (group A), *Neisseria gonorrhoeae*, *Legionella pneumophila*, *Campylobacter fetus*, and *Clostridium* spp., among others. Subspeciation may be helpful in differentiating between new and reemergent etiologic strains of an infectious agent. Moreover, the precise identification of a microorganism may have clinical importance in determining the prognosis of an infection; for example, identification of gram-positive cocci as *Staphylococcus aureus* in a blood culture of a patient with endocarditis implies a significantly worse prognosis than a definitive identification as *Streptococcus* of the viridans group.

The attending physician, not the laboratory worker, is in a position to assess the clinical relevance of laboratory data. Frequently, the causal relationship between a microorganism recovered from a specimen and the disease is tenuous. Knowledge of indigenous microbial flora, if any, of the specimen's source and of the suspected virulence of the microorganism recovered are essential for the interpertation of the report and successful management of the patient.

NORMAL FLORA

In certain anatomical sites of normal individuals, microorganisms either are absent or are present only transiently. These locales include the following: blood, spinal fluid, larynx, trachea, bronchi, bronchioles, alveoli, accessory nasal sinuses, esophagus and stomach (before ingestion of food), liver, and gall bladder. Bladder urine, transudates, and exudates are also usually sterile. Whereas tissue of internal organs normally is free of microorganisms, infectious agents may be introduced into sterile sites by prostheses, indwelling catheters, sutures, and other foreign bodies. The physician must judge whether the presence of bacteria in cultures from these sites reflects infection or contamination of the specimen examined. Autopsy material may provide invaluable information if the specimen is collected within 6 hours after the death of the patient. Unless the specimen is obtained aseptically during this time period, heart blood cultures and excised tissue will have microbial flora reflecting postmortem invasion by microorganisms from the large intestine. Regardless of the source, conclusions concerning the clinical significance of a microbial isolate from a

Table 16.1.   Quantitative Estimation of Normal Flora

Source	Microbial Population
Skin	100 per cm^2 in palm 10^4-10^6 per cm^2 in outer ear 10^6-10^7 per ml of axillary sweat
Gastrointestinal tract	10^9 anerobes per g of feces 10^7 aerobes per g of feces
Vagina	10^7 per ml of secretions
Oropharynx	10^7-10^8 aerobes per ml of secretions 10^8-10^9 anaerobes per ml of secretions

(Miller, J.M. Basic Clinical Microbiology, Part I, Host-Parasite Relationships. HEW Publication No. (CDC) 79–70, 1978.)

physiologically sterile area must be on the basis of a properly collected specimen that was transported expeditiously and examined promptly.

In assessing the role that any microorganism plays in disease, it is important to keep in mind the fact that these minute entities are not only ubiquitous in our environment but also are found in very large numbers on and in our body, even during the best of health. The composition of these microbial populations is never static. Therefore no single hard and fast rule may be followed that clearly interprets the actual or potential clinical significance of a microbial isolate recovered from a site normally colonized with bacteria. Of importance is the fact that on and within the human host there are such sites with large microbial populations comprising many species. Quantitative estimates of the size of these populations are presented in Table 16.1

DIAGNOSIS OF BACTERIAL INFECTIONS; TRADITIONAL PROCEDURES

The accuracy, reproducibility, and reliability of methods used in isolating and identifying etiologic agents are directly related to the reagents and procedures employed. These procedures must be monitored by appropriate standards and controls. Controls are without value, however, if the specimen itself is collected carelessly or not transported promptly to the laboratory.

Also of paramount importance for proper processing and interpretation of results is the requirement for every specimen to be accompanied by a legibly written requisition containing the following: patient identification (name, sex, age, admission or social security number, location in the hospital), preliminary diagnosis, specific anatomic site of the specimen, date and time of collection, chemotherapeutic agent or agents currently being administered, specific or

unusual bacteria suspected, and the requesting physician's name.

Collection and Transportation of Specimens

It is not our purpose to present a litany of specimens and to discuss proper ways for their collection and handling; admittedly, there are many acceptable variations on a theme and equally reliable approaches. Instead we address the ground rules for obtaining and handling those specimens that are required most frequently from hospitalized patients.

Urine. Urine from untreated patients that yields bacterial counts of 10^5/ml or more may be indicative of infection. Counts of less than 10^4/ml are regularly found in clean-voided specimens from healthy individuals and usually result from extraneous bacterial contamination by urethral flora, particulate matter from the perineal area, and clothing. Bacterial counts reflecting infection of the urinary tract are highest in specimens provided by patients who have not voided for several hours. During this period, bacteria influxed into the normally sterile bladder increase in number in a similar way as during incubation in nutrient broth.

Urine obtained by the clean-voided midstream technique is a useful specimen for examination. However, when repeated clean-voided cultures yield equivocal numbers or species of microorganisms, other methods of collection may be required. These include diagnostic catheterization, collection from an indwelling catheter, or suprapubic aspiration. Diagnostic catheterization and suprapubic collection carry definite risks of introducing infection; the indwelling catheter is acceptable only if the area of the tubing most distal from the drainage bag is cleaned with a disinfectant prior to puncture with a sterile needle attached to a syringe. Because bacteria, contaminants and pathogens alike, multiply at room temperature, invalid results are obtained unless collected urine is processed within 2 hours or refrigerated.

Blood. Although bacteria may be present transiently and harmlessly in small numbers in the vascular network after certain innocent functions (e.g., chewing hard candy, vigorous tooth brushing, straining during bowel movement), their persistence in the blood is clinically significant. Therefore the detection of bacteremia and identification of the causative microorganism are critically important laboratory procedures. Unfortunately, blood cultures are subject to contamination by skin bacteria during collection. However, contamination should not be inferred arbitrarily just because a species usually considered nonpathogenic is recovered. The final decision on the significance of the isolate is the clinician's. This decision is based on the conviction that the blood was obtained from a properly disinfected venipuncture site at times or during intervals when the etiologic agent should characteristically be present. As a general guide for life-threatening septicemia, samples of blood should be collected immediately before the start of therapy. In cases of suspected low grade intravascular infection, blood samples should be obtained three times at 1 to 2 hour intervals during the first 24 hours prior to treatment. Obviously, in the absence of positive blood cultures and in the presence of clinical signs requiring continuous or intermittent parenteral therapy, multiple specimens should be drawn at strategic times until the diagnosis in question is either supported or excluded.

Sputum. There is much controversy regarding the value of expectorated specimens in the diagnosis of lower respiratory tract infections. These specimens are routinely contaminated with indigenous flora of the oropharynx and mouth. This flora may include 100 different species of anaerobic and aerobic bacteria. The total population of microorganisms may vary from 10^8 to more than 10^{10} per ml of saliva. Interpretation of cultures from such specimens must be based on knowledge of the quality of specimen examined. In this regard many laboratory technicians tacitly assist physicians by refusing to culture expectorated sputum contaminated with an unacceptable volume of saliva. A paucity of leukocytes in the presence of many squamous epithelial cells and mucus are criteria used to disqualify a specimen. Considering the clinical symptoms and in the absence of confirming data from the laboratory, the physician may weigh the value of collecting a suitable specimen by such potentially traumatic or compromising procedures as bronchoscopy, transtracheal, infralaryngeal, or lung aspiration, or lung biopsy by thoracotomy. These are invasive techniques associated with 10 to 20 percent complication rates (bleeding or pneumothorax).

Feces. The fact that a stool may normally contain as many as 10^{11} bacteria per gram should not discourage the clinician from submitting feces as a valuable specimen for the diagnosis of enteric infection. A 0.5 g specimen of feces is sufficient for culture. If a sterile, cotton tipped applicator stick is used in collecting the specimen, it should be inserted beyond the anal sphincter, rotated, and withdrawn. The swab should be placed in a tube containing a suitable preservative or transport medium before it is sent to the laboratory. Routinely, all enteric specimens should be taken immediately to the laboratory, since a number of pathogenic species will not survive the changes in pH that accompany a drop in temperature. In preparing a culture, laboratory technicians should select portions of the stool that display mucus or blood; these areas usually harbor the microorganisms involved in the intestinal infection. On selective and differential media (discussed below), the enterobacterial pathogens can be isolated readily from properly collected and expeditiously examined specimens. Nevertheless, repeated specimens are always indicated when the clinical picture suggests an intestinal infection and previous stool cultures were negative.

Cerebrospinal Fluid (CSF). Bacterial meningitis may be a rapidly fatal disease unless appropriate antimicrobial therapy is started promptly. Therefore the examination of CSF should be undertaken whenever meningitis is suspected. However, lumbar puncture to obtain a specimen should be performed under conditions of strict asepsis because contamination of spinal fluid by skin bacteria occurs easily. As a result there may be confusion regarding the role of any microorganisms seen or grown in the meningitis in question. Ideally, the laboratory should be alerted by telephone that a CSF specimen is to be submitted for microbiologic examination. Upon receipt the specimen must be tested immediately. Both negative and positive findings of the microscopic examination of a stained preparation should be telephoned to the attending physician. The culture media selected will usually include those necessary to isolate not only bacteria but fungi as well.

Wound, Surgical, Biopsy, and Aspirates Specimens. Because healthy tissue is normally sterile the presence of bacteria may result from contamination, colonization, or infection. It has been reported that 10^5 bacteria per gram of tissue will prevent proper healing of a wound and can play a major determinative role in systemic infection of the compromised host. Collection of a specimen shortly after incision or injury is without value in the absence of overt signs of infection. Even after thorough debridement, it is unlikely that carefully excised tissue will reveal an infectious agent in sufficient numbers to encourage therapy. Therefore symptoms of infection (e.g., cellulitis, swelling, inflammation, suppuration) should be employed as criteria for dictating the need for bacteriologic examination. When these criteria are met, the skin surrounding the site of infection as well as the site itself (if open) or its surface (if closed) must be cleansed thoroughly. These procedures are required prior to taking a specimen.

The mere brushing of a wound, incision, or open abscess with a cotton tipped applicator stick is not likely to capture viable anaerobic bacteria, which frequently cause tissue infection (see the following section). It is always best, although admittedly not always practical, to collect specimens in the absence of ambient air. With a cellulitis this may be accomplished by first injecting a small volume of sterile Ringer's solution and then aspirating with a needle and syringe. Pus from a closed abscess and synovial fluid should also be aspirated with sterile needles and syringes. With all aspirates, care must be taken to expel any air bubbles present in the syringe prior to injecting the fluid or pus into a vial containing CO_2 and transporting it to the laboratory. Alternatively, the syringe with aspirate may be sent directly to the laboratory after the needle end is either plugged with paraffin or inserted into a rubber stopper to preclude exposure to air. In the case of open abscesses, incisions, and wounds it is best to excise a small quantity of tissue and submit this, under appropriate anaerobic conditions, for examination. Gram-stained smears of minced and homogenized tissue and of aspirates should be studied microscopically for the presence of bacteria. In addition, for quantifying and speciating isolates, suitable media should be inoculated with measured amounts of these preparations.

Collection of Specimens for Isolation of Anaerobes. Special oxygen-free containers or anaerobic media must be used for proper collection of specimens to be cultured for anaerobes. For specimens to be taken on swabs, a commercial set of oxygen-free tubes is available. Fluid specimens must be collected using a sterile needle and syringe. The latter method is very useful, since a large volume of fluid can be obtained, aspirated air immediately expelled, and the end of the needle secured with a rubber stopper. If the diagnostic laboratory is in the hospital, the syringe with the material can be immediately delivered to the laboratory. Otherwise, the collected fluid must be injected into an oxygen-free bottle and sent to the laboratory for examination. Tissues and semisolid materials are placed into special transport containers and immediately sent for examination. Any specimen, when conditions require, may be placed directly into enriched anaerobic fluid medium even at bedside or in the operating room.

It has to be stressed that during manipulation, small volumes of oxygen might penetrate into the containers. Therefore the samples must be immediately delivered to the laboratory where they will be inoculated under oxygen-free conditions into special media.

Other Specimens. The specimens delineated and discussed above constitute a major portion of the workload of a microbiology laboratory. Other specimens are also collected and examined. These include, but are not limited to, exudates, fluids or expressions from the following: ear, eye, throat, nasopharynx, pericardium, peritoneum, urethra, vagina, and cervix. In general their collection and handling are in accordance with ground rules followed for those specimens discussed in detail earlier. However, specific instructions should be requested from a responsible laboratory worker.

Processing

The microbiologist uses many reagents and procedures as tools in determining the morphologic, cultural and biochemical characteristics of bacteria. Information gleaned from numerous laboratory tests helps categorize the microorganism in question into the genus, species, and frequently subspecies. The procedures used most often are discussed briefly in the following sections; details of methods are found in manuals or texts on laboratory technology.

Microscopic Examination. Because of their size and transparency, microorganisms are difficult to see in unstained preparations. However, pertinent information may be obtained from the observation of motile forms, which gives an undistorted view of morphology and arrangement of cells, and from histocytologic characteristics, including phagocytosis, in fresh preparations. In preparation for staining, a minute volume of specimen or bacterial culture is smeared on the surface of a glass slide, air dried, and then fixed to the slide by heating. After the brief application — followed by removal with water — of a basic dye (e.g., crystal violet, methylene blue, or safranin), the stained preparation is examined under the oil immersion objective of a microscope; morphology, size, and arrangement of cells are easily seen.

The Gram Stain. Differential staining techniques, which incorporate more than one dye, a fixing agent, and intermittent washings with water, will reveal additional microbial characteristics. A universally used differential stain is the Gram stain. The ingredients and sequence of application to a heat-fixed bacterial film on a glass slide are crystal violet (primary stain), Gram's iodine (fixing agent), ethanol or acetone (decolorizer), and safranin (counterstain). On the basis of their color under the microscope, bacteria are differentiated into two groups by the Gram stain — gram-positive microorganisms stain violet, whereas gram-negative cells stain red.

The mechanism of the Gram stain is related not only to the permeability of the cell membrane but to the thickness, porosity, and chemistry of the cell wall. If osmotic integrity is lost by rupture of the plasma membrane, characteristically gram-positive bacteria will stain gram-negatively. Also, autolyzed, old, or dead gram-positive microbial cells may stain gram-negatively.

The Acid-Fast Stain. Another differential stain, the Ziehl-Neelsen stain, is widely used to identify a small group of microorganisms that resist losing their red primary stain, carbol fuchsin, during rinsing with dilute HCl; cells that remain bright red in color are called *acid-fast*. Microorganisms that are not acid-fast accept the blue counterstain (methylene blue) and thereby may be differentiated microscopically from those that retain the carbol-fuchsin dye.

The Ziehl-Neelsen stain is directed toward bacteria that contain large amounts of lipids and are difficult to stain by conventional methods. Phenol, in the primary dye, and the application of heat aid the penetration of fuchsin through the lipid of the bacterial cell. After staining, lipophilic microorganisms resist decolorization by weak acids.

Special Stains or Techniques. In addition, special techniques (employed less frequently) are available for staining bacterial spores, flagella, and intracellular inclusion bodies. The presence of capsules on some microorganisms may be revealed with dyes for these structures or, better, by staining the background of a specimen. This is accomplished by mixing India ink or nigrosin with the microbial suspension, which is then spread on a glass slide, air dried and examined microscopically. Capsules, if present, are seen as areas or halos without color surrounding the bacteria, which may be stained by any convenient dye.

Culture Media. Whereas blood, spinal fluid, and closed abscesses may yield only single bacterial species, other specimens (e.g., stool, sputum, and contaminated wound swabs) contain mixtures of different bacteria. It is necessary to separate the bacterial population into pure cultures of the component bacterial species in order to carry out the appropriate tests for identification. Tests on mixed cultures are invalid. Isolation in pure culture is accomplished by streaking the inoculum over the surface of solid medium to effect a separation of bacterial cells. Subsequent incubation will allow growth of cells into macroscopically visible colonies. Each colony is the progeny of a single ancestral cell. As detailed below, the morphological characteristics of colonies are valuable aids in identification.

The ability to obtain pure cultures of the pathogens from specimens with many bacteria can present a number of technical problems. The etiologic agent may (1) be missed if present in small numbers in mixtures of different bacteria; (2) be overgrown by other microorganisms; (3) be killed by metabolic products from competing nonpathogens; or (4) fail to grow if its growth requirements are not met. Therefore media are used that allow for the selection or differentiation of bacteria. These special media, of which there are many varieties, have, in addition to the nutrients required by a pathogen in question, chemical inhibitors, proper pH and ionic strengths, and indicators of metabolic activity. Alternatively, enriched media comprised of additional nutrients or growth factors required by certain bacteria may be employed to isolate fastidious pathogens. After inoculation all media are incubated, usually at 35°C, for a minimum of 18 hours; certain microbial species require a lower (22°C) or higher (42°C) incubation temperature and a longer incubation time. Individual colonies may be characterized according to certain criteria, then picked and transferred to suitable nutrient media to reveal distinguishing biochemical or metabolic attributes.

Methods of Anaerobic Cultures. The toxic effect of oxygen on some anaerobes necessitates the production and maintenance of an oxygen-free environment for successful cultivation. The method selected to collect specimens should preclude or minimize contamination by normal anaerobic microflora. It must also allow for the

234   Medical Microbiology

immediate introduction of the specimen into a sterile test tube designed for transporting specimens in the absence of atmospheric oxygen. After receipt in the laboratory, it is important to manipulate and culture the specimen under anaerobic conditions. This may be accomplished in a glove box devoid of atmospheric oxygen and by the use of special media prereduced to support the growth of anaerobes.

Good anaerobic conditions also may be obtained by simple methods, such as the anaerobic brewer's jar. This is a glass container with a leak-proof closure in which prereduced media (tubes or plates) can be kept. The jar is equipped with a disposable hydrogen- and carbon dioxide-generating unit. An indicator demonstrating the presence of oxygen is placed inside the jar to monitor the proper anaerobic conditions. The jar with the inoculated media is incubated at 35°C. This acceptable method for anaerobic culture is rather simple and can be used in almost any laboratory.

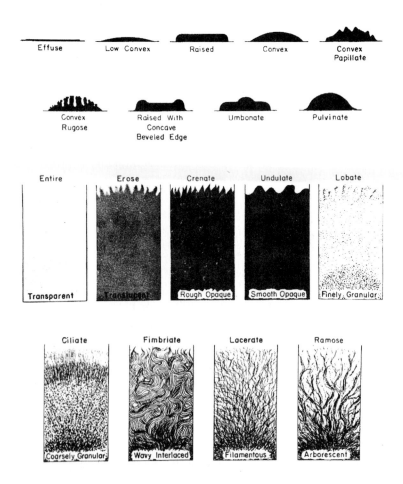

Fig. 16.1. Types of colony morphology, showing the structure of colonies, elevation, and the nature of the edges. (Joklik, W.K. and Willett, H.P., Eds.: Zinsser Microbiology, 16th Ed. Appleton-Century-Crofts, Englewood Cliffs, N.J., 1976).

Growth Characteristics

In a fluid medium (i.e., nutrient broth), turbidity, as a result of bacterial growth, may be uniform, granular, or flocculent; certain species form a pellicle on the broth's surface and minimal or no visible turbidity below this surface. On solid medium, colonies frequently exhibit shared or unique and identifiable features including size, type of elevation (e.g., raised or convex), form (e.g., circular or irregular), margin (e.g., entire or undulate), presence of pigment (e.g., opalescent, fluorescent, soluble in water), opacity (e.g., transparent or opaque), and surface characteristics (e.g., mucoid, glossy; smooth, rough). (For the type of colony morphology, including structure, elevation, and nature of edges, see Fig. 16.1.) In addition, some bacteria produce distinctive odors on various media. The characteristics presented above may be subtle or pronounced, reflecting not only the microbial species studied but the constituents of the medium employed.

Biochemical Tests

Genera, species, and subspecies of bacteria may exhibit characteristic patterns of substrate use, metabolic product formation, and carbohydrate fermentation. We can take advantage of the very active metabolic machinery of cells and their wide variation in degradative ability by identifying or measuring the products of their enzyme catalyzed reactions. Some of the more common biochemical tests are discussed below.

Fermentation. The fermentative capacities of a bacterium are determined by inoculating a pure culture into several media, each containing a different sugar, for example, lactose, sucrose, glucose, galactose, maltose. If the sugar is used by the microorganism, the pH of the medium changes and gas may evolve. These salient reactions are detected by a pH indicator (e.g., phenol red in the medium) and by the inclusion of an inverted vial in the medium prior to inoculation; gas collects in the vial during fermentation. For the differentiation of bacteria that use a sugar oxidatively and not fermentatively, a special medium and procedure are employed. In addition to the sugar in question, peptone, various salts, and bromothymol blue (as the pH indicator) are added to the medium. After inoculation of two tubes with the same medium, the surface of one medium is overlayed with paraffin oil. Oxidative use of the carbohydrate is evident by a color change only in the tube without paraffin oil.

Starch Hydrolysis. The hydroloysis of starch is accomplished by an enzyme, amylase, excreted into the surrounding medium by certain bacteria. The monomeric units of glucose resulting from this breakdown of starch are assimilated by the microorganism during its growth. In a medium containing starch, hydrolysis is noted (after flooding with iodine reagent) by the appearance of a clear zone around colonies of those bacteria attacking starch. Unhydrolzyed starch is dark blue in the presence of iodine.

Gelatin Hydrolysis. The breakdown of gelatin reflects the production by bacteria of gelatinase, an enzyme that digests the substrate protein into its constituent amino acids. At 35°C gelatin is liquid; below 25°C, gelatin is semisolid. Therefore if gelatin is hydrolyzed during incubation of a culture, it will remain liquid even after immersion in ice water.

Nitrate Reduction. The reduction of nitrates to nitrites is accomplished by a large number of microorganisms that produce nitrase. This catalytic reduction can be determined by adding a reagent that reacts with the nitrite to produce a red ring. The test is negative not only in the absence of nitrate reduction but also if the nitrite is further reduced to nitrogen or ammonia.

Indole Production. Indole is a cyclic compound produced by bacteria growing in nutrient broth containing tryptophan. Production of indole is evidenced by the appearance of a red ring after the addition of an indicator (Kovac's reagent).

Hydrogen Sulfide. Generation of H_2S results from the reduction of sulfur by bacteria growing in a medium containing high concentrations of cysteine or other sulfur-containing amino acids. Iron salts are incorporated to detect the H_2S. The appearance of a brown or black precipitate, ferrous sulfide, is a positive reaction.

Other Biochemical Procedures. Many procedures are used to reveal specific enzymatic activity or characteristic patterns of substrate utilization by bacteria. These include, among others, tests to demonstrate oxidase, urease, catalase, lysine and ornithine decarboxylases, arginine dehydrolase, phenylalanine deaminase, and β-galactosidase. Many of these are discussed or alluded to in other chapters that address specific genera or species of bacteria. In essence, data generated from the many tests are assembled to characterize a microorganism and to identify it at the genus and subgenus levels. These data are used to determine unique biochemical characteristics of a bacterium. A compilation of these characteristics defines the biogroup of the species or biotype of the subspecies or strain studied.

Serologic Diagnosis of Bacterial Diseases

Almost all serologic methods that have been devised have found application in the diagnosis of infectious diseases. Traditionally, bacterial agglutination tests, such as the Widal test, have been used to detect antibodies to various surface antigens of bacteria. The appearance of antibodies or a rise in their titer is interpreted as evidence of infection. Conversely, precipitation tests for the detection of bacterial antigens in body fluids have been used only recently. This is due to technical developments, such as counterimmunoelectrophoresis, that enhance and accelerate the precipitation reaction.

A number of highly sensitive techniques that can be adapted to detection and quantification of antigens or antibodies have become very widely used recently. Principal among these techniques are radioimmunoassay (RIA) and enzyme-linked immunosorbent assay (ELISA). Both techniques rely on the immunologic binding of a labeled component (antigen or antibody) as the basic indication of reaction. The techniques can be applied as a direct binding assay. For example, to determine the titer of antibodies to *Legionella pneumophila* by ELISA, soluble antigen, prepared from heat-killed bacteria, is adsorbed to a solid surface, such as a polystyrene plate or tube, and incubated with the patient's serum. Any *Legionella* antibody present will react with and be bound to the adsorbed antigen. After unreacted serum proteins are washed away, a reagent antibody specific for human Ig (class specificity can be determined by use of anti-α, γ or μ chain reagents) is added. This second antibody is chemically conjugated to an enzyme, horseradish peroxidase. The conjugated antibody is bound to the antibody molecules fixed to antigen in the first step. After the serum is again washed to remove unreacted conjugate, a substrate (orthophenylenediamine) is added to the mixture, which will yield a colored rection product after being hydrolyzed by the enzyme. The test is incubated under suitable conditions of time and temperature, and the concentration of reaction product is measured. This concentration is directly related to the amount of *Legionella* antibody bound. Amounts of antibody can be determined by the use of appropriate standards.

These tests can also be used as inhibition assays. For example, RIA technique for the detection of *Haemophilus influenzae* type b (HI_b) polysaccharide antigen in a patient's cerebrospinal fluid requires the incubation of known quantities of ^{125}I labeled HI_b and unlabeled anti-HI_b with the patient's cerebrospinal fluid sample. An anti-human Ig reagent is added and the immune complexes precipitated. After the precipitate is washed, the amounts of radioactivity in the decanted supernatant and in the precipitate are determined. The presence of soluble bacterial antigen in the cerebrospinal fluid competitively inhibits the interaction of the labeled antigen with the antibody and thereby reduces the amount of radiolabel in the precipitate. This results in a high ratio of supernatant label to precipitate label. Standard curves generated from data using known quantities of bacterial antigen can be used to determine concentrations of the antigen in a specimen.

Both the direct binding and inhibition forms of these tests are extremely sensitive and as such they require stringent specificity control.

Passive agglutination techniques are also widely used. These tests take advntage of the sensitivity of agglutination reactions by attaching soluble antigens to the surface of particles, such as erythrocytes or latex particles, and producing clumping of the particles by antibody. These tests can also be used in an inhibition format for detection of soluble antigens.

Antigen-antibody reactions may be detected directly or indirectly by immunofluorescence (IF). Direct IF (DIF) employs an antibody that is covalently bound (conjugated) to a fluorescent dye. Intact bacteria or their antigens in culture or tissue are then incubated with the conjugated antibody, washed, and examined under a microscope with an ultraviolet light source. Antigen that binds the antibody fluoresces brightly and is readily visible. In indirect IF (IDIF), fluorescent dye is conjugated to IgG of an antiimmunoglobulin serum and used to detect antibody bound to antigen. In either case the techniques have the added advantage of giving a histologic or cytologic location of the antibody-antigen reaction.

Other methods are used to identify bacterial antigens by antisera of known specificity. These methods include, among others, complement fixation, capsular "swelling," immobilization, opsonization,

and toxin-neutralization. The bacterial antigens investigated may be in the form of whole cells (living or dead) or soluble preparations. The serologic recognition of the latter in body fluids — for example, cerebrospinal fluid — has obvious clinical significance when there is a need to treat the patient before a culture report is available. The term *serodiagnosis* is more often and more correctly used to describe procedures for both qualitative and quantitative analysis of a patient's serum for antibodies. In each of these procedures a known antigen is employed. The sensitivity and specificity of serologic reactions depend upon many factors, including the antigen, the patient's serum, and the serologic methods used.

The interpretation of test results requires knowledge and experience. For example, in the serodiagnosis of typhoid fever (Widal test), the following must be considered: (1) *Salmonella typhi* shares antigens with other species of *Enterobacteriaceae*; (2) O and H agglutination titers to typhoid and other antigens may rise during unrelated febrile illness, especially in recently vaccinated individuals; (3) the significance of titers must be assessed against titers found in the normal population of that environment or geographic area; (4) *S. typhi* antibodies may be absent or in low titers owing to the stage of infection, poor antigenic stimulus, immunoincompetence of the host, or nutritional hypoproteinemia; (5) the patient may have a history of typhoid infection or have been actively immunized; and (6) in endemic areas significantly elevated titers are encountered during the early stages of infection.

No serologic test is ideally specific. The use of reagents that are of assured quality (appropriate positive and negative control sera) and protocols that are revised or updated in accordance with new techniques form a basis for the reliability and reproducibility of test results. These results, in conjunction with knowledge of the patient's history and current status, become valuable diagnostic guides in the absence of a recoverable pathogen. For further discussion of serodiagnostic tests, see Chapter 8.

Animal Inoculation

Historically, animals have played major roles in satisfying requirements of the Henle-Koch postulates regarding etiology of infection. Recently, chicken embryos and guinea pigs were used to isolate and characterize *Legionella pneumophila*. However, in the clinical bacteriology laboratory today, animals have negligible diagnostic use; current technology is sufficiently sophisticated to provide for the recovery *in vitro* and identification of most pathogens responsible for bacterial diseases. If laboratory animals are required to isolate *Streptococcus pneumoniae* from mixed flora or to establish the virulence of *Listeria monocytogenes* or the toxigenicity of *Corynebacterium diphtheriae*, reference laboratories may provide assistance.

Antibiograms

Antibiotics may vary in their effect on bacterial species, even on strains of the same species and individual cells within a single population. Therefore any clinically significant isolate requires testing *in vitro* for its susceptibility to chemotherapeutic agents unless susceptibility is predictable from knowledge of the microorganism's identity. An antibiogram includes information on the microorganism's sensitivity and resistance to formulary antimicrobial agents. Usually, antibiograms are not performed on *Str. pyogenes* and *Neisseria meningitidis*, which are universally susceptible to penicillin. The recent reporting of strains of *Str. pneumoniae* and *N. gonorrhoeae* with increased resistance to penicillin provides the warning that the blind use of penicillin in the management of these infections may no longer be justified. Of course, alternate drugs have to be adminis-

tered to patients allergic to penicillin. In these cases antibiograms are indicated. In all cases, however, antibiogram patterns serve only as guides to the attending physician, who must weigh both the projected efficacy and potential harm of treatment.

Many procedures are available for measuring *in vitro* the susceptibility of a microorganism to antimicrobial agents. However, an agar diffusion disk test, based on the test described in 1966 by Bauer, Kirby, Sherris, and Turck, is used routinely in most clinical microbiology laboratories. In the agar diffusion disk test the principles of standardized methodology and zone diameter measurement are correlated with minimal inhibitory concentration of the drug against the control bacteria known to be sensitive or resistant to therapy. This test, currently called either the Kirby-Bauer or Bauer-Kirby test, is the most completely described procedure for which interpretive standards have been developed and supported by both laboratory and clinical data. The protocol is easy to follow, the steps are well defined, and the results are reproducible.

Briefly, the test is performed as follows: a standard volume of a pure culture of the isolate, of appropriate concentration, in nutrient broth is seeded over the entire surface of Mueller-Hinton agar in a Petri dish. This medium is the one approved by the National Committee for Clinical Laboratory Standards. After drug-impregnated paper disks are placed on the surface of this medium, the plates are incubated at 35°C in air and then examined. The diameters of the zones of complete inhibition (as determined by the unaided eye), including the diameters of the disks studied, are measured to the nearest whole millimeter. The sizes of the zones of inhibition are interpreted from a reference table. Accordingly, in the laboratory report the microorganism is characterized as S (susceptible), I (intermediate), or R (resistant) to a particular antimicrobial agent. A categorization of S implies that an infection caused by the strain studied may be effectively treated with the dosage of drug recommended for that infecting species and that type of infection. Conversely, R indicates a strain that will not be inhibited by concentrations of the antimicrobial agent achieved in blood or tissue with the usual dosage regimen. It should be understood that R does not invariably mean nonresponsiveness to therapy, nor does S invariably mean responsiveness to therapy. The I category includes strains that may be inhibited by chemotherapy with doses greater than those usually recommended for S strains.

It should be noted that special methods are necessary to test the antibiotic susceptibility of anaerobic organisms. The broth disk method is most frequently employed for this purpose.

Antibiotic susceptibility testing mandates carefully prescribed, controlled, and monitored procedures. The following will affect results: medium (ingredients, thickness in Petri dish and pH); inoculum (a tenfold difference from the size required, 1.5×10^8/ml, yields misleading information); atmosphere and temperature of incubation (a standard incubator at 35°C); disk potency; and measurement of zone size. Also, the Kirby-Bauer method described above has been standardized for assessing only rapidly growing bacteria, especially species of Enterobacteriaceae, Staphylococcus, and Pseudomonas. Under certain conditions or in a supplemented medium, species or strains of Haemophilus, Neisseria, and Str. pneumoniae may be tested.

Within the past decade, strains of Haemophilus influenzae have acquired resistance to penicillin (e.g., ampicillin) and cephalosporin classes of antibiotics. Both classes may be inactivated by β-lactamase enzymes elaborated by bacteria. These enzymes may be constitutive, inducible, or conveyed by a plasmid; their production by bacteria can be determined in the laboratory. Test results will help guide the proper selection of a chemotherapeutic agent.

Depending upon the underlying disease, location or site of the infection, etiologic agent, and anticipated length of treatment, the physician may require quantitative information regarding the lowest concentration of drug that inhibits growth or kills the strain tested. This is expressed by the laboratory as the minimal inhibitory concentration (MIC) or minimal bactericidal concentration (MBC).

It is always important to remember that a patient may be adversely affected by the drug administered; the possible sequelae of therapy must always be a major preliminary consideration. If a decision to treat is made on the basis of available clinical and laboratory information, one must appreciate that the efficacy of a particular preparation depends upon its dosage, biologic and pharmacologic properties, the concentration required at the infected site, the pathophysiologic condition of the patient, and the natural history of the infection. After treatment has started, it may be necessary to monitor the dosage schedule by serum bactericidal tests (to ensure desired levels and preclude toxic concentrations of the agent).

Quality Control

Documented and monitored standards that define expected results are required to guarantee precision, reproducibility, and reliability in the isolation and identification of pathogens and in the accurate performance of serologic and antibiogram tests. These procedures include the collection and handling of specimens prior to examination and the prompt reporting of test results. For official approval, clinical laboratories must have a quality control program with documents, logs, and data to support their efficiency.

DIAGNOSIS OF BACTERIAL INFECTIONS; RAPID AND NEWER PROCEDURES

For seriously ill patients, information about the causal agent of infection is desired as quickly as possible in order to evaluate the patient's clinical status and to make decisions on therapy. For example, in acute bacterial endocarditis the mortality rate may be very high, depending on the etiologic agent and stage of infection. Serious sequelae leading to death may ensue in the absence of early diagnosis and intervention. Equally important diseases frequently requiring heroic measures based on specific microbiologic information are meningitis, septicemia, epiglottitis (primarily a problem in children), anaerobic myonecrosis or clostridial gaseous gangrene, postoperative infection, and subdiaphragmatic and other intraabdominal abscesses. In myonecrosis and abscesses early and appropriate use of the best drug may minimize the need for surgery.

Microscopy is too often neglected as a major expedient; the value of the Gram stain cannot be overstressed. Information derived from this basic and simple procedure, in concert with the clinical impression, frequently provides the presumptive knowledge necessary to start rational management of the patient. In this regard one must not conclude that only positive laboratory findings are of value to the attending physician; negative results per se may be very helpful. They may indicate a poorly collected specimen or may suggest a redirection of diagnostic appraisal. Also, the absence of clinically significant laboratory data does not rule out the presence of fastidious or slow-growing pathogens.

Although usually not considered as rapid methods, the newer techniques, diagnostic kits, and semiautomated and automated devices currently are contributing time- and laboratory-saving steps in diagnostic microbiology. Predictably, the results of their implementation at strategic times will provide information clinically significant for early diagnosis. These expedients are presented and discussed briefly below.

Gas-Liquid Chromatography (GLC)

The implementation of techniques using GLC methods is one of the more important advances taking place in diagnostic microbiology. The analysis of alcohol and volatile acid products of bacterial metabolism is applied in identification of certain anaerobes in culture. To detect these products, cultures are acidified and extracted with ether; the extracts are then chromatographed. Fumaric, pyruvic, succinic, and lactic acids are not volatile, but their methyl derivatives are. Their identification or characterization depends on the amounts of the volatile end products. More precise information is obtainable by comparing peak heights on the chromatogam of each of the products in the test solution with known concentrations in standards. Analysis of metabolic products by GLC is an effective means of differentiating certain species not only of anaerobic bacteria but also of a variety of aerobes, including species of *Neisseria, Pseudomonas, Salmonella,* and *Mycobacterium*. Each strain produces a characteristic chromatogram (fingerprint) that in conjunction with other laboratory data helps identify the microorganism.

Ultraviolet Spectroscopy

Characteristic absorption of ultraviolet light by bacterial cells may be used to provide distinctive spectral patterns that are characteristic of the species studied.

Fluorescent Antibody (FA) Tests

A considerable number of FA tests for identification of bacteria are available; however, they do not supplement conventional bacteriologic methods for identification. Instead, they are used as tools for the rapid screening of cultures or clinical specimens for such pathogens as *Str. pyogenes* (group A), *Legionella* spp., and *Bordetella pertussis*. Reliable results by FA tests require high quality reagents that must be thoroughly characterized. Proper interpretation requires an understanding of the optical system, including the mercury-arc light source.

Counterimmunoelectrophoresis (CIE)

This technique makes use of the fact that during electrophoresis antibodies are displaced toward the cathode and many antigens move toward the anode. When antigen and antiserum are driven by electrophoresis against each other in an agar or agarose gel, a precipitation line develops and usually reaches its maximum intensity within 20 to 90 minutes, depending upon the concentration of antigen and amount of precipitating antibody. The need for a rapid diagnosis of meningitis has justified the use of CIE for detecting bacterial products in cerebrospinal fluid. Soluble polysaccharides from the following organisms have been used in CIE: *Str. pneumoniae, H. influenzae*, serogroup B streptococci, *N. meningitidis*, and *E. coli* K1 and K92. However, interpretation of results of CIE must always consider the existence of several intraspecies and intergeneric cross-reactions.

Diagnostic Kits

There are a variety of multitest systems comprised of paper strips impregnated with reagents or of plastic compartments with nutrient media, substrates, and end point indicators. The major advantage of these kits is their suitability for rapid inoculation and, after incubation, for the easy translation of results into an identification. The kits, available commercially, have been used primarily, although not exclusively, for identifying species of *Enterobacteriaceae*.

Semiautomated and Automated Devices

Although basic methods employed by the clinical bacteriologist have not changed drastically during the past 50 years, semiautomated and automated devices are finding application in the laboratory. The mechanical dispenser for simultaneously depositing multiple paper disks impregnated with various antibiotics to be tested likely represents the earliest, and most widely accepted, mechanical device. Other devices or trends in design to expedite current procedures are in the direction of rapid detection and identification of microorganisms in specimens or in cultures. These include, to mention a few, (1) a mechanical gram-staining device; (2) automated and semiautomated equipment for quantitating and identifying bacteria in urine; (3) a multiagar column or multiwelled plastic tray to determine distinguishing biochemical characteristics or carbohydrate fermentation reactions by using inoculum from a single bacterial colony.

A major approach to systematic bacteriology was introduced approximately 10 years ago in an automated radiometric system that measures the $^{14}CO_2$ generated by bacteria during metabolism of ^{14}C substrates incorporated into the culture medium. This system is reliable, accurate, and fast for detecting bacteremias. It allows for the monitoring of blood cultures 24 hours per day; the bacteriologist is alerted by sound signal when a significant amount of microbial growth occurs. The use of this instrument has obvious clinical implications; the rapid recovery and identification of bacteria, coupled to automated antimicrobial susceptibility testing, frequently allows the treatment and management of a patient at risk within 24 hours. Moreover, during this same period, one can employ additional semiautomated procedures to determine the minimal inhibitory concentration (MIC) or minimal bactericidal concentration (MBC) of chemotherapeutic agent necessary at the site of infection to be effective. Subsequently, the clinician can request that the bacteriologist assess, by manual or currently available semiautomated devices, the patient's serum for antibiotic levels. This knowledge will assist the physician in monitoring the patient for therapeutically effective, nontoxic levels of antimicrobial agent.

The employment of semiautomated devices in the bacteriology laboratory clearly is playing a major role in the rapid diagnosis and treatment of infection. No doubt other equipment to enhance and expedite current methodology, and instruments to retrieve and assemble data, are in various stages of evolution or development. After the implementation of federal regulations regarding proof of reliability and accuracy, and prior to marketing, such test systems will be evaluated impartially and objectively by reference laboratories.

Aside from diagnostic microbiology, the most productive application of automation likely has been in the handling of laboratory data. Computerization is a multifaceted procedure. A primary function is to transmit, expeditiously, test results to patients' records. A second, equally important function includes the storage, retrieval, and analysis of data for a number of management and scientific reasons.

Although not of the magnitude that they have transformed methodology in the clinical chemistry laboratory, automation and computerization are now finding application in the clinical microbiology laboratory. Microbiologists must become acquainted with the technology and hardware designed to expedite information processing without sacrificing accuracy and reproducibility in the process.

DIAGNOSIS OF MYCOTIC INFECTIONS

The collection and handling of most specimens for mycologic examination are similar to those practiced for bacteriologic examination. For certain specimens or special procedures, selection and processing require emphasis on site preparation, timing, and use of transport media. In this regard, microscopic criteria for qualifying sputum samples as acceptable for culture have not been developed. Therefore multiple specimens are required to support or refute a clinical impression of a mycotic respiratory infection. If the patient is not able to produce sputum spontaneously, ultrasonic nebulization may be employed. Concentrating the sputum for isolating fungi is contraindicated; the reagents usually used for species of *Mycobacterium* will inhibit or kill fungi.

Obtaining swab specimens from any site has equivocal usefulness, except for certain yeastlike microorganisms. Material from wounds or sinus tracts should be tissue biopsy or curettage specimens. These are homogenized in the laboratory and then transferred to appropriate media. Scrapings of skin and nails in addition to infected hair are required for the isolation and characterization of dermatophytes. The direct examination of these materials for fungi is the usual protocol after employing a potassium hydroxide preparation and/or the periodic acid–Schiff (PAS) staining technique. PAS, methenamine silver, and Giemsa stains are recommended for identifying fungi in tissues.

Blood cultures for fungi should remain negative after incubation in a special medium at 35°C for 14 days before they are reported as sterile. It is important that the blood culture bottles should be vented with a sterile, cotton plugged needle to ensure growth of fungi.

All specimens collected for mycologic examination should be submitted to the laboratory and processed without delay. Whereas refrigeration may prevent overgrowth by contaminants, this method for preservation should be used only with discretion; *Histoplasma capsulatum* becomes nonviable quickly at refrigerator temperatures. If the length of time between collection and examination is anticipated to be longer than 2 hours, it is advisable to use a transport medium containing antibiotics to inhibit overgrowth by bacteria. Dried specimens have very little value in mycologic diagnosis.

Unless a pure culture of yeast is recovered from urine, quantitation and speciation are not indicated without justification by the attending physician. However, complete identification to species level should be obtained on all yeasts isolated from blood, cerebrospinal, synovial, pleural, and peritoneal fluids, tissue biopsies, and intravenous catheter tips. If a disseminated yeast infection is suspected, multiple media should be inoculated with specimens from different sites.

Patients with immune deficiencies that are either inherent or induced by disease or immunosuppresive treatment are inordinately prone to mycotic infections. Clearly, their susceptibility is linked to the absence or ineffectiveness of their immune responses. Therefore monitoring cellular and humoral events during fungal infection not only helps reinforce the clinical impression of immune deficiency but, in an immunocompetent individual, may be diagnostically significant. Depending upon the chemical nature of the mycotic immunogen and its mode of presentation, quantitative and qualitative variations take place in the host's immune responsiveness. It is likely that cellular responses are fundamentally important in the resistance that is acquired after mycotic infection. These responses frequently can be demonstrated by skin tests for delayed hypersensitivity that use fungal extracts or culture filtrates. Tuberculinlike reactions occur in 24 to 48 hours in positive tests. However, caution must be exercised in the interpretation of results; a positive skin test simply infers sensitization and is not necessarily associated with active infection. Also, a positive skin test does not always indicate sensitivity to a specific organism. For example, trichophytin sensitivity is specific for dermatophytes but is not species specific. *In vitro* cellular hypersensitivity can be measured by blast formation of sensitized lymphocytes in the presence of antigen or by macrophage migration inhibition.

Although antibodies to fungi are produced in most mycotic infections, humoral responses depend in part on contact between the fungus or its metabolite and immunocompetent cells. Although evidence is fragmentary and largely inconclusive that humoral antibodies per se protect against mycotic disease, serologic tests play important roles in the diagnosis of deep-seated infections and in monitoring the patient's response to therapy. Different techniques are applied to detect and quantitate the different classes of antibodies that may result from infection. For example, serologic tests directed toward recognizing agglutinating, precipitating, and complement-fixing immunoglobulins are valuable in the major respiratory mycoses (coccidioidomycosis and histoplasmosis). Titer and predominant class of antibodies depend upon the pathogen, host, and type or specific site of infection. The methods used for recognizing and characterizing these antibodies are hemagglutination, latex agglutination, indirect immunofluorescence, immunodiffusion or immunoelectrophoresis in agarose gel. However, these tests are of limited value unless results are related to history and condition of the patient, including the stage of infection. With all serologic reactions, limitations are imposed by the cross-reactivity of antigens and differences in the immunochemical character of the antigens produced at different stages of infection.

Standardization of mycotic antigens used for skin or serologic testing has only recently received serious consideration in diagnostic mycology. Whereas commercially produced and quality controlled diagnostic antigens are available for certain serologic tests, other tests are still being developed or explored. At present these tests are undertaken usually by microbiologists in reference or special laboratories. The serologic tests that may be employed in the diagnosis of systemic mycotic infections include the following: immunodiffusion, counterelectrophoresis, complement fixation, latex agglutination, and, more recently, enzyme-linked immunosorbent assay. Although an increase in the use of serologic tests can be anticipated, their diagnostic value will be limited to the degree of coordination established or pursued between laboratory and clinical findings. This coordination must always acknowledge that a serologic diagnosis usually is a retrospective diagnosis and must never be more persuasive than isolation and identification of the incipient pathogenic fungus.

There are a limited number of antimycotic agents available for the treatment of mycoses. Among those currently used are the following: nystatin, amphotericin B, 5-fluorocytosine, griseofulvin, tolnaftate, miconazole, and ketoconazole. As with all chemotherapeutic agents, the selection, dosage, and route of administration are prerogatives of the attending physician. Results of antimycotic susceptibility tests may be equivocal and misleading if standard antibiogram procedures are employed; therefore these tests are rarely performed.

DIAGNOSIS OF VIRAL INFECTIONS; TRADITIONAL PROCEDURES

The laboratory diagnosis of viral infections traditionally has been done by isolation of the agent from clinical specimens and identification by serologic methods. In addition, serologic diagnosis has been done by demonstration of a rising titer of antibodies to the causative virus. In the past, viral diagnosis was usually retrospective, since 1 to 2 weeks were often required to complete isolation and identification or secure the convalescent serum sample for serologic diagnosis. However, several recent developments have shortened this time; therefore a greater impact on clinical management of patients will be felt in the future.

Aside from benefits to patient management, several other reasons exist for viral diagnosis. It is a vital component of the community's medical intelligence. The presence of influenza A virus or of an arbovirus in a geographic area can be important in certain clinical diagnoses. Recognition and elimination of nosocomial viral infections are important in hospital practice; therefore diagnoses of viral hepatitis or rotavirus infection are critical.

There is also the need to collect and assess data on the possible viral causes of a number of diseases for which a definite etiology has not been established. Many diseases — multiple sclerosis, diabetes mellitus, systemic lupus erythematosus, and others — are suspected of having viral etiology, yet well documented evidence is required to help establish their causes. Finally, there is the need to isolate and characterize new or unknown viruses that continue to present themselves as agents of human disease.

Collection and Transportation of Specimens

As with bacterial infections, proper selection, collection, and transport of the specimen are of critical importance. Specimen selection is based on the clinical presentation of the patient; the signs and symptoms of disease will suggest to the physician the possible diagnosis. Knowledge of the

Table 16.2. Specimens for Virus Isolation

Clinical Manifestations	Virus Frequently Found	Most Useful Specimens[a]
Aseptic meningitis	Coxsackievirus	CSF, stool or rectal swab, throat swab
	Echovirus	CSF, stool or rectal swab, throat swab
	Mumps virus	CSF, swab of buccal mucosa, throat wash, urine
	Poliovirus	Stool or rectal swab, throat swab, CSF
Congenital or neonatal infections	Cytomegalovirus	Urine, throat wash or swab
	Rubella virus	Throat wash or swab, urine
	Herpes simplex virus	Lesion aspirate or swab, throat swab
Encephalitis	Arbovirus	Blood, CSF
	Herpes simplex virus	Brain biopsy, CSF, vesicle aspirate or swab
	Measles virus	CSF, throat wash or swab, urine
	Poliovirus	Stool or rectal swab, throat swab, CSF
Exanthematous diseases	Coxsackievirus	Stool or rectal swab, throat swab
	Cytomegalovirus	Throat wash or swab, urine
	Echovirus	Stool or rectal swab, throat swab
	Epstein-Barr virus	Throat wash or swab
	Herpes simplex virus	Lesion aspirate or swab, throat swab
	Measles virus	Throat wash or swab, urine
	Rubella virus	Throat wash, nasopharyngeal wash
	Vaccinia virus	Lesion aspirate or swab, throat swab
	Varicella zoster virus	Lesion aspirate or swab, throat swab
Eye infections	Adenovirus	Conjunctival swab, throat swab, rectal swab
	Herpes simplex virus	Conjunctival swab, lesion aspirate or swab, throat swab
	Vaccinia virus	Conjunctival swab, lesion aspirate or swab, throat swab
Respiratory infections	Adenovirus	Throat swab, rectal swab
	Cytomegalovirus	Throat wash or swab, urine
	Influenza virus	Throat wash or swab
	Parainfluenza virus	Throat wash or swab
	Reovirus	Throat swab, stool or rectal swab
	Respiratory syncytial virus	Throat wash or swab, nasopharyngeal wash
Other infections		
Cytomegalic inclusion disease	Cytomegalovirus	Urine, throat wash
Mononucleosis syndromes	Cytomegalovirus	Urine, throat wash
	Epstein-Barr virus	Throat wash or swab
Pericarditis, myocarditis	Coxsackievirus B	Pericardial fluid, stool, throat swab
	Echovirus	Pericardial fluid, stool, throat swab

[a] The specimens are listed in order of their relative value for diagnosis.

pathogenesis of the various viral infections allied with accurate epidemiologic intelligence should enable the clinician to form an opinion about the possible cause. The usual specimens examined for viruses are cerebrospinal fluid (CSF), stool and rectal swab, vesicle aspirate and swab, throat washing and swab, nasal swab and nasopharyngeal washing, pleural or pericardial effusions, urine, tissue biopsy, and tissue taken at autopsy. Table 16.2 shows the various specimens usually examined in selected viral infections.

In general, viral infectivity is a labile property and is better preserved at lower temperatures. Most viruses survive in the frozen state — the lower the temperature, the longer the survival. Therefore specimens are usually kept cold by refrigeration if transportation to the virus laboratory is possible within 1 to 2 hours or by freezing if a longer time is required. Shipment of specimens to distant laboratories requires freezing. Experience shows that the more rapidly a specimen is examined after collection, the greater the chance of successful virus isolation.

Processing

In the virus laboratory the specimen will be processed for inoculation of the various laboratory hosts used for isolation. Since viruses are intracellular parasites, suitable living cells are required for their culture from clinical material. Not all human viruses will grow in a single type of cell culture or laboratory animal; therefore the laboratory must be guided in its selection of the host by the clinical description of the case and the suspected diagnosis. This information is critical for the efficient function and ultimate usefulness of the virus laboratory and must accompany all specimens submitted.

Cell cultures of various types constitute the principal laboratory host for virus isolation, although embryonated chicken eggs

and suckling mice are used for certain viruses (e.g., influenza virus A and coxsackievirus A). Once the host has been selected and inoculated with the specimen, growth of viruses may be detected. For example, cell cultures are observed over a period of several days, up to 3 weeks in some cases, for the development of cytopathologic effects (CPE) associated with lytic growth of virus. The development of CPE in an inoculated culture and its absence in control cultures signals the presence of a virus; however, the agent must be passaged and titrated before the identification phase of the process can be undertaken.

Not all viruses cause CPE or other obvious manifestations of growth; therefore indirect means of detecting replication must be employed. Hemagglutination, hemadsorption, and immunofluorescence are applicable only to certain viruses, again emphasizing the need for complete and accurate clinical information to guide the laboratory in the selection of methods.

Identification

Identification of viral isolates is accomplished by serologic tests. Therefore the laboratory must have available a panel of specific antisera for use. A variety of methods are employed; among these are viral neutralization, hemagglutination inhibition, inhibition of hemadsorption, both direct and indirect immunofluorescence, and complement fixation. Selection of the appropriate test and antiserum is guided by clinical information and various laboratory characteristics of the isolate itself. For example, vesicular lesions on the genitalia that yielded a rapidly cytopathic agent upon inoculation of human diploid cell cultures would suggest herpes simplex virus. In this case an appropriate type-specific antiserum could be used in an immunofluorescence test to confirm the identity of the isolate.

The report from the laboratory usually will describe the isolate by virus name and serotype if this designation is significant. The complete process may take 2 to 3 weeks; however, in many cases a useful presumptive diagnosis may be made within a few days. Virus growth may be quite rapid, especially from good specimens. Characteristics of growth in the laboratory host, along with the clinical picture, often are used to form an accurate presumptive diagnosis.

Cytopathology Effected by Viruses

The growth of certain viruses in cells, whether *in vivo* or *in vitro*, is accompanied by the development of characteristic changes that can be helpful in diagnosis. Most prominent among these changes are the development of inclusions within the infected cell. These inclusions, in some cases, are aggregates of progeny viruses. They are often identifiable not only by visualization in fixed and stained preparations but by immunofluorescence as well. For example, the inclusion that develops in neurons infected with rabies virus is a mass of virus protein that can be stained specifically with fluorescein-conjugated antirabies antibodies. Demonstration of this inclusion constitutes the definitive diagnosis of rabies.

Some viruses cause intranuclear inclusions, while others cause cytoplasmic inclusions; still others may cause both types (e.g., measles virus). It should be realized, however, that many viruses do not cause any inclusions and that those that do may require special methods for demonstration of inclusions.

Another characteristic change effected by viruses is the development of syncytial giant cells, or polykaryocytes. This change manifests as large, usually circumscribed areas of cytoplasm containing many nuclei. The viruses causing such changes are usually those that form progeny by budding through the plasma membrane of infected cells. Giant cells can be detected in tissues as well as in cell cultures.

A number of other cytopathic changes, such as ballooning, cytolysis, and cell rounding, are caused by various viruses; however, these are of little diagnostic value *in vivo*. *In vitro* they do offer some indications useful in identification of viruses.

Serologic Diagnosis of Viral Diseases

Another general approach to viral diagnosis is the demonstration of viral antibodies in the serum of patients. In most cases the diagnosis depends on demonstrating at least a fourfold increase in antibody titer to the suspected agent between the acute and the convalescent phase of the disease. The taking of the two serum specimens is usually separated by 2 to 3 weeks; therefore the diagnosis is almost always retrospective.

Many serologic tests are used in viral diagnosis, e.g., virus neutralization, hemagglutination inhibition, indirect immunofluorescence, complement fixation, and ELISA.

In many systemic viral infections, antibodies are demonstrable during the acute phase of illness or very soon thereafter. For example, hemagglutination inhibition tests for rubella antibodies are usually positive within 7–14 days of onset and often in high titer. Subsequent tests may not reveal a four-fold increase, thus failing to support the diagnosis of rubella. The problem may be overcome by demonstrating the IgM class of antibodies in the acute phase and IgG antibodies in the convalescent phase of the disease.

Aside from its role in diagnosis of viral infections, viral serology also can be used to determine the immune status of persons to a number of virus diseases, e.g., rubella, measles, mumps, and poliomyelitis. This information is useful in predicting the outcome of recent exposure to the incipient agent and, in selected cases, the need for immunization.

DIAGNOSIS OF VIRAL INFECTIONS; RAPID METHODS

In recent years a variety of methods and instruments have been marshaled to effect a rapid response to problems of viral diagnosis. Most of these procedures are focused on the direct detection of viruses in clinical specimens without the need to isolate the agent in a laboratory host. The electron microscope has become the principal tool in detection of some viruses, whereas various serologic procedures for detecting viral antigens are used with other viruses. Table 16.3 shows the viruses for which rapid methods have been developed and the particular method for each.

Specimen selection, collection, and the inclusion of clinical information for these methods are just as critical as for the classical methods. Specimens from which exfoliated cells are to be examined should be processed immediately. It is common practice in many virus laboratories to process specimens for examination by rapid methods and simultaneously inoculate cell cultures for traditional isolation. Many of the antigen detection methods used for direct examination of specimens also can be used for early detection of viral growth in cell cultures.

DIAGNOSIS OF PARASITIC INFECTIONS

In contradistinction to diseases caused by bacteria, fungi, or viruses, diagnosis of parasitic infections is not readily supported by the identification of colony forms on artificial culture media, of inclusion bodies, or of cellular changes in tissue culture or by biochemical reactions. Instead, recognition of a parasite depends largely upon knowledge of the microscopic morphology of the organism that may be present during the course of infection. In support of this recognition and, more frequently, when the specimen or stage of infection does not yield recognizable forms of the etiologic

agent, the results of immunologic tests may play major roles in affirming or refuting the physician's clinical impression. Outstanding examples are toxoplasmosis, amebiasis, malaria, trichinosis, schistosomiasis, and filariasis.

Parasites causing disease have been recovered from every organ and lumen or cavity of the body. Specific sites of infection include blood, intestine, brain, muscle, liver, spleen, lymph node, eye, skin, prostate, and uterine cervix. The collection and processing of organ or tissue excisions is not addressed in this chapter; these specimens are handled best by histopathologists with experience in recognizing multiple aspects of parasites in two-dimensional tissue sections. Specimens other than solid tissue are managed best by microbiologists with expertise in parasitology. These specimens present special problems because of the fragile nature of parasites and the need for identifying them solely on the basis of morphological details. Therefore deliberate attention must be exercised during collecting handling, and processing. Because training of nurses and physicians in these three important phases of specimen management usually is deficient or lacking, it may be necessary to communicate directly with the microbiologist for specific instructions. This consultation will also alert the laboratory to the projected time for receiving and processing the sample.

The timing and collection of specimens for blood parasites, including species of *Plasmodium*, *Trypanosoma*, and *Leishmania*, are discussed in Chapters 51 and 52. After applying the appropriate stain to a thin or thick film of blood on a slide and viewing microscopically under a high power or oil immersion objective, the examiner must be careful to distinguish between parasite and artifact. For example, a misdiagnosis of malaria may result from incorrectly identifying platelets superimposed on red blood cells for plasmodia.

For diagnosis of parasitic infection of the

Table 16.3.   Rapid Methods of Viral Diagnosis

Virus	Method
Adenovirus	Demonstration of viral antigen in exfoliated cells from nasophayngeal washings by immunofluorescence
Cytomegalovirus	Demonstration of viral antigen in exfoliated cells from urine sediments by immunofluorescence
Hepatitis virus A	Demonstration of typical virion morphology and aggregation of virions by specific antibodies by means of electron microscopic examination of specimens from stool
Hepatitis virus B	Demonstration of various viral antigens, HB_sAg, HB_cAg, HB_eAg, and others, in serum by various serologic methods including RIA and ELISA
Herpes simplex virus	Demonstration of viral antigen in brain biopsies, in exfoliated cells from lesion swabbings or throat washings by immunofluorescence; demonstration of typical virions in vesicle fluids by electron microscopy
Parainfluenza viruses	Demonstration of viral antigen in exfoliated cells from nasopharyngeal or throat washings by immunofluorescence
Rabies virus	Detection of viral antigen in brain tissue of animals by immunofluorescence; detection of viral antigen in exfoliated cells from cornea (human infection) by immunofluorescence
Respiratory syncytial virus	Detection of viral antigens in exfoliated cells from nasopharyngeal washings by immunofluorescence
Rotavirus	Demonstration of typical virions in stool by electron microscopy; detection of viral antigens in stool by ELISA or complement fixation
Varicella-zoster virus	Demonstration of typical virions in vesicle fluid by electron microscopy

intestinal tract, feces, duodenal aspirates, and sigmoidoscopy specimens may be submitted for examination. With some parasitic infections (amebiasis, giardiasis, strongyloides), diagnostic stages are not always present in feces. Therefore examination of three fecal specimens selected over a period of 7 to 10 days will help ensure accurate diagnosis. These specimens should be placed in clean containers and should be free of mineral oil, barium, and urine. Also, the patient should not have recently received any antimicrobial agent. For example, tetracycline may suppress for several weeks the appearance of *Entamoeba histolytica* in feces. For the diagnosis of pinworm infections, special cellulose tape collection kits usually are available in the laboratory.

The microscopic study of intestinal specimens for parasites should always include direct examination, concentration procedures, and permanently stained slides. The direct examination is best done on fresh specimens; motile trophozoites, if present, are readily detected. Concentration procedures are required to accumulate parasites present in small numbers during certain diagnostically important stages. Both saline and iodine wet mounts are employed with raw and concentrated preparations. Prepared and fixed slides may be stained permanently by a number of different procedures unique to parasitology. A careful study of these slides will reveal the parasite's morphology and cellular components. Both positive and negative slides should be catalogued and filed for future reference.

There is nothing unique about host response to parasites; most infections elicit elevated antibody titers at one stage or another. However, the multiplicities of antigens compounded by the different stages in the life cycle of the parasite, and, in certain cases, by antigenic variation within a single stage, make serologic diagnosis with impure preparations unreliable. With purified antigens employed in tanned cell hemagglutination, immunofluorescence techniques, and, more recently, ELISA, immunodiagnosis is becoming a more dependable, albeit retrospective, tool.

As in a wide variety of bacterial and viral diseases, immunodepression, autoimmunity, and elevated serum immunoglobulins may occur during infection caused by certain parasites. An appraisal of these humoral responses may contribute significant information regarding the immunologic status of the patient.

REFERENCES

Bartlett, R.C.: Medical Microbiology; Quality Cost and Clinical Relevance. John Wiley & Sons, New York, 1974.

Dick, G., Ed.: Immunological Aspects of Infectious Diseases. University Park Press, Baltimore, 1979.

Friedman, H., Linna, T.J., and Prier, J.E., Eds.: Immunoserology in the Diagnosis of Infectious Diseases. University Park Press, Baltimore, 1979.

Haley, L.D. and Callaway, C.S.: Laboratory Methods in Medical Mycology. HEW Publication No. (CDC) 78–8361, Washington, D.C., 1978.

Holloway, J.W., Ed.: Infectious Disease Reviews, Volume 4. Futura Publishing, Mount Kisco, N.Y., 1976.

Isenberg, H.D., Schoenknecht, F.D., and von Graevenitz, A., Eds.: Processing and Collection of Bacteriological Specimens. Cumulative Techniques and Procedures in Clinical Microbiology (CUMITECH 9). American Society for Microbiology, Washington, D.C., 1979.

Lennette, E.H., Balows, A., Hausler, W.J., Jr., and Truant, J.P., Eds.: Manual of Clinical Microbiology. 3rd Ed. American Society for Microbiology, Washington, D.C., 1980.

Lorian, V., Ed.: Significance of Medical Microbiology in the Care of Patients. Williams & Wilkins, Baltimore, 1977.

Milgrom, F., Abeyounis, C.J., and Kano, K., Eds.: Principles of Immunological Diagnosis in Medicine. Lea & Febiger, Philadelphia, 1981.

17

Staphylococcus

C. John Abeyounis

Staphylococci were among the first pathogenic bacteria to be recognized, having been discovered in pus by Koch in 1878, cultivated by Pasteur in 1880, recovered from purulent infection by Ogston in 1881, and characterized in the early 1900's by Rosenbach. Members of the genus *Staphylococcus* are ubiquitous organisms that are closely associated with man and his environment. These organisms are also found on the body surfaces of many other animals, as well as in air, dust, milk, food, and sewage. Strains from various animal species apparently form distinct populations. In man, staphylococci are found on the skin, in the nasopharynx, and in the gastrointestinal tract.

The three recognized species in the genus are *Staphylococcus aureus*, which is the pathogenic member, *Staphylococcus epidermidis*, which only occasionally produces human disease, and *Staphylococcus saprophyticus*, which rarely causes disease.

Pathogenic staphylococci cause a wide variety of pyogenic infectious diseases ranging from localized skin infections (boils and carbuncles) to pneumonia, exfoliative dermatitis, osteomyelitis, and food poisoning. The nonpathogens may produce diseases such as subacute bacterial endocarditis and urinary tract infections in the compromised host.

MORPHOLOGY AND PHYSIOLOGY

Staphylococci are gram-positive, nonmotile, nonspore-forming, facultative anaerobes that grow optimally at 37°C. They are spherical organisms measuring approximately 1 μm in diameter. Some pathogenic strains are encapsulated. Staphylococci may appear singly or in pairs, but they are seen most frequently in irregular, grapelike clusters (Fig. 17.1).

Staphylococci grow abundantly on unenriched media. On solid agar they form colonies that are smooth, opaque, and glistening in appearance, measuring 1 to 2 mm in diameter after overnight incubation at 37°C. *S. aureus* characteristically forms golden yellow colonies due to the production of carotenoid pigments, and many strains produce clear hemolysis on blood agar. *S. epidermidis* and *S. saprophyticus* usually form white colonies, but occasionally the colonies are yellow or orange. They are rarely hemolytic, but otherwise they are quite similar to *S. aureus* in colonial features.

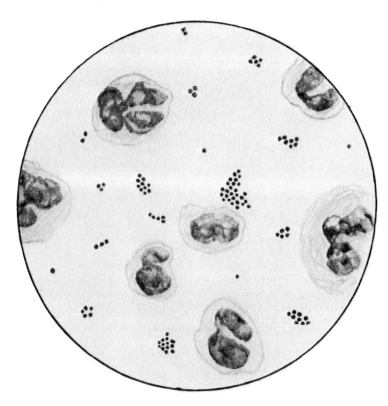

Fig. 17. 1. Staphylococcal pus (about × 800). (Neisser, M.: Die Staphylokokken. In Kolle, W., Kraus, R., and Uhlenhuth, P., Eds.: Handbuch der pathogenen Mikoorganism. Gustav Fischer, Jena/Urban & Schwarzenberg, Berlin, 1930.)

Staphylococci are more resistant than most vegetative forms of bacteria to heat, drying, and certain disinfectants; killing by heat requires 60°C for 30 minutes; viable organisms can be recovered from dried pus after 2 to 3 months; and staphylococci are more resistant than most bacteria to phenol and mercuric chloride. However, they are very sensitive to aniline dyes such as crystal violet. Staphylococci are capable of growth at high salt (12 percent NaCl) or sucrose concentrations. Proteolytic activity of staphylococci varies; they ferment many carbohydrates slowly, producing lactic acid but no gas. Significantly, most strains of S. aureus ferment mannitol anaerobically, whereas most strains of S. epidermidis and S. saprophyticus do not. Staphylococci produce catalase, which distinguishes them

from streptococci. Cultivation on tellurite medium is useful in isolating S. aureus from specimens such as feces that are contaminated with other bacteria.

CELLULAR ANTIGENS

Staphylococci produce a number of structural components, as well as toxins, and enzymes that are antigenic (Table 17.1). More than 30 staphylococcal antigens have been detected by serologic procedures such as agglutination, precipitation, and passive hemagglutination; however, their usefulness in serologic typing is limited.

An important group-specific antigen resides in the teichoic acid component of the cell wall. Staphylococci form two antigeni-

Table 17.1. Antigens of Staphylococci

Structural antigens
  Capsule — polysaccharide moiety with multiple antigenic determinants
  Cell wall
    Protein A — *S. aureus*
    Teichoic acid
      Ribitol — *S. aureus*
      Glycerol — *S. epidermidis*
      Ribitol and glycerol — *S. saprophyticus*

Secreted antigens
  Toxins
    α-, β-, δ-, γ-, ε-lysins
    Leukocidin
    Exfoliatins
    Enterotoxins
  Extracellular enzymes
    Coagulases
    Penicillinase
    Lipases
    Hyaluronidase
    Staphylokinase
    Proteases
    Nucleases

cally distinct types of teichoic acid. One contains a ribitol polymer (*polysaccharide A*), which is characteristic for *S. aureus*; the other contains a glycerol polymer (*polysaccharide B*), which is characteristic for *S. epidermidis*. Both types are found in *S. saprophyticus*.

Most strains of *S. aureus* produce a cell wall protein termed *protein A*, which is located at the cell surface and is often shed into the culture medium. The amount produced by different strains is variable. Two important properties of protein A are its capacity to inhibit phagocytosis and its capacity to bind to the Fc portion of IgG from many mammalian species. The latter feature causes clumping of the organisms when they are mixed with normal serum, hindering study of pathogenic staphylococci by agglutination tests.

The polysaccharide capsule, which is found in some strains of *S. aureus*, con-tains several antigenic determinants. Interestingly, the polysaccharide capsule of a particular strain may contain more than one determinant. Capsular material sometimes can be demonstrated serologically when it is not discernible morphologically.

In addition to the antigenic substances described above, staphylococci produce a number of exotoxins and extracellular enzymes that are also antigenic.

EXOTOXINS AND EXTRACELLULAR ENZYMES

Pathogenic staphylococci produce a number of proteinaceous exotoxins (Table 17.2) and enzymes that exhibit a variety of biologic activities and that have been implicated in contributing to the virulence of the organism. The capacity to produce some (penicillinase, α-toxin, exfoliatin, enterotoxin) and probably most of the toxins and enzymes is conferred on strains of staphylococci by infection with the proper bacteriophage. For some of these substances (e.g., exfoliatin, enterotoxin, and penicillinase) a pathogenic role has been established; for the others this role is not so clear. Antibodies to these substances often either diminish or abolish biologic activity.

Exotoxins

S. aureus may produce any or all of four immunologically distinct toxins, termed α, β, γ and δ lysins (also called toxins or hemolysins) that are active against erythrocytes and other cells such as leukocytes, macrophages, and platelets. Cells from a variety of animal species, including man, are susceptible. Cytolytic potency of these lysins varies with respect to cell type and the animal species. Some strains of *S. epidermidis* may produce a hemolytic toxin known as ε-lysin. No lysin from *S. saprophyticus* has been described.

Table 17.2.   Exotoxins of *Staphylococcus aureus*

Toxin	Hemolytic Activity[a]	Other Biologic Properties	Comments
α-Lysin	Rabbit	Dermonecrotic, lethal for mammalian platelets and leukocytes	Mechanism of cell disruption not clear, but may be proteolytic
β-Lysin	Sheep, ox	Slight lethal activity, toxic for mammalian leukocytes and macrophages	Enzymatically degrades sphingomyelin
γ-Lysin	Rabbit	Lethal for mice, toxic for human leukocytes	Mechanism of cell membrane damage not clear; probably not enzymatic
δ-Lysin	Rabbit, human, sheep, monkey	Slight dermonecrotic and lethal activity; toxic for variety of mammalian cells, as well as lysosomes and bacterial protoplasts	Disrupts cell membrane by detergent-like action
Leukocidin	None	Lyses neutrophils and macrophages	Increases cell membrane permeability to cations; mechanism unknown
Exfoliatin	None	Produces exfoliation of skin	Disrupts intercellular cement, reducing cell adhesion
Enterotoxin	None	Causes food poisoning	Probably acts on emetic receptors in intestine, thereby stimulating vomiting center; mechanism unknown

[a]Only the more sensitive erythrocytes are listed.

S. aureus also produces a nonhemolytic toxin, termed leukocidin, which affects leukocytes but not erythrocytes; a toxin known as exfoliatin, which causes an exfoliative dermatitis; and an enterotoxin, which causes food poisoning.

α-**Lysin.** This toxin is produced by a vast majority of strains of *S. aureus* (>90 percent) and is believed to play a significant role in the pathogenesis of staphylococcal diseases. The toxin is probably responsible for much of the tissue damage that occurs after the initial infection becomes established. Experimentally, rabbit erythrocytes are most susceptible, with those from guinea pig, horse, and man much less so. α-Lysin is also active against other cells, in-cluding leukocytes and platelets. It disrupts the cell membrane, but the precise mechanism of this effect is not clear. Experimental studies also have shown that α-lysin is dermonecrotic following subcutaneous injection and lethal when injected intravenously, with the toxin concentrating primarily in the kidneys, lungs, and brain.

β-**Lysin.** This toxin acts enzymatically on sphingomyelin in the membrane of a variety of cell types. It is hemolytic, possessing strong activity against ovine and bovine erythrocytes but weak activity against human and rabbit erythrocytes. It is also active against platelets, leukocytes, and macrophages from a variety of animals. β-Lysin is responsible for the laboratory phenomenon called "hot and cold" lysis. At 37°C the lysin binds to erythrocytes, but lysis does not occur until the erythrocytes are chilled to 4°C. β-Lysin is produced predominantly by staphylococci recovered from animal sources.

δ-Lysin. This factor disrupts membranes by a detergentlike action on cell surfaces, where it binds to straight chain fatty acids. This toxin is lytic for erythrocytes from a variety of mammals, is dermonecrotic, and is lethal to laboratory animals when injected intravenously. Inhibition of its membrane activity by serum proteins casts doubt on its significance in disease.

γ-Lysin. γ-Lysin acts on a variety of mammalian erythrocytes, is toxic for human leukocytes, and is lethal for mice upon intravenous injection. It is the weakest of the four lysins. The mechanism of activity is unknown, but it is likely to be enzymatic.

Leukocidin. This nonhemolytic toxin, also known as the Panton-Valentine leukocidin, is restricted in activity to neutrophils and macrophages. It presumably enhances pathogenicity of staphylococci by inhibiting phagocytosis. Leukocidin is electrophoretically separable into a fast and a slow component, both of which are required for toxic activity. Only leukocytes from rabbits and man appear to be susceptible. Toxicity appears to result from increased permeability of the cell membrane to cations. The precise mechanism of action is not clear, but it probably relates to stimulation of two membrane associated enzymes, acyclophosphatase and adenylate cyclase.

Exfoliatin. This toxin is produced by S. aureus in two serologically unrelated forms, A and B. Exfoliatin A is relatively heat stable, retaining activity after heating to 100°C for 20 minutes; it is produced primarily by pathogenic staphylococci in phage group II (see below). Exfoliatin B is heat labile, losing activity upon heating to 60°C for 30 minutes; it usually is produced by strains other than those in phage group II. Exfoliatin disrupts the intercellu-

lar cement of epidermal cells in the stratum granulosum of newborn mice and humans, resulting in exfoliation. The mode of action is not known, but biologic activity of the toxin can be abolished by proteolytic enzymes such as trypsin.

Enterotoxins. Pathogenic staphylococci produce five immunologically distinct enterotoxins, designated A to E, the ingestion of which causes food poisoning. Most strains of S. aureus are enterotoxigenic to a certain extent according to sensitive immunologic studies. Production of enterotoxin correlates well with coagulase production. However, some coagulase-negative enterotoxigenic strains have been reported. Of significance is the fact that staphylococcal enterotoxins are odorless, colorless, tasteless, heat resistant, and relatively resistant to proteolytic enzymes. Susceptibility to staphylococcal enterotoxins is restricted to man although chimpanzees and certain monkeys are susceptible to a limited extent. Little is known concerning the mechanism of action because there is no suitable animal model for study.

Extracellular Enzymes

Coagulase. Production of this enzyme, which clots plasma, is a characteristic of pathogenic staphylococci. Indeed, determination of coagulase activity is the best criterion for designation of a particular staphylococcal strain as being S. aureus. Production of coagulase occurs independently of other staphylococcal products, but over 90 percent of coagulase-positive strains also produce α- and δ-lysin.

Coagulase is produced in a cell-free form, which is secreted into the medium, and in an immunologically unrelated cell-bound form. Four antigenically distinct cell-free coagulases have been described.

Detection of both cell-free and cell-bound coagulase is easily accomplished in the diagnostic laboratory. Free coagulase is shown by incubating staphylococci at 37°C in a tube containing rabbit plasma. Formation of a plasma clot within 3 to 4 hours is a positive reaction. The presence of bound coagulase on the bacterial cell surface is indicated by the formation of a gelatinous clump of cells when a staphylococcal colony is mixed with rabbit plasma on a glass slide.

Free coagulase acts in a manner similar to thrombin in converting fibrinogen to fibrin. For this activity a plasma factor known as coagulase-reacting factor (CRF) is required. It is not clear whether CRF combines with coagulase to form a complete enzyme or whether CRF merely acts as an accelerator. Bound coagulase acts differently in that it converts fibrinogen to fibrin directly.

Although the actions of coagulase are not firmly established, some researchers believe that coagulase contributes to the pathogenicity of staphylococci (1) by inhibiting the bactericidal activity of normal serum, since coagulase-positive but not coagulase-negative strains of staphylococci can grow in normal serum and/or (2) by inhibiting phagocytosis, which reportedly results from deposition of fibrin on the bacterial cell surface.

Hyaluronidase. This enzyme depolymerizes hyaluronic acid, which is the ground substance of tissues. Hyaluronidase is produced by most strains of *S. aureus* and some strains of *S. epidermidis*. The enzyme presumably facilitates spread of the organism in tissues. Antigenically, staphylococcal hyaluronidase is homogeneous, but it is distinct from hyaluronidase produced by other bacteria.

Lipases. *S. aureus*, as well as some strains of *S. epidermidis*, produce a group of enzymes capable of hydrolyzing lipids, including the fats and oils of the skin. These enzymes presumably facilitate invasion by pathogenic staphylococci of healthy cutaneous and subcutaneous tissue. There is a high correlation between lipase production and production of skin lesions by staphylococci.

Staphylokinase. This fibrinolytic enzyme, which is produced by pathogenic staphylococci, is similar in activity to streptokinase, which is produced by streptococci. The enzyme dissolves fibrin clots by mediating the conversion of plasminogen to plasmin. Production of this enzyme is a phage-mediated property resulting from lysogenic conversion. It is interesting that strains lose the ability to produce β-lysin when they acquire the capacity to produce staphylokinase. There is little evidence that this enzyme plays a significant role in pathogenicity.

Other Enzymes. In addition to those described above, a number of other enzymes — including phosphatase, nucleases, catalase, lysozyme, and β-lactamase (penicillinase; see below) — are produced by pathogenic staphylococci.

BACTERIOPHAGE TYPING

Although staphylococci possess a number of antigens, some of which are characteristic for the species, serologic typing of strains is utilized only by a few specialized laboratories in which proper reagents are available. Nevertheless, the acute need for an epidemiologic tool to identify staphylococcal strains responsible for epidemics became apparent in the 1950s with the emergence of drug-resistant strains of staphylococci, strains that had increased virulence and were found predominantly in the hospital environment. Development of bacteriophage typing during this period met this need. The method was based on the specificity of the bacteriophage–bacterium interaction. Some viruses lysed some strains of staphylococci and not others. A given strain of staphylococci would be characterized by its pattern of susceptibility to various bacteriophages. It should be stressed that many strains of *S. aureus* cannot be typed in this manner.

The typing procedure, which is useful only for coagulase-positive staphylococci, is based on the use of some 21 different bacteriophages, each of which can lyse some strains of *S. aureus* but not others. The pattern of sensitivity or lysis allows division of many strains of *S. aureus* into four major phage groups.

Group I: 29, 52, 52A, 79, 80
Group II: 3A, 3B, 3C, 55, 71
Group III: 6, 7, 42E, 47, 53, 54, 75, 77
Group IV: 42D
Unclassified: 81, 187

Assignment of a strain to a given group depends on lysis by any combination of phages in that group. Bacteriophage typing has yielded important epidemiologic information concerning staphylococcal disease. For example, most staphylococci that cause serious skin infections, such as impetigo and scalded skin syndrome, belong to phage group II; more than 40 percent of exfoliatin-producing staphylococci are in this group. Enterotoxin-producing staphylococci are predominantly in groups III and IV. The procedure has also become invaluable in identifying sources of pathogenic staphylococci responsible for outbreaks in hospitals.

GENETIC VARIATION

Variation in genetic features is a significant characteristic of staphylococci. Loss of pigmentation, alteration of phage sensitivity pattern, and loss or acquisition of the capacity to produce a particular toxin or enzyme are frequent in the genus. Medically, the most significant variation is drug resistance.

The widespread use of penicillin therapy after World War II for treatment of staphylococcal diseases resulted in the emergence of strains resistant to this antibiotic. As new antibiotics for treatment were introduced (e.g., tetracycline, erythromycin, chloramphenicol) strains resistant to these agents soon appeared, with many strains ex-

hibiting multiple-drug resistance. Furthermore, drug-resistant strains became more prevalent in the hospital environment. Indeed, the frequency of drug-resistant strains today is such that management of serious staphylococcal disease recalls the days before antibiotic therapy. Even the development of semisynthetic penicillins such as ampicillin has alleviated the situation only temporarily.

Penicillin resistance results from the production of the enzyme β-lactamase (penicillinase), which cleaves the β-lactam ring of the antibiotic, thereby inactivating it. The gene for β-lactamase production is carried by plasmids, which penicillin-sensitive strains of staphylococci acquire by transduction. Some plasmids carry genes not only for penicillin resistance but also for resistance to other antibiotics and even to other agents such as the heavy metals mercury and cadmium.

In addition to staphylococcal strains that are drug resistant by virtue of penicillinase production, strains are appearing that are resistant to synthetic penicillins (which are not inactivated by penicillinase) such as methicillin. The mechanism for this type of resistance is not yet clear.

Some strains of staphylococci in phage group II produce a bacteriocin (Ch. 3) similar to those produced by enteric bacteria. The lethal activity of the staphylococcal bacteriocin is against most gram-positive bacteria, including strains of staphylococci that do not produce a bacteriocin. Gram-negative bacteria and bacteriocin-producing staphylococci are resistant.

EPIDEMIOLOGY

Human skin is normally populated by *S. epidermidis*. *S. aureus* is also present on human skin, being spread to that area from the nose, which is the most significant reservoir for pathogenic staphylococci in man. The organisms are spread to other individuals or objects by direct contact or by airborne means.

Most individuals are asymptomatic carriers of *S. aureus*; that is, they have no overt signs of staphylococcal disease. The carrier rate is highest in infants in hospitals; in 4 to 6 weeks the rate approaches 90 percent. The carrier rate in the hospital environment, considering both patients and personnel, is often as high as 70 percent. In contrast, in the general population the carrier rate in infants after 1 year is 10 to 20 percent, in adults, 35 to 50 percent, and in the elderly, 20 to 30 percent.

Some individuals are occasional carriers of *S. aureus*; that is, they are carriers for some weeks, and then for some weeks they are free of the microorganism. Other individuals are transient or intermittent carriers; that is, they carry one strain of *S. aureus* for a few days or weeks lose it, and are immediately repopulated by another strain. Still others are persistent carriers, harboring the microorganism for several weeks or months.

Interestingly, colonization by staphylococci is not without benefit; it has been recognized for years that the presence of one strain of *S. aureus* can interfere with colonization by another strain. This observation has been verified by experiments; indeed, this principle of bacterial interference has been used in clinical situations. For example, in nurseries in danger of an epidemic caused by a strain of high virulence, this strain can be eliminated by antibiotics and replaced by a strain of lesser virulence.

It is important to be aware that invasive staphylococcal infections most often occur in individuals whose state of health has been compromised by either trauma or disease. Predisposing factors include surgery, accident, burns, and debilitating illness such as diabetes mellitus and malignancies. The healthy individual possesses a high degree of resistance to staphylococcal disease, with most infections in the general popula-

tion being limited to superficial lesions of the skin such as folliculitis, acne vulgaris, and hidradenitis. Studies on human volunteers have shown that to produce a lesion in healthy skin a subcutaneous injection of approximately 5×10^6 pathogenic staphylococci is necessary, whereas a similar lesion can be produced by contaminating a surgical suture with less than 100 of the organisms.

In the hospital environment, several factors converge to make pathogenic staphylococci most dangerous. It is there that a susceptible population with a high carrier rate is exposed to strains of staphylococci with high virulence, a high percentage of which are drug resistant. Compared to the general population, in which 5 to 15 percent of strains of *S. aureus* are penicillin resistant, the percentage of penicillin-resistant strains isolated in hospitals is much higher — 65 to 90 percent. Furthermore, 50 percent are tetracycline resistant and 20 percent are erythromycin resistant.

HUMAN DISEASES

Localized, Contiguous, and Metastatic Lesions.

Staphylococcal infections may remain localized, or may spread by extension to contiguous sites, or may enter the vascular system and spread hematogenously to metastatic sites that are far removed from the initial lesion.

Localized staphylococcal disease is probably the most prevalent of human bacterial diseases, with hair follicles, sweat glands, and sebaceous glands of the skin being the most commonly involved sites. Other sites of local infection include the nose, throat, vagina, urethra, and gastrointestinal tract.

Localized lesions may spread to contiguous sites. For example, a local infection in the skin that forms a "boil" or furuncle may become larger and more extensive and a carbuncle may develop. Occasionally, the localized skin lesion may begin to spread by extension through the subcutaneous tissues, producing a cellulitis. For most individuals, localized lesions are the extent of their experience with staphylococcal disease.

Localized skin lesions generally are not a major concern, except for the area of the nose, where such lesions should be treated as potentially life threatening because the staphylococci may have direct access to the brain.

A purulent abscess is the characteristic lesion produced by pathogenic staphylococci. Establishment of a focus of infection triggers an inflammatory response, with migration and subsequent accumulation of phagocytes, deposition of fibrin in the area, and formation of fibrous tissue around the lesion. The center of the lesion becomes necrotic, and purulent fluid, or pus, is formed, which contains dead bacteria and dead leukocytes. On occasion, the infection may break through the walled-off site and become invasive. More serious consequences arise if the vascular system is invaded. Septicemia may ensue, or viable organisms may spread hematogenously, generally within thrombi or phagocytes, to other sites, such as the brain, bones, and heart. Although phagocytosis is considered the principle immune defense against staphylococci, some of these organisms are capable of surviving within phagocytes.

Scalded Skin Syndrome. This staphylococcal disease appears in several clinical forms; it has been termed Ritter's disease, bullous impetigo, acute exfoliative dermatitis, toxic epidermal necrolysis, and generalized exfoliative dermatitis. It is seen most often in infants and young children. Common features include a diffuse, tender erythema of the skin, followed by formation of bullae and subsequent desquamation of the skin due to splitting of the epidermal layer in the stratum granulosum. Patients are frequently febrile and often lose copious amounts of fluid. Sometimes,

but not always, staphylococci may be recovered from the bullae or the denuded skin. Absence of the organism in the lesion should not be unexpected, since this disease is a toxemia. It is caused by the staphylococcal toxin exfoliatin, which may be produced by toxigenic staphylococci at a local site. The toxin spreads systemically to produce the disease.

Staphylococcal Enterocolitis. This disease is most often a consequence of attempts to eliminate the normal intestinal flora by oral administration of a broad-spectrum antibiotic to patients being prepared for abdominal surgery. Reduction of the normal flora permits overgrowth of staphylococci that are resistant to the administered antibiotic. The staphylococci invade the intestinal mucosa, and necrotizing lesions are produced. Disease manifestations include fever, abdominal cramps, and diarrhea with subsequent dehydration and electrolyte imbalance. In the most severe cases, staphylococci are virtually the only microorganisms present, and they constitute a great part of the fecal mass. Frequently, a pseudomembrane forms which consists of necrotic intestinal mucosa, fibrin, and leukocytes.

Staphylococcal Food Poisoning. This is the most common form of bacterial food poisoning and, similar to botulinum food poisoning (Ch. 30), it is due to ingestion of food containing preformed toxin rather than to ingestion of bacteria. This feature distinguishes it from the food poisoning caused by clostridia (other than *C. botulinum*) or salmonellae, which results from ingestion of the organisms. In staphylococcal disease, symptoms appear 2 to 6 hours after ingestion of the enterotoxin; there is nausea, severe vomiting, abdominal cramps, and, frequently, watery diarrhea. Of significance is the fact that there is usually no fever. The short incubation time and the absence of fever serve to distinguish staphylococcal food poisoning from that caused by clostridia or salmonellae. In

260   Medical Microbiology

most victims the disease is mild and self-limiting, and there is a rapid, uneventful recovery. However, on rare occasions staphylococcal enterotoxin can produce shock and even death. Foods most frequently involved in staphlococcal food poisoning are custards and other bakery products, foods with mayonnaise (such as potato, egg, or chicken salad), cheeses, ham, and processed meats. Contamination of such food with enterotoxin-producing staphylococci followed by an incubation period of 4 to 6 hours at a temperature of about 28°C results in production of sufficient toxin to produce disease. The enterotoxin has no effect on the appearance, taste, or odor of the food. Furthermore, heating the food does not ensure destruction of the toxin.

IMMUNITY

Man has a high degree of natural resistance to staphylococcal disease, with phagocytosis being the principal mechanism involved. Although antibodies to various staphylococcal antigens are produced by man, the protective role of these antibodies, even when they are in high titer, has not been clearly established. Indeed, staphylococcal diseases occur in patients in whom antistaphylococcal antibodies can be readily demonstrated. Conceivably, the effectiveness of antibodies in protection may be diminished by the nature of staphylococcal infections, which in most cases is in areas where accessibility of antibodies is low. It is also possible that binding of the Fc portion of IgG to protein A-bearing staphylococci may sterically hinder the binding of potentially destructive antistaphylococcal antibodies.

Autogenous vaccines have been used in attempts to actively immunize patients against staphylococcal infections. This procedure, which has been used primarily in patients who have repeated skin infections, such as pustular acne, has been only somewhat successful.

PREVENTION

Because of their close association with man, staphylococci probably will never be completely eliminated. However, means can be

Table 17.3. Distinguishing Features of Staphylococci

	S. aureus	S. epidermidis	S. saprophyticus
Coagulase	+	−	−
β-Hemolysis	+	−	−
Colony pigmentation	Yellow to golden	White	White
Protein A	+	−	−
α-Toxin	+	−	−
Teichoic acid	Ribitol type	Glycerol type	Ribitol and glycerol
Mannitol: acid, anaerobically	+	−	−
Novobiocin susceptibility	Sensitive	Sensitive	Resistant

+, 90 percent or more of strains are positive; −, 90 percent or more of strains are negative. (Modified from Baird-Parker, A.C.: The basis for the present classification of staphylococci and micrococci. Annals of the New York Academy of Sciences 236: 7, 1974.)

taken to control the spread of the organisms both in and outside of the hospital environment. Because of the frequency and seriousness of hospital acquired staphylococcal diseases, it is there that control efforts have been concentrated. These consist of (1) good hygienic care and proper disposal of material contaminated with pus, (2) isolation of patients with staphylococcal diseases, particularly those with open wounds or pneumonia, (3) barring contact of known carriers, particularly nasal carriers, with highly susceptible individuals, such as newborn infants or compromised patients, (4) avoiding indiscriminate use of antibiotics, and (5) strict adherence to proper operating room procedures.

LABORATORY DIAGNOSIS

Identification of *S. aureus* as a causative agent is based on microscopic, cultural, and biochemical evidence (Table 17.3). Direct smears of specimens such as sputum, pus, and other purulent exudates are stained by Gram's procedure. The finding of gram-positive cocci in typical irregular clusters is only presumptive evidence for staphylococci. Differentiation of gram-positive cocci should not be made on microscopic evidence alone. More definitive evidence is obtained with the appearance of typical colonies of *S. aureus*, when specimens are cultured on blood agar. Such colonies are readily distinguished from those of other gram-positive cocci, such as streptococci or pneumococci. For isolation of staphylococci from material such as feces, which may have other microorganisms present, a medium containing tellurite or a high salt concentration (7.5 percent of NaCl) may be used. Identification of *S. aureus* rests on microscopic examination of isolated colonies and a positive coagulase test given by a pure culture of the microorganism. Other procedures that may be employed include tests for mannitol fermentation, catalase production, gelatin liquefaction, and serologic tests for various antigens. However, these procedures are not performed routinely in most diagnostic laboratories.

TREATMENT

Penicillin and its derivatives, as well as erythromycin, the tetracyclines, the sulfonamides, and chloramphenicol are among the antibiotics that are effective against sensitive strains of staphylococci. However, because of the extraordinary proclivity of pathogenic staphylococci to acquire resistance to these antibiotics and even to more newly developed ones, and because of the prevalence of drug-resistant strains, especially in the hospital, it is essential that indiscriminate use of antibiotics be avoided. This is particularly important in the treatment of serious staphylococcal diseases such as pneumonia, septicemia, and endocarditis. Furthermore, an antibiotic sensitivity test should be performed before institution of therapy. If exceptional circumstances should preclude this, then a penicillinase-resistant penicillin, such as oxacillin or clindacillin, should be used. However, the adverse side effects of these drugs should be noted.

REFERENCES

Bernheimer, A.W.: Cytolytic toxins of bacteria. In Ajl, S.J., Kadis, S., and Montie, T.C., Eds.: Microbial Toxins. Vol. 1. Academic Press, New York, 1970.

Cohen, J.O., Ed.: The Staphylococci. Wiley-Interscience, New York, 1972.

Freeman, B.A., Ed.: Burrows Textbook of Microbiology. 21st Ed. W.B. Saunders, Philadelphia, 1979.

Joklik, W.K., Willett, H.P. Amos D.B., Eds.: Zinsser Microbiology. 17th Ed. Appleton-Century-Crofts, New York, 1980.

Lacey, R.W.: Antibiotic resistance plasmids of *Staphylococcus aureus* and their clinical importance. Bacteriol. Rev. *39*: 1, 1975.

Lennette, E.H., Balows, A., Hausler, W.J., Jr., and Truant, J.P., Eds.: Manual of Clinical Microbiology. 3rd Ed. American Society for Microbiology, Washington, D.C., 1980.

Rogolsky, M.: Nonenteric toxins of *Staphylococcus aureus*. Microbiol. Rev. *43*: 320, 1979.

Schlessinger, D., Ed.: Microbiology — 1975. American Society for Microbiology, Washington, D.C., 1975.

Yotis, W.W., Ed.: Recent advances in staphylococcal research. Ann. N.Y. Acad. Sci. *236*: 1, 1974.

18

Streptococcus

Cornelius J. O'Connell

The streptococci are distinguished by their round shape and habit of repeated division in the same direction to form chains resembling strings of beads. The chains are held together by intercellular bridges. The streptococci are gram-positive and nonmotile, and do not form spores. Often they require complex media such as blood agar for growth, on which they produce various types of hemolysis: α, in which the erythrocytes in the medium are intact but changed to an olive drab color; β, with complete lysis of red cells producing a clear pinkish zone in the agar; and γ, in which there is no hemolysis. The type of hemolysis produced is an aid to classification.

Other features include the presence of substances, the C polysaccharides, extractable with hot acid, which precipitate with one of a series of antisera (the Lancefield grouping sera), as well as growth under adverse circumstances and the production of specific capsules. On the basis of these and other characteristics, streptococci may be broadly divided as follows:

1. *Pyogenic group.* Generally β-hemolytic organisms, reacting with Lancefield antisera as groups A, B, C, or G. Require complex media.

2. *Enterococcus group.* Variably hemolytic organisms, capable of growing on simple media in the presence of bile. Lancefield group D.

3. *Viridans group.* Generally α-hemolytic organisms, not usually groupable by Lancefield sera. No prominent capsules.

4. *Pneumococci.* α-Hemolytic, encapsulated, become elongated before division, require complex media.

5. *Peptostreptococci.* Anaerobic or microaerophilic streptococci.

Members of the genus *Streptococcus* are incapable of fermenting sugars completely, the end product of fermentation being lactic acid rather than carbon dioxide and water. In this they resemble the closely related genus *Lactobacillus*.

THE PYOGENIC GROUP

Group A β-Hemolytic Streptococci (*Str. pyogenes*)

Historical Note. The history of the discovery of these organisms is intertwined with that of the great early microbiologists and is almost exactly one century old. In 1874, Billroth noted chains of globules in tissues involved by erysipelas, and 5 years later Pasteur noted the same organisms in puerperal sepsis. In 1881, the organisms

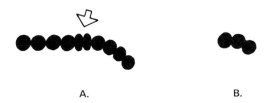

Fig. 18.1. Diagram of various coccus forms (× 5000). A. Typical chain of pyogenic cocci is represented. The individual organisms are a little smaller than 1 μm in size, are fairly uniform, and are arranged in a fairly straight chain. The arrowhead indicates two adjacent flattened cells, the products of recent cell division. These flattened organisms resemble the beads on a Chinese abacus and are a hallmark distinguishing streptococci generally from *Str. pneumoniae* in particular, since the latter organisms do not show these forms. B. Three associated cocci are seen. It is impossible to tell whether these are a short chain (streptococci) or a small cluster (staphylococci). The distinction can only be made if collections of at least four cocci are seen.

were isolated from abcesses by Ogston and demonstrated to be regularly present in erysipelas by Koch. Rosenbach isolated them in 1884 and named them *Streptococcus pyogenes*.

General.   The cell walls of these organisms contain a polysaccharide that after extraction reacts with Lancefield group A antiserum. Fluorescein may be chemically coupled with an anti–group A serum to allow one to rapidly detect the presence of such streptococci by use of a fluorescence microscope; under this type of microscope these organisms glow after treatment with the serum. The test has pitfalls due either to crossreaction of the fluoresceinated serum with other organisms (group C streptococci and some strains of *Staphylococcus aureus*) or to coating of streptococci in clinical specimens by interfering antibodies. However, experienced laboratory technicians, using absorbed sera (to remove crossreacting antibodies) and organisms that

have been allowed to multiply briefly in culture (to remove adhering antibodies), may reliably identify the organisms by this method in only a few hours.

Although the specific group A polysaccharide is the major component of the cell wall, other components play a role in forming this complex structure and contribute to the pathogenic ability of the organism.

The M proteins are present in the substance of the cell wall, sending forth hairlike protrusions that contribute to the organism's ability to adhere to epithelial surfaces. They also confer the ability to resist phagocytosis. On rapid serial passage of the organism from person to person, as in epidemics, the M protein content of the organism increases, changing the colony appearance from the usual mucoid or glossy type to a dull matte appearance. A number of different M proteins exist, and a panel of specific antisera against them may be used to further classify group A organisms into more than 60 specific types. Typing is important in epidemiologic investigations as well as in the prediction of pathogenicity, since certain types are associated with glomerulonephritis (the "nephritogenic strains") but others are not. This is in contrast to rheumatic fever, which may be provoked by infection with any group A organism, regardless of type.

Antibodies directed against the M proteins occur after infection and confer typespecific immunity against reinfection.

Other proteins in the cell wall include the T and R proteins. The former occur in several serologically distinct varieties that are analogous to those of the M proteins. Since the T types are independent of the M types, their determination adds further refinement to epidemiologic studies by allowing a distinction to be made between different strains of the same M type.

A cell wall lipoteichoic acid is formed from polymerization of substituted glycerophosphates. It also contributes to the virulence of the organism and to its ability to attach to epithelial cells.

Surrounding the complex cell wall is a capsule of hyaluronic acid, identical in composition to the hyaluronic acid of human tissues and therefore not antigenic.

Strains with well developed capsules grow as mucoid colonies; those with little or no capsule appear glossy. In either case the organisms grow on blood agar to produce small — about 1 mm in diameter — colonies after overnight incubation. Because of their somewhat complex nutritional requirements, they do not grow on simple media.

Soluble Products. An amazing variety of products are liberated by these organisms during their growth, many of which are toxic or contribute to the ability of the organism to invade tissue in other ways.

Two separate hemolysins are produced, both capable of producing complete or β lysis of erythrocytes. One, streptolysin O, is oxygen labile. This toxin not only dissolves red blood cells but is capable of damaging a variety of parenchymal cells of various organs, including the heart, on which a cardiotoxic action is produced. This hemolysin is antigenic in humans, stimulating the production of an antibody of diagnostic usefulness in detecting recent infection.

The other hemolysin, streptolysin S, is stable in the presence of oxygen but inactivated by serum. It also has far-reaching actions on the host, generally produced by its ability to activate lysosomes. This ability accounts for its anti-leukocytic properties. Streptolysin S is a poor antigen.

Strains of *Str. pyogenes* vary in their ability to produce these hemolysins and may make one type only. For this reason it is usual to cut into the agar with the bacteriologic loop when streaking a plate for demonstration of the organisms in throat cultures. Strains producing only streptolysin O show hemolysis around the slice because the oxygen labile hemolysin is protected from contact with air in the depths of the slit.

Hyaluronidase, which is produced by some strains, aids dissemination of the organism by its ability to dissolve the hyaluronic acid ground substance of tissues. It has been noted before that encapsulated strains of the organism are coated with hyaluronic acid apparently identical to that of tissues that would be susceptible to the action of this enzyme. As might be expected, strains with prominent capsules do not produce this enzyme, which is usually associated with unencapsulated strains. The enzyme is harvested from streptococcal cultures commercially and purified as a therapeutic substance, and it is used to loosen subcutaneous tissue ground substance to allow better absorption of injected materials.

Streptokinase brings about the dissolution of fibrin clots through its ability to activate the plasmin enzyme system of serum. Presumably, like hyaluronidase it contributes to pathogenicity by acting as a spreading factor; by tearing down fibrin walls in the infected area, it defeats the host's attempts to localize infection. It also is obtained from cultures and processed into a material used in the treatment of thrombi.

A mixture of four distinct enzymes, all capable of hydrolyzing DNA, is referred to as streptodornase. The action of these enzymes on the large amounts of nuclear debris present in pus leads to the consequent liquefaction of viscid DNA and accounts in part for the thin, runny pus seen in streptococcal abscesses. A combination of streptokinase and streptodornase is available for therapeutic use in situations where fibrinopurulent exudates must be liquefied, as in empyema. This material, streptokinase-streptodornase, is also useful in the investigation of anergic states. Since most adults should have developed delayed hypersensitivity to this material from past infections, lack of induration 48 hours after intradermal injection of 0.1 ml of the substance may indicate defective cellular immunity.

Other hydrolytic enzymes include those

active on proteins, starches, and esters, proteinase, amylase, and esterase, respectively, whose actions contribute to tissue destruction.

Finally, an NADase is produced and is important for two reasons: it contributes to leukotoxicity and it stimulates the production of an antibody whose late appearance, 3 to 6 weeks after infection, is useful in the late retrospective diagnosis of streptococcal infections. This is particularly useful in the diagnosis of Sydenham's chorea, which occurs so long after the initiating infection that the usual serologic tests, such as the tests for antibodies to streptolysin O, are often negative.

Diagnosis. Culture of appropriate material may be done on blood agar — preferably made with sheep blood — on which hemolytic patterns are most characteristic; β-hemolytic colonies of appropriate appearance should be smeared and stained to establish that they are composed of gram-positive cocci in chains. Usually these will prove to be group A, but definitive identification requires demonstration of the ability to react with specific grouping serum, a difficult and expensive procedure for routine use. In practice, a slightly less accurate but far simpler test is used, the presence or absence of a significant zone of inhibition around a paper disk containing 0.02 units of the antibiotic bacitracin. β-Hemolytic streptotoci inhibited by the disc may be described as *group A* and those not inhibition around a paper disk containing 90 percent reliability.

Recently, other reagents for indicating whether streptococci belong to Lancefield groups A, B, C, or G have become commercially available. They are composed of particles (staphylococcal cells or latex spherules) coated with specific antisera. Coagglutination of streptococci with the indicator particles to produce visible aggregates is an indication of the Lancefield group. Properly used, this test is more accurate than the bacitracin disk test.

During a patient's convalescence from infection, antibodies are formed against streptococcal products. The classic procedure to detect these is the anti-streptolysin O (ASO) test, in which the titer of antibodies to streptolysin is determined by observing the ability of diluted serum from the patient to inhibit the lysis produced by a standardized solution of hemolysin. Todd, who originated the test, devised an arbitrary series of dilutions of serum, reported as *Todd units*, which may be taken as equal to titers (e.g., 133 Todd units equals a titer of 133 in the test). More sensibly, the test may be done using standard twofold dilutions with reports of titers of 10, 20, 40, and so forth.

A fourfold rise in titer or a titer above 100 in a single specimen indicates recent infections. Patients likely to develop rheumatic fever as a complication tend to develop higher titers, usually above 400, than do those with uncomplicated disease. The ASO test is more reliable in diagnosing pharyngeal infections than those of skin because of the presence in skin of sterols that bind streptolysin O and inhibit antibody production.

Another routinely available serologic test is the streptococcal exoenzyme test which is available commercially. This uses latex particles coated with a mixture of several streptococcal enzymes, including streptolysin O, hyaluronidase, and streptodornase. Sera containing antibodies to these products agglutinate the particles; with serial dilutions, a titer may be measured. This test, in contrast to the ASO titer, is equally reliable in indicating skin and pharyngeal infections.

Pharyngitis. In the temperate zone the ordinary residence of *Str. pyogenes* is the human pharynx, with person-to-person spread by droplet infection. Tissue invasion with the production of pharyngitis is favored by various factors, some known and others not. The former include age (preschool to first grade and pubescence) and the production of the virulence-enhancing type-specific proteins by the organism, as in epidemic spread of the disease. The throat becomes bright red and intensely painful, with fever and enlargement of the cervical nodes. This clinical picture is not specific for streptococcal disease, since a number of other bacteria and viruses capable of infecting the throat may produce a similar appearance. Severe pain on swallowing and tender cervical adenopathy are probably the signs best correlated with streptococcal disease, provided that one realizes that diagnosis solely on clinical grounds is always uncertain.

The accessory air spaces of the head, sinuses, middle ear, and mastoid air cells, may be invaded by streptococci, either as a complication of pharyngitis or as a primary process. This type of invasion occurs especially in children.

Skin Infections. In the tropics streptococcal impetigo due to strains with specific predeliction to infect the skin is the most common form of streptococcal disease and it is spread by contact infection rather than by droplets as seen in temperate areas. A subacute condition, the infection evolves through a minor, brief pustular phase into a phase of formation of thick, dark, varnish-like crusts. Clinically, this is in contrast to the lengthy and more marked pustular phase and the golden yellow crusting of the common form of impetigo caused by staphylococci.

Erysipelas is another form of skin infection by hemolytic streptococci; in this infection an abrupt chill is followed by systemic toxicity. About 12 to 24 hours later reddened skin lesions appear with advancing borders that are raised, purple, and sharply demarcated. On the limbs infection often enters through a minor skin break due to trauma or fungal infection; on the face the disease may occur without an obvious entryway, and it is assumed that entry is from inside the nose. It is probable that certain strains of streptococci are more likely to cause the disease, since a patient with erysipelas can spread the same disease to others.

Ordinary cellulitis, a spreading infection of the skin and subcutaneous tissues (without specific features of erysipelas, such as initial chill, systemic toxicity, or characteristic raised purple border), can be produced by streptococci as well as other organisms.

Gangrene, another form of skin infection caused by hemolytic streptococci, is rare. This severe disorder is marked by subcutaneous spread of the organisms after introduction by trauma, which may range from obvious to trivial. Destruction of the subcutaneous tissues leads first to numbness and finally to frank gangrene. The process evolves rapidly in 1 to 2 days and is marked systemically by profound toxicity and locally by full-thickness loss of skin. Diagnosis is made by blood culture, which usually yields the organism, or by culture of the lesion itself.

Puerperal and Surgical Wound Sepsis. In the past, death from streptococcal sepsis was a leading cause of mortality in the puerperium, the period after giving birth. The organisms invaded the uterus through the raw attachment site of the placenta, spread rapidly to the pelvic tissues, and finally entered the blood, producing a grave illness that was usually fatal in the preantibiotic era. Fortunately, the studies of Semmelweiss over a century ago showed the means of transmission of this disease and emphasized the preventive role of cleanliness, handwashing, and aseptic technique in examinations during labor and in delivery. The disease is now rare in countries where these principles are followed. Surgical wounds may be similarly infected if aseptic technique is not followed. Outbreaks of surgical wound sepsis, when they occur, are often traceable to one or more pharyngeal carriers of the organism among the staff of the unit involved.

A clinical clue to streptococcal surgical wound infection is the rapid onset of fever and local signs, within 12 to 24 hours of surgery, and the issue of thin, runny, blood-tinged material from the wound. The character of the discharge is determined to some extent by the proteolytic and fibrin-hydrolyzing effect of the organism's enzymes.

Pneumonia. Pneumonia elicited by hemolytic streptococci may occur sporadically or in epidemic form during epidemics of measles or influenza; it was a common cause of death during the influenza pandemic of 1918 and 1919.

The disease differs from ordinary pneumonia by its rapid, widespread extension to large areas of the lung, its tendency to cause necrosis with multilocular cavities, and the high percentage of patients who develop a bloody pleural effusion as a complication.

Scarlet Fever. This disease is produced by systemic poisoning by the erythrogenic toxin produced by some strains of group A β-hemolytic streptococci. Chills, fever, and greater systemic toxicity than expected from a localized streptococcal infection are followed by an evolving picture of dermal toxicity. At first, perifollicular edema creates a bumpy appearance similar to that of a plucked chicken or coarse sandpaper. Within hours, confluent erythema spreads over the body and onto the limbs and face, where it usually avoids the area around the mouth and thus leads to a characteristic circumoral pallor. After evolving to its fullest extent, the rash gradually fades and is followed by desquamation. The peeled skin is usually in the form of large, thick strips, in contrast to the fine branlike desquamation following other rashes (for example, measles); this is especially so at the tips of the extremities, where actual casts may be shed.

During the evolution of the eruption, parallel changes occur in the tongue. At first, red, swollen papillae are seen protruding through a diffuse white coating, the "strawberry tongue" phenomenon. Later the white coating disappears and the mucosa desquamates, leaving a purplish, swollen organ, the "raspberry tongue".

The disease is dependent on two factors, the acquisition of a streptococcus capable of producing erythrogenic toxin and the lack of immunity to this toxin. Most adults are immune to scarlet fever as a result of a previous disease or through subclinical episodes. Since there are at least three antigenically distinct erythrogenic toxins, it is conceivable that the disease could be contracted more than once, but this is unusual. While scarlet fever is almost invariably a consequence of infection with group A hemolytic streptococci, it occasionally occurs with infection by streptococci of other groups or even by staphylococci, which can produce erythrogenic toxin in rare instances.

Serologic methods for diagnosing the disease or predicting immunity are of historic interest. The Dick test for immunity used the intradermal inoculation of a small amount of erythrogenic toxin; local erythema indicated susceptibility. The Schultz-Charlton reaction for diagnosis used an intradermal injection of antiserum prepared against erythrogenic toxin; the injection was given into the involved skin. In early stages of the rash, the antiserum neutralized local toxin and blanching occurred. These two tests are no longer useful because of unavailability of the necessary materials, the recognition that at least three distinct serologic types of toxins are involved, and the fact that the serum used in the Schultz-Charlton test occasionally produced serious allergic reactions.

Nonsuppurative Complications

Acute Poststreptococcal Glomerulonephritis. Infections with certain types of group A streptococci, the nephritogenic strains, may be followed by acute glomerulonephritis marked by protein and red blood cells in the urine. Microscopic examination of kidney biopsies reveals changes in the glomeruli with disruption of the basement membrane, subepithelial lumps, and secondary changes in the epithelial cells covering the glomerulus. The disease is apparently due to the deposition of immune complexes composed of streptococcal antigens and their antibodies on the glomerular basement membrane.

The disease may be acute or may enter a chronic phase with long continued activity of glomerular disease ending in complete destruction of renal function. It may follow either pharyngeal or extrapharyngeal infection with the streptococci. In the former case the most frequent nephritogenic strains are 1, 4, 12, and Red Lake; in the case of nephritis provoked by impetigo in tropical areas other types, specifically skin-associated nephritogenic types, have been noted.

Rheumatic Fever. Certain individuals who are apparently genetically predisposed may develop rheumatic fever following infection of the pharynx with group A β-hemolytic streptococci. In contrast to nephritis, extrapharyngeal infections seem incapable of producing the disease or causing recurrences. The clinical expression of the infection may vary from almost asymptomatic to a severe pharyngitis, but in practically all cases a significant ASO titer rise occurs following infection. After an interval, acute rheumatic fever occurs with a mixture of involvement of the skin (erythema nodosum or erythema marginatum), the myocardium (inflammatory foci), the heart valves (inflammation resulting in deformities), the joints (a migratory polyarthritis), or the nervous system (Sydenham's chorea). The long range importance of the disease is due to progressive valvular deformity; repeated attacks can add further insult to valves that previously have had only minor involvement. Because of this, until the age where further infections are unlikely to produce further valve damage (variously estimated at between 25 and 35

years), antibiotic prophylaxis against group A streptococci is recommended for all who have had one attack of rheumatic fever. In contrast to nephritis, there are no particular rheumatic fever-inducing strains; instead, infection with any strain may initiate the disease or a recurrence.

Immunofluorescence experiments have shown that antisera prepared against the cell membranes of group A streptococci fix to components of human heart muscle and valves, and it is hypothesized that this cross-reactivity is involved in the pathogenesis of the cardiac lesions.

Other Nonsuppurative Complications. Young adult women are especially prone to have benign poststreptococcal arthritis, a symmetric involvement of medium to large joints, such as the knees, that follows soon after an attack of streptococcal pharyngitis and that has minimal effusion (in contrast to the marked inflammatory signs of rheumatic fever).

Another complication is erythema nodosum, in which arthralgias are associated with a low fever and tender, purplish, medium sized (0.5 to 3 cm) nodules characteristically distributed over the shins. While this may be one of the manifestations of acute rheumatic fever, it may also exist as a sole complication of streptococcal infection.

Treatment of Group A Streptococcal Disease

These organisms are highly sensitive to penicillin and have not developed resistance during the antimicrobial era. Blood levels of the drug easily achieved by oral administration on a fasting stomach or by procaine or benzathine penicillin injections are adequate to eradicate the organism. The treatment of streptococcal pharyngitis in young persons is governed by the possibility of rheumatic fever and by the fact that continuously effective levels of the drug should be maintained for 10 days in order to minimize this risk; it is important to impress upon the patient the need to finish a full course of treatment even though symptomatic improvement or remission may occur earlier.

The best regimen to prevent flare-ups of rheumatic fever is the monthly administration of at least 1.2 million units of benzathine penicillin G intramuscularly until the patient reaches approximately the age of 30. Oral penicillin may be given twice daily in doses of 500,000 units, but this method of prophylaxis is associated with a high attack rate of acute rheumatic fever, apparently because of poor compliance.

In the presence of allergy to penicillin, group A streptococcal disease may be adequately treated with erythromycin, clindimycin, or trimethoprimsulfas.

Group B β-Hemolytic Streptococci

General. This bacterium was first described in outbreaks of infections of cattle udders, and because the infection halted milk production the organism was named *Streptococcus agalactiae*. In addition to infections of cows, fish, and other animals the organism began to be noticed in human disease and was uncovered with increasing incidence as the years passed, especially after its distinguishing characteristics allowed it to be separated from the more common group A streptococci. The organism produces abundant group-specific material that is excreted freely into the medium, so that extraction with hot acid for Lancefield typing is not necessary. While the precipitin reaction is necessary for definitive demonstration that an organism is group B, other characteristics are more important in routine identification. About 95 percent of the organisms resist the bacitracin used in group A testing disks. Hippurate hydrolysis with the release of benzoic acid is characteristic of these organisms, and a rapid test for this is used in some hospital laboratories to identify group B organisms. Other labor-

atories rely on the CAMP* phenomenon, which is a partial hemolysis of red cells in the medium around *Str. agalactiae* colonies that can be potentiated by a β-hemolysin extracted from *Straphylococcus aureus* to produce complete clearing. Disks impregnated with staphylococcal β-hemolysin are commercially available for use in the test. Other laboratories use the production of a yellow or orange pigment around colonies grown on Columbia agar as an indication of the presence of group B organisms.

Sheep blood agar is an excellent medium for growing these bacteria, and it may be supplemented with 8 μg/ml nalidixic acid to inhibit the growth of other microbes. This selective medium increases the rate of recovery of the organism from clinical specimens up to twofold, providing a useful medium for screening populations for the carrier state.

Serology. Although the organisms produce a great deal of group specific B substance, antibody directed against this material is not protective. However, protein substances in the cell wall stimulate the protective antibodies, and antigenic variation from strain to strain in these proteins allows separation into three types, I, II, and III, in a manner analogous to the separation of group A organisms into various types. Subtle antigenic variations within type I allow further division into three subtypes: Ia, Ib, and Ic. Maternal antibodies against specific types of group B streptococci carried by a pregnant woman can cross the placenta, conferring temporary immunity to the offspring.

As is discussed below, the major feature of infection with group B β-hemolytic steptococci is the production of severe disease in newborns. Within this context, there is some epidemiologic significance to the various types: type Ia is the agent most frequently producing the rare condition of fatal overwhelming septicemia of the new-

---

*An acronym for the investigators who described the phenomenon.

born, while the more common but fortunately less severe infections of newborns, including meningitis and other disorders, are due to type III about 85 percent of the time.

Epidemiology. The principal reservoir of the organism is the female vagina. About one in six women of college age carries the organism in the vagina, and this rate about doubles with pregnancy. The vaginal carrier state is usually asymptomatic; sexual partners of female carriers may harbor the organism in their urethras, also as an asymptomatic infection. The organism also may be carried in the rectum or throat, but this is less common than genital carriage.

Organisms from the mother's vagina can colonize the newborn infant during delivery. Once colonized, the newborn continues to carry the organism in sites such as the throat, ear, umbilical stump, or rectum and can transmit the organism to other infants in the nursery. Colonized infants who lack protective maternal antibody, as happens if the mother had never acquired the organism or acquired it too late in pregnancy to form antibodies, are at risk of developing disease.

Infections of Newborns. There has been a rising incidence in infections of newborns by group B hemolytic streptococci over the past two decades, and this organism is now the single most common cause of meningitis of newborns, accounting for almost one-third of such cases. Some form of group B infection is expected to attack 3 to 4 newborns per 1000 within the first week of life, a form of infection arbitrarily defined as *early onset type. Late onset disease* between the second and fourth weeks of life, may be expected in 1 infant out of every 2000.

The early onset type by definition occurs within the first week of life, usually in the first 2 days, and the mother's vagina is usually found to carry a serotype of the organism identical to that infecting the infant. There is a relation between premature labor or prolonged rupture of the membranes prior to delivery and group B streptococcal disease. The infection presents as septicemia, meningitis, and/or pulmonary involvement in various combinations.

Pulmonary involvement may resemble hyaline membrane disease clinically but has several distinguishing characteristics, including a greater frequency of cardiovascular collapse or apnea as well as higher pulmonary compliance (as manifested by the need for less pressure to ventilate the infant). If the infant dies, routinely stained sections of autopsied lung tissue will resemble those of hyaline membrane disease, but Gram staining of the tissue sections will show masses of organisms within the membrane, proving the bacterial cause of the disease.

The less common late onset disease presents several contrasts to the early onset type. Serotyping shows that this form of the infection is not related to maternal carriage of the organism in the vagina but rather is probably acquired by nosocomial transmission. The infection is less overwhelming, often presenting as a meningitis, a septicemia, or a postsepticemic purulent localization of the organisms in bones or joints. Even more localized minor disease such as cellulitis, otitis, or sinusitis, may occur.

Adult Infections. In adults group B streptococci produce a variety of pyogenic diseases generally similar to those produced by organisms of group A, including pharyngitis, cellulitis, and septic arthritis. While in the past, group A organisms were almost invariably the cause of puerperal fever and septicemias originating from the female genital tract, organisms of group B are now seen with increasing frequency in these situations.

Other Pyogenic Streptococci

From time to time other streptococci may cause pyogenic diseases similar to those caused by group A and B organisms. Usually these are members of groups C or

G. Often, there is a history suggestive of animal contact as a source of infection.

In the past, epidemics of milk-borne pharyngitis due to organisms of group C occurred from time to time, and such epidemics are still possible in areas where pasteurization of milk is not routinely practiced.

In general, streptococci of groups other than A are not associated with the production of glomerulonephritis or of rheumatic fever.

THE ENTEROCOCCUS GROUP

General

The enterococcus group is characterized by the presence of an extractable antigen reacting with group D Lancefield antiserum; in contrast to the other streptococci these organisms grow quite well on simple media such as those used for the isolation of gram-negative enteric bacteria. When grown on blood agar they may show any type of hemolysis: α, β, or ɤ. These organisms are normal residents of the intestine and, as might be expected in bacteria that thrive in this site, they are resistant to bile, a feature distinguishing them from many other streptococci. Another distinguishing characteristic is the ability of these organisms to produce a black precipitate when grown in the presence of the carbohydrate esculin. These two properties are revealed

on bile-esculin agar, on which group D organisms are the only streptococci that thrive and produce blackening of the medium — a characteristic that suffices to identify them as members of this group without further serologic testing.

Most group D organisms also possess the property of resistance to a variety of adverse circumstances, such as high salt concentration (6.5 percent NaCl), temperature as high as 40°C or as low as 33°C, or the presence of inhibitory substances such as sodium azide or methylene blue. The ability to thrive despite one or more of the above-mentioned adverse factors separates group D streptococci into the true enterococci and those not tolerant to these factors, the nonenterococcal group D streptococci.

Among the true enterococci there are five subspecies grouped under two species, *Streptococcus faecalis* and *Streptococcus faecium*. Their distinguishing characteristics are displayed in Table 18.1. From the table it can be seen that a ɤ-hemolytic organism (that is, one that produces no hemolysis) must be one of the subspecies of *Str. faecalis*, whereas an α-hemolytic enterococcus must be a variety of *Str. faecium*. No conclusion can be drawn from β-hemolysis, since this could represent a variant of either species.

The group D streptococci that do not resist adverse environmental factors and therefore are nonenterococcal are divided

Table 18.1. Classification of the Enterococci

	Reduction of Litmus and Resistance to Tellurite	Hemolysis	Gelatin Liquefaction	Acid Production From Arabinose
Str. faecalis				
variety *faecalis*	+	ɤ	−	−
variety *zymogenes*	+	β	+	−
variety *liquefaciens*	+	ɤ	+	−
Str. faecium				
variety *faecium*	−	α	−	+
variety *durans*	−	α or β	−	−

Codes used: +, phenomenon listed in heading occurs; −, phenomenon listed in heading does not occur.

Table 18.2.   The Nonenterococcal Group D Streptococci

	Blackening Bile-Esculin Agar	Growth in *Str. faecalis* Broth	Growth in 6.5% NaCl	Growth on Eosin-Methylene Blue Medium
Enterococcus group	+	+	+	+
Str. bovis[a]	+	+	−	−
Viridans group	−	−	−	−

Codes used: +, phenomenon in heading occurs; −, phenomenon in heading does not occur.

[a]The intermediate position of *Str. bovis* between the true enterococci and the viridans group can be seen.

into two species, *Streptococcus bovis* and *Streptococcus equinus*. Of these, only the former is important in human infections. Table 18.2 displays some of the characteristics of this organism and demonstrates its intermediate position between the true enterococci and the viridans group of streptococci.

Role in Urinary Tract Infections

The enterococci are the only gram-positive bacteria significantly associated with urinary tract infection, in contrast to the more frequent and greater variety of gram-negative rods. While it is usual to expect 100,000 colony-forming units of an infecting organism per milliliter of urine in infections of the urinary tract, smaller numbers than these may be encountered in enterococcal infection because a number of cells of this organism are associated together in chains; since each chain produces only one colony on inoculation of the plate, each colony-forming unit represents several individual bacteria. There is a definite association of enterococcal urinary tract infection with instrumentation and catheterization. Despite this, infections due to the organism are not particularly hospital-associated but occur equally often in outpatients and hospitalized ones; hospital-associated outbreaks of enterococcal disease occur more rarely (if at all) than those due to gram-negative rods. Fortunately, these organisms tend to cause simple cysti-

tis more often than invasion of the upper tract with pyelonephritis; they cause only 1 to 3 percent of cases of the latter.

Role in Endocarditis

The presence of enterococci in endocarditis varies from reported series to series; generally they cause 3 to 17 percent of cases of this disease, possibly with frequency increasing over the past few decades. The infection is spread to the heart valves by surgery or manipulation of the gastrointestinal tract or, more frequently, the urogenital tract. Because of this it tends to be a disease of young women, who are predisposed to bacteremia by gynecologic procedures, and of old men, who develop prostatic conditions requiring cystoscopy or prostate surgery.

Str. faecalis liquefaciens accounts for almost 60 percent of cases of heart valve infections; when the two other varieties of this species are added, *Str. faecalis* as a species accounts for 95 percent of cases. The disease is remarkably indolent in its progression; for example, in one series infections due to enterococci had a mean duration before diagnosis of 5 months. Despite its indolent progression, enterococcal endocarditis is ulcerative and destructive with the formation of bulky vegetations that can throw off large emboli in contrast to the tiny ones seen in viridans-produced disease. Thus major emboli are more common in enterococcal endocarditis than in other types and minor emboli are less common. In about one fourth of the cases of enterococcal endocarditis significant numbers of enterococci grow on culture of the urine, a useful diagnostic aid. It cannot be stated with certainty whether this growth is due to the fact that involvement of the urinary tract with enterococci serves as the cause of the endocarditis or whether enterococci from the bloodstream produce secondary renal infection with bacteruria.

Another peculiarity of endocarditis due to these organisms, as compared with that due to others, is the relatively high incidence of metastatic suppuration and abscess formation, especially in the spleen. Enterococci can attack previously normal valves, resembling in this respect staphylococci.

Str. bovis, the nonenterococcal species of group D important in human diseases, can also cause endocarditis. The organism may be recognized by the characteristic laboratory features alluded to above or by the fact that it, in contrast to true enterococci, usually appears to be completely sensitive to penicillin on routine susceptibility tests, whereas, as discussed below, most true enterococci will be partially or completely resistant to this drug.

It is important to recognize *Str. bovis* endocarditis, since there is a distinct relation between this disease and lesions of the colon. One estimate gives a 20 percent probability that either a polyp or an actual carcinoma will be found if careful investigation is done in cases of *Str. bovis* endocarditis.

Antibiotic Treatment

The true enterococci are seldom completely sensitive to penicillin G. Even when they appear to be, more thorough investigation will show that the action of the drug is merely bacteriostatic and not bactericidal.

It was appreciated early in the antibiotic era that streptomycin often synergized with penicillin, changing its action to a bactericidal one and in many cases producing cure of enterococcal endocarditis. For a long time this synergistic action of streptomycin, which occurred with some strains but not with others, was puzzling. More recently, it has become apparent that enterococcal strains tested at extremely high concentrations of streptomycin, at least 125 mg/ml, may be divided into two groups — those that are inhibited at this extraordinarily large concentration and those that are not — and that behavior of strains at high concentrations is predictive of the ability of the drug to synergize with penicillin at the lower concentrations produced by ordinary therapeutic doses. A similar relation has been observed for other aminoglycosides, and it has been shown that kanamycin and gentamicin almost uniformly inhibit enterococci at high concentrations and show synergism with penicillin at lower, clinically achievable concentrations. Tobramycin is similarly active but is less reliable showing synergism with only about three-quarters of the strains.

Ampicillin is more active against enterococci than penicillin and usually is actually bactericidal rather than merely bacteriostatic. Cephalosporins are inferior to penicillin and do not synergize reliably with aminoglycosides. For that matter, macrolidelike antibiotics such as erythromycin and clindimycin usually either do not inhibit enterococci or do not synergize with aminoglycosides. The cell-wall-active antibiotic vancomycin, however, does synergize with aminoglycosides and is prefered in the treatment of patients allergic to penicillin.

When a patient with known previous valvular damage is to undergo gynecologic, prostatic, or colonic surgery, prophylaxis against enterococcal endocarditis can be given by the temporary administration of large doses of ampicillin with gentamicin during the operative and immediate postoperative period.

The nonenterococcal group D organism

Str. bovis does not display the penicillin resistance seen with the true enterococci; infections due to these organisms may be treated with high doses of penicillin alone, although some authorities feel that the addition of aminoglycosides provides additional insurance against relapse or failure of treatment.

THE VIRIDANS GROUP

General

The separation of streptococci into species is still suffering from considerable taxonomic confusion. Nowhere in the genus is this more evident than in the so-called *Streptococcus viridans* group. In the first place, the term *viridans* has no authority as a species name but is merely used by laboratories as a handy method of designating these organisms. Secondly, although the name viridans, with its implication of a green color, implies that all these organisms are α-hemolytic, in fact a great number are nonhemolytic and occasional strains are β-hemolytic. Finally, while these organisms are usually considered to be ungroupable by Lancefield antisera, in fact a number of strains react with these sera, usually with group K. They are quite uniform in being tolerant to the presence of bile and resistant to the chemical substance optochin, features that serve to separate them from the closely related pneumococci.

Their normal habitat is the oral cavity, where they adhere to various surfaces including the teeth and cheeks, with various areas serving as specific ecologic niches in which one or another type prefers to grow. The specificity of these niches is in part dependent on the ability of certain strains to adhere selectively to various oral tissues by as yet imperfectly understood attachment mechanisms.

Although the classification of the group is somewhat unclear, it seems certain that at least two distinct divisions can be made. First, there is *Streptococcus salivarius*, a usually nonhemolytic organism that can react with group K antisera and that produces mucoid colonies on sucrose agar due to the production of levan. The other is the *Streptococcus mitis* group, consisting of organisms that are generally α-hemolytic and produce dry colonies on sucrose agar owing to the production of dextran. The latter group can be broken further into species such as *mitis*, *mitior*, *sanguis*, *mutans*, and "MG" on the basis of classification schemes using a battery of biochemical tests. Although complete agreement has not yet been reached regarding their classification, the most recent tendency has been to use acid formation in mannitol, lactose, and inulin as well as hydrolysis of hippurate and esculin as the characteristics distinguishing at least ten species of the viridans group.

The viridans group makes up a large proportion of the aerobic flora of the normal mouth; circumstances that inhibit their growth, such as antibiotic administration, mouth breathing, or parenteral feeding, are associated with colonization and overgrowth of the oral cavity by staphylococci and gram-negative rods, which are normally inhibited by these bacteria.

Because viridans streptococci are present in great numbers in saliva, the inexperienced microscopist is often confused by their resemblance in expectorated sputum to pneumococci. The problem may be resolved by noting that viridans streptococci are common in specimens heavily contaminated by saliva. This is revealed by a large number of polygonal oral epithelial cells compared to lower respiratory tract cells, such as neutrophils or ciliated epithelial cells. In a properly collected sputum specimen the lower respiratory cells should outnumber buccal cells by at least five to one, and a preponderance of the latter type of cells indicates admixture of saliva in the sputum. Also, when viridans streptococci simulate pneumococci in a smear they are usually seen adhering to the surfaces of polygonal cells rather than being associated with neutrophils.

Role in Endocarditis

The viridans group of streptococci is the most common cause of endocarditis, accounting for slightly over half the cases and there is a suggestion that some strains, for example, *Str. sanguis* and *Str. mitis*, may infect heart valves more frequently than other members of the group. The usual route of infection is the production of bacteremia by dental procedures, which may range from tooth extraction or root canal treatment to even minor procedures such as routine periodontal cleaning. Other factors, including vigorous tooth brushing or the use of pulsating water appliances for cleaning the teeth, may also cause bacteremia with these organisms but this type of bacteremia normally is quite harmless and is easily cleared by the reticuloendothelial system. However, in the presence of preexisting valvular damage, particularly of a type that roughens endothelium, organisms may become attached to the damaged site, invade the valve, and set up an endocarditis vegetation. The predisposing lesion is usually due to rheumatic fever, but other valvular lesions, including those of congenital malformations, syphilitic disease of the aortic valve, or even calcification due to aging, may serve as sites predisposing to endocarditis.

Endocarditis due to the viridans group is less destructive and ulcerative than that due to other organisms, for example, enterococci or *Staphylococcus aureus*. It is revealed by ordinary blood cultures that generally are positive if a total of three cultures are taken at various times during 1 day. Rarely, viridans organisms with special nutritional requirements may need media supplemented with sulfhydryl compounds or pyridoxal for growth.

The susceptibility of this group of organisms to penicillin allows treatment of endocarditis with penicillin alone, usually for shorter periods than necessary for endocarditis due to more resistant organisms. On the other hand, the addition of aminoglycosides to penicillin has been shown to potentiate bacterial killing and some advocate using them in treating the disease for the same reasons that this regimen is proposed in the case of *Str. bovis* infections. Prophylaxis against endocarditis due to viridans bacteria consists of the administration of penicillin to patients with known valvular lesions who undergo dental procedures. It is customary to administer the drug before the procedure to produce bactericidal levels in the blood stream at the time of the bacteremia, i.e., during the performance of the dental surgery, and to continue it throughout the day of the surgery to maintain bactericidal levels for 24 hours after completion of the procedure.

Role in Dental Disease

Viridans streptococci in the oral cavity present a complex picture. The numbers and species present vary with site of isolation and with the individual's oral health. *Str. salivarius*, for example, is found in high numbers in saliva and on the dorsum of the tongue, and only rarely in dental plaque. Dental plaque, the bacterial mass adherent to the tooth surface, on the other hand, is composed predominately of *Str. sanguis*, *Str. mitior*, and, when associated with active caries, *Str. mutans*. The last species has been extensively studied because of this association with caries.

For *Str. mutans* to initiate caries two conditions must be met: the organism must adhere to the tooth surface, and acid production must be sustained. The means by which these organisms first adhere to the enamel surface is not entirely clear, but in the later stages a water-insoluble glucan formed by the organism from sucrose acts as an adhesive. Other viridans streptococci can form a similar glucan, notably *Str. sanguis* and *Str. mitior*. *Str. salivarius* forms a fructan from sucrose.

Str. mutans is saccharolytic, forming lactic, formic, and acetic acids from glucose under the conditions found in dental plaque and is able to sustain this acid production by utilization of both exogenous dietary carbohydrate sources and an intracellular polysaccharide.

Since the role of *Str. mutans* in caries was identified, control of caries through the use of dietary restriction of sucrose, chemotherapeutic methods, and by immunization has been attempted with varying degrees of success. The use of fluorides as a control measure is effective presumably because of two actions, the ability of fluoride to make enamel more resistant to acid dissolution and inhibition of metabolic pathways leading to acid production by the organisms.

Although less well studied than *Str. mutans*-induced caries, other viridans streptococci cause oral diseases. *Str. mitior* and *Str. sanguis*, for example, have been recovered from purulent oral lesions in high numbers, and *Str. milleri* is frequently recovered from dental abscesses and infected root canals. The oral origins of these organisms have been well documented in diseases outside the oral cavity, with *Str. sanguis*, *Str. mitior*, and *Str. mutans* frequently isolated from infective endocarditis and *Str. milleri* from brain abscesses.

Role in Atypical Pneumonia

A member of the *Str. mitis* group, *Str.* MG has often been found in the sputum of patients suffering from atypical pneumonia. Its pathogenic role is unclear because a quite distinct organism, *Mycoplasma pneumoniae*, has been shown to be the cause of most cases of this disease. Nevertheless, many people with previous mycoplasmal pneumonia develop serum agglutinins against *Str.* MG. This was once a routine test for atypical pneumonia but is falling into disuse because the simpler test for cold agglutinins is positive more often following mycoplasmal pneumonia and considerable overlap exists between the two tests. Thus little additional case-finding results from adding the MG agglutinin test to the already standard cold agglutination test.

THE PNEUMOCOCCI

Historical Note

These organisms were first isolated from human saliva by Sternberg in New York City in September 1880. Three months later in Paris, Pasteur also isolated the organism from saliva. Since Pasteur published his findings only a month later but Sternberg's article did not appear until April of 1881, the honor of prior discovery is generally accorded to Pasteur. In 1884 the studies of several microbiologists, including Fraenkel, Friedländer, and Weichselbaum, clearly linked these organisms to lobar pneumonia.

Later, experiments in transforming one type of pneumococcus to another were instrumental in proving the role of DNA in the transmission of genetic information. These began with the observations of Griffith in 1928 that showed that a crude extract of killed type III pneumococci could transform another strain to type III and culminated in the work of Avery, MacLeod, and McCarty, who demonstrated that the transforming material was in fact DNA.

General

The pneumococci were formerly referred to as *Diplococcus pneumoniae* but are now classified *Streptococcus pneumoniae*. They consist of α-hemolytic cocci, which in human infections are always encapsulated,

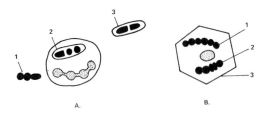

Fig. 18.2. Diagram of pneumococci in sputum (× 2000). A. Three chains of organisms associated with a neutrophil. (1) A triplet of organisms without a visible capsule but suggestive of *Str. pneumoniae* because of the shortness of the chain and the characteristic elongation of one cell prior to division, resulting in a dot-and-dash configuration; (2) within the leukocyte, a similar chain, with a capsule; (3) a classic encapsulated diplococcal form with bullet shaped cells arranged base to base. B. Viridans streptococci. (× 1500). They are recognizable by (1) their long chains, (2) occasional flat "abacus bead" forms, and their association with (3) polygonal epithelial cells, rather than with neutrophils.

although noncapsulated laboratory variants may occur. They are distinguished by their habit of forming short chains in infected tissues, usually composed of only two organisms, accounting for their previous designation as *Diplococcus*. In longer chains, which are more frequent in laboratory cultures, these organisms elongate before division, forming bacilluslike forms; while in the diplococcal form, seen in smears from infections, a characteristic bullet shape is usually seen, with the flat ends of the cocci opposed and the rounded or pointed ends facing away from one another.

These α-hemolytic organisms closely resemble the viridans group of streptococci. In the past their ability to ferment inulin was used to separate them from the latter group, which is generally inulin-negative. Unfortunately, the inulin reaction is not completely reliable for this purpose, since not all strains give the expected reaction; presently pneumococci are distinguished by their sensitivity to bile and to optochin. A neutral pH bile (either as a 10 percent solution or as a 1 percent solution of sodium deoxycholate or taurocholate) triggers autolysis of pneumococci, resulting in the complete clearing of a turbid suspension of the organisms. Bile impregnated discs are also available for use on agar plates, where pneumococci are recognized by the absence of growth near the discs. The organisms are also inhibited by ethylhydrocupreine hydrochloride, a substance known as *optochin*, and discs impregnated with this material are also available for use in an analogous manner to bile discs. In the preantibiotic era, when optochin was used therapeutically, occasional strains of pneumococci were noted to be resistant to the drug, and it is possible that such strains of the organism even now are mistaken for viridans organisms due to this resistance.

The organisms are surrounded by a well developed polysaccharide capsule, and in the presence of specific anticapsular serum, swelling of the capsule, the *Quellung phenomenon*, occurs. Since there are more than 80 antigenic types of capsular substances, it is useful for routine identification of pneumococci to have a polyvalent serum containing antibodies against all capsular serotypes. This serum is available from the Danish State Serum Institute and is marketed as *Omniserum*. When this is mixed with a specimen of fresh sputum, the capsules of any pneumococci present swell, becoming refractile and glassy in appearance, a characteristic reaction.

In heavily infected fluids or tissues, capsular polysaccharide may be produced in such great abundance that it is secreted freely into the medium. Immunologic tests for this material using counter electrophoresis or similar assays have proven useful in demonstrating pneumococcal antigens in cerebrospinal fluid in cases of meningitis and in the sputum or even the blood in cases of pneumococal pneumonia.

The capsule is critical to the production of disease by these organisms; laboratory variant strains that have lost their ability to make capsules are nonpathogenic. These noncapsulated bacteria grow as rough colonies on agar, and it is these "rough" strains that were transformed to other types in the transformation experiments mentioned before.

A final characteristic of these organisms more interesting from a theoretical than a practical diagnostic viewpoint is the fact that regardless of capsular type all pneumococci contain an identical substance — the C polysaccharide — in their cell walls that is like the Lancefield substances extractable from β-hemolytic streptococci. In effect, the possession of this common C substance by all members of the species is equivalent to their constituting a specific Lancefield group of streptococci.

A β-globulin in human serum, the C-reactive protein, reacts with pneumococcal C substance to form a precipitate. It should be emphasized that this is a chemical reaction, rather than an antigen–antibody interaction. In infections and inflammatory states, the amount of C-reactive protein increases. Tests for this material in serum thus provide a sensitive indication of the degree of inflammation a patient is experiencing and are useful in following the progress of a variety of diseases, including rheumatic fever and osteomyelitis. For routine purposes, the C-reactive protein is conveniently detected by means of a precipitation test with an antiserum of rabbit origin.

Pneumococcal cell walls also contain M proteins, similar to those of group A streptococci. Their role in disease is obscure, but it is known that immunity to pneumococcal infection is entirely dependent on antibodies directed against capsular polysaccharides, in contrast to the situation in group A organisms where type-specific antibodies to M proteins determine immunity.

The pneumococci require rich media for isolation; blood agar promotes their growth not only by providing complex nutritional factors but by supplying catalase. The latter is needed for their preservation and growth, since they generate hydrogen peroxide by their metabolism but lack the necessary enzymes for disposal of this material. A further refinement in culture of pneumococci consists of the addition of gentamicin to blood agar in a concentration of about 5 μg/ml. Since pneumococci are uniformly resistant to the aminoglycosides, the addition of this antibiotic inhibits competing microorganisms that might obscure a small number of pneumococcal colonies, resulting in a useful medium for studying the nasopharyngeal carrier state.

While most pneumococci are facultative aerobes, on occasion strains have been cultured from cases of human disease that are obligately anaerobic, the so-called paleopneumococci.

The biologic niche for pneumococci is the human nasopharynx. Once introduced there they persist for weeks to months resulting in an asymtomatic carrier state. Spread through families occurs and is facilitated by rhinovirus infections and similar factors. Under certain circumstances, such as during winter in crowded communities, the carrier rate may approach 70 percent, but usually it is below 25 percent. Thus pneumococcal disease may be considered to be an accidental phenomenon in which a commonly carried organism gains an opportunity to invade tissues because of an occurrence such as aspiration of pneumococcus-containing material, a viral respiratory infection to inflame the respiratory tree and interfere with normal defense mechanisms, or other temporary factors.

Pneumococcal toxins have been searched for to explain the obvious clinical toxicity of disease produced by these bacteria. While they are important in allowing infection to occur, capsular polysaccharides cannot be shown to be toxic in themselves. The α-hemolysin, called *pneumolysin*, has been purified; it is capable of causing some toxic manifestations in experimental animals, mainly by affecting their erythrocytes. An even more likely candidate for a toxic factor is a neuraminidase produced by the organism, which is profoundly toxic, even lethal, in mice. Further work is necessary to clarify the role of this substance in human disease.

Role in Pneumonia

Lobar Pneumonia. This form of infection is marked by a dramatic, sudden onset with chills, dyspnea, and cough. Infecting organisms in alveoli stimulate the outpouring of a wave of edema fluid that sweeps them through the pores of Cohn of adjacent aveoli, and the process stops only when the wave reaches fibrous septa, usually those between major lung lobes. This accounts for the lobar distribution of the infection. At other times, the presence of marked septation between lobules may produce lobular disease rather than complete lobar involvement.

The pneumococci are the most common cause of lobar pneumonia, and this infection is the most important disease caused by them. Over 50 percent of pneumonia in the adult population of the United States is caused by types 1, 2, and 3; in children type 14 is most frequent. Three factors are involved in the production of lobar pneumonia: there must be a nasopharyngeal carrier state for pneumococci, there must be a deficiency of specific circulating antibody against the capsular type being carried, and finally, there must be some accidental factor such as exposure to alternate chilling and warmth, a viral infection, or aspiration of pneumococci to precipitate the disease. Once pneumococci have become lodged in alveoli, edema fluid forms and spreads the infection as described above. During this phase of invasion, the patient has a chill that may resemble malaria in its severity.

Since the disease spreads from the hilar area outwards and may not have yet reached the peripheral area of the lung, physical signs in the involved lobe may be lacking for awhile. Ultimately, the process reaches the pleural surface and chest pain with aveolar rales develops.

In the preantibiotic era the patient remained gravely ill with a consolidated lobe until the crisis occurred. At this time, flushing and sweating occurred with a rapid fall of temperature to normal and disappearance of toxicity, followed by signs of clearing of the pneumonia. It is interesting that the crisis occurred when production of specific anticapsular antibodies had reached the point where they were beginning to appear as excess free antibody in the serum; this suggested that the crisis was brought about by an immunologic mechanism. This idea was reinforced by the finding that the intravenous administration of antiserum could produce the crisis by itself. In the antibiotic era, crisis is not often seen in lobar pneumonia; instead the resolution of fever by lysis over 24 to 48 hours is more common following the institution of antibiotic therapy.

Lobar pneumonia may be complicated by a pleural effusion that is usually sterile but occasionally is infected, leading to empyema. If the effusion is large, a diagnostic tap will help in differentiating the two conditions: a clear fluid not infected by organisms demonstrable in Gram stain or culture and with few white cells implies a benign effusion that needs to be completely drained only if it is prolonging the fever; on the other hand, a purulent effusion containing pneumococci represents empyema and demands surgical drainage.

The diagnosis of pneumococcal lobar pneumonia is made by the Gram stain and Quellung reaction on expectorated sputum, by culture of the sputum, and by blood culture, which may be positive in one-fourth to one-third of cases if examined early in their course.

Bronchopneumonia. In bronchopneumonia, organisms are not swept from alveolus to alveolus through the pores of

Cohn but instead set up a bronchiolitis with penetration of adjacent tissue to involve the interstitium and parabronchiolar alveoli. The disease is less dramatic in its onset and resolution and tends to occur at extremes of life, thus involving children and the elderly. The physical and radiographic findings are those of a patchy, generally bilateral, and usually basilar pneumonia.

This form of pulmonary infection is often caused by pneumococci, especially when it occurs in elderly people as a complication of viral infection or of preexisting chronic heart or lung disease. Conditions such as mitral stenosis that produce chronic congestion of the lungs and moist alveoli predispose the patient to pneumococcal bronchopneumonia. Because of this, immunization against pneumococci is an important feature of management of these individuals.

Meningitis

Pneumococcal meningitis can attack at any age and can occur without an apparent primary focus or may follow obvious infections such as otitis media, mastoiditis, or pneumonia. Meningitis due to this organism is marked by the rapid onset of somnolence leading to coma without an intervening maniacal phase as often seen in meningococcal disease. Pneumococcal infection is noted for the thick exudate that forms about the base of the brain, often trapping cranial nerves during the phase of healing and fibrous organization, and for this reason some clinicians use corticosteroids in order to minimize the inflammatory component and prevent later cranial nerve involvement.

Other peculiarities of pneumococcal meningitis are its appearance at times in alcoholics without an obvious primary focus and with minimal prodromal signs and the important role that these organisms play in recurrent episodes of meningitis associated with cerebrospinal fluid leaks. The episodes

of meningeal infection in the latter situation may be extraordinarily rapid in onset and usually are due to pneumococci.

Diagnosis of pneumococcal meningitis is made by culture of the cerebrospinal fluid on blood agar. A simultaneous blood culture should also be done, since bacteremia may coexist. In heavy infections, direct smears of the spinal fluid often reveal the organism after Gram staining. In less severe infections, the organisms may not be seen but the disease may be diagnosed promptly if counterelectrophoresis is performed. In this case the production of a line of precipitate with the spinal fluid by antipneumococcal serum reveals the pneumococcal etiology of the infection.

Pneumococcal Bacteremia

As mentioned before, bacteremia occurs in a significant number of cases of lobar pneumonia, and this seeding of the bloodstream at the onset of the pulmonary infection is responsible for such metastatic suppurative complications as meningitis and septic arthritis. Occasionally pneumococcal bacteremia occurs without an obvious primary focus, producing a septicemic clinical picture with a positive blood culture. If such cases are carefully examined it is often possible to conclude that a pneumococcal infection of an accessory air space of the upper respiratory tract (a sinus, middle ear, or mastoid air cell) was probably the focus of the septicemia. In children younger than 2 years, cellulitis of the medial gingiva over the posterior maxillary teeth can result in pneumococcal bacteremia. Swelling of the involved area spreading onto the hard palate is seen and frequently ulceration occurs later.

Bacteremia in the Asplenic Host. Loss of splenic function by surgical removal or by atrophy of the organ as in sickle cell disease predisposes the patient to a fulminant, often rapidly fatal, pneumococcal bacteremia. While this catastrophe can happen any time following loss of splenic function for any reason, it appears most often in children under the age of 5 years, during the first few years following loss of the spleen, and in those whose spleens were removed intact (generally for hematologic reasons such as hereditary spherocytosis) in contrast to those in whom removal was done for traumatic rupture. The relative protection afforded by splenic rupture is due to spillage of spleen cells into the peritoneal cavity at the time of rupture. When this occurs, half the patients will subsequently regenerate nodules of splenic tissue from peritoneal implantation of the spilled material, a condition known as splenosis. The regenerated splenic tissue provides some protection against bacteremia, a protection which does not happen after removal of the intact, unruptured organ.

The asplenic individual is not only at risk of fulminant septicemia due to pneumococci, but other encapsulated organisms such as *Haemophilus influenzae* may cause similar rapidly progressive infections. When spleen function has been lost through repeated infarctions and atrophy as in sickle cell anemia, the situation is compounded by a defect in the alternate pathway of complement activation, the properdin system, resulting in an aggravation of the risk of rapidly fatal septicemia.

Waterhouse-Friderichsen Syndrome. This disorder, a combination of shock, vascular injury, and activation of clotting with consumption of coagulation factors, is classically produced by meningococcal septicemia. On occasion, other organisms may initiate this syndrome with its characteristic cardiovascular collapse, bleeding, and skin petechiae or ecchymoses, and the pneumococci are the second most common cause of this syndrome after the meningococci.

Septicemia of the Newborn. Rarely, pneumococcal septicemia of the newborn may occur due to organisms acquired from the mother's vagina, and syndromes similar to the more common newborn infections

produced by group B β-hemolytic streptococci may be seen.

Miscellaneous Purulent Local Diseases

Endocarditis. In the preantibotic era about 15 percent of cases of endocarditis were due to the pneumococci. With the introduction of penicillin, this frequency has fallen and now fewer than 3 percent of cases are due to this organism. Despite its declining frequency, the disease remains important because of its high fatality rate even when correct antibiotic treatment is used. This form of endocarditis is acute, ulcerative, and rapidly destroys valves, and this accounts for the high fatality.

Peritonitis. Patients with preexisting ascites can develop spontaneous peritonitis as a result of implantation of blood-borne organisms in the peritoneal cavity. In children with ascites due to the nephrotic syndrome, this type of peritonitis is commonly caused by pneumococci. Patients with ascites due to Laennec's cirrhosis are also subject to spontaneous bacterial peritonitis, and although in this condition the usual organisms are staphylococci or gram-negative enteric rods, pneumococcal peritonitis also occurs.

Periorbital Cellulitis in Children. Both *Str. pneumoniae* and *H. influenzae* are capable of producing facial cellulitis in children before the age of 5 years. The site of entry is usually a sinus from which extension to the orbital and periorbital areas occurs. In cellulitis due to these organisms a peculiar violet discoloration of the involved area is characteristic and distinguishes this form of the disease from the more common facial cellulitis caused by hemolytic streptococci.

Pericarditis. During the course of lobar pneumonia a purulent pericarditis may occur. While dissemination to the pericardium via the bloodstream is possible, the disease usually spreads by extension from a contiguous area of lung, as shown by the fact that it occurs most often in pneumonia involving the left lower lobe, which is in intimate contact with the pericardium.

Bone and Joint Infections. A painful, monarticular, purulent arthritis often involving a large joint may occcur as a complication of known bacteremic pneumococcal disease such as pneumonia or it may occur spontaneously; in young children, cases of actual osteomyelitis due to pneumococci occur as well as septic arthritis.

Gastrointestinal Tract Involvement. During the course of pneumococcal bacteremia, the digestive tract may become infected, causing a pneumococcal diarrhea manifested by dysentery with the organisms in pure culture in the stool. A rare involvement of the digestive tract is diffuse, errosive, phlegmonous gastritis. This is associated with epigastric pain (which is diminished by rising into a seated posture), severe tenderness in the central epigastrium, and gastrointestinal bleeding. The condition will probably be recognized with increasing frequency now that endoscopy has become routinely available. When it is found, emergency gastric resection should be considered, since the disorder is usually fatal, even with appropriate treatment.

Upper Respiratory Tract Infections. In young children including the newborn, pneumococci are an important cause of severe laryngitis, otitis, sinusitis, and infection of the mastoid air spaces.

Prevention and Treatment of Pneumococcal Diseases

As mentioned above there are more than 80 capsular serotypes of pneumococci, and immunity to pneumococcal diseases depends on the presence of specific anticapsular antibody. Therefore vaccination against pneumococcal disease would require more than 80 antigens. Fortunately, however, 14 capsular types — 1, 2, 3, 4, 6, 8, 9, 12, 14, 19, 23, 25, 51, and 56 — account for about two-thirds of bacteremic pneumococcal infections in adults, and a vaccine containing the polysaccharide capsular substances of these types is commercially available. It is recommended for those at high risk of developing serious pneumococcal disease — such as asplenic individuals, the elderly, and those with cardiac or pulmonary disease — and has been successful in lowering morbidity and fatality from pneumococcal infection in these groups.

When using the vaccine one should keep a few points in mind. First, as with any polysaccharide vaccine, repeated administration in high doses may cause accumulation of polysaccharide in macrophages, resulting in immunologic paralysis rather than heightened immunity. Therefore the recommended dosage should not be exceeded and repeat inoculations should not be given at short intervals. Presently it is believed that booster injections are not required until at least 5 years after the initial one. Secondly, children under 2 years of age do not produce much antibody after the vaccine, and it is best to defer inoculation until after this age in order to achieve maximum benefit. Finally, some of the individuals who need the vaccine most, such as children with sickle cell anemia, are poor producers of antipneumococcal antibody following inoculation.

With few exceptions, pneumococci in the United States are extremely sensitive to penicillin. Although there has been a slight loss of penicillin sensitivity since the introduction of the drug, still practically all organisms are inhibited by a few tenths of a $\mu g/ml$. In the patient who is allergic to penicillin, erythromycin or clindamycin are reliable, although resistant strains occur occasionally. The tetracyclines are less reliable, and up to one-sixth of the pneumococcal strains tested have shown resistance.

The appearance of absolutely penicillin-resistant pneumococci in certain areas of the world has raised concern. These organisms were first noted in New Guinea, where penicillin was widely used in the treatment and prophylaxis of streptococcal and pneumococcal diseases. More recently, a strain has appeared in South Africa with multiple resistance to ordinary drugs, sensitive only to antibiotics not commonly used in pneumonia, such as rifampin, vancomycin, and fusidic acid. Whether these strains will occur in the United States and elsewhere or whether they will remain localized to the areas in which they arose is yet unknown.

ANAEROBIC STREPTOCOCCI

Microaerophilic Forms

A number of so-called anaerobic streptococci grow on first isolation only under reduced oxygen tension, forming small colonies. On repeated subcultures they become progressively tolerant to oxygen, finally producing large colonies under fully aerobic circumstances. After this has been accomplished, they may be found to correspond to well known, ordinary aerobic streptococci. These may be termed the *microaerophilic streptococci* and are found in a variety of infections stemming from foci involving the mouth, the bowel, or the female genital tract. One characteristic syndrome produced by them is chronic subcutaneous burrowing or undermining ulcer, which may follow contamination of an extremity wound or may occur in a wound of the trunk after intestinal surgery. At other times, the focus can be in a lesion in the anus or rectum with involvement of the buttock or thigh. An ulcer appears with undermined skin edges, and tracts burrowing from the undermined area penetrate to remarkable distances, emerging again at the surface to produce further undermined ulcers. Relentless progression of the untreated condition can undermine large areas of skin, finally resulting in sloughing and denudation.

Another characteristic lesion in which microaerophilic streptococci are involved is *postoperative bacterial synergistic gangrene.* This condition follows penetration of an area that harbors a mixture of organisms, such as drainage of putrid empyemas or abdominal abscesses. An infection then occurs due to a synergistic combination of microaerophilic streptococci with aerobes, usually *Proteus* or *Staphylococcus* spp. The lesion is not undermined as in burrowing ulcer but, on the contrary, is saucer shaped. Surrounding the necrotic center is a zone of dying tissue whose skin has a characteristic "suede leather" appearance. Around this is a zone of dusky erythema that is exquisitely tender, a diagnostic feature of the condition. Microaerophilic streptococci are found by injection and needle aspirations of the red advancing edge; the synergistic aerobes are more abundant in specimens taken from the necrotic center.

Truly Anaerobic Streptococci

Truly anaerobic streptococci have been grouped into the genus *Peptostreptococcus*, of which there are at least six species. These tend to grow as single cells, double cells, or short chains of organisms in tissues. Because their counterparts, the microaerophilic staphylococci, also tend to grow in small groups under the same circumstances, direct Gram-stained smears taken from infected areas usually are not reliable for revealing the difference between anaerobic streptococcal and staphylococcal infections. In culture the organisms produce large characteristic chains or clusters, respectively, and this allows easier morphologic differentiation.

The assignment of peptostreptococci to individual species may be done in a number of ways, but present practice is to distinguish them on the basis of gas chromatographic patterns of the volatile substances produced by their growth. About half of these organisms have a sharp, pungent odor that suggests their presence clinically, since anaerobic staphylococci usually have a foul fecal or petroleumlike odor.

Anaerobic streptococci inhabit the mouth and may produce infection after dental or oral surgery, such as tonsillectomy. They may also spread into the accessory cavities of the respiratory tract such as the sinuses, middle ears, or mastoids and by extension along veins may enter the cranial cavity to produce brain abscess. In the latter situation they usually are members of a mixed bacterial flora together with aerobes.

The organisms also live in the lower digestive tract and the female urogenital tract, where they participate in mixed bacterial infections that originate in these areas (e.g., pelvic and intraabdominal abscesses, pelvic inflammatory disease and liver abscess).

Because they are present in the oral cavity they are an important member of the group of mouth bacteria that produce serious complications following human or animal bites or hand injuries resulting from delivery of a blow to the mouth.

Treatment

The anaerobic and microaerophilic streptococci are uniformly sensitive to penicillin and are nearly uniformly sensitive to clindamycin and erythromycin. They are not regularly sensitive to the tetracyclines. Among the cephalosporins, they tend to be resistant to the parent compound, cephalothin, but sensitive to newer members of the series, including cefamandole and cefoxitin.

REFERENCES

Anderson, C.B., Marr, J.J. and Jaffe, B.M.: Anaerobic streptococcal infections simulating gas gangrene. Arch. Surg. *104*: 186, 1972.

Austrian, R. and Gold, J.: Pneumococcal bacteremia with especial reference to bacteremic pneumococcal pneumonia. Ann. Intern. Med. *60*: 759, 1964.

Beaty, H.N., Turck, M., and Petersdorf, R.G.: Ampicillin in the treatment of enterococcal endocarditis. Ann. Intern. Med. *65*: 701, 1966.

Collins, R.N. and Nadel, M.S.: Gangrene due to the hemolytic streptococcus — A rare but treatable disease, N. Engl. J. Med. *272*: 578, 1965.

Dorff, G.J., Coonrod, J.D., and Rytel, M.W.: Detection by immunoelectrophoresis of antigen in sera of patients with pneumococcal bacteraemia. Lancet *1*: 578, 1971.

Gibbons, R.J. and van Houte, J.: Selective bacterial adherence to oral epithelial surfaces and its role as an ecological determinant. Infect. Immun. *3*: 567, 1971.

Gopal, V. and Bisno, A.L.: Fulminant pneumococcal infections in "normal" asplenic hosts. Arch. Intern. Med. *137*: 1526, 1977.

Hoppes W.L. and Lerner, P.I.: Nonenterococcal group-D streptococcal endocarditis caused by streptococcus bovis. Ann. Intern. Med. *81*: 588, 1974.

Jacobs, M.R., Koornhof, H.J., Robins-Brown, R.M., et al.: Emergence of multiply resistant pneumococci. N. Engl. J. Med. *299*: 735, 1978.

Mannik, M., Baringer, J.R., and Stokes, J., III: Infections due to group B beta-hemolytic streptococci. Report of three cases and review of the literature. N. Engl. J. Med. *266*: 910, 1962.

Merrill, C.W. Gwaltney, J.M., Handley, J.O., and Sunde, M.A.: Rapid identification of pneumococci: Gram stain vs. the Quellung reaction. N. Eng. J. Med. *288*: 510, 1973.

Miller, J.M.: Prophylaxis of rheumatic fever and rheumatic heart disease. N. Eng. J. Med. *260*: 220, 1959.

Peter, G. and Smith, A.L.: Group A streptococcal infections of the skin and pharynx. N. Engl. J. Med. *297*: 311; 365, 1977.

Roy, S.B., Sturgis, G.P., and Massell, B.F.: Application of the antistreptolysin-O titer in the evaluation of joint pain and the diagnosis of rheumatic fever. N. Engl. J. Med. *254*: 95, 1956.

Standiford, H.D., de Maine, J.B., and Kirby, W.M.M.: Antibiotic synergism of enterococci. Arch. Intern. Med. *126*: 255, 1970.

Lennette, E.H., Balows, A., Hausler, W.J., Jr., and Truant, J.P., Eds.: Manual of Clinical Microbiology, 3rd Ed. American Society for Microbiology, Washington, D.C., 1980

Rogolsky, M.: Nonenteric toxins of *Staphylococcus aureus*. Microbiol. Rev. *43*: 320, 1979.

Schlessinger, D., Ed.: Microbiology—1975. American Society for Microbiology, Washington, D.C., 1975.

Yotis, W. W., Ed.: Recent advances in staphylococcal research. Ann. N. Y. Acad. Sci. *236*: 1, 1974.

19

Introduction to the Enterobacteriaceae

Eugene A. Gorzynski and Erwin Neter

The *Enterobacteriaceae* comprise an extraordinarily large family of bacteria. The name is appropriate because some members, such as *Escherichia coli*, are normal inhabitants of the intestinal tract of all mammals and because others, such as those of the genera *Shigella* and *Salmonella*, are enteric pathogens. Certain important features are common to all members, such as cell structure, growth characteristics, enzymatic activities, and even antigenic determinants. The members of the family are gram-negative, non–acid-fast rods (0.5 by 3.0 μm). If motile, the organisms have peritrichous flagella. Certain members (klebsiellae) possess capsules; none form spores. They grow either aerobically or anaerobically; glucose is fermented with the production of acid or acid and gas, and many members ferment other substrates as well. The organisms are oxidase-negative and, with rare exceptions, catalase-positive. Most members reduce nitrates to nitrites. As far as the DNA is concerned, G + C content ranges from 39 to 59 mole percent. Cell wall consists of, among other substances, lipopolysaccharide, protein, lipopro-

tein, lipid, and peptidoglycan. A common antigen has been described that is present in essentially all smooth strains of the family.

The lipopolysaccharide portion of the cell wall has been studied extensively both biologically and biochemically. Chemically, it consists of a core polysaccharide, lipid A, and sugar moieties that characterize the S forms. It is the polysaccharide side chains that endow the lipopolysaccharide molecules with the O specificity of the various types and groups of *Enterobacteriaceae*. Loss of these side chains results in conversion from the S (smooth) to the R (rough) form. R forms may have, additionally, deletions' of parts of the core polysaccharide (Fig. 2.14). As endotoxin, lipopolysaccharide produces an extraordinary large number of biologic effects, including fever, alterations of the hematopoietic system, limulus lysate gelation, changes in metabolism, nonspecific modulation of the immune system, the Shwartzman and Sanarelli phenomena, tumor necrosis, and death. The susceptibility to endotoxin varies from animal species to animal species; man is highly susceptible. These effects are largely due to the lipid A component. Since lipid A is present in the R form, its endotoxicity is maintained.

Surface antigens on the bacterial cell play an important role in virulence and other phenomena. For example, the presence of certain surface antigens, referred to as K antigens, plays a key role in the attachment of bacterial cells to host cells, such as epithelial cells of the gastrointestinal or urinary tracts, and thus helps to initiate the pathologic process. Serologically, surface antigens, such as the Vi antigen, interfere with agglutination by antiserum against the O antigenic component. Heating of bacterial cells abolishes this agglutination inhibitory effect. It was previously assumed that the Vi antigen greatly contributes to virulence, hence its name. It is now known to have only a limited effect, notably in *Salmonella typhi* infection. Motile strains are characterized by the respective protein antigens of the flagella (H antigens). As discussed in the section dealing with salmonellae, the antigenic makeup of the flagella may undergo genetically controlled changes, referred to as phase 1 and phase 2. The determination of the antigenic makeup of the flagella in the two phases permits serotype identification of the particular strain.

In addition to the above-mentioned variation, changes in the genetic makeup of *Enterobacteriaceae* may occur also due to the acquisition of DNA through transduction or conjugation. This genetic material may be integrated into the chromosome or replicate as a separate unit in synchrony with the chromosome; when separate, this genetic material is referred to as plasmid. Plasmids play important roles in enterobacterial infections, since they may code for antibiotic resistance and/or for the production of virulence factors, such as enterotoxin. The widespread occurrence of strains resistant to commonly used chemotherapeutic agents, including antibiotics, is largely associated with the presence of plasmids. Of great clinical significance is the fact that such plasmids may be transferred not only from strain to strain of the same species but also from one species to another. Plasmids may also code for the production of substances, the so-called *bacteriocins*, that may kill other microorganisms. These products may be used for typing purposes. Plasmids may also code for changes in metabolic activities; as a result, for example, salmonella strains may acquire the capacity to ferment lactose, complicating its identification when isolated from clinical specimens.

Enterobacteriaceae may be killed by commonly used methods, such as heat (e.g., pasteurization) and chlorination. These microorganisms are rather resistant to the action of bile salts; hence *S. typhi* may readily proliferate in the gall bladder, and culture media containing bile salts are widely used selectively to grow *S. typhi* (Ch. 16). Numerous antibiotics and other chemotherapeutic agents are effective against members of the family; however, the susceptibility pattern frequently varies from strain to strain, and it is for this reason that the determination of the antibiogram of a patient's isolate may guide the physician in the selection of the appropriate chemotherapeutic agent.

Various members of the family *Enterobacteriaceae* can be differentiated from each other on the basis of motility, growth factors and inhibitors, and biochemical activities. Numerous substrates (sugars, alcohols, etc.) are used to this end. Representative characteristics are presented in Table 19.1. It is important for the diagnostician to realize that all activities do not contribute to the same degree to identification of a strain isolated from a patient. Clearly, activities that occur in more than 95 percent of all isolates are more important than those that occur with lower frequency (e.g., 70 percent). Thus the percentages of positive reactions become important features for identification; for an ex-

Table 19.1 *Enterobacteriaceae*: Salient Characteristics of Genera

	Genus and Reactions											
Characteristics	Esch- erichia	Shi- gella	Salmo- nella	Kleb- siella	Entero- bacter	Ser- ratia	Proteus	Provi- dencia	Citro- bacter	Edward- siella	Edwinia	Yer- sinia
Motility	+/−	−	+	−	+/−	+	+	+	+	+	+	−
Oxidase	−	−	−	−	−	−	−	−	−	−	−	−
NO$_3 \rightarrow$ NO$_2$	+	+	+	+	+	+	+	+	+	+	+	+/−
Indole	+/−	−/+	−	−/+	−	−	+/−	+	+/−	+	−/+	−/+
Methyl red	+	+	+	−	d	−/+	+	+	+	+	−/+	+
Voges-Proskauer	−	−	−	+	d	+	−/+	−	−	−	+/−	−
Citrate	−	−	d	+	d	+	d	+	+	−	+/−	−
H$_2$S	−	−	+/−	−	−	−	+/−	−	+/−	+	+	−
Urease	−	−	−	−/(+)	d	d	+/−	−	d	−	−	+/−
KCN[1a]	−	−	−/+	+	+	+	+	+	+/−	−	−/+	−
Phenylalanine deaminase	−	−	−	−	−	−	+	+	−	−	−	−
Lactose	+	−[b]	−	+	d	+/−	−	−	d	−	+/−	−/+
Gas from glucose	+	−	+	+	+	−/+	d	d	+/−	+	−	−

Abbreviation used: +, ≥90 percent are positive; −, ≥90 percent are negative; +/−, majority are positive; −/+, majority are negative; (+) delayed positive; d, can be +, (+), or − depending on strain or species.
[a] Growth in KCN.
[b] *Shigella sonnei* is (+).

ample see Table 20.1. For further details, the interested reader is referred to the *Manual of Clinical Microbiology*, the volume by Edwards and Ewing entitled *Identification of Enterobacteriaceae* and to tables supplied by manufacturers of various test kits and semiautomated equipment. In addition, strains are identified on the basis of their antigenic structure, such as the K, O, or H antigens.

The clinical relevance of the family is evident from the following facts: (1) *E. coli* is responsible for infection of the urinary tract in many tens of thousands of patients a year; (2) approximately two million infections a year in the United States are caused by members of the genus *Salmonella*; (3) low virulence members of the family have become increasingly important as opportunistic pathogens in subjects with low resistance to infection (e.g., *Serratia marcescens*); and (4) *E. coli*, together with other species, is an important component of the normal intestinal flora and contributes to resistance of infection.

Recently, the family has been enlarged to include the genus *Yersinia*. Whereas one member, *Yersinia enterocolitica*, is indeed related to enteric disease, another member, *Yersinia pestis*, is totally different in its pathogenic potential.

Human infections by *Enterobacteriaceae* may be endogenous or exogenous in nature. Examples of endogenous infections, originating from the microbial flora of the patients themselves, are *E. coli* infection of the urinary tract and peritonitis following intestinal perforation. Examples of exogenous infections, caused by microorganisms acquired from outside, are typhoid fever, salmonella gastroenteritis, and nosocomial infections originating from other patients or the hospital environment.

Species of *Enterobacteriaceae* are not fastidious in their nutritional requirements; usually they grow well on simple culture media. Therefore growth and recovery of an enteric microorganism from a body site

normally sterile technically is not difficult. On the other hand, isolating a suspected enteric pathogen from a source, such as feces or respiratory secretions, that has its own microbial flora or a source that has been grossly contaminated may present a problem analogous to looking for a needle in a haystack. Under these conditions, special media or procedures must be used that suppress the growth of indigenous bacteria but favor the growth or survival of the pathogen in question. However, these media are of limited value if the source (i.e., body site) is contaminated with feces or has not been cleansed properly prior to the taking of the specimen. This is especially significant with specimens obtained from extraintestinal areas. For example, accepting the fact that 1 gram of feces contains about 10^{11} bacteria, contamination with as little as 1 ng will introduce about 100 bacteria. In less than 4 hours under appropriate conditions, this microbial population may increase 10- to 2000-fold. Clearly, this number of microorganisms may suppress or mask the presence of insidious causes of infection. Equally important, a clinician may start unnecessary or inappropriate therapy on the basis of laboratory data that do not discriminate between contaminant and pathogen. Independent of the source, specimens should be transported to the laboratory immediately after collection and processed as soon as practicable after receipt. Although methods for processing specimens vary from laboratory to laboratory, proper selection of adequate media and conditions of incubation are very important. It is fruitful to employ blood agar plates together with MacConkey or eosin methylene blue agar for specimens of extraintestinal origin and to use a variety of differential and selective media for feces. The subjects of specimen collection, transport, and cultural methods are addressed in Chapter 16.

Most media for enteric bacilli contain various acid–base indicators to reveal fermentation of the carbohydrate lactose. The majority of enteric microorganisms normally present in fecal material will ferment lactose; intestinal pathogens usually do not. This is only a provisional aid, since strain variation within species does occur. After a suspected enteric bacterium is isolated, oxidase and nitrate reduction tests should be performed; all species of *Enterobacteriaceae* are oxidase-negative, and very few fail to reduce nitrate to nitrite. The latter are screening tests that help save much time and labor spent needlessly pursuing the identity of a microorganism that except for peripheral similarities is not a member of the family *Enterobacteriaceae*. A few of the characteristics that distinguish the genera of this family are shown in Table 19.1.

After preliminary identification, additional biochemical tests are required for accurate determination of species. Major or characteristic reactions, as applicable, are covered under the specific genera discussed in the two succeeding chapters. Briefly, species identification may be accomplished with as few as two or three tests or may require analysis of many biochemical results. With conventional methods, the microbiologist employs time-consuming manipulative procedures. Within recent years diagnostic kits have become commercially available that allow for the performance of multiple tests in microtubes by one-step inoculation from a single bacterial colony on nutrient agar. Overall correlation between results of these tests and conventional tests is high, ranging between 93 and 98 percent.

It is important to emphasize that for treatment purposes identification of an enterobacterial isolate even to species level frequently is not necessary; subspeciation to serogroup or serotype level is rarely justified. The multiplicity of serogroups and serotypes within the family *Enterobacteriaceae* make complete characterization of all isolates both expensive and impractical. However, the cost may be justified as an aid in controlling nosocomial infections or outbreaks of disease such as salmonellosis. The serologic procedures available and relevant are addressed in the two succeeding chapters.

In certain enteric infections, notably in typhoid fever, the microbiologic diagnosis may be facilitated also by the documentation of a specific immune response, namely by means of the Widal test. This approach may be used also to provide suggestive evidence of the etiologic role of opportunistic pathogens, including many members of *Enterobacteriaceae*.

Depending upon the etiologic agents and the particular circumstances, prophylaxis of enterobacterial infections can be accomplished by vaccination, e.g., against typhoid fever; by sanitation of water (chlorination), milk (pasteurization), and other food; occasionally by antibiotic prophylaxis; and by numerous infection control procedures practiced in hospitals.

REFERENCES

Brenner, D.J., Farmer, J.J., Hickman, F.W., et al.: Taxonomic and nomenclature changes in *Enterobacteriaceae*. HEW Publication No. (CDC) 78-8356, Washington, D.C., 1977.

Buchanan, R.E. and Gibbons, N.E., Eds.: Bergey's Manual of Determinative Bacteriology. 8th Ed. Williams & Wilkins, Baltimore, 1974.

Edwards, P.R., and Ewing, W.H.: Identification of *Enterobacteriaceae*, 3rd Ed. Burgess Publishing Company, Minneapolis, 1972.

Lennette, E.H., Balows, A., Hausler, W.J., Jr., and Truant, J.P., Eds.: Manual of Clinical Microbiology. 3rd Ed. American Society for Microbiology, Washington, D.C., 1980.

Enterobacteriaceae I

Erwin Neter

ESCHERICHIA COLI

Escherichia coli shares many characteristics with the other members of the family *Enterobacteriaceae*. The genus name was coined to honor the discoverer of this microorganism, the pediatrician Escherich. The microorganism grows readily on ordinary culture media and, in addition, on selective culture media, notably MacConkey agar. This selective medium is widely used in diagnostic laboratories, since it favors the growth of many "enterics" and essentially prevents the growth of numerous other microorganisms, such as staphylococci. A somewhat similar medium is Endo agar. *E. coli* grows both aerobically and anaerobically. It produces acid and gas from numerous substrates, including glucose, lactose, and mannitol. Other characteristics are listed in Table 20.1. Antigenically, it is characterized by the presence of three major antigens: *H* or *flagellar antigen* in motile strains; *O antigen* of the lipopolysaccharide complex; and certain *surface* or *K antigens*. Unfortunately, these surface antigens are not homogeneous chemically, and some make up even anatomic structures, such as fimbriae, that play a significant role in the attachment of the microorganisms to host cells. Certain K antigens are polysaccharide in nature and may interfere with O agglutination.

So far as the clinical significance of *E. coli* is concerned, three major facts should be kept in mind: (1) the organism is a normal inhabitant of the large intestine in all mammals and contributes, either directly or indirectly, to health and resistance to infection; (2) certain strains of *E. coli* produce enteric illness and are referred to as *enteropathogenic* or *diarrheagenic*; and (3) *E. coli* frequently causes extraintestinal infections, notably of the urinary tract.

E. coli as Enteric Pathogen

Enteropathogenic E. coli. A few decades ago severe outbreaks of diarrheal disease occurred in nurseries, often associated with a high fatality rate. The disease affected otherwise healthy infants. Search for a known pathogen was fruitless until the association of the illness with serologically characterized strains of *E. coli* was recognized. Only relatively few among more than 140 serotypes were associated with this illness. In support of the assumption

Table 20.1.   Reactions of *Escherichia*, *Shigella*, and *Salmonella*

Test or Substrate	*Escherichia* Reaction	%+	*Shigella* Reaction	%+	*Salmonella* Reaction	%+
Indol	+	98.6	− or +	39.8	−	1.1
Methyl red	+	99.9	+	100	+	100
Voges-Proskauer	−	0	−	0	−	0
Simmon's citrate	−	0.2	−	0	d	80.1
Hydrogen sulfide (TSIA)	−	0	−	0	+	91.6
Urease	−	0	−	0	−	0
KCN	−	2.4	−	0	−	0.3
Motility	+ or −	69.1	−	0	+	94.6
Lysine decarboxylase	d	88.7	−	0	+	94.6
Arginine dihydrolase	d	17.6	− or (+)	9.5	+ or (+)	58.5
Ornithine decarboxylase	d	64.2	d	20	+	92.7
Phenylalanine deaminase	−	0	−	0	−	0
Gas from glucose	+	91.1	−[a]	2.1	+	91.9
Lactose	+	90.8	−[a]	0.3	−	0.8
Sucrose	d	48.9	−[a]	0.9	−	0.5
Mannitol	+	96.8	+ or −	80.5	+	99.7

Codes used: +, 90% or more positive in 1 or 2 days; −, 90% or more negative; + or −, majority positive; − or +, majority negative; d, different biochemical types [+, (+), −]; (+), delayed positive.

[a]Certain biotypes of *S. flexneri* 6 produce gas; *S. sonnei* cultures ferment lactose and sucrose slowly and decarboxylate ornithine.

(Adapted from Edwards, P.R. and Ewing, W.H.: Identification of *Enterobacteriaceae*. 3rd Ed. Burgess Publishing Company, Minneapolis, 1972.)

that these strains were indeed responsible for the illness were the following facts: (1) the particular strain usually was the predominant *E. coli* strain isolated from affected patients; (2) clinical illness occurred almost exclusively in infants and young children; (3) these strains were found much less frequently in healthy infants and older children or adults; (4) these serotypes are hardly ever found in extraintestinal infections; (5) appropriate chemotherapy resulted in clinical improvement and, when used prophylactically, in the termination of outbreaks; (6) a specific immune response to the corresponding O antigens was documented in some of these subjects; and (7) infection of volunteers resulted in mild illness and a specific immune response. Although highly suggestive, these facts do not prove beyond doubt the etiologic role of the serotypes nor do they explain the mechanism of pathogenicity.

It also became clear that some serotypes were far less contagious than others; thus, *E. coli* 026:60(B6) has been associated mainly with sporadic cases in contrast to *E. coli* 0111:58(B4) and 0127:71(B16), which were associated with large outbreaks. Among the more important serotypes are the following: 026:60(B6), 055:59(B5), 0111:58(B4), 0125:70(B15), 0126:71(B16), and 0127:63(B8). The first number refers to the O antigen, which may have a single or two antigenic determinants; the second number, followed by the designation in brackets, refers to the so-called K or surface antigen. The identification of a special K antigen referred to as B type does not necessarily indicate that it exists as a separate moiety. The strains are identified further on the basis of the flagellar or H antigens. Thus *E. coli* 055:59(B5), depending upon lack of H antigen (nonmotile) or the presence of H antigens 6 or 7, is designated as 055:59(B5):NM, 055:59(B5):6, or 055:59(B5):7. For further details refer to the volume by Edwards and Ewing. These serotypes of *E. coli* have been referred to as enteropathogenic *E. coli* (EEC).

During the past two decades these epidemics have either disappeared or become far less common, and the infection associated with the presence of these serotypes has become much milder. Accordingly, serotyping at the present time is not recommended as a routine procedure in the absence of epidemics, particularly since it does not identify those strains of *E. coli* whose pathogenic potential has been elucidated, the diarrheagenic strains.

Diarrheagenic E. coli. One mechanism whereby *E. coli* causes diarrheal disease was discovered following clarification of the pathogenesis of cholera. It was established that *Vibrio cholerae* produces clinical illness mainly through the production of enterotoxin. This enterotoxin has been purified and its mode of action elucidated. It causes fluid accumulation in the intestinal lumen through increase in intracellular cyclic AMP. This enterotoxin is antigenic and its toxicity can be abolished by specific antitoxin. A ganglioside of the host cells serves as its receptor. Subsequent studies have revealed that certain strains of *E. coli* produce a very similar enterotoxin. Since this enterotoxin is sensitive to elevated temperatures, it is referred to as *heat labile enterotoxin*. A plasmid is responsible for its production, implying that this genetic material can be transferred from one bacterial cell to another and even from one species to another; whether or not it was originally acquired from *V. cholerae* is of course not known.

Certain strains of *E. coli* produce a second enterotoxin, referred to as *heat stable enterotoxin*. It is smaller in size and antigenically distinct. It also produces the characteristic fluid accumulation within the intestinal lumen, but probably via accumulation of cyclic GMP. Enterotoxigenic

strains of *E. coli* produce either the heat labile or the heat stable enterotoxin or both.

Although enterotoxins are produced more frequently by some serotypes of *E. coli* than by others, determination of the O and H antigens alone should not be taken as adequate evidence of enterotoxicity, except when patients are studied during epidemics. It has been clearly established that the above-mentioned enteropathogenic strains of *E. coli* are not necessarily identical with enterotoxic and enteroinvasive strains. Finally, certain strains of *E. coli* have the propensity to invade the mucous membrane of the intestinal tract, leading to diarrhea. For the sake of clarity, strains with these properties have been referred to as diarrheagenic *E. coli*.

Clinical illness due to strains producing enterotoxins or with enteroinvasive capacity has been documented in both children and adults, particularly in patients with traveler's diarrhea; it is not restricted to infants, and nursery epidemics have not been encountered.

For the detection of the enterotoxins, three major kinds of laboratory procedures are available — *in vivo*, cell culture, and immunologic tests. The first category is represented by the intestinal loop procedure carried out in the adult or infant rabbit or mouse, rabbit skin test, and by infection of animals, for examples, suckling pigs. The second category is exemplified by the Chinese hamster ovary, Y-1 (mouse adrenal tumor), and the Vero (green monkey kidney) cell tests. The third category comprises the radioimmunoassay (RIA) and the enzyme linked immunosorbent assay (ELISA), also referred to as enzyme immune assay (EIA). Detection of the heat stable enterotoxin can be accomplished by the rabbit ileal loop and infant mouse tests. The latter is considered to be more reliable than the former. Enteroinvasiveness can be detected experimentally by the application of the strains to the conjunctiva of guinea pigs (Serény test). Unfortunately, these tests are not available as routine procedures in most diagnostic laboratories. Recent observations indicate that *E. coli* enterotoxins may not be detected by conventional methods but can be identified by measuring water secretion during *in vivo* perfusion of the rat jejunum. Thus enterotoxin production may take place in strains that presently are considered as enterotoxin-negative. For this reason certain enteropathogenic strains may be reclassified in the future as toxigenic.

Surface or K antigens play a key role in the pathogenesis of enteritis. For example, in the porcine infection, absence of the K 88 antigen results in loss of pathogenicity even when enterotoxin is produced. Of further interest is the fact that immunization with the K 88 antigen results in protection against enterotoxin induced illness. In calves, ingestion of K antibodies through colostrum protects the newborn calf against experimental enterotoxic colibacillosis. As yet, these findings have not found application for the prevention of illness in man.

Extraintestinal *E. coli* infections

E. coli is responsible for numerous kinds of extraintestinal infections. Particularly important are those of the urinary tract, including cystitis, pyelonephritis, and asymptomatic bacteruria. The last is characterized by lack of evidence of infection other than the presence in the urine of *E. coli* (or other potential pathogens) in significant numbers (10^5 or more organisms per ml). Other infections include peritonitis, particularly following perforations (e.g., appendicitis, trauma), septicemia, meningitis, pneumonia, prostatitis, and abscesses in many parts of the body. Certain serogroups of *E. coli*, such as 04, 06, and 07, but not the enteropathogenic ones, are encountered with undue frequency. In fact, some 10 serogroups out of more than 140 account for roughly 50 percent of extraintestinal in-

fections. The precise mechanisms whereby these strains produce extraintestinal infection is not entirely clear, but attachment of the bacteria to host cells may play a significant role. The diagnosis of extraintestinal infections is made by the bacteriologic examination of appropriate specimens, such as urine, blood, pus, and spinal fluid.

With regard to urinary tract infection, care must be taken in the procurement of voided urine lest contamination from the urethra complicate interpretation of the results. It has been established that in infection voided urine usually contains 10^5 or more microorganisms per ml. The large number of bacteria present is due to the fact that urine is an excellent culture medium. When urine from a patient with infection remains in the bladder for some hours, rapid multiplication of the microorganisms occurs, accounting for the fact that usually more than 10^5 cells/ml are present. In contrast, when sterile urine from a person free of infection passes through the urethra, it may become contaminated by the normal flora, but the number of microorganisms is low, usually less than 10^3/ml. Urine obtained by catheterization or suprapubic aspiration may be examined when voided urine yields unclear results. Quantitation can be established by a variety of methods, including the use of special bacteriologic loops, delivering 0.01 or 0.001 ml. Local production of antibodies of several immunoclasses (IgG, IgM, and/or IgA) is seen more frequently in patients with pyelonephritis than in those with cystitis. If at the time of antibody production the infecting strain of the same antigenic specificity is still present in the urine, antibodies become attached to the surface of the bacterial cells and can be demonstrated by the FA technique, using antibodies to human immunoglobulin. It must be kept in mind that some patients with lower tract infection have antibody coated bacteria in the urine and others with upper tract infection do not. Determination of microbial susceptibility to chemotherapeutic agents, including antibiotics, frequently is helpful to the clinician in the selection of appropriate specific therapy.

SHIGELLA

Shigella is another genus of microorganisms belonging to the family *Enterobacteriaceae*. The members of this genus are responsible for bacillary dysentery, or shigellosis.

Historical Background

In 1875 Loesch discovered the protozoan *Entamoeba histolytica* as the causative agent of amebic dysentery. Some 20 years later the Japanese microbiologist Shiga, investigating causes of dysentery, discovered a bacillus which bears his name, the Shiga bacillus. That this microorganism is in fact the causative agent of the disease was supported by the observation that serum of patients following recovery from the illness specifically agglutinated this microorganism. During the following years other members of the group were discovered, namely, the Flexner, Boyd, and Sonne bacilli; all are responsible for shigellosis. The genus was named *Shigella* to honor its discoverer.

The Genus *Shigella*

Members of the genus have the characteristics of the family *Enterobacteriaceae* but differ from other genera of this family (Table 20.1). Briefly, the microorganisms are nonmotile, gram-negative rods that grow readily under both aerobic and anaerobic conditions. The organisms produce acid from glucose and some genus members produce acid from other substrates as well. The microorganisms are agglutinated by the corresponding antibodies that differentiate the various species and serotypes. The characteristics of these microorganisms are summarized in Table 20.2.

The four major groups of microorganisms can be differentiated from each other on the basis of biochemical activities and O antigenic characterization. Thus subgroup A, *Shigella dysenteriae*, fails to attack mannitol and lactose; subgroup B, *Shigella flexneri*, and subgroup C, *Shigella boydii*, produce acid from glucose and mannitol but not from lactose; and subgroup D, *Shigella sonnei*, produces acid from all three substrates, mannitol, lactose, and glucose. On the basis of additional biochemical activities and, more importantly, on the basis of antigenic structure, subgroup A is divided into 10 serotypes, subgroup B into 6 serotypes, and subgroup C into 15 serotypes. Changes in classification, particularly as re-

Table 20.2.   Major Biochemical Reactions of Members of the Genus *Shigella*

Test or Substrate	S. dysenteriae	S. flexneri 1 to 5	S. flexneri 6	S. boydii	S. sonnei
Indole	− or +	+ or −	−	− or +	−
Ornithine decarboxylase	−	−	−	−	+
Gas from glucose	−	−	− or +	−	−
Lactose	−	−	−	−	d
Mannitol	−	+	+ or −	+	+
β-Galactosidase	− or +	−	−	− or +	+

Codes used: +, 90% or more positive within 1 or 2 days; −, 90% or more negative; − or +, most strains negative, some positive; + or −, most strains positive, some negative; d, different reactions [+, (+), −]).

(Adapted from Lennette, E.H., Balows, A., Hausler, W. Jr., and Truant, J.P., Eds.: Manual of Clinical Microbiology. 3rd Ed. American Society for Microbiology, Washington, D.C, 1980.)

lated to the genetic characteristics of various strains, may be anticipated.

Smooth, virulent strains form translucent colonies. As with other bacteria, mutants may arise with loss of virulence. Certain nonvirulent strains form opaque colonies.

Since the members of the genus *Shigella* are nonmotile bacteria, thus differing from those of the genus *Salmonella*, H antigens are not present. In accord with the other members of the family *Enterobacteriaceae*, lipopolysaccharides characterize the O antigens of the various members, the polysaccharide side chains determining the antigenic specificity. Loss of these structures leads to the emergence of antigenically rough (R) strains. Pathogenicity is lost, although endotoxicity remains unaltered.

Shigellosis

Shigellosis refers to any and all infections caused by members of the genus *Shigella* or, in a more restrictive sense, to bacillary dysentery only. This infection affects mostly the colon, producing clinical pictures from mild to severe colitis; subclinical infection also occurs. Depending on the pathologic process, frank blood, leukocytes, and/or mucus are present in the feces. When medical care is not readily available, shigellosis may be associated with a significant fatality rate, notably in children. Such was the case a decade ago during an epidemic in Central America.

Shigellosis is a worldwide disease and still occurs even in countries with advanced sanitation and medical care. In the United States some 13,000 to 22,000 cases are reported on an annual basis to the Center for Disease Control. Clearly, this figure does not include many patients with mild infection or subjects whose medical care does not include appropriate cultural examination. Statistical data suggest that this infection was encountered somewhat less frequently during the years 1975 to 1977 than during 1972 to 1974. Clinical illness is encountered far more frequently in young children than in older children or adults, the highest frequency occurring in children between 1 and 3 years of age.

All members of the genus *Shigella* are potential pathogens. However, for reasons that are not entirely clear *S. sonnei* infection is far more common in the United States than shigellosis by the other members; *S. flexneri* infection is the second, *S. boydii* the third, and *S. dysenteriae* the fourth and last in frequency. In striking contrast, *S. flexneri* is more commonly encountered in some countries of Asia than is *S. sonnei*. The reasons for these differences are unexplained.

Dysentery bacilli possess the intrinsic capacity to invade the mucous membrane of the gut. Evidence is provided by the fact that this property can be transferred experimentally to noninvasive microorganisms, such as *E. coli*, through genetic manipulation. Surprisingly few bacterial cells of a virulent strain (a few hundred) suffice to produce clinical illness in human volunteers. Several experimental models have been used for the study of the pathogenic activities of shigellae, such as oral infection of monkeys and starved guinea pigs, infection of the eye resulting in keratoconjunctivitis of the guinea pig, and infection of tissue culture cells. The particular nature of the invasive factor, however, has not been fully elucidated.

It has been known for many years that the classical Shiga bacillus produces an exotoxin that is lethal to the mouse and is considered to be a neurotoxin. Patients with Shiga bacillus infection produce antibodies to the neurotoxin. A toxin similar to the neurotoxin of the Shiga bacillus has been demonstrated in strains of other *Shigella* species. Products of shigellae with cytotoxicity for HeLa cells and enterotoxicity in the rabbit ileal loop test have been identified. Their role in human shigellosis remains moot.

The incubation period of shigellosis is rather short, usually less than 4 days; the range is from 1 to 7 days.

Shigellae, almost without exception, cause natural disease only in man and very rarely in other animals. For totally unexplained reasons, another important member of the family *Enterobacteriaceae*, *Salmonella*, is a pathogen for numerous animal species. The very factors responsible for these striking differences in the host-parasite relationship deserve study.

Shigellae are transmitted from person to person either directly or indirectly. Fecal material from patients and carriers represents the major source. Transmission may occur directly through manual contamination or indirectly through contaminated water, food, flies, etc. Common-source outbreaks have been associated with food-borne infections and water-borne disease due to inadequate chlorination of water. In the United States epidemics attracting the attention of public health officials are relatively rare; sporadic infections predominate. In the past, outbreaks of shigellosis have played havoc in institutions for mentally ill and other patients, and such epidemics have been referred to as asylum dysentery. Even today in the United States, outbreaks of shigellosis do occasionally occur in custodial institutions, such as child care centers. It must be kept in mind that epidemics occur occasionally, although they go unrecognized because the infection, particularly in older children and adults, may be so mild as not to attract medical attention; even when such patients are seen by physicians, cultural examination is usually not carried out. Evidence for the rather frequent occurrence of mild or subclinical infections in families in the presence of an overt case of shigellosis is based in part on the isolation of the microorganism from family members and, more incisively, on the basis of a definitive antibody response. In epidemiologic studies other tests can be utilized, such as bacteriophage typing.

Since shigellosis usually is a localized enteric infection, isolation and identification of the causative agent present in feces is the main approach to the etiologic diagnosis. Specimens should be seeded promptly or, when delay is inevitable, placed into a transport medium, such as buffered glycerol saline solution. Among the selective media favoring the growth of the pathogen in comparison to that of non-pathogenic enteric bacteria are SS (shigella-salmonella) agar, deoxycholate-citrate agar, and Hektoen agar. Less inhibitory enteric media include MacConkey, eosin methylene blue (EMB), and deoxycholate agars. One of the latter group of media is used in the event that a given strain does not grow well on the highly selective media. When the specimen is examined for the presence of all pathogens, other culture media are needed; for example, to detect *Staphylococcus aureus* blood agar or similar noninhibitory media should be employed. It is also advisable to use an enrichment medium, such as selenite broth, which, after incubation, is used for seeding of the above-mentioned agar media. Fishing of appropriate lactose-negative colonies should result in the procurement of pure cultures, which, in turn, are identified on the basis of motility, biochemical activities, and antigenic properties. Polyvalent antiserum may be used for tentative antigenic identification, followed by tests using monospecific antisera.

Strains differ in their susceptibility to various antibacterial agents. In fact, plasmid induced resistance to several antibiotics was discovered by Watanabe in Japan during a study of shigellosis. Thus determining the *in vitro* susceptibility of a given isolate from a patient serves as a valuable guide to chemotherapy, and such determinations are particularly important when one is dealing with outbreaks, both small and large.

A rise in the titer of antibodies specific for the particular serotype of *Shigella* can be demonstrated rather frequently. However, immunologic diagnosis, similar to the Widal test, is not employed routinely for the diagnosis of shigellosis.

Only rarely do shigellae cause extraintestinal infections, such as bacteruria, vaginitis, or bacteremia. For the microbiologic diagnosis, appropriate specimens (urine, pus, blood) are cultured.

Chemotherapy of bacillary dysentery has proved to be effective both clinically and bacteriologically. It is used in severe cases of shigellosis and whenever the carrier state should be eliminated for the control of outbreaks. The susceptibility to clinically available antibacterial agents, including antibiotics, may differ from strain to strain. Resistance to multiple antibiotics is due to the presence of R factors, that is, plasmids. Therefore *in vitro* susceptibility tests are indicated and serve as a guide to clinicians. Generally speaking, absorbable drugs are more effective than nonabsorbable agents. Among the compounds used with success are ampicillin, tetracycline, sulfonamides, chloramphenicol, and, most recently, trimethoprim/sulfamethoxazole. Even a single dose of tetracycline has proved to be effective in the treatment of shigellosis in adults.

A number of studies, both experimental and clinical, have been carried out on the possible effectiveness of a *Shigella* vaccine. Killed, attenuated, and antibiotic dependent strains and mutant hybrids were used. In view of the fact that in this country shigellosis is a mild disease and immunity would be type specific, active immunization of the population is neither indicated nor feasible.

SALMONELLA AND SALMONELLOSIS

Historical Comment

The genus *Salmonella* represents an important member of the family *Enterobacteriaceae*. The prototype, *Salmonella*

choleraesuis, was first described by the American bacteriologist Salmon, and the genus is named in his honor. Another member is responsible for typhoid fever, the etiologic agent having been discovered by Eberth.

General Characteristics and Classification

The members of the genus *Salmonella* are gram-negative motile rods that do not produce spores. The organisms grow readily on simple culture media. Enzymatically, they are endowed with the capacity to produce either acid and gas or acid from certain substrates, notably glucose, maltose, mannitol, but not from lactose and sucrose; they do not produce indol from tryptophan, and most strains produce H_2S (Table 20.1).

The classification of the members of this large genus is based largely on their antigenic makeup. Fundamentally, two major antigens are involved: the somatic or O antigen and the flagellar or H antigen. The O antigen is part of the cell wall lipopolysaccharide. This macromolecule is referred to, on the basis of other biological activities, as endotoxin. The serologic specificity is largely related to the polysaccharide moiety (side chain) and the endotoxic activity to the lipid A (Fig. 2.14). Antibodies may be directed against more than one antigenic determinant of the lipopolysaccharide. The H antigen is a protein present in the flagella of motile strains. A given strain may produce flagella of different composition at different times; this change is referred to as *phase variation*. The antigenic characterization of the two phases is used for classification of the strains. In addition to the O and H antigens, some members of the genus produce yet another important antigen, present on the surface of the bacterial cell. This antigen is referred to as *Vi antigen*, since it originally was considered to be a major determinant of virulence. Based on the characteristic polysaccharide or O antigens, the entire genus is divided into O groups: A, B, C, etc. Within each O group, members are classified further on the basis of their H antigens into serotypes (Table 20.3). This classification is frequently referred to as the *White-Kauffmann scheme*. Presently, some 1700 members are recognized, although only a small fraction plays the major role in human and animal disease.

In one classification, only three species are recognized: (1) *S. choleraesuis* as the prototype; (2) *Salmonella typhi* as the specific etiologic agent of typhoid fever; and (3) *Salmonella enteritidis* comprising all other members of the genus. Thus organisms are described as *S. enteritidis* ser. paratyphi, *S. enteritidis* ser. heidelberg, etc. (Table 20.3). Alternatively, all serotypes of the genus can be considered as species and referred to as *Salmonella paratyphi, Salmonella heidelberg*, etc. While the former classification is preferred and is used by the

Center for Disease Control, the latter nomenclature provides greater simplicity and will be used here, without implying species status for all serotypes.

Morphology and Growth Characteristics

The microorganism has peritrichous flagella (Figure 2.18A). Morphologically, it cannot be differentiated from other motile enteric bacteria. *Salmonella* strains grow readily in simple culture media, both aerobically and anaerobically, including infusion broth and nutrient agar. Characteristically, like other members of the family, the organisms also grow on selected media, such as MacConkey and Endo agars. These culture media also support the growth of *Escherichia, Klebsiella*, and other members of the family. More restrictive and selective culture media for growth of *Salmonella* are available, notably SS agar, Hektoen enteric agar, and others. Enrichment media, such as selenite broth and G-N broth, are used

Table 20.3. Antigenic Scheme of *Salmonella*

Species and Serotype		Group	O Antigens	H Antigens Phase 1	H Antigens Phase 2
S. enteritidis	bioser. paratyphi A	A	1, 2, 12	a	—
	ser. paratyphi B	B	1, 4, 5, 12	b	1, 2
	ser. saintpaul		1, 4, 5, 12	e, h	1, 2
	ser. typhimurium		1, 4, 5, 12	i	1, 2
	ser. heidelberg		1, 4, 5, 12	r	1, 2
S. choleraesuis		C_1	6, 7	c	1,5
S. enteritidis	ser. montevideo		6, 7	g, m, s	—
	ser. thompson		6, 7	k	1, 5
	ser. manhattan	C_2	6, 8	d	1, 5
	ser. newport		6, 8	e, h	1, 2
S. typhi		D	9, 12, Vi	d	—
S. enteritidis	ser. enteritidis		1, 9, 12,	g, m	—
	bioser. pullorum		9, 12	—	—
	ser. anatum	E_1	3, 10	e, h	1, 6

(Adapted from Edwards, P.R. and Ewing, W.H.: Identification of Enterobacteriaceae. 3rd Ed. Burgess Publishing Company, Minneapolis, 1972.)

in the diagnostic laboratory. The major characteristic enzymatic reactions are summarized in Table 20.1. Smooth (S) colonies may change to rough (R) colonies; biochemically this genetic change is associated with the loss of the characteristic O antigenic determinant. Intermediate forms exist, also. Since the loss of the O specific determinant or side chain leaves intact the lipid A portion of the endotoxic macromolecule, the toxicity of the LPS obtained from the R mutant is essentially identical with that from the S form. In addition to the endotoxin, some strains of *Salmonella* probably produce enterotoxin responsible for diarrhea. At the present time, information is not available why some strains, such as *S. typhi*, so frequently produce a unique systemic disease in man and others, such as *Salmonella typhimurium*, almost exclusively produce localized intestinal infection. Certainly, neither the known antigens nor the biochemical activities account for these striking differences.

Distribution of Salmonellae

A few members of the genus are host adapted. *S. typhi* is a pathogen for man only and *Salmonella gallinarum* for certain animals. Most of the other members are found in numerous animal species, including man, monkeys, cattle, pigs, dogs, cats, chicken, ducks, and flies. The reasons for these striking differences in host-parasite relationships are unknown.

S. typhi and Typhoid Fever

S. typhi. *S. typhi* has certain features that separate it from the other salmonellae. It does not produce gas from any of the substrates that are fermented with the production of acid, in contrast to almost all other members. Antigenically, it shares the O antigen of group D with some 60 other members. In addition to the 9,12 components of the O antigen, most strains also produce Vi antigen. Characteristically, the flagellar antigen (d) exists only in phase I (Table 20.3). Bacteriophage typing of Vi-positive *S. typhi* strains is of value in the study of the epidemiology of typhoid infections, particularly when relating a suspected source to given cases. More than 70 types have been identified. Among selective media, this microorganism grows on bismuth sulfite (Wilson-Blair) agar in addition to MacConkey and SS agars.

Typhoid Fever. *S. typhi* is the only causative agent of the clinical illness referred to as *typhoid fever*. The name of the illness is derived from one of the clinical features of the malady: stupor.

Since *S. typhi* essentially is a pathogen for man only, the infection arises from human subjects, either patients or carriers. The organism may be transmitted from person to person by contaminated hands or indirectly through contaminated food, flies, etc. When the organism is present in communal supplies, such as water or food, large-scale epidemics may arise. In the past such epidemics have contributed greatly to morbidity and mortality. Even in modern times and in countries with excellent sanitary facilities such outbreaks have occurred occasionally, such as the epidemics at Zermatt, Switzerland; Aberdeen, Scotland; West Germany; and Florida. Recently a widespread epidemic, probably the largest of this century, occurred in Central America, the problem being complicated by the fact that the strains were resistant to chloramphenicol. Today, in this country fewer than 500 cases a year are reported to the Center for Disease Control. Among these patients were medical technologists who acquired typhoid fever by inappropriate handling of proficiency test specimens.

In contrast to *Salmonella* gastroenteritis characterized by a short incubation period of several hours to a few days, the incubation period of typhoid fever is relatively long, usually between 1 and 3 weeks. The incisive effect of the infecting dose on the

Table 20.4. Infective Doses of *S. typhi* in Humans

Number of Microorganisms Swallowed	Number of Subjects	Percentage of Subjects With Illness
10^9	42	95
10^8	9	89
10^7	32	50
10^5	116	28
10^3	14	0

(Reprinted, by permission from Hornick, R.B., Greisman, S.E., Woodward, T.E., et al.: Typhoid fever: Pathogenesis and immunologic control. The New England Journal of Medicine, *283*: 686–691, 1970.)

development of clinical illness in man is clearly evident from the data shown in Table 20.4.

Following ingestion of viable typhoid bacilli, the organisms penetrate the wall of the small intestine, reach the regional lymph nodes, and subsequently invade the bloodstream; thus bacteremia is an early feature of the disease. The microorganisms then are seeded into various organs, including the small intestine (notably the Peyer's patches), skin, gall bladder, spleen, kidneys, and lungs. It is in the intestine that the major local pathologic changes occur, resulting in diarrhea and occasionally in hemorrhage or perforation. Dissemination to the kidneys and the lungs results in the presence of *S. typhi* in the urine and, less frequently, in sputum. When the corresponding antibodies are produced (see below), typhoid bacilli may be caught in capillaries of the skin as clumps, resulting in the development of a characteristic lesion, the rose spot.

Based on the above considerations of the illness, the microbiologic diagnosis becomes self-evident. Early in the course of typhoid fever, notably during the first week or 10 days, blood cultures should be obtained, which often reveal the presence of the pathogen. At this time cultures of

feces usually yield negative results. During the second week and later, blood cultures become negative and the microorganism can be recovered from the feces. In some patients, sputum and/or urine cultures are positive. In addition to the isolation and identification of *S. typhi*, the antibiogram should be determined. During the epidemic in Central America it became evident that this pathogen was resistant to chloramphenicol and/or other antibiotics of potential use in the treatment of this infection.

The diagnosis of typhoid fever can be made also on the basis of the specific immune response of the patient. Typically, antibodies are produced from the second week of illness on against both the O and H antigens of *S. typhi*. Thus an increase in the titers of antibodies of both specificities can be documented when early and later serum specimens are available. Alternately, titers exceeding those found in healthy individuals of similar age in the particular environment provide strongly suggestive evidence of the existence of the disease — the higher the titer, the more significant the result. The immunologic diagnosis of typhoid fever was first introduced by Widal; hence this test is referred to as the Widal test. For screening purposes the slide bacterial agglutination test is used. For a definitive result serial dilutions of serum are tested by means of the standardized agglutination test with formalinized suspensions of *S. typhi* for the detection of H antibodies and heat-killed suspensions for the titration of O antibodies. For the interpretation of the test it is important to keep in mind that patients with infection due to *Salmonella* group D, other than *S. typhi*, often produce O antibodies, but these subjects do not form the H antibodies characteristic of *S. typhi*. On the contrary, following immunization with typhoid vaccine (see below) antibodies against the H antigen of *S. typhi* may be present in elevated titers. Finally, it should be mentioned that chronic carriers often have antibodies against the Vi antigen in increased amounts in the blood. Vi anti-bodies may be quantitated by means of the bacterial agglutination or the passive hemagglutination test. For the former test, living or formalinized suspensions of a Vi-positive strain of either *S. typhi* or an unre-lated microorganism (e.g., *Citrobacter*) may be utilized. Supernates obtained from heat-ed Vi-positive cultures can be used in the hemagglutination test. Recent observations suggest that the fluorescent antibody test may be superior to the bacterial agglutina-tion procedure for the detection of carriers.

For the treatment of typhoid fever, chlor-amphenicol continues to be the drug of choice, provided that the strain is suscepti-ble. Alternatively, ampicillin and trimetho-prim-sulfamethoxazole have been used.

Prevention of typhoid fever rests largely on appropriate sanitary measures, including the provision of safe water (chlorination), milk (pasteurization), and other food. In addition, special care must be exercised for chronic carriers, and the isolation of pa-tients with typhoid fever is mandatory. The disease is reportable to the appropriate health authorities. Illustrative of the danger of the chronic carrier is Typhoid Mary, who, many years ago, went from family to family as a servant and became responsible for numerous cases of typhoid fever.

Unfortunately, a highly effective method for the elimination of the chronic carrier state is not available. Ampicillin may be effective in some individuals; removal of the gall bladder, alone or together with chemotherapy, is also used. It is important that chronic carriers be excluded as em-ployees in hospitals with patient contact and as food handlers in restaurants and other establishments. Carriers must be in-structed in personal hygiene. Table 20.5 illustrates the development of the *S. typhi* carrier state in males and females of var-ious age groups.

Additionally, immunization with typhoid vaccine protects individuals to a significant degree. It is of interest to note that the

Table 20.5. Development of the *S. typhi* Carrier State

Age of Subjects	Percentage Carriers	
	Male	Female
0–10	0.6	—
10–20	0.4	0.2
20–30	2.1	2.1
30–40	2.8	6.2
40–50	3.5	16.4

(Adapted from Wilson, G.S. and Miles, A., Eds.: Topley and Wilson's Principles of Bacteriology, Virology and Immunity. 6th Ed. Vol. 2. Edward Arnold Ltd., London, 1975.)

typhoid vaccine, consisting of killed bacte-rial cells, was introduced into general use long before its effectiveness was proved. It is to the merit of the World Health Orga-nization to have undertaken careful studies on the effectiveness of several typhoid vac-cines in the field. Particularly noteworthy is the inclusion of a control group immunized with enteric bacteria other than *S. typhi*, which provided evidence that endotoxin or some other common component is not re-sponsible for the observed efficiency of the typhoid vaccine. Under these conditions it was shown that the vaccine prevents the disease under natural conditions in some 70 to 80 percent of subjects (Table 20.6). Some differences exist between vaccines prepared by different methods; thus the acetone-killed vaccine appears to be some-what better than the ethanol treated vac-cine. Immunity is established by two injec-

Table 20.6. Effectiveness of Typhoid Vaccine

Country	Number of Subjects	Effectiveness (%)
Yugoslavia	5,028	79
Guiana	24,046	94
Poland	81,534	87

(Adapted from Wilson, G.S. and Miles, A., Eds: Topley and Wilson's Principles of Bacteriology, Virology and Immunity, 6th Ed. Vol. 2. Edward Arnold Ltd., London, 1975.)

tions several weeks apart. Since viable bacteria are not used, the vaccine does not have special danger for immunologically incompetent individuals. A better immune response is obtained by properly spaced injections of the vaccine. When needed, immunity is reestablished in immunized individuals by the administration of a single dose given 3 years after primary immunization. In the United States, in the absence of an epidemic, routine immunization is not indicated. In the past, a mixed vaccine, consisting of *S. paratyphi* A and B in addition to *S. typhi*, was used, but there is no evidence that this vaccine prevents infection by salmonellae other than *S. typhi*. Therefore its use is not recommended. The possible role of cellular immunity resulting from immunization has not been clarified.

Salmonella Fever

An illness similar to, but usually milder than, typhoid fever is referred to as *salmonella fever*. It is caused by *S. paratyphi* A or *S. paratyphi* B. Pathogenesis, microbiologic diagnosis, and management are similar to those of typhoid fever. The disease is unusually rare in this country at the present time.

Salmonellosis

Salmonellosis is a disease caused by any member of the genus *Salmonella*. As mentioned above, *S. typhi* and *S. paratyphi* are excluded, since their respective diseases are unique and referred to as typhoid and paratyphoid or salmonella fever.

Most common among human infections is *gastroenteritis*. This illness is sometimes referred to as *food poisoning*, particularly when an epidemic can be traced to contaminated food. In addition, members of the genus may cause extraintestinal infections.

Essentially all smooth strains of the genus may cause disease; however, certain serologic types are far more prevalent than others. Thus *S. typhimurium* is by far the most frequently encountered etiologic agent of disease in man around the world. The more prevalent serotypes, accounting for 55 percent of all isolates encountered in the United States in 1977 as reported in 1979 by the Center for Disease Control, are *S. typhimurium, S. newport, S. heidelberg,* and *S. enteritidis*.

Gastroenteritis. Since most of the serotypes responsible for this illness are not host adapted, the infection may be acquired, either directly or indirectly, from human as well as animal sources. Salmonellae are encountered essentially in all animal species, both wild and domestic, from turtles, chickens, ducks, cats, dogs, and cattle to man. The infectious agent may be transmitted directly or indirectly. Examples of indirect transmission are as follows: chickens harboring salmonellae contaminate eggshells and thus the eggs themselves; when such eggs are used for mass production of egg powder, widespread illness may result from its consumption. Such an epidemic took place during World War II. A large scale water-borne outbreak of salmonellosis occurred in California and involved more than 10,000 subjects. It is of interest to note also that salmonellae have been transmitted through drugs, such as the dye carmine red prepared from flies and used for the study of motility of the gastrointestinal tract, as well as through hormone preparations obtained from endocrine glands of animals. The incubation period of gastroenteritis, in contrast to that of typhoid fever, is short, ranging from 6 to 72 hours (usually 12 to 36 hours). The microorganisms invade the mucous membrane, causing inflammation. Recent observations suggest that enterotoxin production by salmonellae may be more common than is currently recognized.

The microbiologic diagnosis of gastroenteritis, or food poisoning, caused by salmonellae is based on the isolation and identification of the pathogen from appropriate specimens, notably feces, from affected subjects and suspected food. Documentation of the antibody response for diagnostic purposes is not a routine procedure, although it may provide strongly suggestive evidence of infection in bacteriologically negative individuals and/or be useful for the diagnosis of subclinical infection. Antibiotic therapy usually is not indicated and, in fact, often contraindicated. The latter conclusion is based on the observation that administration of antibiotics, such as chloramphenicol, neomycin, and others, is usually ineffective both clinically in producing faster recovery and bacteriologically in eliminating the pathogen from the intestinal tract. In fact, the duration of excretion of the pathogen is often prolonged. In one particular study reported by Clementi, untreated subjects excreted the pathogen for 52 days and antibiotic treated individuals for 160 days. More recent information suggests that trimethoprim-sulfamethoxazole, a chemotherapeutic agent, may aid in the termination of the excretor state in some individuals. Antibiotic therapy may be indicated when spread to the systemic circulation occurs or threatens in subjects with abnormally low resistance, such as infants and patients with malignancy. Prevention of the disease is best accomplished by appropriate sanitary conditions, education of food handlers and homemakers, diagnosis of infection of domestic animals and pets, and early recognition of outbreaks. An effective vaccine for active immunization is not available.

Extraintestinal Salmonellosis

While in the vast majority of subjects with gastroenteritis due to salmonellae the pathogen remains localized in the intestinal tract, extraintestinal infections do occur and do not necessarily represent a complication of clinically overt enteric disease. Salmonellae may cause infection of the urinary tract, endocarditis, meningitis,

osteomyelitis, arthritis, pneumonia, and other problems. Usually these infections are the result of hematogenous spread of the pathogen, which probably enters the systemic circulation from the gastrointestinal tract. Noteworthy is the fact that salmonella osteomyelitis is seen relatively more frequently in individuals with sickle cell disease than in other individuals. This is due to the fact that, because of the hematologic disorder, the pathogen invades the bloodstream from the gastrointestinal tract more readily and becomes trapped in the bone marrow. It is as yet unknown why certain serotypes of *Salmonella* (*S. choleraesuis*) are seen relatively more frequently in this condition than others.

The microbiologic diagnosis of extraintestinal salmonellosis is made by isolating and identifying the pathogen from appropriate specimens, such as blood, spinal fluid, sputum, pus, and urine. Clearly, antibiotic therapy is indicated, the selection being guided by the results of the antibiogram. In patients with underlying illnesses, such as malignancy, antibiotic prophylaxis may be used in those with gastroenteritis due to salmonellae to prevent serious hematogenous disease.

CONCLUDING REMARKS

By design the foregoing discussion deals with individual pathogens and the respective diseases. Therefore it is appropriate to point out that mixed infections also occur. For example, enteropathogenic *E. coli* may be isolated together with a member of the genus *Salmonella* and in children is encountered more frequently when rotavirus is present in the intestinal tract. Also, two different species or serotypes of either enteropathogenic *E. coli*, *Salmonella*, or *Shigella* can be present simultaneously in the gastrointestinal tract. Too frequently, the assumption is made that when two potential pathogens are isolated from a single fecal specimen both contribute to the illness. It therefore must be kept in mind that infection may be due only to one of the microorganisms in a patient who is a carrier of the other. Documentation of the immune response to one or both aids in the differentiation between a single and a mixed infection.

When suspected pathogens are obtained from a given specimen, such as feces from a patient with diarrhea, often only a single colony is used for identification. Thus it is unlikely that the presence of two serotypes of *Salmonella* or *Shigella*, perhaps differing only in antigenic composition, are recognized. For this reason, mixed infection is diagnosed less frequently than it actually occurs.

Finally, it is important to realize that with the transfer of plasmids from one to another species, diagnostically important biochemical activities may be altered in the recipient strain. Thus a strain of *Salmonella* acquiring DNA coding for lactose-fermenting enzyme becomes lactose-positive, and the correct identification of this pathogen at best is very difficult or not made at all. The diagnosis of enterotoxin induced enteritis is rendered particularly difficult when the plasmid coding for the synthesis of this important pathogenetic factor is transferred from *E. coli* to another genus, such as *Citrobacter* or *Klebsiella*. Fortunately, these plasmid induced alterations appear to be rather uncommon but nonetheless must be kept in mind.

REFERENCES

Buchanan, R.E. and Gibbons, N.E., Eds: Bergey's Manual of Determinative Bacteriology. 8th Ed. Williams & Wilkins, Baltimore, 1974.

Carpenter, C.C.J.: Mechanisms of bacterial diarrheas. Am. J. Med., *68*: 313, 1980.

Edwards, P.R. and Ewing, W.H., Eds.: Identification of *Enterobacteriaceae*. 3rd Ed. Burgess Publishing Company, Minneapolis, 1972.

Grieco, M.H., Ed.: Infections in the Abnormal Host. Yorke Medical Books, New York, 1980.

Lennette, E.H., Balows, A., Hausler, W. Jr., and Truant, J.P., Eds: Manual of Clinical Microbiology. 3rd Ed. American Society for Microbiology, Washington, 1980.

Mandell, G.L., Douglas, R.G., and Bennett, J.E.: Principles and Practice of Infectious Diseases. John Wiley & Sons, New York, 1979.

Neter, E: The Microbiologic Aspects of Urinary Tract Infection. In Rubin, M.I., Ed.: Pediatric Nephrology. Williams & Wilkins, Baltimore, 1975.

Rodriguez-Leiva, M: Typhoid fever 1979 — A new perspective on an old disease. J. Infect. Dis., *140*: 268, 1979.

Rose, N.R. and Friedman, H., Eds: Manual of Clinical Immunology. 2nd Ed. American Society for Microbiology, Washington, 1980.

Washington, J.A. II: Medical Bacteriology. In J.B. Henry, Ed.: Todd, Sanford, Davidsohn, Clinical Diagnosis and Management by Laboratory Methods, 16th Ed., Vol. 2. W.B. Saunders, Philadelphia, 1979.

21

Enterobacteriaceae II

Eugene A. Gorzynski

A significant change in the spectrum of etiologic agents of infectious diseases has evolved during the past 20 years. Whereas species of *Salmonella* and *Shigella* persist as enteric pathogens, and *Yersinia pestis*, discussed at the end of this chapter, causes a nonenteric infection, the remaining members of the family *Enterobacteriaceae* have emerged as overt, contributing, or suspected causes of disease. However, to characterize the latter arbitrarily as pathogens, when present in microbiologic specimens, is not justified; the recognition of opportunistic infections attributable to these microorganisms clearly requires clinical judgment supported by laboratory data. For example, the presence of enteric bacilli in the respiratory tract is not uncommon, but the species isolated are not necessarily responsible for pneumonia. Also, burns and wounds frequently harbor a few or many different species of *Enterobacteriaceae*, none of which may play a major role as invasive agents. Therefore if we are to address the pathogenicity or virulence of *Enterobacteriaceae* other than species of *Salmonella* or *Shigella* or *Y. pestis*, the patient as a compromised subject must be considered as a determinant. In this regard, the following host factors or conditions are

known to modulate or predispose to primary or superinfections: advanced age, stress, diet deficiency, debilitation, malignancy, antibiotic therapy, trauma, instrumentation, humoral/cellular immune incompetence, and disease. The identity, characteristics, and pathogenicity of members of the family *Enterobacteriaceae* regarded as opportunistic invaders comprise a major portion of this chapter.

KLEBSIELLA

Characteristics

Four species are distinguished in the genus *Klebsiella*: *K. pneumoniae*, *K. ozaenae*, *K. oxytoca*, and *K. rhinoscleromatis*. All members are nonmotile, usually encapsulated, rods. Owing to similarity in colonial characteristics and biochemical reactions, *Klebsiella* strains may be confused with *Enterobacter* strains. Major biochemical reactions are presented in Table 19.1.

On nutrient agar, the large, moist colonies generally formed may coalesce and often are very mucoid in appearance; in broth, growth is stringy. The capsules, easily seen in moist India ink slide mounts, are composed of hexoses and uronic acids. The polysaccharides account for the many capsular antigens characterized. These antigens can be determined by means of the swelling or *Quellung* (Neufeld) reaction. However, it must be emphasized that actual capsular swelling does not occur in the presence of specific antisera. Instead, a precipitin reaction takes place at the surface of the capsule or slime layer. This precipitation of antibody causes the capsule or slime layer to become highly refractile and easily seen in unstained moist preparations. Alternatively, the capsular antigens present in klebsiellae may be identified by agglutination or precipitation tests with appropriate antisera.

Because crossreactions occur between certain capsule types, many sufficiently strong to cause confusion, the employment of specific absorbed capsular antisera is required for the unequivocal identification of type. Currently, additional serologic procedures are being assessed as diagnostic tools for detecting specific soluble microbial antigens in specimens or body fluids of patients with putative infection notably caused by species of *Streptococcus*, *Neisseria*, *Haemophilus* and *Klebsiella*. These include latex agglutination, counterimmunoelectrophoresis, enzyme linked immunoassay, coagglutination, and radioimmunoassay.

Five O antigens have been characterized for *Klebsiella*. However, their determination is difficult because required treatment to remove blocking capsular material frequently converts them to the rough form devoid of O antigen. Moreover, most of the O antigens of *Klebsiella* species are identical or closely related to O antigens of certain *Escherichia coli*.

Clinical Relevance

Klebsiellae rank second to *E. coli* in number of facultatively anaerobic enteric bacilli found in the bowel of a normal, healthy individual. Therefore as with other *Enterobacteriaceae* these microorganisms may be present innocently in specimens contaminated by feces or may be recovered as the cause of an overt, sometimes fatal infection. Klebsiellae have emerged as frequent causes of hospital associated infections. Significantly, the most common species, *K. pneumoniae* (Friedländer's bacillus), is a cause of pneumonia and septicemia. Also, occasionally it has been associated with other suppurative conditions including liver abscess, meningitis, peritonitis, and wound infection. The presence of this facultatively anaerobic microorganism in deep wounds provides an excellent growth environment for obligate anaerobes present at the same time. *K. pneumoniae* is responsible for 0.5 to 4 percent of all pneumonias; in untreated cases, the fatality rate may be 90 percent or greater. In this disease, sputa frequently are viscid, mucoid or stringy, and often bloody. In experimental animals, there appears to be a vast virulence difference between the lower capsular types (type 1 through type 6) and the higher types that have been isolated. With the lower types, 10 bacteria are sufficient to kill a mouse in 48 hours, whereas with the higher types 10^6 to 10^9 are required. Compromised patients, uncontrolled diabetics and alcoholics in particular, are inordinately susceptible to *K. pneumoniae* infection.

The remaining species of *Klebsiella* (*K. ozaena*, *K oxytoca*, and *K. rhinoscleromatis*), are less frequently encountered in the United States; routine microbiologic procedures often do not include their differentiation. The latter are etiologic agents of chronic infections of the upper respiratory tract, including nasal muscosa and pharynx, endemic in the South and Central Americas and in North Africa.

ENTEROBACTER

Characteristics

This genus is comprised of the following species: *E. cloacae*, *E. sakazakii*, *E.*

aerogenes, E. agglomerans, and *E. gergo- viae*. Except for occasional variants, these microorganisms are motile. Although strains inoculated on nutrient agar usually produce fimbriate and slime-forming colonies, no defined capsule is visible in moist India ink slide mounts. Of the family *Enterobacteriaceae*, this genus is the least effectively distinguished; it has many biochemical characteristics that are close if not identical to species of *Klebsiella*. Owing to these similarities, laboratories practicing only rudimentary microbiology frequently do not attempt routinely to speciate *Klebsiella* or *Enterobacter*. Instead, isolated strains arbitrarily are categorized and reported as members of the poorly defined "klebsiella-enterobacter" group. Nonetheless, speciation is feasible if one employs sufficient biochemical data, as addressed in *Bergey's Manual of Determinative Bacteriology* and in *Identification of Enterobacteriaceae*. A few of these data are shown in Table 19.1.

All motile strains of *Enterobacter* possess both O and H antigens. Owing to a multiplicity of inter- and intrageneric crossreactions, no specific serologic test currently is useful in diagnosis of an enterobacter infection.

Clinical Relevance

Because species of *Enterobacter* are saprophytes and may be recovered from the intestinal tract of both man and animals, it is expected that they may also be found in soil, water, and even dairy products. They are opportunists in patients conditioned by disease or treatment. However, compared to the klebsiellae, *Enterobacter* species are only infrequent causes of infection. Nonetheless, like many *Enterobacteriaceae*, species of *Enterobacter* are capable of producing infection in body tissue, most frequently the urinary tract. *E. cloacae* accounts for the majority of *Enterobacter* isolates reported. Antibiograms are recom-

mended to help select the most effective, least toxic drug.

SERRATIA

Characteristics

Several species are present in the genus *Serratia*; *S. marcescens, S. liquefaciens*, and *S. rubidaea* are most frequently encountered clinically. All members are flagellated aerobes and facultative anaerobes that grow readily on simple nutrient agar. Less than 6 percent of isolated strains are chromogenic; they produce red pigmented colonies at room temperature but seldom at 37°C or above.. The pigment is not soluble in water. Because lactose may be fermented slowly, if at all (depending upon strain or species of *Serratia*), fermentation of this carbohydrate should not be employed as a reliable guide for preliminary identification of the genus or any of its species. When gas is formed from fermentable substrates, the volume is small (< 10 percent). Gelatin is liquefied rapidly, lysine and ornithine may be decarboxylated, and lipase is produced. Other biochemical reactions are shown in Table 19.1.

Fifteen somatic (O) antigen groups and 13 flagellar (H) antigens have been established or characterized. With monospecific O and H antisera, it is feasible to determine the serotype (i.e., both O and H antigens) of at least 95 percent of clinical isolates. Acceptable serologic procedures include bacterial agglutination (O and H) and coagglutination. Recently described as specific and easy to perform and interpret is the H (flagellar) immobilization test. Knowledge of the serotype and biotype (a numerical profile of biochemical reactions in known substrates) will help determine whether two or more isolates are the same strain and likely causes of a hospital acquired infection. In addition, susceptibility patterns derived from antibiograms, discussed below, will strengthen or discredit this essential determination.

Clinical Relevance

Serratia spp., once regarded as harmless saprophytes, are being recovered and reported with increasing frequency as agents responsible for hospital acquired infections. The degree of virulence displayed by these species varies according to strain. Moreover, in the absence of a history of infection, normal human subjects may have both bactericidal antibodies and complement dependent opsonins, characterized as IgM, against serratiae. Serum from newborn infants is deficient in opsonic antibody against this microorganism. The potentiators or stimulators of these immunoglobulins later in life are not known, nor is the role of antibody in protection against serratia infection clearly understood. Recent findings suggest that serum resistance, that is, a microbial factor that blocks bactericidal or opsonic activity, contributes to the virulence of *S. marcescens*. Whereas serum sensitive strains of *Serratia* isolated from urine, wounds, and sputum usually cause manageable or self-limited infections, serum resistant strains may be recovered from the blood; they cause septicemia that is predictably difficult to control. These latter infections frequently occur in a hospital where serum-resistant strains are prevalent.

The pathogenic potential of *Serratia* spp., when present in colonized patients, often is not clear. However, their prompt recognition is a requirement of every hospital laboratory. Of the *Serratia* spp. isolated from clinical specimens, most are identified as *S. marcescens*. Although most strains are recovered from urine specimens, there are reports of pneumonia, septicemia, endocarditis, arthritis, and wound infections caused by *S. marcescens*. Most urinary isolates have a high probability of multiple drug resistance. Gentamicin, once considered the drug of choice, should not be employed empirically; many isolated strains of *S. marcescens* are now resistant to this chemotherapeutic agent. Amikacin, an aminocyclitol antibiotic, currently is effective in treating serious gram-negative bacillary infections, including *S. marcescens*, that are resistant to gentamicin. Obviously, to preclude or retard the emergence of resistant strains, the use of amikacin should be reserved for those life-threatening or recrudescent infections caused by bacteria refractory to formulary drugs but sensitive *in vitro* to amikacin.

PROTEUS

Characteristics

Two species are included in the genus *Proteus*: *P. mirabilis* and *P. vulgaris*. Two other species, *P. morganii* and *P. rettgier*, were listed initially in this genus, but according to current taxonomy, the latter microorganisms are classified *Morganella morganii* and *Providencia rettgeri*.

All *Proteus* species are actively motile at 35°C. Characteristically, these microorganisms produce urease. This enzyme is responsible for the alkalinization of urine and the subsequent damage to renal epithelium in patients with urinary tract infections caused by *Proteus* species. Lactose is not fermented. Salient biochemical characteristics are shown in Table 19.1. Although aberrant strains occasionally are encountered giving atypical biochemical reactions, differential properties may be employed in preliminary speciation.

Species of *Proteus* grow luxuriantly on the moist surface of nutrient agar devoid of inhibitors. *P. mirabilis* and *P. vulgaris* usually swarm, producing confluent blue-gray growth over the entire surface of the medium. As a result the uninhibited growth of either species in a specimen or culture will make it difficult to isolate or identify other bacteria concurrently present.

Swarming is reduced significantly on a medium containing a high concentration (e.g., 5 percent) of agar and in a medium containing 0.25 percent phenylethanol.

Many O and H antigens have been characterized for species of *Proteus*. Numerous intergeneric crossreactions have been encountered between these and other antigens of *Enterobacteriaceae*, including serotypes of *Salmonella* and *Escherichia*; however, correlative studies on antigenic interrelationships between species of *Proteus* are lacking. Therefore serologic procedures alone have limited use as epidemiologic tools in monitoring hospital associated infections caused by these bacteria. Additional or more specific markers, such as biotype, antibiogram spectrum and bacteriocin* production/sensitivity pattern, currently are being assessed at the Center for Disease Control. On the other hand, certain strains of *P. mirabilis* (OXK) and *P. vulgaris* (OX2 and OX19) are employed as antigens in the Weil-Felix test, useful in the diagnosis of certain rickettsial infections, discussed in Chapter 37. However, because humoral antibodies may be absent or inconsistently elevated, depending upon etiologic species of *Rickettsia*, the clinical significance of either positive or negative test results is debatable.

Clinical Relevance

Proteus spp. have evolved as causes of urinary tract infections, wound and burn infections, pneumonia, and septicemia. As with any cause, pneumonia and septicemia may be fatal in patients debilitated by underlying disease or compromised by therapy. On the other hand, urinary tract infections intrinsically are less grave; they may present a spectrum of clinical manifestations ranging from asymptomatic to acute or chronic. The importance of urinary tract infections, independent of cause, is revealed by their frequency, likelihood of recurrence, and difficulty in prevention or management. More significantly, there always exists a potential not only for their reemergence, but for their recrudescence as serious renal disease, bacteremia, and, in pregnancy, possible fetal prematurity. The major pathway by which the kidneys become infected is via the ascending route (i.e., the urethra and bladder). Less frequently, the hematogenous route is implicated.

The retention of urine because of mechanical obstruction or functional failure provides an excellent opportunity for potential pathogens to reach the kidneys by reflux from the bladder. Therefore these opportunists first must colonize and then penetrate the pelvic epithelium before growing in renal parenchyma.

Principal etiologic agents are species of *Escherichia*, the *Enterobacter-Klebsiella* group, *Pseudomonas*, *Serratia*, as noted above and *Proteus*. Although any species of *Proteus* may initiate infection of the urinary tract, indole-negative *P. mirabilis* is responsible for the majority of hospital associated and community acquired proteus infections in man. The possession of pili may play a significant role in aiding colonization by *Proteus* species of the mucosa. However, because these organelles render the microorganism susceptible to phagocytosis, pili may actually diminish nephropathogenicity by restricting access to renal parenchyma. Urease produced by *Proteus* species in bladder urine may hydrolyze urea to ammonia; a rise in pH will result. This increased alkalinity will precipitate magnesium and calcium salts and result in the formation of calculi and in predictable damage to renal epithelium.

It is speculated that in the presence of

---

*Bacteriocins are proteins elaborated by many bacteria during their exponential phase of growth. These proteins are bactericidal for strains of the same or closely related species. Bacteriocins are detected by the inhibitory zone they produce against a suitable indicator strain.

certain antimicrobial agents, species of *Proteus* may persist as viable cells lacking a structured wall and, accordingly, be refractory to those agents impairing cell wall biosynthesis. It is likely that these osmotically fragile cell wall deficient bacteria (referred to as protoplasts, L forms, or spheroplasts) remain susceptible to antimicrobial drugs (e.g., tetracycline and erythromycin) acting upon the cell metabolism per se and not cell wall formation.

It must be emphasized that any gram-negative enteric bacterium may cause urinary tract infection. Therapy should not be arbitrary or empirical except as a heroic means in life-threatening infections. Ideally, treatment should reflect the results of antimicrobial susceptibility tests on the isolated and speciated microorganism. However, selecting a predictably effective regimen may be a problem because antibiograms are oriented toward blood, and not urine, levels.

PROVIDENCIA

Characteristics

Three species are present in the genus *Providencia*: *P. alcalifaciens*, *P. stuartii*, and *P. rettgeri*. These bacteria do not form H$_2$S; this clearly separates them from *Proteus*. The fact that they are motile and utilize citrate as a source of carbon distinguishes them from shigellae. Additional biochemical characteristics are shown in Table 19.1.

Clinical Relevance

Any species of *Providencia* may be the etiologic agent of a urinary tract infection; patients with underlying urologic disorders are excellent candidates. Like other gram-negative enteric rods mentioned earlier, providenciae are implicated as causes of hospital associated infection and can infect wounds and burns. The knowledge that

most isolates are resistant to many antimicrobial agents makes empirical therapy untenable. Successful treatment requires use of data retrieved from antibiograms of the isolate in question. Currently, the aminocyclitol antibiotic amikacin appears to be effective against resistant strains of *Providencia*.

CITROBACTER

Characteristics

This genus is comprised of three motile species, *C. freundii*, *C. diversus*, and *C. amalonaticus*, which grow in citrate medium. Differentiation is made by observing for growth or the by-products of growth in selective media; for example, *C. freundii* and *C. amalonaticus* but not *C. diversus* grow in a medium containing potassium cyanide, whereas *C. diversus* and *C. amalonaticus* but not *C. freundii* produce indole in peptone broth. Other biochemical characteristics are presented in Table 19.1. Although a number of both somatic (O) and flagellar (H) antigens have been characterized for species of *Citrobacter*, the O antigens of many serotypes have an intergeneric relationship with other members of *Enterobacteriaceae*, including *Salmonella* and *Escherichia*. To date, the development of a serologic test scheme for species of *Citrobacter* has not evolved.

Clinical Relevance

Both *C. freundii* and *C. diversus* may be encountered in stool specimens of healthy individuals. Their role as mediators or etiologic agents of enteric infection has not been clearly established. They are frequently found in urine specimens of patients with a history of recent instrumentation or with underlying urologic disease. With almost equal frequency, *Citrobacter* spp. are recovered from the respiratory tract where, most often, they appear in mixed flora and as secondary invaders not contributing significantly to pneumonitis. Cerebrospinal infections caused by *C. diversus* recently have been documented in newborn children. In compromised patients, *C. freundii* has been isolated as the causative agent of meningitis, endocarditis, septicemia, and osteomyelitis. *Citrobacter* infections should not be treated empirically; species indentification and knowledge of antibiogram patterns are required for the effective treatment of a patient at risk. In this regard, several species-related differences are notable. Whereas most *C. freundii* isolates are susceptible to ampicillin and carbenicillin, strains of *C. diversus* usually are resistant to these two antibiotics. In contrast, *C. diversus* is susceptible to cephalothins; *C. freundii* is resistant.

It is known that septicemia may occur in any patient receiving intravenous therapy, independent of the fluid administered. The majority of ensuing septicemias likely are due to extrinsic contamination reflecting breaks in aseptic or manipulative techniques. However, intrinsic contamination of injected fluid by species of *Enterobacteriaceae* should not be ruled out arbitrarily only because the fluid administered was quality controlled during preparation or purchased from commercial sources.

EDWARDSIELLA

Characteristics

The genus *Edwardsiella* is comprised of one species, *Edw. tarda*, that may have clinical relevance. Because of its superficial resemblance to *Escherichia coli*, *Edw. tarda* occasionally and erroneously is reported as "atypical *E. coli*." *Edw. tarda* is a motile rod. *E. coli* does not produce H_2S in an appropriate medium containing inorganic sulfur compounds, and more than 88 percent of *E. coli* strains ferment both lactose

and mannitol. In contrast, *Edw. tarda* does produce H_2S and fails to ferment lactose and mannitol. It must be emphasized, however, that these latter observations alone will not distinguish *Edw. tarda* from other *Enterobacteriaceae*; additional tests or substrates (summarized in Table 19.1) must be evaluated.

Clinical Relevance

Edw. tarda has been isolated from both cold and warm blooded animals. It is not considered a member of the normal enterobacterial flora of the human host. In man, this microorganism rarely causes infection.

ERWINIA

Taxonomy and Significance

Controversy exists regarding the placement of the genus *Erwinia* in the family *Enterobacteriaceae*. Most taxonomists justify this placement on the basis that these gram-negative, motile rods reduce nitrates to nitrites and share other biochemical reaction patterns with *Enterobacteriaceae*, in particular species of *Klebsiella*, *Enterobacter*, and *Citrobacter* (Table 19.1). *Erwina herbicola* likely is an opportunistic pathogen of compromised human subjects. In the absence of other suspected bacteria, the presence of *Erw. herbicola* may be clinically significant.

YERSINIA

Characteristics

The genus *Yersinia* is comprised of three species: *Y. pestis*, *Y. pseudotuberculosis*, and *Y. enterocolitica*. After Gram staining these relatively large (about 0.8 by 2 to 6 μm, depending upon species) bacteria are ovoid, rod shaped, or coccobacillary in appearance. *Y. pestis* displays bipolar bodies; that is, the microoganism has a "safety pin" appearance when stained with Wayson's carbol fuchsin-methylene blue reagent. These dark blue bodies, more frequently found in *Y. pestis* than in other yersiniae, are pronounced in preparations of tissue or pus and are vague or absent in smears of cultures. *Y. pestis* is nonmotile at any temperature; the remaining two species are motile at 22 to 25°C but not at 37°C. *Yersinia* spp. produce small (1 to 2 mm), nonpigmented colonies on artificial media after 24 to 48 hours incubation at 28 to 35°C. Chains of 4 to 16 bacilli frequently are seen in smears of broth cultures. The major biochemical characteristics (summarized in Table 19.1) are similar to those of other representatives of the family *Enterobacteriaceae*. A *Yersinia* species should be suspected if an isolate, nonmotile or motile only at room temperature, ferments carbohydrates other than lactose, is oxidase- and phenylalanine-negative, and does not produce H_2S. Differentiation between species of *Yersinia* is accomplished best in special reference laboratories.

Yersiniae are facultative intracellular parasites. *Y. pestis* causes plague, a severe systemic disease of rodents and man. In sharp contrast, the other species of *Yersinia* cause localized syndromes. In humans *Y. pseudotuberculosis* may be responsible for a mild mesentery lymphadenitis mimicking appendicitis, whereas *Y. enterocolitica*, avirulent in laboratory animals, has been implicated as a cause of the following infections: acute mesentery lymphadenitis, enterocolitis, and wound infection. Also, *Y. enterocolitica* has been recovered from blood cultures. In the compromised host, septicemia with a 50 percent fatality has been reported. *Yersinia* spp. and the diseases they cause are considered in further detail below.

Y. pestis

Virulence Factors. The endotoxic role, if any, played by the cell wall lipo-polysaccharide of *Y. pestis* in humans is unclear; in rabbits, both local and general Shwartzman reactions are produced. More than 20 different antigens have been determined; specificity of somatic (O) antigen is conferred by 3,6-dideoxyhexoses shared with *Y. pseudotuberculosis* and *Salmonella* groups B and D. Because of crossreactivity between these shared antigens, identification of isolated microbial strains by serologic procedures alone has questionable merit. Certain antigens of the yersinae, as well as other factors, are determinants of virulence. They likely account for the extracellular dissemination of the pathogen by promoting growth in plasma and interstitial fluid, by mediating adsorption to and invasion of host tissue, and by enhancing multiplication within phagosomes and cytoplasm of infected cells. The determinants of virulence and their modes of action are listed below:

1. *Antigens V and W* protect the microorganisms against phagocytosis.

2. *Pesticin I*, a bacteriocin produced by *Y. pestis*, inhibits growth of *Y. pseudotuberculosis* and certain strains of *Y. enterocolitica* and *E. coli*. Pesticin converts sensitive bacteria to nonviable, osmotically stable "spheroplasts."

3. *Pigmentation determinant*, found in virulent strains, is an unidentified surface component that allows for the adsorption of low molecular weight chromatophores, resulting in the formation of colored colonies. In mice, administration of hemin, Fe^{2+}, or Fe^{3+} will restore the virulence and pigmentation of avirulent *Y. pestis*.

4. *Fraction I antigen*, present within the microorganism's envelope, is highly immunogenic; antibodies appear to be protective. Although this antigen is required for virulence of yersiniae in the guinea pig, its role in human infections has not been determined.

Clinical Relevance. *Y. pestis* is the etiologic agent of plague, a disease not frequently found in the United States. Between 1960 and 1980, 148 cases of plague were reported in the United States, 90 from New Mexico. In 1980, 18 cases were reported; five deaths occurred. Nine cases were documented during the first 10 months of 1981. Plague is encountered most frequently in Central and South Africa, Asia and South America. Specimens (blood, sputum, aspirate, tissue), cultures, and animal and human carcasses containing the plague bacillus are potentially dangerous to all exposed personnel. The clinical manifestations and pathogenesis of plague are more appropriately addressed in books on pathology and infectious diseases. The bubonic form characteristically is transferred from infected rodents, usually rats, via fleas to man. In the United States, the incidence of this disease is highest in individuals who have professional or avocational contact with wild animals. From the infected skin site the microorganism travels to regional lymph nodes, usually in the groin. The enlarged nodes (buboes), indistinguishable clinically from lymphadenitis of other causes, may suppurate. Notably, even in mild cases, *Y. pestis* may be recovered in small numbers from the blood. However, in the insidious septicemic form of plague, many bacteria are present in the blood prior to clinical evidence of a bubo. Independent of therapy, rapid peripheral vascular collapse and death frequently ensue. With all forms of plague, there may be disseminated intravascular coagulation with concurrent features of the generalized Shwartzman phenomenon. Highly contagious pneumonic plague may be an extension of the bubonic or septicemic forms or may be acquired by inhaling contaminated droplets contributed by an infected patient.

The microbiologic diagnosis of plague requires a laboratory with special facilities and personnel with expertise to handle and to culture, isolate, and identify *Y. pestis*. Aspirates from buboes, pus from the area of flea bite, blood, and sputum specimens must be collected with care, placed in appropriately labeled containers or media, and transported without delay to the laboratory. The diagnosis suspected must be communicated clearly via telephone to the laboratory *and* by a written order accompanying each specimen. After culture, the identification of suspected isolates may be made or confirmed by serologic procedures, including bacterial agglutination, precipitation tests, and FA tests with anti–*Y. pestis* hyperimmune serum globulins conjugated with fluorescein isothiocyanate. Also, known strains of bacteriophage will lyse *Y. pestis* at 20°C and, concurrently, *Y. pseudotuberculosis* only at 37°C. Because of the existence of crossreactions and the use of reagents not always quality controlled or clearly standardized, results of all confirmatory tests must be interpreted with caution. Animal inoculation and the subsequent autopsy and microbiologic/serologic examination of target organs or tissue provide reliable, albeit potentially hazardous, tools.

It was noted above that the envelope antigen (fraction I) of *Y. pestis* is immunogenic. A rise in titer of humoral antibodies 2 weeks or more after onset of clinical disease may be detected against tannic acid treated erythrocytes coated by fraction I antigen. Whereas these latter antibodies are present for several years after recovery from plague and their presence may help label a quiescent human focus, the titer of complement-fixing antibodies decreases rapidly after recovery.

Currently, tetracycline and streptomycin are preferred chemotherapeutic agents. Penicillin, effective *in vitro* against *Y. pestis*, is ineffective in therapy.

Killed virulent *Y. pestis* with a high content of fraction I antigen is effective in active artificial immunization against bubonic but not pneumonic plague. Administration should be limited to persons at risk or travelers to areas defined as endemic by American Public Health authorities.

Y. pseudotuberculosis

Clinical Relevance. *Y. pseudotuberculosis*, like the other yersiniae, is a zoonotic bacterium. This microorganism is excreted in the feces of infected animals and probably is spread to human hosts by skin contamination and accidental oral ingestion. Gastroenteritis, usually self-limited or benign in the uncompromised subject, may be preliminary to acute septicemia and to the formation of abscesses in patients with preexisting hepatic disease or in patients treated with corticosteroids. Virulence is enhanced in the presence of free iron compounds. *Y. pseudotuberculosis* shares with *Y. pestis* both V and W antigens; fraction I antigen usually is absent. Bacteriophages against the former microorganism will lyse all strains but not *Y. pestis* or *Y. enterocolitica*.

Y. enterocolitica

Clinical Relevance. *Y. enterocolitica* is being recognized with increasing frequency as a cause of acute diarrheal disease in the United States. The etiologic agent is an invasive enterobacterial pathogen. Pus cells usually are present in large numbers in stools from which *Y. enterocolitica* may be recovered and identified by appropriate biochemical tests. By agglutination and hemagglutination tests, several serotypes of *Y. enterocolitica* have been established on the basis of their O and H antigens. These antigens have little relationship to other yersinae; most isolates from patients in the United States are serotype 8. Elevated antibody titers are demonstrable by serologic procedures in subjects with frank infections.

The effectiveness of antimicrobial therapy is equivocal. Antibiotics, effective *in vitro* according to established criteria, do not alter significantly the mean duration of symptoms in infected patients.

REFERENCES

Anderson, R.L. and Engley, F.B., Jr.: Typing methods for *Proteus rettgeri*: Comparison of biotype, antibiograms, serotype, and bacteriocin production. J. Clin. Microbiol. *8*: 715, 1978.

Brenner, D.J., Farmer, J.J., Hickman, F.W., et al.: Taxonomic and Nomenclature Changes in *Enterobacteriaceae*. HEW Publication No. (CDC) 78–8356, Washington, D.C., 1977.

Buchanan, R.E. and Gibbons, N.E., Eds.: Bergey's Manual of Determinative Bacteriology. 8th Ed. Williams & Wilkins, Baltimore, 1974.

Cluff, L.E. and Johnson, J.E., Eds.: Clinical Concepts of Infectious Disease. 2nd Ed. Williams & Wilkins, Baltimore, 1978.

Edwards, P.R. and Ewing, W.H., Eds.: Identification of *Enterobacteriaceae*. 3rd Ed. Burgess Publishing Company, Minneapolis, 1972.

Hodges, G.R., Degener, C.E., and Barnes, W.G.: Clinical significance of *Citrobacter* isolates. Am. J. Clin. Pathol. *70*: 37, 1978.

Lennette, E.H., Balows, A., Hausler, W.J., Jr., and Truant, J.P., Eds.: Manual of Clinical Microbiology. 3rd Ed. American Society for Microbiology, Washington, D.C., 1980.

Prier, J.E. and Friedman, H., Eds.: Opportunistic Pathogens. University Park Press, Baltimore, 1974.

Rabson, A.R., Hallett, A.F., and Keornhof, H.J.: Generalized *Yersinia enterocolitica* infection. J. Infect. Dis. *131*: 447, 1975.

Simberkoff, M.S., Ricupero, I., and Rahal, J.J., Jr.: Host resistance to *Serratia marcescens* infection: Serum bactericidal activity and phagocytosis by normal blood leukocytes. J. Lab. Clin. Med. *87*: 206, 1976.

Youmans, G.P., Paterson, P.Y., and Sommers, H.M., Eds.: The Biologic and Clinical Basis of Infectious Diseases. 2nd Ed. W.B. Saunders, Philadelphia, 1980.

22

Vibrio and Campylobacter

Eugene A. Gorzynski

VIBRIO

The genus *Vibrio*, of the family *Vibrionaceae*, contains species associated with surface and marine waters. Members are gram-negative, single cell rods that are slightly curved or straight; each has one polar flagellum (Fig. 22.1). Both indophenol oxidase and catalase are produced; glucose is fermented without the formation of gas. Speciation is accomplished by bochemical tests, susceptibility to a specific bacteriophage (phage IV test), ability to hemolyze sheep red blood cells, and the capacity for growth in nutrient broth devoid of NaCl or containing 3 to 7 percent of this salt. Distinguishing characteristics will be identified below, as applicable, for the two species, *V. parahaemolyticus* and *V. cholerae*, that are relevant in clinical microbiology.

V. parahaemolyticus

Of the two species of *Vibrio*, *V. parahaemolyticus* is the most frequently isolated in the United States. Whereas it has long been recognized that this species is responsible for more than 50 percent of acute diarrheal diseases in Japan, in the United States it has only recently been shown to cause outbreaks and symptoms similar to shigella dysentery. Since 1975 these outbreaks have involved at least 1000 people. The ingestion of raw or poorly cooked seafood, shrimp in particular, appears to be a common mechanism. Like shigellae, *V. parahaemolyticus* is invasive. Twelve to 72 hours after exposure the infected patient presents with diarrhea, fever, vomiting, and cramping abdominal pain. Illness is self-limiting. Like other enteropathogens, *V. parahaemolyticus* also has been recovered from a variety of extraintestinal in-

V. cholerae

V. cholerae is the causative agent of cholera, an enteritis precipitated by colonization of the small intestine with this organism (Fig. 22.2). Man is the only documented natural host. Whereas *V. parahaemolyticus*, salmonellae, *Y. enterocoli*fected sites (e.g., ears and extremities of individuals contaminated by the marine environment). If clinical symptoms of bacillary dysentery persist in the absence of recoverable *Shigella* spp. from stool specimens, a purposeful attempt should be made to biochemically test a number of lactose nonfermenting isolates.

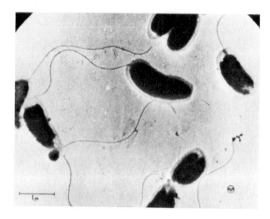

Fig. 22.1. Electron micrograph of *Vibrio cholerae*. (Neter, E.: Medical Microbiology. 5th Ed. F.A. Davis, Philadelphia, 1966.)

ca, and shigellae are invasive pathogens, *V. cholerae* is not, nor does it cause detectable morphologic or structural damage to the small bowel or its mucosa. Epidemiologic studies reveal that cholera usually is asymptomatic; however, it also occurs as mild or acute cases. In its acute form there is massive loss of fluid leading to severe dehydration; only the restoration of fluid and electrolytes will preclude incipient shock and likely death.

Acute enteritis caused by *V. cholerae* currently is rare in the United States. It appears to be endemic and limited to those rural areas in the Bengal region of India, Bangladesh, Africa, and the Philippines where water and food sanitation are poor. In these locations, cholera predominantly is a disease of indigenous children and old people. In nonendemic areas, adults and children equally are affected after consumption of grossly contaminated water or food, the acknowledged vehicles of transmission. The ingestion of an inordinately large number of *V. cholerae* is necessary for overt infection. In volunteers, 10^{11} viable vibrios usually are required to allow a sufficient infective dose to circumvent the hostile acid environment in the stomach; administered with 2 g of $NaHCO_3$, 10^6 *V. cholerae* organisms are infective. Because

an understanding of the pathogenesis of cholera may help the clinician deal more rationally with other enteric infections, *V. cholerae* is discussed in this chapter only as it relates to the classical, more severe form of disease.

V. cholerae is easy to grow on simple media at pH 7.0 to 9.5; the microorganism does not survive at pH < 6.0. In broth cultures and in fluid-stool specimens *V. cholerae* is not distinguishable from other vibrios by light or dark-field microscopy. However, in the presence of species-specific antisera, flagellated strains are immobilized. Flagella play a significant role in the pathogenesis of *V. cholerae*. In contradistinction to motile vibrios, nonmotile bacteria of the same strain will not adhere to brush border membranes of the intestinal surface. It is reasoned that this adherence enables the microorganism to resist removal by peristalsis and to multiply at the site

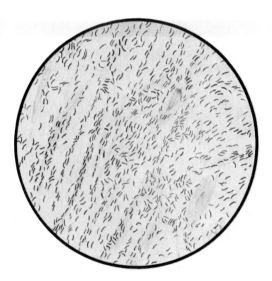

Fig. 22.2. Smear of mucus from small intestine of a cholera patient (about × 500). Streams of mucus covered by vibrios can be recognized. (Kolle, W., and Prigge, R. Cholera asiatica. In Kolle, W., Kraus, R., and Uhlenhuth, P., Eds.: Handbuch der pathogenen Mikroorganismen. Gustav Fisher, Jena/Urban & Schwarzenberg, Berlin, 1928.)

Table 22.1.   Differentiating Characteristics of *Vibrio* Species

Characteristics	V. cholerae biotypes		V. parahaemolyticus
	Classical	El Tor	
Growth in NaCl-free broth	+	+	–
Sucrose fermentation	+	+	–
Susceptibility to polymyxin B (50 units)	+	–	a
Susceptibility to bacteriophage IV	+	–	a
Voges-Proskauer reaction	–	+	–
Hemolysis of sheep RBC	–	+	–

[a]Data not available.

of action. Pili, possessed by all vibrios, may also contribute to or be involved in this adhesion. These events are preliminary to penetration by the microorganism of the mucous layer covering the intestinal epithelium. Mucinases produced by *V. cholerae* may play a role in this process.

V. cholerae has been classified into the "classical" and El Tor biotypes on the basis of certain tests, including Voges-Proskauer and susceptibility to polymyxin B and specific bacteriophage typing. These same characteristics also allow for distinguishing the biotypes from *V. parahaemolyticus*, which may also cause enteritis. Either biotype of *V. cholerae* may cause mild or severe cholera; however, differentiations should be made for epidemiologic reasons. A few of the major distinguishing characteristics are presented in Table 22.1.

Like other motile, gram-negative enteric species, *V. cholerae* possesses both flagellar (H) and somatic (O) antigens. The heat labile protein (H) antigen is common to all strains; the heat stable polysaccharide fraction of the endotoxic lipopolysaccharide determines the antigenic O group. *V. cholerae* is classified into six such groups; serotypes O2 to O6 have limited epidemic potential. Serotype O1, which contains the classical and El Tor biotypes, is comprised of two or three antigenic factors (A, B, and C) that account for the microorganism's serotype. Factors A and B are found in serotype

Ogawa, A and C in serotype Inaba, and A, B, and C in serotype Hikojima. Except for identifying *V. cholerae* per se, knowledge of the specific etiologic serotype has no clinical significance and limited epidemiologic relevance because conversion among these serotypes can occur in natural infections.

In addition to containing endotoxin, all pathogenic strains of *V. cholerae* elaborate an enterotoxin that is responsible for the loss of fluid in cholera. This enterotoxin (choleragen) is a heat labile protein (destroyed at 50°C) with a molecular weight of approximately 84,000. Its activity is sharply decreased at pH <6.0 and is destroyed by pronase but is resistant to trypsin. During infection the major action of *V. cholerae* enterotoxin is to bind irreversibly to receptors on the brush border membrane of mucosal cells and to stimulate the activity of membrane bound adenyl cylase. This results in an increase in intracellular levels of cyclic 3',5'-adenosine monophosphate (cAMP) and hypersecretion of fluid and electrolytes into the lumen of the intestine. The rate of fluid loss from the gut may exceed 1 liter/hour. This fluid is clear, free of inflammatory cells and leukocytes, odorless, virtually devoid of protein, and concentrated with electrolytes. Rapid intravenous fluid therapy restores the critically ill or moribund patient to a state of well being within an hour.

Cholera is not readily transmitted by

direct contact with patients or carriers. Proper sanitation alone, with particular emphasis on water and food, will prevent epidemics. In an endemic area, active artificial immunization with whole cell vaccines provides some protection, for less than 6 months, to adults only. The observation that children, who are more prone than adults to cholera, receive little benefit from immunization suggests that the vaccine boosts the immunity of an individual primed by an earlier latent or overt infection. It is controversial whether or not commercial vaccines provide protection to a *V. cholerae* virgin population in nonendemic areas. United States travelers to endemic areas are not required to be actively artificially immunized against *V. cholerae*.

CAMPYLOBACTER

Members of *Campylobacter* are gram-negative, slender, curved bacilli that are motile because of a single polar flagellum at one or both ends of the cell. The ends of the cells usually are pointed. All are microaerophilic *in vitro*; they do not grow under strict anaerobic conditions nor aerobically as surface colonies. Microscopic examination of fresh cultures in broth shows the organisms, which may appear ribbon shaped due to the arrangement of cells, in chains of single curved rods. In old cultures, these rods may appear coccoid. Species of *Campylobacter* differ from species of the closely related genus *Vibrio*; the former are nonfermentative, with no acid end products of metabolism.

Studies by electron microscopy reveal an outer cell membrane that is double layered, fitting loosely over the cell wall comprised of an outer lipoprotein layer, a middle lipopolysaccharide layer, and an inner mucopeptide layer adjacent to the cytoplasmic membrane. In consonance with endotoxins of other gram-negative bacilli, lipopolysaccharides of *Campylobacter* spp. induce fever and generalized Shwartz-man reactions in experimental animals. Also, bacteria free supernatant fluids of broth cultures of *Campylobacter fetus* abort pregnant cows injected intravenously.

The major reason for removing species of *Campylobacter* from their previous taxonomic location in the genus *Vibrio* is based on nucleic acid content. The mole percent guanine plus cytosine (mole percent G + C) of the DNA for the former is about 30 to 35; the mole percent G + C for *Vibrio* spp. is about 46 to 47. Whereas an antibody response to the homologous strain of *Campylobacter* may be detected by hemagglutination, by latex agglutination, or by precipitin lines in the immunodiffusion test, species of *Campylobacter* appear antigenically heterogeneous; therefore a serotyping scheme currently is not available.

This genus is familiar to veterinarians; *Campylobacter fetus* subsp. *fetus* (formerly *Vibrio fetus*) has been known for many years to cause an enzootic venereal disease of cattle, resulting in infertility or abortion. As far as we know, this subspecies does not cause infection in man.

Subspecies of *C. fetus*, *C. intestinalis* and *C. jejuni*, are responsible for a variety of infections in both animals and man. The sources and modes of transmission of the latter infections are moot questions. Whereas campylobacter are widespread as either commensals or pathogens among animals, currently only a small number of human infections are attributable directly to transmission from animals or their products. The shedding of *C. fetus* subsp. *jejuni* in feces of domestic animals, puppies in particular, suggests that household pets may constitute a reservoir for human campylobacteriosis. Also, unpasteurized milk and undercooked poultry have been reported as vehicles of transmission.

A variety of symptoms, most commonly fever, accompanies campylobacter infection in man. It appears that responsible subspecies (*jejuni*, *intestinalis*) may be involved in

such conditions as acute enteritis, bacteremia, septic arthritis, endocarditis,
meningitis, meningoencephalitis, and Reiter's syndrome. Although initially it was
believed that these subspecies were opportunistic microorganisms, primarily infecting
debilitated or immunosuppressed patients,
it is now recognized that the majority of infections are in previously healthy individuals. A number of reports indicate that
in children gastroenteritis caused by campylobacter occurs with a higher incidence
than that caused by salmonellae or
shigellae. Symptoms include elevated
temperature, bloody diarrhea, and, frequently, severe abdominal pain. In untreated patients campylobacter may persist in
the stool for as long as 7 weeks; 48 hours
after initiation of treatment with erythromycin, the microorganism is no longer
detectable in stool specimens.

Subspecies of *Campylobacter fetus* have
fastidious growth requirements. A selective
isolation medium (Campy-BAP) is comprised of brucella agar base, 10 percent
sheep red blood cells or 7 percent lysed
horse red blood cells, and the following
antimicrobial agents (to suppress growth of
bacteria normally found in feces): vancomycin, trimethoprim, polymyxin B,
amphotericin B, and cephalothin. Because
subsp. *intestinalis* will grow best at 25°C
and subsp. *jejuni* at 42°C, the selective
medium should be inoculated in duplicate
and incubated 48 hours in the following
atmosphere: 5 percent oxygen, 10 percent
carbon dioxide, and 85 percent nitrogen.
Identification of bacteria in isolated colonies is in accordance with established
criteria presented in *Bergy's Manual of Determinative Bacteriology*.

At present, many antibiotics are effective
in the treatment of patients with campylobacter infection; erythromycin and gentamicin currently are the most active.
However, because resistant strains have
been reported, antibiogram patterns should
be determined preliminary to the initiation
of therapy.

REFERENCES

Blaser, M.D., LaFarce, F.M., Wilson, N.A., and Wang, W.L.L.: Reservoirs for human campylobacteriosis. J. Infect. Dis. *141*: 665, 1980.

Buchanan, R.E. and Gibbons, N.E., Eds.: Bergy's Manual of Determinative Bacteriology. 8th Ed. Williams & Wilkins, Baltimore, 1974.

Cluffs, L.E. and Johnson, J.E., Eds.: Clinical Concepts of Infectious Diseases. 2nd Ed. Williams & Wilkins, Baltimore, 1978.

Holmgren, J. and Svennerholm, A.M.: Mechanisms of disease and immunity in cholera: A review. J. Infect. Dis., Suppl. *136*: S105, 1977.

Lenette, E.H., Balows, A., Hausler, W.G., Jr., and Truant, J.P., Eds.: Manual of Clinical Microbiology. 3rd Ed. American Society for Microbiology, Washington, D.C., 1980.

Richards, K.L. and Douglas, S.D.: Pathophysiological effects of *Vibrio cholerae* and enterotoxigenic *Escherichia coli* and their exotoxins on eucaryotic cells. Microbiol. Rev. *42*: 592, 1978.

Silbert, R.M.: The genus *Campylobacter*. Annu. Rev. Microbiol. *32*: 673, 1978.

23

Pseudomonas

Eugene A. Gorzynski

This genus is classified under the family *Pseudomonadaceae*. All species are single cells (not occurring in pairs, chains, or groups), gram-negative straight or slightly curved rods, usually indistinguishable from the *Enterobacteriaceae* with polar flagella. According to *Bergey's Manual of Determinative Bacteriology*, the genus *Pseudomonas* is comprised of 235 species, although a number of those assigned possess staining or biochemical attributes not consistent with the generic characteristics. A further paradox is the assignment to other genera of at least 25 species that conform to the current description of *Pseudomonas*.

Pseudomonads inhabit the marine environment, fresh water, and soil. Several species are notable plant pathogens; a few others cause infections in animals and man that are difficult to treat. Only the latter type of species is addressed in this chapter. In this regard, because no morphological or biochemical character of a strain or species is immutable or serves as a foundation for immediate recognition or differentiation, the assessment of multiple test reactions is required for speciation. With pathogenic pseudomonads many morphological or biochemical analyses may be required. On-

ly a few salient characteristics are included in this introduction or below, when the specific pathogens are described.

Pseudomonas spp. are not fastidious; they are easy to cultivate on simple laboratory media, including those selective or differential preparations designed for species of *Enterobacteriaceae*. Although most will tolerate pH 5.6 growth is best at neutral or slightly alkaline pH. The temperature range for growth is 4 to 43°C; 35°C is optimal for pathogens.

Under appropriate conditions, catalase and oxidase usually are produced. Pseudomonads obtain their energy from carbohydrates by oxidative rather than fermentative metabolism. In the presence of peptone, these oxidative bacteria cause the accumulation of alkaline amines that mask low levels of acidity produced; therefore, special-base media must be used to reveal whether carbohydrate metabolism, if any, is oxidative or fermentative. Species of *Pseudomonas* are categorized as strict aerobes, although a few employ denitrification as a means of anaerobic respiration. The pseudomonads most frequently associated with human infections are presented and discussed below.

PSEUDOMONAS AERUGINOSA

Characteristics

P. aeruginosa may be found in small numbers in stools from normal, healthy human subjects. Also, it is a common contaminant of the hospital environment; it has been recovered from bedside water decanters, sinks and water faucets, baths and shower stalls, forceps, oral and rectal thermometers, ward utensils, floors, Zephiran, and liquid soap, including hexachlorophene. Moreover, it is encountered in clinical specimens more frequently than any other glucose-nonfermenting gram-negative rod. Clinical isolates grown on blood agar frequently are β-hemolytic. This microorganism is unique in that in culture and in infected tissue it may produce pyocyanin (a chloroform-soluble blue pigment), water-soluble fluorescent pigments, and/or other water-soluble pigments that are brown to black in color. In contrast to *Enterobacteriaceae*, the side chains of the lipopolysaccharide (LPS)-rich cell wall of *P. aeruginosa* are devoid of neutral sugars; instead, these side chains are comprised of amino sugars.

Clinical Relevance

Healthy human subjects usually are resistant to infection by *P. aeruginosa*. It appears that this resistance collapses when the host's granulocytes are defective or are significantly reduced in number. When infection does occur, morbidity is enhanced not only by LPS but possibly by elaborated exotoxins. In addition, proteolytic enzymes (proteases) have been reported to increase virulence. Moreover, pyocyanin may contribute to necrosis of tissue cells and leukocytes by precluding uptake of oxygen. The role played by pili, when present, is not clear; they may allow for adsorption to target cells and may be responsible for the observed resistance to phagocytosis.

P. aeruginosa has been recovered as the causative agent of primary and secondary infections in compromised subjects. Accordingly, specimens from wounds, sputum, pus, exudate, blood, urine, stool, and biopsy and autopsy tissue, may yield this microorganism. Not infrequently, this microorganism is a member of the polymicrobic flora of the infected site; in this regard it may play a synergistic role. Summarized below are conditions or infections wherein *P. aeruginosa* may contribute a significant role requiring careful clinical appraisal and measures to treat or stabilize.

Respiratory Tract Infections. The respiratory tract has become a major or initial site for *P. aeruginosa* infection in older children and adults. The organism is seldom isolated from pediatric patients with chronic respiratory tract disease other than cystic fibrosis. In cystic fibrosis this microorganism is prevalent in the upper and lower respiratory tract. Almost 100 percent of those patients who die of pulmonary tract complications yield *P. aeruginosa* in their sputa; 90 percent of recovered strains are very mucoid, and frequently there is cocolonization or coinfection by several different strains or serotypes of *P. aeruginosa*. Pneumonia caused by this microorganism is associated with an 80 percent fatality in immunosuppressed and neutropenic patients. A hemolysin, phospholipase, produced by *P. aeruginosa* may contribute to its invasiveness by destroying the surfactant that protects pulmonary tissue.

Sepsis. *P. aeruginosa* may cause severe sepsis with endotoxin shock. In renal transplants, it is an important contributor to early deaths due to sepsis. Whereas pseudomonad sepsis or bacteremia previously affected the very old and very young, currently afflicted are middle age patients with acute or chronic nonneoplastic disorders or solid tumors. Depending upon the underlying clinical problem, the spectrum of mortality may be high in subjects with burns, endocarditis, urologic problems, pneumonia, or renal transplants. Of significance and independent of therapy, is the finding that a majority of patients with *P. aeruginosa* bacteremia die. Therefore, at present, control of the underlying disease contributes most toward survival.

Prognosis is always guarded in patients with severe sepsis or pulmonary tract infections complicated by *P. aeruginosa*. Therapy with the synergistic combination of carbenicillin plus either gentamicin or tobramycin may be effective. Also of value may be the administration of granulocytes and hyperimmune serum. A polyvalent vaccine comprised of the 16 internationally recognized serotypes of *P. aeruginosa* may have value. In mice a ribosomal vaccine containing protein and RNA appears highly effective against lethal infectious challenge. However, the potential or projected efficacy of active immunization in man must be considered with care; according to recent information, immune complexes with *P. aeruginosa* may play an important role in the pathogenesis of infective endocarditis.

PSEUDOMONAS PSEUDOMALLEI

Among species of *Pseudomonas*, colonies of *P. pseudomallei* on nutrient media have a unique and characteristic appearance: they are umbonate (raised central papilla, raised rim, and radial striae). Cultures have a musty, earthy odor. *P. peudomallei* is a natural inhabitant of moist soil in Southeast Asia and in North Australia. In man this microorganism is the cause of melioidosis, an infection of major concern to military personnel serving in Southeast Asia. Interest in this disease has waned since conclusion of the Vietnam War. Nonetheless, the physician must be alert to the fact that melioidosis may occur as a recrudescent infection in humans who have been injured in a country where the etiologic agent is endemic. This disease presents a clinical picture that varies from unsuspected and asymp-

tomatic infection to acute, severe pneumonia or fatal septicemia. Significantly, activation of subclinical infection can occur after prolonged latency periods. The latter infections can be precipitated by other infections and even by trauma or surgery in an aseptic field.

PSEUDOMONAS MALLEI

This nonmotile rod is the etiologic microorganism of an infectious disease, *glanders*, which primarily affects horses. *P. mallei*, transmitted to man by direct contact with an infected animal through abraded skin or by inhalation of contaminated dust, may result in wound or respiratory tract infections.

PSEUDOMONAS CEPACIA

There is an increasing association between *P. capacia* and endocarditis among intravenous users of illicit drugs. *P. cepacia* represents a good argument for the importance of speciation. Whereas carbenicillin plus gentamicin or tobramycin may be effective in treating *P. aeruginosa* infection, these antibiotics are without value in treating patients with *P. cepacia* infection; speciation and antibiogram patterns of the isolated pathogen are required.

OTHER PSEUDOMONAS SPECIES

By using only symptomatology or the microscopic or cultural morphology of isolated colonies, one cannot identify with certainty the isolated pseudomonad. Multiple tests frequently are required to speciate and to determine the antimicrobial agent that likely will be the most effective in therapy. The listing of the following *Pseudomonas* species without the presentation of detailed biochemical or antigenic characteristics should not suggest that these microorganisms are innocuous; they are important causes of infection and are not unusual isolates: *P. putida, P. maltophilia, P. stutzeri, P. fluorescens,* and *P. alcaligenes.*

REFERENCES

Buchanan, R.E. and Gibbons, N.E., Eds.: Bergey's Manual of Determinative Bacteriology. 8th Ed. Williams & Wilkins, Baltimore, 1974.

Doggett, R.G., Ed.: *Pseudomonas aeruginosa.* Academic Press, New York, 1979.

Kulczycki, L.L., Murphy, T.M., and Bellanti, J.A.: *Pseudomonas* colonization in cystic fibrosis. JAMA *240*: 30, 1978.

Lennett, E.H., Balows, A., Hausler, W.G., Jr., and Truant, J.P., Eds.: Manual of Clinical Microbiology. 3rd Ed. American Society for Microbiology, Washington, D.C., 1980.

Lieberman, M.M.: *Pseudomonas* ribosomal vaccines: Preparation, properties, and immunogenicity. Infect. Immun. *21*: 76, 1978.

Mackowiak, P.A. and Smith, J.W.: Septicemic melioidosis. JAMA *240*: 764, 1978.

Prier, J.E. and Friedman, H., Eds.: Opportunistic Pathogens. MacMillan, London, 1974.

Schlessinger, E., Ed.: Microbiology 1977. American Society for Microbiology, Washington, D.C., 1977.

Seale, T.W., Thirkill, H., Tarpay, M., et al.: Serotypes and antibiotic susceptibilities of *Pseudomonas aeruginosa* isolates from single sputa of cystic fibrosis patients. J. Clin. Microbiol. *9*: 72, 1979.

24

Legionella

Joseph H. Kite, Jr.

Legionnaires' disease is the name given to an unusually explosive outbreak of pneumonia that occurred among some of the delegates to an American Legion convention in Philadelphia in the summer of 1976. Over 200 people became ill, and 34 of them died of pneumonia or its complications. The etiology was at first unknown, and it required 5 months of intensive investigation to isolate and identify the causative rod shaped microorganism, given the interim designation of Legionnaires' disease bacterium. It was found later that the causative microorganism could be responsible also for a milder form of the disease, called Pontiac fever, in which there was pleuritis but no pneumonia or fatalities. More recently, a group of related bacteria have been recongized as additional human pathogens. On the basis of genetic characteristics, it has been proposed that all these microorganisms be classified in a new family, *Legionellaceae*, and the term legionellosis has been suggested to encompass all disease processes caused by it. Members of the single genus *Legionella* share common morphologic and cultural characteristics and probably flagellar antigens. Six species

have been proposed on the basis of differences in genetic composition as determined by DNA homology studies, antigenic characteristics, and cell wall constituents. *Legionella pneumophila*, the causative agent of Legionnaires' disease, is the most important species in terms of pneumonia produced and the frequency of isolation. This species has been subdivided into six serogroups on the basis of antigenic structure. Eighty-five percent of the isolates of *L. pneumophila* have been serogroup 1 strains. This chapter will be devoted principally to Legionnaires' disease, with a concluding section on pneumonias caused by other species of *Legionella*. Legionnaires' disease appears to be spread by inhalation of air or dust containing the microorganism. Person-to-person spread apparently does not occur. Currently, erythromycin is the drug of choice for treatment.

DESCRIPTION OF THE PATHOGEN

Legionella pneumophila is an aerobic, gram-negative (lightly stained with safranin), pleomorphic bacterial rod, 0.3 to 0.5 μm wide by 2 to 3 μm long, with

329

filamentous forms equal to or greater than 20 μm in length. The microorganisms are fastidious, nonsporulating, and usually not flaggelated. Examination by electron microscopy reveals a typical prokaryotic morphology, vacuolated, dividing by binary fission, and similar in appearance to other gram-negative bacteria. Although the usual bacteriologic stains give poor results, the Dieterle silver impregnation stain is useful for the recognition of the microorganism in tissues but is not specific.

L. pneumophila is unable to grow on many standard bacteriologic media such as blood agar or unenriched chocolate agar. The bacterium can be grown on medium containing Mueller-Hinton (M-H) agar base without antibiotics supplemented with 1 percent hemoglobin or ferric pyrophosphate to supply iron and 1 percent IsoVitaleX to supply L-cysteine. Plates of agar medium are incubated at 35°C in a 5 percent CO_2 atmosphere or in a candle jar for up to 7 days. The generation time of the organism is over 3 hours, and it usually requires 4 or 5 days before growth is visible. Nutrient requirements of *L. pneumophila* are not particularly complex, and good growth has been obtained in liquid or solid media containing only 21 amino acids and inorganic salts. A critical factor for good growth appears to be an adequate concentration of amino acids in the medium. Analysis of all constituents has led to the formulation of a new medium, Feeley-Gorman (F-G) agar, on which colonies grow more rapidly and in greater numbers. Recently, a semiselective medium, charcoal yeast extract agar (CYE) supplemented with polymyxin B and vancomycin, has been used to isolate *L. pneumophila* from contaminated specimens. It is likely that additional improvements and new formulations will be made. A highly efficient selective medium should permit recovery of the organism from expectorated sputum and from soil and other environmental samples.

The bacterium will grow intraperitoneal-ly in guinea pigs and in the yolk sac of embryonated eggs. When the organism is grown on agar medium containing sufficient L-tyrosine or L-phenylalanine, a soluble brown pigment is produced that may represent melanin formation. Under some conditions *L. pneumophila* also produces one or more substances that fluoresce under Wood's light (ultraviolet). *L. pneumophila* does not ferment any known carbohydrate.

No toxins have been clearly identified, but some detectable "endotoxicity" appears to be different in several respects from the classical endotoxicity generally associated with gram-negative organisms. The active principle may represent a new type of bacterial lipopolysaccharide. Toxic products could account for the pathology observed in organ systems other than the lungs. Final identity of isolated *L. pneumophila* requires serologic testing, usually with fluorescent labeled antiserum. Six serotypes have been identified. *L. pneumophila* has not been found to be related to other bacteria examined to date using the DNA homology technique. All strains behave as a single species. The strain type is Philadelphia 1, and Pontiac 1 is the most divergent strain. *L. pneumophila* contains a high content of branched chain fatty acids — a unique profile that may serve as an important means of identifying the organism. From these observations suggestions have been made that the organism be classified in a family separate from the presently recognized microorganisms.

EPIDEMIOLOGY

Investigations of the cause of Legionnaires' disease illustrate the importance of an epidemiologic approach to understanding disease. It was determined early that the illness was not confined to legionnaires. However, those affected persons not associated with the convention had one thing in common with the sick conventioneers — for one reason or another they had been in or near the Bellevue-Stratford Hotel in Philadelphia. Those persons who stayed overnight at the hotel showed a higher rate of illness than those who stayed elsewhere. The only family contacts who became ill had been in Philadelphia for the convention, indicating that the disease had not been spread from person to person. Also, the obvious possibility that the disease might have been spread by food or drink was ruled out. Other observations suggested that the disease might have been spread through the air, pointing suspicion toward the air conditioning system. Those who became ill had spent more time in the lobby of the hotel than those who remained well. Members of a second group of seriously ill patients were found to have a clinical illness indistinguishable from that originally defined as Legionnaires' disease, but these patients had not attended the American Legion Convention. Since they had been within a one block area of the convention headquarters hotel without entering it, they were defined as having Broad Street pneumonia.

The clinical symptoms produced could have been caused by a variety of agents, including heavy metals, toxic organic substances, and infectious organisms. Six months after the convention in Philadelphia, Fraser, McDade, and Shepard at the Center for Disease Control succeeded in isolating a previously unrecognized bacterium and identified it as the causative agent. Success was achieved by inoculation of guinea pigs with tissue specimens obtained from autopsy. This technique had been useful for isolating rickettsial organisms that cause a pneumonia called Q fever. Spleen tissue taken from inoculated guinea pigs was found to contain small rod shaped organisms. Growth of the organisms could be achieved by inoculating them into the yolk sac of embryonated eggs.

After the finding of the organisms, the next critical step was to prove that they caused the disease. An indirect immunofluorescent test was performed on the isolated bacteria to detect antibodies in patient's serum. This was done by adding serum from a patient to a smear of the bacteria followed by fluorescein conjugated rabbit antibody to human antibody. When many patients' sera were tested in this fashion, more than 90 percent of the serum specimens were positive and in more than 50 percent there was a rise in titer between paired specimens. These findings indicated that the patients had been infected recently by this particular microorganism. The question remained as to whether the organism was a rickettsia or a bacterium. With a specially enriched agar medium the organism could be grown outside of guinea pigs or eggs and thus was shown to be a bacterium.

The habitat of *L. pneumophila* appears to be the inanimate environment, particularly soil and water. The natural occurrence of the organism in a variety of habitats has not been extensively explored because isolation of the organism in the past has required inoculation into guinea pigs in order to obtain growth. Transmission of the disease appears to be airborne, and person-to-person spread has not been documented. A frequent source of organisms appears to be aerosols from air conditioning cooling towers or evaporative condensers. There is also some association with inhaled dust from excavation sites. It appears that the organism is widespread in nature and may be transmitted with dust, as occurs in the fungal disease histoplasmosis. Little is known about the size of the infectious dose of *L. pneumophila*.

The disease is more frequent in the summer, but sporadic cases occur in all seasons. Most patients are middle aged to elderly, although the disease can occur in persons of any age. An increased predominance among men may reflect an increased exposure risk among them. There appears to be an increased risk for cigarette smokers and patients receiving immunosuppressive therapy. *L. pneumophila* appears to be an opportunistic pathogen.

Legionnaires' disease has been found frequently to occur in outbreaks. At the end of 1978 more than 600 epidemic associated cases of Legionnaires' disease (12 epidemics) and 270 sporadic cases had been detected. Legionnaires' disease has been reported in all parts of the United States and Canada and in Europe, Israel, and Australia. It is probable that cases will be found throughout the world. Three outbreaks and several isolated cases have involved renal homograft recipients and other patients receiving immunosuppressive therapy. It is possible to acquire the disease as a nosocomial infection.

Two recognized forms of legionellosis have clearly different incubation periods. Legionnaires' disease has an attack rate of 1 to 5 percent and an incubation period of 2 to 10 days, whereas Pontiac fever, which occurred in 1968 and was recognized retrospectively, has an attack rate of 95 percent and an incubation period of 36 hours. At this time one can only speculate that differences in the pathogenicity of the responsible strains, perhaps in addition to differences in dose and the underlying health of groups affected, may have resulted in different incubation periods and clinical manifestations in these two outbreaks.

No consistent common factor has been identified as the source of infection, although several outbreaks have been associated with particular buildings or their environment. In Pontiac, Michigan, the air conditioning system was clearly identified as the vehicle that spread the infection, while an excavation site seemed to be associated with at least one other outbreak. The air treatment system may serve as an amplifier as well as a delivery system for *L. pneumophila*.

Selective and enriched media are needed for more rapid and efficient detection of the organisms from environmental sources such as water and soil. More than 200 water samples from 23 lakes in Georgia and South Carolina were screened by fluorescent antibody tests for *L. pneumophila*. Over 90 percent were positive, and *L. pneumophila*, serogroup 1, was isolated from four of these samples. It is known that the organism can live in tap water for as long as a year.

Although the causative agent of Legionnaires' disease was recognized only recently, results of serologic, cultural, and DNA relatedness studies have shown that *L. pneumophila* and three unclassified agents isolated in 1947, 1959 and 1968 are the same species. Thus this organism has been in the environment and the cause of disease for over 30 years.

PATHOGENESIS

Legionella pneumophila may cause disease ranging from a mild pneumonitis not requiring hospitalization to that of a multilobar pneumonia with a fatal outcome resulting from respiratory failure. In Legionnaires' disease there is a typical pattern of lobar pneumonia. The alveoli are filled with many neutrophils, macrophages, and abundant fibrin. Extensive necrosis of the cellular exudate is common, and focal necrosis of alveolar septa is occasionally seen. When the Dieterle silver impregnation stain is used, many bacteria can be seen in the exudate, often inside macrophages. Bronchi are notably spared, a fact that may help explain the infrequency of sputum and the lack of observed person-to-person spread. Although the fatality rate has been 15 to 20 percent in the past, clinical recognition and treatment have probably lowered this rate considerably.

Other organs may be involved, producing an effect on cerebral, renal, and hepatic function. It is not clear at present whether these organs are affected by bacterial invasion, by toxin produced by the bacteria, or by antigen–antibody complexes.

While this infection may affect the healthy host, the immunosuppressed patient appears to be at greatest risk for developing Legionnaires' disease.

In Pontiac fever there is pleuritis but no pneumonia, and no other organ systems are affected. No fatalities have been reported. Guinea pigs that were exposed during the Pontiac fever outbreak to an aerosol condensate from the air conditioning system developed a nodular pneumonia from which a bacterium was recovered that is indistinguishable from that which causes Legionnaires' disease. It is not known whether or not routes of infection other than inhalation can function naturally.

CLINICAL MANIFESTATIONS

The earliest symptoms include malaise, diffuse myalgia, and headache. Within 12 to 48 hours there is a sudden onset of high nonremittent fever (40 to 40.5°C), recurrent shaking chills, and severe prostration. A dry cough is common early, and later may become productive. Three additional groups of symptoms can be seen: (1) chest pain, often pleuritic, (2) diarrhea, abdominal pain, or vomiting, and (3) confusion and delirium. The latter symptoms may indicate some degree of toxic encephalopathy. Legionnaires' disease may vary from a mild respiratory illness without pneumonia to a severe multisystem disease involving lungs, liver, gastrointestinal tract, kidneys, and the central nervous system.

Physical examination often reveals few abnormal findings other than an acutely ill, febrile patient with pulmonary rales or rhonchi but with no evidence of consolidation. Clinical laboratory tests usually show a slight elevation of the white blood cell count. Sputum production is uncommon; however, microscopic examination of Gram-stained smears of sputum shows few leukocytes and few or no bacteria. Chest roentgenograms show a patchy infiltrate that may have an interstitial or a consoli-

dated appearance early but typically progresses to a nodular consolidation that may be unilateral or bilateral.

Clinically, the disease can be difficult to distinguish from other "atypical" pneumonias including mycoplasmal pneumonia, psittaocosis. Q fever, influenza, viral pneumonia, tularemia, and plague. Such diseases must be considered in making a differential diagnosis. Factors favoring the diagnosis of Legionnaires' disease include occurence in older adults, diarrhea, rigors, an obtunded state, the nodularity of a pulmonary consolidation, and perhaps time of year.

The disease often becomes progressively worse over the initial 4 to 6 days of hospitalization. About 15 percent of the cases have been fatal; death is associated with respiratory failure or shock.

Mild cases of this disease have been documented by a fourfold or greater rise in antibody titer in paired serum specimens. The outbreak at Pontiac, Michigan had no instances of pneumonia and no deaths in 144 cases. The syndrome of fever, myalgia, and headache of acute onset and short duration seen in that outbreak clearly differs from the classical cases described above and from that seen in other outbreaks that have been investigated. It is likely that the full spectrum of Legionnaires' disease will be found to be much broader than is now recognized.

DIAGNOSIS

Legionnaires' disease should be suspected in acutely ill patients who have clinical or radiologic evidence of pulmonary consolidation but lack significant microorganisms on microscopic and cultural examination. Any available material (i.e., sputum, transtracheal aspirates, pleural fluid, or lung tissue) should be inoculated onto appropriate media and examined for the presence of *L. pneumophila*. An acute phase serum should be collected im-

Table 24.1. Laboratory Diagnosis of
Legionnaires' Disease

Demonstration of the organism in tissues or
body fluids
  Stains
    Dieterle silver impregnation stain
    Giménez stain
  Smears of sputum or respiratory secretions
    Direct fluorescent antibody test
    Enzyme-linked immunosorbent assay
    (ELISA)
  Detection in urine
    ELISA
    Reversed passive hemagglutination

Demonstration of a rise in titer of serum anti-
bodies
  Antigen used
    Polyvalent suspension of six serotypes
  Tests
    Indirect fluorescent antibody
      Positive test: A fourfold rise in titer of
            paired sera to $\geq$ 128 or a ti-
            ter $\geq$ 256 on a single serum
    Hemagglutination
      Positive test: A fourfold rise in titer of
            paired sera to $\geq$ 80 or a ti-
            ter $\geq$ 80 on a single serum

Isolation of the causative organism
  Growth on
    Mueller-Hinton medium plus iron and cys-
    teine[a]
    Feeley-Gorman agar
    Charcoal yeast extract agar[b]
  Identification
    By fluorescent labeled rabbit antiserum to
    L. pneumophila

---

[a]Cultivation is possible from lung tissue or pleural
fluid, but *L. pneumophila* cannot be cultured on this
medium from sputum or transtracheal aspirates.

[b]Charcoal yeast extract agar may be used to grow *L.
pneumophila* from sputum and environmental
samples.

mediately, so that the titer can be compared with that of a second serum drawn 3
to 5 weeks later. The laboratory diagnosis
of Legionnaires' disease can be made by (1)
demonstration of the presence of the

organism in the patient's tissues or body
fluids, (2) demonstration of a four-fold rise
in titer of serum antibodies to the organism, and (3) isolation of the organism from
the patient. These procedures are outlined
in Table 24.1.

Demonstration of the Presence of the Organism in the Patient's Tissues or Body Fluids

L. pneumophila cannot be stained satisfactorily in tissues or exudates by conventional staining methods such as the Gram stain,
but the microorganism may be seen in tissues by the nonspecific Dieterle silver impregnation stain (Fig. 24.1) or the Giménez
stain. Bacteria can be seen in cellular exudates, often inside macrophages. A specific and more sensitive method for demonstrating the organisms is the use of the
direct fluorescent antibody (FA) test in
which tissues or smears of sputum or respiratory secretions are exposed to fluorescein-labeled antibodies to *L. pneumophila*.
The most practical means is to use a
polyvalent conjugate prepared against
strains representative of the six serologic
groups. A third method for the detection of
antigens or organisms in sputum and urine
is the enzyme-linked immunosorbent assay
(ELISA). In this test an enzyme (peroxidase) is chemically linked to rabbit antiserum to *L. pneumophila*. The antiserum is
then added to the clinical material containing the suspected organism and is allowed
to incubate, and then the substrate to the
enzyme is added. Following an additional
period of incubation, a color change in the
altered substrate is measured. The ELISA
test is rapid and can detect antigen in 3
hours. Soluble antigen can be detected in
the absence of living bacteria and in specimens such as urine and sputum.

Since measurable amounts of *L.
pneumophila* antigen can be detected in the
urine during the course of the disease, examination of this clinical specimen may be

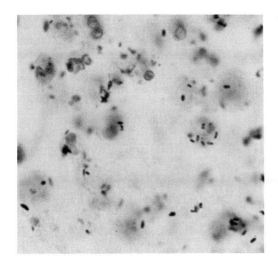

Fig. 24.1. Photograph of *Legionella pneumophila* in tissue section of lung from a patient with Legionnaires' disease. Dieterle silver impregnation stain. (× 9700) (Slide obtained through courtesy of Dr. W.C. Winn, University of Vermont, College of Medicine.)

useful when sputum cannot be obtained. In addition to the ELISA test, a reversed passive hemagglutination test is also rapid and highly sensitive for detection of antigen. It is performed by using sheep erythrocytes tanned and coated with anti-*L. pneumophila* globulin. These two tests do not require radioactive reagents or specialized equipment, and thus they are particularly suited to the study of large numbers of specimens in a wide range of laboratory conditions.

Demonstration of the Rise in Titer of Serum Antibodies to the Organism

The indirect fluorescent antibody test is used with known organisms of each serogroup (six serogroups identified) or with a polyvalent antigen suspension. The Center for Disease Control criterion for diagnosis is a four-fold rise in titer of paired sera to ≥ 128 or a titer of ≥ 256 on a single serum. Antibodies may be detected as early as 5 to 7 days after onset of symptoms, but as in most other infections, serologic studies generally do not assist the clinician in the differential diagnosis early in the course of the patient's illness.

A microhemagglutination test has been established by coating red blood cells with extracts of *L. pneumophila*. The hemagglutination (HA) procedure compares favorably with the indirect FA technique for detecting antibody. Because the hemagglutination method is simpler, more rapid, and less expensive than the indirect FA procedure, the HA test is well suited for large seroepidemiologic surveys. The upper limit of titer in normal individuals is 8, and 32 is considered the lowest titer suggestive of infection (but not necessarily disease).

Isolation of the Organism From the Patient

Examination of sputum by Gram stain will reveal no predominant bacterial species and few polymorphonuclear leukocytes. Blood, sputum, pleural fluid, and lung tissue may be inoculated in guinea pigs, on supplemented M-H medium, F-G agar, or CYE agar. Incubation of the agar plate medium is made at 35°C in 5 percent CO_2 for up to 7 days because the organism is slow growing. Confirmation of the identity of the organism is made by fluorescent labeled antiserum.

When a supplemented M-H medium has been used, *L. pneumophila* has not been isolated on culture from sputum or transtracheal aspirates, although direct culture is possible from lung tissue and pleural fluid. It may be anticipated that isolation attempts and characterization of colonial growth will improve as new media are devised. Recent success with charcoal yeast extract agar for primary isolation would suggest the importance of including this medium in routine cultivation of certain specimens.

THERAPY

The antibiotic of choice in treatment of patients with Legionnaires' disease is erythromycin. It is also effective against mycoplasmal pneumonia, streptococcal pneumonia, and pneumonias caused by some strains of *Staphylococcus aureus*. No cultures of *L. pneumophila* resistant to erythromycin have been found to date. For the patient with confirmed Legionnaires' disease who is faring poorly on erythromycin therapy alone, consideration should be given to rifampin therapy. Although rifampin is effective, it probably should be used only in combination with erythromycin because of the risk of developing rifampin-resistant organisms. Penicillin is not effective against *L. pneumophila*, probably because the organism produces a β-lactamase.

PREVENTION

Although person-to-person spread has not been documented, respiratory isolation of patients with Legionnaires' disease pneumonia may be warranted until more information is available on whether debilitated hospitalized patients are at risk of contacting Legionnaires' disease from other patients with this illness.

The recognition that some outbreaks of Legionnaires' disease may result from spread of aerosols of *L. pneumophila* from contaminated air conditioning cooling towers or evaporative condensers raises the possibility that decontamination or preventive maintenance of air conditioning systems may halt or prevent some outbreaks. The outbreak in Pontiac ceased after the health department building was closed and the air conditioning system was repaired. *L. pneumophila* is susceptible to a variety of commonly recommended hospital and laboratory disinfectants, often in low concentrations. Chemicals such as phenolics, quaternary ammonium compounds, glutar-

aldehyde, formaldehyde, and hypochlorite could be used to eradicate potential reservoirs of human infection.

Immunity, as measured by seropositivity, does develop among persons in the same environment as those who contract the disease. Complement and bactericidal antibodies appear to play an important role in mediating the resistance to infection in laboratory animals. However, *L. pneumophila* appears to exist as a facultative intracellular pathogen, capable of growing to high titers in human monocytes and macrophages. Evidence suggests that for *L. pneumophila*, as for tuberculosis and leprosy bacilli, the presence of serum antibodies directed against the bacteria does not protect the individual from infection. Thus cell-mediated immunity, regulated by lymphokine-producing T cells, may be the more important mechanism which operates by stimulating monocytes and macrophages to inhibit the growth of *L. pneumophila*. This hypothesis would explain why individuals who have defective cell-mediated immunity are more susceptible to the disease. It would also suggest that a vaccine for Legionnaires' disease must elicit cell-mediated immunity to be effective.

OTHER LEGIONELLA THAT CAUSE PNEUMONIAS

The recent observation that pneumonia can be caused by a previously unrecognized bacterium, *L. pneumophila*, has legitimized findings that otherwise may have been unreported or given skeptical attention. Within 1 year after the Philadelphia epidemic, investigators in Pittsburgh and in Charlottesville, Va. recognized that an unusual acid-fast bacterium was producing acute fibrinopurulent pneumonia in renal transplant patients. An organism was isolated in guinea pigs by the Pittsburgh group and named the Pittsburgh pneumonia agent (PPA). Two other rickettsialike organisms, originally named HEBA and TATLOCK, were later found to be identical to PPA. Although the name *L. pittsburgensis* has been proposed for this organism, the name presently accepted is *L. micdadei*. The clinical illness produced by this organism is similar to Legionnaires' pneumonia as it occurs in compromised hosts. All patients have been immunosuppressed, and the administration of corticosteroids has been a common feature. Although *L. micdadei* is weakly acid-fast in infected human lung tissue, all of the isolates grown on agar have not been acid fast with standard or modified (1% H_2SO_4) Ziehl-Neelsen stains.

Pneumonia has also been produced by *L. bozemanii* (a rickettsialike agent formerly called WIGA) and *L. dumoffii* (formerly called TEX-KL). Although clinical information relating to these patients is very limited, two of the original patients had experienced accidental submersion in water. The other three patients probably developed nosocomial infections; two of these patients had chronic renal failure, and the third had a carcinoma of the lung. Two cases of pneumonia caused by *L. dumoffii* have been reported in immunosuppressed patients; a similar bacterial isolate has been obtained from a cooling tower.

A fourth new bacterial species, *L. gormanii*, was isolated from the environment and has been serologically, although not yet culturally, implicated in human pneumonia. A fifth species, with the proposed name *L. longbeachae*, has been isolated recently from the respiratory tract of four patients with pneumonia.

These new species of *Legionella* are all gram-negative rods that share the fastidious growth requirements of *L. pneumophila* and cause human pneumonia difficult to distinguish clinically from that caused by *L. pneumophila*. This rapidly expanding number of phenotypically similar species of etiologic agents of human pneumonia is due to the increasing awareness of their presence by the medical profession and clinical laboratory personnel and to the use of CYE agar or buffered CYE agar as primary isolation media in culturing organisms from specimens of the respiratory system in cases of suspected legionellosis.

The discovery of legionellosis and other "new" bacterial diseases should serve to reemphasize the determinant role of the host in overt clinical manifestations of infection. Also it should serve to remind the physician and the laboratory worker that many so-called saprophytes can be pathogenic by virtue of the state of health and immunity of the host.

REFERENCES

Balows, A. and Fraser, D.W.: International Symposium on Legonnaires' Disease. Ann. Intern. Med. *90*: 489, 1979.

Fraser, D.W. and McDade, J.E.: Legionellosis. Sci. Am. *241*: 82, 1979.

Jones, G.L. and Hébert, G.A., Eds.: "Legionnaires'," the Disease, the Bacterium and Methodology. HEW Publication no. (CDC) 79–8375, 1979.

Meyer, R.S. and Finegold, S.M.: Legionnaires' Disease. Annu. Rev. Med. *31*: 219, 1980.

Winn, W.C. and Myerowitz, R.L.: The pathology of the legionella pneumonias. Human Pathol. *12*: 401, 1981.

25

Haemophilus, Bordetella, and Brucella

Reginald M. Lambert

HAEMOPHILUS

A small, gram-negative bacillus was isolated by Pfeiffer from the nasopharynx of many patients with influenza during the pandemic of 1890. This bacillus was recovered with such high frequency from the patients that it was considered to be the etiologic agent of influenza. A similar experience during the influenza pandemic of 1918 seemed to support the same conclusion. In 1923, the bacillus was named *Haemophilus influenzae*. It is now known, however, that influenza is caused by a virus, not *H. influenzae*.

As the name indicates, members of the genus *Haemophilus* require media enriched with blood or constituents of erythrocytes for primary isolation. The type species of the genus is *H. influenzae*, an important etiologic agent of acute bacterial meningitis, especially in children. Other species of medical significance are *H. parainfluenzae, H. ducreyi, H. aegyptius, H. haemolyticus,* and *H. parahaemolyticus*. One species, *H. suis*, has special biologic interest owing to its synergistic participation with a virus in producing influenza of swine.

Morphologic Characteristics

H. influenzae is a small, gram-negative coccobacillus that is about 0.2 to 0.3 μm in width and 0.5 μm in length. In smooth colonies of fresh isolates and in smears prepared directly from sputum and exudates, the organisms are seen single or in pairs and may give bipolar staining. In thick preparations the cells may be confused with the gram-positive pneumococci because of difficulty in the decolorizing step of the Gram stain procedure. In older cultures the cells exhibit marked pleomorphism with longer cells (1.0 to 2.0 μm in length), short chains, and long, threadlike filamentous forms. Members of the genus *Haemophilus* are not motile and do not produce spores. Capsules are formed by *H. influenzae* but are quickly lost after only 6 to 8 hours in culture. Cells in exudates from older lesions lose the capsules as the pleomorphic forms appear.

Cultural Characteristics

The *Haemophilus* spp. are facultative in the requirement for oxygen and need one or both of two substances, the X and V factors, for primary isolation and growth under aerobic conditions. The X factor in blood is *hematin* or *hemin*, the heme portion of hemoglobin that diffuses from erythrocytes; it is readily available in media containing blood. Other iron-containing pigments that are able to furnish the tetrapyrrole compounds necessary for synthesizing the iron-containing respiratory enzymes cytochrome, cytochrome oxidase, catalase, and peroxidase can presumably substitute for the X factor in blood. The X factor is not required for anaerobic growth.

The V factor, nicotinamide adenine dinucleotide (NAD [DNP] or NADP [TPN]), is also present in intact red cells but diffuses poorly through the membrane into the medium. In addition, blood plates contain heat sensitive enzymes that inactivate V factor reducing the amount available. Consequently, *H. influenzae* and other V factor–dependent species grow very poorly if at all on blood agar. Chocolate agar supports the growth of *Haemophilus* spp. much better than blood agar. Chocolate agar is prepared by adding blood to a heated basal medium that effectively inactivates the enzymes that destroy V factor. It is commonplace to add commercially available supplements containing both X and V factors to chocolate agar. Such a medium is very useful for primary isolation of not only *Haemophilus* spp. but for *Neisseria gonorrhoeae* and *Neisseria meningitidis* as well.

In mixed cultures on blood agar, colonies of *H. influenzae* can be seen around colonies of other organisms, especially staphylococci, that are supplying V factor to the medium. This has been called the *satellite phenomenon*. It can be readily demonstrated by streaking the entire surface of a blood plate with a pure culture of *H. influenzae* followed by adding a single or a few straight streaks with a pure culture of *Staphylococcus aureus* or by adding a strip of filter paper that has been impregnated with a solution of commercially prepared V factor.

Colonies of *H. influenzae* are small (0.5 to 1.0 mm), round, entire, convex, colorless, and transparent. The loss of colonial irridescence after 6 to 8 hours of incubation is due to the loss of capsules and to the smooth-rough cultural phase variation. A mucoid–smooth–rough phase change has been described for *H. influenzae* in which the mucoid (M) phase is the fully encapsulated, serologically typeable form with small, coccobacillary cells occurring singly and in pairs. The smooth (S) phase has only patches of capsular material on the cell surface, is very difficult to type, and is characterized by an increased pleomorphic mi-

Table 25.1.   Requirements for X and V Factors and Hemolytic Properties of the Genus *Haemophilus*

Haemophilus Species	Growth Factors		Blood Plate Hemolysis
	X	V	
H. influenzae	+	+	−
H. parainfluenzae	−	+	−
H. haemolyticus	+	+	+
H. parahaemolyticus	−	+	+
H. aegyptius	+	+	−
H. ducreyi	+	−	+
H. suis	+(?)	+	−

croscopic appearance. The rough (R) phase is not serologically typeable with antisera specific for capsular substances and microscopically exhibits marked pleomorphism.

H. influenzae is reminiscent of *Streptococcus pneumoniae* not only in the phenomenon of smooth–rough phase variation and loss of serologically typeable capsules, but both organisms undergo autolysis in older cultures and are bile soluble.

H. influenzae is sensitive to most antiseptics and is killed by drying and exposure to 50 to 56°C for 30 minutes. Lactose is not fermented and other carbohydrates are attacked with high variability.

Antigenic Characteristics

Encapsulated strains of *H. influenzae* can be serologically typed with capsular antisera into six types designated a, b, c, d, e, and f. The capsular materials of types a, b, c, d, and f have been identified as polysaccharides, with all but type d containing phosphorus. Types a, c, and f have been found to be polyglucophosphate, polygalactophosphate, and polygalactosamine phosphate, respectively. Type b capsular substance contains a pentose sugar, ribose, rather than a hexose sugar and is composed of pairs of polyribophosphate (PRP) chains forming a structure similar to the backbone of ribonucleic acid (RNA). Recent studies indicate that the chains are probably polyribosylribitol phosphate.

Serologic typing of *H. influenzae* can be performed using type specific antisera and soluble capsular material either in a fluid phase or agar gel precipitation reaction or with encapsulated organisms to produce a capsular swelling (*Quellung*) reaction. For agglutination and capsular swelling reactions, organisms from solid media are best because the capsular material is quickly solubilized and lost from the cells in liquid media or spinal fluid.

Somatic O antigens have been reported as well as other nonendotoxic antigens, such as P antigen that is strain specific and an M antigen that appears to be present in all strains of *H. influenzae*.

Pathogenic Characteristics

H. influenzae is a strict parasite of man. Its normal habitat is the upper respiratory tract; it is not normally found elsewhere in the body. It is an invasive organism that is a primary, pyogenic agent of disease, and it can be found as a secondary complication of infections primarily caused by other organisms. It was in the latter capacity that *H. influenzae* was recovered from sputum and autopsy material of influenza patients during the pandemics of 1890 and 1918.

The carrier rate of *H. influenzae* among children is 30 to 50 percent and in adults 30 to 80 percent. Only 1 percent or less of the carriers have an encapsulated strain; all others are nonencapsulated. Serious infections by *H. influenzae* are caused predominantly by encapsulated strains of type b. Nonencapsulated strains are recovered from less severe infections. The list of diseases caused by *H. influenzae* includes meningitis, epiglottitis, otitis media, cellulitis, pneumonia, chronic bronchitis, other respiratory diseases, laryngitis, systemic infections, septic arthritis, and many others. Severe infections found with greatest frequency are meningitis, epiglottitis and obstructive infections of the respiratory tract, pyarthrosis, pneumonia, and empyema.

Acute bacterial meningitis due to *H. influenzae* remains one of the few serious life-threatening diseases of childhood that has not been brought under effective control. In fact, *H. influenzae* is the most frequent cause of bacterial meningitis in children, except during epidemics of meningitis caused by *N. meningitidis*. The use of antibiotics has reduced the fatality rate from 90 percent to the current 5 to 10 percent. However, 30 to 50 percent of those who recover suffer permanent neurologic sequelae such as blindness, deafness, mental retardation, hydrocephalus, and cerebral palsy. Since the introduction of antibiotics about 30 years ago, there has been no further decline in the mortality rate. During the same time period, the incidence of the disease has increased three or four times. Meningitis due to *H. influenzae* is not a reportable disease, but it has been estimated that the disease has a frequency of 4.8 per 100,000 population and 35 to 50 per 100,000 children under 5 years, representing about 10,000 cases each year in the United States.

H. influenzae enters the respiratory tract and establishes a nasopharyngitis with fever. Any portion of the lower respiratory tract may become involved from which a bacteremia and septicemia may develop. The bloodstream carries the organisms throughout the body, with the meninges and joints preferential sites for localization.

All of the infections listed above occur in adults, but with a much lower frequency. However, the incidence of these infections in adults may be higher than is realized. Many clinical laboratories do not use chocolate agar or other media rich in V factor for cultures from adults and, consequently, *H. influenzae* is not recovered or recognized.

Diagnosis

Since the infections including meningitis caused by *H. influenzae* do not differ in clinical appearance from those caused by other pyogenic bacteria, such as staphylococci, streptococci, pneumococci and meningococci, diagnosis must be made bacteriologically. Sputum, pus, or sediment of spinal fluid is used for culture on blood and chocolate agar, for direct examination of Gram-stained preparations and for examination of capsular swelling, immunofluorescence, and agglutination reactions. Spinal fluid may be used for fluid phase and agar precipitation studies, for inhibition of

agglutination, and for passive hemagglutination and inhibition of passive hemagglutination reactions.

Reactions with organisms in the sediment of centrifuged spinal fluid specimen may not always be successful, since the capsular material dissolves in the spinal fluid very readily. Organisms from 6 to 8 hour cultures on solid media have better capsules and give more reliable serologic reactions.

Treatment

H. influenzae is susceptible to the penicillins, chloramphenicol, and other chemotherapeutic agents. Ampicillin is the drug of choice. In recent years, strains resistant to ampicillin because of a plasmid-mediated production of β-lactamase have been encountered with increasing frequency. For serious infections chloramphenicol is the drug of choice because high cerebrospinal fluid levels can be achieved and resistant strains are rare. For minor infections erythromycin, tetracycline, and sulfamethoxazole-trimethoprim are useful.

Prevention

Many workers believe that the persistent high mortality rate, high morbidity rate, increasing incidence, and increasing resistance to antibiotics indicate the need for effective vaccine control of *H. influenzae* infections. Such vaccines are not yet commercially available.

Prophylactic use of chemotherapeutic agents should be restricted to children at risk from close contact with patients with serious infections of *H. influenzae*. The entire family should be treated, not just the children at risk, since the original infection may have derived from an adult carrier. However, short term use of antibiotics will not prevent reestablishment of the carrier state later or prevent further infections. On the other hand, wide scale prophylactic use of antibiotics should be discouraged.

H. aegyptius

The *Koch-Weeks bacillus* or *H. aegyptius* causes a highly contagious conjunctivitis that has been called *pink-eye*. The organism was originally seen in smears from eye infections in Egypt by Koch in 1883. The bacillus was first recovered in pure culture by Weeks in 1887. *H. aegyptius* resembles *H. influenzae* both morphologically and culturally. It does not have a capsule and, consequently, does not have irridescent colonies. Species specific antigens of this organism have been reported. Topical treatment with sulfonamides has been found effective for eye infections with *H. aegyptius*. Ampicillin and other antibiotics may be just as effective.

H. ducreyi

H. ducreyi causes a venereal disease called *soft chancre* or *chancroid*. A pustule surrounded by an area of redness and inflammation appears on or around the genitalia 4 to 10 days after exposure. The pustule quickly becomes a necrotic ulcer with soft, irregular edges. The infection frequently spreads to the lymph nodes in the groin, causing swelling. Several lesions may be present at the same time.

Microscopically, *H. ducreyi* occurs singly, in pairs, or in small clumps and may appear in parallel rows. The organism requires both X and V factors for growth. Material for culture should be taken from the floor of the ucler, streaked onto rabbit blood agar and incubated at 37°C in a reduced oxygen tension. Colonies are small, gray, glistening, convex, and have entire margins.

H. ducreyi appears to be antigenically homogeneous. Many patients develop a hypersensitivity to the organism, but skin testing with killed intact organisms is not a useful diagnostic aid. Direct smears from the lesion are positive in 40 to 65 percent of cases; positive cultures are obtained in 60 to 90 percent.

H. ducreyi causes about 10 percent of venereal disease and may be present in mixed infections with syphilis. Antibiotic treatment of soft chancre is promptly effective.

H. suis and Swine Influenza

In 1931 Shope showed that influenza of swine was caused by combination of a virus and a bacterium. Swine influenza is similar to that of humans, with high morbidity and low mortality. In the period between epidemics the virus survives in lung worms that live in the lungs of swine in a symbiotic relationship. *H. suis* is found in the nasopharynx of hogs in increasing numbers when climatic conditions are adverse and the virus ceases to be dormant and produces the disease. Experimentally, both the bacillus and the virus were required to cause the disease. The relationship of *H. influenzae* to human viral influenza is that of a secondary invader rather than as a primary partner with influenza virus to cause the disease.

BORDETELLA

The genus *Bordetella* includes the three species *B. pertussis*, *B. parapertussis*, and *B. bronchiseptica*. These bacteriologically and serologically related bacteria are associated with respiratory tract infections. The medically most important member of the genus is *B. pertussis*, which cause whooping cough. Infections of *B. parapertussis* are less common than those caused by *B. pertussis* but more common than generally realized. *B. bronchiseptica*, which is primarily a resident of the respiratory tract of animals, is recovered from humans after close contact with pets and domestic animals. Infections by this organism are infrequent.

B. pertussis is an obligate parasite of man, although experimental infections can be induced in several different species of animals. It is a delicate bacterium that survives outside the human host for only 1 to 2 hours. It is sensitive to chemical antiseptics, disinfectants, and ultraviolet light and is killed by temperatures as low as 50 to 55°C in 30 minutes. Transmission is by inhalation of droplets produced by the cough or sneeze of an infected person.

Microscopic Characteristics

On primary isolation, bordetellae are small, coccoid, gram-negative bacilli ranging in size from 0.3 to 0.5 μm in diameter and 0.5 to 1.0 μm in length. Older cultures characteristically exhibit increased pleomorphism and may have filamentous forms as well. Only B. bronchiseptica is motile. Spores are not formed. Capsules are present but cannot be demonstrated by capsular-swelling techniques.

Cultural Characteristics

Bordetellae require complex media for primary isolation and growth. Bordet-Gengou agar is the medium of choice. Originally devised by Bordet and Gengou in 1906, this medium has been used with various modifications for many years. Potato

infusion, glycerol, and defibrinated blood of sheep, horse, rabbit, or human origin are mixed with agar to produce a solid medium. Penicillin may be included to suppress the growth of streptococci, neisseriae, and other penicillin sensitive oral flora that may be present on primary isolation. Peptone may be added to the medium for batch cultures in the production of vaccines.

Colonies of B. pertussis on Bordet-Gengou agar are smooth, raised, entire, glistening, and less transparent than those of H. influenzae and have a grayish color. They are about 1.0 mm in diameter and have a pearllike appearance in reflected light. A zone of hemolysis is produced around the individual colony. The size and definition of the hemolytic zone depend on the age, species, and concentration of blood in the medium in addition to the time and temperature of incubation. The colonial appearance of B. parapertussis and B. bronchiseptica resembles that of B. pertussis. Colonies appear in 24 to 48 hours and may be larger, especially in older cultures.

Cultures of B. pertussis exhibit S→R (smooth to rough) phase changes. Primary isolates on enriched media have a smooth colonial appearance, are virulent with a full

Table 25.2. Summary of Selected Growth and Biochemical Characteristics of *Bordetella*

Characteristic	B. pertussis	B. parapertussis	B. bronchiseptica
Aerobic growth	+	+	+
Anaerobic growth	–	+	+
Motility	–	–	+
Urease produced	–	–	+
Nitrate reduction	–	–	+
Sugars fermented	–	–	–
Indole produced	–	–	–
Acetylmethylcarbinol produced	–	–	–
H$_2$S produced	–	–	–
X and V required	–	–	–

range of antigens, and, microscopically, have small, coccobacillary forms. With passage on unenriched media, the colonies become rough and avirulent and are composed of larger, pleomorphic cells. This change from phase I through intermediate forms II and III to the phase IV is accompanied by a loss of certain antigens.

Biochemical Characteristics

Members of the genus *Bordetella* are relatively inactive metabolically. Sugars are not fermented; H_2S, indole, and acetylmethylcarbinol are not produced; gelatin is not liquefied. During growth the pH rises in media containing amino acids, which are used as a source of energy. The X and V factors are not required for primary isolation or growth. A summary of some of the growth characteristics and biochemical reactions is presented in Table 25.2.

Although the requirements for growth of *B. pertussis* are simple, constituents of media such as casamino acids, yeast extract, and agar act as inhibitors of good growth. Passage of media through ion-exchange resins removes many of the inhibitory properties. Blood and charcoal may be added to media to neutralize the inhibitors.

Adaptation of *B. pertussis* to media, such as blood, chocolate, and brain-veal infusion agar, is associated with the microscopic appearance of increased pleomorphism and phase changes from smooth to rough colonies and with alterations in antigenic structure.

Antigenic Characteristics

Serologic differentiation and identification of the members of the genus *Bordetella* are possible by agglutination reactions with immune sera made in rabbits. Fourteen cell-surface agglutinogens (antigens) called *factors* are recognized in smooth, phase 1 cultures. Factor 1 is a species-specific antigen present only in *B. pertussis*. Factor 14 is unique to *B. parapertussis*, and factor 12 is found in *B. bronchiseptica*. Factor 7 is present in smooth strains of all three species of *Bordetella*. In addition to factor 1, which is present in all smooth strains of *B. pertussis*, factors 2, 3, 4, 5, and 6 are also specific to *B. pertussis* (but not all strains) and provide the basis for strain differentiation and recognition useful in epidemiologic investigations. Consequently, serotypic combinations such as *1, 3, 7; 1, 2, 5, 7; 1, 2, 4, 7;* and so on are produced. Factor 13 is found in *B. pertussis* but is also present in strains of *B. bronchiseptica*. The agglutinogens of *Bordetella* are summarized in Table 25.3.

In addition to the eight agglutinogens mentioned above, cells of *B. pertussis* have several other immunologically active substances. A heat labile hemagglutinin (HA) is present as a cell surface antigen. It can be detected in cell-free liquid media following culture and is readily extracted from cells with $2 M$ NaCl solution. The extracted HA agglutinates the erythrocytes of chickens, mice, guinea pigs, rabbits, sheep, horses, and humans. It binds to receptors on the red cell surface other than those reacting with influenza virus. Antibodies to HA can

Table 25.3. Antigenic Factors (Agglutinogens) of the Genus *Bordetella*

Bordetella Species	Genus Specific Factors	Species Specific Factors	Other Factors[a]
B. pertussis	7	1	2, 3, 4, 5, 6, 13
B. parapertussis	7	14	8, 9, 10
B. bronchiseptica	7	12	8, 9, 10, 11, 13

[a]All factors not present in all strains.

be demonstrated in convalescent sera but appear to have no role in protection to whooping cough.

An antigenic, heat labile, protoplasmic endotoxin (HLT) is present in cells of *B. pertussis* as well as a cell wall, heat stable endotoxin that is similar to the somatic O antigen of other gram-negative bacilli. The HLT produces inflammation and necrosis of the respiratory tract of experimental animals and induces lesions in the brain and meninges when injected intracutaneously into guinea pigs. These observations strongly suggest that the HLT contributes significantly to the pathogenesis of whooping cough and to the encephalopathies sometimes seen in this disease.

The heat stable endotoxin of *B. pertussis* is serologically distinct from that of *B. parapertussis* and *B. bronchiseptica*. It is antigenically weak, but it contributes to the adjuvant effects of *B. pertussis* that are useful for the experimental stimulation of antibodies to other antigens.

Four additional factors or activities have been described that appear to be properties of a single substance called *pertussigen*. These four activities or factors include (1) a mouse protective antigen (PA) that protects mice injected with pertussis vaccine from intracerebral challenge with living, virulent *B. pertussis*, (2) a histamine-sensitizing factor (HSF) that increases the susceptibility of mice to shock by histamine, serotonin, bradykinin, and endotoxin and increases susceptibility to active and passive anaphylaxis, anoxia, cold stress, and x-rays, (3) a lymphocyte-promoting factor (LPF) that induces leukocytosis with marked lymphocytosis, and (4) an adjuvant activity that enhances the production of IgM-, IgG-, and IgE-type antibodies in experimental animals that have been immunized with antigens unrelated to *B. pertussis*.

The heat labile pertussigen present in cells of smooth cultures has not been chemically defined. It may be responsible for many of the immunologic, physiologic, and pharmacologic reactions associated with whooping cough.

Although pertussis vaccines have been outstandingly effective for many, many years, attempts to identify a single antigenic substance responsible for the development of protective immunity in humans have not been successful. It may be that protective immunity is the total immune response, both humoral and cellular, to several antigens in combination with the adjuvant property intrinsic to cells of *B. pertussis*.

Clinical Course and Pathology of Whooping Cough

The clinical course of whooping cough in man is variable but three stages are identifiable, each lasting about 2 weeks. Following an incubation period of 10 to 14 days, the first, or *catarrhal*, stage begins with development of symptoms of a common cold, sneezing, low grade fever, and a mild progressive cough. The organisms multiply on the mucous membranes of the respiratory tract and begin to produce necrosis of the bronchial epithelium with infiltration of leukocytes. The organisms are shed in large numbers in the droplets produced by sneezing and coughing. During this stage, the patient is most infective for other persons.

During the second, or *paroxysmal*, stage, the infection extends to deeper structures, producing peribronchiolitis and interstitial pneumonia. The development of mucous plugs causes obstruction of the lower airways and atalectasis. These changes result in poor oxygenation of the blood and anoxia. Paroxysms of many, rapid explosive coughs followed by a sudden long inspiration (the whoop) produce prostration, vomiting, and cyanosis. A single paroxysm may include several whoops. The paroxysms of coughing may be induced by cold drinks, cold air, smoke, exertion, or imitation of others' coughing. The whoop may be absent in infants and in patients with mild disease. The leukocytosis and marked lymphocytosis decline as the organism disappears.

The third stage, *convalescence*, brings a reduction in severity of the disease and a disappearance of the paroxysms of coughing. Although the whoop ceases, it may return many months later as a learned response when other respiratory infections occur.

Secondary respiratory infections by other bacteria and viruses constitute serious complications. Ear infections by *B. pertussis* are extremely rare, but otitis media may be caused by other organisms during the course of the disease.

The number of reported cases of whooping cough has decreased dramatically in the United States over the last 30 years primarily because of the extensive immunization of infants and young children. From over 120,000 cases with about 11,000 deaths in 1950, the number has fallen to less than 2000 with fewer than 100 deaths in recent years (Fig. 25.1). The diagnosis of whooping cough (with the whoop) is now made clinically, rarely with laboratory confirmation. Mild forms of the disease (without the whoop) and other respiratory tract infections due to *Bordetella* go unrecognized and are treated symptomatically or with antibiotics. In fact, few laboratories prepare or stock Bordet-Gengou medium.

Many laboratories depend on chocolate agar for the recovery of *Bordetella* because it is in routine use for the isolation of *Haemophilus* and *Neisseria*. However, many laboratories do not even use chocolate agar routinely. Consequently, the incidence of infections with bordetellae are probably much higher than is reported.

Laboratory Diagnosis

A nasopharyngeal swab is passed through the nostril until it touches the postpharyngeal wall. A paroxysm of coughing is usually induced by this procedure, increasing the chance of recovering organisms. The swab can be used to streak two Bordet-Gengou agar plates, one with penicillin and one without, or blood agar and chocolate agar plates. Alternatively, the swab may be placed in a casamino acid solution before streaking the plates. This solution can then be used for the preparation of films for Gram staining and for fluorescent antibody (FA) staining.

After the incubation of the plates for 48 to 72 hours, the colonies may be used for direct staining, agglutination and fluorescent antibody identification, and subculture. Examination of patients' sera for antibodies is not useful for diagnosis because detectable antibodies do not appear until 2 to 3 weeks after infection. Such studies can

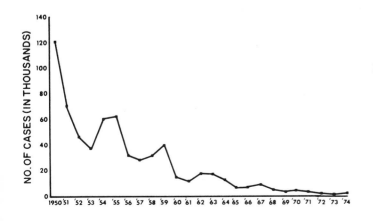

Fig. 25.1. Reported cases of whooping cough in the United States, 1950 to 1974. (with permission, Munoz, J.J. and Bergman, R.K. Bordetella pertussis. In Rose, N.R., Ed.: Immunological and Other Biological Activities. Marcel Dekker, Inc., New York, 1977.)

be useful in confirming the clinical and bacteriologic diagnosis.

Treatment

Antibiotic therapy has little, if any, effect on the clinical course of whooping cough. Since diagnosis is usually made when the paroxysms of coughing and the whoop appear, the physiologic and pathologic reactions are already well advanced and must "run their course." The administration of erythromycin and tetracyclines may cause a disappearance of the bacilli from the body more rapidly than would be expected without treatment.

It is conceivable that antibiotic treatment initiated after diagnosis very early in the catarrhal stage might lessen the severity of the disease and shorten its course. However, there are no data to support this practice, and, as pointed out previously, diagnosis is rarely made early in the catarrhal stage.

Prophylactic use of antibiotics is warranted for infants, young children, and other susceptible individuals at high risk, such as family members of a patient.

Immunity to Whooping Cough

Immunity acquired after recovery from whooping cough is longlasting but not permanent or absolute. Second attacks are mild, and most are never recognized as being due to *B. pertussis*. Immunity is diminished in the elderly, and second attacks can be serious. Reimmunization may be indicated for the elderly at high risk.

Pertussis vaccines in current use are prepared with an extract of smooth phase I cells rather than with chemically killed intact cells. Such extracts are usually administered as DPT (diphtheria-pertussis-tetanus) vaccine. Since transplacental transfer of maternal immunity is poor or absent in newborns, it is recommended that immunization of infants with DPT vaccine be initiated as early as 1 month of age and be followed by two more injections at 6 week intervals and a booster injection 1 year later. Primary or booster immunization for individuals over 6 years old should be carried out with single vaccines rather than with combined preparations because reactions due to sensitivity to the proteins of diphtheria and pertussis organisms are more frequent and more severe.

B. parapertussis

In children clinical disease caused by *B. parapertussis* resembles mild whooping cough with a less severe cough. In adults it may produce a prolonged bronchitis attributed to a viral infection. In both instances treatment is symptomatic. Second attacks have not been reported, suggesting that immunity is conferred by the first attack. There is no reciprocal immunity between *B. pertussis* and *B. parapertussis*. Vaccines of *B. parapertussis* are not commercially available.

Long term studies (15 to 24 years) have indicated that 2 to 5 percent of all nasopharyngeal cultures positive for *Bordetella* are positive for *B. parapertussis*. However, serologic studies suggest that infections with *B. parapertussis* are more frequent than suspected. In one study 91 percent of adults had demonstrable antibodies to *B. parapertussis*, and in another study 40 percent of children had antibodies to this organism. Clinically recognized infections occur primarily in children less than 10 years old. Less than 20 percent of infected children have symptoms of clinical pertussis, and about 40 percent are asymptomatic. In contrast, asymptomatic infections of *B. pertussis* in children are rare. However, in very young infants, less than 6 months of age, infections with *B. parapertussis* can be very serious; deaths have been reported.

In the most severe cases of pertussis, dual infections with *B. pertussis* and *B. parapertussis* are not uncommon when more than one or two colonies of the primary culture are examined.

B. bronchiseptica

This organism frequently causes sporadic and epidemic respiratory infections in rabbits and guinea pigs. It is transmitted to humans by close contact with pets, especially dogs, and other animals. In children a respiratory tract disease resembling whooping cough may be seen.

BRUCELLA

The history of brucellosis extends back to the description of the clinical disease by Marston in 1861. In 1887 Bruce isolated a small, gram-negative coccobacillus from the spleens of British military personnel who had died of Malta fever. This coccoid shaped organism, called *Micrococcus melitensis* by Bruce, was isolated some years later from milk and urine of healthy goats. The human disease was brought under control on the isle of Malta with elimination of raw goat's milk from the diet.

A similar bacillus was recovered by Bang in 1897 from contagious abortion of cattle and was named *Bacillus abortus*. This organism was also isolated from the fetus of a sow by Traum in 1914 and was considered

to be a separate species, *Bacillus abortus suis*. The genus *Brucella* was created to accommodate the three species *Brucella melitensis*, *Brucella abortus*, and *Brucella suis*. The species *Brucella ovis* of sheep and *Brucella canis* of dogs are also recognized.

The disease of man is called *brucellosis* (undulant fever, Malta fever, Bang's disease). It is an acute septicemia with fever that may become chronic and last for several years. Many organs and tissues may become involved.

Morphologic Characteristics

The genus *Brucella* is comprised of small, pleomorphic, gram-negative coccobacilli that become more bacillus shaped after primary isolation. They do not produce spores and are nonmotile. Freshly isolated smooth strains are encapsulated, but the capsules do not appear to be related to virulence.

Cultural Characteristics

Species of *Brucella* are aerobic; their growth is enhanced by 1 percent CO_2. They form colonies that are round, convex, smooth, translucent, and may require 3 to 4 days to appear. Colonies in older cultures may become brownish. Brucellae grow best

Table 25.4. Differentiation of *Brucella* Species

Brucella Species	H$_2$S Production	CO$_2$ Requirement	Thionine (1:50,000)	Basic Fuchsin (1:25,000)	Agglutination by Antisera A	M
Br. abortus	++	+	−	+	++++	+
Br. melitensis	−	−	+	+	+	++++
Br. suis	+	−	+	−[a]	+++	+
Br. ovis	−	+	+	+	−	−
Br. canis	−	−	+	−	−	−

[a]Certain biotypes not inhibited.

at 37°C with a range of 10 to 42°C. *Br. abortus* requires 10 percent CO_2 for primary isolation.

Brucellae exhibit S→R variation with intermediate forms (I). The S→R variation is accompanied by reduced virulence, a decrease in specific agglutination, and increased colonial opacity and brownish color.

Biochemical Characteristics

Differentiation of the species of the genus is based on requirement of CO_2, H_2S production, inhibition of growth by certain dyes, and growth in certain carbohydrates. Some of the characteristics are presented in Table 25.4. These properties are not absolute; each species has several biotypes that are recognized on the basis of variations of these characteristics.

Antigenic Characteristics

Injection of killed, smooth phase organisms of *Br. melitensis* or *Br. abortus* induces an immune response in animals to both species, and unabsorbed antisera do not distinguish between the two. Repeated absorption of the *Br. melitensis* antiserum with *Br. abortus* eventually results in a monospecific serum for *Br. melitensis*. Absorption of *Br. abortus* antiserum with *Br. melitensis* produces a serum combining with *Br. abortus* and *Br. suis*. *Br. abortus* and *Br. suis* have relatively large amounts of the abortus antigen (A) and small amounts of the melitensis antigen (M). Conversely, *Br. melitensis* has relatively large amounts of M antigen and small amounts of A antigen. *Br. suis* cannot be distinguished from *Br. abortus* serologically.

Agglutination reactions can be performed with absorbed antisera, and fluorescent antibody reactions are also useful. The patterns of A and M antigens in *Brucella* are shown in Table 25.4.

Pathogenic Characteristics

Brucellosis is a disease of animals that is transmitted to man. The organisms are carried by healthy animals following a febrile infectious episode. They have an affinity for placental tissue and cause infectious abortion of pregnant animals. The predilection for placental tissue appears to be due to the presence of a substance called *erythritol*, which is not present in human placental tissue.

Man becomes infected by consumption of raw, infected milk and milk products or by direct contact with infected animals. After entry into the body through the alimentary tract, conjunctiva, or skin, the organisms are engulfed by polymorphonuclear cells and are transported to the regional lymph nodes by way of the lymphatics. The bacteria multiply within the polymorphonuclear cells, are released when the cells die, and are engulfed by mononuclear cells that are attracted to the area in response to the local tissue reaction. If the infection is not contained and overcome, the organisms are carried by the phagocytic cells to the blood stream and distributed throughout the body.

Infectious granulomas develop in the lymph nodes, liver, spleen, and kidney. In addition, lesions of the endocardium involving both mitral and aortic valves may develop. In mammals other than humans, the organisms accumulate in the mammary glands and are shed into the milk. They also accumulate in the genital organs, especially in the pregnant uterus, causing abortion.

The onset of brucellosis in man may be abrupt, with chills and fever, or be insidious and ill defined after an incubation period of between 10 and 30 days. Symptoms include chills, weakness, headache, jointache, night sweats, and a diurnal fever of 101 to 105°F resulting from repeated showering of organisms into the blood stream from foci in the reticuloendothelial system.

Without treatment the disease lasts 3 to 4 months and may become chronic and persist for several years. Fatal cases result from (1) an acute septicemic form of the disease, (2) a focalized form, or (3) a chronic lymphogranulomatous course extending several months.

Diagnosis

Bacteriologic isolation and identification is the only reliable means of diagnosis. Multiple blood cultures should be made. Other specimens, such as urine, lymph node aspirations, surgical specimen, and spinal fluid, should be plated on tryptose agar. All media should be incubated at 37°C under 10 percent CO_2 and held for up to 3 weeks. Differential culture media are then used with pure cultures. Agglutination and fluorescent antibody studies can be performed with organisms in the smooth phase.

Immunity

Protective immunity to brucellosis is low, although agglutinins appear relatively early in the disease due to the long incubation period. Most infections are probably subclinical because many persons have demonstrable antibodies without a history of the disease. A cellular hypersensitivity develops that can be demonstrated by the injection of an extract of *Brucella* called *brucellergen*. The skin test used with this material is not considered a reliable diagnostic test.

Treatment

Tetracyclines, streptomycin, and ampicillin are effective in causing relatively quick response. Since the organisms are found intracellularly in tissues and mononuclear phagocytes, retreatment may be required as relapses occur. The sudden death of large numbers of bacilli may result in the release of endotoxin and antigenic substances inducing shock-like reactions.

Prevention and Control

Infections of animals with *Brucella* are worldwide. It is now clear that each of the species of the genus can infect a wide range of both domestic and wild animals. Attempts to control brucellosis among domestic animals have included animal testing programs to determine evidence of past or current infection, segregation and/or eradication of serologically positive animals, immunization of calves with an attenuated live vaccine of *Br. abortus*, and regulations governing movement of animals across state lines. In spite of the fact that it is estimated that 20 percent of the cattle herds are infected, the incidence of brucellosis in humans in the United States has declined steadily over the last 25 years. However, after reaching a low point in 1971, the number of human cases has risen each year since.

In the period of 1965 to 1974, 51 percent of the reported cases were due to *Br. suis*, 21 percent to *Br. abortus*, 11 percent to *Br. melitensis* (most of foreign origin or in laboratory personnel), 2.6 percent to *Br. canis*, and 14.6 percent to undifferentiated *Brucella*, which may or may not have included *Br. ovis*.

REFERENCES

Brucellosis Surveillance, Annual Summary. HE 20-7011/16, Annual Reports, C.D.C. 1975/8186. U.S. Department of Health, Education and Welfare, Center for Disease Control, 1975.

Davis, B.D., Dulbecco, R., Eisen, H.N., Ginsberg, H.S., Wood, W.B., Jr., and McCarty, M.D., Eds.: Microbiology. 2nd Ed. Harper & Row, New York, 1973.

Joklik, W.K., Willett, H.P., and Amos, D.B., Eds.: Zinnsser Microbiology. 17th Ed. Appleton Century Crofts, New York, 1980.

Munoz, J.J. and Bergman, R.K.: Bordetella pertussis, In Rose, N.R., Ed.: Immunology Series, Vol. 4. Marcel Dekker, New York, 1977.

Sell, Sarah H.W. and Karzon, D.T.: Hemophilus Influenzae, Proceedings of a Conference on Antigen-Antibody Systems, Epidemiology and Immunoprophylaxis, April 24–25, 1972, Vanderbilt University Press, Nashville, 1973.

Solotorovsky, M. and Lynn, M.: Haemophilus influenzae: Immunology and Immunoprotection. CRC Crit. Rev. Microbiol., 6: 1, 1978.

26

Pasteurella, Francisella, and Eikenella

Reginald M. Lambert

PASTEURELLA

The genus *Pasteurella* was given its name in honor of Louis Pasteur; he first described the bacterium responsible for fowl cholera (*P. multocida*) and, through work with this organism, developed the concept of microbial attenuation — that microorganisms may lose their virulence but retain their antigenic properties. He demonstrated that a vaccine of living fowl cholera bacilli that had been attenuated by aging of the bacterial cultures could safely be used to immunize and to protect chickens from challenge with fully virulent bacilli.

The genus *Pasteurella* includes a group of organisms that are primarily pathogenic for animals. However, human infections do occur, ranging from local abcesses to fatal septicemias. Microorganisms that were members of the genus *Pasteurella* at one time but which have been moved to other genera in recent years include *Yersinia pestis* (plague), *Yersinia pseudotuberculosis*, *Yersinia enterocolitica* (enterocolitis), and *Francisella tularensis* (tularemia). The four species remaining in the genus *Pasteurella* are *P. multocida*, *P. haemolytica*, *P.*

pneumotropica, and *P. ureae*. *Pasteurellosis*, or hemorrhagic septicemia, is an infectious disease of cattle and buffalo and to a lesser extent of pigs, sheep, goats, dogs, cats, and other animals. The term *hemorrhagic septicemia* was first used by Hueppe in 1886 as a collective term for fowl cholera, rabbit septicemia, pasteurellosis of cattle, and swine plague. By the turn of the century, hemorrhagic septicemia included any disease caused by *P. multocida*. Pasteurellosis is now known to be caused by a specific serotype of *P. multocida*, designated type B. Type E has recently been recovered from cattle with pasteurellosis in Africa.

Pasteurellosis occurs in a septicemic form and in a respiratory form. When resistance is lowered, as when animals are shipped, the organisms cause pneumonia and septicemia and may spread to other animals. This disease state, called *shipping fever*, has been thought to be caused by the combination of a paramyxovirus and *Pasteurella* spp. Nevertheless, only killed vaccines of *Pasteurella* are now used to protect animals from shipping fever and to control fowl cholera.

All of the *Pasteurella* spp. are normal inhabitants of the respiratory tract of animals. Man is not the primary host or reservoir of these organisms and becomes infected only accidently. *P. multocida* is the most important member of the genus as far as animals are concerned and, consequently, for man as well.

Morphologic Characteristics

Microscopically, the bacilli of this genus are small, ovoid, gram-negative coccobacilli that display marked bipolar staining. They vary in size from 0.15 to 0.25 μm in width and 0.30 to 1.25 μm in length. The cells are arranged singly, in pairs, or in small bundles. Spores are not formed, and cells do not have flagella. The cells are not acid fast. Capsules may or may not be formed.

Cultural Characteristics

Members of this genus are facultative anaerobes that grow on ordinary laboratory media over a wide temperature range (0 to 43°C). However, primary isolation is facilitated by growth on enriched media, such as blood agar, chocolate agar, or serum agar, at 37°C with increased CO_2 tension. Colonies are small (about 1.0 mm in diameter), convex, round and grayish-white. Only *P. haemolytica* is hemolytic on blood agar, but *P. ureae* may produce a greenish discoloration.

P. multocida is nonhemolytic on blood agar. Cultures have a musty odor resembling burning hair. Mucoid (M), smooth (S), and rough (R) colonial forms are recognized after a 24 hour growth on serum agar at 37°C. Smooth colonies 1.0 to 1.5 mm in diameter are irridescent when exposed to obliquely transmitted light and are produced by highly virulent strains of *P. multocida* with a capsule of type-specific polysaccharides. The M strains produce larger colonies, 2 to 3 mm in diameter. The capsules of these strains are made up of hyaluronic acid and may or may not have demonstrable type-specific polysaccharides. The M strains are of low virulence and are often isolated from the normal or chronically infected respiratory tract. The R strains do not differ much in appearance from the S strains but no type-specific polysaccharides are present. The R strains are avirulent.

Antigenic Characteristics

The S strains can be serologically classified into five types, A, B, C, D, and E, based on the capsular polysaccharides. Intact, young (6 hour) cells can be used in a slide agglutination reaction. The capsular polysaccharides can be solublized by heating a suspension of encapsulated *P. multocida* at 56°C; the cellular material is sedimented and the soluble antigenic material is removed. This "extracted" antigen can be used to coat human erythrocytes for the passive hemagglutination reaction (Ch. 16) with type-specific antisera.

Biochemical Characteristics

Members of the genus *Pasteurella* produce catalase and oxidase and are negative for methyl red and Voges-Proskauer reactions and show no growth in sodium citrate. Indole is produced by *P. multocida* and *P. pneumotropica*. Glucose and sucrose are usually fermented without production of gas. Lactose is generally not fermented. However, fermentation of carbohydrates is widely variable and of little value for speciation. Some differential characteristics are shown in Table 26.1.

Pathologic Characteristics

P. multocida is commonly isolated from wild and domestic animals and is an opportunistic pathogen for man. Infections in

Table 26.1.   Differential Characteristics of *Pasteurella* Species

Pasteurella Species	Blood Plate Hemolysis	Growth on MacConkey Agar	Mannitol Fermentation	H$_2$S	Indole	Urease	Ornithine Decarboxylase
P. multocida	–	–	+	+	+	–	+
P. haemolytica	+	+	+	v	–	–	v
P. pneumotropica	–	–	–	+	+	+	v
P. ureae	–	–	+	–	–	+	+

v, variable

man generally occur in one of the following ways: a local soft tissue infection following an animal bite or scratch, especially by a cat; chronic respiratory infections such as chronic bronchitis and bronchiectasis most commonly found in farmers, ranchers, slaughterhouse workers, and pet owners; and systemic infections such as septicemia and meningitis, often without any apparent contact with animals. *P. multocida* has also been found to cause pyogenic arthritis, brain abcess, pyelonephritis, endocarditis, peritonitis, conjunctivitis, and mouth ulcers.

Clinical findings and anatomical changes are not unique to *P. multocida* or to the other species of *Pasteurella*. Diagnosis is dependent upon the isolation and identification of the organisms. Sputum, bronchial washings, nasal swabs, spinal fluid, purulent exudate, and blood are useful specimens for culture, depending upon the clinical findings. Specimens should be plated directly on blood agar and chocolate agar, and the cultures incubated under increased CO$_2$ tension. Gram-stained films and biochemical reactions are essential to proper identification.

Although penicillin resistant strains of *P. multocida* have been reported, penicillin is the antibiotic of choice. Tetracycline is also useful.

P. ureae

P. uraeae resembles *P. multocida* with certain exceptions. Colonies are mucoid and about 2 mm in diameter after 24 hour incubation. On blood agar, *P. ureae* causes a greenish discoloration of the blood agar around the colony and some of the red cells are lysed. Most strains are lactose-negative, although lactose-positive strains have been reported. Urease production is exceptionally good. *P. ureae* has no known animal host; it is also avirulent for mice, guinea pigs, and rabbits.

P. ureae is primarily an opportunistic pathogen for humans, establishing itself following trauma or primary infections by other pathogens. It has been recovered in about 1 percent of routine sputum specimens. Pure cultures have been obtained from patients with sinusitis, pneumonia, endocarditis, meningitis, and septicemia. In general *P ureae* seems to have a predilection for patients with chronic respiratory disease. *P. ureae* is susceptible to a wide range of antibiotics including penicillin, the antibiotic of choice.

P. haemolytica

P. haemolytica differs bacteriologically from other members of the genus *Pasteurella* in that it produces blood plate hemolysis and that it will grow in the presence of bile salts and on MacConkey agar. It is also serologically distinct from the other members of the genus. This species is a known pathogen for sheep and cattle, but it has low pathogenicity for laboratory animals and is avirulent for rabbits. Only one documented infection of man by *P. haemolytica* has been reported, a case of endocarditis.

P. pneumotropica

P. pneumotropica has been responsible for a human case of meningitis and three cases of local infection following animal bites. A case of endocarditis was probably due to this organism as well.

FRANCISELLA

Tularemia is an infectious disease of wild mammals and other animal hosts with insects acting as reservoirs and vectors. Man enters the infectious cycle accidentally by contact with infected animals or contaminated water or by the bites of infected insects. Tularemia in man is an acute febrile disease with a tendency for pneumonic complications.

The adaptation of the infectious agent to the ectoparasites of rodents suggests that tularemia is not a new disease and that it has been endemic in North, Central, and South America and Asia for a long time. Tularemia was discovered by McCoy in 1910 in ground squirrels that were shot or found dead in Tulare County, California. The disease in these rodents was characterized by lesions similar to those of plague. Later, McCoy and Chapin (1912) isolated a gram-negative bacillus from diseased rodents and named it *Bacterium tularense*. Tularemia in man was first diagnosed by Wherry and Lamb in 1914. In recognition of the pioneering field, laboratory, and clinical investigations of Francis and his associates in the United States Public Health Service in the early 1920s, the genus *Francisella* has been created to accommodate the etiologic agent of tularemia, *F. tularensis*.

Microscopic Characteristics

F. tularensis is a gram-negative bacillus that is very pleomorphic; cells may be large and small, coccoid and bacillary, oval, minute, and bean shaped and dumbbell shaped, and they are found singly and in filaments. Rod shaped forms exhibit bipolar staining. Capsules and spores are not produced, and flagella are not formed.

Cultural Characteristics

A glucose-cysteine agar enriched with defibrinated rabbit blood is the medium of choice for the cultivation and isolation of *F. tularensis*. This medium, which was originally devised by Francis, is available commercially (without rabbit blood) and includes the 13 amino acids that this bacillus requires as well as thiamine and spermidine. Minute, pinpoint colonies may appear as early as 24 hours after inoculation from other cultures and then develop into larger (1.0 to 1.5 mm) smooth, gray colonies after 48 hours. Primary culture may require 7 to 10 days for colonies to form. The rabbit blood agar may become green around large masses of confluent colonial growth.

F. tularensis grows facultatively, but aerobic culture is best. Optimal temperature for growth is 37°C. Glucose, maltose, mannose, and fructose are fermented with production of acid but no gas. H_2S is produced if the medium contains cysteine. Increased CO_2 tension is not required for growth.

Antigenic Characteristics

There appears to be only one serotype, although a polysaccharide antigen, a protein antigen and an endotoxin have been described.

Host Range

Over 48 different species of animals are naturally infected hosts of *F. tularensis*. In

North America, cottontail rabbits, jackrabbits, and snowshoe rabbits (the last two are actually hares) are the principal hosts, with cottontail rabbits being the direct source of most human cases of tularemia. Other animal sources of human infections include gray squirrels, fox squirrels, oppossums, woodchucks, muskrats, skunks, coyotes, foxes, cats, sheep, deer, voles, and bull snakes. Wild rats, field mice, chipmunks, lemmings, calves, dogs, and several species of squirrel have been found to be naturally infected also. In Russia, epizootics among many species of voles have resulted in explosive outbreaks. Quail, pheasants, prairie chickens, and domestic chickens have been avian sources of human infections.

Tularemia is carried from animal to animal primarily by flies, fleas, lice, and ticks. In ticks *F. tularensis* is passed via the ovaries to the eggs and through the larval and nymph stages to the adult tick, which transmits the disease. Man may acquire tularemia from the bite of the deerfly and several species of infected ticks.

F. tularensis is known to survive under many different environmental conditions, such as in streams, still water, moist soil, animal hides, infected carcasses, and food. The contamination of one stream in Montana lasted for 33 days. Water-borne epidemics have been reported in both the United States and Russia, with sporadic cases resulting from handling of fish. The organism has survived in water for up to 3 months, in animal hides for 40 days, in carcasses for 133 days, in cultures for 22 years at 10°C without transfer, and in muscle of rabbit carcasses that have been refrigerated for 4 months. The organisms are readily killed at 60°C for 10 minutes or by thorough cooking of infected meat.

It has been reported that the water-borne strains of *F. tularensis* are less virulent than those carried by insects. Correlation of virulence with colonial morphology and smooth-rough variation is not consistent.

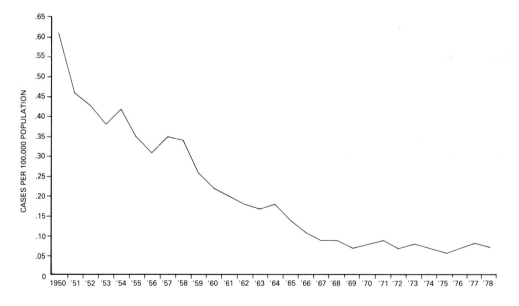

Fig. 26.1. Reported cases of tularemia by year in the United States, 1950 to 1978 (Center for Disease Control: Reported Morbidity and Mortality in the United States, 1978. Morbid. Mortal. Weekly Rep. 27 (54 Annual Suppl.), 1979).

Pathologic Characteristics

Infection of man by *F. tularensis* occurs most commonly by handling of infected animals and birds but also by insect bites, ingestion of contaminated water or improperly cooked meat, and inhalation of airborne organisms (laboratory infections or from aerosolization from dead rodents during threshing of grain). The basic types of infections have been described as *ulceroglandular*, *oculoglandular*, *typhoidal*, and *pulmonary*. The number of reported cases in the United States declined steadily during the 20-year period beginning in 1950. Since 1970 the number of cases has stabilized around 10 cases per 100,000 population each year (Fig. 26.1).

The organisms usually gain entrance to the body through a break in the skin or by the bite of an insect. After 3 to 4 days, a papule develops at the site of entrance and becomes an open ulcer after 7 to 8 days. By this time the organisms have spread to the regional lymph nodes. If the infection is not contained here, the organisms are spread via the blood to other parts of the body, especially the lungs, liver, and spleen. The ulceroglandular form has a better prognosis than other forms of the disease provided that it does not become generalized.

Oculoglandular tularemia results from infection of the conjunctivae usually by contact with contaminated fingers and hands and by blood droplets and dust. A local ulcer on the conjunctivae may develop with a spread to the regional lymph nodes. Prognosis is good and is similar to that of ulceroglandular tularemia.

Pulmonary tularemia may develop from inhalation of aerosolized organisms. Spread to other organs via the blood is common. There is probably some pulmonary involvement in all forms of tularemia, but full-blown lung infections have a poor prognosis.

Typhoidal tularemia develops following ingestion of contaminated water or infected meat. Ingestion of the organisms can also result in local abcesses of the mouth and enlargement of submaxillary and cervical lymph nodes.

In untreated cases the case fatality rate of the ulceroglandular and oculoglandular types is about 5 percent (1 percent in Russia), but it is much higher, about 30 percent, in the pulmonary or ingestive forms of the disease.

Diagnostic Characteristics

Diagnosis of tularemia can be accomplished microbiologically and, in most instances, serologically. Pathologically, the disease resembles plague, and clinical diagnosis is not possible. In general the diagnosis of tularemia is made when there is absence of growth on ordinary media and little or no growth on blood agar that does not contain cysteine; relatively slow growth on special media; distinctive microscopic morphology and staining properties of the organisms; slide agglutination reactions; direct and/or indirect fluorescent antibody reactions; and an increase in agglutination titers in sera from the acute and convalescent phases. As with brucella infections, most laboratories make the diagnosis of tularemia simply on the basis of agglutination titers of patients' sera. In the absence of a previously known infection, a titer of 1:40 is diagnostic, although it must be confirmed by a rise in titer in a later specimen. Such serologic reactions do not become positive until the second week of the disease.

Antimicrobial Agents

Streptomycin is bactericidal for *F. tularensis* and is the drug of choice. Bacteriostatic agents, such as tetracycline and chloramphenicol, are effective, but relapses are often seen. Even with streptomycin relapses may occur probably because the organisms invade the cells and become in-

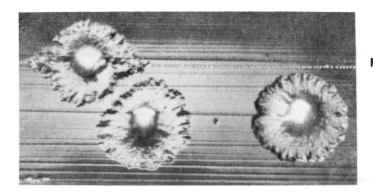

Fig. 26.2. Colonies of *Eikenella* depressed into the agar. (With permission, Eiken, M.: Studies on anaerobic, rod-shaped, gram-negative microorganism *Bacteroides corrodens* N. sp. Acta Pathol. Microbiol. Scand. *43*: 406, 1958.)

tracellular and are protected from the effects of the antibiotics. *F. tularensis* has not yet developed resistance to the antibiotic of choice.

Vaccines

An effective vaccine of living, attenuated organisms has been developed and is available from the Center for Disease Control for individuals at risk, including laboratory personnel.

EIKENELLA

In 1958 Eiken suggested the name *Bacteroides corrodens* be given to fastidious, slow-growing, gram-negative bacilli producing colonies that pitted or "corroded" the agar surface (Fig. 26.2). Later studies by Jackson and coworkers (1971) revealed that such "agar-corroding" isolates could be separated into an obligately anaerobic group and a facultatively anaerobic group of bacilli that grow under aerobic conditions if hemin is added to the culture medium. Since these workers also demonstrated that the two groups differ biochemically, antigenically, and in percentage of guanine + cytosine in DNA, the facultative, agar-corroding bacilli have been reclassified *Eikenella corrodens* in the family *Brucellaceae*. The obligate anaerobes formerly known as *Bacteroides corrodens*

are now referred to as *B. ureolyticus* (Ch. 31).

Other bacterial isolates that resembled *B. corrodens*, except that all were microaerophilic (requirement of an amount of O_2 less than that of air) or capnophilic (requirement of an increased amount of CO_2 over that of air), have been found to be identical with *corrodens* by Riley, Tatum, and Weaver (1973).

Morphologic Characteristics

E. corrodens is a straight, slender, gram-negative bacillus, 0.3 to 0.4 μm by 1.5 to 4.0 μm, with rounded ends and a characteristically regular morphology. Unbranched filaments up to 12 μm long may occasionally be formed. The organism is nonencapsulated, nonsporulating, and nonmotile.

Cultural Characteristics

E. corrodens is aerobic and faculatively anaerobic. Colonies on blood agar are gray, translucent, and nonhemolytic; they may have a small, greenish zone around the edge after 48 hours or more of incubation. After 24 hours colonies are about 0.5 mm in diameter; after 48 hours the size increases to about 1.0 mm. Corroding or pitting strains produce colonies that appear to be in a shallow pit in the agar (Fig. 26.2). The margin of the colonies may be circular or irregular. Noncorroding strains produce dome shaped colonies 0.5 to 1.0 mm in diameter. The odor of cultures of *Eikenella* is similar to that of hypochlorite bleach.

Aerobic growth typically requires the addition of hemin to the culture medium. Growth is also enhanced by 5 to 10 percent CO_2. Fluid media support growth poorly, but it may be improved by the addition of cholesterol or sheep serum. The organisms grow best at pH 7.3 and 37°C, with a temperature range of 25° to 42°C.

Eikenella are oxidase-positive and catalase-negative, lysine decarboxylase-positive, and urease-, indole-, and gelatinase -negative; nitrate is reduced to nitrite; glucose, lactose, sucrose, and many other carbohydrates are not fermented. The guanine plus cytosine content of DNA is higher (57 to 58 mole percent) in *Eikenella* than in *Bacteroides* and a number of other genera, including *Actinobacillus, Haemophilus, Moraxella, Pasteurella,* and *Yersinia.*

Antigenic Characteristics

There appear to be four major recognizable antigens in the genus *Eikenella* as determined by agglutination and immunodiffusion studies. A given strain may not have all four antigens. There also appears to be considerable quantitative variation from strain to strain. The antigens are not shared by *Bacteroides ureolyticus, B. fragilis, B. oralis, Vibrio* spp., or *Brucella abortus.*

Normal Habitat and Pathologic Characteristics

E. corrodens is a normal inhabitant of the mouth and upper respiratory tract of man. This organism is probably an opportunistic pathogen. Although it may occur alone in infections, it is more commonly present with one or more other bacteria in abcesses and other infections anywhere in the body. The organisms have been recovered in blood cultures obtained from patients following tooth extractions.

Antibiotic Susceptibility

All of the *E. corrodens* strains studied to date appear to be susceptible to ampicillin, penicillin, carbenicillin, and the tetracyclines. Most strains are susceptible to colistin, chloramphenicol, and rifampin. These organisms show variable susceptibility to gentamicin and kanamycin and are resistant to methicillin, cephalothin, clindamycin, vancomycin, and metronidazole. In contrast, *B. ureolyticus* is susceptible to clindamycin and metronidazole. The inclusion of clindamycin or vancomycin in selective media is useful in the recovery of *E. corrodens* from mixed infections.

REFERENCES

Brooks, G.F., O'Donoghue, J.M., Pissin, J.P., Soapes, K., and Smith, J.W.: *Eikenella corrodens*, a recently recognized pathogen: Infections in medical-surgical patients and in association with methylphenidate abuse. Medicine, *5:* 325, 1974.

Dubos, R.J., Ed.: Bacterial and Mycotic Infections of Man. 3rd Ed. J.B. Lippincott, Philadelphia, 1958.

Jackson, F.L. and Brodman, Y.V.: Transfer of the facultatively anaerobic organism *Bacteroides corrodens Eiken* to a new genus, *Eikenella*. Int. J. System. Bacteriol. *22:* 73, 1972.

Lennette, E.H., Balows, A., Hausler, J.W., Jr., and Truant, J.P., Eds.: Manual of Clinical Microbiology. 3rd Ed. American Society for Microbiology, Washington, 1974.

Neisseria

Kyoichi Kano

The term *gonorrhea*, meaning "flow of sperm", was coined by Galen as early as 130 A.D. to describe the manifestations of gonorrheal urethritis. However, the contagious nature of the disease was not clearly understood until the 13th century, when Gulielmus de Saliceto apparently treated many patients suffering from gonorrhea and realized its venereal origin. Arderne, in 1376, was probably the first to describe clinical features of the contagious urethritis that are comparable to those considered now characteristic for gonorrhea.

After the discovery of syphilis in the 15th century in Europe, the misconception that gonorrhea was an initial stage of syphilis was proposed and was the dominant theory of gonorrhea etiology for over 300 years. This misconception was potentiated by the experiment performed by Hunter in 1767: he inoculated himself with pus taken from a patient apparently suffering from both syphilis and gonorrhea and developed both diseases. At the end of the 18th century, Hill and Bell clinically differentiated gonorrhea from syphilis. However, their observations were largely neglected until Ricord, in the middle of the 19th century, distin-

guished syphilis and gonorrhea as two different venereal diseases beyond any doubt.

Neisser, in 1879, was the first to discover diplococci that were present inside polymorphonuclear leukocytes of purulent urethral discharges from 35 patients with gonorrhea. The name of the genus, *Neisseria*, was given in his honor. It was Bumm, however, who succeeded in 1885 in culturing the organism and proving its pathogenicity by inoculating human volunteers with the culture.

In 1887 Weichselbaum found similar diplococci within phagocytes of spinal fluids obtained from six patients suffering from epidemic cerebrospinal meningitis. He named the organism *Diplococcus intracellularis meningitidis*. His observations were fully confirmed by Lingelsheim in 1905 during an epidemic of cerebrospinal fever.

GENUS NEISSERIA

The genus *Neisseria* comprises six species, including two pathogens, *N. gonorrhoeae* (gonococci) and *N. meningitidis* (meningococci). Members of the genus are saprophytes of mucous membrane; man is the

Table 27.1.   Differential Characteristics of Neisseriae

Species	Glucose	Acid but No Gas From: Maltose	Fructose	Sucrose	Production of H₂S	Pigment
N. meningitidis	+	+	−	−	−	−
N. gonorrhoeae	+	−	−	−	−	−
N. sicca	+	+	+	+	+	−
N. subflava	+	+	±	±	+	+
N. flavescens	−	−	−	−	+	+
N. mucosa	+	+	+	+	+	−

only known reservoir of these organisms. They are nonmotile, gram-negative cocci, 0.6 to 1.0 μm in diameter, occurring often in pairs with adjacent sides flattened. They divide in two planes at right angles to each other. They are structurally similar to other gram-negative organisms. The guanine and cytosine content of DNA of neisseriae range from 47 to 52 mole percent. *Neisseria catarrhalis*, formerly a member of this genus, with guanine and cytosine content of 40 to 44 mole percent, was therefore transferred to the genus *Branhamella*.

Neisseriae are aerobes or facultative anaerobes. They are chemoorganotropic and can utilize a few carbohydrates, producing acid but no gas. As seen in Table 27.1, patterns of sugar fermentation can be used to differentiate gonococci from meningococci. All neisseriae produce catalase and cytochrome oxidase. Since only a few other bacteria produce cytochrome oxidase so abundantly, this characteristic has been customarily used for identification of neisseriae. They all possess autolytic enzyme systems, and therefore they are bile soluble. They are extremely sensitive to physical and chemical agents. Exposure of neisseriae to sunlight, desiccation, disinfectants, detergents, and metal salts kills the organisms within a matter of minutes.

The two pathogenic species of *Neisseria* are quite fastidious and require enriched media for their growth. Free ions are required, and starch, cholesterol, and serum or albumin must be added to the media.

Their growth is optimal at 37°C and is greatly enhanced in the presence of 5 to 10 percent CO_2 in the atmosphere. In contrast the remaining nonpathogenic neisseriae can grow in ordinary media such as nutrient agar at 22°C. For primary isolation of the pathogenic neisseriae a nonselective medium such as blood agar or chocolate agar can be used. However, the Thayer-Martin selective medium, which contains vancomycin, colistin, and nystatin in addition to chocolate agar, allows the growth of these two pathogenic neisseriae, while the growth of most other bacteria including nonpathogenic neisseriae and the growth of fungi are inhibited.

MENINGOCOCCI AND GONOCOCCI

The two pathogenic species of *Neisseria* are very similar to each other morphologically, physiologically, genetically, and immunologically. However, their initial sites of infection are distinct — meningococci invade the mucous membranes of the upper respiratory tract, whereas gonococci invade the mucous membranes of the urogenital tract.

The ultrastructure of the cytoplasm and cell wall is very similar in both species. The cell wall consists of a triple layer: an outer membrane, a dense layer of peptidoglycan, and an inner membrane. The outer membrane contains lipopolysaccharides, phospholipid, and proteins. Most of the pathogenic strains of meningococci possess a capsule to which their pathogenicity is attributed. The question of whether or not gonococci also possess a true capsule has been debated since the 1920s. The fragile, capsulelike structure of gonococci appears to be present, but it is very difficult to demonstrate. The presence of pili on gonococci has been claimed to be associated with their virulence. However, doubts have been cast on the pathogenic role of pili because pilated cocci are rather rare in fresh isolates and pilated gonococci with a mutation of the gene for the O-polysaccharide components of the lipopolysaccharide failed to establish lethal infections in chick embryos.

As mentioned, neither meningococci nor gonococci grow on nutrient agar, and both require enriched media. Their optimal temperature is 37°C, and their growth does not occur at 22°C. The Thayer-Martin selective medium has been widely used to isolate these organisms. Blood agar colonies of meningococci are small, slightly convex, transparent, and glistening. The average diameter of the colonies is approx-

imately 1.0 mm. Colonies of gonococci from initial isolates are small and transparent. The gonococci of small colonies (T_1 and T_2 types) possess pili and are pathogenic. Colonies of older cultures develop a lobate margin, and their size becomes larger (T_3 and T_4 types). The gonococci of the larger colonies do not have pili and are usually nonpathogenic. As mentioned, recent studies do not seem to support the exclusive role of pili in the virulence of gonococci and indicate that some other factors are definitely involved.

Meningococci are aerobes; gonococci are aerobes or facultative anaerobes. Meningococci ferment glucose and maltose, and gonococci ferment glucose only (Table 27.1). These characteristics are used to differentiate one species from the other.

Guanine and cytosine contents of meningococci and gonococci show very similar values, 49.6 and 50.5 mole percent, respectively. Sulfonamide resistant mutants are commonly found in both of these pathogenic species of *Neisseria*. Since 1976

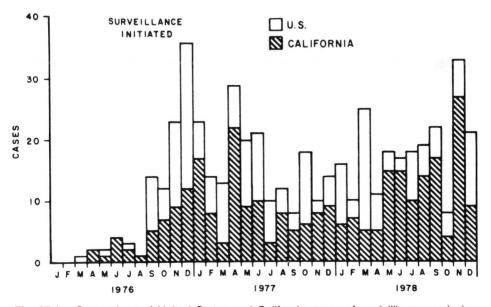

Fig. 27.1. Comparison of United States and California cases of penicillinase-producing *N. gonorrhoeae*, by month of onset, March 1976 through December 1978. The United States classification includes territories but excludes California. (MMWR *28* (8): 86, 1979, Center for Disease Control.)

Table 27.2. Group-Specific Polysaccharide Antigens of *N. meningitidis*

A	*N*-acetyl-3-O-acetylmannosamine phosphate (α-1-6)
B	*N*-acetylneuraminic acid (α-2-8)
C	*N*-acetyl- and *O*-acetylneuraminic acid (α-2-9) or *N*-acetylneuraminic acid (α-2-9)
X	*N*-acetylglucosamine phosphate (α-1-4)
Y	*N*-acetylneuraminic acid: glucose
Z′	3-Deoxy-D-mannooculosonic acid: *N*-acetylgalactosamine
W135	*N*-acetylneuraminic acid: galactose
D and Z	Unknown

penicillinase-producing gonococci have been found with increasing frequency and have worldwide distribution (see Fig. 27.1).

Meningococci and gonococci share many antigens that are recognized by immune sera. Antiserum to gonococci, after extensive absorption with meningococci, has been conjugated with fluorescein dye and used to identify gonococci in the direct smear preparations (fluorescent antibody test, FA test). Certain protein antigens of the outer membrane have been shown to be associated with virulence of some strains of both meningococci and gonococci.

Serogroups of meningococci based on group specific antigens of capsular polysaccharides have been well established. As seen in Table 27.2, nine serogroups can be distinguished: their antigenic determinants, except of groups D and Z, have been identified. Serogrouping of meningococci in fresh isolates can be accomplished by a variety of serologic tests, such as agglutination and complement-mediated bactericidal tests.

More recently, attempts have been made to identify group-specific antigens of gonococci. Based on protein antigens of the outer membrane, 16 serogroups can be distinguished. The presence of group-specific antigens of a polysaccharide nature has also been claimed.

MENINGOCOCCAL INFECTIONS

Meningococcal infections are relatively uncommon. However, meningococci can

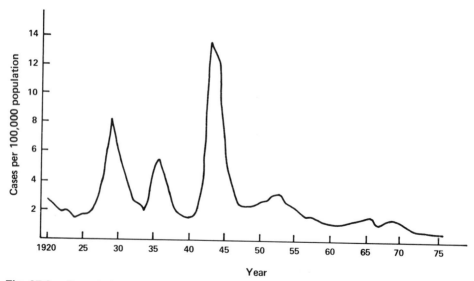

Fig. 27.2. Reported cases of meningococcal infections in the United States, 1920 to 1975. (Modified from MMWR *25* (53): 50, 1977, Center for Disease Control.)

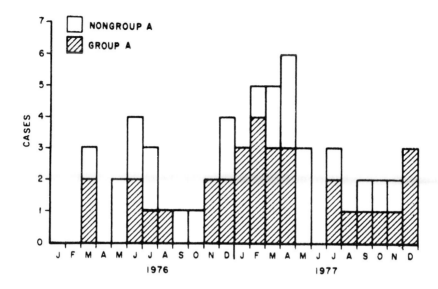

Fig. 27.3. Meningococcal meningitis cases in Alaska, 1976 to 1977. (MMWR *27* (14): 121, 1978, Center for Disease Control.)

cause a variety of clinical problems: bacteremia, sepsis, meningitis, arthritis, pneumonia, pleuritis, pericarditis, urethritis, epididymitis, petechiae, purpura, and conjunctivitis. In rare cases death may be sudden, within a few hours after the initial symptoms.

Epidemiology

In the past, there was a cyclic occurrence of epidemics of meningococcal infections in the United States, at intervals of 8 to 12 years (Fig. 27.2). The current incidence in the United States is 1500 to 1600 per year. The disease often occurs as an isolated event, but it may occur as an epidemic in closed populations, such as military camps, schools, institutions and jails. The past outbreaks in closed populations and the severity of the disease created mass hysteria and social problems. During World War II the death rate of United States soldiers due to meningococcal infections was higher .than that from any other bacterial infection.

The epidemics in the 1940s and 1950s

were caused mainly by group A. Group C became the main culprit in epidemics in the 1960s. The incidence of group B and F infections increased in the early to mid-1970s. As exemplified by the data in Figure 27.3, group A infections became prevalent in the late 1970s. The cyclic occurrence of epidemics and the shifting of one serogroup to another seem to indicate that meningococci of a particular serogroup are "waiting" for a new nonimmunized population to be infected.

Over 70 percent of the cases of meningococcal infections occur in persons younger than 25 years, and 40 percent of patients are children 3 months to 4 years old. The low incidence of newborns clearly indicates their protection by maternal antibodies.

Pathogenesis

The source of meningococcal infection is exclusively man, either patients or healthy carriers. The carrier rate is about 5 percent in the normal population and may increase sharply in a closed population prior to an outbreak of an epidemic. The portal of entry is the upper respiratory tract, and transmission occurs by droplet infection. There have been reports on exceptional cases in which mouth-to-mouth resuscitation or renal transplantation transmitted meningococci.

Once meningococci are implanted in the mucous membrane of the upper respiratory tract, they penetrate into the bloodstream and cause transient bacteremia. At this point over 90 percent of those infected remain healthy, but 10 percent develop bacteremia. Following bacteremia, patients may develop sepsis (35 percent), meningitis (20 percent), or both (45 percent).

Clinical Manifestations

Meningococcal sepsis starts with the same symptoms as those of sepsis elicited by any other pyogenic cocci. Fever, chills, malaise, and headache are common symptoms. In many patients with sepsis, skin lesions appear very rapidly. Petechiae may appear on the trunk and fuse together, forming massive purpura. Necrotic centers in skin lesions may develop owing to emboli in small vessels and release of endotoxin from degraded meningococci. In the fulminating cases of sepsis called *Waterhouse-Friderichsen syndrome*, massive hemorrhage and necrosis occur in adrenals, resulting in hypoadrenalic shock and sudden death. Following the sepsis, many other organs and structures may be involved: eyes, heart, lungs, joints, and ears. Meningitis begins with signs of acute meningeal irritation, such as severe headache, nausea, vomiting, and stiff neck. Abnormal reflexes may be noted.

The fatality rate dropped from 70 to 10 percent following the wide application of antibiotics. A survey of autopsy cases in the 1960s showed involvement of heart (80 percent), skin and mucous membranes (70 percent), central nervous system (70 percent), and adrenals (50 percent). Diffuse myocar-

ditis is the major pathologic finding in the heart; vasculitis, thromboemboli, and hemorrhage are seen in the skin. Acute inflammation of leptomeninges in central nervous system and hemorrhage and necrosis in adrenals are marked pathologic changes of these fatal cases.

Laboratory Diagnosis

In the case of meningococcal sepsis, cultures should be prepared from a nasopharyngeal swab, blood, and spinal fluid on chocolate agar and Thayer-Martin medium. The oxidase test on colonies on the agar plates shows the presence of neisseriae. Sugar fermentation reactions then identify the meningococci in cultures. Direct smears from skin lesions often reveal the presence of the organisms.

Cerebrospinal fluid from patients with symptoms of meningitis should be examined immediately after collection. A cloudy look of the specimen indicates infection with pyogenic cocci. Gram-stained smears of the sediment of the cerebrospinal fluid should reveal the presence of typical coffee bean shaped gram-negative diplococci within phagocytes. These laboratory findings along with clinical symptoms give good presumptive evidence for meningococcal meningitis, and the antibiotic therapy should be instituted without any delay.

For differential diagnosis it is important to remember that *Haemophilus influenzae* and *Streptococcus pneumoniae*, besides meningococci, are frequently isolated from cerebrospinal fluids of patients with bacterial meningitis. The incidence of meningitis due to *Escherichia coli* infection among children is also increasing (Table 27.3).

Immunity

Seroepidemiologic studies show that most adults possess IgM, IgG, and IgA antibodies against group A meningococci that were presumably acquired through inappar-

Table 27.3.   Incidence of Bacterial Meningitis in the United Kingdom — 1974

Bacteria	Isolations in Cerebrospinal Fluid	Age of Patients Who Died Total	≤4	5–24	25–65
Neisseria meningitidis	1091 (50%)	74	51	8	15
Haemophilus influenzae	342 (17%)	13	10	3	0
Streptococcus pneumoniae	288 (14%)	51	10	1	40
Streptococci other than *S. pneumoniae*	69 (3%)	20	11	1	8
Escherichia coli	81 (4%)	22	18	1	3
Staphylococci	79	5	1	0	4
Mycobacterium tuberculosis	30	4	1	0	3
All other organisms	56	18	5	0	13
Total	2036	207	107	14	86

(MMWR *24* (No. 38): 322, September 20, 1975, Center for Disease Control.)

ent infections. It has also been observed that no reinfection occurs with the same strain. It appears therefore that group-specific bactericidal antibodies are responsible for the immunity against infection with meningococci. Clinical studies provided further evidence that an inverse relationship exists between incidence of antibodies and the number of cases at different age groups in epidemic areas and that the majority of patients in an epidemic at an army camp were those who did not have antibodies against the particular strain of meningococci. Antibodies to LPS and outer membrane protein antigens may also play an important role in immunity against meningococcal infections.

Treatment and Prophylaxis

Penicillin or penicillin and rifampin are the drugs of choice. Most strains of group B and C and possibly group A are markedly resistant to sulfonamides. Therefore sulfonamides should not be used.

In the early 1970s group A and C vaccines became available and World Health Organization field trials with group A vaccine were successfully conducted in the Middle East. In the 1970s 350,000 military personnel were vaccinated with group A and C vaccines. A significant reduction in the incidence of infections with meningococci of these groups was observed. This was confirmed in the second field trial by showing that the incidence of cerebrospinal meningitis caused by group A organisms was 89 percent lower in the immunized group than in the control group after 1 year. Prophylaxis with oral penicillin gave inconclusive results. Rifampin and minocycline were shown to be effective in prophylaxis and in elimination of the organisms from the carriers.

GONOCOCCAL INFECTION

Gonorrhea is the most frequent venereal disease all over the world. In the United States its incidence reached epidemic proportions in the 1970s. Therefore the control of gonorrhea became one of the major public health problems of today. The number of factors characteristic for gonorrhea make it very difficult to achieve this goal. These factors are (1) a short incubation period, (2) the lack of natural or acquired immunity against infection, (3) the presence of

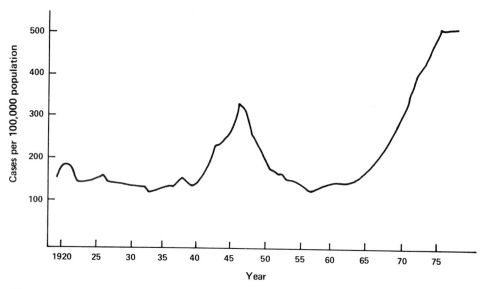

Fig. 27.4. Reported cases of gonorrhea in the United States, 1920 to 1975. (Modified from MMWR *25* (53): 67, 1977, Center for Disease Control.)

large numbers of asymptomatic patients, and (4) emergence of penicillinase-producing mutants and increased resistance of gonococci to penicillin.

Epidemiology

As seen in Figure 27.4, the decreased incidence of gonorrhea immediately after World War II and the early 1950s coincided with the time when antibiotics became widely available. Thereafter the incidence increased sharply, especially in the early 1970s, and reached its plateau in the mid- to late 1970s. The total number of reported cases in the United States at present is 2.5 to 3 million annually. However, the real numbers, including asymptomatic patients and unreported cases, may well be twice the reported numbers. Over 70 percent of the reported cases were in persons under 25 years of age, and 30 percent of the patients were 15 to 19 years old. The incidence in the latter age group has been increasing every year. According to the statistics compiled by the Center for Disease Control, in 1977 the overall incidence of gonorrhea in the United States was 470 per 100,000; Alaska had the highest incidence (1216 per 100,000), followed by Georgia and Tennessee.

Source of Infection

Transmission of gonococci occurs in adults almost exclusively by sexual contact, and the sources of infection are the exudate and purulent discharge from urethra or cervix. Among children transmission may result from sexual abuse or through contact with contaminated fomites. Newborns may acquire the organisms from the mothers with gonorrhea during passage through the infected birth canal.

Recent studies indicate that the risk of an unprotected healthy male to acquire the organisms from an infected female is about 20 percent. The risk of a healthy woman in contact with an infected man is not known but it may well be higher than 20 percent.

The most serious source of infection are asymptomatic patients, especially females. The incidence of asymptomatic female patients is up to 80 percent depending on the

Table 27.4.   Results of Gonorrhea Culture Tests on Females — United States, January 1978 to June 1978

	No. Tested	No. Positive	(%)
VD clinics	459,071	86,675	(18.9)
Hospitals			
Outpatients	689,092	29,560	(4.3)
Inpatients	32,720	774	(2.4)
Correctional centers	29,812	1,286	(4.3)
Manpower training centers	14,793	580	(3.9)
Private family planning centers	543,119	8,136	(1.6)
Student health centers	107,244	1,342	(1.3)

(Modified from MMWR *27* (No. 45): 448, November 10, 1978, Center for Disease Control.)

population studied. This is why the Center for Disease Control has been conducting mass screening programs for gonorrhea. As exemplified by the results of the screening in 1978, which are shown in Table 27.4, the positivity rates among various populations other than patients of venereal disease clinics ranged from 1.3 percent in student health centers to 3.9 percent in manpower training agencies and 4.3 percent in correctional or detention centers.

Pathogenesis

As described previously, the concept of virulence factors of gonococci originated from the observations that the colonies of T_1 and T_2 organisms are usually pilated and predominantly found in fresh isolates whereas gonococci of T_3 and T_4 colonies possess pili rarely or not at all and are avirulent. The organisms from virulent colonies are relatively resistant to phagocytosis. However, the role of pili in pathogenesis of gonorrhea has not been definitely elucidated.

In acute gonorrhea, gonococci infect the columnar epithelium of the urethra and periurethral ducts and glands. Other portals of entry are the mucosa of the cervix uteri, conjunctiva, and rectum. Infection is established soon after the contact, possibly by the anchoring of pili to the surface of the mucosa. The organisms penetrate through intercellular spaces of the columnar epithelium, reach the subepithelial tissues by the third day of infection, and elicit an inflammatory response characterized by dense infiltration by polymorphonuclear leukocytes. The spread of infection occurs usually through local lymphatic channels. Similar mechanisms are believed to be operating in infection of other urogenital organs.

Clinical Manifestations

The clinical course of gonococcal infection can be divided into three phases: acute, chronic, and systemic. The incubation period in primary infection by gonococci in man is 2 to 8 days, averaging 4 days. The burning sensations during urination and discharge from urethra and/or vagina are initial signs of acute gonorrhea. In addition, female patients often present with fever and abdominal pain. Paraurethral glands, Littré's glands of the male, and Skene's glands as well as Bartholin's glands of the female are most probably involved in the acute phase of the disease. It should be mentioned again that many female patients and a few male patients may be asymptomatic but they retain fully the capacity to infect others.

Unless they are treated properly for the

acute phase of the disease, the patients may enter the chronic phase, which results in serious complications. In a male patient the infection spreads directly from the anterior urethra to the posterior urethra and Cowper's glands. The common complication is stricture of the urethra. Gonococci reach the bladder neck and the vesical trigone and incite inflammation, which causes urination urgency and pain. Increased intravesicular and abdominal pressure forces infected secretions through the prostatic duct into the prostate and through the ejaculatory ducts into the seminal vesicle and the ductus deferens. The prostatic portion of the male urethra offers many openings of ducts and crypts, which harbor the organisms and act as conduits for its spread. The kidneys, ureter, and most of the bladder escape from the infection.

The inflamed prostate is softly enlarged and very tender on rectal examination. The prostate is the most serious reservoir for infection, since its secretion containing gonococci is expelled through the ducts by contraction of prostatic muscles and is added to the ejaculate upon intercourse. Acute seminal vesiculitis is also a complication of the posterior urethritis and may cause peritoneal irritation. Swelling of the terminal portion of the ductus deferens adjacent to the ureter may result in ureteral block with severe renal pain. Right sided funiculitis and seminal vesiculitis have often been misdiagnosed as appendicitis. Extension of the infection to epididymis causes painful inflammation and swelling of the whole epididymis. Bilateral involvement of the epididymis may lead to permanent obstruction of the lumina resulting in lasting sterility. The testis usually escapes the infection.

In chronic gonorrhea of female patients the paraurethral Skene's glands as well as Bartholin's glands are involved and act as a reservoir for further extension of the infection. Unlike the situation in male patients, ascent of the infection to the bladder is rare, but an abscess may develop in the Skene's glands. Because the stratified squamous epithelium is resistant to the gonococcal infection, the vagina of an adult female is not involved in infection. The branching folds of the cervix with columnar epithelial lining and mucous formation form an excellent soil for multiplication and spread of gonococci during the chronic phase of the disease.

It has been generally assumed that menstrual contractions of the uterus facilitate passage of the organisms to the fallopian tubes. However, according to recent studies, the changes in the phenotype of the organisms and in the nutrients in the environment that occur during menses, as well as other factors such as hormonal action on the organisms and the pH of cervical secretion, play a much more significant role in the dissemination of gonococcal infection during menses. Soon after the spread of the infection to the tubes, an inflammatory reaction in the surrounding connective tissues causes edema and hyperplasia with enlargement and thickening of the tubes. The exudate in the tubes becomes purulent and is sometimes pushed into the peritoneal cavity causing pelvic peritonitis before adhesions and scarring close the openings. Later, the closure of the peritoneal end or other portion of the tubes may take place and cause permanent sterility. The major consequence of chronic gonorrhea in females is the development of *pelvic inflammatory disease* resulting from the infection of the fallopian tubes with gonococci and some anaerobes.

It should be mentioned that about 50 percent of females with gonorrhea have colonization of gonococci in the rectum, which occasionally results in proctitis. A few male patients have such rectal colonization of the organism. However, this is common in male homosexuals. Another extragenital site of colonization is the pharynx, causing, in rare cases, pharyngitis.

Systemic infection with gonococci results in bacteremia, which is a rather rare event;

the incidence is approximately 1 percent of all cases of gonorrhea. Asymptomatic patients of both sexes are also at a risk to develop bacteremia. The portals of entry are believed to be the penile and prostatic veins in males and venous plexuses around genital organs in females. Lymphatic invasion by gonococci can occur at any site of the infection. However, the involvement of lymphatic vessels is benign and hardly ever leads to formation of lymph node abscesses or disseminated infection. The most common manifestation of the systemic infection is gonococcal arthritis-dermatitis syndrome, which is characterized by fever, chills, malaise, polyarthritis, and development of unique skin lesions. At the initial stage the small distal joints are involved and joint fluids are usually sterile. The petechial or papular skin lesions appear on the distal dorsal surface of wrists, elbows, and ankles. Central necrosis of the skin lesions is common. Without proper treatment at this stage, which lasts several days, the patients may develop pyarthritis, which becomes more prominent in a single joint. Other forms of the systemic infection are subacute endocarditis, meningitis, uveitis, and panophthalmitis.

Gonococcal Infection in Children

Recently, amniotic transmission of the organisms to the fetus has been reported. This type of infection may result in abortion and perinatal death. In the perinatal period, infection of the eye, *ophthalmia neonatorum*, is the most common manifestation. Since the establishment of Credé's prophylactic administration of 1 percent silver nitrate into the conjuctival sac of newborns, this disease only rarely causes blindness. All states now require applica-

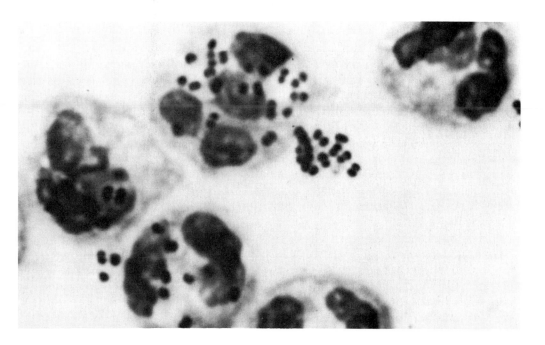

Fig. 27.5. *N. gonorrhoeae.* Gram stain of urethral smear (× 2400). Diplococci located in clumps within polymorphonuclear leukocytes of exudate. (With permission, Freeman, B.A.: Neisseria: The Gram-negative pathogenic cocci. In Freeman, B.A., Ed.: Burrow's Microbiology. 21st Edition. W.B. Saunders Company, Philadelphia, 1979.)

tion of Credé's procedure; however, this treatment is not satisfactory for an already established infection.

Gonococcal vulvovaginitis is occasionally seen among girls 2 to 8 years old. The alkaline pH of the vagina is believed to be one of the factors facilitating the disease in this age group. The disease is usually limited, but it may progress to the fallopian tubes or peritoneum.

Laboratory Diagnosis

Gram staining of the purulent urethral discharge from a male patient with the typical symptoms of the acute phase of gonorrhea, the purulent synovial effusion of patients with gonococcal arthritis, and the conjunctival discharge from patients with eye infection usually gives a good presumptive laboratory diagnosis. Examination of smears prepared from scrapings of skin lesions may reveal the organisms on Gram staining. These specimens contain many polymorphonuclear leukocytes and intracellular gram-negative displococci (Fig. 27.5).

Gram staining of smears prepared from cervical swabs of female patients is often not sensitive enough and may be misleading because of the presence of other bacteria. Therefore repeated culturing of endocervical swabs and rectal swabs on chocolate agar and Thayer-Martin medium is recommended. Culture of rectal swabs must also be performed in the case of homosexual males. Complete identification of the organisms in the isolate is necessary when infection with meningococci is suspected.

Serologic identification of gonococci has been applied to those cases in which proper endocervical cultures are very difficult to obtain. The fluorescent antibody (FA) test using immune serum to the organisms appears to be useful. More recently, a similar test with antiserum to the pili was developed. The FA test is rapid and does not require living organisms. Clinical studies by FA tests showed that these tests can iden-

tify 80 to 90 percent of asymptomatic women with the endocervical infection.

Although many studies have shown that there are humoral as well as cellular responses to gonococcal antigens in patients with gonorrhea, a reliable and useful serodiagnostic test based on the immune responses still remains to be established.

Treatment and Prophylaxis

Because of the constant increase of resistance to penicillin and the emergence of penicillinase-producing mutants (see Fig. 27.1), it is impossible to describe a solid guideline for the treatment that will be useful in the immediate future. Physicians should always consult with the latest recommendation for treatment, published each year by the Center for Disease Control.

According to the currently recommended treatment, a single injection of aqueous procaine penicillin G with oral probenecid is the regimen of choice for uncomplicated gonorrhea of both sexes. An alternative regimen is oral ampicillin with probenecid. For those patients who are allergic to penicillin or probenecid, oral tetracycline or injection of spectinomycin may be used. Patients infected with penicillinase-producing strains should be treated with spectinomycin.

Follow-up urethral and other appropriate cultures from men and cervical and rectal cultures from women should be studied to decide about the effect of treatment.

Chemoprophylaxis by oral penicillin was tried on military personnel on leave, and a significant decrease in the incidence of gonorrhea was reported.

REFERENCES

Craven, D.E. and Frasch, C.E.: Protection against group B meningococcal disease. Infect. Immun. *26*: 110, 1979.

Feldman, H.A.: Some recollections of the meningococcal diseases. JAMA *220*: 1107, 1972.

Lachman, E.: The anatomy of male gonorrhea. Med. Times *101*: 47, 1973.

Lachman, E.: The anatomy of female gonorrhea. Med. Times *103*: 67, 1975.

Low, A.C. and Young, H.: Modern trends in the laboratory diagnosis of gonorrhea. Med. Lab. Sci. *36*: 279, 1979.

28

Corynebacterium and Listeria

C. John Abeyounis

CORYNEBACTERIUM

The genus *Corynebacterium* consists of a large group of bacteria that includes free-living saprophytes and plant pathogens as well as parasites and pathogens of animals and man. Corynebacteria are closely related to mycobacteria and nocardiae as judged on the basis of cell wall structure and serologic analysis. *Corynebacterium diphtheriae* (diphtheria bacillus, Klebs-Loeffler bacillus), the causative agent of diphtheria, is the only major human pathogen in the genus. It is found almost exclusively in man, predominantly in the nasopharynx of patients and in healthy carriers.

Diphtheria as a clinical entity was first described in 1826 by Bretonneau, but its bacterial etiology was not established until much later. Klebs first described the diphtheria bacillus in 1883, and the following year Loeffler recovered the organism from several cases of diphtheria.

Diphtheria is the classical example of a toxigenic disease that arises from a bacterial infection, but its unique pathogenesis did not become apparent until the discovery of the diphtheria toxin in 1888 by Roux and Yersin. These investigators showed that sterile filtrates of cultured diphtheria bacilli were lethal for guinea pigs and could produce lesions identical to those produced by injection of viable organisms.

Morphology and Physiology

C. diphtheriae is a gram-positive, non-sporulating, nonmotile bacillus measuring 1 to 8 μm in length and 0.3 to 0.8 μm in breadth. The organism is highly pleomorphic with curved, club shaped, and filamentous forms seen frequently in stained preparations. Old cultures tend to decolorize readily and appear gram-negative. Diphtheria bacilli are characteristically arranged in a palisade or "picket fence" fashion, often resembling Chinese characters. The bacilli stain irregularly, particularly with methylene blue, giving a beaded or banded appearance, with some areas staining more intensely than others (Fig. 28.1). These areas of intense staining, termed *metachromatic* granules (also called Babes-Ernst or volutin granules), represent an aggregation of polyphosphate polymers. Although these microscopic and tinctorial features are typical for *C. diphtheriae*, they

375

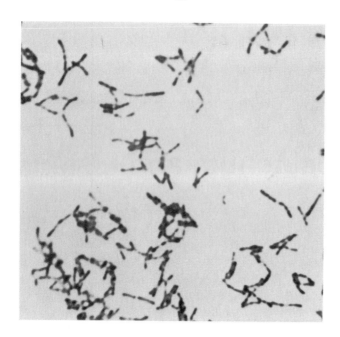

Fig. 28.1. Smear of diphtheria bacilli grown on blood agar showing the characteristic barred appearance and irregular staining. Methylene blue stain (× 1200). (Freeman, B.A., Ed.: Burrows Textbook of Microbiology. 21st Ed. W.B. Saunders, Philadelphia, 1979.)

are not diagnostic. Growth of the organism occurs over a wide temperature range, 15 to 40°C, but is optimum from 34 to 37°C. Diphtheria bacilli are considered facultative anaerobes; however, the organisms grow best under aerobic and slightly alkaline conditions (pH 7.8 to 8.0).

The bacilli grow on ordinary laboratory media, but for isolation in the diagnostic laboratory, the two preferred media are Loeffler's coagulated serum and chocolate agar-tellurite medium. Colonies on Loeffler's medium are small, gray to buff in color, and have a granular appearance. Smears from colonies grown on this medium show the most characteristic microscopic and tinctorial features. On a tellurite-containing medium diphtheria bacilli grow well, but growth of other microorganisms that colonize the throat, such as streptococci and pneumococci, is suppressed. Colonies of diphtheria bacilli are dark gray to black in color due to reduction of tellurite. Of significance is the fact that staphylococci, which also may be isolated with diphtheria bacilli, reduce tellurite and produce black colonies.

The biochemical activities of *C. diphtheriae* are not remarkable. The organism does not liquify gelatin or hydrolyze urea but it does ferment a variety of sugars, producing acid but never gas.

C. diphtheriae survives well under certain cultural conditions. Viable organisms may be recovered from agar after 7 to 8 weeks and from sections of the diphtheric membrane after as long as 3 months. On the other hand, they are readily killed by the usual disinfectants and by heating to 60°C for 10 minutes.

Three morphological types of *C. diphtheriae*, termed *gravis*, *mitis*, and *intermedius*, have been described. On tellurite medium colonies of the *gravis* strains are large (1 to 2 mm) at 18 hours, gray to gray-black, and dull in appearance. *Intermedius* strains form small (<1 mm) gray colonies that are also dull in appearance, and *mitis* strains form small (<1 mm) black colonies with a glistening appearance.

In addition to cultural differences, the three types of diphtheria bacilli differ in microscopic morphology and biochemical properties. For example, *gravis* strains stain more uniformly than the other two types and ferment both glycogen and starch. Neither of these substances is fermented by either *intermedius* or *mitis* strains.

Initially, it was believed that the *gravis* and *intermedius* strains produced a more severe disease; however, this has not been clearly established. Now, this distinction is more of biologic than medical interest.

Antigenic Structure

Diphtheria bacilli are antigenically heterogeneous, with several somatic and surface antigens having been described. The somatic antigens (O antigens) are heat stable polysaccharides, and the surface antigens (K antigens) are heat labile proteins.

Serotypes of *C. diphtheriae*, based on these O and K antigens, have been described. In addition, *gravis* and *mitis* strains also can be typed on the basis of bacteriophage and bacteriocin susceptibility. The O antigens are shared not only by other corynebacteria but also by closely related nocardiae and mycobacteria. However, neither serologic analysis nor bacteriophage typing is routinely utilized in the diagnostic laboratory.

Certain strains of *C. diphtheriae* are toxigenic. They elaborate a powerful exotoxin (see below) that causes the systemic symptoms of diphtheria. Diphtheria toxin is a potent immunogen and is antigenically identical in all toxigenic strains.

Pathogenic Factors

Diphtheria Toxin is the principal pathogenic factor of *C. diphtheriae* and is responsible for the systemic manifestation of diphtheria. Toxin production is contingent upon a lysogenic state in which *C. diphtheriae* are infected with a bacteriophage that carries the *tox$^+$* gene. This gene, which apparently serves no function for the virus, codes for the production of diphtheria toxin when it is integrated into the bacterial genome. This lysogenic state is apparently quite stable. The Park-Williams 8 strain of *C. diphtheriae*, used for the commercial production of the toxin, is still highly toxigenic after more than 80 years of culture. Interestingly, a number of serologically unrelated bacteriophages can carry the *tox$^+$* gene, but the most widely studied is the β-phage.

Optimum production of the toxin depends not only upon the *tox$^+$* gene that codes for the protein structure of the toxin but also upon certain metabolic and environmental factors to which the bacilli are exposed. An alkaline pH, 7.8 to 8.0, and aerobic conditions are requisite, but most important is the iron concentration in the medium, the optimum being 0.14 μg/ml. Interestingly, this concentration is below that required for optimum growth of the diphtheria bacilli.

Diphtheria toxin is a heat labile protein of 62,000 daltons. Toxicity of the molecule resides in its capacity to inhibit protein synthesis in eukaryotic cells. Trypsinization of diphtheria toxin results in two polypeptide fragments, A and B. Fragment A, of 24,000 daltons, is responsible for enzymatic activity (toxicity) of the toxin. Fragment B, of 38,000 daltons, binds to receptors on sensitive cells. The intact molecule is required for toxicity to cells. In reacting with sensitive cells, the B component of the toxin molecule binds to receptors at the cell surface. Subsequent to this binding the A component is cleaved from the molecule by cellular enzymes, enters the cell, and exerts its toxic action by inhibiting protein synthesis. Fragment A splits nicotinamide adenosine dinucleotide (NAD) to nicotinamide and adenosine diphosphoribose. The latter binds to and inactivates elongation factor II (transferase II), an enzyme that together with the enzyme transferase I is required for the construction of polypeptide chains on ribosomes.

Susceptibility to diphtheria toxin varies

considerably among animal species. Humans, monkeys, guinea pigs, rabbits, and birds are highly susceptible to the toxin, with an amount equivalent to 130 ng/kg of body weight being lethal. Rats and mice are relatively insensitive, presumably because their cells lack the receptor for fragment B.

Components A and B bear several distinct antigenic determinants, and antitoxin contains a mixture of antibodies that is specific for each of these determinants. Antibodies to the A component block enzymatic activity *in vitro* but afford no protection to animals or cells against the lethal action of the toxin, whereas antibodies to the B component effectively neutralize the toxin and are protective.

Other Pathogenic Factors that contribute to the disease potential of diphtheria bacilli include (1) the cord factor, which is a toxic glycolipid (trehalose 6,6'-dicorynemycolate) similar to that produced

by mycobacteria and which is capable of disrupting mitochondria and affecting cellular respiration, (2) K antigens, and (3) enzymes such as neuraminidase and *N*-acetylneuraminate lyase. It is believed that these substances contribute by yet undefined mechanisms to the virulence and invasiveness of diphtheria bacilli.

Human Disease

Epidemiology. Diphtheria was once one of the most feared infectious diseases. The incidence was highest in children, with a morbidity rate of 20 to 30 percent. The fatality rate in untreated cases was 7 to 10 percent but in some epidemics was as high as 40 percent. Since the 1920s there has been a sharp decline in both the morbidity rate and fatality rate in the United States (Fig. 28.2) and most other Western countries. This dramatic drop has been attri-

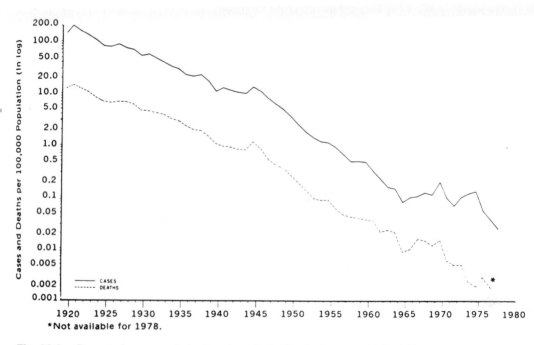

Fig. 28.2. Reported case and death rates of diphtheria by year, United States, 1920 to 1978. (Morbidity and Mortality Weekly Report, Annual Summary, 1978. MMWR *27*: 23, 1979, Center for Disease Control.)

buted to the introduction of mass immunization of pre-school children during that period. However, this may not be the full explanation since the incidence of diphtheria began to drop even before mass immunization. Also, a similar drop in the incidence of scarlet fever occurred during this same period of time, even though there was no immunization program for this disease.

Paradoxically, the dramatic drop in the incidence of diphtheria in children has been accompanied by an increase of the disease in the 30 to 60 year old age group. This may be explained by the low incidence in children, which affords little opportunity for acquiring a booster response from subclinical infection, which in turn leads to a weakening of immunity in early adulthood. Scattered epidemics of diphtheria still occur in the United States. These are seen generally in rural areas or crowded slums.

Pathogenic Manifestations. Man is the only significant natural reservoir for diphtheria bacilli; however, they reportedly also have been isolated from horses and monkeys. The bacilli are carried in the upper respiratory tract, which becomes infected, most commonly directly by droplets. Respiratory infection also may occur indirectly from cutaneous lesions or fomites. The incubation period is 1 to 7 days. If toxigenic diphtheria bacilli become established in the throat, the organisms invade the mucosal epithelium and begin to multiply and produce toxin. Local necrosis occurs, which provides favorable conditions for additional bacterial growth and toxin production. The toxin is absorbed and produces systemic manifestations in the susceptible individual. Significantly, the organism rarely invades deeper tissues. An inflammatory response at the site of infection leads to production of an exudate that eventually forms a characteristic pseudomembrane, which may spread upward into the nasopharynx or downward into the larynx and trachea. Occurrence of the latter is particularly dangerous, because

death by suffocation can frequently result by mechanical obstruction.

Diphtheria shares clinical features with streptococcal pharyngitis, with which it often times is confused. However, unlike the streptococcal infection, pharyngitis in diphtheria does not spread but remains localized, and fever is usually moderate.

Systemic manifestations of the disease appear after entry of the toxin into the general circulation. Serious complications usually involve the kidney — in the form of an acute interstitial nephritis — as well as the heart and nervous system, particularly in the nasopharyngeal form of the disease. Cardiac involvement, which usually appears during the second week of the disease, is produced by toxin-induced fatty degeneration of the myocardium. This leads to dysfunction, circulatory collapse, and frequently, death. Indeed, about one-half of the fatalities seen in diphtheria are due to this complication. Involvement of the nervous system usually appears between the third and fifth week of disease, with both cranial and peripheral nerves being affected. Involvement of cranial nerves characteristically results in paralysis of the soft palate. Peripheral nerve involvement is manifested by polyneuritis in the extremities. If the patient recovers, there generally is no permanent damage to the involved organs.

Extrarespiratory sites such as the conjunctiva, middle ear, and mucous membrane of the genitalia may also be infected, but much less commonly than the upper respiratory tract. The cutaneous form of the disease, which at one time was rare, is becoming more prevalent, especially among those living in poor sanitary conditions or in a tropical climate. Although systemic toxemia does not usually result from cutaneous diphtheria, individuals with this form of the disease serve as a reservoir for the spread of respiratory tract infections.

Laboratory Diagnosis. Diagnosis of diphtheria depends primarily on the demonstration that the organisms isolated from a patient produce diphtheria toxin. For this isolation, specimens such as a throat swab are cultured, ideally on Loeffler's medium, a medium containing tellurite and blood agar. Colonies of diphtheria bacilli are apparent in 12 to 24 hours. The appearance of the throat in diphtheria, especially in the early stages, may be confused with streptococcal pharyngitis or with Vincent's angina. Inoculation of blood agar facilitates isolation of streptococci, and a direct smear, prepared from the swab and stained with gentian violet, aids in diagnosing Vincent's angina. Examining the direct smear for diphtheria bacilli provides only suggestive evidence, since nontoxigenic *C. diphtheriae* or other corynebacteria are often seen normally in the upper respiratory tract. Microscopic evidence for diphtheria bacilli is best obtained from growth on Loeffler's medium, since smears of colonies grown on tellurite medium often do not have the characteristic morphology. It should be noted that on tellurite medium staphylococci or micrococci, in addition to diphtheria bacilli, form black colonies.

Toxin production by diphtheria bacilli is established by either *in vivo* tests for toxicity in animals or an *in vitro* test employing immune precipitation in gel. *In vivo* toxigenicity tests are generally carried out in guinea pigs. Twenty-four hours prior to the test one guinea pig is protected by injection of 250 antitoxic units (see below) of diphtheria antitoxin. The next day, this guinea pig and another untreated guinea pig are injected subcutaneously with a saline suspension of the suspected organism prepared from the growth on the Loeffler slant. Toxigenic diphtheria bacilli kill the unprotected animal in 3 to 5 days, whereas the protected animal survives. On autopsy, edema at the site of inoculation and enlarged, hemorrhagic adrenal glands are seen in the unprotected animal.

Tests for a local rather than a systemic reaction can also be performed in guinea pigs. In these tests the bacterial suspension is inoculated intradermally, usually in the shaved abdominal area. By this technique several specimens may be examined. Development in the unprotected animal of a necrotic lesion at the injection site in 2 to 3 days is a positive reaction. Other animals, particularly rabbits, have also been used for *in vivo* tests.

The *in vitro* test for toxigenicity utilizes the procedure of gel precipitation. An appropriate medium, such as peptone maltose lactate agar, containing 20 percent horse serum, is used. A strip of filter paper soaked in diphtheria antitoxin is placed either in molten agar or on top of solidified agar. A heavy inoculum of the suspected microorganism is then streaked on the agar

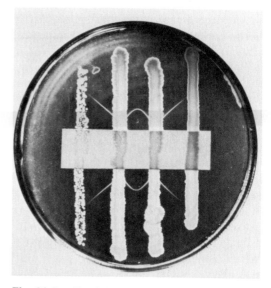

Fig. 28.3.   Precipitation test for toxigenicity. Filter paper was impregnated with diphtheria antitoxin and placed on the agar plate. The agar plate was subsequently inoculated with four bacterial specimens, with streaks made perpendicular to the filter paper. The outer two bacterial strains are nontoxigenic. The precipitation lines formed between the two inner bacterial strains, which are toxigenic, merge to form a reaction of identity. (King, E.O., Frobisher, M., and Parsons, E.I.: The *in vitro* test for virulence of *Corynebacterium diphtheriae*. Am. J. Pub. Health *39*: 1314, 1949.)

surface at right angles to the paper strip. If the organism produces diphtheria toxin, a precipitation line consisting of toxin–antitoxin complexes will form after 24 hours of incubation (Fig. 28.3).

Immunity. The history of studies on immunity to diphtheria is dotted with scientific landmarks that contributed not only to conquering a specific disease but also to microbiology in general. These include the demonstration by Roux and Yersin (1888) that systemic effects in diphtheria were caused by a soluble toxin; studies by von Behring and Kitasato (1890) that serum from animals immunized with diphtheria toxin could protect susceptible animals from the disease; the courageous step by von Behring and Wernicke in 1891 of injecting a child suffering from diphtheria with antitoxin; experiments by Smith (1909) showing that toxicity, but not antigenicity, is reduced or even lost when toxin combines with antitoxin; the discovery by Schick in 1913 of a test that distinguishes immune individuals from those susceptible to the toxin; and, finally, the demonstration by Ramon (1923) that formalin treated toxin, or toxoid, is nontoxic but is fully antigenic.

Immunity to diphtheria is primarily antitoxic — the protected individual has a sufficient amount of circulating antibodies to neutralize the pathologic effects of the toxin. The protective antibodies are directed principally against the B component of the toxin. The immune state may be acquired actively by clinical or subclinical infection or by immunization with toxoid. Immunity also may be transferred passively by administration of antitoxin or by transplacental passage of antibodies from mother to fetus. Although it is clear that immunity is largely directed against the disease-producing diphtheria toxin, there is some question whether antibodies to other components of *C. diphtheriae*, such as the cord factor, the somatic antigens, or the K antigens, also may contribute to protection.

Standardization of Toxin and Antitoxin. The pioneering work in this field was performed by Paul Ehrlich. He first defined diphtheria toxin in terms of the minimum lethal dose (MLD), the least amount of toxin that kills a guinea pig weighing 250 g within 4 days after subcutaneous inoculation. A unit of antitoxin was defined as the smallest dose of antitoxin serum that was capable of completely neutralizing 100 MLD of toxin.

Ehrlich and others soon realized that because of its unstable nature, toxin was an unsuitable reference standard, since by various treatments and even on storage it converts to toxoid (i.e., it becomes nontoxic but still reacts with antitoxin).

Subsequently, Ehrlich devised a reference based on a standard antitoxic serum, which is accepted today as the International Standard. All diphtheria antitoxin preparations used for therapy are measured against the activity of Ehrlich's original antiserum. Potency of antitoxin is given in terms of antitoxin units (AU).

To standardize a particular antitoxin preparation, one first determines the smallest amount of a potent toxin that when mixed with an amount of a standard antitoxin containing 1 AU and subsequently injected subcutaneously into a 250 g guinea pig will still kill the animal within 4 days. This amount of toxin is termed the *L+* (*Limes Tod*) *dose.*

To learn the combining power of an antitoxin of unknown potency that is to be used for therapy, one determines its capacity to neutralize the L + dose of toxin. The smallest amount of this antitoxin that will *protect* a guinea pig when mixed with the L+ dose of toxin is considered to contain 1 AU.

The potency of toxin and antitoxin preparations may be determined more conveniently by a skin test in which guinea pigs or rabbits are injected with toxin–antitoxin mixtures intracutaneously rather than subcutaneously. The smallest amount of toxin that gives a minimal skin reaction when mixed with 1 AU of standard antitoxin is determined. This amount of toxin is termed the *Lr* (*Limes inflammatory reaction*) *dose*.

Potency of antitoxin can also be determined by an *in vitro* test by taking advantage of the observation that neutral mixtures of toxin and antitoxin flocculate more rapidly than toxic mixtures. The smallest amount of toxin that flocculates most rapidly with 1 AU of standard antitoxin is termed the *Lf* (*Limes flocculation*) *dose*.

More recently, *in vitro* neutralization tests utilizing cultured cells, which give good correlation with *in vivo* protection tests, also have been developed for titration of antitoxin.

Shick test. Over 65 years ago Shick developed the first test for diphtheria that could distinguish susceptible and resistant individuals. This test greatly contributed to the conquering of diphtheria. In the test, 1/50 of the MLD of purified diphtheria toxin usually in a volume of 0.1 ml, is injected intradermally into the forearm. As a control, similar material, but heated at 60°C for 30 minutes to destroy toxicity, is injected into the other forearm. The following results may be seen:

1. No reaction in either forearm, indicating that the person is protected against diphtheria, i.e., antitoxin is present in the circulation. The amount of antitoxin in the circulation required for protection varies with the individual. Positive reactions have been noted in individuals with as much as 0.03 units of antitoxin per ml; in contrast, no reactions have been seen in individuals with as little as 0.0005 units of antitoxin.

2. Positive reaction in the test arm, no reaction in the control arm, indicating that the person is susceptible to the toxin. A positive reaction appears usually after 24 to 48 hours with a maximum response seen after 4 to 7 days. In some individuals, the time of initial appearance and maximum response may be after 5 to 7 days. The response appears as a raised erythematous

area around the injection site, reaches a maximum, and then fades slowly and disappears within 3 to 4 days. Sometimes, a brownish coloration of the skin remains followed by loss of the epidermal layer.

3. Pseudoreaction is seen in resistant individuals who are allergic to the inoculum. A reaction of similar intensity appears in both arms within 24 hours. The reaction in both arms fades more rapidly and disappears more quickly than true positive reactions (number 2, above).

4. Combined reaction is seen in individuals who are at the same time susceptible to toxin and allergic to the inoculum. A positive reaction is seen in the test arm and a pseudoreaction is seen in the control arm.

Treatment. The only effective means of treating diphtheria is administration of antitoxin. This therapy should be followed whenever a presumptive clinical diagnosis of diphtheria is made, without waiting for confirmation by the laboratory. Binding of toxin to the tissue is rapid and irreversible. Consequently, the sooner antitoxin is administered, the better the prognosis. For rapid dissemination, antitoxin is given intramuscularly or intravenously.

The amount of antitoxin that should be administered is still a debated point. According to one conservative protocol, mild cases should receive 10,000 to 20,000 AU, intramuscularly. Severe cases should be injected intravenously with 50,000 to 100,000 AU.

It is important to note that commercial antitoxin is prepared in an animal species foreign to man, usually horses. Consequently, the patient should be tested for hypersensitivity to the serum of the appropriate animal species prior to treatment. In hypersensitive or allergic individuals, the antitoxin must be administered slowly in small doses.

Antibiotic therapy, though not effective against diphtheria, is used to combat secondary infection by *C. diphtheriae* and to abolish the carrier state. The latter is important in view of the fact that up to 15 percent of those who recover from diphtheria become carriers for several weeks if not given antibiotics. Diphtheria bacilli are susceptible to penicillin, erythromycin, and tetracycline.

Prevention. Toxoid, prepared by alum precipitation of formalin inactivated toxin, is presently used for active immunization. Initial immunization is given to infants 2 to 3 months of age, usually with pertussis vaccine and tetanus toxoid (DPT). A second injection is given 1 year later, and a third injection is administered just before the child begins school.

Studies have shown that almost 50 percent of individuals over 15 years of age are hypersensitive to the toxoid inoculum. Consequently, this age group should be skin tested, prior to immunization, by intradermal injection of 0.1 ml of a 1:10 dilution of toxoid (Moloney test). Schick-positive individuals usually become Schick-negative if the Moloney test is repeated 2 or 3 times at weekly intervals.

Susceptible individuals who have been in high risk situations can be protected by passive immunization with 1000 to 3000 units of antitoxin and simultaneous active immunization with toxoid.

Other Corynebacteria

The corynebacteria that are commonly associated with man and animals are listed in Table 28.1. Members of the genus other than *C. diphtheriae* that are associated with man are *C. pseudodiphtheriticum*, which is found in the nasopharynx, and *C. xerosis*, which is present on skin and mucous membranes, particularly the conjunctiva. The latter two organisms, which are commonly referred to as diphtheroid bacilli, are considered nonpathogenic and, indeed, are part of the normal flora of man. They are often confused with *C. diphtheriae* on microscopic examination and even on isolation. Neither organism produces a soluble

exotoxin. However, one should be aware that under the proper conditions, diphtheroid bacilli may become opportunistic pathogens. These bacilli have been known to cause endocarditis, meningitis, and osteomyelitis. Aside from toxigenicity, these organisms may be distinguished on the basis of fermentation of glucose and maltose (Table 28.1).

Several species of *Corynebacterium* are pathogenic for lower animals, and some, on rare occasions, produce disease in man.

C. pseudotuberculosis causes a caseous lymphadenitis in sheep and horses and ulcerative lesions in other domestic animals such as cattle and pigs. The bacillus produces a soluble exotoxin that is antigenically distinct from, and less potent than, diphtheria toxin.

C. renale produces pyogenic lesions in the urinary tract of cattle, sheep, horses, and dogs and is related serologically to *C. pseudotuberculosis*. *C. equi* produces pneumonia in foals and is responsible for other infections in horses.

C. pyogenes and *C. hemolyticum* (not listed in the table) are only tentatively included in the genus *Corynebacterium* because they differ from other members in several important aspects. For example, the cell wall composition of these two species is completely different from other corynebacteria. Both *C. pyogenes* and *C. hemolyticum* produce pyogenic infections in domestic animals. Interestingly, *C. pyogenes* produces a soluble exotoxin that is much weaker than diphtheria toxin and is antigenically unrelated to diphtheria toxin and the toxin produced by *C. pseudotuberculosis*.

LISTERIA

Of the four species in the genus *Listeria*, *L. monocytogenes* is the only one of medical interest. This organism has been recognized for many years as a significant pathogen in domestic and wild animals. Only in recent

Table 28.1.   Some Distinctive Characteristics of Corynebacteria That Parasitize Man and Animals

Species	Hemolysis	Fermentation of: Sucrose	Glucose	Maltose	Reduction of Nitrate	Other Features
C. diphtheriae	+	–	+	+	+	Human pathogen; exotoxin producer; infected by specific bacteriophages
C. pseudodiphtheriticum	–	–	–	–	+	Human parasite; present in nasopharynx; nonpathogen
C. xerosis	–	+	+	v[a]	+	Human parasite; present on skin and mucous membranes; nonpathogen
C. pseudotuberculosis	+	v	+	+	v	Related to pyogenic infections in domestic animals; exotoxin producer; infected by specific bacteriophages
C. renale	–	–	+	v	–	Related to cystitis and pyelonephritis in domestic animals
C. kutscheri	–	+	–	–	–	Parasite of rats and mice
C. equi	–	–	–	–	+	Pathogenic for horses
C. bovis	–	–	v	v	–	Parasite of cows; may cause mastitis

[a]Variable

(Modified from Bucharan, R.E. and Gibbons, N.E. (Eds.): Bergey's Manual of Determinative Bacteriology, 8th Ed. © (1974) The Williams and Wilkins Co., Baltimore.)

years has its importance in human disease been widely recognized.

Morphology and Physiology

L. monocytogenes is a small, gram-positive, nonencapsulated bacillus. It produces no spores and is motile by means of peritrichous flagella. Of significance is the finding that motility is greater at 20 to 25°C than at 37°C. Rod forms are seen on initial isolation, but coccoid forms tend to predominate in cultures. The organism measures 0.5 to 2 μm in length and 0.4 to 0.5 μm in breadth. Both smooth and rough strains are seen on culture. Filamentous forms up to 20 μm in length are seen in old cultures or cultures of rough strains. Also, in old cultures the tinctorial properties become irregular.

Listeriae grow well on enriched laboratory media. In fluid media all but rough strains show diffuse growth. Characteristic bluish-green colonies are seen on a clear solid medium such as tryptose agar, and β-hemolysis is formed on blood agar.

Although *L. monocytogenes* is aerobic, optimum growth is seen under reduced O_2 and increased CO_2 tension as well as at neutral or slightly alkaline pH. The organisms are capable of growth at a pH as high as 9.0 and in sodium chloride concentrations of 10 percent or even higher. Diagnostic advantage is often taken of the feature that this organism continues to grow at temperatures as low as 4°C.

L. monocytogenes shows low biochemical activity. It is not proteolytic, does not produce H_2S or indole, and does not reduce nitrates or hydrolyze urea. However, it does produce catalase, and it ferments a variety of sugars, producing acid but not gas.

Antigenic Structure

Four major serogroups of *L. monocytogenes*, designated 1 to 4, have been described on the basis of heat labile flagellar (H) antigens and heat stable somatic (O) antigens. These groups are further subdivided into 11 serotypes. Significantly, antisera to listeriae crossreact with a number of other bacteria including corynebacteria, *Streptococcus faecalis*, *Staphylococcus aureus*, and *Escherichia coli*; consequently, diagnosis based on serology is not reliable.

Human Listeriosis

Pathogenic Determinants. Pathogenic determinants of *L. monocytogenes* include a lipid, termed monocytosis-producing agent, which presumably is responsible for the characteristic monocytosis seen in listeriosis. The organism also produces a diffusable hemolysin that is heat labile and O_2 sensitive. The hemolysin is lethal for mice, and there is evidence that it is cardiotoxic. A lipolytic protein, which is cytotoxic for cultured murine peritoneal macrophages, has also been described. There appears to be a good correlation between virulence and the activity of these substances.

Epidemiology. *L. monocytogenes* produces disease worldwide in a variety of animals, including man. The organism is present in soil and silage, but its natural reservoir is believed to be rodents and fowl. It also has been recovered from ticks, fish, crustaceans, and even plants.

Listeriosis may be sporadic or epizootic in lower animals. Young animals are more susceptible than older animals, and under natural conditions disease manifestations may vary with different species. A generalized septicemia is most common in rodents, a massive myocarditis in fowl, and central nervous system involvement in ruminants. Listeriae also have a tendency to localize in the reproductive system of pregnant females, leading to abortion.

Infection of man by *L. monocytogenes* is usually by the oral route and may occur from soil, by direct contact with animals, or

Table 28.2. Principle Clinical Forms of Human Listeriosis

Meningitis, meningoencephalitis — most common in neonates and adults over 40 years of age

Low grade septicemia (influenzalike) in pregnancy — usually results in abortion or stillbirth

Septicemia — in neonates
— in adults as complication of pharyngitis, tonsillitis, sinusitis, otitis media

Endocarditis

Localized abscesses — external or internal

Pneumonia

Conjunctivitis

Infectious mononucleosislike syndrome

Pharyngitis

Cutaneous papules and pustules

Urethritis

(Modified from Gray M.L. and Killinger, A.H.: *Listeria monocytogenes* and listeric infections. Bacteriol. Rev. *30*: 309, 1966.)

by ingestion of contaminated food such as raw milk. Human-to-human transmission is uncommon except for transplacental passage. Approximately 1 percent of the normal population and 4 to 5 percent of those in close contact with animals — e.g., slaughterhouse personnel — excrete the organism in their feces. Particularly susceptible to listeriosis are newborns, the elderly, and individuals whose health has been compromised.

Clinical Manifestations in human listeriosis may occur as a local or systemic infection, and the disease may be manifested in a variety of ways (see Table 28.2). Abscesses or granulomas are characteristically produced. Localized infections often involve the mucous membranes, which leads to upper respiratory symptoms. The regional lymphatics and conjunctiva also may be affected. Generalized infections are more common and are much more severe. Purulent meningitis, meningoencephalitis, and septicemia are the clinical entities most frequently associated with *L. monocytogenes* in man. Invasion of various organs, such as the liver, spleen, and adrenal gland, may result from septicemia. Invasion of the central nervous system often gives rise to a meningitis or meningoencephalitis.

Almost 50 percent of cases of human listeriosis are perinatal. Characteristically the

mother develops mild influenzalike symptoms during the last trimester of pregnancy. This may lead to abortion or stillbirth, or the child may develop meningitis if born alive.

Diagnosis of listeriosis based on clinical signs alone is extremely difficult, if not impossible. Generalized infection may produce disease that may mimic other diseases such as typhoid fever or infectious mononucleosis.

In adults over 40 years old and in the newborn, the most common form of the disease is meningitis, a meningitis that is indistinguishable clinically from that produced by other bacteria or viruses. The case fatality rate in untreated cases of meningitis is 70 to 90 percent. Onset of the disease is usually sudden. In fulminating listeriosis death can occur within 24 to 72 hours.

Listerial meningitis or septicemia may arise in patients debilitated from malignancy, diabetes, or alcoholism. Corticosteroid therapy is believed to increase the likelihood of listeriosis in compromised patients. It should be noted that subclinical infections can occur, with excretion of the organism in the feces by carriers.

Immunity to listeriae is principally by cellular mechanisms, being mediated by T cells and activated macrophages. Humoral

Table 28.3. Distinguishing Features of *Listeria monocytogenes* and Certain Other Gram-Positive Bacteria

Feature	*Listeria monocytogenes*	*Erysipelothrix rhusiopathiae*	*Corynebacterium* spp.	*Lactobacillus* spp.	*Streptococcus pyogenes*	*Streptococcus faecalis*
Morphology	Bacillus	Bacillus	Bacillus	Bacillus	Coccus	Coccus
β-hemolysis	+	–	v[a]	–	+	–
Glucose	+	+	v	+	+	+
Mannitol	–	–	v	v	–	+
Catalase	+	–	+	–	–	–
Motility	+	–	–	–	–	–
Keratoconjunctivitis	+	–	–	–	–	–

[a]Variable within the genus.

(Buchner, L.H. and Schneierson, S.S.: Clinical and laboratory aspects of Listeria monocytogenes infections, Am. J. Med. *45*: 904, 1968.)

antibodies to listeriae are produced, but their protective role is not clear.

Treatment of listeriosis by administration of antibiotics is effective. Ampicillin is considered the drug of choice; erythromycin and the tetracyclines also are effective.

Laboratory Diagnosis. Diagnosis of listeriosis depends on isolation of *L. monocytogenes* from the proper clinical specimen, such as swabs of lesions, blood, or cerebrospinal fluid. Of major importance is direct examination of smears stained by the Gram procedure. Isolation of listeriae by culture is enhanced by storage of specimens for several weeks at 4°C. Listeriae may be confused with a number of other nonsporulating gram-positive bacteria, particularly corynebacteria. Several tests are available for differentiation (Table 28.3). The Anton test has also been used to distinguish *L. monocytogenes* from other gram-positive organisms. In this test a purulent keratoconjunctivitis is produced within 24 to 36 hours after instillation of *L. monocytogenes* into the conjunctival sac of a young rabbit.

REFERENCES

Andrewes, F.W., Bulloch, W., Douglass, S.R., Freyer, G., Gardner, A.D., Fildes, P.,

Ledingham, J.C.G., and Wolf, C.G.L.: Dipththeria, Its Bacteriology, Pathology and Immunity. H.M.S.O., London, 1923.

Barksdale, L.: *Corynebacterium diphtheriae* and its relatives. Bacteriol. Rev. *34*: 378, 1970.

Bojsen-Møller, J.: Human listeriosis. Diagnostic, epidemiological and clinical studies. Acta Pathol. Microbiol. Scand. B *229*: 157, 1972.

Bonventre, P.F.: Diphtheria. In Schlessinger, D., Ed.: Microbiology — 1975. American Society for Microbiology, Washington, D.C., 1975.

Busch, L.A.: Human listeriosis in the United States, 1967–1969. J. Infect. Dis. *123*: 328, 1971.

Collier, R.J.: Diphtheria toxin: Mode of action and structure. Bacteriol. Rev. *39*: 54, 1975.

Freeman, B.A., Ed.: Burrows Textbook of Microbiology. 21st Ed. W.B. Saunders Company, Philadelphia 1979.

Gray, M.L. and Killinger, A.H.: *Listeria monocytogenes* and listeric infections. Bacteriol. Rev. *30*: 309, 1966.

Pappenheimer, A.M., Jr.: The Schick test 1913 –1958. Int. Arch. Allergy Appl. Immunol. *12*: 35, 1958.

Pappenheimer, A.M., Jr., and Gill, D.M.: Diphtheria. Science *182*: 353, 1973.

Watson, B.B. and Lavizzo, J.C.: Extracellular antigens from *Listeria monocytogenes*. II. Cytotoxicity of hemolytic and lipolytic antigens of *Listeria* for cultured mouse macrophages. Infect. Immun. *7*: 753, 1973.

29

Bacillus

Konrad Wicher

Bacillus and *Clostridium* are two genera of the family *Bacillaceae*; both are spore-bearing and gram-positive but *Bacillus* is aerobic and *Clostridium* anaerobic. *Clostridium* is of greater clinical relevance.

The genus *Bacillus* consists of over 25 species, but only a few are of medical significance — *B. anthracis*, *B. cereus*, *B. megaterium*, *B. mycoides*, and *B. subtilis*. Of these only *B. anthracis* is considered a true pathogen. *B. cereus* might play a role in food poisoning; the remaining are opportunists causing disease in compromised hosts. Other saprophytic bacilli are present in soil, dust, water, milk, animal wool, feces, or plants and, as contaminants, may cause problems in health care institutions.

GROUP CHARACTERISTICS

Morphology

Members of the genus *Bacillus* are rod shaped organisms varying from 3 to 9 μm in length and 1 to 1.5 μm in width. Depending on the source of clinical specimens or the media used for growth, the organisms appear in a stained film usually in chains or groups but also in single or diplobacillary form. They are motile by peritrichous flagella and form spores only in the presence of oxygen. The spores may be localized in various parts of the cell and, with some exceptions, do not exceed the width of the bacillus. *B. anthracis* is the only species that has a prominent capsule, especially when it is seen in a film from a clinical specimen or when it is grown in a 10 percent CO_2 atmosphere, and it is the only species without flagella. The organisms are gram-positive, but considerable variation in staining may be observed.

Culture

All members of the genus grow on simple media. The colonies are usually large (2 to 7 mm) with a granular surface, mealy or wrinkled in appearance. In broth a surface scum may be formed with or without turbidity or heavy flocculant deposit. Growth may be improved by enriching the medium with glucose but not with serum or blood. The optimum growth temperature varies from 25°C to 37°C; few grow below 12°C and, except for the thermophilic members, which grow at 60°C, none grow above 55°C. All members grow aerobically, but some, such as *B. anthracis* and *B. cereus*, can also grow under anaerobic conditions.

Resistance

The spores vary greatly in resistance to heat; for example, spores of *B. anthracis* can be destroyed by boiling for about 10 minutes, whereas those of *B. subtilis* may withstand boiling for many hours. Autoclaving (120°C) contaminated material destroys most spores within 40 minutes.

Germicidal detergents of sporicide type,* in order to affect spores, must act for 6 to 8 hours. Floor and wall finishes can hardly be kept wet by a biocide for 6 to 8 hours without damage to wood or plaster. There are no available practical sporicides for area disinfection. Dialdehyde and formaldehyde products are available that are intended for surgical instruments, but even they have to act for 2 or 3 hours. A gaseous disinfectant, such as β-propiolactone, in proper conditions can kill spores of *B. subtilis* in 2 hours. The stronger germicidal detergents (e.g., tuberculocide) destroy the vegetative forms of bacilli.

Metabolic Reactions

Members of the genus *Bacillus* produce yellow-brownish, pink, or black pigment. These characteristics vary and are not a good parameter for differentiation. The organisms liquefy gelatin rapidly. Fermentation reactions tend to be weak and irregular and only in a very few cases helpful for identification. In practice the differentiation between *B. anthracis* and other *Bacillus* spp. is required and can be achieved without difficulty by comparing, besides metabolic activi-

---

*Germicidal detergents are classified depending on their activity as *germicide, tuberculocide, fungicide,* or *sporicide*.

ties, other characteristics. Biochemical differentiation between *B. anthracis* and *B. cereus* is very difficult, and a variety of parameters have to be used (see Table 29.1).

Antigenic Structure

The antigenic heterogeneity among the members of the genus *Bacillus* is known. However, there are no known serologic biotypes of *B. anthracis* and serologic tests are not used in diagnostic laboratories.

Pathogenicity

Under natural conditions *B. anthracis* causes disease in humans, sheep, cattle, and other animals. *B. cereus* has been associated with gastroenteritis and *B. subtilis* with severe eye lesions in man. In a compromised host — especially in terminal cancer, after extensive surgery of the gastrointestinal tract, or during prolonged treatment with immunosuppressants — any of the saprophytic members of the genus *Bacillus* may invade the host and be isolated from blood. If the organisms are found in such specimens as sputum, urine or wound discharge, this may indicate contamination rather than be of clinical significance.

ANTHRAX

Anthrax is a zoonotic disease. Those who are handling materials which may be harboring *B. anthracis* (e.g., abattoir workers, veterinarians, workers handling hides and wool, farmers) may be affected. In the United States anthrax is a disease of the past. In the last 10 years, only 2 to 5 cases a year have been reported.

Pathogenesis

In man the infection occurs in three forms: cutaneous, respiratory, and gastrointesti-

Table 29.1. Properties Useful in Distinguishing *B. anthracis* From Other Bacilli

Characteristics	B. anthracis	B. cereus	B. subtilis
Anaerobic growth	+	+	–
Hemolysis on blood agar	–	+	+ (not all)
Motility	–	+(usually)	+
Methylene blue reduction	– (or late +)	+	+
Salicin	– (or late +)	+	+
Egg yolk reaction	+	+	–
Peptonization of milk	– (or late +)	+	+
Animal pathogenicity	+	– (+ when large dose)	–

nal. Cutaneous anthrax follows the deposition of *B. anthracis* spores under the epidermidis, where they germinate into vegetative forms that multiply and produce toxin. Infection with vegetative forms has a shorter incubation time than infections with spores, but it causes similar symptoms. Depending on the number of organisms infecting the host, the incubation period may vary from 2 to 7 days. As the initial lesion, a small papule develops that progresses to a vesicle. Slight erythema and edema may surround the vesicle. After a few days the vesicular fluid becomes blueish-black. A characteristic sharp-walled depressed ulcer with a black eschar may be seen in the center within 7 to 10 days after onset. Mild systemic symptoms with low fever and enlarged regional lymph nodes may be observed. The organism is very invasive and may, if the patient is untreated, cause septicemia and general toxemia. The fatality rate in cutaneous anthrax was 10 to 20 percent; with effective antibiotic treatment it dropped to less than 1 percent.

In respiratory infection the spores of *B. anthracis* colonize the terminal alveoli of the lungs. They are ingested by macrophages, which carry them to the regional lymph nodes. Some spores survive the phagocytic process; they germinate into vegetative forms that mutiply and produce toxins. Toxemia and septicemia may result as a consequence of the respiratory infection. The incubation period may vary from 2 to 6 days, with nonspecific symptoms of mild fever and malaise resembling an upper respiratory infection. Death may occur very rapidly owing to general toxemia and respiratory failure secondary to pulmonary capillary thrombosis. The fatality rate is almost 100 percent. History of exposure to an aerosol containing *B. anthracis* or identification of the organism in pleural fluid may be of help in diagnosis.

Gastrointestinal anthrax is acquired by ingestion of contaminated meat. The spores pass through the intestinal mucosa and germinate. The organisms multiplying in the submucosal tissue produce a toxin that causes necrotic, ulcerative lesions in the terminal ileum or cecum. The incubation period is usually 2 to 5 days. The patient may react with non-specific symptoms of abdominal pain, nausea, vomiting, fever, and diarrhea. The leukocyte count may be moderately elevated. The disease may lead to general toxemia, shock, and death. History or better, examination of ingested meat, help in diagnosis. Gastrointestinal anthrax was fatal in 25 to 50 percent of cases. In recent years this type of anthrax is hardly ever seen, and it no longer exists in the United States.

The drug of choice in cutaneous and respiratory infections is penicillin. The dose and route of administration vary. In gastrointestinal anthrax tetracycline should be used. All cases of anthrax should be reported to local public health authorities.

Anthrax vaccine is available for use in man. Employees in high risk industries should be immunized.

Laboratory Examination

Anthrax cannot be diagnosed for certain without bacteriologic confirmation. It should be stressed that specimens must be taken prior to initiation of antibiotic therapy.

In cutaneous infections, a sterile swab soaked in sterile saline or, better, in brain heart infusion is rotated beneath the edge of the eschar without removing it. As much as possible of the vesicular fluid should be absorbed on the swab. The swab, placed in a sterile tube, should be sent immediately to the laboratory. For direct examination, tissue impression films obtained by gently pressing a sterile (flame sterilized) microscopic slide to the exposed area of the wound should be made, if possible. Several slides should be prepared.

In respiratory infections sputum should be collected into a sterile glass container. If pleural fluid is available, it should be aspirated and injected into a sterile tube.

In gastrointestinal infections fecal material should be obtained for laboratory examination. Efforts should be made to obtain the suspected meat for culture.

Since in all forms of anthrax septicemia may develop, blood (10 to 20 ml) for cultures should be obtained from patients with systemic symptoms.

For direct examination, films from specimens, including an impression film, are heat fixed and stained. Gram stain shows large, 3 to 9 μm long, square ended gram-positive rods either singly or in chains (Fig. 29.1). Spores may be seen as refractile spots (unstained) within the cells. The capsule may be made visible by changing

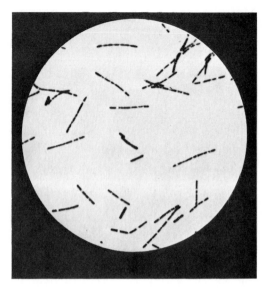

Fig. 29.1. *Bacillus anthracis*. Smear from spleen of infected guinea pig ($\times$ 1000). (With permission, Wilson, G.S. and Miles, A.A., Eds.: Topley and Wilson's Principles of Bacteriology, Virology and Immunity. 6th Ed. Edward Arnold Ltd., London, 1975).

the focus of the microscope. The capsule is characteristic for *B. anthracis*, and efforts should be made to demonstrate it with toluidine blue, methylene blue, or other stains. Fluorescent staining is also helpful in identification of organisms in direct smears. Antibodies to *B. anthracis* are labeled with fluorescein isothiocyanate and used in proper dilution as a staining reagent. This procedure is usually not available in hospital diagnostic laboratories; it is more popular in veterinary institutions, where the number of samples is larger.

Culture of *B. anthracis* can be obtained in medium that does not contain growth inhibitory substances. Plates should be incubated overnight at 37°C. On blood agar the colonies of *B. anthracis* are nonhemolytic, 3 to 5 mm in diameter, grayish with a dull appearance, and flat with irregular waved bridal margin (medusa head) (Fig. 29.2).

Biochemically, *B. anthracis* is very similar to *B. cereus*. The characteristics dif-

Fig. 29.2. Edge of a colony *B. anthracis*, demonstrating irregular waved bridal margin (medusa head) (× 18). (With permission, Wilson, G.S. and Miles, A.A., Eds.: Topley and Wilson's Principles of Bacteriology, Virology and Immunity. 6th Ed. Edward Arnold Ltd., London, 1975).

ferentiating the two and *B. subtilis* are outlined in Table 29.1.

Serologic examination differentiating antigenic structure of members of the genus *Bacillus* is not practiced. Detection of antigen(s) of *B. anthracis* in various products is done by the classic Ascoli test, which is a precipitation reaction using a specific antibody to *B. anthracis* and saline extract of the examined product. This test has some application in veterinary medicine.

INFECTION BY OTHER BACILLI

Species other than *B. anthracis* have been isolated from patients with a variety of diseases. *B. cereus* affects the gastrointestinal tract by the elaboration of enterotoxins and has been associated with food poisoning. In Europe this organism has been recognized as an important source of food-borne outbreaks of gastroenteritis for the last 25 years. Most likely because of the rigid hygienic rules it is rather seldom seen as a source of food poisoning in the United States. Various other members of this group have been isolated from blood of patients with debilitating diseases such as carcinoma, multiple myeloma, lymphoma, cirrhosis of the liver, and severe diabetes, in a variety of severe wounds, after open heart surgery, and in many other diseases compromising the immune response of the host.

REFERENCES

Bodily, H.L., Updyke, E.L., and Mason, J.O., Eds.: Diagnostic Procedures for Bacterial, Mycotic and Parasitic Infections. American Public Health Association, New York, 1970.

Lennette, E.H., Balows, A., Hausler, W.J., Jr., and Truant, J.P., Eds.: Manual of Clinical Microbiology. 3rd Ed. American Society for Microbiology, Washington, D.C., 1980.

Wilson, G.S. and Miles, A.A., Eds.: Topley and Wilson's Principles of Bacteriology, Virology and Immunity. 6th Ed. Edward Arnold, Ltd., London, 1975.

30

Clostridium

Konrad Wicher

ANAEROBIC MICROORGANISMS

It is difficult to provide a definition of anaerobic microorganisms acceptable to all specialists. The following practical definitions of the anaerobes may be satisfactory for the medical professions:

Obligate anaerobes are bacteria that cannot survive exposure to air for more than 20 minutes and require for growth oxygen tension ≤ 4 mm Hg.

Facultative anaerobes are those microorganisms that can be exposed to air for 100 minutes and grow in an atmosphere with oxygen tension of 60 mm Hg.

Microaerophilic bacteria are organisms that prefer reduced oxygen tension such as that provided by 10 percent CO_2 in air; these organisms grow poorly or not at all in aerobic conditions but they grow well in anaerobic conditions.

Oxygen is toxic to anaerobic microorganisms; substances eliminating or reducing oxygen in the environment enhance the growth of anaerobes. Chemical reducing agents such as cysteine or glutathione are used in the laboratory to lower the redox potential (E_h) in media. In naturally occurring infection a low redox potential is created by various means. Local anaerobic conditions can be created by medical manipulation (iatrogenic anaerobiosis). For example, a tight cast may cause impairment of local circulation and result in edema or tissue anoxia. These conditions cause accumulation of lactate, leading to local acidosis, lowering of pH, and proteolysis. If this is localized in an area where anaerobic organisms are present, conditions for propagation of anaerobes are created and the infection process may start. Aerobic infection (e.g., by *Streptococcus pyogenes*) can also lower the redox potential, creating conditions for mixed infection with anaerobic organisms.

The anaerobic bacteria consist of a variety of morphological types, including gram-positive and gram-negative bacilli and cocci, comma shaped organisms, and spirochetes. Anaerobic bacteria may be conveniently divided into two groups: the spore-forming organisms (clostridia) and the nonsporulating anaerobic bacteria.

General Characteristics of Clostridia

Clostridia are gram-positive anaerobic spore-forming bacilli. Most species are obligate anaerobes, but a few are air tolerant and grow under reduced atmospheric pressure. The pathogenicity of the organisms is based on production of potent soluble exotoxins. Some species are saccharolytic, producing acids and gas from carbohydrates, and many are proteolytic. Clostridia are widely distributed in nature and are present in soil and in the intestinal tract of humans and animals.

Pathogenic clostridia, depending on the disease they produce, can be divided into two groups: histotoxic clostridia, causing a variety of tissue infections usually as a consequence of wound infections, and microorganisms, represented by *C. tetani* and *C. botulinum*, causing intoxication of the body by potent toxins. *C. tetani* is the causative agent of tetanus. The microorganism is not invasive; it enters the body usually through a wound and, if conditions are suitable, produces exotoxins that are responsible for the clinical symptoms of the disease. *C. botulinum* is the causative agent of botulism, a food poisoning caused by ingestion of the toxins produced by the organisms in the contaminated food. The organism in botulism does not necessarily have to enter the body; however, botulism due to wound infection by *C. botulinum* has been reported in sporadic cases.

HISTOTOXIC CLOSTRIDIA

These organisms cause a severe infection of muscles called clostridial myonecrosis (gas gangrene). The most important histotoxic species of *Clostridium* are *C. perfringens*, *C. novyi*, and *C. septicum*. A few other organisms, less important, such as *C. his-*

tolyticum or *C. sordellii*, are very seldom responsible for clostridial myonecrosis.

Morphologic and Cultural Characteristics

C. perfringens varies considerably in length, from 1 to 8 μm, and is approximately 1 μm wide. The ends are truncated or slightly rounded. Spores are seldom seen in cultures but are commonly formed under natural conditions. The spores are oval and located subterminally. Sporulation occurs more frequently with some strains than with others. Capsules are formed readily only in an infected host. The organism is nonmotile.

C. perfringens grows well in enriched media. On solid media, after incubation at 37°C for 4 days the colonies are 2 to 4 mm in diameter, low convex, amorphous, grayish-yellow, and smooth-surfaced. Variation in the form may be observed. In chopped meat-glucose broth, clostridia grow well with moderate turbidity, powdery deposit, and slight sour odor.

Toxin Production

All of these histotoxic clostridia produce a variety of toxins and enzymes of different potencies, and each toxin is designated by a Greek letter in order of importance or discovery. The toxins formed by types A and C of *C. perfringens* are given in Table 30.1. α toxin is a lecithinase that splits lecithin (lecithin + lecithinase $\rightarrow$ lysolecithin + phosphorylocholin). The lysolecithin causes lysis of erythrocytes. *In vivo* α toxin apparently acts on the lecithin-containing

Table 30.1.   Toxins Produced by *C. perfringens* in Clostridial Myonecrosis or Food Poisoning

Type	α	β	ϵ	ι	δ	θ	κ	λ	μ	ν
A	+	−	−	−	−	+	+	−	−	+
C	+	+	−	−	−	+	+	−	+	+

lipoprotein complex in the cell membranes and probably on mitochondria. β, ε, and ι toxins have lethal and necrotizing activity. δ and θ toxins have lethal and hemolytic activity. κ toxin is a collagenase, λ a proteinase, μ a hyaluronidase, and ν a deoxyribonuclease.

C. perfringens is divided into five types, and some types may be divided further into subtypes on their production of the four major lethal toxins, and are designated types A to E. C. perfringes type A produces α, θ, κ, and ν antigens and is primarily responsible for disease in man as the cause of myonecrosis, less severe wound infections, and food poisoning. C. perfringens type C, besides being responsible for diseases in domestic animals, has been associated with necrotic enteritis in man. C. perfringens of types B to E usually affects animals.

Infection

Infection with histotoxic clostridia may be due to exogenous or endogenous organisms. In traumatic injuries the source of clostridia is usually soil dust carried into the tissues. The incidence of contamination and infection depends on the concentration of C. perfringens in the soil, which varies with the geographic location. Endogenous infections are due to organisms present on the skin or escaping from the bowel when its integrity is disrupted by disease (e.g., carcinoma of the colon), trauma, injury, or surgery. One of the essential factors predisposing to clostridial myonecrosis is trauma associated with deep and lacerating wounds. Settings that may lead to this disease include automobile and motorcycle accidents, gunshot wounds, compound fractures, industrial accidents, surgical complications, and septic abortions. When C. perfringens is introduced into tissue the primary requirement for initiation of an infection is a lowered redox potential, which may take place even without tissue dam-

age (e.g., when obstruction of blood circulation takes place). In areas of reduced oxygen the pyruvate of muscle is incompletely oxidized and lactic acid accumulates, causing a drop in pH. The combination of lowered redox potential and lowered pH may activate endogenous proteolytic enzymes, resulting in tissue autolysis. Proliferation of the organism in such conditions is accompanied by the production of soluble toxic products.

Clinical Manifestations

Wound and soft tissue infections can be divided into three categories of increasing severity: simple wound contamination, anaerobic cellulitis, and clostridial myonecrosis. Two additional clinical settings, uterine infections and clostridial septicemia, are special types of wound and soft tissue infections with certain unique features. The symptomatology of the three categories, however, may overlap, and infection may evolve from a cellulitis into true clostridial myonecrosis.

Simple Wound Contamination. In simple wound contamination clostridia may be present without an obvious pathologic process. Either the clostridia present may be nontoxic or the environmental conditions in the wound may be unsuitable for toxin production and the initiation of progressive infection by toxigenic strains.

Anaerobic Cellulitis. This is a more serious form of wound infection in which the clostridia infect tissue already dead as a result of ischemia or direct trauma. The organisms in this case spread through subcutaneous tissue but do not invade healthy, intact muscle. Growth of C. perfringens within the necrotic tissue is extensive, and gas is normally a prominent feature. Patients, however, do not develop extreme toxemia, and the overall prognosis is considerably better than in clostridial myonecrosis.

Clostridial Myonecrosis. Following

injury there is an incubation period of usually 12 to 14 hours before symptoms suddenly appear. The characteristic initial symptom is pain in the affected area, which increases in severity as the infection spreads. There is local edema and blood-stained exudate. The infection is associated with profound toxemia, extensive local edema, variable amounts of gas, and massive tissue damage. Untreated cases end with death from shock.

It has to be kept in mind that not all wound infections demonstrating the presence of gas or the clinical picture of myonecrosis are due to the clostridia.

C. perfringens is the major cause of myonecrosis, with *C. septicum* responsible for approximately 5 to 20 percent of the total number of cases. The clostridia next in rates of occurrence are *C. novyi*, *C. histolyticum*, and *C. sordellii*. Clostridial myonecrosis due to *C. novyi* generally is characterized by a high fatality rate and large amounts of edema and fluid, with little gas production; the presence of these organisms in a contaminated wound has to be interpreted with caution.

Not widely appreciated is the fact that infection with anaerobic streptococci or facultative bacteria, such as *Klebsiella*, *E. coli*, or synergistically acting *E. coli* and one of anaerobic or aerobic streptococci, may also be accompanied by gas formation. Although a tentative diagnosis of myonecrosis can be based on clinical symptoms, the final diagnosis must be based on the laboratory findings.

In wound and soft tissue infections one frequently sees more than one kind of microorganism, and it is not easy to establish which is the causative and which is the metabolically supporting organism. The use of a wide spectrum antibiotic acting on all major organisms will take care of the synergistic liaison of the microorganisms.

Uterine Infections. Prior to legalized abortions many cases of uterine infection followed illegal mechanically induced abortions by untrained practitioners. The source of *C. perfringens* could be exogenous or endogenous. In contrast to clostridial myonecrosis, in uterine myonecrosis septicemia and intravascular hemolysis are common and lead to secondary renal failure. This disease progresses rapidly and has a high fatality rate.

Clostridial Septicemia. Invasion of the bloodstream may occur in association with malignancy and may involve a localized myonecrosis in addition to a fulminating clostridial septicemia. There usually is no history of external tissue damage. The source of the organism appears to be endogenous and to result from a lesion of the patient's intestinal tract as a consequence of the malignant process or surgery. *C. septicum* and *C. perfringens* are the most frequently isolated species from blood.

Food Poisoning. A mild form of food poisoning has been recognized with increasing frequency since its association with *C. perfringens* was first demonstrated in 1945. The organisms usually involved are strains of type A that produce heat resistant spores and minimal amounts of θ toxin. Some 8 to 24 hours following ingestion of contaminated food, the patient develops acute abdominal pain and diarrhea. Nausea may occur, but vomiting, fever, and headache are uncommon. Symptoms normally last for 12 to 18 hours, and recovery is usually complete except for rare fatalities in elderly or debilitated patients. The symptoms are attributed to enterotoxin that is synthesized during sporulation of the organism and are probably the results of action of enterotoxin on the intestinal mucosa. Repeated attacks indicate the absence of immunity. This type of food poisoning usually results from the ingestion of beef, pork, poultry, or fish heavily contaminated with *C. perfringens*.

Antibiotic-Associated Colitis. *C. difficile* has been associated with antibiotic-induced pseudomembranous enterocolitis. This severe gastrointestinal disease may be triggered by such antibiotics as clindamycin, ampicillin, cephalothin, and probably metronidazole to which the organism is resistant. The clinical symptoms are due to action of a cytotoxin released by *C. difficile*. The toxin can be detected in stool filtrates of affected patients or in culture filtrates by a cytotoxic test using monolayers of cell cultures or by counterimmunoelectrophoresis (CIE). Antitoxin to *C. sordellii* can neutralize the cytopathic effect of the *C. difficile* toxin or react in the CIE, demonstrating an antigenic crossreactivity. Although *C. difficile* is part of the normal fecal flora of humans and animals it has been detected in only a small percentage of examined subjects and in low concentrations. Improved culture methods introduced very recently may allow more frequent isolation of the organisms.

Laboratory Diagnosis

An early diagnosis of myonecrosis is essential and must be made on clinical grounds. However, only the laboratory findings permit a final classification. Important information can be gained from a direct Gram-stained smear of material taken from deep within the wound. The laboratory identification of *C. perfringens* or other species of clostridia involved in myonecrosis does not present a special problem. The microorganisms grow well in chopped meat-glucose medium at 37°C. There is abundant growth with gas formation, which is characteristic for *C. perfringens*. *C. perfringens* also produces a characteristic pattern of hemolysis on blood agar plates. After overnight incubation on rabbit, sheep, ox, or human blood agar, colonies of most strains demonstrate a characteristic double hemolysis resulting from a narrow zone of complete hemolysis due to the θ toxin and a much wider zone of incomplete hemolysis due to the α toxin. This double zone pattern of hemolysis may fade during a prolonged incubation.

Whether or not an organism can produce lecithinase is readily recognized by using nutrient agar containing egg yolk. The examined culture of *C. perfringens* and positive and negative control strains are streaked in parallel lines across the total surface of the medium and incubated overnight. Lecithinase produces a zone of opacity. The results can be accepted only if the control strains demonstrate positive and negative reactions as expected.

In litmus-milk medium most strains of *C. perfringens* produce "stormy fermentation" due to the fermentation of the lactose in milk, which results in a large amount of acid, causing the casein to coagulate. The acid clot is then disrupted and torn apart by the large volume of gas formed from the lactose fermentation. This action in litmus-milk medium is useful in identification of *C. perfringens* but when used alone is not diagnostic, since the reaction may also be produced by a number of other clostridial species, including *C. septicum*. To speciate *Clostridium*, fermentation reactions on a variety of sugars must be used.

The characteristic features of *C. perfringens* are production of gas, double zone hemolysis, egg yolk reaction, and stormy fermentation in the litmus-milk medium.

Prevention and Treatment

The most important preventive measure against clostridial myonecrosis is early and adequate wound debridement. The severity of the infection markedly increases with delayed debridement. Adequate cleaning, removal of necrotic tissue, delay in primary closure of large wounds, maintenance of drainage, and avoidance of tight packing are all of prime importance in prevention. Administration of prophylactic antibiotics for gram-positive organisms — if possible penicillin (*C. perfringens* is thus far sensitive to penicillin 100 percent) — will reduce the risk of anaerobic infection particularly if administered shortly after the wound is sustained. Large doses of penicillin have to be administered.

An infected patient can be intermittently given oxygen in a hyperbaric chamber pressurized to 3 atmospheres, with five to seven exposures. This treatment is supposed to exert a direct inhibitory action on the organism and on the toxin production. It increases also the redox potential of the tissue, preventing the spread of infection. Both successes and failures have been reported, and experiments on animals demonstrated that the hyperbaric oxygen chamber is not effective in preventing the disease. However, there remain differences in opinion, and the use of the hyperbaric oxygen chamber is an individual clinician's decision.

CLOSTRIDIA CAUSING SYSTEMIC INTOXICATION

Tetanus

C. tetani was described by Nicolaier in 1884 and isolated by Kitasato in 1889. It can be found in the human intestinal tract in approximately 10 to 25 percent of the population. It can also be found in feces of horses, dogs, cats, and various other animals. Most cases of tetanus result from contamination of wounds by soil or various objects. Tetanus may also be transmitted between drug addicts by injections performed under nonsterile conditions. Contaminated, neglected umbilical cords in the offspring of nonimmunized mothers might be the cause of neonatal tetanus.

Morphological and Cultural Characteristics. *C. tetani* ranges from 2 to 5 μm in length and 0.5 to 1 μm in width; however, considerable variation in size may be observed. The organisms are motile and under appropriate cultural conditions produce terminally located spores that are of considerably greater diameter than the vegetative cell, giving the characteristic

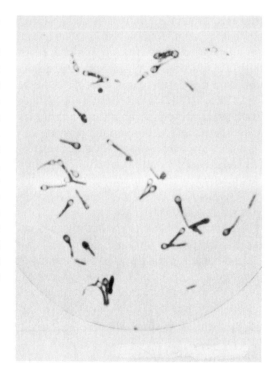

Fig. 30.1. *Clostridium tetani.* Seven day culture (× 1000). (With permission, Wilson, G.S. and Miles, A.A., Eds.: Topley and Wilson's Principles of Bacteriology, Virology and Immunity. 6th Ed. Edward Arnold, Ltd., London, 1975.)

drumstick appearance to the organism. The spore does not take up the Gram stain and appears as a colorless oval structure (Fig. 30.1). The spores are resistant to wide temperature changes and may remain viable for years in soil and in cicatrized wounds. Spores of *C. tetani* resist boiling; they can be destroyed by autoclaving at 120°C for 25 minutes; 5 percent phenol destroys the spores only after 15 hours of contact. Nutritional requirements of *C. tetani*, like those of other clostridia, are complex but they can be readily met by blood agar or chopped-meat broth. On a solid medium after incubation at 37°C for 4 days the colonies are 2 to 5 mm in diameter, glistening, translucent and with an irregularly granular surface. In chopped-meat-glucose medium the growth is poor to moderate with slight turbidity and a granular deposit. *C. tetani* produces an offensive odor of manure. As a rule the organisms are not biochemically active, and they do not ferment sugars. The only positive reactions are liquefaction of gelatin, clotting of milk, digestion of meat in the broth, production of indole, and β-hemolysis. The lack of saccharolytic and proteolytic enzymes tends to minimize the inflammatory reaction that may develop in the host.

Properties of Tetanus Toxin. The production of a toxin of a single antigenic type by all strains of *C. tetani* and its neutralization by a single antitoxin is of practical importance. The purified active toxin is a protein with a molecular weight of about 68,000. The toxin, a tetanospasmin, is extremely potent; 1 mg of pure toxin can kill 15 million mice. There is wide variation among animals in susceptibility to tetanus toxin; humans and horses are probably the most sensitive, whereas birds and cold blooded animals are usually resistant.

Infection. *C. tetani* enters the body through wounds of various types: lacerations, slivers, compound fractures, gunshot wounds burns, frostbite, penetrating scratches, puncture by a drug addict's needle, and so on. At times tetanus might be related to various infectious processes or to surgery. The incubation period for tetanus varies from days to weeks or even months (1 to 54 days), but it is usually between 6 and 15 days, with a median of 7 or 8 days. The molecular basis for the action of tetanus toxin is unknown. The site of action is the synaptosomes that are high in toxin-fixing capacity. Gangliosides in synaptic membranes are responsible for the binding of tetanus toxin.

The mode of action is the blocking of synaptic inhibition in the spinal cord, presumably at inhibitory terminals. The obliteration of inhibitory reflex responses of nerve fibers permits the uncontrolled spread of impulses initiated in the central nervous system, which results in the hyperflexia of the skeletal muscles. In other words, tetanus toxin blocks transmission of inhibiting impulses of the internuncial neurons, producing prolonged muscular spasms of both the flexor and extensor muscle groups.

Manifestation. A wound may or may not be present at the time of onset of manifestations. Early symptoms and signs often consist of irritability, restlessness, headache, and low grade fever. Two basic forms of tetanus may be distinguished: local and general. Local tetanus consists of spasms and increased muscle tone confined to muscle near the wound; there are no systemic signs. General tetanus is far more frequent; the most characteristic symptom is lockjaw or trismus, the inability to open the mouth because of spasms of the facial muscles. It leads to a grotesque, grinning expression termed *risus sardonicus*. Spasms of the somatic musculature in general tetanus may be widespread, resulting in opisthotonos (arching of the back) and board-like rigidity of the abdomen. Acute paroxysmal incoordinate widespread spasms of the muscles are characteristic of moderate and severe tetanus. Such tonic convulsions occur intermittently and irregularly and are unpredictable; they persist for a few seconds to several minutes. The paroxysmal spasms, which are painful, severe, and exhausting, may occur spontaneously or may be precipitated by a variety of external stimuli, such as drafts of cold air, noise, light, and attempts to move the patient. Cyanosis and even sudden death from respiratory arrest may result from these spasms.

The diagnosis of tetanus is a clinical one. In typical fully developed cases the diagnosis is easy. However, one must be alert in order to detect early cases. Many different conditions may be considered in the differential diagnosis of tetanus. Trismus due to tetanus may be erroneously attributed to alveolar abscesses, peritonsilar abscesses, temporomandibular joint disease, or functional causes.

Treatment.   Treatment of tetanus varies with the severity of the disease, but in general it is definitely designed to prevent further elaboration and absorption of toxin. Antitoxin is administered. Because of hypersensitivity reactions resulting from the administration of antitoxin prepared in a horse or sheep, human antitoxin from pooled hyperimmune donors is recommended. There is no need for repeated injections. It is desirable to give the antitoxin in the proximal part of an extremity where the wound is located, when this is feasible. In addition, debridement of the wound and the removal of any foreign body is essential. Large doses of penicillin should be given; if the patient is allergic to penicillin, tetracycline or clindamycin may be used. Once clinical manifestations of tetanus are established, the prognosis is grave, and only a few patients recover. Indeed, proper treatment must be instituted before clinical manifestations occur in order to effect a favorable prognosis.

Prevention.   Tetanus can be prevented by active or passive immunization. When this is properly applied the disease disappears almost completely. During World War I out of 1000 British soldiers wounded, 8 died of tetanus. In World War II incidence of tetanus in the United States Army was very low; of approximately 2,750,000 admissions for wounds and injuries only 12 cases of tetanus were reported. In the Vietnam war not even one case of tetanus was noted among American soldiers.

Routine active immunization with tetanus toxoid should begin at 1 to 3 months of age using a combination of tetanus and diphtheria toxoids and pertussis vaccine (DPT). Three doses of DPT should be given at 3 or 4 week intervals, with booster doses 1 and 4 years later. Immunity to tetanus should be maintained by single booster doses of toxoid every 10 years. In the past, wounded patients were exposed to booster shots whenever brought to emergency rooms. In addition, school, camp, and military requirements have led to an inordinate exposure to tetanus toxoid. For these reasons patients coming to an emergency room with a history of the basic immunizing series and a history of a booster injection within 5 years probably do not need an additional booster injection. Individuals who come to the emergency room with no history of immunization or a history of partial immunization should receive antitoxin in one arm and the first of a series of toxoid injections in the other arm.

Passive immunity may be conferred by the administration of antitoxin. The prophylactic administration of a single 250 IU dose of antitoxin should be administered to patients with a soil contaminated wound who have no record of previous active immunization. The presence of 0.01 IU of antitoxin per milliliter of serum is generally considered protective.

Laboratory Diagnosis.   The hospital diagnostic laboratory can be helpful only in a limited way concerning the diagnosis of tetanus and is very seldom used for this purpose. Usually state public health laboratories or laboratories of the Center for Disease Control are helpful in the confirmation of a tetanus case. If the assistance of the hospital laboratory is desirable, material obtained from the treated wound or any other material for culture should be transported to the laboratory in a container free of oxygen. It must be stressed that *C. tetani* is very sensitive to oxygen and that tension of 10 mm Hg inhibits the growth of the organism. The material should be used for immediate inoculation of both prereduced solid and liquid media, such as chopped-meat-glucose, and incubated under strict anaerobic conditions. The isolation of the organisms from a wound may be difficult because of the presence of other organisms in the specimen. In any case, heating the fluid culture medium at 80°C for 20 minutes after an initial 24 hour incubation period will kill nonsporulating organisms and permit recovery of *C. tetani*. Mice, which are very sensitive to tetanus toxin, are used for detection of toxin in body fluids. However, this examination is considered to be the function of a rather specialized laboratory and is hardly ever done in a hospital diagnostic laboratory.

Botulism

Botulism is a disease usually caused by ingestion of a food containing toxin elaborated by *C. botulinum*. The organism is widely

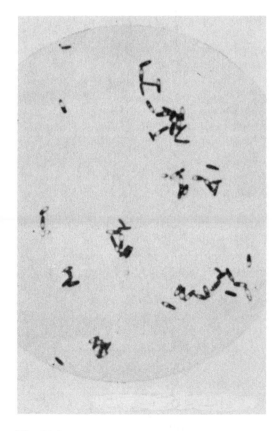

Fig. 30.2. *Clostridium botulinum*. Two day culture (× 1000). (With permission Wilson, G.S. and Miles, A.A., Eds.: Topley and Wilson's Principles of Bacteriology, Virology and Immunity, 6th Ed. Edward Arnold, Ltd., London, 1975.)

distributed in nature as a saprophyte and thus commonly contaminates vegetables, fruits, and various marine products.

Morphological and Cultural Characteristics. *C. botulinum*, discovered by van Ermengem in 1896, is a straight or slightly curved gram-positive rod with rounded ends, from 3 to 9 μm long, and motile by use of peritrichous flagella. It produces heat-resistant spores that are oval and subterminal and that tend to distend the bacillus (Fig. 30.2). The spores survive at 105°C up to 100 minutes but they are killed at 120°C in 20 minutes. They survive food processing and then germinate. Vegetative forms are the only forms that elaborate toxin. *C. botulinum* is a strict anaerobe. On the basis of the type of toxin produced, the species *C. botulinum* is divided into seven serologically distinct types A to G. Immunologic differences among these types are clearcut and of epidemiologic significance. Type A can be found in vegetables, fruits, meat, and fish; type B in meat, usually pork; type E in fish and marine mammals; type F in liver paté. Types A, B, E, and F affect humans and animals; the remaining types — C, D, and G affect animals only.

The nutritional requirements of the organism are complex. On solid media after incubation at 37°C for 4 days, colonies appear irregularly round, 5 to 10 mm in diameter, glistening, translucent, and filamentous, with alternately smooth and granular surface. In chopped-meat-glucose medium the organisms demonstrate abundant growth with dense turbidity and a moderate powdery and granular deposit. On blood agar all except type G are β-hemolytic. There is considerable diversity among the various types in the utilization of carbohydrates and proteolysis. Biochemical reactions using, besides fermentation of carbohydrates, such characteristics as gelatin liquefaction, action in litmus-milk medium and H_2S production can to some extent differentiate the various types;

however, owing to the large variations in biochemical characteristics, it is impossible to apply a general definition of the species.

Properties of the Botulinum Toxin. Botulinum toxin is the most potent toxin known; 1 mg of the purified toxin can kill 200 million adult mice. Another example of potency of the toxin can be demonstrated by a case of fatal intoxication that occurred in a person who licked a fingertip covered with the juice of spoiled preserves. Botulinum toxin differs from classical exotoxins in that it is excreted not from a viable organism but only after autolysis of the cell. Crystalline (pure) toxin has been dissociated into two biologically active fractions: α, a toxin protein of 128,000 daltons, and β, a potent hemagglutinin that is an aggregate of three molecules, 250,000 to 750,000 daltons.

Pathogenesis. Human botulism results from the ingestion of preformed toxin in contaminated food. The toxin is absorbed primarily from the upper gastrointestinal tract, but toxin reaching the lower small intestine or colon may also be slowly absorbed, perhaps accounting for the delayed onset and prolonged duration of symptoms in some patients. The toxin gains access to the peripheral nervous system and blocks the release of acetylcholine, causing impairment in neural transmission. The usual incubation period is 18 to 36 hours; however, the onset of signs and symptoms may occur as soon as a few hours or as late as 8 days or more after ingestion of contaminated food. In general, patients with a short incubation period (less than 24 hours) are more severely affected and are more likely to die. The length of the incubation period and the severity of the illness correlate with the amount of toxin ingested.

Manifestation. Botulism should be strongly considered in patients who have acute cranial nerve impairment with symmetrical descending weakness or paralysis. Symptoms of botulism are due to a progressive decrease of skeletal muscle function that eventually results in paralysis. First to become affected are the small muscles of the eye, larynx, and pharynx. In consequence, diplopia, dysathria, and dysphagia are seen. Pupils are often but not invariably dilated and fixed. Mucous membranes of the mouth and pharynx may be extremely dry and even painful. Later, weakness of the extremities and impairment of the muscles of respiration may occur. Death usually is caused by cardiac arrest due to inadequate respiratory exchange. The differential diagnosis of botulism includes myasthenia gravis, cerebrovascular accident, Guillain-Barré syndrome, and intoxication with carbon monoxide.

Treatment. The trivalent A, B, and E preparation of antitoxin is the therapy of choice in cases of botulism in which the toxin type has yet to be determined. Monovalent preparations should be used only in cases in which the toxin type is definitely known. It must be stressed that while it is true that most cases of type E botulism have been associated with fish products and types A and B with food of plant origin, there are enough exceptions so that this information cannot be relied upon, particularly when the physician is faced with treating a patient. Antibiotic treatment usually has no influence unless spores or organisms are present in the patient's tissues. Polyvalent antiserum (A, B, C, D, E, F) is available commercially. Individuals at high risk (e.g., laboratory technicians working with C. botulinum or its toxin) should be immunized. Such individuals may be immunized with polyvalent toxoid, which is available through the Center for Disease Control.

Prevention. Although existing preventative measures for the control of botulism are simple and effective when properly carried out, the fact that outbreaks still occur each year indicates the need for control measures. Only 37 cases of botulism were recorded in 1976 in the United States;

in most cases intoxication was due to home-made canned food.

Laboratory Diagnosis. The laboratory can do little to help the clinician in establishing the diagnosis. Diagnostic confirmation depends primarily on detection of toxin in the patient or in the food. Most hospital diagnostic laboratories are not staffed or equipped to conduct the necessary laboratory procedures required; usually the laboratories of the state public health departments or the Center for Disease Control can provide assistance with the examination. Specimens to be examined in botulism include blood (20 ml), gastric contents, or vomitus and feces. The specimens should be obtained as soon as possible, but always before antitoxin is given; this is particularly important in the case of blood specimens. A significant volume of the specimens should be collected in order to extract the toxin. All specimens should be refrigerated (not frozen) after collection if they cannot be examined immediately. Whenever possible, food should be kept sealed in the original container. Sterile, unbreakable containers should be used for samples to be mailed to distant laboratories. The samples must be placed in leak-proof containers, packed in a second leak-proof insulated container labeled "Medical Emergency" and "Danger Hazardous Material," and shipped by the most rapid means possible. The receiving laboratory should be notified in advance as to how and when specimens will arrive.

The most reliable technique for the detection of toxin is the mouse neutralization test. Detection of the organism itself may be done by culture, preferably using the spore selection procedure, by fluorescent antibody technique, and in a presumptive manner, by gas chromatography. All of the laboratory procedures are rather complex.

Wound and Infant Botulism. In recent years two other types of botulism have been recognized, wound botulism and infant botulism. Thus far only a few cases of wound botulism have been described. All patients had a typical clinical illness with cranial nerve palsy, weakness, and respiratory impairment. The symptoms appeared 7 to 10 days after contamination of a deep lacerated wound or compound fracture. In some of the patients the diagnosis was bacteriologically confirmed. This type of botulism appears most frequently in young males, reflecting their greater outdoor activity.

Botulism has been diagnosed in a few infants 3 to 20 weeks of age. Infant botulism is characterized by involving only individual cases, unlike cases of food-borne botulism in adults, where a large number of people can be affected. The cases described thus far have shown a remarkably similar pattern. The affected infants usually have been perfectly healthy up to the onset of illness. With the appearance of botulism some infants initially showed only mild lethargy, weakness, and slow feeding; others, however, became acutely ill, with severe feeding problems. Weakened sucking, swallowing, and crying with pooling of oral secretions and a diminished gag reflex were common in the more severely affected children. Some also had alterations in oculomotor function and facial expression. Others manifested a generalized weakening of the striated muscles, which may become evident as loss of head control, with the child appearing "floppy." In the clinical diagnosis of the syndrome one has to consider sepsis, dehydration, viral infections, poliomyelitis, meningitis, acute infantile polyneuropathy, and many other conditions. The problem with infant botulism appears to be in the difficulty of demonstrating the presence of toxin(s) and/or isolating *C. botulinum* from the surrounding environment of the infant. For example, of the 58 cases reported in the United States through 1978 that were thoroughly investigated, potential sources for *C. botulinum* spores were identified only six times; these were found in vacuum cleaner dirt, soil, and honey. Regularly used to dip infant pacifiers, honey has been considered as a cause of infant botulism through contamination with spores of *C. botulinum*. Because of this some authorities recommend that honey not be fed to infants less than 1 year of age. The present evidence suggests that ingested *C. botulinum* can colonize the gut of a susceptible infant and when conditions permit produce botulinum toxin. Absorption of the toxin results in neurologic impairment typical of botulism.

Infant botulism has been associated with sudden infant death syndrome; however, this association has not been well proved.

REFERENCES

Finegold, S.M.: Anaerobic Bacteria in Human Disease. Academic Press, New York, 1977.

Joklik, W.K., Willett, H.P., and Amos. D.B., Eds.: Zinsser Microbiology. 17th Ed. Appleton-Century Crofts, New York, 1980.

Lennette, E.H., Balows, A., Hausler, W.J., Jr., and Traunt, J.P., Eds.: Manual of Clinical Microbiology. 3rd Ed. American Society for Microbiology, Washington, D.C., 1980.

Wilson, G.S., and Miles, A.A., Eds.: Topley and Wilson's Principles of Bacteriology, Virology and Immunity. 6th Ed. Edward Arnold, Ltd., London, 1975.

31

Nonsporulating Anaerobes

Konrad Wicher

The distribution of anaerobic microorganisms in man are summarized in Table 31.1. Anaerobic nonsporulating bacteria are prevalent throughout the body as indigenous flora. Anaerobic bacteria outnumber aerobic and facultative anaerobic bacteria in a variety of body sites — mouth, colon, vagina. They are numerous on all mucosal surfaces, and some of them populate the skin as well. It is of clinical importance to

Table 31.1. Distribution of Anaerobic Normal Flora in Man

	Skin	Upper Respiratory Tract	Mouth	Intestine	External Genitalia	Urethra	Vagina
Gram-positive							
Actinomyces	−	+	+	±	−	−	−
Clostridium	−	−	±	+ +	−	±	±
Bifidobacterium	−	−	+	+ +	−	−	+
Eubacterium	±	±	+	+ +	?	?	±
Lactobacillus[a]	−	−	+	+	−	±	+ +
Propionibacterium	+ +	+	±	±	?	−	+
Gram-negative							
Peptococcus,							
Peptostreptococcus	+	+	+ +	+ +	+	±	+
Bacteroides	−	+	+ +	+ +	+	+	+
Fusobacterium	−	+	+ +	+	+	+	±
Campylobacter	−	+	+	±	−	±	+
Veillonella	−	+	+ +	+	−	?	+

Key to symbols: −, not found or very rare; ±, irregular; +, usually present; + +, present in large numbers.
[a]Includes anaerobic, microaerophilic, and facultative strains.
(Modified from Finegold, S.M.: Anaerobic Bacteria in Human Disease, Academic Press, New York, 1977.)

know the distribution of the normal flora at certain sites because many anaerobic infections arise in proximity to mucosal surfaces where the anaerobic organisms are colonized. The clinician may therefore be able to predict which microorganism(s) may be involved in an infection.

Nonsporulating anaerobes are more pleomorphic in appearance than most aerobic bacteria. This property can sometimes be helpful in identification of these organisms. Colonial morphology of most anaerobes on solid media and appearance of their growth in liquid media is not sufficiently characteristic to aid appreciably in their identification. It has been stressed

that colonial morphology, like cellular morphology, is extremely dependent on the culture environment. The pathogenicity of these organisms is not well determined nor understood. No exotoxins similar to those produced by the organisms of the genus *Clostridium* are produced by nonsporulating organisms.

Although only two genera of the family *Bacteroidaceae*, namely *Bacteroides* and *Fusobacterium*, will be discussed here in some detail, a physician has to be aware that other anaerobic microorganisms are responsible for a variety of infections. In Table 31.2 are listed the anaerobic microorganisms of medical importance and in

Table 31.2. Selected Anaerobic Bacteria of Medical Importance

Characteristic	Genus	Species
Sporulating Gram-positive bacilli	*Clostridium*	*C. tetani* *C. botulinum* *C. perfringens* *C. septicum* *C. novyi* and many others
Nonsporulating Gram-negative bacilli	*Bacteroides*	*B. fragilis* *B. thetaiotaomicron* *B. vulgatus* *B. distasonis* *B. ovatus* *B. melaninogenicus* Subspecies *melaninogenicus*, *intermedius*, and *levii* *B. oralis* *B. ureolyticus*
	Fusobacterium	*F. nucleatum* *F. necrophorum* and others
Gram-positive bacilli	*Actinomyces* *Bifidobacterium* *Corynebacterium* *Eubacterium* *Propionibacterium*	Many various species
Gram-negative cocci	*Veillonella*	*V. parvula*
Gram-positive cocci	*Peptococcus* *Peptostreptococcus*	*P. magnus* *P. anaerobius* *P. intermedius*
	Sarcina	*S. ventriculi*

Table 31.3.   Infections Commonly Involving Anaerobes

Infection	Organism[a]	Comment
Bacteremia	*Bacteroides* *Fusobacterium* *Clostridium* *Peptostreptococcus* *Peptococcus* *Bifidobacterium* *Eubacterium* *Veillonella*	*B. fragilis* accounts for 58 to 90% and fusobacteria for 4 to 20% of the anaerobic gram-negative bacilli; clostridia and gram-positive cocci were isolated in 1 to 3%, and the remaining organisms less frequently

Central nervous system
   Brain abscess
   Extradural or subdural
   empyema
	Peptostreptococcus
	 Bacteroides
	 Veillonella
	 Fusobacterium
	 Actinomyces
		In brain abscesses, 89%, and in extra- or subdural empyema, 10% of organisms recovered were anaerobes

Ear, nose, mouth, throat
   Chronic otitis media
 	
   Chronic sinusitis
 	
   Dental and oral infection
	Bacteroides
	 Fusobacterium
	 Clostridium
	 Peptostreptococcus
	 Peptococcus
	 Bacteroides
	 Fusobacterium
	 Bacteroides
	 Fusobacterium
	 Peptostreptococcus
	 Peptococcus
		The incidence of anaerobic organisms isolated in this group is approximately 50%

Thoracic
   Aspiration pneumonia
 	
   Lung abscess
 	
   Bronchiectasis
   Empyema
	Gram-positive cocci
	 Bacteroides
	 Fusobacterium
	 Fusobacterium
	 Bacteroides
	 Peptostreptococcus
	 Peptococcus
	 Eubacterium
	 Fusobacterium
	 Gram-positive cocci
	 Fusobacterium
		Also microaerophilic streptococci
		 B. melaninogenicus
		 F. nucleatum
		 F. nucleatum
		 B. melaninogenicus
		
		 Spirochetes are also involved
		 Also microaerophilic streptococci
		 F. nucleatum
		 In the group of thoracic diseases anaerobes are isolated in 76 to 93%

Intraabdominal General infection	*Bacteroides* *Fusobacterium* *Clostridium* *Peptococcus* *Peptostreptococcus* *Eubacterium* and others	The incidence of anaerobes isolated in diseases of the intraabdominal group ranges from 50 to 100%

Table 31.3.   *Continued*

Infection	Organism[a]	Comment
Liver abscess	*Bacteroides*	
	Fusobacterium	
	Clostridium	
	Gram-positive cocci	
Biliary tract infections	*Clostridium*	
Appendicitis with peritonitis	*Bacteroides*	
	Fusobacterium	
	Gram-positive cocci	
	Clostridium	
Obstetric–gynecologic		The incidence of anaerobes iso-
Postabortal sepsis	*Bacteroides*	lated in diseases of this group
Puerperal sepsis	*Fusobacterium*	ranges from 56 to 74%
	Gram-positive cocci	
	Clostridium	
Tuboovarian and pelvic abscess	Gram-positive cocci	
	Bacteroides	
Bartholin's gland abscess	*Bacteroides*	
Other infections of the female urogenital tract	*Bacteroides*	
	Fusobacterium	
	Peptococcus	
	Peptostreptococcus	
Soft tissue and miscellaneous		
Anaerobic myonecrosis	*Clostridium*	
	Peptostreptococcus	
Progressive bacterial synergistic gangrene	Microaerophilic streptococci, *S. aureus,* or other aerobic cocci	
Decubitus ulcers	*Bacteroides*	
	Clostridium	
Intrauterine infection	*Bifidobacterium*	
	Bacteroides	
	Peptostreptococcus	

[a]The microorganisms in each group are listed in frequency of isolation.
(Modified from Finegold, S.M.: Anaerobic Bacteria in Human Disease, Academic Press, New York, 1977.)

Table 31.3 infections commonly involving anaerobes.

BACTEROIDES

General Characteristics

All species in the genus *Bateroides* are gram-negative rods, and vary widely in morphology depending on medium and gaseous environment. The bacilli may be either quite pleomorphic (Fig. 31.1A through 31.1D) with vacuoles and swelling when grown in some liquid media containing glucose or fairly uniform with rounded ends when grown on blood agar plates. Some of them are strict anaerobes, and others may be facultative anaerobes. The differences may occur within species and sometimes even within strains. The surface of the colonies on an enriched blood agar plate is

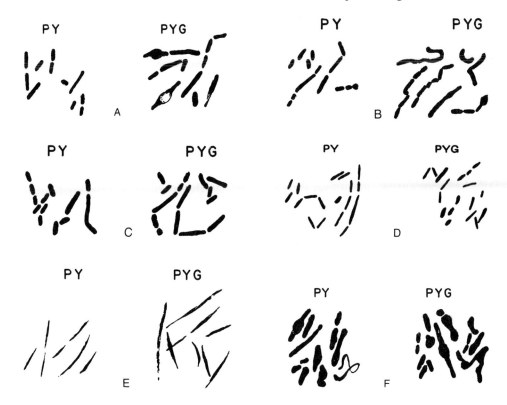

Fig. 31.1. (A) *B. fragilis.* (B) *B. melaninogenicus* subsp. *melaninogenicus.* (C) *B. oralis.* (D) *B. ureolyticus.* (E) *F. nucleatum.* (F) *F. mortiferum.* Drawings of microorganisms grown in peptone-yeast estract (PY) and in peptone-yeast extract–glucose (PYG) media. Pleomorphism is more pronounced under more oxidizing conditions. (With permission, Holdeman, L.V., Cato, E.P., Moore, W.E.C., Eds.: The Anaerobe Laboratory Manual, 4th Ed. The Virginia Polytechnic Institute and State University Anaerobe Laboratory, Blacksburg, Va., 1977.)

convex, white to gray, translucent, and glistening. The colonies tend to undergo autolysis in a few days. Some strains may be hemolytic. In fluid media they produce uniform turbidity with a whitish deposit. Bile (10 percent) in the medium improves the growth of some organisms. Cultures have a fetid odor but form little gas. They are biochemically active, producing acid from various sugars, and can be differentiated on the basis of their biochemical properties. Some of the species may produce black pigment. The antigenic composition of *Bacteroides* is not yet well explored; some (*B. fragilis*) have species-specific antigens and others (*B. the-*

taiotaomicron) strain-specific antigens. Subcutaneous inoculation of these microorganisms into guinea pigs produces abscesses. An endotoxin associated with a lipopolysaccharide component has been isolated from various strains of *Bacteroides*. Lipid (fraction A) from some *Bacteroides* may enhance coagulation.

Until 1977, the species *Bacteroides fragilis* consisted of 5 subspecies, *fragilis*, *thetaiotaomicron*, *vulgatus*, *distasonis*, and *ovatus*. However, on the basis of the DNA-DNA homology studies all subspecies are now considered as separate species of the genus *Bacteroides*.

B. fragilis can be isolated from the respiratory, gastrointestinal, and urogenital tracts. Despite their ubiquity in the human host, these organisms are known to cause various life-threatening infections. They can cause abscesses in various organs, infection of the respiratory tract and infection of the genital tract, and they are implicated in decubitus ulcers. *B. fragilis* accounts for approximately 60 to 80 percent of the gram-negative anaerobic bacilli isolated from blood. *B. fragilis* in clinical terms is resistant to penicillin. *B. thetaiotaomicron*, *B. distasonis*, *B. vulgatus*, and *B. ovatus* play a less important role than *B. fragilis*; however, they may also be implicated in various anaerobic infections.

B. melaninogenicus is divided into three subspecies, subsp. *melaninogenicus, intermedius*, and *levii*. *B. asaccharolyticus*, once a subspecies of *B. melaninogenicus*, has been classified as a separate species. The organisms of the *B. melaninogenicus* group are pleomorphic and vary from small coccobacilli to rods. They are β-hemolytic, and most strains form pigment. The pigment develops slowly and is said to consist of colloidal ferrous sulfide. By the time pigmentation is fully developed the culture is often dead. This may account for difficulties in isolating this microorganism. In fluid medium the culture forms uniform turbidity, and growth is inhibited by the presence of 10 percent bile. The cultures have a foul odor. *B. melaninogenicus* is biochemically less active than *B. fragilis* and is considered nonsaccharolytic but proteolytic. The organisms of the *B. melaninogenicus* group are part of the normal flora of the mouth, the gastrointestinal tract, and probably the urogenital tract and may be expected to be responsible in certain instances for infection of these locations. Their pathogenicity is probably low, but some organisms produce collagenase, an important factor in infections. They have been isolated from purulent lesions, usually along with other pathogenic bacteria, and infrequently from blood culture as a consequence of tooth extraction.

B. oralis are small rods that are weakly saccharolytic and grow on blood-enriched media. A characteristic of this organism is a lack of pigment production and the fact that almost invariably it grows close to other microorganisms. The latter feature causes difficulty in isolation because on solid medium the colonies of *B. oralis* fuse with colonies of other microorganisms. The organism is a common resident of the upper respiratory tract, but it also may be found in the gastrointestinal and urogenital tracts. It used to be considered as a nonpathogenic organism; however, it has been isolated from blood culture, particularly after extraction of teeth and after surgery of the respiratory or genital tract.

B. ureolyticus is a bacillus variable in size with a diphtheroid arrangement on smear. It is a fastidious microorganism and possesses a peculiar feature consisting of the formation on agar of small colonies (0.5 mm) depressed below the surface of the medium (pitting the agar). Although not saccharolytic, it produces H_2S, liquefies gelatin, and is nitrate and urease positive. *B. ureolyticus* is part of the normal flora of the mouth and may cause oral and pulmonary infections.

There are a variety of other species within the genus *Bacteroides* that have not been closely associated with disease in man. The sensitivity to antimicrobial agents of the genus *Bacteroides* varies, and Table 31.4 lists susceptibility data for some of the major microorganisms encountered in infections.

FUSOBACTERIUM

General Characteristics

The members of the genus *Fusobacterium* are gram-negative rod-shaped organisms with great variation in size. They may be coccobacilli as short as 2 μm or may grow into long filaments of up to 15 μm. Their width is also variable; quite frequently they are wider near the middle of the organism

Table 31.4. Susceptibility of Anaerobes to Antibiotics

Antibiotics	B. fragilis	B. melaninogenicus	Fusobacteria	Cocci
Penicillin G	+	+++	+++	+++
Lincomycin	+ to ++	+++	+ to +++	+++
Clindamycin	+++	+++	+ to +++	++ to +++
Chloramphenicol	+++	+++	+++	+++
Vancomycin	+	+	+	+++
Tetracycline	+ to ++	++ to +++	++	++
Metronidazole	+++	+++	+++	++

Key: +, poor activity; ++, moderate activity; +++, good activity.
(Modified from Finegold, S.M.: Anaerobic Bacteria in Human Disease, Academic Press, New York, 1977.)

than at the end. The fusiform rod may be thin with delicately pointed ends. (*F. nucleatum*) or with central swelling (*F. mortiferum*) (Figs. 31.1E & 31.1F). Pleomorphism is a striking characteristic of some of the species, particularly in fluid culture. Staining of the organisms is often irregular. They demonstrate very weak saccharolytic activity. Very little is known about the antigenic structure of the organisms.

F. nucleatum includes strains formerly identified as *F. fusiforme*. They are part of the normal flora of the mouth and upper respiratory, gastrointestinal, and urogenital tracts. Cells are from 2 to 15 μm long and are thin, usually with tapered ends. Darkly stained in the Gram method, intracellular granules usually are apparent, particularly in culture from fluid media. Colonies on blood agar, usually after incubation for 48 hours, may be surrounded by a zone of deep, greenish discoloration particularly after exposure to air; they appear to have a flecked or crystalline structure and produce an unpleasant odor. In fluid medium the growth appears as flocculent. The organisms are weak fermenters of fructose and glucose and fail to ferment other sugars, and they are indol positive. A neuraminidase detected in *F. nucleatum* may play a role in pathogenicity. *F. nucleatum* is the most common species of *Fusobacterium* isolated from infections. It is an important

agent in oral and pleuropulmonary infections and lung abscesses. Among the anaerobes it is, after the bacteroides, the most frequent isolate from blood.

F. necrophorum is usually more pleomorphic than *F. nucleatum*. Cells often are of different lengths and filaments are common. Cellular swellings and free round forms may be present in cultures of some strains. Except in young cultures, staining is irregular, and beaded forms are common. Growth occurs under strictly anaerobic conditions. After 48 hours incubation at 37°C on solid media enriched with serum, colonies are circular, convex, about 1 mm in diameter, almost water clear, and glistening. Deviations from this appearance may be observed. Cultures in liquid media show "wooly balls" and have a foul odor. *F. necrophorum* is only moderately active biochemically. It is indole and H_2S positive and reduces methylene blue. It differs from *F. nucleatum* by production of β-hemolysin, lipase, and leukocidin. These organisms are usually present in the upper respiratory and the gastrointestinal tracts and are associated with a variety of human infections, primarily of abdominal or pelvic regions. They are important in liver abscess.

Other species of *Fusobacterium* have been associated with a variety of different infections involving almost every organ of the human body.

OTHER ANAEROBIC MICROORGANISMS OF MEDICAL IMPORTANCE

Gram-Positive Cocci

This group is represented by two genera, *Peptococcus* and *Peptostreptococcus*. Each genus consists of several species, such as *Peptococcus niger, Peptococcus magnus, Peptococcus prevoti, Peptococcus saccharolyticus, Peptococcus asaccharolyticus, Peptostreptococcus anaerobius, Peptostreptococcus productus*, and *Peptostreptococcus parvulus*. Peptococci and peptostreptococci may vary in size from 1 to 3 μm in diameter. The peptococci frequently are arranged in irregular clumps and the peptostreptococci more frequently in chains. On blood agar species of both genera appear after 2 or 3 days of incubation at 37°C as small (0.5 to 2 mm), white colonies. These colonies may be convex, opaque and shiny. Occasionally, strains of both genera may be hemolytic or demonstrate α-hemolysis. *P. asaccharolyticus* may produce black colonies or black sediment in broth. Biochemically, the organisms are very weakly active or not active at all.

Observations of infections caused by anaerobic gram-positive cocci support the concept that these are opportunistic bacteria that in a compromised host can produce a clinically apparent infection, especially in areas of normal habitation, such as skin, oral cavity, urogenital tract, and gastrointestinal tract.

Gram-Negative Cocci

Veillonella is a representative genus and *V. parvula* a representative species of this group. Members of this genus are small, 0.3 to 0.5 μm in diameter. On smears they can be seen in pairs, short chains, or groups. Colonies on blood agar have small opaque centers with translucent edges. Organisms of the genus *Veillonella* are part of the endogenous flora of the mouth, respiratory tract, intestine, and vagina. They are rarely involved in human disease.

Gram-Positive Bacilli

Gram-positive nonsporulating anaerobic bacilli that may be encountered in clinical specimens include species of *Eubacterium, Lachnospira, Actinomyces, Arachnia, Propionibacterium, Bifidobacterium*, and *Lactobacillus*. Most are obligate anaerobes, but some are microaerophilic or facultative anaerobes. The gram-positive anaerobic nonsporulating rods are rarely involved in human disease. These microorganisms can easily be confused with such gram-positive aerobic bacilli as *Corynebacterium, Listeria*, or *Erysipelothrix*. A wide morphological variation between and within genera may be seen; some species may occur as small rods and others as large, evenly stained rods or club-rods or rods with bifid ends, with filaments or without branching. Organisms of *Propionibacterium* may be found most commonly on the skin or as normal vaginal flora. *Eubacterium* and *Lactobacillus* may be found as normal flora of cervix uteri. Almost all of these organisms may be found in feces. Differentiation of the gram-positive anaerobic bacilli to the genus and/or species level may be readily accomplished by the use of gas chromatography and examination of cultural characteristics and biochemical reactions.

REFERENCES

Finegold, S.M.: Anaerobic Bacteria in Human Disease. Academic Press, New York, 1977.

Joklik, W.K., Willett, H.P., and Amos, D.B., Eds.: Zinsser Microbiology. 17th Ed. Appleton-Century-Crofts, New York, 1980.

Lennette, E.H., Balows, A., Hausler, W.J., Jr., and Truant, J.P., Eds.: Manual of Clinical Microbiology. 3rd Ed. American Society for Microbiology, Washington, D.C., 1980.

Wilson, G.S., and Miles, A.A., Eds.: Topley and Wilson's Principles of Bacteriology, Virology, and Immunity. 6th Ed. Edward Arnold, Ltd., London, 1975.

32

Spirochaetaceae

Felix Milgrom

The order *Spirochaetales* is composed of spiral organisms all of which are called colloquially *spirochetes*. Three anatomic entities can be distinguished in spirochetes, an *axial filament*, a *protoplast*, and an *ènvelope*. The axial filament is composed of fibrils that are responsible for the rigidity of the organism; they are considered analogs of bacterial flagella. The protoplast, or protoplasmic cylinder, is twisted around the axial filament in a helical fashion, like a spiral staircase built around a central pillar (Fig. 32.1A); otherwise, the axial filament is wound helically around the helical protoplast, like a railing along a spiral staircase (Fig. 32.1B and C). The envelope covers the protoplast.

In large spirochetes these structural components are distinguishable by means of the light microscope. Isolation of muramic acid from spirochetes and their susceptibility to lysozyme and penicillin provide evidence that these organisms have structures analogous to the bacterial cell wall.

All spirochetes are motile. Their motility, however, is due not to flagella, as in other bacteria, but to the movements of the cell itself. In this respect, spirochetes resemble protozoa. The axial filament is likely to play the most important role in spirochetal motility.

Movements of spirochetes are best studied by darkfield illumination. Three types of movements can be distinguished: *rotation, translation*, and *flexion*. Rotation is the movement of the whole spirochete around its long axis. Sometimes rotation of fine spirochetes is difficult to note. If, however, the cell is bent on one or both ends, rotation is readily recognizable by the appearance of a structure resembling the letters T, L, and O or the digit 8 at the end(s) of the cell. Translation is the movement of the cell from one place to another. This movement results from a propellerlike driving created by rotatory movements. Flexion is a movement that produces various kinds of bending and twisting of the cell.

Similar to other bacteria, spirochetes multiply by binary transverse fission. If they can be stained by the Gram procedure, spirochetes are gram-negative. Some are too thin to be visible with the light microscope after ordinary bacterial staining; however, they can be made visible by impregnation with silver nitrate (procedure of Levaditi) because as a result of the deposition of metallic silver the spirochetes become thicker.

The order *Spirochaetales* is composed of one family only, *Spirochaetaceae*, which

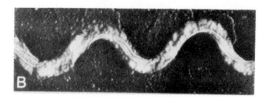

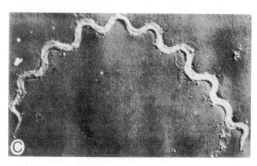

Fig. 32.1. (A) *Leptospira canicula* showing the central axial filament with a protoplast twisted around it. (Electron micrograph, × 1700.) (With permission, Swain, R.H.A.: The electron-microscopical anatomy of *Leptospira canicola*. J. Pathol. Bacteriol. *73*: 155, 1957.) (B) *T. pallidum* after treatment with trypsin, showing fibrils of axial filament wound around the protoplast. (Electron micrograph, × 3900.) (With permission, Swain, R.H.A.: Electron microscopic studies of the morphology of pathogenic spirochaetes. J. Pathol. Bacteriol. *69*: 117, 1955.) (C) *B. recurrentis* with axial filament wound around the protoplast. (Electron micrograph × 10,300.) (With permission, Swain, R.H.A.: Electron microscopic studies of the morphology of pathogenic spirochaetes. J. Pathol. Bacteriol. *69*: 117, 1955.)

contains five genera. The genera *Spirochaeta* and *Cristispira* each comprise many species of nonpathogenic spirochetes that are frequently found as free-living organisms in fresh or sea water and in sewers. Some *Cristispira* are found in the digestive tracts of mollusks. Some organisms (especially *Spirochaeta*) are very long, up to 500 μm. The genera *Treponema*, *Borrelia*, and *Lep-*

tospira contain pathogenic species of spirochetes; several of them cause well defined diseases.

TREPONEMA

Syphilis

Syphilis, or lues, is the most serious of veneral diseases. There are many who believe that it was not known in Europe in antiquity and the Middle Ages and that at the end of the 15th and beginning of the 16th century it was brought to Europe from Central America by Spanish sailors. This view, however, has been criticized by several authors, some of whom believe that stigmata of congenital syphilis are recognizable in European medieval sculptures and carvings. Syphilis spread in Europe in the 16th century as an epidemic, acute, and highly malignant disease with high mortality. In the following centuries it became a much milder, chronic disease.

In 1905 Schaudinn and Hoffmann described the causative agent for syphilis, a spirochete, in material from a syphilitic lesion. It is called at present *Treponema pallidum*.

Morphology. *T. pallidum* is 5 to 20 μm long and 0.1 to 0.2 μm broad. The resting organism has regular spirals with a wavelength of 1 μm and an amplitude of 0.5 μm. It can be readily observed under darkfield illumination (Fig. 32.2A). For observation of fine structure *T. pallidum* has to be examined by means of an electron microscope. It contains an axial filament composed of several fibrils wound around the protoplast. The axial filament arises from a base plate in the protoplasmic cylinder, wraps itself around this cylinder end, and terminates with a free end on the envelope. The whole cell is surrounded by an envelope that is quite fragile and is readily disrupted by osmotic shock.

T. pallidum stained by ordinary bacte-

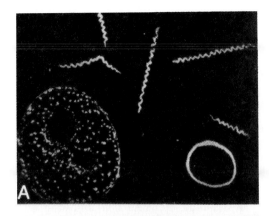

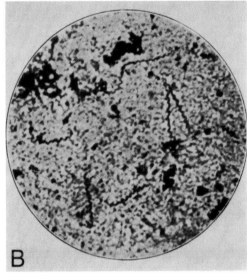

Fig. 32.2. (A) *T. pallidum* in darkfield illumination (× 2000). (With permission, Smith D.T.: Treponema pallidum and syphilis. In Joklik, W.K. and Smith, D.T., Eds.: Zinsser Microbiology. 15th Ed. Appleton-Century-Crofts, New York, 1972.) (B) *T. pallidum*. Silver impregnation (Lavaditi procedure) (× 1000). (With permission, Sobernheim, G.: Syphilisspirochate. In Kolle, W., Kraus, R., and Uhlenhuth, P., Eds.: Handbuch der pathogenen Mikroorganismen. Gustav Fischer, Jena; Urban & Schwarzenberg, Berlin and Wien, 1930.)

riologic methods is hardly visible by light microscopy, which is not surprising, since its thickness barely exceeds resolution power of the light microscope. In the Giemsa stain *T. pallidum* appears as a pinkish

"pale" organism (hence "pallidum"). On the other hand, the Levaditi procedure of silver impregnation makes *T. pallidum* readily visible by light microscopy (Fig. 32.2B). This procedure is frequently used for staining histologic sections of syphilitic lesions.

In spite of many claims, no one has succeeded in culturing virulent *T. pallidum* on artificial media. There are available many cultured strains of treponemes, for example, the Reiter strain, propagated for many years under anaerobic conditions. These strains are nonpathogenic though they were originally obtained from syphilitic lesions. Most likely the cultures were established by nonpathogenic treponemes contaminating syphilitic lesions. An alternative explanation — that these strains represent a true *T. pallidum* that has lost its pathogenicity — appears less likely and has to be repudiated on the basis of recent DNA hybridization studies.

It is possible to propagate virulent *T. pallidum* by animal inoculation. The first successful inoculation of apes with the material from syphilitic lesions was reported at the beginning of the 20th century, still before the discovery of *T. pallidum*. At present rabbits are most frequently used for propagation of *T. pallidum*. In succeeding rabbit-to-rabbit passages the frequency of successful inoculations reaches 100 percent. The best known and most frequently used strain of *T. pallidum* propagated in rabbits is the Nichols strain. In spite of being maintained in rabbits for over 60 years, this strain is still pathogenic for man, as has been shown by accidental laboratory infections. The intratesticular route is used frequently in rabbit inoculation. The incubation time is 8 to 10 days, after which time the testicles become swollen and cannot be pressed into the inguinal canal (Fig. 32.3). From animal experiments the generation time of *T. pallidum* was roughly estimated at 30 hours. Infected rabbits develop secondary lesions that resemble human secondary syphilis. They develop neither tertiary syphilis nor congenital syphilis.

Experimental syphilis has been of great value in examining several characteristics of this disease, including immunity and treatment. Also, therapeutic procedures have been examined in experimental syphilis. Importantly, testicular syphilomas serve as a source of *T. pallidum* for serodiagnostic procedures. On the other hand, inoculation of animals with human pathologic material has hardly any diagnostic value.

T. pallidum is very sensitive to temperature; it is killed within 2 hours at 41°C. It is also very sensitive to many physical and chemical agents. However, *T. pallidum* remains alive indefinitely if preserved as a suspension in liquid nitrogen.

Human Infection. The intact skin is resistant to infection by treponemes; however, they penetrate the skin or mucous mem-

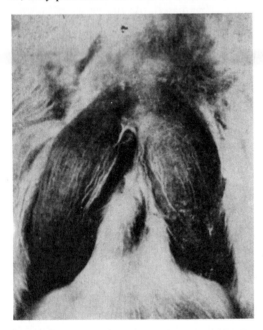

Fig. 32.3. Experimental syphilis in rabbits injected with Nichols strain of *T. pallidum*. Bilateral orchitis 18 days after intratesticular inoculation. (With permission, Milgrom, F., and Wicher, K.: Iconographia syphilidis experimentalis. Arch. Immunol. Terapii Doswiadczalnej *2*: 185, 1954.)

branes upon prolonged contact. Sexual relations are by far the most frequent mode of transmission of syphilis, but nonsexual transmissions are still encountered. They are caused mostly by direct contact, for example, kissing. Infections of physicians' fingers are occasionally noted; they are promoted by vigorous brushing of hands, which favors penetration of treponemes. Infants and small children raised in poor hygienic conditions may contract syphilis from contaminated sponges, towels, and other washing utensils. The following discussion of syphilis presents the clinical course of an untreated disease. The methods for laboratory diagnosis are stressed.

Until 3 years after infection syphilis is referred to as *early syphilis*. The incubation time of syphilis in humans is 1 to 6 weeks, with an average of 3 weeks; however, treponemes are in the bloodstream within a few hours after infection. The manifestations of *primary syphilis* appear at the portal of entry, usually on the genitals as an indurated, sometimes ulcerated lesion that is accompanied by enlargement of the regional lymph nodes. (Figure 32.4A shows a primary lesion on a finger, a rather unusual localization.) Syphilis is highly contagious in the primary stage. The diagnosis is conveniently made by a dark-field examination of the exudate from a primary lesion. Serodiagnostic tests are not reliable; Wassermann and flocculation tests are positive only in a small proportion of patients with the incipient primary syphilis. As time progresses and the disease approaches the secondary stage, the proportion of positive serodiagnostic tests increases considerably. The primary lesion resolves slowly, and it is quite frequently still present at the beginning of secondary syphilis.

Lesions of *secondary syphilis* usually appear 2 months after infection. At that time there is very pronounced spirochetemia. Secondary syphilis is a systemic disease with metastatic lesions in various organs. Most pronounced are skin man-

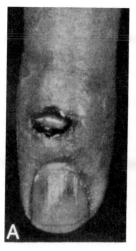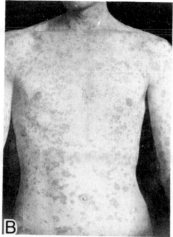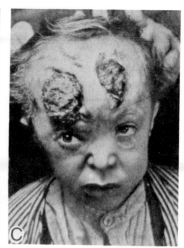

Fig. 32.4. Clinical manifestations of syphilis. (A) Primary syphilis on finger. (With permission, Kierland, R.K.: Syphilis. In Ormsby, O. and Montgomery, H., Eds.: Diseases of the Skin. 18th Ed. Lea & Febiger, Philadelphia, 1954.) (B) Secondary syphilis, macular eruption. (With permission, Kierland, R.K.: Syphilis. In Ormsby, O. and Montgomery, H., Eds.: Disease of the Skin. 18th Ed. Lea & Febiger, Philadelphia, 1954.) (C) Late congenital syphilis. (With permission, Milgrom, F.: Opis preypadku kily wrodzonej poznej. Kronika Wenerol. *4:* 137, 1950.)

ifestations in the form of generalized macular or papular eruptions (Fig. 32.4B). In places exposed to irritation and maceration, such as the genitals, anus, and armpits, eroded papules appear that shed treponemes. Secondary syphilis is the most contagious stage of this disease. Diagnosis of secondary syphilis may be made by dark-field examination of material from lesions, but serodiagnostic tests are more convenient. Wassermann and flocculation tests are positive in practically all patients.

The incidence of primary and secondary syphilis reached a peak in the United States in 1947, when 75 cases of recent infections per 100,000 population were observed. With successful penicillin treatment and energetic preventive measures, this incidence dropped to four cases per 100,000 population in 1957. The incidence of new syphilitic infections increased again in the 1960s and 1970s to reach 10 to 12 cases per 100,000 population.

Lesions of secondary syphilis undergo slow regression. Most treponemes are destroyed. There are periods without manifestations, referred to as *asymptomatic syphilis*. These periods are interrupted by relapses in which the recurrent lesions are usually not generalized and, most frequently, appear as single lesions. In recurrent secondary syphilis contagiousness is much lower than in generalized secondary syphilis. The diagnosis is made by means of serologic tests.

More than 3 years after infection, the disease is called *late syphilis*. The lesions occurring at that time are referred to as lesions of *tertiary syphilis*. These are granulomas of the skin and internal organs, including the heart and arteries. Death occurs from heart failure or rupture of the aorta. There are very few treponemes in the lesions of tertiary syphilis, and these lesions have very low potential for transmission of the disease. The diagnosis is made by serodiagnostic tests; Wassermann and flocculation tests are positive in about 90 percent of the cases of late syphilis of the skin and internal organs.

Late neurologic manifestations of syphilis, which appear many years after infection, take two forms. *General paresis* is an inflammatory, degenerative disease of the entire brain that causes severe mental disturbances. Diagnosis based on serologic examination of serum and cerebrospinal fluids is positive in close to 100 percent of cases. *Tabes dorsalis* is a degenerative disease of the sensory routes in the dorsal columns of the spinal cord. This is a severe disease resulting in pronounced crippling. It is diagnosed by serologic examination of serum and cerebrospinal fluid, which are positive in about 90 percent of cases. Fortunately, these neurologic manifestations of syphilis appear only in a few percent of patients and only in those who had received no treatment or inadequate treatment. Patients with general paresis and tabes dorsalis are practically noncontagious.

In late syphilis there are long periods without manifestations, referred to as *latent syphilis*. The disease may be diagnosed only by means of serodiagnostic tests. The death rate from syphilis in the United States was 14,000 cases annually in 1940. It declined considerably and has been recently only about 200 cases per year.

Congenital syphilis used to occur frequently; in 1941, 18,000 cases were reported in the United States. At present there are less than 1000 cases per year. The term *hereditary syphilis*, used several decades ago, was a misnomer because syphilis is not inherited but is transmitted to the fetus as an infection *in utero*. Therefore the old concept of syphilis transmitted to the baby by the father without infection of the mother was wrong. Infection of the fetus usually occurs at the beginning of the second half of gestation, but occasional infections in the first trimester have been well documented. The severity of congenital syphilis depends on the intensity of the infection of the fetus and its gestational age at the time of infection. Massive and early infections lead to abortions or stillbirths.

With a milder infection suffered in later gestational stages the child is born at term with congenital syphilis.

Early and late manifestations of congenital syphilis are similar to those of acquired syphilis (Fig. 32.4C). Diagnosis of early congenital syphilis may be made quite readily by means of darkfield examination of exudate from skin lesions. Serodiagnostic tests are carried out on umbilical blood or, later, blood taken from the baby. It should be remembered that IgG antibodies in the newborn are of maternal origin. Therefore in some cases the reaction with the baby's blood may be positive because of passive transfer of maternal antibodies even though the child has escaped the infection. On the other hand, IgM antibodies do not cross the placenta; therefore positive tests with the IgM fraction of the baby's serum are reliably indicative of active syphilitic infection. Six months after birth most IgG antibodies are of the baby's origin, and then the test with whole serum becomes reliable.

Immunity. As mentioned before, since the 16th century syphilis has changed from an acute and frequently fatal into a chronic and rarely fatal disease. This phenomenon may have resulted from the selection of people who had inborn resistance. They did not die of syphilis and left progeny with inherited resistance. Alternatively, a decrease in microbial virulence could be considered.

The manifestations of syphilis characteristic for a particular stage of this disease, discussed above, depend undoubtedly upon the immunologic status of the host. Early spread of syphilitic infection occurs because of the weakness of resistance on the part of the host. This is the case in primary and early secondary syphilis. In the later stages of early syphilis, immunity begins to be expressed. The treponemes are destroyed and the lesions subside. The disease frequently becomes asymptomatic. The balance between the invasiveness of treponemes and the strength of immunity probably accounts for the manifestations of the disease at any given time. Relapses in early syphilis show that the aggressiveness of treponemes is stronger than the defense of the patient; a lack of symptoms shows that the opposite is the case. Manifestations of late syphilis are elicited by cell-mediated immunity, and they are characterized by a rather vigorous, exaggerated response to a few organisms, a hallmark of this type of immunity.

Because the immune response determines the extent and character of lesions in each stage of syphilis, a patient with patent or asymptomatic syphilis will never develop a primary lesion. This observation of early syphilologists was frequently referred to as "immunity to reinfection" (premunition).

Following complete eradication of treponemes by drugs (e.g., penicillin) in early syphilis, the resistance to reinfection disappears very quickly. Interestingly, such eradication of organisms at the very beginning of primary syphilis leaves practically no immunity and the patient may be reinfected within a few days. On the other hand, efficient treatment instituted in secondary syphilis is followed by an immunity that lasts for at least a few weeks.

No definite information is available about the immune mechanisms responsible for the control of the spread of treponemes and resistance to reinfection. Humoral antibodies may play some role because antibody-containing serum reduces the infectivity of a treponemal suspension in the rabbit. Furthermore, passive protection was observed in rabbits injected with sera of rabbits infected with syphilis. On the other hand, the greatest spread of treponemes occurs in secondary syphilis, when there is the highest titer of humoral antibodies. Of the two types of antibodies encountered in syphilis, Wassermann antibodies are not considered protective. In contrast, a protective role has been attributed to antibodies that immobilize treponemes even though there is no definite evidence for this contention. In recent years evidence has emerged that cell-mediated immunity plays an important role in recovery from syphilis.

In untreated syphilis or inadequately treated syphilis roughly one-third of patients recover spontaneously in that they do not suffer from any manifestations of disease and even eventually show negative Wassermann tests. It should be stressed, however, that denial of treatment for syphilis is unethical and dangerous for both the patient and the community.

Treatment. From the 17th through 19th centuries the treatment of syphilis was based on the application of mercurials in the form of ointments. In 1909 Ehrlich introduced arsphenamine, which is diaminohydroxyarsenobenzene, a compound of trivalent arsenic. In 1920 Levaditi introduced treatment with bismuth. Then, for about a quarter of a century, the treatment of syphilis consisted of injections of arsphenamine and bismuth. Since the late 1940s penicillin has been employed as the drug of choice in the treatment of syphilis. Penicillin has very remarkable treponemocidal activity. It has shortened treatment of syphilis from multiple injections administered over a period of 1 to 2 years to a few injections given within a few days or weeks.

Since penicillin is also the major drug used for treatment of gonorrhea and since it is administered in much smaller doses for this disease than for syphilis, treatment of gonorrhea may occasionally suppress the manifestations of syphilis. Therefore after each penicillin treatment of gonorrhea the patient should be submitted to serologic examination for syphilis to diagnose or rule out a double infection.

Since the 1910s neurologic manifestations of late syphilis have been treated by infecting the patient with malaria (which later is controlled by antimalarial drugs). The efficacy of this treatment is most likely due to the high fever so induced.

In spite of some efforts vaccination against syphilis has never been successfully developed. Prevention of the disease is based on the detection and treatment of sources of infection.

Serodiagnosis of Syphilis. The first serodiagnostic test for syphilis was described in 1906 by Wassermann, Neisser, and Bruck. They selected a complement fixation reaction described a few years earlier as the test procedure. Because the causative organism was not available in any pure form (in fact, it is not available today), Wassermann and his associates selected extracts from syphilitic lesions of man and animals as well as from livers of stillborn syphilitic fetuses as antigens for their tests. They obviously hoped that such extracts would contain antigenic components of syphilis organisms. After a few months of experimentation they reported that they could detect antibodies in patients' sera and that they had developed a useful serodiagnostic procedure.

It soon became obvious that many important controls were not included in these studies. It was shown that syphilis sera combined with extracts of normal tissues equally as well as they did with extracts of syphilitic lesions. Still, the diagnostic significance of the test remained valid. Ethanol extracts of various normal tissues, primarily bovine heart, were successfully employed as antigens in the Wassermann test. Such extracts constitute solutions of tissue lipids that are devoid of organ or species specificity. After dilution in saline these tissue lipids form a colloidal suspension that is used as the proper Wassermann antigen. Significant improvement in the Wassermann test was achieved by the addition of cholesterol to tissue extracts. Colloidal suspensions obtained from cholesterolized extracts are composed of larger particles and are more sensitive test antigens than suspensions prepared from extracts without cholesterol.

Flocculation tests for syphilis were developed in the 1920s. The extracts used for these tests are also cholesterolized ethanol extracts of heart. They are prepared in such a way that the saline suspension of lipids is composed of large colloidal particles, about 0.1 μm in diameter. Such suspensions undergo visible clumping in the presence of syphilis sera. The flocculation tests most frequently used in this country are the VDRL (Veneral Disease Research Laboratory) test and the Kahn test. Flocculation tests detect the same antibody as the Wassermann test, but they are much easier to perform and therefore have almost completely replaced the Wassermann test in recent years.

Isolation in the 1940s of a phospholipid named *cardiolipin* from ethanol extracts of bovine heart was of paramount importance. Cardiolipin is the active principle of the crude ethanol extracts that had been used in Wassermann and flocculation tests. Cardiolipin is preserved as an ethanol solution. By itself it cannot serve as the Wassermann antigen; thus to the ethanol solution of cardiolipin are added lecithin and cholesterol. When this preparation is mixed with saline, a colloidal suspension, composed of particles that apparently have cardiolipin on their surface, is formed. Cardiolipin, lecithin, and cholesterol are used in different relative concentrations in preparations employed for the Wassermann and for the flocculation tests.

We discussed previously the frequency of positive Wassermann and flocculation tests in various stages of syphilis. This feature of a serodiagnostic test — the frequency of positive results, among patients suffering from the disease for which the test had been designed — is called sensitivity. The figures presented previously showed that the Wassermann and flocculation tests are quite sensitive in that they give positive results in close to 100 percent of cases of secondary syphilis and over 90 percent in late syphilis. The specificity of Wassermann and flocculation tests should also be discussed. The specificity of a serologic test is measured in a negative sense by the frequency of positive results in patients with diseases other than the one for which the test had been designed and in normal human beings. Wassermann and flocculation tests are positive in the tropical treponemal diseases yaws and pinta almost as frequently as in syphilis. They are also positive, although less frequently, in other spirochetal diseases (e.g., in relapsing fever). These tests give positive results in lepromatous leprosy with the high frequency of 70 percent, and up to 20 percent of patients with systemic lupus erythematosus show positive tests.

Nonspecific positive Wassermann and flocculation tests have also been noted in patients with most febrile infectious diseases (tuberculosis, malaria, vaccinia, scarlet fever, infectious mononucleosis, and many others) and in those with malignancies. However, with modern procedures positive tests in these diseases are noted only exceptionally. One can readily avoid an erroneous diagnosis when positive Wassermann or flocculation tests are encountered in acute febrile diseases. It suffices to repeat the test a few weeks after the symptoms subside.

In addition to reactions in the diseases named above, Wassermann and flocculation tests give nonspecific reactions in people without any apparent abnormalities. The frequency of such reactions is low, only about 1 in 4000, but still this constitutes a major problem because of mass examinations. Each year a few million people in the United States are examined by means of flocculation tests (medical checkups, hospital admissions, premarital examinations, pregnancy, etc.). With millions of tests performed, thousands of positive reactions are encountered that prove to be nonspecific. Therefore it has been very important to develop serologic tests capable of excluding nonspecific results in Wassermann and flocculation tests. Such tests are discussed later in this chapter, but now some explanation of the mystery of the formation of Wasser-

mann antibodies in the course of syphilis should be offered.

When it became clear that in the Wassermann test syphilis sera combine with ubiquitous tissue lipids rather than *T. pallidum*, some investigators entertained the notion that the serum factor responsible for these reactions was not a true antibody but some undefined "reagine." This term is still occasionally used in some publications. However, it is completely obvious that the reactions of syphilis serum with lipid antigen are due to antibodies. Wassermann antibodies are immunoglobulins of the IgM and the IgG classes, and they show serologic specificity for cardiolipin.

Currently, there are two major theories explaining the mode of formation of Wassermann antibodies. One theory assumes that patients suffering from syphilitic infection respond to *T. pallidum*. Because of shared lipid antigens between *T. pallidum* and normal tissues, antibodies to *T. pallidum* crossreact with ubiquitous tissue lipids (cardiolipin). The second theory postulates that Wassermann antibodies are formed in response to the patient's own tissue lipids, liberated from syphilitic lesions in a strongly immunogenic form. It is impossible to state at present which of these two theories is correct because there are experimental data supporting both of them. However, one has to admit that the second theory is more comprehensive, since it accounts for formation of Wassermann antibodies not only in syphilis but also in all other conditions in which tissue destruction would release lipids in immunogenic form.

As mentioned previously, a procedure distinguishing between specific and nonspecific results of Wassermann and flocculation tests had been badly needed. Such a procedure was described in 1949 by Nelson and Mayer as the *T. pallidum immobilization* (*TPI*) test. Treponemes for this test are obtained from rabbit syphilomas developed 8 to 10 days after intratesticular injection of the Nichols strain of *T. palli-*

dum. The suspension of treponemes is prepared in a medium that contains a number of amino acids and vitamins. In this medium, under anaerobic conditions at 37°C, treponemes survive and remain motile for several days.

For the test the treponemal suspension is mixed with the patient's serum and guinea pig complement. The mixture is incubated under anaerobic conditions for up to 18 hours. The result of the test is evaluated by comparing the motility of treponemes in the test proper and in controls. Immobilizing antibodies detected in the TPI test are different from Wassermann antibodies, and removal of Wassermann antibodies by means of a flocculation reaction does not affect the TPI test. The TPI test becomes positive 6 to 8 weeks after infection (i.e., later than the Wassermann and flocculation tests). In treated cases the TPI test remains positive longer than the Wassermann test. In untreated cases the TPI test practically never becomes negative.

In spite of its rather simple principle, the TPI test is difficult and expensive to perform. Simple modifications of this test were developed. The most popular of them is the *fluorescent treponemal antibody (FTA)* test. In this test freeze-dried treponemes from rabbit testicular syphilomas are employed. They are not alive and do not require any special methods of preservation. Such a treponemal preparation is incubated with the patient's serum and then with fluorescein-labeled antiserum to human gamma globulin. In a positive test fluorescence of treponemes is observed.

A modification of the FTA test was developed in which the patient's serum is preabsorbed with a culture of Reiter treponemes. The purpose of this absorption is removal of antibodies to nonpathogenic treponemes. The resulting test, called *FTA-ABS*, appears indeed to be more specific than the FTA test, even though the precise effect of the absorption is not yet clear.

Endemic Syphilis, Tropical Treponematoses

In several countries of the Middle East as well as in Europe, Scotland, Bosnia, and the eastern Carpathian Mountains, the occurrence of endemic nonvenereal syphilis has been reported. The disease is transferred through direct contact, but the occurrence of primary lesions is rare. However, the clinical course of this form of syphilis does not differ from venereal syphilis, and there is no reason to suspect any difference between treponemes causing venereal and endemic syphilis.

Yaws (frambesia) appears in tropical Africa, Asia, and America, whereas pinta is a disease limited to the Western Hemisphere, Mexico, and Central and South America. Yaws is caused by *T. pertenue* and pinta by *T. carateum*. These treponemes are morphologically and immunologically indistinguishable from each other and from *T. pallidum*. Significantly, DNA hybridization experiments showed almost complete homology between *T. pallidum* and *T. pertenue*, indicating that these organisms may be variants of the same species. Similar to *T. pallidum*, they cannot be cultured on artificial media.

Yaws and pinta occur most frequently in childhood and are acquired through direct contact under poor hygienic conditions. Transfer by flies and other insects is suspected. There is no evidence for venereal transfer. The lesions of both diseases are mostly limited to the skin, but in yaws, bone lesions have also been described. There is no involvement of internal organs or of the central nervous system. Congenital forms have not been described. In both yaws and pinta the Wassermann and flocculation tests are positive, although in pinta they are positive less frequently than in syphilis. Treatment with arsenicals and penicillin is effective.

Oral Treponemes

Spirochetes, now classified as treponemes, are detectable in the normal human oral cavity, and their numbers frequently increase under pathologic conditions. Of these, *T. vincentii* has attracted the most attention. These are helical cells 5 to 16 μm long and 0.2 to 0.3 μm wide. They grow on artificial media (e.g., peptone-yeast extract, with the addition of animal serum) under anaerobic conditions. The role of this treponeme, along with anaerobic fusiform bacilli in Vincent's angina, has been discussed for many years. Vincent's angina is an acute throat disease with congested tonsils and grayish pseudomembranes, resembling diphtheria. The disease may descend and form pulmonary gangrene. The etiologic role of spirochetes or both fusiforms and spirochetes in this disease remains at best questionable. *T. vincentii* is present in the mouth and throat of about 25 percent of the normal population. They and the fusiform bacteria increase in number probably as the result of several noxious factors, such as deficient nutrition, and may act as opportunistic pathogens.

Other oral treponemes, such as *T. microdentium*, *T. refringens*, and *T. denticola*, have been distinguished as separate species from *T. vincentii*.

BORRELIA

The genus *Borrelia* comprises spirochetes 3. to 20 μm long and 0.2 to 0.5 μm broad. Each organism contains 3 to 10 irregular coils. With the electron microscope a helical cytoplasmic cylinder may be distinguished around which 15 to 20 fibrils (axial filaments) are wound. Borrelias stain quite well with the usual bacterial dyes and are gram-negative. They can survive in liquid blood for many months but are susceptible to desiccation. They are strictly anaerobic. The growth of borrelias on artificial media

is still controversial. They multiply abundantly in chick embryos. Also, they may be propagated in mammals (e.g., rats or hamsters) and in ticks.

Borrelias are pathogenic organisms causing relapsing fever in man. They are transmitted by the body louse and by ticks of the genus *Ornithodoros*. Some investigators believe that each species of *Borrelia* is transmitted by a different arthropod. Accordingly, several species of *Borrelia* were distinguished depending on the species of the *Ornithodoros* vector. The range of animal hosts depends to a great extent on the feeding habits of the arthropod vector. Of numerous species of *Borrelia*, *B. recurrentis*, transmitted by the body louse, is considered the species responsible for human louse-borne recurrent fever. This organism was first described by Obermeier in 1873 in a patient's blood during an epidemic of relapsing fever in Berlin. The 8th edition of *Bergey's Manual of Determinative Bacteriology* lists 19 species of *Borrelia* with greater or lesser pathogenicity for man (Table 32.1).

Epidemiologic and Clinical Characteristics

Relapsing fever occurs as an endemic tick-borne disease in several places throughout the world. The vertebrate reservoir is mostly small wild animals, from which the organisms are transmitted to man. In the United States endemic outbreaks have been reported, mostly in the Southwest. Borrelias multiply in the ticks and may be transmitted through eggs to the next generation (transovarian passage). The ticks transfer the organisms from one animal to another. After sucking the blood from an animal or human, the tick becomes infected, at first in the celomic cavity and then throughout the body. Infection of the salivary glands may account for infectivity of the bite itself. Otherwise, infection is transmitted by body

Table 32.1.   Genus *Borrelia*

From birds	*B. anserina*
From animals other than birds	
From man; cause of relapsing fever	
Arthropod vector is the louse *Pediculus humanus humanus*	*B. recurrentis*
Arthropod vector is a tick of the genus *Ornithodoros*	
Transmitted by *O. erraticus erraticus*	*B. hispanica*
Transmitted by *O. hermsi*	*B. hermsii*
Transmitted by *O. moubata*	*B. duttonii*
Transmitted by *O. parkeri*	*B. parkeri*
Transmitted by *O. rudis*	*B. venezuelensis*
Transmitted by *O. talaje*	*B. mazzottii*
Transmitted by *O. tholozani*	*B. persica*
Transmitted by *O. turicata*	*B. turicatae*
Transmitted by *O. verrucosus*	*B. caucasica*
From animals other than man	
From ticks (*Ornithodoros*)	
From *O. brasiliensis*	*B. brasiliensis*
From *O. dugesi*	*B. dugesii*
From *O. graingeri*	*B. graingeri*
From animals other than arthropods	
From rodents	
Transmitted by *O. erraticus sonrai*	*B. crocidurae*
Transmitted by *O. tartakovskyi*	*B. latyschewii*
Transmitted by *O. zumpti*	*B. tillae*
From ruminants and horses	*B. theileri*
From primates	*B. harveyi*

(Buchanan, R.E., and Gibbons, N.E., Eds.: Bergey's Manual of Determinative Bacteriology. 8th ed. Copyright ©, 1974 The Williams & Wilkins, Co., Baltimore.)

fluids and feces of ticks that are rubbed into the skin. Infection of the tick's gonads accounts for the transovarian passage of the borrelias. Borrelias remain viable in ticks throughout the life of the host, which may extend for over 20 years.

Louse-borne relapsing fever used to be widespread in Europe, Asia, and Africa and was responsible for decimating epidemics, especially in times of famine. In the United States epidemics of relapsing fever were noted in the first decades of the 20th century, especially in immigrants from Eastern Europe.

The louse-borne and tick-borne diseases are clinically similar. The incubation time of relapsing fever is usually 1 week. The disease has sudden onset with chills and fever above 40°C (104°F). Enlargement of spleen, jaundice, and reddish spots on the skin are frequently observed. In 3 to 10 days after onset of the disease there is a sudden drop in fever, but within a few days there is a relapse. Whereas the first attack has an average duration of 6.2 days, the average duration of the second attack is 4.3 days. If a third attack is to come, the symptomless interval between the second and third attack is longer than that between the first and second. The average duration of the third attack is 3 days. The interval between the third and fourth attack is longer than any of the previous intervals, and the average duration of the fourth attack is only 2 days. This time sequence is shown in Figure 32.5. There may be up to ten re-

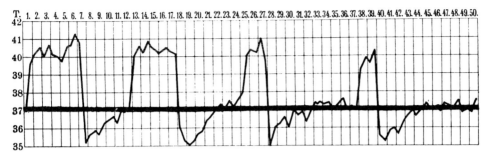

Fig. 32.5. Typical course of temperature in relapsing fever. Ordinate, temperature (°C); abscissa, time of onset of disease (days). (With permission, Nocht, B., Paschen, E., and Hegler, C.: G. Jochmann Lehrbuch der Infektionskrankheiten. Julius Springer, Berlin, 1924, p. 266.)

lapses, with the severity of the attacks decreasing and the length of afebrile periods increasing. The disease has a rather low fatality rate of 4 to 5 percent, but in some epidemics the fatality rate reaches 50 percent. During relapse but not remission, borrelias are found in large numbers in the blood.

The recurrent character of the disease is explained by the emergence of serologic mutants of the borrelias. One would assume that after the first attack antibodies produced against the invading borrelias would eliminate most but not all organisms; the surviving borrelias are mutants differing serologically from the original invader. After these borrelias causing the second attack are eliminated, some mutants remain to multiply again and cause the third attack. In these terms ultimate recovery would depend on production of a broad enough spectrum of antibodies to cover the entire antigenic "flexibility" of the organism. In accordance with this trend, many serotypes have been recognized in several species of *Borrelia*.

Diagnosis of relapsing fever is made by demonstration of borrelias in the blood, and this demonstration is quite readily achieved during the febrile periods. Borrelias can be seen in stained smears. The staining procedures most frequently used are those of Wright and Giemsa. Also, dark-field examination of blood is quite a reli-

able procedure. Cultures are not helpful in diagnosis, but inoculation of blood into young rodents, such as rats, mice, and hamsters, may sometimes be a helpful diagnostic method.

Patients suffering from relapsing fever form antiborrelial antibodies. These can be detected by means of agglutination or immobilization of borrelias. Up to 20 percent of patients form Wassermann antibodies. Also, the Weil-Felix test frequently shows moderately elevated titers.

The demonstration of borrelias in infected lice and ticks can be achieved by injecting laboratory animals with crushed arthropods or by culture on chick embryos.

Relapsing fever is treated with tetracyclines; chloramphenicol and streptomycin have also been successfully used.

The measures for prevention of the disease are based on avoiding contact with ticks and lice. Insect-repelling agents are helpful. No effective vaccine has been developed.

LEPTOSPIRA

In 1886 Weil described an infectious disease characterized by jaundice, which was transferred to man from rats. The disease was called Weil's disease, infectious jaundice, or 7-day fever. In 1915 and 1916 Inada and Ido isolated the causative agent of this disease, a leptospire. According to the present classification the genus *Leptospira* contains only one species, *Leptospira interrogans*. Leptospires are helical organisms, 6 to 20 μm long and 0.1 μm in diameter; they are frequently bent on one or both ends (Fig. 32.1A).

The organisms are motile, and the motility can best be observed under darkfield illumination. Rapid rotation about the long axis results in the formation of figures appearing as T, L, O, or 8 at one or both ends of the organisms seen under darkfield illumination. This is caused by the bent terminal part of the organism rapidly rotating. Rotation drives the organism by a propellerlike action to perform translation. Finally, flexion of the body is also a frequent movement. In stained preparations leptospires are hardly visible because of their small diameter, which is close to the resolution power of the light microscope. On the other hand, the silver impregnation method makes leptospires readily recognizable in microscopic preparations. Electron microscopic studies reveal a protoplast bound helically around the axial filament and an envelope encasing both structures.

Leptospires can be readily propagated on artificial media containing inorganic salts and buffered saline. Some media are supplemented with rabbit serum; others contain bovine serum albumin and/or Tween 80. Growth is better in liquid or semisolid media than on solid media. Leptospires are strict aerobes; their optimal growth occurs at temperatures of 28 to 30°C. A temperature of 56°C is lethal for all leptospires. They also grow readily on the chorioallantoic membrane of the chick embryo. No toxins have been described. Some strains cause hemolysis.

In previous years classification of leptospires was based on their antigenic structure, geographic distribution, species of the affected host, and clinical data. The genus encompassed several species. In the most recent recommendation of the International Committee on Systematic Bacteriology,

Leptospira interrogans was recognized as the only species. For practical purposes subdivision into two complexes is used, the interrogans complex, composed mostly of pathogenic strains, and the biflexa complex, with saprophytic strains. Some investigators feel that these two complexes should be considered separate species on the basis of their DNA structure. The interrogans complex now contains 130 serotypes belonging to 16 serogroups: icterohaemorrhagiae, hebdomadis, automnalis, canicola, australis, tarassovi or hyos, pyrogenes, bataviae, javanica, pomona, ballum, cynopteri, celledoni, grippotyphosa, panama, and shermani. Identification of an isolated strain for serogroups and serotypes is performed by means of an agglutination test comparing the reaction elicited by standard antisera with the reaction produced by the antiserum to the strain under investigation. This analysis is highly complex; it suffices to say that leptospires possess more that 250 agglutinogens. Cross-absorption experiments are of primary importance. The guidelines presented by the World Health Organization in 1967 state, "Two strains are considered to belong to different serotypes if, after cross-absorption with adequate amounts of heterologous antigen, 10 percent or more of the homologous titer regularly remains in at least one of the two antisera in repeated tests."

Agglutination tests are evaluated microscopically and macroscopically. Formalin-killed leptospires are agglutinated into clumps resembling cotton-wool, whereas live organisms are agglutinated into highly reflectile spheroid masses. For many years the term "agglutination lysis" was used to denote the reaction with live leptospires because it was observed that masses of agglutinated leptospires seemed to disappear when the reaction was performed at high serum dilution. It was shown, however, that this "lysis" was complement independent and that debris of allegedly lysed spirochetes were really composed of clumped organisms. Therefore this misnomer was discarded. Serologic analyses of leptospiral strains were also conducted by precipitation and passive agglutination. Classification has been quite arbitrary; not rarely, identical organisms were described under different names.

Epidemiologic and Clinical Characteristics

Leptospirosis is a widespread disease. It affects a variety of domestic and wild animals, with rats being the most important reservoir. Many strains may infect several animal species, whereas others are more species-restricted. In several instances the animal infection is not apparent. Most likely pathogenic leptospires do not multiply outside the host, but when shed in the urine they survive in water or soil for several days or weeks. Human infection occurs directly by contact with urine or tissues of infected animals or, more frequently, through contaminated water. Abraded skin or mucous membranes serve as portals of entry. Children and young or middle-aged adults comprise the most frequently affected age groups. The disease is more prevalent in males than females. People exposed to hazards of infection with leptospirosis are those who stay in poorly drained places infested by rats and other rodents — for example, coal miners, ricefield workers, slaughterhouse workers, and soldiers in trenches.

The incubation period of leptospirosis is in most cases 7 to 13 days. In typical Weil's disease, fever, chills, headache, and conjunctivitis are very characteristic from the onset of the disease. In this period, referred to as the first phase of the disease, leptospires may be found in the blood. Usually in the second week of the disease the patient develops jaundice, hemorrhages of the skin, and extreme weakness. At this time, referred to as the second phase of the disease, leptospires disappear from the blood

and are found in the urine. Jaundice appears only in 10 percent of cases; these patients are severely ill, and fatality among them reaches 30 percent. In milder, nonicteric forms the fatality rate is only 5 percent. Recovery usually occurs within 1 to 2 weeks and is followed by solid immunity mediated by humoral antibodies.

Aseptic meningitis and myocarditis occasionally accompany leptospirosis. Subclinical infections are also quite frequent in humans as judged by serologic studies and observations on resistance to infection. An interesting outbreak of leptospirosis, referred to as peritibial or Fort Bragg fever, was described in 1942. The characteristic features in this form of leptospirosis were rash and erythematous lesions noted over peritibial areas. A very high proportion of these patients had splenomegaly.

Laboratory Diagnosis

Diagnosis of leptospirosis may be made by darkfield examination of the patient's serum early in the disease. Mistakes have been made in which the strings of erythrocyte stromata were taken for leptospires; therefore confirmatory tests should be done. The reliable diagnosis of leptospirosis is made by culturing the organisms on artificial media. Most of these media are composed of salts buffered to pH 7.3 to 7.4 and supplemented with 7 to 10 percent of pooled normal rabbit serum. Some media use peptone; others use hemoglobin or yeast extract. Synthetic media composed of chemically defined ingredients have also been employed. Through the addition of 0.2 to 0.5 percent of agar to fluid media the latter become semisolid, or through the addition of 0.8 to 1.3 percent of agar the media become solid. In the first phase of the disease, isolation of leptospires is readily achieved from blood. During leptospiruria, urine is the material of choice for culturing leptospires. At autopsy, renal cortex may be minced and cultured. The cultures are incubated under aerobic conditions at 28 to 30°C and inspected after 1 week and thereafter at weekly intervals for a total of 6 weeks. Only cultures negative after 6 weeks are discarded. Some investigators recommend initial incubation at 37°C for 2 to 3 days to accelerate the growth of leptospires. Inspection of cultures is made by darkfield microscopy, observing living, motile leptospires.

Another useful diagnostic procedure is the inoculation of susceptible animals with pathologic material. Young animals are more susceptible to leptospiral infection than adult animals. One-week-old guinea pigs and 3 week old hamsters are preferably employed. Mice and rats may also be used, but only if it is proved that they originated from a colony free of leptospirosis; weanling mice and rats are preferred. The tested specimen in a volume of 0.5 to 1.0 ml is injected intraperitoneally. It should be stressed that some serotypes of leptospires elicit patent disease in laboratory animals, whereas other serotypes may cause an inapparent infection. After inoculation the animals are observed daily for weight loss and fever. Examination of peritoneal exudate for leptospires is performed by means of darkfield illumination. Postmortem examination is conducted on all animals 3 weeks after inoculation; kidneys are examined for the presence of leptospires, primarily by means of cultures but also through further inoculation of animals.

Serodiagnostic tests for leptospirosis are performed in the second stage of the disease. Two types of tests may be distinguished: *genus-specific* and *strain-specific*. For the genus-specific tests several procedures can be used. The most important are the passive agglutination and passive hemolysis tests, in which the patient's serum is tested against erythrocytes coated by soluble substances extracted from leptospires. The complement fixation test may also be conducted using antigens of the biflexa complex. In addition, plain agglutina-

tion of leptospires has been employed. The genus-specific test usually becomes positive 1 to 2 weeks after the onset of symptoms, and its titer reaches the peak in the third week. The test becomes negative 1 to 2 years after infection. The genus-specific test is useful in establishing the diagnosis of leptospirosis.

The strain-specific test accomplishes the identification of the strain against which the patient's antibodies are directed. In most instances this test is not reliable. At the beginning of the disease the titers of cross-reactions with noninfecting strains may be higher than the titer with the infecting strain. Still, some information about the nature of the infecting strain may be obtained by means of absorption experiments. The dependable identification of the infecting leptospire is made by serologic tests in which the isolated organism is used.

Therapy. A number of antibiotics, including penicillin, streptomycin, and chloramphenicol, are efficient in the treatment of leptospirosis; however, only antibiotics administered within the first 4 days of disease are effective.

REFERENCES

Alston, J.M. and Broom, J.C.: Leptospirosis in Man and Animals. E.S. Livingstone, Edinburgh, 1958.

Eagle, H.: The Laboratory Diagnosis of Syphilis. C.V. Mosby, St. Louis, 1937.

Felsenfeld, O.: Human relapsing fever, and parasite-vector-host relationships. Bact. Rev. 29: 46, 1965.

Jadassohn, J.: Handbuch der Haut-u. Geschlechtskrankheiten. Vol. 15/1. J. Springer, Berlin, 1927.

Jadassohn, J.: Handbuch der Haut- u. Geschlechtskrankheiten. Vol. 15/2, J. Springer, Berlin, 1929.

Kolle, W., Kraus, R., and Uhlenhuth, P.: Handbuch der pathogenen Mikroorganismen. Vol. VII, Part 1. Gustav Fischer, Jena; Urban & Schwarzenberg, Berlin and Wien, 1930.

Stokes, J., Beermann, H., and Ingraham, N.R.: Modern Clinical Syphilology. W.B. Saunders, Philadelphia, 1945.

Turner, L.H.: Leptospirosis I. Trans. R. Soc. Trop. Med. Hyg. *61*: 842, 1967.

Turner, L.H.: Leptospirosis II. Serology.Trans. R. Soc. Trop. Med. Hyg. *62*: 880, 1968.

Turner, L.H.: Leptospirosis III. Maintenance, isolation and demonstration of leptospires. Trans. R. Soc. Trop. Med. Hyg. *64*: 623, 1970.

Wilson, G.S. and Miles, A.A., Eds.: Topley and Wilson's Principles of Bacteriology, Virology and Immunity. 6th Ed. Vols. 1 and 2. Edward Arnold, Ltd., London, 1975.

World Health Organization: Treponematoses Research, Report of a Scientific Group. Technical Report Series, No. 455, 1970.

Mycoplasma

Joseph H. Kite, Jr.

Mycoplasma pneumoniae is the primary cause in humans of an acute pneumonia now referred to as mycoplasmal pneumonia, but previously called cold-agglutinin-positive primary atypical pneumonia. Although it was considered a primary form of lung disease, it was atypical in that it did not have the characteristic features of other bacterial and viral pneumonias, and its cause was unknown. Patients did not respond dramatically to treatment with penicillin as they did in infections caused by *Streptococcus pneumoniae*. Also, the atypical pneumonia could be correlated with the presence of antibodies, termed cold agglutinins, in the serum.

Mycoplasmal pneumonia is seen principally in older children and young adults. It is spread by droplet infection. The disease may be treated with erythromycin or tetracyclines. Patients usually recover, but convalescence may be prolonged.

In recent years evidence has accumulated to demonstrate that the mycoplasmas are important agents of other human diseases. *M. pneumoniae* can cause severe disease not limited to the respiratory tract, e.g., central nervous system complications, in-travascular problems, mucocutaneous lesions, and gastrointestinal disturbances. *Ureaplasma urealyticum* is a cause of non-gonococcal urethritis in men and continues to be implicated in infertility, spontaneous abortion, and stillbirth. *Mycoplasma hominis* is a cause of postpartum fever and a likely cause of pelvic inflammatory disease and pyelonephritis.

THE CLASS MOLLICUTES

Mycoplasmas have characteristics that are so different from those of other bacteria that they have been placed in the separate class *Mollicutes*. The major criterion for this classification is the type of cell boundary. Some important characteristics of mycoplasmas are presented in Table 33.1. Bacteria of the class *Mollicutes* do not have a cell wall but a triple-layered membrane that may or may not contain cholesterol. Without a cell wall the organisms are pleomorphic. In size they are the smallest organisms that contain all the necessary enzyme systems and genetic information that are compatible with a free-living existence.

Table 33.1. Characteristics of Mycoplasmas

Procaryotic organisms that have no cell wall but a triple-layered membrane that contains sterol in species found in humans

Pleomorphic; can be stained with Giemsa stain but are not stained well with Gram stain

Smallest free-living microorganisms (smallest cell is 125 to 250 nm); coccoid, but has tendency to form filaments; can pass through filters that retain most bacteria

Very small colonies (10 to 600 μm in diameter); frequently show a "fried egg" appearance

Multiplication by binary fission or by release of elementary bodies through fragmentation and distintegration of the filaments

Resistant to penicillin and its analogs

Growth and metabolism specifically inhibited by antibody

Culture, Growth, and Morphology

The organisms can be cultured on artificial but enriched medium in the laboratory without living cells as are required by viruses and rickettsiae. The smallest cell is 125 to 250 nm in size and has a tendency to form filaments, which may vary in length up to 150 μm. The smallest mycoplasma cell is approximately one-tenth the diameter of a staphylococcus. The organisms are sufficiently small in size that they are able to pass through the pores of filters (0.45 μm in diameter) that ordinarily retain bacteria. Thus for many years these organisms were considered viruses because they were filterable and could not be grown on the usual bacteriologic media.

Mycoplasmas do not stain well with Gram stain (gram-negative) but can be stained with Giemsa stain. Growth medium usually requires sterol plus some protein, the latter most often derived from serum. Some mycoplasmas do not require sterols; these are placed in the genus *Acholeplasma*. Mycoplasmas are facultative anaerobes and exhibit a gliding motility.

The smallest mycoplasma is referred to as an elementary body. It is quite small (about 0.1 to 0.2 μm in diameter) but can change in shape and size as it grows. The elementary body may develop into a fairly long filament. Multiplication may be by binary transverse fission of coccoid and filamentous cells or by condensation of protoplasm and segmentation within filaments, leading to the multiple release of elementary bodies, which may repeat the cycle. On solid media mycoplasmas form very small colonies (10 to 600 μm in diameter), and low magnification of the microscope is usually needed to visualize them. A colony is seen as a central, opaque, granulated area that penetrates into the agar. A surrounding flat peripheral zone grows on the surface of the agar and is lighter in density. This type of growth is referred to as a "fried egg" colony.

Occurrence and Classification

The first disease that was recognized as being caused by a mycoplasma was a contagious pneumonia of cattle that occurred in Europe in the 19th century. At that time the organisms responsible for causing pneumonia were called pleuropneumonia organisms, or PPO. In humans the causative agent of primary atypical pneumonia was designated Eaton's agent in 1944 and thought to be a virus when filtered secretions from naturally occurring cases produced pneumonia in rats and hamsters. Later, when the organism was successfully cultured on artificial medium, it was found to resemble PPO cultured from cattle. Therefore these organisms were given the name pleuropneumonialike organisms, or PPLO. Later characterization demonstrated that PPO and PPLO were similar and sufficiently different from other bacteria that they should be placed in a separate family, the *Mycoplasmataceae*. A definite role for these microorganisms in human respiratory disease was demonstrated by the fulfillment of Koch's postulates in human volunteers. The official name given to the human respiratory pathogen is *Mycoplasma pneumoniae*.

At present more than 60 species of mycoplasmas are recognized as pathogenic, producing diseases in a variety of mammalian, avian, insect, and plant hosts. A classification of human mycoplasmas is presented in Table 33.2. Ten species representing three genera may be found in the human respiratory or urogenital tracts. Members of the family *Mycoplasmataceae* require sterol for growth, have a genome size about 5.0×10^8 daltons (half the size of that of the smallest bacterium), and have an NADH oxidase localized in the cytoplasm. A second family, *Acholeplasmataceae*, does not require sterol for growth and has its natural habitat in sewage or soil. One species, *Acholeplasma laidlawii*, may be found in humans on the skin or in the oral cavity.

One group of mycoplasmas was formerly designated as "T strains" because they produced "tiny" atypical colonies that were smaller in size (10 to 50 μm) than the classical "large" colonies of mycoplasmas. This heterogeneous group of organisms, which possesses the enzyme urease, is now classified under the genus *Ureaplasma* in the family *Mycoplasmataceae*. A single species, *U. urealyticum*, has been designated, but it has eight serotypes.

The mycoplasmas may be saprophytic, parasitic, or pathogenic. They are ubiquitous organisms and have been isolated from many tissues and even from tumors. In a variety of animals, mycoplasmas have been recognized as pathogens of the respiratory tract, urogenital tract, and joints. Usually the diseases are chronic and often

Table 33.2. Classification of Human Mycoplasmas

Class:	*Mollicutes*	Procaryotic organisms bounded by a single triple-layered
Order:	*Mycoplasmatales*	membrane
Family I:	*Mycoplasmataceae* — requires sterol for growth	
Genus I:	*Mycoplasma* — utilizes glucose or arginine, does not hydrolyze urea	
	M. pneumoniae	
	M. hominis[a]	
	M. salivarium[b]	
	M. fermentans	
	M. orale[b]	
	M. buccale	
	M. faucium	
	M. primatum	
Genus II:	*Ureaplasma* — hydrolyzes urea	
	U. urealyticum	
Family II:	*Acholeplasmataceae* — does not require sterol for growth	
Genus I:	*Acholeplasma*	
	A. laidlawii	

Note: *Mycoplasma* spp. and *U. urealyticum* listed above may be found in the oral and/or urogenital tract. A second family, *Acholeplasmataceae*, has its natural habitat in sewage or soil, and consists of five species in the genus *Acholeplasma*; *A. laidlawii* is found on skin and in the oral cavity. A third family, *Spiroplasmataceae*, contains helical shaped organisms classified in one genus, *Spiroplasma*, and is important as an arthropod-borne plant pathogen.

[a]Common isolate from urogenital tract.
[b]Common isolate from respiratory tract.

of multifactorial origin, making it difficult to establish the etiologic importance of mycoplasmas. However, the proven role of mycoplasmas in chronic diseases of animals suggests that more careful systematic studies should be undertaken in humans.

The most common mycoplasmas isolated from the genital tracts of humans are *M. hominis* and *U. urealyticum*. *U. urealyticum* has been proved to be responsible for nongonococcal urethritis in men, causing at least 10 percent of cases; this organism continues to be implicated in infertility, spontaneous abortion, and stillbirth. *M. hominis* has been shown to be a cause of postpartum fever and a likely cause of pelvic inflammatory disease and pyelonephritis. *U. urealyticum* induces both cytonecrosis and ciliostasis in animals while *M. hominis* causes marked ciliary swelling. The absence or reduction of ciliary activity may interfere with conception and early embryonic development. Both *U. urealyticum* and *M. hominis* adsorb to spermatozoa and may reduce motility, induce morphologic alteration, or interfere with normal metabolism. Recently, all three species of mycoplasmas known to be pathogenic in humans (*M. pneumoniae, M. hominis,* and *U. urealyticum*) have been isolated directly from joints of patients with acute arthritis. New information about the pathophysiology of mycoplasmas suggests that these organisms should be reevaluated for their possible role in arthritis in humans.

In addition to the widespread occurrence of mycoplasmas as animal parasites and pathogens, there is recent evidence that related organisms — spiroplasmas — are arthropod-borne plant pathogens. Another area in which mycoplasmas are of great importance is the inadvertent infection of human and animal cell cultures used for viral diagnostic assays. Here the most frequent source of mycoplasmas is either the oral cavity of the technical worker or contaminated animal sera used in the growth medium.

DESCRIPTION OF THE PATHOGEN M. PNEUMONIAE

The etiological agent of mycoplasmal pneumonia was first thought to be a virus, designated Eaton's agent. Marmion and Goodburn in 1961 first suggested that the agent could be a mycoplasma by demonstrating extracellular minute coccobacilli in chick bronchial epithelium using the Giemsa staining technique. Conclusive proof that Eaton's agent was a new *Mycoplasma* species was developed by Chanock, Hayflick, and Barile in 1962 when they succeeded in growing the organism on artificial medium for the first time. Shortly thereafter, experimental disease was produced in human volunteers inoculated with the organism isolated in the laboratory, thus fulfilling Koch's postulates. Subsequently, the name *M. pneumoniae* was proposed for the organism, the nomenclature providing a parallel to that of the common cause of bacterial pneumonia, *Str. pneumoniae*.

M. pneumoniae possesses all the properties described for the class *Mollicutes* except that it is an aerobe and not a facultative anaerobe. On primary isolation *M. pneumoniae* grows as a granular colony, usually showing only the darker granular center. The "fried egg" appearance with the lighter peripheral growth occurs after some passages *in vitro*. The organism is hemolytic, a property shown to be due to peroxide formation during growth. A major antigenic determinant is a lipid hapten. *M. pneumoniae* is quite distinct from other mycoplasmas of human origin by serologic and DNA homology tests. Organisms growing in broth culture ferment a variety of carbohydrates. Observations of mycoplasmas growing on a glass surface by phase-contrast microscopy and time-lapse cinephotomicrography have indicated that individual cells are motile and that they divide by binary fission. Ultrastructural studies have revealed a differentiated organelle at one pole that may be responsible for attachment and/or motility. For attachment *M. pneumoniae* produces a surface-reactive protein, and binding is accomplished through sialic acid receptor sites on the surface of host tissue cells (respiratory ciliated epithelium). A fully virulent strain of *M. pneumoniae* adsorbs to cell surfaces by this attachment phenomenon. Avirulent organisms apparently are not able to adsorb to cell surfaces.

Epidemiology

Transmission of mycoplasmal pneumonia from infected individuals to susceptible contacts is thought to occur by the airborne route. Mycoplasmas can be isolated from the nose, throat, trachea, and sputum of patients, indicating diffuse involvement of the respiratory mucosa. This extensive parasitism, coupled with a persistent cough characteristic of the disease, implies that infected secretions are the vehicle of spread. Organisms are present in sputum in large numbers but tend to associate with desquamated cells or cell fragments. Thus relatively large droplets may be required for transmission. This concept is supported by evidence that epidemic settings generally involve the type of close personal contacts present in families, schools, and institutions. Restricted population groups demonstrating a high incidence of *M. pneumoniae* infection include young adults in university and military settings.

M. pneumoniae appears to represent one of the more common etiologic agents causing lower respiratory tract disease in humans. It is probable that epidemic waves of infection tend to occur at approximately 4 to 5 year intervals, so that the incidence varies markedly from year to year. In one study of the general population, 20 percent of all pneumonias observed were due to *M. pneumoniae* over a 5-year period of surveillance.

M. pneumoniae infections probably occur throughout the world and appear to occur throughout the year. However, there is a tendency for more cases to be seen during the colder months. *M. pneumoniae* is probably the most common cause of pneumonia in school-age children and young adults, although milder disease can occur in infants and small children. Clinical disease is uncommon below age 4 and after age 50. The disease occurs equally in both sexes. It has been demonstrated that asymptomatic subjects may have radiographically demonstrable infiltrates. Reinfections are not uncommon, even among those who have preexisting antibodies.

Pathogenesis

Pathogenesis of mycoplasmal pneumonia has been deduced in part from the natural disease, where limited information is available, and in part from experimental animal models. The motility of *M. pneumoniae* allows it to penetrate the mucociliary blanket covering the epithelium, and a specialized terminal organelle permits attachment to epithelial cell surfaces. It has been speculated that in the absence of opsonic antibody the organisms may evade phagocytosis by alveolar macrophages. The parasitized epithelial cells show a reduction in glucose utilization, amino acid uptake, and macromolecular synthesis. These biochemical alterations are followed by reduction and loss of ciliary activity, histopathologic changes, and finally, exfoliation of all or part of the infected cell. Although the mechanism of cell injury has not been defined, one suggestion is that it results from the action of peroxide produced by mycoplasmas.

One property of *M. pneumoniae* that may allow it to overcome natural defense mechanisms is the antigenic similarity between its glycerophospholipids and those of host tissues. Mycoplasmas also appear able to evade the host immune response by causing an immunosuppressive effect during infection. Evidence to support this comes from the occurrence of tuberculin anergy for weeks or months during and following pneumonia. *M. pneumoniae* may act directly on lymphocytes to cause nonspecific mitogenic activity for both B and T lymphocytes, interferon production, and depression of cell-mediated immune reactions to unrelated antigens.

Host cell injury may be caused by the release of peroxide, nutritional deprivation of cells, or elaboration of other toxic products by the organism. Toxic products may cause headache, malaise, and fever. Small T lymphocytes respond to antigenic products, and lymphokines are produced that augment recruitment of additional cells and modify the activity of macrophages and leukocytes. The accumulation of lymphocytes and plasma cells within the lamina propria constitutes a peribronchial infiltration, while accumulation of the same cells in the alveolar wall leads to interstitial pneumonia, both characteristic features of *M. pneumoniae* disease.

In the lung, plasma cells synthesize antimycoplasma immunoglobulins of the major classes. The earliest immunoglobulin response is IgM. Initially these antibodies have broad specificity; this explains agglutinins for *Streptococcus* MG and the erythrocyte I antigen. IgG, IgM, and IgA antibodies transude through the damaged mucosa. They may serve to supplement the limited amount of secretory IgA (11S) by providing the mechanism for complement-mediated opsonization and lysis of organisms.

One of the components of *M. pneumoniae* disease may be an involvement of immunopathologic phenomena. Patients with mycoplasmal pneumonia frequently develop a variety of heterogenic antibodies during disease, including cold agglutinins and antibodies to heart, lung, liver, and brain tissues and to Wassermann antigen (cardiolipin). The development of antibodies to various tissues is due to serologically crossreacting glycolipids present in membranes of *M. pneumoniae* and host tissue cells There is evidence also that there are circulating immune complexes in serum during active phases of the disease. The various complications and sequelae following pulmonary mycoplasma infection may be the result of the localization in tissues of immune complexes.

Another complicating feature of the immune response appears to be the possibility that prior exposure of the host to the organism may somehow sensitize the host for future infections. Thus if injection of vaccine has failed to produce serum antibodies, a challenge inoculation with the vaccine sometimes may lead to more severe disease than expected. On the other hand, some patients with immunodeficiency syndromes characterized by B cell dysfunction fail to develop any radiographic evidence of pulmonary infiltration; however, they are more severely ill than expected in regard to systemic symptomatology and persistence of cough. In summary, factors both from the *M. pneumoniae* organism and from the host appear to be involved in the pathogenesis of *M. pneumoniae* disease and its various complications.

Although most cases of mycoplasmal pneumonia follow a benign course, there are several reports of fatal disease. In these cases the microscopic picture of the lung included features of both interstitial pneumonitis and desquamative bronchitis and bronchiolitis. Infiltration of mononuclear cells was prominent in the peribronchial tissues, while the airways were filled with necrotic epithelial cells, mononuclear and polymorphonuclear cells, and fibrin.

Clinical Course

Pneumonia produced by *M. pneumoniae* is generally mild, self-limited, and infrequently accompanied by complications or known long term sequelae. Only 3 to 10 percent of infected persons develop clinically apparent pneumonia. However, *M. pneumoniae* probably accounts for up to 20 percent of all cases of pneumonia in the general population and for up to 50 percent in closed populations. The onset of symptoms is usually insidious, following a relatively long incubation averaging between 3 and 4 weeks.

The most common manifestation of *M. pneumoniae* infection is a cough that can vary from mild to a severe pertussislike syndrome. Low-grade fever is usually present. General symptoms include malaise and headache, often aggravated by the persistent coughing. The patient may complain of having a dry or scratchy throat. Many clinical studies report the occurrence of pneumonic infiltrates demonstrable by chest x-ray, which are accompanied by minimal or no physical findings. When pneumonia is present it is most often unilateral, involving one of the lower lobes. The duration of clinical *M. pneumoniae* disease is variable and is dependent upon the site of infection. In untreated patients with tracheobronchitis or pneumonia, the acute febrile phase lasts about a week, while cough, malaise, or lassitude may persist an average of 2 additional weeks. In appropriately treated patients it can be demonstrated that the duration of symptoms and signs is significantly shortened.

Severe mycoplasmal respiratory disease, resembling necrotizing bacterial pneumonia, occurs more widely than previously recognized. It can occur in otherwise healthy children and adults of all ages. A number of nonpulmonary complications have been found in association with *M. pneumoniae* infection. Central nervous system (CNS) involvement has included meningoencephalitis, aseptic meningitis, brainstem encephalitis, ascending paralysis (resembling Guillain-Barré syndrome) and transverse myelitis. Approximately 0.1 percent of all patients with *M. pneumoniae* infection and 7 percent of those requiring hospitalization have CNS complications.

The presence of circulating antibodies to *M. pneumoniae* in healthy young children suggests the occurrence of infection without significant symptomatology. By following a defined population of children, it has been observed that clinical expression of the disease becomes more marked as increasing age provides the opportunity for repeated exposure to the organism and thus for the development of immunity; this observation is in contrast to most acute respiratory tract infections, which cause less illness with recurrent exposure and increasing age. However, these findings do support the hypothesis that the immune response to *M. pneumoniae* may be partially responsible for the pathology produced.

Diagnosis

As the physician examines a patient for suspected pneumonia, some features of nonbacterial pneumonias should be recognized that would indicate the disease may not be a classical bacterial pneumonia as produced by streptococci, *Klebsiella pneumoniae*, or staphylococci. These features include marked headache in adults, definite occurrence of nasopharyngal findings, and presence of nonproductive or minimally productive cough. Also, there may be an absence of shaking chills, significant pleural pain, purulent or bloody sputum, and lack of a predominant organism on smears examined after a Gram stain. Also, there is a peripheral leukocytosis with neutrophilia. Other types of atypical pneumonia include Q fever, psittacosis, Legionnaires' disease, and those caused by the respiratory viruses. Consideration of the former two might be substantiated by a history of exposure. The latter two cases may be suggested by age and epidemiologic circumstance. Other causes of pulmonary infiltrates, such as tuberculosis, mycotic infection, pulmonary infarction, and malignancy, must also be considered.

Laboratory diagnosis of mycoplasmal pneumonia may be made by indirect or

Table 33.3. Laboratory Diagnosis of
Mycoplasma pneumoniae

Indirect tests (nonspecific):
  Cold hemagglutinins in serum

Definitive tests (specific):
  Growth and identification of microorganism
    Biochemical tests:
      Hemadsorption
      β-hemolysis
      Reduction of tetrazolium chloride
    Immunologic test:
      Reaction with fluorescent labeled anti-
      serum

  Detection of serum antibodies
    Complement fixation test
    Passive hemagglutination test
    Inhibition of growth or metabolism

presumptive tests and by definitive tests. The useful tests are summarized in Table 33.3.

Indirect tests are those that are not specific for the organism but give a presumptive diagnosis. Sera of patients may be tested for cold hemagglutinins. This test is generally available. Cold hemagglutinins are antibodies that agglutinate group O human red blood cells at low temperatures, about 2 to 5°C, but not at 37°C. It has been proposed that mycoplasmas produce a toxic product, such as hydrogen peroxide (H_2O_2), that alters or removes the I antigen of human red blood cells. These altered red blood cells would be recognized as foreign by the body, with an autoimmune response resulting. The test is "nonspecific" in that it measures antibodies to altered red blood cells but not antibodies to mycoplasma antigens. Although only a minority of cases of "cold-hemagglutinin-positive, nonbacterial pneumonias" are caused by *M. pneumoniae*, the majority of cases with titers equal to or greater than 128 are caused by *M. pneumoniae*. Tests for cold hemagglutinins are still useful, since some laboratories are not equipped to grow and identify mycoplasmas or to perform serologic tests with them.

Historically another presumptive test involves the recognition of agglutinins to *Streptococcus* MG. This test is not considered useful at present, since patients develop these antibodies less frequently than cold hemagglutinins. *Streptococcus* MG is a nonhemolytic microorganism that was frequently isolated from patients who had mycoplasmal pneumonia, and at one time it was thought that it could be the causative organism of the disease. Apparently *Streptococcus* MG shares glycolipids with *M. pneumoniae*, but only about 30 percent of patients with mycoplasmal pneumonia have demonstrable antibodies to *Streptococcus* MG. Serodiagnosis of primary atypical pneumonia was made by the detection of cold agglutinins and agglutinins to *Streptococcus* MG long before the causative agent of the disease was established.

Definitive diagnosis of mycoplasmal pneumonia is made by isolation and identification of the organism and/or demonstration of specific antibody. Since *M. pneumoniae* parasitizes the entire respiratory tract mucosa, suitable specimens for isolation attempts include nasopharyngeal or oral pharyngeal throat swabs, sputum, tracheal aspirates, or lung tissue samples. When appropriate, isolation should be attempted from extrapulmonary sites, including vesicles, neural tissues, and cerebrospinal fluid. Growth medium consists of beef heart infusion, horse serum, and yeast extract. Serum provides cholesterol, which is one of the necessary constituents for growth. Penicillin and thallium acetate are frequently added to inhibit growth of bacteria and fungi in specimens. While methylene blue may be added to inhibit mycoplasmas other than *M. pneumoniae*, this is no longer recommended, since some isolates of *M. pneumoniae* are inhibited by this procedure.

A biphasic or semisolid medium and a solid growth medium are used for inoculation. Aerobic conditions are satisfactory, but growth is improved in the presence of 5

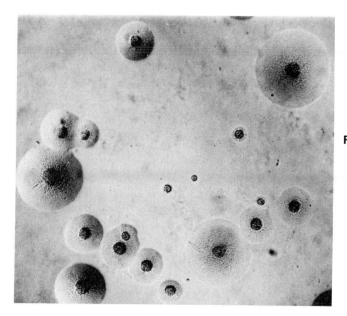

Fig. 33.1. Colonies of *Mycoplasma pneumoniae*. (× 1000) Typical "fried egg" colonies are produced on enriched agar medium. On primary isolation colonies of *M. pneumoniae* will show a dense granular central zone, but little or no peripheral zone. A few colonies on this plate lack a peripheral zone, but this characteristic is usually lost on subculture.

percent carbon dioxide. Colonies on agar plates are not evident before 5 days, and 7 to 10 days of incubation is optimal (Fig. 33.1). Four to six passages through semisolid medium are made before specimens are reported as negative. The cultivation of clinical specimens should become more common with improvement of the cultural procedures and a reduction in time required for colony growth. For example, a modified NYC (New York City) medium can support the growth and presumptive identification of large-colony mycoplasmas and *U. urealyticum* within 1–3 days. Fresh isolates of *M. pneumoniae* on agar medium frequently appear as circular, dome-shaped, granular structures, measuring 30 to 100 μm in diameter and lacking the peripheral zone common to many mycoplasmas. Dienes stain applied to the colonies aids in their recognition as mycoplasmas.

To identify isolates, several procedures may be followed. *M. pneumoniae* colonies can be identified by their biochemical properties. Among the human oral respiratory mycoplasmas, only *M. pneumoniae* demonstrates the properties of hemadsorption and

hemolysis. *M. pneumoniae* produces clear hemolysis of sheep or guinea pig red blood cells that have been spread in a thin agar sheet over the mycoplasma colonies. Other mycoplasmas do not give these reactions. The cultured organisms may also be detected or identified serologically according to species by inhibition of growth using specific antiserum prepared in laboratory animals. Colonies on agar medium can also be identified directly by immunofluorescence using a suitably labeled reagent.

The immune response to mycoplasmas is stimulated by two main classes of antigens: membrane glycolipids and lipid-free proteins. Gylcolipid antigens take part in most of the common serologic reactions; they serve as receptors for antibody in complement-mediated lysis and in growth inhibition. Protein antigens are reactive in eliciting cell-mediated immunity, which may be demonstrated *in vivo* by skin tests and *in vitro* by macrophage migration inhibition. A variety of serologic procedures have been described for demonstrating a rise in specific antibodies to *M. pneumoniae* between acute and convalescent phases. Complement fixation (CF) is the most frequently available procedure, and reports indicate that a rise in titer may be detected in as many as 80 percent of the cases, although a rate as low as 50 percent also has been reported. Titers of 80 or higher are accepted as presumptive evidence for infection. The CF test is quite specific if glycolipid antigen is used as a test antigen.

A very sensitive method for detection of serum antibody has been the use of passive hemagglutination tests, in which mycoplasmas are attached to tanned erythrocytes and then agglutinated in the presence of antibody. Growth inhibition and mycoplasmacidal tests are more sensitive assays for antibodies, but they require experience with cultivation techniques that are generally not available. Antibody and complement kill *M. pneumoniae* by lysis, and growth of mycoplasmas is not detected. Antiserum may also be used quantitatively to inhibit the metabolism of *M. pneumoniae*, specifically the reduction of triphenyltetrazolium.

There are four additional serologic tests that are quite sensitive for the detection of serum antibodies but are more elaborate and time-consuming to perform. These tests include indirect immunofluorescence, radioimmune precipitation, platelet aggregation, and enzyme linked immunosorbent assay (ELISA).

In general, the laboratory tests discussed above do not offer the physician immediate help when dealing with acutely ill patients. Recovery and identification of mycoplasmas require 1 to 2 weeks although improved media may reduce this time; serodiagnosis requires a comparison of acute- and convalescent-phase samples. Rapid diagnostic methods are not practically available at the present time. *M. pneumoniae* can be demonstrated in sputum samples by immunofluorescence methods, but this method has not been widely tested.

Treatment

Erythromycin is at present the antibiotic of choice in the treatment of *M. pneumoniae* pneumonia. Significantly it is also effective in Legionnaires' disease which may have a similar clinical course. However, tetracycline and its derivatives are also effective against mycoplasmal pneumonia and have the additional advantage of proven effectiveness against psittacosis and Q fever. Tetracycline is also effective against both *U. urealyticum* and *M. hominis*, although as many as 10 percent of ureaplasma isolates are resistant. At present the only clear indication for antibiotic treatment of urogenital problems is for patients with nongonococcal urethritis and their sexual contacts.

Additional reasons for recommending erythromycin come from the facts that standard doses give higher blood levels, there is good diffusion into respiratory secretions, and there is a greater sensitivity of the organism by *in vitro* tests. While treatment has been shown to reduce the period of time that a given patient is symptomatic, it does not seem to reduce the time of carriage of the organism in the respiratory tract. *M. pneumoniae* is resistant to penicillin, since it lacks a cell wall.

Prevention

At present there is no effective method for the prevention of *M. pneumoniae* infection and disease. Vaccine trials have included both inactivated and live attenuated agents. In large field trials in the military with inactivated vaccine preparations, only about 50 percent protection was obtained. Live attenuated vaccines have been produced using temperature-sensitive mutants. Although animal studies have indicated that intranasal inoculation of the live vaccine might be successful, evaluations in humans have not been performed. Stimulation of systemic antibodies may prevent clinical manifestations of pneumonia, but additional local stimulation with live or killed organisms may be necessary to evoke resistance to colonization. Currently, there is less interest in live vaccines because of indications that the disease is mediated by immune responses, that immunity is short-lived, and that potentially serious extrapulmonary disease may result from *M. pneumoniae* infections. Nevertheless, it may be feasible to protect against mycoplasma infection with a vaccine prepared from the components of the organism responsible for epithelial cell attachment.

M. pneumoniae is inactivated by treatment with lipid solvents, formalin, and a variety of antiseptics.

CELL WALL-DEFECTIVE MICROBIAL VARIANTS

In addition to mycoplasmas, which normally lack a cell wall, other bacteria can exist with damaged or deficient cell walls. *Wall-defective microbial variant* is a general term denoting microorganisms that have undergone changes in morphology, physiology, and/or cultural characteristics as a result of damage to or deficiency of their cell walls. These changes are more profound than those normally associated with the species in its vegetative bacterial phase. However, the term variant does not imply a change in genetic constitution.

Most bacteria with damaged cell walls undergo marked morphologic and physiologic changes and can exist in at least four phases — the protoplast phase, spheroplast phase, transitional phase, and L phase, each differing from the others and from the classical bacterial phase (Ch. 2). Although several characteristics are shared between mycoplasmas and wall-defective

variants, the pathogenicity of the latter should be considered separately.

L-Phase Variants

L-phase variants are wall-defective microbial variants that can replicate as nonrigid cells and that on solid media produce colonies composed of a core growing into the agar and superficial growth around the core, giving them a "fried egg" appearance resembling colonies of mycoplasmas. The individual organisms vary in size from "large bodies," larger than the bacterial form, to "small bodies," smaller than some viruses. They are gram-negative, indifferent to penicillin, and usually spherical or pleomorphic. The term L form derives from the Lister Institute, where they were first studied extensively.

The term L form refers solely to the distinct morphology of colonies composed of L-phase variants. Some L-phase variants revert to the bacterial phase upon removal of the substance that induced the L phase (unstable L-phase variants); some revert only under special conditions (relatively stable L-phase variants); and some do not revert under any conditions (stable L-phase variants). For some years it was suspected that mycoplasmas might represent stable L-phase variants that were incapable of reverting to a bacterial form. However, when comparisons were made between the DNA of mycoplasma and DNA from many L forms of bacteria or DNA from some bacteria originally thought to be the cause of mycoplasmal pneumonia (e.g., *Streptococcus* MG), no genetic relatedness could be demonstrated. Thus *Mollicutes* are phylogenetically and taxonomically unrelated to other bacteria or their L forms.

Virtually all species of bacteria can form L-phase variants, spheroplasts, or protoplasts under appropriate circumstances. It has been stated that patients with continued fever or illness during adequate therapy for documented bacterial infections should be studied intensively for these forms. At the present time it would seem prudent to culture specimens in hypertonic medium as well as in regular medium when cultures unexpectedly remain positive after antibiotic therapy. The pathogenic potential of L-phase variants and their prevalence during antibiotic therapy deserve further study, particularly in patients with defective immunologic or phagocytic function. L-phase variants may be capable of pathogenicity through the production of toxins (e.g., *Clostridium tetani* or *Vibrio* spp.). Also, L-phase variants are known to be present in certain infections, particularly those of the urinary tract, and perhaps in the blood during salmonella infections and in brucellosis. There is some suggestion that L forms may play a role in some cases of pyelonephritis or endocarditis. However, the pathogenicity of L forms is not clearly established.

In general, tetracyclines, erythromycin, lincomycin, and chloramphenicol are more effective against L-phase variants than are aminoglycosides, cephalosporins, or penicillins. During treatment, bacteria may persist in the patient as L forms resistant to the antibiotics being used and then revert to the parent bacterial form on routine cultures, thus giving misleading results in routine testing for sensitivity to antibiotics. Also, when antibiotic therapy is discontinued, the L form in the body may revert to the pathogenic parent form.

Transitional-Phase Variants

Most clinical isolates of wall-defective variants are probably transitional-phase variants. These variants are characterized by instability of cellular morphology associated with an inherent tendency to revert to the vegetative bacterial phase. Individual organisms in a culture vary markedly in

size, shape, characteristics in the Gram stain, content of cell wall constituents, osmotic fragility, and penicillin sensitivity. Colonial morphology varies from passage to passage. Transitional-phase variants differ from L-phase variants primarily by the inability of the former to propagate serially in a distinctive colonial form on agar. However, they may undergo conversion to L-phase variants.

Following infection, bacteria in the body may become transitional-phase variants after reaction with one or more of the following: antibiotics, antibody and complement, phagocytes, or lysosomal enzymes. Such altered bacteria may be difficult to recognize and culture and therefore difficult to identify as the causative agent of disease. To the physician these facts should serve to stress the importance of taking clinical specimens prior to the administration of antibiotics, if at all possible.

REFERENCES

Barile, M.F. and Razin, S.: The Mycoplasmas. I. Cell Biology. Academic Press, New York, 1979.
Cassell, G.H. and Cole, B.C.: Mycoplasmas as agents of human disease. N. Engl. J. Med. *304*: 80, 1981.
Fernald, G.W. and Clyde, W.A.: Pulmonary immune mechanisms in *Mycoplasma pneumoniae* disease. In Kirkpatrick, C.H. and Reynolds, H.Y., Eds.: Immunologic and Infectious Reactions in the Lung. Marcel Dekker, New York, 1976.
Kite, J.H.: Immunodiagnosis of mycoplasma pneumonia. In Milgrom, F., Abeyounis, C.J., and Kano, K., Eds.: Principles of Immunological Diagnosis in Medicine. Lea and Febiger, Philadelphia, 1981.
Stanbridge, E.J.: A reevaluation of the role of mycoplasmas in human disease. Ann Rev. Microbiol, *30*: 169, 1976.
Tully, J.G. and Whitcomb, R.F.: The Mycoplasmas. II. Human and Animal Mycoplasmas. Academic Press, New York, 1979.

34

Mycobacterium

Ernst H. Beutner and
Richard L. Miner

The genus *Mycobacterium* includes *M. tuberculosis*, the most important of the causative agents of tuberculosis, some less common causative agents of human tuberculosis, *M. leprae*, the causative agent of leprosy, some less common human pathogens, and a number of animal pathogens and saprophytes. All mycobacteria are *acid-fast bacilli* (*AFB*). That is, extraction of stained bacteria with acid or acid alcohol under conditions that remove the stains from other bacteria fails to destain AFB. Also, a fluorochrome stain can serve to identify AFB. *M. tuberculosis* is commonly referred to as "tubercle bacilli." Similarly, *M. leprae* is frequently called the leprosy or Hansen bacillus (after its discoverer).

MYCOBACTERIUM TUBERCULOSIS

The discovery of tubercle bacilli by Robert Koch and his demonstration of their role as causative agents of human tuberculosis in 1882 fulfilled Jacob Henle's criteria (1840) for the documentation of the etiologic significance of microorganisms.

Two varieties of tubercle bacilli were differentiated by Theobold Smith in 1898, the human and the bovine varieties (*M. tuberculosis* and *M. bovis*). These differ in their spectra of animal infectivity — that is, the bovine variety infects cattle, goats, cats, pigs, horses, and rabbits, while the human variety fails to do so. Both varieties of tubercle bacilli are pathogenic for primates, guinea pigs, and certain other rodents as well as some species of birds.

Basic Characteristics

Staining Properties. The human tubercle bacilli are slender rods, about 0.5 μm in width and ranging from 1 to 4 μm in length. In smears of fresh cultures they appear as cords of acid-fast rods. In smears of infected material from patients they may appear singly or as pairs of solidly stained or granular AFB (Fig. 34.1A).

The crystal violet used in the Gram stains usually fails to stain acid-fast tubercle bacilli. Young bacilli that are not yet acid fast stain gram-negative, while full-grown cultures may stain weakly gram-positive. Neither of

445

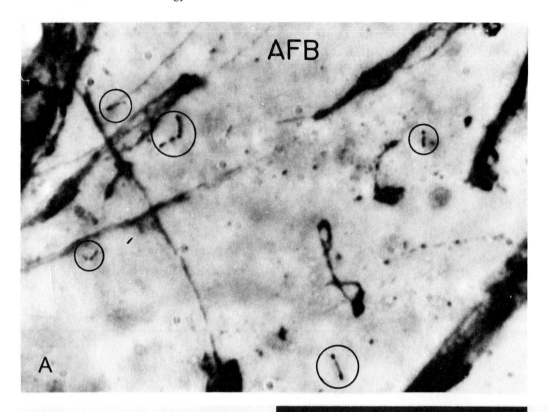

AFB

A

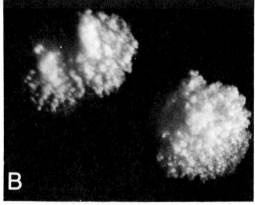

B

Fig. 34.1. (A) Acid-fast (Ziehl-Neelsen) stain of a smear of sputum from a case of active tuberculosis. Encircled acid fast bacilli (AFB) are red, and the remaining material is blue. Note beaded or polar staining of AFB ($\times$ 1000). (B) Colonies of *M. tuberculosis* isolated from sputum on a plate of Middlebrook's 7H 10 agar as seen by incident light. Note rough texture ($\times$ 10). (Photograph obtained through courtesy of Dr. W.R. Bartholomew, Erie County Laboratory, Buffalo, New York.)

these findings is of value in studies of AFB.

In order to stain mycobacteria, a strong dye such as carbol fuchsin (3 percent basic fuchsin in 5 percent phenol with 90 percent ethanol) together with heat is used, as in the Ziehl-Neelsen staining procedure (and with a nonionic detergent in the Kinyoun modifications of it). Destaining with acid alcohol (3 percent HCl in 95 percent etha-

nol) or with 15 to 20 percent HCl serves to remove the dye from all bacteria that are not acid fast. A counterstain with methylene blue reveals the presence of other microorganisms.

Some strains of *Nocardia asteroides*, *Nocardia brasiliensis*, and *Nocardia caviae* are weakly acid fast (an acid-alcohol rinse for 5 to 10 seconds fails to destain them), but the standard Ziehl-Neelsen method used to stain mycobacteria gives negative reactions for AFB with these *Nocardia* species.

Cultivation. The cultural isolation and identification of tubercle bacilli affords the only completely reliable basis for diagnosing tuberculosis.

M. tuberculosis is a strict aerobe with simple nutritional requirements. The tubercle bacilli can grow on media that contain only ammonium salts as a nitrogen source, glycerol as a carbon source, inorganic salts, and water. Aspartate enhances growth. Such simple, defined media, however, can support the growth of tubercle bacilli only if large inocula are used.

Primary isolation of tubercle bacilli (e.g., from sputum specimens) requires the use of media enriched with animal proteins. The classic Loewenstein-Jensen medium contains potato extract, coagulated egg, aspartate, glycerol, and malachite green. This medium is now used along with more defined media such as Middlebrook's 7H 10 Tween albumin agar, which contains albumin in a broth or agar base of Tween 80, aspartate, ammonium salts, and inorganic salts. During the logarithmic growth phase (Ch. 2) the generation time of tubercle bacilli is approximately 14 hours, as contrasted to a generation time of 20 minutes for pyogenic bacteria such as staphylococci. Thus growth of tubercle bacilli even on enriched media requires at least 10 days and frequently 2 months or more. Growth first appears as hard, rough, buff colored, pinpoint colonies on solid media. If growth of AFB appears more rapidly or if colonies are soft, they are the product of other species of mycobacteria. The colonies of tubercle bacilli grow to a diameter of several mm over a period of a month (Fig. 34.1B). They are so hard that the bacteriologic loops used to remove them must be made of a heavier wire than is used for routine bacteriologic studies. In broth cultures *M. tuberculosis* forms a granular deposit.

Biochemical and Physical Properties. Lipids make up 20 to 40 percent of the dry weight of *M. tuberculosis*. Most is in the cell walls; about 60 percent of their dry weight is lipid. Other species of *Mycobacterium* also have a relatively high lipid content, though not as high as that of the tubercle bacilli. The lipids of mycobacteria account for at least three of their distinctive characteristics — acid-fast staining, resistance to the bactericidal action of chemical agents, and adjuvant action (see below). Tubercle bacilli are resistant to acids such as HCl and oxalic acid, alkalies such as NaOH and Na_3PO_4, oxidizing agents such as chlorine, and surfactants such as cationic detergents. The resistance of AFB to alkali is utilized in culturing tubercle bacilli from specimens such as sputum that are heavily contaminated with other, more rapidly growing bacteria. That is, treatment of the sputum with NaOH kills most of the contaminating bacteria, but the viability of the tubercle bacilli is affected to a much smaller extent. Though tubercle bacilli and other AFB are resistant to the bactericidal action of chemical agents, they are as susceptible as most other bacteria to the action of physical agents such as heat and ultraviolet irradiation. For example, pasteurization of milk kills tubercle bacilli. This assumes considerable importance because bovine tuberculosis transmitted by milk was in part responsible for a very high infant mortality rate from tuberculosis in the 19th and early 20th centuries.

The adjuvant effect of tubercle bacilli and other mycobacteria results from a lipid, wax D. Freund's adjuvant, which is a suspension of dried tubercle bacilli in mineral oil and a detergent, markedly enhances immune responses. Thus intradermal immunization of animals with emulsions of aqueous solutions or suspensions of antigens in this adjuvant are commonly used to obtain immune sera or elevated cell-mediated immunity (CMI).

Mycolic acid makes up about 11 percent

of the total lipid of tubercle bacilli. This fatty acid together with tuberculoprotein can serve as sensitizing antigen for a normal animal in that a CMI would be elicited. However, neither the protein alone nor the mycolic acid itself elicit CMI, even though the tuberculoproteins serve as skin test reagents.

Mycolic acid together with the sugar trehalose comprises cord factor. This substance is responsible for the formation of cords or strands of *M. tuberculosis* and certain other species of *Mycobacterium* when cultured in broth. Most nonpathogenic species of the genus grow in the form of clumps or irregular clusters, but distinction of cord formation is not of diagnostic value in recognizing pathogenic strains.

M. tuberculosis cultures form niacin, which affords a basis for an important differential test used in laboratory diagnosis. In addition to the tubercle bacillus, only *M. simiae*, *M. marinum*, and some strains of *M. bovis* such as BCG (see below) form niacin. With the advent of the niacin test it is no longer necessary to infect guinea pigs with AFB to prove that these bacilli are *M. tuberculosis*.

True tubercle bacilli, which are resistant to the chemotherapeutic agent isoniazid, are negative for the enzyme catalase. Thus catalase tests assume practical importance. These and other biochemical tests also serve as aids in the differentiation of groups and species of mycobacteria.

Other Mycobacterial Agents of Tuberculosis. Most tuberculosis in humans is caused by the human tubercle bacilli. However, since a few cases are due to other species of mycobacteria, species differentiation assumes some practical importance. In principle, the differentiation of species of *Mycobacterium* rests variously on their cultural characteristics, spectrum of animal pathogenicity, biochemical reactions, or serologic characteristics.

Infections with the bovine variety of tubercle bacilli, which can be distinguished by their pathogenicity for rabbits, are almost nonexistent in the United States now. The

Table 34.1.   Runyon Scheme for Classification of *Mycobacterium* spp.

Group	Common Name	Examples of Bioreactions			
		Niacin[a]	INH susceptibility[b]	Catalase[c]	Pathogenicity[d]
I	Photochromogens	$-^a$	$\pm^b$	$\pm$	$++ - +++$
II	Scotochromogens	$-$	$-$	$+$	$\pm - +++^e$
III	Battey-avian-swine	$-$	$-$	$+$	$\pm - ++$
IV	Rapid growers	$-^a$	$-$	$+$	$\pm - +$
	M. tuberculosis, *M. bovis*	$+$	$+$	$-$	$+++$

[a]One photochromogen, *M. simiae*, produces niacin, and one rapid grower, *M. chelonei*, gives variable reactions.
[b]Susceptibility to 1 μg of isonicotinic acid hydrazide (INH) per ml. Some photochromogens are resistant.
[c]Several catalase tests are used in studies of AFB. See references (Youmans) for details.
[d]Pathogenicity: $+++$, strong pathogenicity; $++$, moderate pathogenicity; $+$, very weak pathogenicity; $\pm$, practically nonpathogenic.
[e]The range of pathogenicity in Runyon groups II and III is broad because the different species in these groups vary widely in terms of their pathogenic potential. It is for this reason that accepted laboratory practice in the United States calls for species identification. The Runyon scheme for classification serves as a first stem to this end.

few cases of pulmonary tuberculosis in the United States caused by other species of *Mycobacterium* fall into two groups from a clinical standpoint. One group includes patients with suppressed CMI responses (e.g., patients with Hodgkin's disease or under treatment with high doses of corticosteroids). Such infections are commonly due to species of *Mycobacterium* that have low virulence (i.e., that rarely cause tuberculosis in subjects with normal T cell responses) (Table 34.1). The second group is, for the most part, caused by *M. kansasii* and the *M. avium* complex. Neither infects guinea pigs.

Isolates of AFB that are not true tubercle bacilli can be classified initially into four groups in clinical laboratory studies according to the scheme of Runyon (see Table 34.1). Group I (e.g., *M. kansasii*) forms soft, smooth colonies (Fig. 34.2) that characteristically give reactions of photochromogen. That is, on media maintained in the dark, buff colored colonies form; on expo-

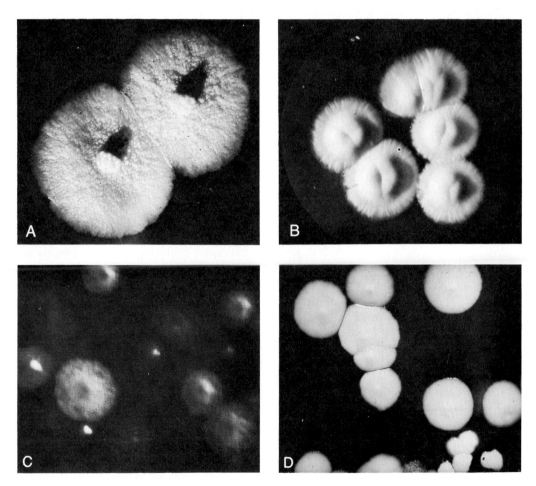

Fig. 34.2 Mycobacteria other than *M. tuberculosis*. Isolates in Middlebrook's 7H 10 agar. (A) *M. kansasii*, Runyon group I; (B), *M. serofalaceum*, Runyon group II; (C) *M. intercellulare*, Runyon group III; (D) *M. fortuitum*, Runyon group IV (× 10). Note granular texture of *M. kansasii* and *M. intercellulare* and smooth texture of *M. serofalaceum* and *M. fortuitum*.

sure to light they turn bright yellow, orange, or red (depending on the strain). This stands in contrast to the group II scotochromogens (Fig. 34.2), which form colored colonies in both light and in the dark. The pulmonary tuberculosis caused by *M. kansasii* is comparable to the disease produced by human tubercle bacilli, while the virulence of scotochromogens is usually low.

M. avium complex, which belong to Runyon group III, forms soft, buff colored colonies (Fig. 34.2). This complex includes not only *M. avium*, which is a pathogen for birds and swine, but also *M. intercellulare*, which causes human tuberculosis. Since these AFB were first demonstrated in human infections in the Battey state sanatorium in Rome, Georgia, they are sometimes referred to as the Battey-avian-swine complex of mycobacteria. Serotyping serves to distinguish different members of this group. Cases of human tuberculosis caused by these organisms occur in the Southeastern United States. Group IV, the rapid growers, includes the *M. fortuitum* complex, which may cause human infections, particularly in immunosuppressed patients. *M. fortuitum* may form rough or smooth colonies (Fig. 34.2).

Primary differentiation into the four Runyon groups rests on cultural characteristics. Selected biochemical tests aid in further identification of species of *Mycobacterium* in each of the groups. Most tuberculosis laboratories use the finding that serves to identify the Runyon group of AFB as a basis for further laboratory studies that aid in identifying their species, since the Runyon scheme affords only a rough first approximation of classifications.

Pathogenic Mechanisms of Tuberculosis

M. tuberculosis, the primary causative agent of tuberculosis, produces pulmonary infections in over 90 percent of human infections at the present time. Primary infection may also occur in the intestinal tract, when the organism is transmitted by infected milk, or in skin (e.g., the pathologist's wart, an infection acquired during the performance of an autopsy). The infection may remain localized or may become disseminated.

Almost all of the pathologic changes in chronic tuberculosis are due to CMI responses to the tubercle bacilli. These CMI responses are mediated by macrophages and by T cells that are specifically sensitized to the tubercle bacilli.

Role of M. tuberculosis. The proof of the etiologic significance of *M. tuberculosis* rests on the following observations: (1) Tubercle bacilli can be isolated from tubercular lesions, and AFB can be detected in smears of such lesions. (2) The isolated tubercle bacilli produce tuberculosis in guinea pigs (or other animals). (3) The tubercle bacilli can be reisolated from and ABF can be detected in tuberculous lesions of guinea pigs. (4) The reisolated tubercle bacilli can infect other guinea pigs. These steps were fulfilled in tests by Robert Koch about 100 years ago. They meet the Henle-Koch postulates for documenting the etiologic significance of microorganisms.

Role of Cell-Mediated Immunity. Robert Koch observed that primary infection of guinea pigs with tubercle bacilli leads to disseminated tuberculosis from which most or all die over a period of months. However, reinfection of guinea pigs before their death with tubercle bacilli elicits a different response pattern than the primary infection. This "Koch phenomenon" merits detailed consideration.

Primary infection provokes the following events: Within the first week little change can be observed grossly. A small papule may be detected at the site of inoculation, but it heals. In the first 1 to 3 weeks the tubercle bacilli multiply rapidly. At the end of this time a nodule develops at the site of inoculation owing to the development of

CMI responses to the tubercle bacilli. This nodule develops into an ulcer. This also fails to heal before the infected animal succumbs to the tubercle bacilli. Autopsies performed 1 to 3 months after infection reveal a large area of necrosis at the site of infection and multiple nodules or tubercles on the omentum, on the spleen and liver, and on other internal organs. The sequence of changes observed following reinfection of guinea pigs harboring tuberculosis differs markedly: An indurated nodule usually develops in 1 to 3 days at the site of reinoculation owing to CMI to the tubercle bacilli. The multiplication of the tubercle bacilli is limited and generally restricted to the site of reinoculation. The nodule at the site of reinoculation ulcerates but goes on to heal even though the ulcer at the site of primary inoculation fails to do so. This altered reactivity to reinfection is known as the Koch phenomenon.

Robert Koch demonstrated that both heat-killed tubercle bacilli and crude extracts of them elicit marked responses in previously infected guinea pigs comparable to those seen after reinfection with viable cultures of the bacteria. We now recognize that these responses are due to CMI or delayed hypersensitivity reactions to tubercle bacilli. Strongly positive reactions produced by large doses of antigens given to a highly sensitized host can be fatal. Minute doses given intradermally serve as skin-test reagents to detect the CMI of the host to tuberculoproteins.

Nature of Skin Tests. Skin tests for tuberculosis reveal CMI to tuberculoproteins. Negative reactions denote absence of detectable CMI. A positive reaction presents as an area of induration due to necrosis; it reaches a maximum 1 or 2 days after intradermal injection of tuberculoprotein.

Mantoux introduced the first quantitative skin test. This is performed with *old tuberculin (OT)*, a crude extract prepared by growing tubercle bacilli in glycerin broth and boiling it to one-tenth of the original volume. Each batch of OT is adjusted to a standard concentration by comparing its reactivity in skin tests with an international reference standard. In the original Mantoux tests 0.1 ml of a 1:10,000 dilution of a standard OT preparation is injected intradermally. If a subject responds with an area of induration of 10 mm or more in 1 or 2 days, the reaction is positive. If the reaction is negative, 0.1 ml of a 1:1000 dilution is tested; if it gives a negative reaction, a 1:100 dilution is used. If this last gives a negative reaction or an area of induration less than 10 mm in diameter, the subject is deemed to be tuberculin negative. Multiple dilutions of OT are used to avoid excessively strong tuberculin reactions.

At the present time OT is largely replaced by purified protein derivative (PPD) prepared from crude extract. Several types of PPD are used in different countries of the world, each standardized more or less in the same way as the original OT. These PPD contain diverse tuberculoproteins but no glycerin. Skin tests are performed essentially as the Mantoux test using graded amounts of PPD. Today tuberculin tests with standard PPD are generally performed with the intermediate and second strength preparations; however, first strength can also be used (e.g., is permitted in the United States). Also, multiple-puncture tests, such as the Sterneedle (Heaf) and tine tests are available commercially. Interestingly, some subjects who give positive skin-test reactions to OT give negative reactions to PPD.

A positive tuberculin skin test denotes past or present infection with tuberculosis. A recent conversion from a negative to a positive skin test or a positive test in an infant is indicative of an active disease. Subjects can have skin tests, that convert from positive to negative over a period of time. While standard Mantoux or PPD skin-test responses of less than 10 mm induration or of mere erythema with no induration are deemed to be negative or doubtful tuberculin hypersensitivity reactions, such subthreshold skin-test responses do not preclude past or present infection. Interestingly, while over 90 percent of patients with active tuberculosis give positive skin tests, they are not infrequently rather weak and sometimes are negative (5 to 10 percent of the cases).

Skin-test surveys carried out with standard PPD and preparations of PPD made from the group III or Battey-avian-swine-type mycobacteria reveal distinct patterns of distribution of tuberculin hypersensitivity in the United States. Positive reactions to the group III reagent occur predominantly in the Southeastern states.

Since tuberculin skin tests with conventional PPD become positive in almost all subjects infected with *M. tuberculosis*, these tests afford a measure of the rate of infectivity. The fatality rate among those infected varies with age, sex, and race. In effect, while most tuberculin-positive subjects do not go on to develop clinically active disease, the probability of their developing tuberculosis is considerably higher than that of tuberculin-negative subjects because the latent infections may become activated.

Mechanism of Defense. Infections with tubercle bacilli elicit both humoral and cellular immune responses. The humoral immune responses play no significant role in defence against the disease, while CMI to tubercle bacilli affords significant protection.

In vitro experiments on tuberculin sensitivity demonstrated that the migration inhibition factor (MIF) (Ch. 13) can be specifically induced by I-RNA (Ch. 8). For example, a mixture of I-RNA specific for PPD plus normal lymphocytes plus normal macrophages can, under appropriate conditions, give positive MIF reactions when challenged with PPD but not with coccidioidin. I-RNA specific for coccidioidin in a similar test system gave rise to MIF with the coccidioidin specificity.

T lymphocytes sensitized to tuberculo-protein release lymphokines (Ch. 13) on encounter with tubercle bacilli. This CMI reaction is particularly severe in tuberculosis, in part because the tubercle bacilli can survive and multiply in the macrophages that ingest them. However, the lymphokines produced in response to the hypersensitivity reaction and the activation of macrophages by them curtail the rate of multiplication of the tubercle bacilli. Also, while these bacteria can survive in the infected tissue for months or years, the massive tissue necrosis induced by the tuberculin hypersensitivity reaction produces a form of localized "self-amputation" that enables the host to survive at the expense of the necrotic destruction of the tissue around foci of infection. These severe hypersensitivity reactions to the tubercle bacilli account for virtually the entire histopathology of chronic tuberculosis.

The tubercle bacilli continue to multiply in patients who produce only weak or not detectable tuberculin delayed hypersensitivity reactions as in the so-called exudative form of tuberculosis. Patients with this exudative form of the disease who do not convert to a more strongly positive tuberculin hypersensitivity reaction go on to die from the disease if it remains untreated with chemotherapeutic and/or antibiotic agents. In the terminal stages of disease the existing tuberculin hypersensitivity detected by skin tests may convert to negative, a condition referred to as anergy.

Basic Clinical Manifestations of Tuberculosis

The tubercle bacillus can invade any organ or tissue in humans. As a result the clinical presentation can be extremely diverse. However, in the majority of cases the lungs are primarily involved, and the picture is that of pulmonary disease with systemic manifestations. The combination of cough and sputum production with the systemic symptoms of weight loss, easy fatigue, weakness, and fever is a common syndrome in pulmonary tuberculosis. Bloody or bloodstained sputum may occur in early or advanced cases or may be absent. Findings on physical examination are often non-specific. Rales may be present in fresh, exudative phases of the infection. In long-standing cases with extensive fibrosis, contraction, and distortion of pulmonary tissues there may be a wide variety of signs: apical dullness, bronchial breath sounds, coarse rales, deviation of the trachea, and decreased mobility of one side of the chest. Two major pathologic types of reaction to pulmonary tuberculosis include the exudative reaction, or tuberculosis pneumonia, and the productive reaction, which consists of tuberculous granulation tissue or tubercles.

Most commonly, a positive skin test affords the first sign of infection; this is a sign of primary tuberculosis. This is usually a self-limiting infection. With the extensive use of x-rays of the chest in routine examinations, early lung involvement may be discovered before any clinical symptoms become prominent. Primary tuberculosis may become reactivated, since the bacilli can survive for years.

Extrapulmonary tuberculous infection gives rise to symptoms originating from the tissue or organ involved, usually accompanied by some of the systemic symptoms mentioned above. Miliary tuberculosis is manifested by infections of many tissues.

Exudative Tuberculosis. This is a pneumonic process that usually occurs without permanent damage to, or destruction of, lung tissue.

Pathologically, exudative tuberculosis is characterized initially by a polymorphonuclear reaction, followed by filling of the alveoli and small bronchi with an exudate of large mononuclear cells. Alveolar walls thicken, and the lymphatics fill with exudate. The cells in the exudate then show degenerative changes.

These exudative changes may show some variation, depending on the numbers of bacilli involved, the host resistance, and the degree and rapidity of the development of hypersensitivity. Frequently this is the earliest reaction to infection. With the institution of drug therapy these changes may clear completely within a few weeks or months. Without treatment they would progress to the productive type of lesion.

Productive Tuberculosis. This is a granulomatous response, consisting of mononuclear cells that phagocytize tubercle bacilli, enlarge in size, and may divide or coalesce into multinucleated Langhans giant cells. At the same time lymphocytes, fibroblasts, new capillaries, and collagenous tissue surround the area, and caseation begins in the center. This, then, is a tubercle, the lesion for which the disease is named.

The caseation occurring in these lesions is a type of necrosis and is the process responsible for the destruction and permanent damage to the tissues that results from tuberculous infection. Caseation gives a cheesy, creamy appearance. The substance may solidify and undergo resorption, fibrosis, or calcification, or it may (especially in large areas of caseation) soften and empty into a bronchus, leaving a cavity and disseminate the infection into other areas of the lung. Spread to other parts of the body by lymphatic and hematogenous dissemination may also occur during this process.

Primary Tuberculosis. Up to about 50 years ago most of the United States population was subject to infection with tubercle bacilli; the same holds true for many other countries today. In nearly all cases the initial exposure is through inhalation; introduction of a significant number of bacilli causes foci of pulmonary infection. This infection usually produces few or no symptoms and, except in infants and young children, no significant radiologic change. However, the infection is associated with a silent bacillemia, which may seed metastic foci in various parts of the body. Over a period of several weeks delayed hypersensitivity and cell-mediated immunity develop in most cases. At the end of this time the patient usually displays a positive reaction to the tuberculin skin test, which may be the only evidence that the events have occurred.

In the occasional case the host defenses prove to be inadequate and chronic tuberculosis immediately follows the primary infection. This is termed progressive primary tuberculosis, but in the vast majority of cases the various lesions heal. However, viable but dormant bacilli are frequently able to survive within the healed, scarred lesions in areas of favorable oxygen tension, such as the lung apices, kidney, spine, long bones, and brain. These dormant foci may erupt at any time in the future without the patient having been exposed to reinfection. Thus it may be stated that tuberculosis is a disease that usually infects a person only once and that all subsequent events are the result of the initial, or primary, infection.

Reactivation Tuberculosis. Immunity controls primary infections throughout life in most cases. In some cases, however, the tubercle bacilli break out of their foci, multiply, and spread to cause clinical, symptomatic tuberculosis. Not all cases can be explained, but a common factor appears to be an impairment of host immunity (e.g., in cases of diabetes, alcoholism, prolonged steroid or immunosuppressive therapy, gastrectomy, silicosis and malignancies).

Although reactivation is probably by far the most common source of clinical tuberculosis, it is reasonable to assume that the occasional case may be brought about by exogenous reinfection owing to an overwhelming exposure to tubercle bacilli from a contagious person.

Extrapulmonary Tuberculosis. The most common extrapulmonary tuberculosis occurs in the urogenital system, with renal, epididymal, or tuboovarian foci. Infections may also occur in bones as manifested by

osteomyelitis, the central nervous system with meningitis or brain abscess, and the serous membranes (pleura, peritoneum, and pericardium).

Such infection is the result of bloodstream dissemination of tubercle bacilli. The usual route of entry to the blood is rupture of a liquefied caseous area into a pulmonary vein. This gives rise to serious and, if unrecognized, frequently fatal generalized tuberculous infection, with small tubercles scattered throughout the body.

Clinical Diagnosis of Tuberculosis and Relevance of Microbiological Studies

Since tuberculosis may have symptoms and signs in common with several other infections, chronic illnesses, and malignancies, it is important to be aware of the possibility of tuberculosis in such patients. With the decreasing incidence of the disease the physician's experience with it has lessened, and it has become more important to keep in mind the possible existence of this infection in the differential diagnosis of any patient who gives positive tuberculin skin-test reactions and shows some of the characteristic symptoms and signs (see above). It should be kept in mind that while tuberculosis was once a disease of the young, it has now become more common in the elderly.

Sputum specimens should be taken in the morning for routine bacteriologic studies (see below). In some cases it is necessary to do a biopsy or surgical resection as a diagnostic procedure. Such specimens should be used for both histopathologic and bacteriologic studies.

When cultures reveal the presence of tubercle bacilli, the physician can proceed with treatment with confidence that the patient does indeed have tuberculosis. However, in some cases culture results and other studies, such as biopsy, leave the question of etiologic diagnosis unanswered. In such cases it may be necessary to make a decision to begin antituberculosis treatment on a presumptive basis. When a patient presents with a suggestive history and typical x-ray and tuberculin-test findings and other diagnoses have been ruled out as well as is possible, a therapeutic trial may provide strong evidence that tuberculosis is the cause of the disease from which the patient is suffering. The administered drugs will usually reduce the patient's cough and render him or her afebrile in approximately 2 weeks and may bring about some x-ray clearing in 1 or 2 months. If these results coincide with the initiation of treatment, they add to the evidence that tuberculosis is present and justify continuation of the treatment.

Laboratory Findings in Tuberculosis

Bacteriologic studies of tubercle bacilli are performed in specialized laboratories with personnel trained for work with these bacteria.

The specimens examined for tubercle bacilli are of two types, those contaminated with rapidly growing bacteria and those that are uncontaminated. Contaminated specimens include sputum, urine, and material from open lesions of the skin. Uncontaminated specimens include cerebrospinal fluid and surgical specimens. Blood specimens are not of diagnostic value.

Most bacteriologic studies for tubercle bacilli are performed on a series of single (10 ml or less) sputum specimens, since over 90 percent of tuberculosis cases take the form of pulmonary infections. Single sputum specimens are collected early in the morning, before food is ingested.

Processing Specimens. Contaminated specimens such as sputum samples must be pretreated to destroy rapidly growing bacteria. This is usually done with NaOH or Na_3PO_4 solutions, with or without pretreatment with hydrolytic enzymes to break down particulate matter. The ex-

tent of pretreatment varies with the type of specimen. While tubercle bacilli and other species of mycobacteria are clearly more resistant to the killing effects of chemical agents such as strong alkali, the difference is a relative one. Thus prolonged treatment (e.g., with NaOH) not only reduces the probability of encountering contaminating bacteria but also decreases the number of tubercle bacilli that can be isolated. In practice, the conditions and times of pretreatment must therefore be controlled with accuracy.

Pretreated specimens are neutralized and centrifuged. The concentrated sediment provides the material for further studies.

Direct Smears for Acid-Fast Bacilli. A Ziehl-Neelsen stain or the Kinyoun modification of it serves to reveal the presence of AFB in smears of concentrated sediments from pretreated contaminated specimens or in smears made directly from specimens. Some laboratories use fluorochrome dyes to stain AFB.

The finding of AFB in urine specimens is open to questions of interpretation because these specimens may contain saprophytic mycobacteria. On the other hand, the detection of AFB in a sputum specimen of a patient with clinical signs of tuberculosis is highly suggestive of a diagnosis of pulmonary tuberculosis, since nonpathogenic mycobacteria are uncommon in sputum. In such cases treatment is started even before cultural studies are completed. However, multiple specimens should be examined to confirm the presence of AFB and cultural studies should be started.

The advantage of examinations of direct smears for AFB is that they provide results rapidly. The disadvantages are that this method is less sensitive in that about 10^5 AFB/ml must be present to detect them in a direct smear. Thus some specimens that contain tubercle bacilli revealed by cultural methods may be negative for AFB on direct smears. Also, since acid-fast stains reveal not only tubercle bacilli but also other mycobacteria, the direct smear stain is not a specific method and cultural isolation and identification of AFB are necessary.

Isolation of Tubercle Bacilli. Concentrated sediments of sputum or other contaminated specimens as well as uncontaminated specimens may be inoculated onto standard solid media for primary isolation. The most widely used media are 7H 10 agar and Loewenstein-Jensen medium. Colonies of AFB that appear in less than 7 days are not *M. tuberculosis*. Identification of colonies that develop in 7 days or more is based on their morphology and their reactions in the niacin test. A positive niacin reaction plus the expected morphology confirms the identification of *M. tuberculosis* and the diagnosis. Niacin-negative AFB are further characterized as groups I to IV of the Runyon classification scheme (Table 34.1) on the basis of their growth rate, colony morphology and color.

When isolates of AFB are identified as members of one of the four Runyon groups (which is rather infrequent), biochemical tests for further identification of the species of *Mycobacterium* are usually carried out, since the pathogenicity of individual species within each group differs. Biochemical reactions that are studied include two catalase tests (a semiquantitative one is used to detect isoniazid susceptibility of tubercle bacilli), a nitrate reduction test, a Tween 80 degradation test, arylsulfatose tests done at two specified time intervals (3 day and 2 week cultures), tellurite reduction and urease production tests, and others. Also, the capacity of mycobacteria to grow at different temperatures (25°C, 36°C, and 45°C), as well as their pigment production after exposure to light, aids in species identification.

Tests for Susceptibility to Antimicrobial Agents. Tests of isolates of tubercle bacilli or other AFB for susceptibility to the antibiotic and chemotherapeutic agents available for treatment of patients provide necessary information to the clinician, since the bacteria can develop resistance to these agents. The most useful antimicrobial agent is isoniazid (isonicotinic acid hydrazide). Isolates of tubercle bacilli resistant to isoniazid can be identified quickly by a catalase test performed on a colony from the primary isolate; susceptible strains give a positive catalase reaction, while resistant ones are catalase negative.

For direct susceptibility tests, dilutions of patients' sputum specimens adjusted in accordance with the number of AFB per high-power field are inoculated onto Middlebrook's 7H 10 medium with and without selected antitubercular agents. Indirect tests of the susceptibility of isolates of tubercle bacilli or other AFB to isoniazid and other antimicrobial agents are now most commonly performed on the same medium with one or more selected concentrations of the indicated agents. For example, two dilutions of a suspension of the tubercle bacilli from a primary isolate (1:100 and 1:10,000) are inoculated onto 7H 10 agar containing (1) no agents (control), (2) 0.2 μg of isoniazid per ml, (3) 1.0 μg of rifamycin per ml, (4) 5 μg of ethambutol per ml, and (5) 2 μg of streptomycin per ml. If necessary, selected concentrations of some additional antitubercular agents now available (see below) are also studied. Because of the slow growth of tubercle bacilli the completion of such a susceptibility test requires about 2 to 3 weeks. Thus standard practice calls for the initiation of therapy with a selected combination of first-line drugs (see below) before the results of susceptibility tests are available. If these tests subsequently reveal resistance to one or more of the agents being administered to the patient, adjustments are made in the therapeutic regimen.

Treatment of Tuberculosis

Antimycobacterial Drugs. These agents fall into two groups, based on effectiveness and toxicity.

The so-called first-line drugs are the most

effective and least toxic agents to be used, in various combinations, where drug resistance is not a factor. These drugs are isoniazid (INH), rifampin (RMP), ethambutol (EMB), streptomycin (SM) and *para*-amino salicylic acid (PAS). PAS is no longer in general use, since the other drugs are much better tolerated by patients. All these drugs can be given orally except SM, which must be given by intramuscular injection.

The second-line drugs are less effective and more toxic; consequently they are more difficult and less satisfactory to use. Those that can be given orally are cycloserine, pyrazinamide, and ethionamide. The others capreomycin, viomycin, and kanamycin, must be given parenterally.

Prophylactic Treatment. This consists of treating with INH for 1 year those patients under the age of 35 who have had recent conversions of their tuberculin tests to positive and those in older age groups who are at high risk of infection or reactivation. This treatment has proved to be highly effective in preventing development of tuberculosis in such individuals.

Original Treatment. This term refers to the treatment with antimycobacterial agents of those patients who are being treated for the first time and who have had no prior exposure to the drugs. This implies that they harbor drug-sensitive organisms, although a few patients may be found to have organisms that are resistant to some of the drugs. This is called primary drug resistance.

Treatment of this group of patients is with a basic regimen of two drugs given concurrently or with the addition of a third agent, depending in part on the degree of illness of the patient. Treatment should be for a duration of 18 to 24 months, or longer if the response is less than desired. The most popular drug combinations are INH-EMB, INH-RMP, INH-SM, INH-EMB-RMP, and INH-EMB-SM. There is little difference in effectiveness among these regimens.

In the 1940s and 1950s, when SM, PAS and INH first became available, many of the patients treated with single agents developed strains that became resistant to one agent after another. However, patients with active tuberculosis treated with combination of two or three agents as indicated above do not develop resistant tubercle bacilli. The reason for this is that the probability of encountering mutants resistant to multiple agents is the product of the probability of single mutations. Thus if the probability of occurrence of an organism resistant to one agent is $1/10^5$, then the probability of simultaneous resistance to two agents is $1/10^{10}$ and to three agents $1/10^{15}$.

Retreatment. This is treatment of patients who have previously had drug treatment and in whom treatment has failed or whose disease has reactivated after apparently successful treatment. Before drug sensitivity studies of the patient's organisms are completed it is wise to assume drug resistance in such cases.

When faced with this situation, the physician should make every effort to find out all she or he can about the patient's prior treatment: which drugs were given and for how long, whether treatment was continuous or interrupted, and the general course and results of the treatment. Armed with such information, he or she may make an intelligent selection from the available drugs and tailor a regimen to the circumstances to ensure as much as possible that the patient's organisms are likely to be sensitive to the drugs chosen.

It is impossible to be accurate in every instance, and one must be prepared to make changes in the regimen if the drug sensitivity studies indicate the need.

Epidemiology

Pulmonary tuberculosis is transmitted by droplet infection. Thus housing in crowded urban areas increases the risk of infection. Poor nutrition reduces resistance to the development of clinically active tuberculosis.

Thus tuberculosis becomes widespread in economically depressed areas. Inhalation of rock dust from silicates and the resultant silicosis specifically predisposes to infection. Bovine tubercle bacilli occur in the milk of infected cattle. Drinking of infected milk causes intestinal tuberculosis. Contact with tubercle bacilli can cause local infections of the skin.

Today, most cases of tuberculosis in the United States occur in the lower socioeconomic classes in the urban areas and among the medical professions (physicians, dentists, nurses); the morbidity rate in males is about twice as great as in females and over twice as great in most nonwhites as in whites.

Decline in Incidence. In the 19th and early 20th centuries tuberculosis was a primary cause of death in Western industrialized countries. For example, in the mid-19th century in England and Wales the death rate from tuberculosis in children under 5 years of age was almost 6/1000 per year and in young adults between the ages of 25 and 35 years over 4/1000 per year. This rate started to decline even before the discovery of tubercle bacilli.

After the discovery of the tubercle bacilli and the bovine variety of the disease, control measures undoubtedly hastened the decline in the morbidity and mortality rates. In the United States legislation was enacted requiring all cattle to be tested for tuberculin hypersensitivity and all positive responders to be destroyed. This program, while costly at the outset, virtually eliminated bovine tuberculosis in this country. In other countries immunization programs were undertaken. Early in the 20th century programs for the isolation of active cases in sanitoriums and, since the 1950s, effective therapeutic agents further reduced the morbidity and mortality rates. It is now less than one-hundredth of the rate at the turn of the century. Up to the 1930s essentially 100 percent of the urban population was infected as demonstrated by positive tuberculin reactions. Now less than 5 percent of the population is skin-test positive. By 1977 the morbidity rate in the United States had dropped to about 14/100,000 persons per year and is declining at the rate of about 5 percent per year.

Selective Effects of Infections. Selective breeding of rabbits that develop strongly positive tuberculin skin tests in response to injection with tubercle bacilli yields resistant strains, while selection of rabbits that respond with weakly positive or negative skin tests yield susceptible strains.

As indicated in the preceding section, while tuberculosis was the most common cause of death in industrialized areas of the West in the 19th and early 20th centuries, the death rate had already started to decline before the finding of the tubercle bacilli or the initiation of effective control measures. The combination of almost 100 percent infection and the high death rate, particularly among children (caused to a large extent by bovine tuberculosis transmitted by milk) and young adults, appears to have had a significant selective effect on the human population. This may in part account not only for the drop in incidence of tuberculosis but also for the capacity of humans to give strongly positive CMI responses.

Prevention of Tuberculosis

In the United States the primary preventive measure is INH treatment of subjects who convert to tuberculin-positive skin tests; immunization with bacillus Calmette Guérin (BCG) is used to a limited extent. In Europe and most other parts of the world BCG immunization serves as the primary preventive measure.

Prevention by Use of Skin Tests and INH. Because of the decreased incidence of tuberculosis and the availability of highly effective drug regimens that render patients noninfectious in a short time, the opportunities for an individual to contract a primary infection have been reduced drastically. This means that with the exception of a small number patients who will develop progressive primary tuberculosis, future cases of active disease will represent reactivation in persons who have a positive skin test, indicating that they harbor viable bacilli as a result of prior primary infection.

The implications of this situation on prevention of tuberculosis are twofold:

1. Those subjects who have positive skin tests are the ones who are at risk of developing active tuberculosis and should be followed carefully for signs of reactivation, especially those in the high-risk groups. Early detection and treatment will reduce still further the chance of their spreading the infection to other, susceptible individuals

2. The skin test offers the opportunity of determining when a primary infection has occurred. Today most children and young adults are tuberculin negative; when a positive reactor is found, especially when prior nonreactivity can be documented, it can be assumed that the infection is of recent origin. In such cases in persons under 35 years old prophylactic therapy with INH is recommended and has proved successful in reducing significantly the future development of clinical tuberculosis in this group (see above).

In older persons the risk of serious INH toxicity to the liver makes prophylactic treatment undesirable except in selected patients who are at a high risk of reactivation.

These measures, together with early detection and isolation of active, infectious cases, should result in a continued fall in the incidence of tuberculosis and, one hopes, its eventual eradication.

Prevention by BCG Vaccination. Bacillus Calmette Guérin (BCG) is a live attenuated strain of bovine tubercle bacilli developed at the Pasteur Institute during World War I by monthly subcultures on cut edges of potatoes for several years. While the history of the use of BCG for immunization of humans has been marked with controversy, BCG is now used by most countries of the world. Skin-test-negative subjects receive BCG by a multiple-puncture injection. If the injection "takes," the subject converts to a positive skin-test reaction. If the skin test converts back to negative over a period of years, the subjects may receive repeated injections of BCG in some countries. While some subjects suffer from severe reactions to repeated injections that fail to heal for months and while primary injections of BCG occasionally give rise to fatal infections (presumably because of defects in T lymphocytes that compromise CMI responses), this immunization program has significantly decreased the incidence of tuberculosis at least in Northern Europe and is widely used in areas with high tuberculosis rates.

MYCOBACTERIUM LEPRAE

Leprosy has afflicted humans since antiquity. Fear of it is reflected in the book of Leviticus in the Old Testament of the Bible, for example. The leprosy bacillus was first observed by the Norwegian physician A.H. Hansen in 1868 and first reported by him in 1874. While this Hansen bacillus was described before the discovery of the tubercle bacilli, little is known about its properties because these bacteria have not been grown on bacteriologic media. That is, while there are numerous claims for the cultivation of *M. leprae*, none has been confirmed to date.

Basic Findings

Acid-fast stains of smears or sections of tissue infected with *M. leprae* reveal clusters of irregularly shaped AFB. They vary in length from 1 to 8 μm, and their width is usually about 0.5 μm. Smears of leprous lesions contain large numbers of these

AFB. These leprosy bacilli take on two types of staining patterns in a standard Ziehl-Neelsen preparation, notably solidly stained bacilli and bacilli with a granular pattern of acid-fast staining. The latter were largely dead bacilli, while the solidly stained ones appeared to be viable *M. leprae*, as demonstrated by studies on an experimental model of mice infected with human *M. leprae*.

Mouse Model of Leprosy

C.C. Shepherd and his associates at the Center for Disease Control reported in 1965 that human *M. leprae* in homogenates of leprous lesions can, under controlled conditions, multiply in the foot pads of a certain strain of mice. Specifically, about 5000 *M. leprae* (predominantly of the type that stain solidly) are injected into the footpads of mice. Starting in 3 months, groups of the mice are killed at monthly intervals up to the end of 1 year. When the leprosy bacilli "take" (i.e., when stained sections of infected footpads reveal 30 to 50 AFB per section) or when gross lesions appear, all mice are killed; the footpads are homogenized and AFB are counted. Several lines of evidence indicate that these AFB are the human *M. leprae*: most specimens from leprosy patients take, there is a quantitative relation between the number of AFB inoculated and the number of takes; no takes occur with control materials; specimens from patients resistant to treatment with sulfones fail to respond to this agent in the mouse footpad; the bacilli can be passaged in mouse footpads but cannot be cultured; the histopathology of human lesions and mouse footpad lesions is comparable.

Since studies of this mouse footpad model indicate that at least most of the solidly stainable *M. leprae* are viable while most or all of those with granular staining are not, the ratio of solidly stained to granular AFB, or the "morphologic index," affords a simplified, quantitative method for assaying the *in vivo* effects of treatment with antimicrobial agents on the leprosy bacilli. According to results of both the mouse footpad asssay and the morphologic index, the antibiotic rifampin was found to be an effective therapeutic agent in leprosy. Such studies afford the basis of most of the advances in our understanding of the therapeutic control of leprosy. Prior to the advent of the mouse footpad model the only known effective therapeutic agents were the sulfone derivatives.

The basic mechanisms of susceptibility and resistance to infections with the Hansen bacillus have been clarified by studies on factors that govern the rate of growth of these bacteria in footpads. In mice the leprosy bacilli usually enter a logarithmic phase of growth between about 3 and 6 months after infection. The doubling time during this *in vivo* logarithmic phase in the mouse footpad is about 24 days. The rate of growth and the number of bacilli that develop in footpads can be increased by treatment with corticosteroids. Rats, which normally have a high resistance to such footpad infections, can be infected after thymectomy and irradiation. Thymic transplants into such infected rats reverse this susceptibility, as seen by a drop in the number of leprosy bacilli in the footpads. These findings confirm and extend earlier findings on the vital role of T cell responses in the defense against leprosy. Armadillos also afford an experimental model for studies on *M. leprae*, which is now widely used in research on the disease.

Immune Responses and Pathogenic Mechanisms

Both humoral and cellular immune response to leprosy bacilli develop in the infected patients. However, the antibody responses (usually detected by serologic tests with other species of mycobacteria that can be cultured) do not appear to have a protective effect and are not of diagnostic significance. Immune responses of T lymphocytes as detected by skin tests are of critical importance.

Skin tests for delayed type hypersensitivity to *M. leprae* can be carried out with *lepromin* or with tuberculin. Tuberculin skin tests with OT or PPD (see above) frequently give positive reactions in leprosy patients because of crossreactions between the tubercle bacillus and Hansen's bacillus. Most experts in the field, however, prefer to use lepromin. This skin-test reagent is prepared from leprous lesions containing large numbers of AFB by boiling and grinding the tissue into a paste. Several forms of lepromin, ranging from the crude paste to partially purified preparations, are in use. One is the Mitsuda reagent. Skin tests with intradermal injections of 0.1 ml lepromin give delayed-type reactions that like the reactions to tuberculin reach a maximum in 48 hours. Also, a second reaction sometimes develops in about 3 to 4 weeks, particularly with crude lepromin preparations. This is thought to be due to sensitization of subjects by the skin-test reagent itself.

Leprosy patients are classified on the basis of their skin tests as having the lepromatous or tuberculoid form (Table 34.2). Patients who give a negative lepromin skin-test reaction are of the lepromatous type; those who give a positive skin test are of the tuberculoid type. Importantly, the prognosis for patients with the lepromatous form is poor, but that for those with the tuberculoid form is good. Quantitative gradations occur in the level of lepromin

hypersensitivity, and the levels of hypersensitivity of a given patient may change, such as in response to skin tests with lepromin or to immunotherapy with BCG.

Clinical Findings

The onset is usually insidious and consists of a few small, flat, ill defined, slightly anesthetic skin lesions that may appear on the face or trunk. This form is called indeterminate leprosy. Thickening of nerve trunks is common to all forms of leprosy and may be apparent in areas where nerves are superficial and palpable, such as the ulnar nerve at the elbows and the peroneals at the knees. The nerve damage is presumably due to invasion of bacilli. The involved nerves become firm and tender. They become enlarged, easily palpable, and sometimes visible. As the nerves degenerate, atrophic, anesthetic, and paralytic involvement of the extremities results.

As indicated above, when CMI fails to develop during the initial stages, lepromatous leprosy will result. If this immunity is well developed, tuberculoid leprosy will result. Many cases, however, fall between these two polar forms and reflect variations in the balance between numbers of bacilli and cellular immunity.

Lepromatous Leprosy. When cellular immunity is absent, the bacilli multiply freely, the entire skin may be infiltrated with bacilli, and there is a continuous bacteremia with invasion of multiple organs. In spite of the vast numbers of bacilli, manifestations of serious infection, such as fever, leukocytosis, and anemia, are absent.

Table 34.2. Significance of Lepromin Hypersensitivity Reactions

Lepromin Skin Test	Type of Leprosy	Number of Solidly Stained AFB	Prognosis
Negative	Lepromatous	Many	Poor
Positive	Tuberculoid	Few	Good

Early skin lesions are multiple and symmetrical. They are ill defined erythematous macules and papules, slowly progressing to plaques and nodules. Late lesions and permanent disabilities may continue to develop after treatment has been started. Confluent masses of granulation tissue on the ears, face, trunk, limbs, and skin lead to thickening and corrugation. Nodularity of skin can cause grotesque appearance of the face and limbs. Perforation and collapse of the nasal septum leads to the "saddle-nose" deformity, and involvement of the eye may bring about keratitis, iridocyclitis, and blindness. Involvement of many internal organs, including liver and kidney, leads to severe impairment. Loss of fingers, toes, or even larger segments of extremities is noted. Sterility may result from infiltration of the testes. In severe cases, secondary amyloidosis may supervene. The prognosis of this form of leprosy is generally unfavorable.

Tuberculoid Leprosy. This clinical form of leprosy, when cellular immunity is well developed, is usually limited to one or two nerves and the related skin areas. The most frequently involved sites are the extremities, face, and buttocks. Typically, the lesions are large erythematous plaques with sharp outer margins and a central flat area that is hypopigmented and anesthetic. Anesthesia in a hypopigmented area of skin almost always means leprosy. Bacilli are very sparse and hard to find in tuberculoid leprosy.

Dimorphous Leprosy. Skin lesions are numerous, smaller, and less anesthetic. The margins are not as sharp as in tuberculoid leprosy. Numbers of bacilli are higher than in the tuberculoid type but are much lower than in lepromatous leprosy. There is a low-grade bacteremia, and granulomatous lesions may develop in lymph nodes, liver, and other organs.

Diagnosis

The important signs are the characteristic skin lesions and thickening of peripheral nerves, with areas of anesthesia. AFB may be demonstrated in smears prepared from scrapings of lepromatous or dimorphous lesions of the skin, earlobes, and nasal septum. Biopsy of the skin may be useful in making the diagnosis and in determining which form of the disease is predominant.

Differential diagnosis includes a large assortment of skin diseases. The associated anesthesia and peripheral nerve involvement will separate leprosy from these conditions.

Treatment

General measures are important and, in some cases, may result in temporary improvement. Such measures include personal and environmental hygiene, good diet, and treatment of concurrent diseases.

Specific treatment at the present time is with the sulfones, of which 4,4'-diaminodiphenyl sulfone (DDS) is the most widely used and effective compound. This drug causes rapid healing of skin ulcers and upper respiratory tract lesions. Tracheostomy, which used to be commonly required, is now seldom needed. Early lepromatous forms are rapidly healed, but advanced cases improve slowly, sometimes requiring years before bacilli disappear from the lesions. The sulfones are not effective against the nerve damage, which sometimes continues to progress while the patient is under treatment. Some promising results are being reported with the use of the antibiotic rifampin.

Another approach to therapy currently under investigation is immunotherapy. Vaccination with BCG not only increases CMI to mycobacteria but also characteristically stimulates general immune responses nonspecifically.

Epidemiology and Prevention

Leprosy is thought to be transmitted by body contact and/or nasal secretion. It afflicts several million people in the tropical regions of Africa, Asia, and Latin America. In the United States less than 1000 cases occur per year, most in Latin American immigrants who acquired the infection in the countries of their origin. In most states of this country, patients are treated on an outpatient basis. Patients who have young children are instructed not to fondle them in order to reduce the chances of transmitting the infection. Isolation of patients in a leprosory is practiced in some Southern states.

In the past leprosy was regarded as a disease that is difficult to transmit and with an exceptionally long incubation time. However, recent studies on lymphocyte activation by lepromin suggest that infection with leprosy may be rather common in endemic regions even though clinical signs appear only rarely. Thus the development of clinically active leprosy may, in fact, be a result of some defects in CMI responses.

OTHER MYCOBACTERIAL PATHOGENS

The genus *Mycobacterium* includes at least three minor human pathogens and a number of animal pathogens. *M. ulcerans, M. marinum*, and *M. fortuitum*, all of which occur as saprophytes, can cause chronic localized skin infections in man. *M. marinum* is a photochromogen (Table 34.1). Still other mycobacteria may cause pulmonary tuberculosis (e.g., *M. kansasii* and *M. avium* group; see above).

John's bacillus, or *M. paratuberculosis*, a small coccobacillary acid-fast organism, causes chronic intestinal infections in cattle. This created significant economic problems in the past. Other mycobacteria are pathogens of pigs, rodents, and other mammals, birds, and cold-blooded vertebrates.

REFERENCES

Baum, G.L., Ed.: Textbook of Pulmonary Diseases, 2nd Ed. Little, Brown, Boston, 1974.

Hunter, G.W., Swartzwelder, J.C., and Clyde, D.F.: Tropical Medicine, 5th Ed. W.B. Saunders, Philadelphia, 1976.

Lennette, E.H., Balows, A., Hausler, W.J., and Truant, J.P., Eds.: Manual of Clinical Microbiology. 3rd Ed. American Society for Microbiology, Washington, D.C., 1980.

Wilson, G.S. and Miles, A.A.: Topely and Wilson's Principles of Bacteriology and Immunology. 5th Ed. Williams & Wilkins, Baltimore, 1964. (Note — the earlier editions such as this one afford more detailed reviews of the topic)

Wolinsky, E.: Nontuberculosus mycobacterial infections of man. Med. Clin. North Am. *58*: 639, 1974.

Youmans, G.: Tuberculosis. W.B. Saunders, Philadelphia, 1979.

35

Actinomyces and Nocardia

Ernst H. Beutner,
Russell J. Nisengard,
Richard L. Miner, and
Daniel Amsterdam

ACTINOMYCES

Actinomyces are indigenous to humans and several animal species. They have been regarded as the causative agents of actinomycosis for about half a century. In the past 20 years their normal habitat in dental plaque (deposits on teeth) has been subjected to detailed studies, and certain species of *Actinomyces* have been implicated as causative agents of two common oral diseases — periodontitis and certain forms of tooth decay.

The classification of bacteria in this genus has undergone a number of changes. Five species of *Actinomyces* are now recognized according to the Eighth Edition of *Bergey's Manual of Determinative Biology* (Table 35.1). Four of them occur in humans, predominantly in the gingival sulcus and the tonsilar crypts.

MORPHOLOGIC AND CULTURAL CHARACTERISTICS

Actinomyces are gram-positive rod shaped bacteria (Fig. 35.1). Some strains grow as filaments about 0.8 μm in diameter and 5 to 10 μm long or longer. Other strains develop filaments that break up into polymorphic diphtheroid forms (i.e., like diphtheria bacilli); these are commonly in the range of 0.5 to 1 μm wide and about 2 μm long. Branching filaments can be seen in microcolonies and sometimes in Gram stains.

The appearance of microcolonies isolated from such specimens aids in presumptive identification. Final identification is made on the basis of biochemical and serologic reaction patterns. *Actinomyces* are facultative anaerobes. Thioglycolate broth enriched with animal proteins supports their growth. A granular growth usually develops in the bottom two-thirds of tubes of broth within 7 days and settles to the bottom. For primary isolation, brain-heart infusion agar plates are inoculated in duplicate, one for anaerobic cultivation in 95 percent N_2 and 5 percent CO_2 and one for aerobic incubation with 5 percent CO_2. Microcolonies up to 1 mm in diameter usually develop in 18 to 24 hours. Observation of these (at 100-fold magnification) aids

Table 35.1.   Habitat and Differentiating Characteristics of *Actinomyces* spp.

Characteristics	A. bovis	A. odont-olyticus	A. israelii	A. naes-lundii	A. viscosus
Natural habitat	Cattle, other animals	Man	Man	Man	Man, rodents
Usual morphology of microcolonies — smooth (S) or filamentous (F)	S	S	F	F	F
Mature colonies red on blood agar	–	+	–	–	–
Examples of biochemical reactions:					
Catalase	–	–	–	–	+
Starch hydrolysis (wide zone)	+	–	–	–	–
Fermentation of ribose[a]	–	–	+	–	–
Serologic groups (fluorescent antibody method)	B	E	D	A	F
Human diseases (suspected pathogens)	None	Root surface caries, actinomycosis	Actinomycosis	Periodontitis, root surface caries, actinomycosis	Periodontitis, root surface caries

[a]Several sugars are used in fermentation reactions for identification of species of *Actinomyces*. Ribose serves as an example in this table.

Excerpted and reproduced with permission from Seack, J.M. In Bergey's Manual of Determinative Microbiology. 8th Ed. R.E. Buchanan & N.E. Gibbons, (Eds.) © 1974, The Williams & Wilkins Co, Baltimore.)

in primary identification (Table 35.1). Most strains of *A. odontolyticus* and *A. bovis* form smooth microcolonies. Filamentous "spider" microcolonies are formed by *A. israelii*, *A. naeslundii*, and *A. viscosus*. Some strains form smooth or granular or "molar tooth"-like colonies. On primary isolation most colonies of *A. odontolyticus* on blood agar can be identified by their red color. Development of mature colonies requires up to 7 days of cultivation. The colony morphology of the four recognized species varies from strain to strain. Most are 0.5 to 1 mm in diameter and may reach 2 mm after 1 to 2 weeks incubation. Many are smooth, convexed opaque, and cream or white in color. Some are granular with a rough texture. Some strains of *A. israelii* and other species form colonies with branching filaments at the edges.

Species Identification

Subculture of primary isolates of suspected strains of *Actinomyces* are identified by biochemical and serologic tests of the type listed in Table 35.1. All species except *A. viscosus* are catalase negative. Other biochemical tests, including fermentation reactions, indole formation, nitrate reduction, and H_2S formation, serve to further identify species.

Serologic tests by direct fluorescent antibody tests (Ch. 16) with absorbed monospecific conjugates serve to differentiate species of *Actinomyces* and their serotypes.

Several other filamentous microorganisms are found in the oral cavity. *Arachnia propionica* is part of the normal oral flora of humans but not animals. It is a gram-positive facultative anaerobe that grows as

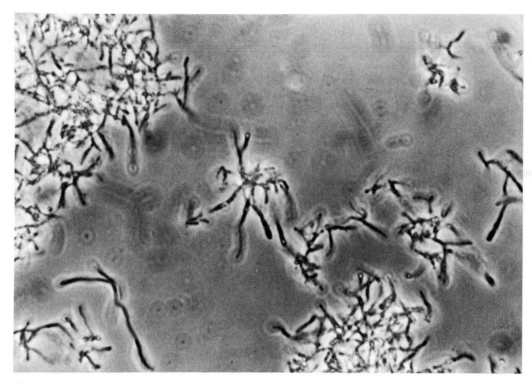

Fig. 35.1.   Phase-contrast photomicrograph of *A. israelii* (× 840). (Photograph courtesy of Dr. P. Mashimo, Department of Oral Biology, School of Dentistry, State University of New York at Buffalo.)

diphtheroid cells or as branching filaments. *Arach. propionica* has been isolated from actinomycosislike lesions. *Bacterionema matruchotii* is a gram-positive facultative anaerobe with pleomorphic cells. Characteristically, there are long, nonseptate filaments with terminal bacilluslike bodies. *B. matruchotii* is found in human saliva and dental supra- and subgingival plaque. *Leptotrichia buccalis* is a gram-negative anaerobe that grows as straight or slightly curved rods, frequently with pointed ends. The cells may form long septate filaments.

Rothia dentocariosa is a gram-positive aerobe that is pleomorphic in cell morphology, ranging from branched filaments to coccoid and bacillary forms. *R. dentocariosa* is found in dental plaque, dental caries within the dentin of teeth, and human gingival tissue from patients with periodontal disease.

ACTINOMYCES IN HUMAN PATHOLOGY

Dental Plaque and Tonsillar Infections

Dental plaque is a soft, sticky, filmlike, concentrated mass of bacterial microcolonies held together by an intermicrobial substance. Plaque that adheres to the enamel of the tooth above the gum line is termed supragingival plaque, while plaque that adheres to the tooth root under the gum line is termed subgingival plaque. The microbial composition of plaque dynamically changes with time and differs subgingivally and supragingivally and even in different mouth locations. The earliest microorganisms in plaque are gram-positive streptococci, including *Streptococcus sanguis* and *Streptococcus mutans*. The composition of plaque continuously changes and becomes more complex so that within a few days after formation, gram-positive rods and filamentous forms make up a significant proportion of plaque bacteria. These include *A. viscosus*, *A. naeslundii*, *A. odontolyticus*, and *A. israelii*. At a later stage, the proportion of gram-negative bacteria increases.

Actinomyces, which also occur in tonsillar crypts, were first implicated in human infection on the basis of observations of "sulfur granules" in draining sinuses of granulomatous lesions. The finding of branching filaments in these granules led to the mistaken view that a fungal infection or "mycosis" produced the lesions. Thus the latter were referred to as actinomycosis. But the agents *Actinomyces* are bacteria, as demonstrated by their typical bacterial cell wall, sensitivity to antibacterial antibiotics and procaryotic nuclear structure.

In recent years studies of plaque bacteria and their pathogenicity in animal models have implicated certain species of *Actinomyces* in two types of very common diseases of the oral cavity. One type includes inflammatory diseases of the gums, notably periodontitis and gingivitis. Periodontitis is the primary cause of loss of teeth in humans. Secondly, some species are implicated in one of the forms of tooth decay, caries that develop below the gum line or gingival margin; most caries, including those on smooth surfaces of teeth, are caused by certain species of streptococci that grow on teeth, notably *S. mutans* and to a lesser extent *S. sanguis* (Ch. 18).

In addition, *Actinomyces* spp. are regarded as the primary causative agents of actinomycosis. (*A. bovis*, which is associated with bovine actinomycosis, is not considered here.) Human actinomycosis is associated primarily with *A. israelii* and *A. naeslundii* and sometimes with certain other filamentous bacteria that reside in the gingival sulcus. Somewhat similar granulomatous infections appear to be caused by wound infections with a broad variety of saprophytic microorganisms. These include members of the strictly aerobic genus

Nocardia (e.g., *Nocardia asteroides* and *Nocardia brasiliensis*) and a number of saprophytic fungi. Emmons and his associates as well as others review this subject in their monographs. Such exogenous infections occur predominantly on the hands and feet, in contrast to the endogenous actinomycosis which occurs primarily in the cervicofacial areas and less frequently in the thoracic and abdominal areas.

Gingivitis and Periodontitis

The periodontium or structures that surround and support the teeth include the gingiva (gum), dentogingival junction (junction of gingiva with tooth), alveolar bone (bone socket), cementum (calcified covering of root dentin), and periodontal ligament (connective tissue between alveolar bone and cementum). Dentobacterial plaque causes inflammatory changes in the periodontium that can be prevented by plaque control through brushing, flossing, and professional cleaning. Gingivitis is the plaque-induced inflammatory disease of the gingiva. The histopathology is characterized by an inflammatory infiltrate of plasma cells and lymphocytes, alterations in fibroblasts and collagen, connective tissue destruction, and vasculitis. Untreated gingivitis is thought to frequently progress to periodontitis. Periodontitis (previously known as pyorrhea) involves not only the gingiva but the other periodontal structures as well. This disease includes osteoclastic bone loss, destruction of the periodontal ligament with collagenolysis, necrosis of cementum, and apical migration of the epithelial attachment. If untreated, periodontitis leads to progressive loosening and eventual loss of teeth.

Bacteriologic Studies. When the gingiva is clinically healthy, plaque is minimal and is composed primarily of gram-positive cocci. As plaque continues to accumulate and gingivitis ensues, there is a change in the microbial composition of plaque. In plaque associated with gingivitis, *Actinomyces* spp. frequently predominate and may comprise over half the bacteria. These species include *A. viscosus*, *A. naeslundii*, and *A. israelii*. In plaque associated with chronic periodontitis, *Actinomyces* spp. constitute approximately 12 percent of the plaque bacteria. Actinomyces occurring in high proportions in plaque are located near the gingival tissues and may thus contribute to the pathogenesis of gingivitis and chronic periodontitis.

Animal Model Studies. Studies on naturally occurring and experimentally induced periodontitis in rodents suggest that actinomyces play an etiologic role. Early studies revealed that golden hamsters were susceptible to spontaneous periodontal disease while albino hamsters rarely developed the disease. Bacterial studies revealed that the plaque in the golden hamsters contained large numbers of *A. viscosus*, while that of albino hamsters did not. The transmissibility of periodontal disease was demonstrated by oral implantation of *A. viscosus* cultures into the albino hamsters and the ensuing development of periodontitis. In rice rats and white rats, species of *Actinomyces* have also been associated with periodontitis. Monoinfection of the oral cavity of germ-free rats with either *A. viscosus* or *A. naeslundii* led to heavy formation of subgingival plaque within 90 days. Accompanying this was severe osteoclastic alveolar bone loss and root surface caries.

Mechanism of Action of Actinomyces. The mechanisms by which actinomyces play a role in gingivitis and periodontitis are not fully understood. Speculation has centered around immune responses to actinomyces antigens and toxic substances produced by the microorganisms. Cellular responses (CMI), immediate hypersensitivity, and IgG antibody type to actinomyces occur in humans. CMI to extracts of *A. viscosus*, *A. israelii*, and *A. naeslundii* is significantly greater in patients with

gingivitis and periodontitis than in periodontally healthy subjects. The incidence of immediate hypersensitivity to actinomyces is significantly greater in periodontitis than in gingivitis or in periodontally healthy subjects. Additionally, IgG antibody titers to *A. naeslundii* and *A. israelii* are significantly greater in periodontitis than in gingivitis.

Dental Caries

Dental caries is a destruction of tooth substance, including the inorganic substance, which is primarily hydroxyapatite, and the protein organic matrix. The carious lesion starts either in the enamel covering the crown of the tooth or in the cementum covering the roots of the teeth. If unchecked, the carious lesion extends into the underlying dentin and eventually causes necrosis of the tooth with partial or full destruction of the crown. Dental caries of the crown enamel, "pit and fissure" caries, and "smooth surface" caries are thought to be caused primarily by *S. mutans*. Filamentous bacteria, however, are thought to play a role in the etiology of "root surface" caries in cementum. Strains of *A. viscosus*, *A. naeslundii*, *A. odontolyticus*, and *Rothia dentocariosa* have been isolated from root surfaces of extracted human teeth. Oral implantation of *A. viscosus* and *A. naeslundii* into gnotobiotic rats leads to large bacterial plaque accumulations along the gum margin and root surface caries.

Actinomycosis

Human actinomycosis usually takes one of three clinical forms — cervicofacial, thoracic, or abdominal lesions. Over 85 percent of the cases are cervicofacial. They appear as chronic granulomatous infections of the subcutaneous tissues that commonly develop draining sinuses. The microbial agents most commonly isolated from such infections are *A. israelii* and *A. naeslundii*.

Isolates of *Arachnia propionica* have also been reported.

Cervicofacial Actinomycosis. The infection starts as a painless swelling and then hardens to a "woody" indurated nodule. The involved tissues proceed to break down, suppurate, and form sinus tracts that open externally and that by direct extension may invade the bones of the skull. Characteristically, there may be healing and scar formation in one area while new sinus tracts are opening nearby.

Pulmonary Actinomycosis. The initial lesions are usually bilateral and in the lung bases, but they may occur unilaterally and in any part of the lung. At the initial site a granulomatous process is begun that may extend to the mediastinum, pericardium, or the pleura with pain and, sometimes, a pleural effusion. Early symptoms are subacute, with cough and purulent sputum, which may be bloody. Eventually, the chest wall is involved, with formation of multiple draining sinuses.

As the disease progresses the patient becomes anemic, with leukocytosis and elevated erythrocyte sedimentation rate, losses of weight and strength, and a spiking fever and night sweats.

The chest film may resemble initially that of bronchopneumonia but may eventually show involvement of the pleura, mediastinal structures, and ribs. The characteristic picture is one of non-homogeneous consolidation with occasional cavitation and evidence of chest wall involvement. Most cases are originally thought to be either carcinoma or tuberculosis.

Abdominal Actinomycosis. The same processes of infection, local invasion, and sinus tract formation may occur in the ileocecal area, the female adnexa, and the rectum. Several recent reports describe cases of actinomycosis induced by intrauterine devices. A hard intraabdominal mass may be felt, and external sinus tracts eventually form from these sites. Any abdominal organ may become involved through direct extension. The symptoms often suggest appendicitis, salpingitis, or carcinoma.

Laboratory Diagnosis. Smears of exudates from draining sinuses or surgical excisions are examined for the presence of sulfur granules. These and/or samples of specimens are examined microscopically and culturally. Direct examination of wet mounts of sulfur granules reveals the presence of clusters of branching filaments, frequently with club shaped ends. Gram stains of smears of such granules also reveal the clumps of filamentous forms resembling smears from granular sediments of broth cultures.

For isolation, specimens are inoculated into broth media, generally thioglycolate or brain-heart infusion broth, enriched with animal protein such as sterile whole sheep serum and onto two plates of blood agar enriched with a brain-heart infusion base, one for aerobic and one for anaerobic incubation. Cultures should be incubated for 1 week before they are discarded as negative. Suspected colonies or growth in broth can be further identified by Gram stains and biochemical tests and, where available, fluorescent antibody tests for species identification.

Treatment. Penicillin is the drug of choice. It is usually effective when used in high dosage for long courses. It has been demonstrated that intermittent or low-dosage regimens are ineffective. Treatment must be continued long after the patient is apparently cured. Treatment for as long as 18 months may be necessary. For patients who are allergic to penicillin, chloramphenicol, clindamycin, or lincomycin may be substituted.

Surgical approaches are often very difficult because of the nature of the pathology, but the principle of drainage of abscesses should be followed, if possible. Resection for diagnosis has been shown to be reasonably safe if the diagnosis is made promptly on the resected section so that treatment can be started without delay.

NOCARDIA

Frequently and conveniently *Nocardia* is thought of as the aerobic counterpart of the *Actinomyces*. Although both genera are members of the same family, they differ in properties other than their oxygen requirements. Of prime importance is the property of acid-fastness displayed by many nocardiae. This acid-fastness differs from that exhibited by the mycobacteria in that a 1 percent aqueous sulfuric acid solution serves as the decolorizing reagent instead of the 3 percent hydrochloric acid in ethanol solution used in the classic Ziehl-Neelsen staining procedure for mycobacteria.

Potentially pathogenic nocardiae are worldwide in occurrence, existing primarily in the soil. The infection of subcutaneous tissues appears in a form of mycetoma usually on the foot (Madura foot) or on hands. It usually follows a puncture wound. The lesion is characterized by abscess formation and excretion of pus that contains granules. This lesion is discussed in Chapter 36. The organisms may also enter the body by the respiratory route. The pulmonary infection with nocardiae follows inhalation of organisms and results in an infiltrative disease that may culminate in cavity formation. In a few instances nocardiosis becomes systemic following the dissemination of organisms through blood circulation. Metastatic lesions may be found in various tissues, most importantly brain and meninges.

Nocardia asteroides and *Nocardia brasiliensis* are the primary causes of nocardiosis. *Nocardia* spp. are thin, gram-positive, nonmotile, frequently branching filaments that may fragment into bacillary or coccoid forms. They grow aerobically on simple media, although growth is variable and slow. When first visible, in 2 to 4 days, colonies are usually white. They remain white or change and become pigmented varying from tan to yellow to orange to red.

Aerial filaments may develop over the surface of the colony; arthrospores* may develop by fragmentation. *Nocardia* spp. grow on media used for culture of mycobacteria, on Sabouraud's dextrose agar, and on blood agar. Growth occurs at 35° to 37°C and is enhanced by 5 to 10 percent CO_2 in atmosphere.

Specimens for diagnosis consist of pus, sputum, spinal fluid, and, where possible, biopsy material. At present, serologic tests are unreliable. Smears stained by the Gram procedure demonstrate bacillary and coccal forms or intertwining groups of branching rods.

The isolation of *Nocardia* spp. is essential in order to establish diagnosis. Further, it is necessary that all tissue biopsy specimens be cultured, since the organism is not readily visualized in tissue sections with the routine stains. Methenamine-silver stain is recommended.

Currently, the sulfonamides are the drugs of choice along with surgical drainage of abscesses and the excision of necrotic tissue when required. Nocardiosis is not communicable.

REFERENCES

Buchanan, R.E. and Gibbons, N.E., Eds.: Bergey's Manual of Determinative Bacteriology. 8th Ed. Williams & Wilkins, Baltimore, 1974.

Emmons, C.W., Binford, C.H., Utz, J.P., and Kwon-Chung, K.J.: Medical Mycology. Lea & Febiger, Philadelphia, 1977.

Gibbons, R.J., and van Houte, J.: Bacteriology of dental caries. In Shaw, J.H., Sweeney, E.A., Cappuccino, C.C., and Meller, S.M., Eds.: Textbook of Oral Biology. W.B. Saunders, Philadelphia, 1978.

Slack, J.M. and Gerencser, M.A.: Actinomyces, Filamentous Bacteria: Biology and Pathology. Burchess, Minneapolis, 1975.

*This term will be discussed in Chapter 36.

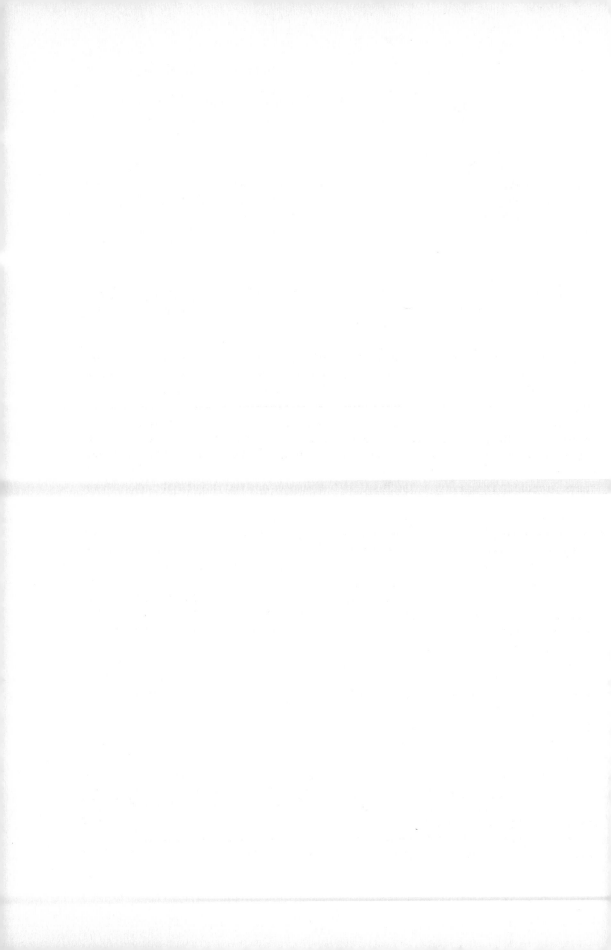

36

Medical Mycology

Joseph H. Kite, Jr.

Mycology is the study of fungi, a major group of microorganisms significantly different from bacteria, viruses, and protozoa. Fungi comprise two predominant forms, yeasts and molds. The presence of fungi as contaminants on bread, vegetables, and a variety of foods that have been kept for a prolonged period is common. There is probably no organic substance that is free from attack by these microorganisms. Fungi are found extensively in the environment and become a frequent source of contamination in the hospital as well. Most fungi are not pathogenic, and some are useful to mankind in a number of ways. For example, some yeasts are used in baking bread and in the brewing industry; other fungi give flavor to cheese, and some are used in industrial processes, such as to produce alcohol and citric acid or to produce antibiotics such as penicillin (from the mold *Penicillium chrysogenum*).

CLASSIFICATION

Fungi are a separate kingdom; this classification indicates the distinction of these organisms from bacteria (Table 36.1).

Bacteria are procaryotic, having a single naked chromosome without nuclear-membrane-bound organelles; fungi are eucaryotic, since cells contain a nucleus with a nuclear membrane, multiple chromosomes, and a specialized mitotic apparatus. Two bacterial genera will be discussed briefly in this chapter because they were classified formerly as fungi and because they exhibit some filamentous growth which is characteristic of fungi. The genera *Actinomyces* and *Nocardia* (Ch. 35) can produce clinical disease similar to that caused by fungi. Thus it is important to consider these organisms when making a differential diagnosis.

The true fungi have a basic structure consisting of a system of branched, tubular filaments called hyphae that contain protoplasm and nuclei. The cell wall contains chitin or a celluloselike material, such as glucan or mannan. Most fungi have cross walls or septae creating multicellular hyphae, but some fungi lack such septations. The septations have "holes" in them that permit the flow of cytoplasmic material between cells. Hyphae that are so divided by transverse walls at regular intervals are said to be *septate hyphae*. A few molds

Table 36.1. Classification of Fungi and Bacteria of Related Interest That Are the Principal Etiologic Agents of Human Disease

Fungi

Zygomycetes — nonseptate; sexual and asexual spores

Mold fungi: *Rhizopus, Mucor, Absidia*

Ascomycetes — septate; sexual and asexual spores

Yeasts and molds

Includes some pathogenic fungi with sexual stages

Basidiomycetes — septate hyphae; have clamp connection for sexual reproduction

Includes mushrooms and toadstools, and possibly some pathogenic fungi with sexual stages

Deuteromycetes (fungi imperfecti) — septate; asexual spores only

Yeast fungi: *Candida, Cryptococcus*

Dimorphic fungi: *Histoplasma, Coccidioides, Blastomyces, Paracoccidioides, Sporothrix*

Mold fungi:

Dermatophytes (*Microsporum, Trichophyton, Epidermophyton*)

Aspergillus

Producing mycetoma (*Petriellidium, Madurella*)

Chromoblastomycotic agents (*Fonsecaea, Phialophora, Cladosporium*)

Bacteria

Funguslike bacteria

Actinomyces

Nocardia

---

have hyphae that do not have cross walls or septa, thus permitting the streaming of protoplasm throughout the multinucleate structure. Such molds are said to have *nonseptate* or *coenocytic hyphae*. The latter type of mycelium is characteristic of the *Zygomycetes* (Table 36.1) and serves to distinguish this group from all other classes of fungi.

Fungi are subject to variations in form according to the temperature at which growth occurs. A fungus may grow as a yeast (without filaments) in the body and at

37°C on laboratory media (tissue phase), but at room temperature (25°C) the same fungus may form a filamentous colony. Such a fungus would be characterized as dimorphic or biphasic. This characteristic is important in the laboratory diagnosis of some fungi. However, not all fungi follow this pattern. Most fungi are routinely incubated both at 37°C and at room temperature. If a clinical isolate grows only at one temperature, attempts are usually made to grow it at the other temperature in order to determine if the organism is dimorphic.

Fungi reproduce by forming either asexual or sexual spores that are specialized, resistant units varying greatly in morphology. Thus morphological appearances of hyphae and spores are of aid in the laboratory identification of some pathogenic fungi. Asexual spores develop from spore-bearing hyphae that have not undergone nuclear fusion, while sexual spores are produced by the fusion of two nuclei. If the nuclei originate from the same thallus (vegetative part of fungus), the fungus is homothallic; if a sexual spore is produced only by fusion of two separate thalli or mating types, the fungus is said to be heterothallic.

Fungi that reproduce sexually are known as *perfect fungi*. The medically important fungi with sexual reproduction are members of the classes *Zygomycetes, Ascomycetes,* and *Basidiomycetes* (Table 36.1). Many of these perfect fungi also reproduce asexually.

In the class *Zygomycetes* a fertilized cell becomes a zygote. These organisms are considered the lower fungi and contain mostly organisms that are saprophytes and occasional contaminants. However, three genera that may be pathogenic under the proper circumstances are *Rhizopus, Mucor,* and *Absidia.*

Ascomycetes have sexual spores that are contained in an ascus or sac. This class contains some nonpathogenic yeasts and some of the perfect forms of pathogenic fungi, such as *Blastomyces* and *Aspergillus*.

Basidiomycetes produce sexual spores on the end of a basidium or club shaped cell. This class contains the mushrooms and toadstools, and some of these can be poisonous because of the toxins produced.

The *Deuteromycetes*, or *imperfect fungi* (*fungi imperfecti*) constitute by far the majority of the fungi pathogenic for humans. They are referred to as imperfect because all reproduce asexually. This class of fungi may be subdivided into yeast fungi, which are not dimorphic but exist only in the yeast form, dimorphic fungi, and mold fungi, which exist only in the filamentous form.

Until recently, most of the fungi of clinical importance were thought to reproduce only asexually. However, the use of special media and improved laboratory techniques has revealed that a sexual stage can be produced in many of these fungi in the presence of opposite mating types. The sexual or perfect stage is usually given a different generic and species name than that of the imperfect stage. Thus many pathogenic fungi now have two names, one for the perfect and another for the imperfect stage. Although this policy may lead to some confusion, it is taxonomically legitimate. For example, a causative agent of ringworm of the feet (athlete's foot), *Trichophyton mentagrophytes*, is an imperfect fungus that is identified as *Arthroderma benhamiae* in its perfect stage. Then it becomes proper to assign such an organism to one of the three classes *Zygomycetes*, *Ascomycetes*, or *Basidiomycetes*. However, it is convenient to know that nearly all the medically important fungi are seen normally in their asexual stage; therefore the diagnostic laboratory may continue to refer to them by their "imperfect" name. The inherent pathogenicity of fungi is not related to their sexual or asexual stage.

The sexual stage is not often observed in the diagnostic laboratory, but the recognition of sexual spores is sometimes helpful in recognizing as nonpathogenic a yeast such as *Saccharomyces* spp., which can be a common contaminant of clinical material. Such a yeast may produce sexual spores in an ascus or sac after meiosis, and these spores can be recognized in a smear (red-staining cells) after application of an ascospore stain.

Pathogenic Fungi

Although there exist over 100,000 species of fungi, only about 50 of these are pathogenic for humans. Furthermore, very few of these are primary pathogens (i.e., able to produce disease in a healthy host). For the most part they represent misplaced soil saprophytes. As a more practical classification scheme, these pathogenic fungi are divided into four groups on the basis of whether the principal disease occurs in (1) the superficial layers of the skin, (2) cutaneous areas (skin, hair, or nails), (3) subcutaneous areas (deeper tissues), or (4) the disease is systemic (Table 36.2). In the last case infection often starts in the lungs and then spreads to other organs. Superficial infections will not be discussed in this chapter, since they are frequently innocuous and no significant pathology is produced. About 20 species of fungi cause cutaneous infections; a dozen are associated with severe localized subcutaneous disease, and about 20 cause systemic infections. In addition, there is also a long list of opportunistic organisms that may cause disease in patients who are debilitated because of other illness, because of treatment with antibiotics that destroy bacterial flora but selectively permit fungi to grow, or because of treatment with steroid and immunosuppressive agents (e.g., in patients receiving transplanted tissue). A few diseases are caused by endogenous organisms (i.e., species that are part of the normal flora) such as candidiasis and actinomycosis, whereas other diseases, such as histoplasmosis and

Table 36.2.   Clinical Types of Fungus Infections

Type	Disease	Causative Organism
Superficial infections	Pityriasis versicolor	*Malassezia furfur*
	Piedra	*Trichosporon beigelii* (white)
		Piedraia hortai (black)
Cutaneous infections	Ringworm of skin, hair and nails	Dermatophytes (*Microsporum* spp., *Trichophyton* spp., *Epidermophyton floccosum*)
	Candidiasis of skin, mucous membrances, and nails	*Candida albicans* and related species
Subcutaneous infections	Sporotrichosis	*Sporothrix schenckii*
	Chromomycosis	*Fonsecaea pedrosoi* and related organisms
	Mycotic mycetoma	*Petriellidium boydii, Madurella* spp. (Funguslike bacteria: *Nocardia*)
Systemic infections	Opportunistic fungus infections	
	Candidiasis, systemic	*Candida albicans*
	Cryptococcosis	*Cryptococcus neoformans*
	Aspergillosis	*Aspergillus fumigatus*, etc.
	Mucormycosis	*Rhizopus* spp., *Mucor* spp., *Absidia* spp.
	Pathogenic fungus infections	
	Histoplasmosis	*Histoplasma capsulatum*
	Coccidioidomycosis	*Coccidioides immitis*
	Blastomycosis	*Blastomyces dermatitidis*
	Paracoccidioidomycosis	*Paracoccidioides brasiliensis*

This table is intended not as a complete list of fungi pathogenic for humans but as a list of the more important microorganisms divided according to their major sites of infection.

Fig. 36.1. Left, yeast (*Candida albicans*). (A) Colonies of yeast on Sabouraud's Dextrose Agar (SDA). Colonies are raised and smooth, have an entire periphery, are soft in texture, and have a light yellow color ($\times$ 2). (B) Microscopic appearance of yeast cells ($\times$ 400). Yeast cells are globose or ovoid (5 to 7 μm in diameter) and reproduce by budding. (C) Diagram of yeast cells, one with a bud ($\times$ 3000). Right, mold (*Trichophyton mentagrophytes*). (D) Colonies of mold on SDA. Colony appearance may vary from cottony to powdery, appears folded, grayish to buff or white ($\times$ 2). (E) Microscopic appearance of mold colony ($\times$ 400). Intertwining branching filaments or hyphae with asexual spores. (F) Diagram of mold ($\times$ 600). (1) Septate branching hyphae; (2) microaleuriospores (2 μm by 3 to 7 μm in size) in clusters or borne singly from hypha; (3) macroaleuriospore is thin-walled, composed of three to five cells, and 6 to 8 by 20 to 50 μm.

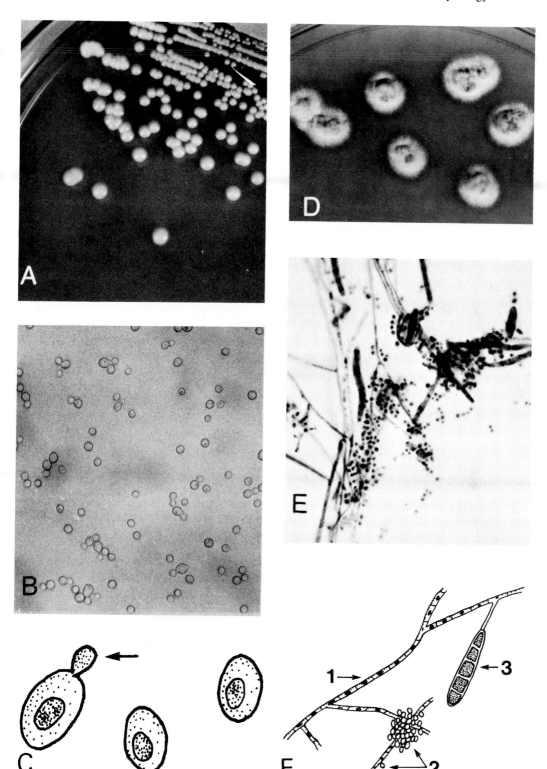

most of the systemic diseases, are caused by fungi exogenous in origin (i.e., coming from outside the body, frequently from the soil). Some fungi appear to have developed a parasitic mode of existence with man, such as the anthropophilic dermatophytes and *Candida albicans*.

The laboratory identification of fungi is made largely on the basis of morphology by examining the type of colony formation observed grossly and the type of specialized spore structure seen microscopically. Fungi produce two principal types of colonies: a yeast colony and a mold or filamentous colony. A yeast colony (Fig. 36.1A) is soft, creamy, and opaque and has a regular border or hairy projections around the edges. Cultures on an agar plate exhibit a yeast odor. Microscopically there are individual oval to round budding cells (Fig. 36.1B and C). Reproduction is by budding of the cells. Under certain environmental conditions some yeasts may elongate to form a *pseudomycelium*. A mold or filamentous colony (Fig. 36.1D) may be cottony, wooly, fluffy, or powdery in consistency, and various pigments may be seen. It is composed of a mat of intertwining, branching filaments (Fig. 36.1E and F). An individual filament is called a *hypha*, and the collective mass of hyphae is called a *mycelium*. The mycelium that penetrates the medium is known as the *vegetative mycelium*, while the growth that projects into the air from the surface of the substrate is called the *aerial mycelium*. The aerial mycelium may produce spores that when released may be carried to other sites, germinate, and develop into new colonies.

Bacterial colonies, as produced by *Nocardia* and *Actinomyces*, are grossly different in appearance; they are rough and heaped up and may be pigmented. Microscopically, branching filaments but no spores are seen.

The microscopic identification of asexual spores is an important step in the labora-

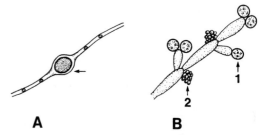

Fig. 36.2. Chlamydospores. (A) Chlamydospores are thick walled structures formed within hyphae (intercalary) or at the ends of hyphae (terminal) (× 400). They are often irregular in form and size but are produced by many fungi. (B) (1) Terminal chlamydospores of *Candida albicans* produced from pseudohyphae; (2) clusters of yeast cells (× 300).

tory diagnosis of pathogenic fungi. Some typical examples of asexual spores are described in the following paragraphs.

A *chlamydospore* develops by the concentration of protoplasm at some point in a hyphal cell (Fig. 36.2). It then enlarges to become wider than other cells in the hypha. With the development of a thick protective wall the spore becomes very resistant to environmental conditions. All fungi produce chlamydospores, and they are often irregular in form and size. The presence of a terminal chlamydospore is helpful in the recognition of *C. albicans*.

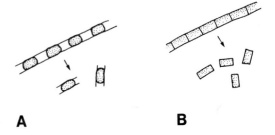

Fig. 36.3. Arthrospores. (A) Barrel shaped arthrospores of *Coccidioides immitis* (× 1000); after the hypha ruptures, a tag of cytoplasm from adjacent cells remains attached to the spore. (B) Rectangular arthrospores of *Geotrichum candidum* (× 500).

Arthrospores develop by fragmentation of hyphae into short, oblong, or rounded structures (Fig. 36.3). Each spore is then capable of forming an entire colony. Only a few fungi form arthrospores (e.g., *Cocci-dioides*, *Geotrichum*, and *Trichosporon*).

Blastospores are unicellular forms of a fungus that reproduce by budding (Fig. 36.1C). The bud increases in size and later breaks off to form a new yeast cell. This method is the common way by which yeasts reproduce (e.g., *Candida*, *Cryptococcus*, *Histoplasma*).

Sporangiospores develop within a swollen enclosed structure called the *sporangium* (Fig. 36.4). The latter is a saclike structure formed at the end of a sporangiophore or stalk projecting from a hypha. Sporangiospores are found in the *Zygomycetes* (e.g., *Rhizopus* or *Mucor*).

Conidiospores are borne openly in the air and are produced by segmentation or by budding of the tips of the hyphae or from the walls of hyphae (Fig. 36.5A and B). The hyphal structure that bears them is a *conidiophore*. An individual spore is called a *conidium*. Conidia that exist as small single cells are termed *microconidia*, while large, multicellular conidia are called *macroconidia*. Both types of spores are usually

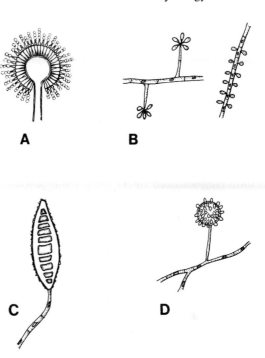

A   **B**

C   **D**

Fig. 36.5. Conidiospores and aleuriospores. (A) Conidiospores or conidia are borne openly. In *Aspergillus niger* (× 100) conidiophores bear a vesicle that is globose and contains two rows or series of sterigmata. The outer series is short and buds off conidia. The conidia are globose, 4 to 5 μm in diameter, brown to black, and very rough. (B) Conidia in *Sporothrix schenckii* (× 500) are produced from long slender, tapering conidiophores produced at right angles from the hyphae. Conidia are formed at the apex, are 2 to 3 by 3 to 6 μm, and are pyriform to oval, and their arrangement suggests a palm tree or a flower head. Sporulation increases with age, so that spores are formed along the sides of the conidiophore and along the undifferentiated hyphae. (C) Macroaleuriospores of *Microsporum canis* (× 250) are 8 to 20 by 40 to 150 μm, have thick walls (2 μm), have up to 15 cells, are spindle shaped and echinulate (prickly surface), and frequently have curved or hooked ends. (D) The characteristic macroaleuriospores of *Histoplasma capsulatum* (× 550) are round or pyriform, 8 to 14 μm in diameter, and contain tubercles or fingerlike projections quite variable in size and morphology.

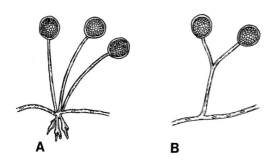

A   **B**

Fig. 36.4. Sporangiospores (× 30). (A) Spores are borne within a sac or sporangium. *Rhizopus* spp. have unbranched sporangiophores and rhizoids or rootlike structure appearing opposite the point of attachment of the sporangiophores. (B) *Mucor* spp. have branched sporangiophores and no rhizoids.

shed when they mature and thus serve to disseminate the species. Successive conidia are frequently formed in a chain in which the terminal spore is the oldest. Examples of conidiospores are found in *Aspergillus* and *Sporothrix* spp.

Aleuriospores resemble conidia in a general way, but they have a thicker point of attachment and are not set free when they mature. *Microaleuriospores* are small and composed of single cells, while *macroaleuriospores* are larger and often multicellular (Figs. 36.1F and 36.5C). In the dermatophytes, classification into three genera is based on the form, size, wall thickness, and presence or absence of echinulations on the macroaleuriospores. The fungi are structurally complex, and variations occur in the type and arrangement of spores that have not been illustrated here. Microscopic identification of spore type and arrangement is very important in laboratory identification of fungi isolated from clinical specimens. Differentiation into genera, species, and varieties is made in large part on a morphological basis, especially the morphology of the reproductive structures. In contrast to bacteria, physiologic and immunologic characteristics of fungi are of minor or sometimes no importance for purposes of identification.

Toxic reactions may be produced by consumption of infected food products. Exotoxins such as aflatoxin are not known to be produced *in vivo* but can be produced *in vitro* by contamination of certain products such as grains, nuts, meal, or animal feed with *Aspergillus*. Ingestion of infected food can lead to toxic reactions. Mushroom poisoning can occur through eating those species that are toxic.

Collection of Clinical Material

The first step in the isolation and identification of fungi is the proper collection of clinical material. The following general comments apply to the various clinical lesions that may be involved:

Cutaneous Lesions; Hair, Skin, Nails. Hairs may be epilated with forceps and placed between glass slides or in a clean pill envelope. Scrapings of skin and nails can be obtained by using a sterile scalpel and should be collected in a sterile Petri dish. In the case of ringworm infections it is important to scrape the border of the lesion rather than the central area, since the latter may have healed and be free from microorganisms.

Subcutaneous Lesions; Draining Fistula or Sinus Tract. If an abscess is open to the outside, drainings or pus can be collected in sterile test tubes. A specimen can best be obtained by curettage from deep in the lesion and should include part of the wall. The specimen should be placed in a sterile tube containing 2 to 3 ml sterile water or saline. If an abscess is closed, fluid can be aspirated with a needle and syringe.

Systemic Mycoses. Specimens may be similar to those collected for bacteriologic examinations. Sputum should be taken early in the morning so that it is likely to contain secretions from the tracheobronchial tree. Specimens should be examined carefully for flecks containing pus or caseous or bloody material. If these are not seen, the sputum may be concentrated. Other specimens may be biopsy material, blood, bone marrow, cerebrospinal fluid, urine, and feces. Additional information on the collection and processing of various clinical specimens may be obtained from the manuals by Haley and Callaway or Lenette *et al* (see references).

Laboratory Diagnosis

It is important to discuss some aspects of the laboratory diagnosis of fungi, since some procedures differ from techniques used in the isolation and identification of bacteria. Initial attention is given to direct microscopic examination of clinical material and cultivation on appropriate media.

Direct Microscopic Examination. Demonstration of fungi in biopsy or tissue sections can be done by many specific stains, including the Gomori methenamine silver method. Fresh clinical material is frequently examined by a wet-mount preparation in which a loopful of material is placed on a glass slide in a drop of water or lactophenol cotton blue for light staining, a coverslip emplaced, and microscopic examination conducted under low and high magnification. In the case of skin, hair, or nails, or with a variety of specimens, a drop of 10 percent KOH may be used in order to lyse pus or skin cells, thus providing better visualization of the fungi. This rapid procedure will demonstrate the presence of mycelial elements of dermatophytes and serve to establish a diagnosis. It is also useful to visualize the short, hyphal strands and yeast forms of pityriasis versicolor as well as the yeast and mycelial elements of mucocutaneous lesions of candidiasis. If yeast or bacteria are suspected, a stained smear is helpful. With periodic acid-Schiff (PAS) stain, fungi stain red. If the Gram stain has been used to detect bacteria, fungi appear dark blue. Many fungi are too weakly gram-positive to be seen well on Gram stain.

Cultivation of Clinical Material. Since fungi are not nutritionally fastidious, the standard most commonly used medium is Sabouraud's dextrose agar (SDA). It is a simple medium that contains beef extract and dextrose at pH 5.6, which discourages bacterial growth. In order to make it more selective for fungi, antimicrobial agents are frequently added. A broad spectrum antibiotic such as aureomycin or chloromycetin reduces bacterial overgrowth, and cycloheximide retards the growth of nonpathogenic fungi. The latter is a general inhibitor of eucaryotic protein synthesis, although most pathogenic fungi are not inhibited by it. As a note of caution, anti-microbial agents should not be included in the medium when clinical material is suspected for *Cryptococcus*, *Aspergillus*, or *Mucor* spp., since they may be inhibited by these agents. Most fungal pathogens grow slowly, so that tubes should be observed for 4 to 6 weeks before a negative report is given.

Identification of Fungal Isolates. Pathogens grow more slowly than nonpathogens and usually require 7 to 14 days on primary isolation. Those colonies or portions of colonies that may be granular in appearance, rather than cottony, more frequently contain asexual spores useful in identification. Two procedures are employed for microscopic examination of fungal growth. A colony may be removed by a bent wire, rather than a bacteriologic loop, transferred to a drop of lactophenol cotton blue on a glass slide, and the filaments teased apart before emplacement of a coverslip. However, this technique can destroy or disrupt delicate sporulating structures, making identification difficult. Therefore for examination of dermatophytes and saprophytes, a slide culture technique is employed. The top of a sterile test tube is used to cut out a block of agar medium so that it can be placed on a glass slide. The sides of the agar block are inoculated with fungus, a coverslip is emplaced, and the slide is incubated in a Petri dish with moist filter paper to provide humidity. After the sporulating structures have developed, the intact growth may be examined microscopically for identification. Production of asexual spores may be stimulated by growth on a low-nutrient or "deficient" medium such as Czapek-Dox agar or cornmeal agar.

Biochemical tests that are sometimes useful in identification include tests for carbohydrate assimilation and fermentation, proteolytic activity, and hydrolysis of casein, starch, and urea. It is usually not necessary to perform pathogenicity tests in laboratory animals for suspected systemic fungi, but mice and guinea pigs can be used if growth fails to occur from clinical materials. Serologic tests are often very useful for diagnosis and prognosis of a systemic fungus disease, but sera from patients should be compared with positive reference sera when tested with a commercial antigen preparation. Serologic tests are of little value in dermatophyte or subcutaneous infections. In systemic infections precipitin titers usually appear first and are often diagnostic for the disease. In some diseases precipitin patterns have been correlated with the presence or absence of active disease in contrast to past infection. This procedure should become more useful as purer preparations of specific antigens are produced. Positive complement fixation tests appear later, and the persistence or disappearance of positivity is correlated with the progress of the patient. Fluorescent antibodies may be very useful for the demonstration of specific fungi in tissue, sputum, and exudate; sometimes it may be the only procedure to establish a diagnosis in the event that cultures fail or were not taken. Current attention is being given to the use of very sensitive techniques for the detection of fungal antigens in body fluids; these tests would be extremely important for the early recognition of invasive diseases, such as candidiasis, aspergillosis, and mucormycosis.

The Immune Response

Infection depends upon exposure to a sufficient number of organisms and upon the resistance of the host. Generally the immune response to fungus infections is very good and is usually sufficient to prevent clinical disease. For example, in endemic areas large numbers of persons may inhale spores from the environment and express few or no symptoms as the infecting organisms are controlled. This is followed by specific resistance to reinfection. On the other hand, if the host defense mechanism is lowered, then many oppotunistic fungi of

low virulence can become established and produce disease. If the patient recovers from such an infection, no specific resistance is produced.

Humoral antibodies appear to play little or no role in the containment of most fungus infections. Cellular immune mechanisms are the primary defense mechanisms. This point is illustrated in patients who have various types of immune deficiencies. In patients who have various degrees of thymus or T cell defects, opportunistic fungus infections are common. However, if the defect is in the B cells, fungal disease is uncommon, although bacterial infections may be frequent. The role of humoral and cellular defense mechanisms is also reflected in the pathologic manifestations produced by infection. For example, pathogenic fungi in the normal host induce a pyogenic reaction followed by a granulomatous reaction. The response that is elicited by invasion of opportunistic fungi is necrotic and suppurative. In the latter case, the host is deficient and cannot contain the organism.

Hypersensitivity and allergy to fungi can be manifested in different ways. Inhalation of the spores of fungi may induce asthma. Other allergic reactions are manifested as "ids" or eruptions associated with cutaneous infections due to dermatophytes or *Candida* spp. In other cases an allergic reaction such as erythema nodosum may be part of the primary infection with systemic disease, as in coccidioidomycosis. Hypersensitivity may be demonstrated by an intradermal test with an extract of a fungus culture (e.g., coccidioidin or histoplasmin). A positive skin test is evaluated in a fashion similar to a tuberculin test (i.e., an area of redness and induration 5 mm or greater after 48 hours indicates previous exposure to the specific organism used for testing). Hypersensitivity is often associated with good resistance to infection or reinfection. Since exposure to the systemic fungi generally confers a lifelong reactivity to the skin-test antigen (e.g., histoplasmin), the skin test is of little diagnostic or prognostic value except in cases of disseminated disease, in which absence of reactivity indicates anergy. However, a negative skin test may also be obtained in patients who have a deficiency in cell-mediated immunity and who thus may be more prone to fungal infections such as candidiasis. The use of serologic reactions in the diagnosis of fungal infections was discussed in the preceding section.

Therapy

It is important to establish a diagnosis of a fungal agent when it is the cause of disease, because treatment is different from that of bacterial infections. Most antibacterial antibiotics are not effective in treating fungus diseases, and the few antifungal agents available are ineffective against bacteria. When one considers therapy for systemic fungal infections, the first question is whether or not any treatment is indicated. Self-limited infections resolve spontaneously, but progressive infections require therapeutic intervention. For example, the small percentage of patients with histoplasmosis or coccidioidomycosis requiring therapy have overwhelming systemic infection. In contrast, all patients with blastomycosis require therapy regardless of the clinical severity of the primary infection. Such differences probably relate to the specific pathophysiologies of the diseases.

Patients with infections caused by opportunistic pathogens also require similar consideration. Candidemia (yeast cells in the blood) is often transient and resolves spontaneously. However, endocarditis or invasive disease in a compromised host requires treatment. A pulmonary cryptococcal infection usually resolves spontaneously, but cryptococcal meningitis is always fatal unless treated.

New drugs, such as corticosteroids and immunosuppresive agents, as well as new medicosurgical techniques employing open-heart surgery or insertion of prosthetic devices and catheters, have modified the host and favored the introduction of endogenous and exogenous yeasts. Deep visceral or septicemic infections are now more common and may be due to yeasts belonging to the genera *Candida, Torulopsis, Cryptococcus, Trichosporon, Rhodotorula,* and *Saccharmyces.*

One group of effective antifungal agents is the polyene antibiotics, having a conjugated double bond system $(CH=CH)_n$ and rings that vary from 26 to 38 carbon atoms. The two most useful of these antibiotics are nystatin and amphotericin B. Both act against the cell membrane of the fungus, combine with sterols unique to these cellular membranes, and cause leakage of intracellular potassium and other metabolites. Nystatin is effective in topical candida infections but not in deep mycoses or dermatophyte infections. Amphotericin B is effective against the deep mycoses (e.g., histoplasmosis, cryptococcosis); however, the usefulness of amphotericin B is somewhat limited by its toxicity, which may vary from the production of a mild headache, chills, and fever to severe hemolytic anemia and acute nephritis.

Another effective group of therapeutic agents is the pyrimidine antimetabolites. The best example is 5-fluorocytosine (flucytosine or 5-FC). It is particularly effective in treating yeast infections, but it is also active against species of *Aspergillus* and fungi causing chromomycosis. It may interfere with pyrimidine metabolism or DNA synthesis. However, it has been cited as a cause of hepatic, gastrointestinal, and bone marrow toxicity.

The imidazole antimycotics make up a group with very broad spectrum, high activity, and tolerable amounts of side effects. Miconazole appears to be very effective in coccidioidomycosis and paracoccidioidomycosis. It is thought to work by interacting with cell membranes and causing leakage of cytoplasmic contents. Ketoconazole is a new, well absorbed oral imidazole with minimum side effects and limited toxicity; it is effective against several fungi, including *Candida albicans*. The mechanism of action is inhibition of ergosterol synthesis, a critical step in synthesis of fungal cell walls and membranes. A good response in chronic mucocutaneous candidiasis with combined 5-FC and ketoconazole may be due to the antimetabolic effect of the former combining with the antimembrane effect of the latter to prevent emergence of resistant strains.

The antibiotic griseofulvin is effective against the dermatophyte infections but not in deep mycoses. It interferes with protein and nucleic acid synthesis. The pathogenic actinomycetes (*Actinomyces, Nocardia*) are bacteria and therefore susceptible to antibacterial chemotherapy (e.g., penicillin, sulfadiazine).

In order to alleviate a deficiency of cell-mediated immunity in some patients, it may be necessary to consider the administration of transfer factor (extract of lymphocytes from sensitized donors), viable lymphocytes, or fetal thymus tissue.

CUTANEOUS INFECTIONS

Dermatophytoses

Cutaneous infections of humans include a variety of diseases involving the skin, hair, and nails. Infection is generally restricted to the nonliving cornified layers, but a variety of pathologic changes can occur in the host because of the presence of the infectious agent and its metabolic products. The majority of these infections are caused by a homogeneous group of keratinophilic fungi called the dermatophytes. These "ringworm" fungi are among the most common infectious agents of man. Dermatophytoses are limited to the keratinized tissues — nails, hair, and stratum corneum of the skin.

Disease produced by dermatophytes is called *tinea* or ringworm. Growth of the fungus in skin and scalp is more or less equal in all directions, so that the lesions produced tend to creep in a circular or ring form. Historically, the Romans associated the lesions with insects and named the disease *tinea*, meaning larva.

Correlation of a specific dermatophyte with a characteristic disease process has been difficult because a single species can cause a variety of clinical manifestations in different parts of the body; also, the same clinical appearance can be caused by dermatophytes of different species or different genera. Therefore dermatologists have frequently employed a terminology based on the part of the body involved. One may define the clinical conditions as tinea capitis (ringworm of the scalp), tinea favosa (favus due to *T. schoenleinii*), tinea corporis (ringworm of the body), tinea imbricata (ringworm due to *T. concentricum*), tinea cruris (ringworm of the groin), tinea unguium or onychomycosis (ringworm of the nails), tinea pedis (ringworm of the feet), tinea barbae (ringworm of the bearded area of face and neck), and tinea manuum (ringworm of the hands).

Clinical Manifestations. All infections begin in the horny layer of the epidemis. Those that involve the hair follicles, hair, and nails soon invade these structures. On the skin the host reaction may be limited to patchy scaling or proceed to a toxic eczemaform eruption. Later an inflammatory reaction may occur. In most cases apparent resolution occurs, although the host may become a normal carrier and stress or trauma may exacerbate clinical disease.

Although dermatophytes can exhibit a keratinolytic activity, their failure to invade living tissues is probably due to inhibitory factors in serum as well as a sensitivity to body temperature (37°C). Invasion usually stops where there are viable multiplying tissue cells.

The three genera of dermatophytes responsible for infection are *Microsporum*, *Trichophyton*, and *Epidermophyton*. The dermatophytes can initiate disease in skin, hair, or nails, depending upon the species and the host response. *Microsporum* spp. may infect the hair or skin, *Trichophyton* spp. can infect hair, skin, or nails, and *Epidermophyton floccosum* may infect the skin and/or nails. Most dermatophyte infections throughout the world are caused by a limited number of species (Table 36.3). Although six of these species cause infection within the continental United States, worldwide travel has increased the possibility of host exposure to species formerly limited to certain geographic areas. The source of human infection by dermatophytes may be anthropophilic (from another human), zoophilic (from an animal), or geophilic (from the soil). When the scalp is infected the physician may be aided by examining the patient's scalp under Wood's light, an ultraviolet light of 3650 Å. Hairs infected by some dermatophytes fluoresce when examined in a darkened room (Table 36.3). Additional examination of hair or skin scrapings are made in the laboratory.

Laboratory Diagnosis. Laboratory diagnosis of dermatophytoses is based on morphology and involves a direct microscopic examination of clinical material and its culture on appropriate media. Microscopic examination of individual hairs may reveal the presence of spores around the hair (ectothrix infection) or inside the hair (endothrix infection). A recognition of small or large spore ectothrix or endothrix infection aids in the diagnosis (Table 36.3). Skin scrapings can be examined in a KOH preparation or stained by periodic acid-Schiff stain to detect hyphal elements.

In order to determine that an infection is due to a dermatophyte, clinical material may be cultured on *dermatophyte test medium*, a selective medium designed to exclude most bacteria and contaminant fungi. As dermatophytes grow they change the color of the medium from yellow to red. For determination of the genus and species of the fungus, cultures are made on SDA. Gross examination of colonies and microscopic examination for characteristic asexual spores are made.

One example of morphological characteristics that aid in species identification is given in Fig. 36.1D, E, and F. Man is most commonly infected by two species of *Microsporum*, *M. audouinii* (transmitted from humans) and *M. canis* (transmitted from animals — cats and dogs). *M. audouinii* was the most common cause of tinea capitis in schoolchildren in the United States. However, with the immigration of people

Table 36.3. Dermatophytes and Their Mode of Hair Invasion

| | Invades Hair and Follicles | | | | Rare or No Invasion of Hair or Follicles |
| | Large Spores | | Small-Spore Ectothrix | No Spores in Hair: "Favic type"[a] | |
Ecology	Ectothrix	Endothrix			
Anthropophilic	T. mentagrophytes (var. interdigitalis)	T. tonsurans	M. audouinii[b]	T. schoenleinii[b]	T. rubrum, E. floccosum
Zoophilic	T. mentagrophytes (var. mentagrophytes) T. verrucosum	—	M. canis[b]	—	—
Geophilic	M. gypseum[c] M. nanum[c]	—	—	—	—

[a]Favus is a clinical description of ringworm (tinea favosa) frequently involving the scalp. It is characterized by dense masses of mycelium and epithelial debris which form yellowish, cup shaped crusts called scutula.

[b]Parasitized hairs usually fluoresce under Wood's light. Fluorescence is usually bright yellow-green except for *T. schoenleinii* where dull bluish-white fluorescence is frequent.

[c]Not commonly isolated from human infections.

from Mexico, Puerto Rico, and other Latin American countries, *Trichophyton tonsurans*, which is endemic in those regions has become quite common in this country. In these areas this dermatophyte tends to supplant *M. audouinii* as the most frequent cause of tinea capitis. The principal etiologic agents of tinea pedis (athlete's foot) in the United States are *Trichophyton mentagrophytes* and *Trichophyton rubrum*. The most frequent cause of other dermatophytoses may vary from area to area. Strain and species differences may also account for differences in the spread of infection.

Many species of dermatophytes are known to have a perfect or sexual stage and can be placed in the class *Ascomycetes*. The major purpose of knowing the perfect stage is for identification in epidemiologic studies, where matings of a clinical isolate can be made with known strains.

Hypersensitivity. Hypersensitivity can be demonstrated by skin tests using trichophytin. At present, preparations used are not species specific and are of limited diagnostic and prognostic value. If immunity exists, it is very transient following infection.

A secondary problem that may rise following infection with dermatophytes is the development of a *dermatophytid* or *id reaction*. This is a secondary eruption occurring in sensitized individuals as a result of the spread of fungi or their products from a site of primary infection. For example, following a primary infection in the foot, secondary eruptions or pustules may occur on the hands. Fungi are found only at the primary site and not in the site of the id reaction. These hypersensitivity reactions disappear following resolution of the dermatophyte infection.

Therapy. Topical agents are used when effective. The antibiotic griseofulvin is uniquely effective against dermatophytes. The drug accumulates in the keratinous structures as they are formed and renders them resistant to infection.

Candidiasis

Candidiasis is a primary or secondary infection produced by yeasts of the genus *Candida*, most commonly *C. albicans*. It is also known by the older term *moniliasis* or by the specific terms *thrush, dermatocandidiasis*, and *mycotic vulvo-vaginitis*. Presently, *Candida* is recognized as one of the most frequently encountered fungal opportunists. *C. albicans* is a normal inhabitant of the alimentary tract and the mucocutaneous regions. It is present regularly in small numbers in the mouths of normal healthy adults. It is present in the vagina in about 5 percent of healthy nonpregnant women, but its frequency may increase to 30 percent in pregnant women.

Clinical Manifestations. Candidiasis can present a diversity of clinical pictures, and all tissues and organ systems may be invaded. There are three basic forms of infectious disease (Table 36.4): acute mucocutaneous and cutaneous candidiasis, chronic mucocutaneous candidiasis, and acute systemic candidiasis. These infections may be localized and self-limited, may exhibit widely disseminated cutaneous lesions, or may be disseminated systemically to various organs. The most serious cases are found in those patients whose resistance is deficient or has been suppressed. In addition to infectious diseases, *Candida* spp. also produce some important allergic manifestations.

In candidiasis, lesions may occur in the mouth, vagina, skin, nails, bronchi, or alimentary tract. Occasionally organisms may progress from these sites to produce septicemia, endocarditis, or meningitis. However, in most cases the infection is mild. The distribution of the disease is worldwide and occurs in all age groups.

The most common form of the disease is an acute or subacute mucocutaneous involvement called oral candidiasis or thrush. A creamy-white or gray pseudomembrane covers the tongue and oral surfaces of chil-

Table 36.4. Infectious Candidiasis

Acute mucocutaneous and cutaneous candidiasis

Caused by environmental changes that act locally (water and sweating); physiologic changes such as pregnancy; alteration of microbial flora by antibiotics; reduction of host resistance by steroid therapy

Localized and self-limited infection — oral, vulvar, or paronychial lesions

Chronic mucocutaneous candidiasis

Caused by defects of cell-mediated immunity that lead to widely disseminated cutaneous lesions.

Oral, vulvar, and paronychial lesions, but no systemic lesions

Acute systemic candidiasis

Caused by inadvertent introduction of yeasts from indwelling catheters; injections in drug addicts; depression of host resistance by drugs in debilitated patients and those with advanced lymphoproliferative diseases (Hodgkin's disease, leukemia)

Visceral organs involved — meningitis, endocarditis, or dissemination to kidneys, lungs, brain, liver, etc.

---

dren or adults. Significant predisposing factors may be the low pH of the mouth of the newborn, endocrine disturbances of older children, and, in adults, vitamin deficiency, diabetes, or prolonged use of antibiotics, steroids, and other drugs.

Cutaneous candidiasis involves the intertriginous areas of the glabrous skin and may occur directly or secondary to preexisting lesions. This form of candidiasis is seen commonly in the axillae, groins, or intermammary folds. The lesions are characteristic and well defined as weeping, "scalded skin" areas with an erythematous base and a scalloped border. This clinical form is seen in two types of patients: those with metabolic disorders such as diabetes, obesity, or sequelae of chronic alcoholism, and those whose skin is predisposed to infections by environmental conditions such as moisture (e.g., frequent immersion in water may occur in a number of occupations).

Involvement of the nails is also quite common.

Chronic mucocutaneous candidiasis describes a clinical manifestation that is associated with genetic defects and occurs primarily in children. One major group of abnormalities is associated with a congenital absence or dysplasia of the thymus leading frequently to lethal immunologic deficiencies. Two examples are Swiss-type agammaglobulinemia and DiGeorge's syndrome. On the other hand, if the genetic defects involve humoral immunity alone (Bruton's hypogammaglobulinemia), then there may be no increased incidence of candidiasis. Another group of abnormalities associated with chronic mucocutaneous candidiasis involves nonlethal immunologic deficiencies and multiple endocrinopathies. A number of lesser deficiencies in T lymphocyte function have been detected in different patients. Sensitized lymphocytes may recognize antigen but fail to become activated or, if activated, may fail to produce active mediators (e.g., chemotactic factors and macrophage inhibitory factor). Thus macrophages are not attracted to or held at the site of antigenic stimulus, so that the *Candida* organisms cannot be phagocytized and destroyed. Other patients may have a defective myeloperoxidase system preventing leukocytes from killing candidae after phagocytosis. The clinical appearance of candidiasis can be related to the type of deficiency encountered. For example, patients who have an effective macrophage system may express clinically a macular or scaling skin lesion, while patients who have defective macrophages may have granulomatous lesions reflecting the failure of candidae to be removed.

Defects in humoral immunity in chronic mucocutaneous candidiasis are important also, since humoral antibodies (especially locally produced secretory IgA) may play a significant role in helping to contain the infection and to opsonize the invading yeast cells. An alteration or deficiency of complement activity may also alter the role of phagocytosis. Thus the effects of humoral and cell-mediated defects in the immune system lead to severe and widely disseminated mucocutaneous lesions.

Systemic candidiasis is a rarer condition resulting from continued inoculations of yeasts into the body (e.g., drug addicts, indwelling catheters, or long-term antibiotic or steroid therapy). Systemic infection may lead to the involvement of the urinary tract, endocarditis, and meningitis. The prognosis in these conditions is poor, and the death rate is high.

Allergic manifestations of candidiasis are due to allergy to the metabolites of candidae. The clinical condition, consisting of sterile vesicular lesions on the hands or other areas of the body, is called candidids and is similar to the id reaction of ringworm infection. Extracellular products of *Candida* spp. can induce both delayed and immediate types of hypersensitivity, and a variety of such reactions may occur, including eczemas, asthma, and gastritis.

Laboratory Diagnosis. Scrapings from cutaneous and mucocutaneous lesions can be examined microscopically in wet-mount preparations or as smears stained by the Gram method. The distinctive picture of yeast cells and pseudohyphae should allow a rapid diagnosis of infection. Pseudohyphae are not an indication of thermal dimorphism, since these structures are determined by nutrient factors and not temperature. Other specimens, such as sputum, vaginal discharge, urine, and fecal samples, usually are more difficult to interpret. The presence of yeasts in such specimens is not by itself diagnostic, since many yeasts, including *C. albicans*, can be found in these specimens originating from normal subjects.

For cultivation of clinical material, fresh specimens should be inoculated on SDA to confirm the presence of yeasts (Figs. 36.1A, B, and C), as well as to obtain a quantitative estimation of the organisms present. Since *C. albicans* is the primary pathogen in man, the next step is to identify the organism isolated. In some circumstances a rapid identification is desirable. One of the most reliable tests is the germ tube test, where a pure culture of yeasts is added to serum and incubated at 37°C for 2 hours. After such incubation only *C. albicans* and occasionally *Candida stellatoidea* will form a short germ tube, the beginning of a pseudohypha. *C. albicans* can then be distinguished by its ability to give a positive sucrose assimilation test (i.e., growth in the presence of sucrose as the sole source of carbohydrates); *C. stellatoidea* gives a negative reaction. Identification of *C. albicans* is done more routinely by inoculation of the isolated and pure yeast culture onto cornmeal agar. The characteristic microscopic structures sought are the terminal chlamydospores produced from pseudohyphae (Fig. 36.2B). These structures are indicative of *C. albicans* or *C. stellatoidea*, and again the sucrose assimilation test can be used to distinguish them. If other species of *Candida* are isolated (i.e., germ tube test is negative and there are no terminal chlamydospores), assimilation and fermentation tests can be performed with a number of carbohydrates for identification. Recently *Candida tropicalis* has been found to be a major pathogen in immunologically compromised patients.

Serologic tests can be of great help in establishing that tissue invasion has occurred and the host's immune response has been stimulated. However, many normal individuals may have antibodies to *Candida* antigens, reflecting superficial colonization of mucous membranes or previous infections. Therefore the detection of a two- to fourfold rise in titer would indicate recent infection and demonstrate that the yeast isolate was more than a mere contaminant. Precipitation tests or counterimmunoelectrophoresis using cytoplasmic protein antigen from yeast-phase cells are recommended. Of greater urgency in diagnosis is the recognition of systemic candidiasis. In such patients a humoral response has been found to mannan, a major surface polysaccharide of several *Candida* spp. Antibody can be detected by a radioimmunoassay or by a passive hemagglutination test using sheep red blood cells coated with purified mannan. Recent studies have indicated that earlier detection of invasive disease, prior to the appearance of antibodies to mannan, can be achieved by testing serum for the presence of mannan antigen using a hemagglutination inhibition assay or an enzyme-linked immunosorbent assay (ELISA).

Therapy. Topical agents such as 1 percent crystal violet may be applied directly to cutaneous lesions. Nystatin has some success for oral, intestinal, or cutaneous candidiasis. It may be used as an ointment or in tablet form for vaginal inserts. It is difficult to decide whether or not to treat for suspected systemic candidiasis. Colonization with various *Candida* spp. is common among hospitalized patients, especially those receiving immunosuppressive agents. When the organism is present as a commensal, treatment is not necessary. For example, positive blood cultures may represent only transient fungemia that can be corrected by removal of a contaminated intravenous catheter. However, in invasive disease the organism may not be isolated. Candida may not be found in the sputum in pneumonia or in urine in pyelonephritis, even when it is the causative agent. Therefore the use of serologic tests may be a guide to treatment. For systemic infection, amphotericin B, 5-fluorocytosine, or a substituted imidazole such as ketoconazole may be used.

After successful antifungal therapy, a fourfold decline in serum antibody titer may denote the successful application of therapy or the elimination of colonization. Alteration of causative environmental factors or control of endocrine problems should be managed as well.

Treatment of chronic mucocutaneous candidiasis may require additional measures because of genetic defects and a lack of adequate host response to the invading yeast cells. It may be possible to correct a defect in cell-mediated immunity by transfer of fetal thymus tissue. A temporary alleviation may be accomplished by using transfer factor, an extract of lymphocytes obtained from a pool of donors already sensitized to *C. albicans*. In some patients combined treatment by chemotherapy and immunotherapy may be desirable.

SYSTEMIC FUNGAL INFECTIONS

The fungi producing systemic disease can be subdivided into two major groups: opportunistic fungi, which are of low virulence and which produce disease almost exclusively in patients debilitated by some other cause, whose defense mechanisms are impaired, and primarily pathogenic fungi, which can cause disease in a normal healthy host provided that sufficient numbers of microorganisms are present in the infecting dose. In debilitated patients the course of infection and disease by pathogenic fungi is exaggerated.

Opportunistic fungi include yeasts, which produce the diseases candidiasis and cryptococcosis, and molds, which produce the diseases aspergillosis and mucormycosis. In present medical practice the advent of cytotoxic drugs, long-term steroid treatment, and immunosuppressive agents has markedly increased the number and severity of diseases caused by opportunistic fungi. The diverse array of organisms being isolated from these treated patients suggests that probably all fungi may be considered potential pathogens when normal defenses are abrogated.

There are several characteristics unique to opportunistic fungi. They are always present in the environment, and they have no particular geographic distribution. *Candida* and *Aspergillus* spp. account for the vast majority of opportunistic fungal infections in debilitated patients. There is no dimorphism exhibited by the causative organisms. The morphological changes demonstrated by candidae, for example, are determined by nutrition rather than by temperature. Infections are often insidious and may not be diagnosed until autopsy. There are no differences in susceptibility according to age, sex, or race. The usual cellular response to opportunistic fungi is a suppurative necrotic process and perhaps some poorly organized granulomatous reaction. Recovery from opportunistic infections does not result in specific immunity.

Primarily pathogenic fungi are the dimorphic fungi, causing histoplasmosis, coccidioidomycosis, blastomycosis, and paracoccidioidomycosis. These fungi grow in the form of molds as soil saprophytes, but when the spores are inhaled or gain entrance by other means into the body they are able to adapt and grow in this unnatural environment. Usually the host is able to contain the organism, and no clinical disease occurs. However, should sufficient numbers of organisms be introduced, there will be drastic changes in the morphology, metabolism, cell wall content and structure, enzyme systems, and methods of reproduction of the invading spores. Thus a yeast or tissue phase of the dimorphic organisms develops. There are some additional characteristics of pathogenic fungi that make them different from opportunistic fungi. Pathogenic fungi have a very restricted geographic distribution, and sometimes to acquire the infection (e.g., coccidioidomycosis) an individual has to be in that location at the particular time of the year when the fungus is sporulating. Agricultural workers and those living in rural areas are especially exposed to pathogenic fungi because of their constant contact with the soil. Sex and race are important factors. Males have more serious disease, and dark-skinned individuals have a greater risk of developing the disseminated form of the disease (coccidioidomycosis). In chronic in-

fections the usual cellular response is a granulomatous process resembling that seen in tuberculosis. Resolution of infection is accompanied by a strong specific resistance to reinfection that is of long duration.

The disease candidiasis was discussed previously under the subject of cutaneous infections. As opportunistic fungi *Candida* spp. can invade the host systemically and produce urinary tract infections, endocarditis, and meningitis. This is especially likely to occur in patients who have defective resistance.

Cryptococcosis

Cryptococcosis is a chronic or subacute systemic infection caused by the yeast *Cryptococcus neoformans*. This disease has also been known as torulosis, Busse-Buschke's disease, European blastomycosis, and malade signal. In man the primary infection is almost always pulmonary, following inhalation of yeasts. Infection is usually subclinical and transitory. However, in debilitated patients or compromised hosts it may arise as a complication of other diseases and then may become rapidly systemic. It has been referred to as the signal disease (malade signal), since it signals or indicates an underlying debilitating disease. *C. neoformans* has a predilection for the central nervous system and is a unique organism because of its production of a broad polysaccharide capsule in the infected host and in culture. The chief vector for the distribution and maintenance of the fungus is the pigeon. The pigeon is not infected, but in the accumulated fecal material found in pigeon roosts the organism can grow because of the alkaline substrate rich in nitrogen and salt. There the yeast can predominate and remain viable for 2 years or more. However, in the soil or other environments the organism is unable to compete with other organisms for survival. *C. neoformans* is worldwide in distribution and is constantly associated with avian habitats. Dust from these environments may contain viable virulent organisms, and infection is frequently associated with cleaning of infected areas. In the desiccated state the organisms may be no more than 1 μm in diameter, a condition that allows them to be inhaled into the alveolar spaces of the lung.

Clinical Manifestations. The portal of entry for cryptococci is the lungs. The clinical types of cryptococcal disease include pulmonary, central nervous system, cutaneous and mucocutaneous, osseous, and visceral.

Most cases of primary infection of the lungs are asymptomatic, although sometimes symptoms may include cough, low grade fever, pleuritic pain, malaise, and weight loss. The infection frequently becomes established in the lower part of the lung, but usually no cavitation, fibrosis, or calcification occurs. The most serious extension of the disease is dissemination of infection from the lung to the central nervous system. The reason for the predilection of *C. neoformans* for the central nervous system has not been explained so far, but it may depend upon additional nutritive factors in the spinal fluid or lack of inhibitory humoral and cellular factors. The patients will have clinical symptoms of headache, which may be frontal, temporal, or retoorbital, intermittent, and of increasing frequency and severity. Additional signs of meningitis can be observed. Cryptococcosis usually causes a rapidly progressive deterioration of the patient, and untreated cases of meningitis are usually fatal.

Although dissemination of the disease from the lungs to produce meningitis is often recognized in the United States, cutaneous or mucocutaneous forms of the disease following dissemination have been recognized more often in Europe (10 to 15 percent). In about 5 to 10 percent of cases of cryptococcosis bone is involved, particularly bony prominences, cranial bones, and vertebrae. Dissemination may result in gran-

ulomatous lesions in any organ or tissue of the body.

Laboratory Diagnosis. Spinal fluid is the specimen of choice to be examined from patients with suspected cryptococcal meningitis. Direct examination of the spinal fluid can be made by three tests:

1. India ink stain (Fig. 36.6). When a smear of spinal fluid mixed with ink is examined microscopically, a clear area surrounding typical budding yeast cells marks the wide capsule. White blood cells (7 to 20 μm in diameter) in the spinal fluid are similar in size to yeasts (5 μm in diameter) and can be mistaken if an unstained preparation is examined. Sputum and pus may also be stained by India ink after digestion with potassium hydroxide to eliminate extraneous cells.

2. Immunofluorescence test. This test is valuable when smaller numbers of cryptococci are present that may not be detected by the India ink stain. A hyperimmune rabbit serum to *C. neoformans* is

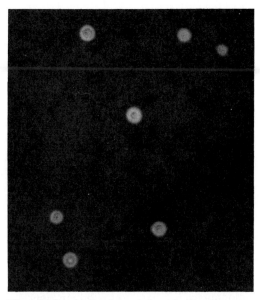

Fig. 36.6. India ink stain of *Cryptococcus neoformans*. Clear area surrounding the yeast cell marks the thick polysaccharide capsule, which is not penetrated by India ink ($\times$ 500).

labeled with fluorescent dye and added to a concentrated smear of spinal fluid. Individual yeast cells fluoresce when examined microscopically under ultraviolet light.

3. Latex agglutination and ELISA tests. A more sensitive test for detection of cryptococcal meningitis is based upon the detection of capsular polysaccharide antigen shed into the spinal fluid. Inert latex particles can be coated with rabbit antibody to the capsular polysaccharide of *C. neoformans* and then mixed with the patient's spinal fluid. The antigen present will cause agglutination of the coated latex particles.

Another technique for the detection of capsular polysaccharide in body fluids is an enzyme-linked immunosorbent assay (ELISA) using rabbit anticryptococcal globulin. This sensitive test can detect cryptococcal capsular polysaccharide at a concentration of 6 ng/ml compared with 35 ng/ml detectable by the latex agglutination test. Thus it may permit earlier diagnosis and initiation of therapy.

Clinical material may be cultured on SDA. The organisms are not dimorphic and grow only as yeasts at 37°C and at room temperature. Colonies tend to be very mucoid owing to the large capsule. Confirmation that the culture is *Cryptococcus* is made by performing a urease test; only species of *Cryptococcus* give a positive test (color of medium changes from pink to red or purple). Further determination that the species is *C. neoformans* can be made by growing the organisms on Niger seed agar, prepared from an extract of thistle or bird seeds. During growth on this medium *C. neoformans* assimilates creatine and absorbs a brown pigment from the seed extract. Consequently, brown colonies indicate the pathogenic *C. neoformans*, while colonies from other, nonpathogenic species of *Cryptococcus* remain white. *C. neoformans* also has the ability to convert a component of esculin to a pigment resembling melanin so that colonies are brown-black in

color on a growth medium containing esculin. Additional assimilation and fermentation tests may be performed to confirm the recognition of *C. neoformans*.

Because of its capsular polysaccharide, *C. neoformans* elicits little humoral or allergic response. Nevertheless, serum antibodies may be detected by an indirect fluorescent antibody test with *C. neoformans* yeast cells. Antibodies may be detected prior to the detection of polysaccharide antigen and again after therapy, when the organisms and antigen have been eliminated.

Therapy. Local lesions of the lung usually heal without treatment. In disseminated cases combined therapy using amphotericin B and 5-fluorocytosine is recommended. Intravenous therapy is adequate for meningeal as well as other forms of disease. The fatality of meningococcal cryptococcosis has been reduced to about 6 percent with proper treatment.

Aspergillosis

The mold *Aspergillus* has been recognized only recently as an important agent of opportunistic infections in debilitated patients. However, the entire range of pathogenic processes can include (1) toxicity due to ingestion of food contaminated by aflatoxin, an exotoxin of *Aspergillus* spp., (2) allergy and sequelae due to the presence of spores or transient growth of the organism in body orifices, (3) colonization without extension in preformed cavities and debilitated tissues, (4) invasive, inflammatory, granulomatous, necrotizing disease of lungs and other organs, and, rarely, (5) systemic and fatal disseminated disease.

Aspergillus spp. are among the most common fungi of all environments throughout the world, and spores are constantly being inhaled from the air. However, only about eight species have been consistently involved in human infectious disease.

Aspergillus fumigatus accounts for almost all diseases, both allergic and invasive. Infection with aspergilli has occurred in all age groups, both sexes, all races, and in all parts of the world. Primary disease is rare but can follow exposure to masses of spores. Secondary aspergillosis has been associated with antibiotics, steroids, radiation, cytotoxins, neoplasias, and tuberculosis. The increased use of immunosuppressive drugs leads to an increased frequency of disseminated aspergillosis.

Clinical Manifestations. The three major categories of disease involving aspergilli are allergic aspergillosis, colonizing aspergillosis, and invasive disease. Asthmatic allergy to spores of the various *Aspergillus* spp. is similar to allergy produced to various types of dander, pollen, or spores. This form of the disease may become more chronic and severe, developing into bronchopulmonary aspergillosis with some airway obstruction. Colonizing aspergillosis (aspergilloma) develops by the colonization or fungus growth in preformed cavities caused by other diseases such as tuberculosis or sarcoidosis. A characteristic "fungus ball" may develop within the cavity, consisting of tangled masses of mycelium that may sporulate if there is air space above them. A frequent clinical picture of aspergilloma is recurrent hemoptysis (spitting of blood from the lungs), which can lead to death. Invasive aspergillosis is not common but can develop from the preceding forms of the disease. Clinically the disease is seen as pneumonia, and mycelia are present in the tissue.

Laboratory Diagnosis. Depending on the form of the disease, direct examination is made of sputum, biopsy material, or surgical specimens. The finding of mycelial elements on direct microscopic examination (Fig. 36.7) is helpful in the final diagnosis because *Aspergillus* spp. are common contaminants, and it is necessary to be cautious in evaluating the culture of the organism from clinical materials. *Aspergillus*

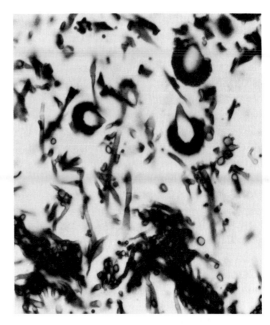

Fig. 36.7. Histologic section of lung from a patient with aspergillosis revealing hyphae of *Aspergillus fumigatus*, which are septate and show dichotomous branching. When organisms grow in a cavity with an airspace (fungus ball), sporulating heads may be observed. The vesicle is flask-shaped and produces on the upper half only a single series of sterigmata (× 200).

spp. grow readily on all laboratory media, and when grown at 37°C and at room temperature they form only mold colonies. The most commonly encountered *Aspergillus* spp. from pathologic material are *A. fumigatus, A. terreus, A. flavus*, and *A. niger*. Colony morphology and pigmentation may vary with the species and aid in identification. Microscopically the characteristic structure of aspergilli is a conidiophore or stalk that enlarges to form a vesicle that may be flask shaped or round (Fig. 36.5A). One or two rows of sterigmata may project from the upper surface of the vesicle, or sterigmata may cover the entire surface. From the sterigmata are borne chains of conidia. Species identification is aided by preparation of slide cultures and examination of conidiophores, conidiospores, and the shape of vesicles.

Serologic tests for antibodies to aspergillus mannan can be made by immunodiffusion tests using filtrates from cultures of *A. fumigatus, A. niger,* and *A. flavus.* The presence of one or more precipitins is indicative of either a fungus ball, allergic bronchopulmonary aspergillosis, or invasive aspergillosis. Although the presence of one or two precipitins could indicate any form of aspergillosis, the presence of three or four precipitins is strong evidence of either a fungus ball or invasive aspergillus. Detection of high levels of IgE antibodies also aids in the diagnosis of allergic bronchopulmonary aspergillosis or aspergilloma.

Therapy. The treatment of aspergillosis depends upon the disease produced. Medical management or surgical resection may be possible in some cases. Amphotericin B is the only agent with possible benefit in the treatment of invasive or disseminated *Aspergillus* infections. 5-Fluorocytosine has been used alone or in combined therapy with amphotericin B with some success. Successful therapy depends in part on the patient's underlying illness and immune competence.

At the other end of the spectrum, antifungal therapies are useless against pulmonary hypersensitivity disease, but glucocorticosteroids are helpful. Between these clinical extremes lies the broad category of chronic, saprophytic aspergillus infection of the lung. The role of corticosteroids, antifungal medications, and surgery for these chronic infections remains a source of debate.

Zygomycosis (Mucormycosis)

Mucormycosis is usually an acute and rapidly developing infection of debilitated patients caused by a mold fungus that commonly grows on bread or fruit. Within the heterogeneous group *Phycomycetes*, only

the class *Zygomycetes* contains fungi of medical importance. In the later class, members of two orders, *Mucorales* and *Entomophthorales*, cause human disease characterized by broad nonseptate hyphae in tissues. Most disease in humans is produced by organisms of the order *Mucorales*, and hence the disease is often called mucormycosis. Another synonym for the disease is phycomycosis, but this term is less precise and is now considered obsolete. Mucormycosis may involve the rhinofaciocranial area, lungs, gastrointestinal tract, skin, or, less commonly, other organ systems. The infecting fungi primarily invade vessels of the arterial system and elicit a suppurative pyogenic reaction rather than granuloma formation. In entomophthoromycosis, however, blood vessel invasion and infarction are usually not found, but rather hyaline material, granulomas, macrophages, and eosinophils are characteristically found in the subcutaneous tissues of the limbs of healthy persons. This latter form of zygomycosis will not be discussed further in this chapter. It has been proposed that the term zygomycosis be used to cover all infections caused by organisms in the class of *Zygomycetes* and that the specific type of infection be designated by a descriptive adjective (e.g., rhinocerebral zygomycosis).

In the *Mucorales* several species of the genera *Rhizopus, Mucor,* and *Absidia* are responsible for disease, but the clinical and pathologic findings are similar regardless of the organs involved. Species of these three genera are ubiquitous and frequently are found in decaying organic debris. They grow rapidly on any carbohydrate substrate, produce numerous sporangia and sporangiospores, and are thermotolerant.

The most frequently encountered agents of human disease are *Rhizopus arrhizus* and *Rhizopus oryzae.* The form of clinical disease produced is based not on age, sex, geography, or race but on factors predisposing the patient to infection. Recently, hospital-acquired cutaneous and sub-cutaneous infections, especially with *R. rhizopodoformis*, have been traced to contaminated adhesive bandages; ethylene dioxide sterilization of rolled bandages is ineffective against *Rhizopus*. Compromised patients in the hospital environment also may risk greater exposure to *Mucoraceae* from the air unless filtered ventilation is instituted. Because of high natural resistance, mucormycosis is a rare disease. The causative organism is normally avirulent, but in a host with the predisposing factors it can grow and produce disease. The spores are also potent allergens.

Clinical Manifestations. Mucormycosis is the most acute and fulminating fungus infection. Several clinical forms of the disease are known to occur. Rhinocerebral disease is most often associated with acidosis of the uncontrolled diabetic. Pulmonary infection is primarily a disease of patients with leukemia and lymphoma. Gastric involvement is encountered most frequently in malnourished individuals, particularly in children with kwashiorkor (malignant malnutrition). Some infections occur in individuals with focal or general tissue debility such as burns or those undergoing surgical procedures. A variety of drugs and chemotherapeutic agents have also been cited as predisposing to mucormycosis.

The most commonly seen form of the disease in the United States is the rhinofaciocranial syndrome. The infection begins in the upper turbinates or paranasal sinuses or, less commonly, in the palate and pharynx, causing severe cellulitis. The symptoms involve first the nose and then the eye, brain, and possibly the meninges. In an uncontrolled diabetic the disease runs a rapid, fatal course, usually within 10 days. Favorable growth of the fungus is provided by an acid pH and a high glucose content of the environment. Fortunately, the disease is comparatively rare even in such predisposed patients.

Laboratory Diagnosis. Rapid diagnosis is extremely important because mucormycosis is such an acute fulminating disease. Since the causative organisms are common contaminants of the environment, direct microscopic examination with demonstration of the organism is more meaningful for diagnosis than is culture. Fungal elements are usually not numerous but can be found in scrapings from the upper turbinates, in aspirated material from sinuses in rhinocerebral disease, and in sputum in the case of pulmonary disease. In KOH preparations hyphae are broad, 10 to 15 μm in diameter, thick walled, refractile, branching, and aseptate. The hyphae may have swollen cells (up to 50 μm in diameter) and may have a distorted appearance. On autopsy the characteristic hyphae are seen around blood vessels.

Clinical material can be cultured on SDA or any standard laboratory media without cycloheximide. The growth is rapid, often detectable in 18 hours, and forms only mold colonies. *Rhizopus* spp. are characterized by the formation of sporangia or sacs attached to unbranched sporangiophores, which arise singly or in groups from nodes directly above rhizoids (Fig. 36.4A). The brown sporangia are dark walled, spherical, and filled with hyaline or colored spores. The genus *Mucor* has species that have branched sporangiophores and no rhizoids (Fig. 36.4B). *Absidia* spp. have unbranched sporangiophores that arise between nodes, so that rhizoids are not opposite their point of attachment. Species identification is usually difficult, and no physiologic reactions have been established. Speciation is based on variations in morphology of the culture and individual spores as observed microscopically.

Serologic detection of antibodies to the three genera has been possible by immunodiffusion tests, although these tests are not yet well developed.

Therapy. Various isolates of the genera *Rhizopus*, *Mucor*, and *Absidia* vary considerably in their sensitivity to amphotericin B, so that sensitivity of individual isolates must be determined. Surgical treatment should also be as extensive as necessary to remove necrotic tissue. Control of the underlying disease (e.g., acidosis of diabetes mellitus) or reduction or discontinuation of immunosuppressive therapy (e.g., in transplant patients) is also essential.

Histoplasmosis

Histoplasmosis is a very common granulomatous disease caused by the dimorphic pathogenic fungus *Histoplasma capsulatum*. It is also known as Darling's disease, reticuloendotheliosis, Ohio Valley disease, and cave disease. Darling first described the disease and observed the causative organisms in histiocytes but had the mistaken impression that they were encapsulated protozoan plasmodia. These observations led to adoption of the current scientific name.

Infection follows the inhalation from the air of spores, which become transformed into small yeasts (2 to 5 μm in diameter) that are found within cells, generally histiocytes, of the reticuloendothelial system. A variety of clinical manifestations are produced. However, 95 percent of infections are inapparent, subclinical, or completely benign. These cases are diagnosed only by x-ray findings and a positive histoplasmin skin test. In the United States it is estimated that there are 200,000 new infections every year. All ages and both sexes are subject to primary pulmonary infection.

The organism grows in soil with high nitrogen content and is generally associated with the fecal material from birds and bats. The organism has been recovered from bird roosts, chicken houses, bat caves, silos, and abandoned residences inhabited by pigeons. Construction workers are frequently infected as old buildings are destroyed and massive amounts of soil are moved. If known infectious sites are not treated with a 3 percent solution of formaldehyde, *H.*

capsulatum may persist for possibly a decade. The most highly endemic area in the United States is the central North American continent, especially the Ohio–Mississippi Valley region, one of the principal habitats of starlings. Scattered areas of high prevalence exist in all parts of the world. As the mold form of the organism grows, it elaborates small (2 to 5 μm) microaleuriospores.

Epidemics of acute respiratory histoplasmosis occur following exposure to numerous spores; instances in which it has occurred include people who clean roosts of chickens and other birds, or who attend parks frequented by starlings, or who breathe air provided by ventilation systems installed near piles of bird droppings.

Clinical Manifestations. Infection by *H. capsulatum* usually occurs by way of the lungs if a sufficient quantity of spores has been inhaled. The resulting disease may be divided into two major categories, pulmonary and disseminated, each of which may have acute and chronic phases. Pulmonary histoplasmosis may appear with mild flulike symptoms if any are present at all. These signs may become exaggerated if the disease becomes more severe, and by x-rays multiple lesions may be detected that are scattered in all areas of the lung. The appearance of the disease may be quite similar to tuberculosis and can be differentiated only by serologic and cultural procedures. An epidemic form of the disease with severe pneumonitis may appear when large quantities of spores are inhaled. A chronic cavitary form of the disease may develop after the acute stage or years later. This form does not resolve, and eventual dissemination with systemic manifestations usually occurs. Disseminated histoplasmosis to the spleen, liver, and other reticuloendothelial areas is a common occurrence as a benign disease, but it may become progressive and fatal. Massive reinfection may result in a fatal acute allergic reaction in highly sensitive lungs.

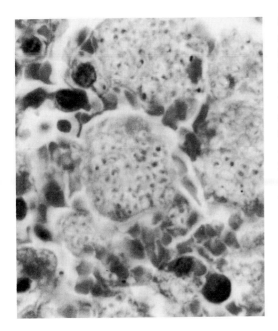

Fig. 36.8. Histologic section of lung from patient with histoplasmosis reveals many histiocytes containing numerous yeast cells (about 3 μm in diameter) of *Histoplasma capsulatum* (× 350).

Laboratory Diagnosis. Detection of the organism in sputum by direct microscopic examination is difficult, and frequently attempts are negative. Biopsy and sternal puncture material may be examined after staining. In the acute rapidly fatal form of histoplasmosis numerous yeast cells are seen only within the histiocytes in areas rich in reticuloendothelial cells, such as the liver, spleen, bone marrow, lymph nodes, and sometimes the adrenals. The yeast cells within the histiocytes are budding, are of uniform size (about 3 μm), and are visible in smears stained by routine procedures (Fig. 36.8). Fluorescein labeled antibody may aid in the detection of antigen.

In cases of pulmonary histoplasmosis, sputum, gastric lavage, or other material may be cultured on blood agar at 37°C and SDA at room temperature. Plates should be kept 4 to 6 weeks. *H. capsulatum* is dimorphic, but if growth occurs only at one

temperature attempts should be made to convert one phase to the other by subculture. The mold phase is white or buff brown, and filaments show the characteristic tuberculate macroaleuriospores important for identification. These diagnostic asexual spores are borne on tubular stalks or aleuriophores, are round or pyriform, are 8 to 14 μm in diameter, and have numerous tubercles or fingerlike projections that are variable in size and morphology (Fig. 36.5D).

Serologic tests may be of both diagnostic and prognostic value in histoplasmosis. A positive precipitation test is diagnostic 2 to 5 weeks after development of symptoms and can differentiate active from inactive disease. It may be performed as an immunodiffusion test or a counterimmunoelectrophoresis test. The standard antigen is histoplasmin, a concentrated broth filtrate of the mycelial growth of *H. capsulatum*. Positive reference sera must be used for comparison and to confirm the designated precipitin lines. The reference control serum should develop two lines, designated H and M. The H precipitin is encountered most commonly among specimens from patients with clinically active histoplasmosis and may be detectable 1 year or more after apparent clinical recovery. The M line may be indicative of active infection, past infection, or recent skin testing for histoplasmosis. The presence of an M band in the absence of a recent skin test may indicate an early infection, since this antibody appears before the H antibody.

The complement fixation test is positive later in the disease (6 weeks or more). A titer of 32 is considered significant, but it is important to determine serial titers. A rise in titer indicates dissemination of disease. Intradermal tests performed with histoplasmin would be minimal or negative if disease disseminates. Thus complement fixation tests and skin tests are useful as prognostic indicators of the disease process. A favorable sign for recovery is a negative or decreasingly positive complement fixation test and a positive skin test, the latter indicating an effective cellular immune response.

Therapy. In most cases of histoplasmosis the disease resolves by bedrest and supportive procedures. However, antibiotic therapy with amphotericin B is required in disseminated disease or chronic cavitary or mucocutaneous lesions.

Coccidioidomycosis

Coccidioidomycosis is an inapparent or mildly severe upper respiratory infection that usually resolves rapidly. However, the disease may progress as a chronic pulmonary condition or as a systemic disease to involve the meninges, bones, joints, and subcutaneous or cutaneous tissues. The disease is also known as San Joaquin Valley fever, desert rheumatism, or valley bumps. The only etiologic agent, *Coccidioides immitis*, is a pathogenic fungus and is probably the most virulent of all of the etiologic agents of human mycoses. The organism is found in the soil in hot semiarid regions. Highly endemic areas include the southwestern United States and northern Mexico, with endemic foci in Central and South America. In the United States, California, Arizona, Nevada, New Mexico, Texas, and Utah are involved. The organism is found in soils with a high content of carbonized organic material and a high salt concentration. *C. immitis* does not survive well in rich soil in competition with other soil microorganisms.

C. immitis is disseminated by dust aerosols (from windstorms, construction work, and farming) that are prevalent from early summer until the first rains of winter. Infection results from inhalation of dust containing arthrospores.

Clinical Manifestations. Infection by *C. immitis* can lead to two very different clinical forms of coccidioidomycosis. The first form, primary coccidioidomycosis, is an inapparent or moderately severe disease followed by complete resolution of the infection and establishment of strong immunity to reinfection. The second and rare form of the disease, secondary coccidioidomycosis, occurs as a chronic progressive disease or an acute, rapidly fatal dissemination. The pattern of diversity in clinical response is similar to that seen in histoplasmosis, paracoccidioidomycosis, and some other fungus infections. About 60 percent of patients have inapparent infections and 40 percent mild infections, while only about 0.5 percent have the serious secondary coccidioidomycosis. It is estimated that in the United States about 100,000 people are infected annually.

Asymptomatic pulmonary disease can be detected by skin-test conversion using a commercially available skin-test reagent, coccidioidin. Other persons may have symptoms ranging from those of a common cold to severe respiratory disease, varying with the number of spores inhaled. The most prominent symptoms include fever, chest pain, shortness of breath, cough, and loss of appetite.

Allergic manifestations are seen in about 5 to 10 percent of cases. One form of allergy is erythema nodosum, consisting of red, tender, itching or painful raised nodules found on the lower extremities, especially about the knees. Such "desert bumps" are almost pathognomonic for coccidioidomycosis and usually indicate strong resistance to the infection. Toxic eruptions similar to erythema multiforme may develop on the upper half of the body. Arthritis that sometimes accompanies primary disease has been called "desert rheumatism."

In secondary coccidioidomycosis pulmonary disease is frequently observed on x-ray as a single, thin-walled cavity. Dissemination is dependent upon factors such as overwhelming exposure and steroid therapy, and has increased incidence in persons of certain races. Epidemiologic studies have shown a significant association of coccidioidomycosis with HLA histocompatibility (HLA-A9). Also, a greater incidence among blacks and Filipinos suggests some racial susceptibility. Further studies may help define high risk subgroups. Meningitis is one of the most common causes of death.

Laboratory Diagnosis. Direct examination of clinical materials such as sputum, pus, gastric washings, and exudates from cutaneous lesions can be made in a KOH mount. The tissue phase of *C. immitis* is a spherule. Spherules vary in size from 10 to 80 μm, have a double refractile wall, and contain many endospores with an average diameter of 2 to 5 μm. Detection of characteristic spherules in tissue or clinical materials is sufficient corroborative evidence for diagnosis.

Cultures are made on SDA in tubes or bottles rather than Petri dishes because of the high infectivity of spores produced in culture. The fungus grows only as a mold, and alternate cells along the hypha become thin walled rectangular or barrel shaped arthrospores that are 2.5 to 4.0 μm by 3 to 6 μm in size (Fig. 36.3A). Spherules do not grow in the laboratory under ordinary conditions; but on special media and incubated in an atmosphere with increased CO_2, limited growth has been achieved.

Precipitation and complement fixation tests are useful in the diagnosis and prognosis of coccidioidomycosis, as has been mentioned for histoplasmosis. The antigen coccidioidin is a preparation of a concentrated broth filtrate of the mycelial growth of *C. immitis*. A single line of precipitation forms in an immunodiffusion test and should give a line of identity with a standard reference serum. A positive precipitin test is highly specific and indicates early active disease. Although an antigenic preparation has been produced from the spherule form (spherulin), it is not as specific as coccidioidin.

Therapy. Primary disease leads to spontaneous recovery in almost all asymptomatic and symptomatic cases. However,

secondary coccidioidomycosis usually has a grave prognosis unless chemotherapy is given. The drug of choice is amphotericin B. Miconazole may be of use in patients who have failed to improve after amphotericin B therapy. Transfer factor, an extract of sensitized lymphocytes, offers an experimental approach to therapy that may offer promise for the future.

Blastomycosis

Blastomycosis is a chronic granulomatous and suppurative disease having a primary pulmonary stage that is frequently followed by dissemination to other body sites, particularly the skin and bones. The disease is also known as North American blastomycosis or Gilchrist's disease. The causative agent is the dimorphic fungus *Blastomyces dermatitidis*. The disease was first described by Gilchrist in 1894 as a new type of skin disease. *B. dermatitidis* appears to be a soil saprophyte, and essentially all infections are acquired by inhalation of spores. Although the disease was first thought to be limited to the North American continent, it has been found in Africa and Israel. On the American continent most cases are found in the Midwest, the Southeast, and the Appalachian states. The disease is most prevalent in middle-aged males. Primary infection appears to occur more frequently during the cooler, wetter months of the year. It is possible that the organism is dormant most of the time, flourishing only rarely under particular climatic and environmental conditions of the colder seasons.

Clinical Manifestations. Blastomycosis may take three forms: primary pulmonary disease, which may be inapparent or severe, chronic cutaneous disease, which may be accompanied by lesions in the bone, and generalized systemic disease. It has been established that essentially all infections begin in the lung. If the host cannot contain the infection, the disease progresses as a chronic infection of skin and bone and eventually becomes systemic. Unlike other common systemic mycoses, there does not appear to be a mild subclinical form, and spontaneous resolution occurs only rarely.

Primary lesions in the lungs often resemble those of tuberculosis or histoplasmosis. The symptoms are those of a mild progressive respiratory infection with cough, fever, and some pleural pain. As the lesions heal, macrophages that have engulfed the organisms may be responsible for spread and deposition of the organism to distant sites of the body. If the lesions in the lung do not heal, pneumonia may develop.

Cutaneous blastomycosis is the most common form of extrapulmonary disease. The first signs to appear are subcutaneous nodules or papulopustular lesions, which ulcerate. Initially they are usually found on exposed peripheral areas such as the face, hand, wrist, and lower legs, but they may spread to the trunk and other areas. Within weeks or months the lesions evolve into ulcerated verrucous granulomas with sharp borders raised 1 to 3 mm.

Laboratory Diagnosis. Direct examination can be made of sputum for pulmonary blastomycosis, or, in the case of cutaneous disease, aspirated material may be taken from pustules at the outer edge of the lesion. A KOH mount can be made and examined for yeast cells. Yeasts are thick-walled spherical cells, 8 to 15 μm in diameter or occasionally larger, and the bud on the parent cell has a characteristic broad base of attachment measuring 4 to 5 μm. Buds may grow to the size of parent cells without detaching, resulting in a cluster of cells. Demonstration of the characteristic broad based bud of the yeast cells is usually sufficient for a diagnosis of blastomycosis. The identity of *B. dermatitidis* in clinical material can be confirmed by fluorescent antibody techniques used to stain organisms in formalized tissue or smears on slides.

Clinical material should be cultured on blood agar and on SDA without cyclohex-imide and incubated at 37°C and room temperature, respectively. The mold phase of the organism does not contain any characteristic spores that are useful in diagnosis. It is the yeast colony, grown at 37°C, that is examined microscopically for yeast cells containing a broad-based bud.

Serologic techniques have not been as useful as in the other systemic mycoses. However, a precipitation test has been developed using a filtrate of the yeast phase of *B. dermatitidis* and positive reference sera. Sera from patients with blastomycosis frequently react and give one or two lines of precipitation. A positive reaction indicates recent or current infection.

Therapy. The treatment of choice in all forms of blastomycosis is amphotericin B. The organism is quite sensitive to the drug, and relapses occur only in cases of inadequate treatment. In cases of significant systemic toxicity, an acceptable alternative is hydroxystilbamidine isethionate.

Paracoccidioidomycosis

Paracoccidioidomycosis produces a primary pulmonary infection, often inapparent, that then disseminates to form ulcerative granulomas of the buccal, nasal, and occasionally the gastrointestinal mucosa. The disease is also known as South American blastomycosis. Paracoccidioidomycosis is similar to blastomycosis and coccidioidomycosis, but the infection is restricted geographically to Latin America. The only etiologic agent is the dimorphic fungus *Paracoccidioides brasiliensis.* The name of the genus was derived from the mistaken idea that the type of sporulation was similar to that of *Coccidioides immitis.* At one time it was placed in the genus *Blastomyces* as a species thought to be similar to *B. dermatitidis* because of the variations in bud formation.

The organism is believed to be found in soil. A large proportion of the population is infected by inhalation of the organisms, but usually a subclinical and self-limited disease develops, since there is a high natural resistance. Patients with severe disease have a deficiency of cell-mediated immunity, although sometimes it appears to be only temporary.

Clinical Manifestations. Paracoccidioidomycosis occurs in three forms: pulmonary, mucocutaneous-lymphangitic, and disseminated. The most commonly encountered form of the disease is the presence of lesions on the oropharynx and gingivae. Primary infection is pulmonary, followed by dissemination of the organism to other areas. During the primary infection and the initial reaction of alveolitis, there is an influx of macrophages and a few giant cells. The macrophage is the probable mode of dissemination of the fungus to other areas of the body.

In the mucocutaneous-lymphangitic form, lesions in the mouth begin as papules or vesicles that then ulcerate. They have a granulomatous appearance and spread slowly to form sometimes extensive vegetations. Lymphadenopathy is a common and characteristic feature of the disease. The predilection of the disseminating organisms for the mucocutaneous areas may be due to the cooling effect of air on these areas. With increased adaptability of the fungus and reduction of host defenses, the disease may spread to other areas.

Laboratory Diagnosis. Direct examination of sputum, biopsy material, crusts, material from granulomatous bases or the outer edge of ulcers, and pus from suppurative draining lymph nodes can be made in KOH mounts. Yeasts can be easily observed and vary in size from recently separated buds of 2 to 10 μm up to mature cells of 30 μm or more. The yeast cells are spherical or oval, have a doubly refractile wall, and produce one to a dozen narrow necked buds of uniform or variable size. The yeast cells may also occur in chains of four or more. The appearance of multiple budding is characteristic of *P. brasiliensis*.

Clinical material should be cultured on blood agar at 37°C and on SDA at room temperature, both without cycloheximide. The mold culture at room temperature does not produce any characteristic spores, so that the yeast form demonstrating the typical morphology is essential for diagnosis.

For serodiagnosis, a precipitation test can be performed with a concentrated filtrate of the yeast culture of *P. brasiliensis*. The result is considered positive if one or more lines formed by the tested serum fuse with corresponding lines of precipitation produced by the reference serum. Although precipitating antibodies are long-lasting, one of the three precipitins that could occur in the patient's serum might disappear after successful chemotherapy.

Therapy. The drugs of choice are amphotericin B and miconazole.

SUBCUTANEOUS INFECTIONS

The subcutaneous mycoses are a heterogeneous group of infections that are the result of traumatic injury to the skin and simultaneous implantation of fungi from soil or plants. Therefore this group is different from the systemic mycoses, where the primary mode of entry is usually pulmonary. In the subcutaneous mycoses a lesion develops at the site of inoculation, and the developing disease either remains localized at this area or spreads slowly to surrounding tissue. In some cases there is a frequent extension via the lymphatic channels (*sporotrichosis*), while in other, rare cases hematogenous and lymphatic dissemination is recorded (*chromoblastomycosis*). Mycetomas are another type of subcutaneous infection in which bacteria (producing actinomycotic mycetoma) or fungi (producing eumycotic mycetoma) are introduced into a skin wound from the soil.

The organisms involved in subcutaneous infections are common soil saprophytes that exhibit varying abilities to adapt to the tissue environment and produce disease.

Sporotrichosis

Sporotrichosis is a chronic infection characterized by nodular lesions of the cutaneous and subcutaneous tissues with invasion of the lymphatics and production along lymph channels of additional lesions that suppurate, ulcerate, and drain. In humans all forms of sporotrichosis are caused by the single species *Sporothrix schenckii*. The organism is only weakly pathogenic, and individual strains vary considerably in their virulence. Following traumatic injury to the skin the organism gains entrance to the body. From the cutaneous and subcutaneous lesions the fungus may spread to muscle, bone, and other sites.

The most common means of entry of *S. schenckii* are scratches from thorns or splinters and cuts from the handling of various grasses, reeds, or sphagnum moss. Frequently there is a history of contamination of wounds with soil. *S. schenckii* has been found frequently on decaying vegetation, but it has an elusive and transient distribution in the soil. Transmission is usually sporadic, but one famous epidemic involved the gold mines of Africa, where the organism was growing on timbers handled by the miners.

At the present time the greatest number of cases come from endemic areas in Mexico, Central America, and Brazil, with a scattered distribution throughout the world. Sporotrichosis is the most common subcutaneous and deep mycosis in Mexico. In the United States infection is usually associated with gardening and may be considered an occupational hazard of greenhouse workers and rose growers.

Clinical Manifestations. Although most cases of sporotrichosis involve the skin, subcutaneous, tissue, and local lymphatic channels, other forms of the disease do occur. The type of disease depends on the site of inoculation and the response of the host to it. Five clinical types of disease may be listed: (1) lymphocutaneous, (2) fixed cutaneous, (3) mucocutaneous, (4) extracutaneous and disseminated, and (5) primary pulmonary. The first four types of disease result from inoculation through a wound, while the last results from inhalation of spores.

In lymphocutaneous sporotrichosis the first evidence of infection may appear about 3 weeks after entrance of the fungus. The first sign is a small, hard, movable, nontender subcutaneous nodule. The lesion becomes discolored, varying from pink to purple and sometimes black; it may penetrate the skin and become necrotic. The initial lesion may remain for weeks or months and tends to heal with scarring as new nodules develop. In chronic sporotrichosis the lymphatics that drain the area of the lesion are involved. Additional subcutaneous nodules develop within a few days or weeks along the local lymphatic channels. The typical picture of an ulcer on a finger with an associated chain of swollen lymph nodes extending up the arm is said to make a "visual diagnosis" possible with considerable confidence.

Fixed cutaneous sporotrichosis occurs in highly endemic areas; since so many people are sensitized to *S. schenckii*, primary infection is restricted to the site of inoculation. Mucocutaneous sporotrichosis is relatively rare. Disseminated sporotrichosis most frequently involves the skeletal system but may occasionally involve other organs. Pulmonary sporotrichosis occurs by inhalation of spores similar to histoplasmosis or coccidioidomycosis, and it is more prevalent among chronic alcoholics. The disease progresses, and the patients usually do not recover spontaneously.

Laboratory Diagnosis. Direct examination may be made of pus, exudates, biopsy material, and aspirates, but in general yeast cells are few in number and may not be seen microscopically. Yeast cells are cigar shaped and 3 to 5 μm in diameter, with up to three buds. Most helpful for the direct recognition and identification of the organism in clinical material is the fluorescent antibody technique.

S. schenckii grows well on most culture media. Clinical material should be inoculated on blood agar and SDA for incubation at 37°C and room temperature, respectively. Colony morphology is variable, but a dirty-white yeast colony develops at 37°C, becoming membranous and developing areas of discoloration. At room temperature a mold colony develops that produces characteristic spores used for identification. Slender conidiophores rise from the hyphae at right angles. At the apex of the conidiophore, ovate conidia are formed in an arrangement that resembles a palm tree or a flower head such as a daisy (Fig. 36.5B). With age, single spores are also formed along the undifferentiated hyphae.

Among the serologic tests for antibody, the yeast cell agglutination and agglutination of latex particles coated with yeast filtrate have been the most sensitive techniques. Agglutination titers of 8 or greater, or latex agglutination titers of 4 or greater, are considered presumptive evidence of sporotrichosis. Titers may range in the hundreds, depending upon the clinical type of disease.

Therapy. The treatment of choice is iodide therapy, which can be administered orally in milk as a saturated solution of potassium iodide. Open lesions can be treated topically with a solution of 2 percent KI containing 0.2 percent iodine. For the treatment of pulmonary and disseminated disease, amphotericin B is the most effective drug.

Chromomycosis

Chromomycosis is a term that has been applied to a group of clinical entities caused by dematiaceous or pigmented fungi whose cell walls are characterized by a brown, olive, or black color. Dematiaceous fungi cause the mycotic infections chromoblastomycosis, keratomycosis (mycotic ulcers of the cornea), mycetomas, phaeohyphomycosis, superficial infections (black piedra, white piedra, tinea nigra, and tinea versicolor), and sporotrichosis. In this section attention will be devoted primarily to chromoblastomycosis.

Most commonly the organisms gain entrance to the body by trauma to the skin. Usually lesions are localized, and the response is one of hyperplasia, characterized by the formation of verrucoid, warty, cutaneous nodules, described as cauliflower lesions, which may be raised 1 to 3 cm above the skin surface. Chromoblastomycosis is also known as verrucous dermatitis.

The causative agents of chromoblastomycosis are frequently found as saprophytes in decaying vegetation, rotting wood, and the soil. The principal etiologic agents are *Fonsecaea pedrosoi*, *Fonsecaea compactum*, *Phialophora verrucosa*, and *Cladosporium carrionii*, although other organisms may also be encountered. The most commonly isolated fungus is *Fonsecaea pedrosoi*.

Although the organisms causing chromoblastomycosis may be found in soils in all parts of the world, the disease is more frequent in tropical and subtropical countries, particularly among poor rural people who do not wear shoes. Most cases come from the American tropics, especially Mexico and Central America. Puncture wounds are the main mode of entrance for the organisms. Repeated trauma and injury are usually needed for disease to be initiated; good hygiene and adequate nutrition may help prevent a potential infection.

Clinical Manifestations. The lesion of chromoblastomycosis or verrucous dermatitis initially appears at the site of some trauma or puncture wound. First it is a small, raised, erythematoid papule that may be violet in color. As new lesions appear in later months or years, they follow the distribution of local lymphatic channels. The lesions become raised above the skin surface, tend to enlarge and become grouped, and become verrucous, resembling the florets of cauliflower. Often the lesions ulcerate and become infected secondarily with bacteria.

Phaeohyphomycosis of the brain is a rare form of the disease resulting from hematogenous spread from a focal lesion elsewhere. Afflicted patients are often debilitated or on steroid therapy. Cystic and nonspecific chromomycosis is another rare form caused by other species of *Phialophora* and *Fonsecaea* less virulent than the usual agents of verrucous chromomycosis. These infections may become more prominent with increased use of immunosuppressive agents, long-term steroids, and cytotoxins.

Laboratory Diagnosis. Skin scrapings, crusts, aspirated debris, and excised material can be examined directly in a KOH mount. Microscopically, the etiological agents of chromoblastomycosis are brown pigmented, branching hyphae, 2 to 6 μm wide, which may become distorted, and pleomorphic brown bodies up to 20 μm wide. In granulation tissue there is a predominance of sclerotic bodies, which are thick walled, brown pigmented, multiply by splitting rather than budding, and may be grouped in a chainlike fashion.

Agents of chromoblastomycosis are seen only as black-brown or olive-gray velvety colonies that grow more slowly than most of the saprophytic organisms of the soil. Identification of organisms is difficult because specific taxonomic criteria have not been developed. Identification depends on spore types, percentage of spore types, and fine details of spore production. Three general types of conidiophores are produced: (1) phialophora type, a vase or flask shaped structure giving rise to conidia that tend to aggregate around the opening; (2) acrotheca type, a terminal or lateral branch that appears as a knotted club and from the ends and sides of which are borne conidia; and (3) cladosporium type, a simple conidiophore that buds to form spores in a branching chain formation. The genus *Phialophora* produces only spores of the phialophora type, while the genus *Cladosporium* produces only spores of the cladosporium type. The genus *Fonsecaea* (formerly genus *Hormodendrum*) has all three types of sporulation varying in proportion in different strains.

Serologic tests do not appear to be of practical value in diagnosis. No consistent patterns have been found in the antigenic relationships between the various etiologic agents that clearly delineate the species of chromomycotic agents.

Therapy. In the early stages of the dissease, removal of the lesion by conventional surgery or cryosurgery may be performed. Amphotericin B may be applied topically or injected into the lesion. Other useful drugs are 5-fluorocytosine and thiabendazole.

Mycetoma

Mycetoma is a clinical syndrome with a triad appearance of tumefaction, draining sinuses, and small particles or granules (grains) in the drainage. The disease has also been called Madura foot or maduromycosis since it is prevalent in the district of Madura in India. Disease results from inoculation of soil organisms into the body through a traumatic wound, usually on the foot or hand. The infection progressively involves and destroys connective tissue, muscles, and bones.

The etiologic agents include a diverse group of organisms from plant debris and soil, bacteria causing actinomycotic mycetoma, and fungi causing eumycotic mycetoma. Although these organisms independently may cause other diseases such as actinomycosis or chromomycosis, the diagnosis of mycetoma is made only when the triad of clinical signs listed above is found.

About 50 percent of cases are due to bacteria (actinomycetes) and 50 percent are due to true fungi. Actinomycotic mycetoma is caused most commonly by bacteria from three genera: *Nocardia*, *Actinomadura*, and *Streptomyces*. Characteristics of some of these bacteria are discussed in Chapter 35. The genera that frequently cause eumycotic mycetoma include *Petriellidium* and *Madurella*. All are soil saprophytes or plant pathogens. The ability of these organisms to induce infection varies even with different strains of the same organism.

Highly endemic areas are equatorial Africa and Mexico. Sporadic cases have been reported from Europe and the United States. Mycetoma has its highest incidence in rural areas, where contributing factors may be frequent exposure to soil, inadequate nutrition and hygiene, and poor health. The most common etiologic agent in the United States is *Petriellidium boydii* (imperfect form, *Monosporium apiospermum*).

Clinical Manifestations. Regardless of the specific bacterial or fungal organism initiating mycetoma, the clinical symptoms are essentially the same. Sometimes case histories have suggested a lapse of several years between a recognized injury and the first signs of disease. It appears that time may be required for the organism to adapt to the host, or possibly several injuries to the same area may be required before disease begins. The initial lesion is a small, painless subcutaneous swelling that slowly enlarges and softens. It ruptures to the surface, forming sinus tracts, and then burrows into the deeper tissues, producing swelling and distortion of the foot. The surface has numerous openings from sinus tracts. The discharge may be a serous exudate or purulent if there is secondary bacterial infection.

The drainage contains numerous small particles or granules referred to as grains, which vary in size from 0.3 to 5 mm or greater. Depending on the microorganism, the grains may be white, yellow, cream, pink, red, brown, or black. Examination of these granules in the laboratory permits the differentiation of actinomycotic mycetoma from eumycotic mycetoma.

After the involved tissue has healed, massive fibrosis occurs, giving a hard, tumorlike appearance to the area. The mycetoma usually remains localized, but it may extend slowly to neighboring tissues and produce severe disfigurement and disability.

Laboratory Diagnosis. Direct examination of pus, exudate, or biopsy material may be made for the presence of grains. They vary in size, and their morphology, texture, color and shape provide an indication as to the identity of the causative organism. Microscopic examination of crushed grains in KOH preparations reveals a mass of intertwining branching filaments. Actinomycetes produce a grain with filaments 0.5 to 1.0 μm in diameter as well as coccoid and bacillary forms. Eumycotic grains have intertwined broad hyphae 2 to 5 μm in diameter. Recognition of the etiologic agent as a bacterium or fungus is important, since treatment will be quite different.

Material for culture is best taken from a deep biopsy so that it is free from contaminating bacteria and fungi. The granules are crushed in a tissue homogenizer and plated on appropriate media. Actinomycetes should be cultured on blood agar and incubated at 37°C both anaerobically and aerobically. Isolated colonies can be identified by biochemical characteristics. Clinical material containing eumycetes can be plated on SDA and incubated at room temperature. Growth is slow, and identification is made by observation of colony morphology, spore types, and carbohydrate assimilation patterns. *P. boydii*, the most common cause of mycetoma in Europe and the United States, produces white to yellowish granules. Colonies are filamentous and white, turning gray. Hyphae produce large pyriform aleuriospores 4 to 9 μm by 6 to 10 μm that are borne singly from aleuriophores or directly from hyphae. Physiologic tests can aid in further identification.

There are no established serologic procedures for the diagnosis or prognosis of mycetoma. The etiologic agents are too many and diverse to make preparation of a polyvalent antigen feasible.

Therapy. Treatment is difficult because of the inability of drugs to penetrate into cystic and fibrotic areas in sufficient concentration to inhibit the causative microorganisms. Bacterial mycetomas are easier to treat than fungal mycetomas. *Actinomyces* is susceptible to high doses of penicillin, while *Nocardia* is treated with sulfadiazine. *Actinomadura* and *Streptomyces* are treated with streptomycin. The eumycotic mycetomas have frequently been treated with amphotericin B, but blood levels achieved are usually below the effective concentration. Iodides have shown some usefulness, apparently acting to cause resolution of the granuloma formed around the fungus, thus enabling host defense mechanisms to help eliminate it.

REFERENCES

Beneke, E.S.: Medical Mycology Laboratory Manual. 2nd Ed. Burgess Publishing, Minneapolis, 1966.

Conant, N.F., Smith, D.T., Baker, R.D., and Callaway, J.L.: Manual of Clinical Mycology. W.B. Saunders, Philadelphia, 1971.

Emmons, C.W., Binford, C.H., and Utz, J.P.: Medical Mycology, 2nd Ed. Lea and Febiger, Philadelphia, 1977.

Haley, L.D. and Callaway, C.S.: Laboratory Methods in Medical Mycology. 4th Ed. HEW Publication No. (CDC) 78-8361, Supt. Documents, Washington, D.C., 1978.

Kite, J.H.: Immunology of mycotic diseases. In Rose, N.R., Milgrom, F., and van Oss, C.J., Eds.: Principles of Immunology. 2nd Ed. Macmillan, New York, 1979.

Kite, J.H.: Serological diagnosis of mycotic infections. In Milgrom, F., Abeyounis, C.J., Kano, K., Eds.: Principles of Immunological Diagnosis in Medicine. Lea and Febiger, Philadelphia, 1981.

Lennette, E.H., Balows, A., Hausler, W.J., and Truant, J.P., Eds.: Manual of Clinical Mycology. 3rd Ed. American Society for Microbiology, Washington, D.C., 1980.

Rippon, J.W.: Medical Mycology. The Pathogenic Fungi and the Pathogenic Actinomycetes. W.B. Saunders, Philadelphia, 1974.

Rickettsiaceae

David T. Mount

The tribe *Rickettsiae* of the family *Rickettsiaceae* has three genera; *Rickettsia, Coxiella,* and *Rochalimaea.* Diseases of man caused by the organisms include the typhus fevers, the spotted fevers, the scrub typhus fevers, Q fever, and trench fever. The rickettsiae are with one exception obligate intracellular parasites. Most require an arthropod vector for transfer from various mammalian reservoir species.

MORPHOLOGY, PHYSIOLOGY, AND CULTURE

The rickettsiae vary in shape from coccobacillary to bacillary. Their length ranges from 2.0 to 4.0 μm and their width from 0.3 to 0.5 μm (Fig. 37.1). The cell wall has the multilayered structure characteristic of gram-negative organisms, and it contains muramic acid and diaminopimelic acid but not the teichoic acids of gram-positive bacteria. The cells have no flagella, but they have a slime layer, which can be seen by electron microscopy. Below the cell wall lies the cytoplasmic membrane, consisting of the typical unit membrane structure found in bacterial cells. Intracytoplasmic invaginations of the cytoplasmic membrane have been observed. A well defined nuclear structure has not been observed, but the DNA exists as irregular fibrous structures.

Host cell penetration by these obligate intracellular parasites is an active process that requires viable rickettsial cells. Both mono- and divalent cations are required for penetration, and stabilizing agents promote the activity. Rickettsiae reproduce by binary fission in the cytoplasm or in some instances in the nucleus of infected cells with a minimum generation time of about 8 hours.

Although these organisms depend on the host cell for essential metabolic reactions, they do show limited metabolic activity. For example, rickettsiae carry out glutamic-aspartic acid transamination and oxidize glutamic acid via the citric acid cycle that leads to the formation of energy-rich ATP. Glucose is not utilized. Limited lipid and protein synthesis has been achieved in complex cell-free systems. An unusual requirement for this cell-free activity is for ATP to be derived endogenously from glutamate and also exogenously from the medium. Nucleic acid synthesis has not been demonstrated *in vitro*.

Most rickettsiae are quite sensitive to extracellular conditions and are readily killed by heat and disinfectants. The rickettsiae may be cultured in appropriate arthropods,

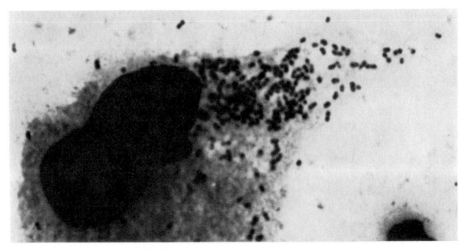

Fig. 37.1. *Rickettsia tsutsugamushi* in the cytoplasm of mesothelial cell of a guinea pig (×2000). (With permission, Freeman, B.A., Ed.: Burrows Textbook of Microbiology. 21st Ed. W.B. Saunders, Philadelphia, 1979.)

mammals, chick embryo yolk sac, and cell culture. The utilization of the chick embryo yolk sac is of great importance because it is a convenient way to obtain great numbers of organisms for vaccine production. The guinea pig infection has been used to identify rickettsiae, since some of these organisms produce a marked scrotal reaction. Large numbers of viable cells injected intravascularly in mice cause an increase in vascular permeability and acute toxic death in a few hours. Neutralization by specific antiserum of this toxicity is one means of differentiating rickettsiae.

SEROLOGY

Antibodies to rickettsial antigens may be demonstrated by various procedures. The Weil-Felix reaction utilizes agglutination reactions to strains of *Proteus vulgaris* (OX-19 and OX-2) and *Proteus mirabilis* (OX-K) that share antigens with certain rickettsiae such as those of the typhus, spotted fever, and scrub typhus groups. The reaction to the several strains is helpful in distinguishing the various rickettsial infections. There are important considera-

tions in the interpretation of these tests; a positive reaction can result from an infection with proteus bacilli and not all rickettsial infections induce antibodies to the strains of *Proteus* (e.g., patients suffering from rickettsial pox, Q fever, and trench fever do not develop these antibodies). The Weil-Felix test is widely available and can be carried out in most clinical laboratories. More specific tests utilizing rickettsial antigens give more reliable information but are generally performed only in reference laboratories. Such specific tests include complement fixation, agglutination, immunofluorescence, toxin neutralization, passive hemagglutination, and radioimmunoprecipitation.

DISEASES

Typhus Fever Group

Epidemic typhus has been one of the most severe diseases in the history of mankind. It has been recognized in Europe since the 16th century. During the Thirty Years War, typhus caused devastating loss of life and was spread throughout Europe. Continuing wars and famine created conditions that provoked typhus fever outbreaks. In the United States epidemic typhus was found primarily in the Eastern coastal cities, where it was introduced from Europe. Even in the conditions of the Civil War epidemic typhus was not prevalent in America. During World War I there were very severe epidemics in Serbia and Russia, where about three million people died of typhus, while on Western front it rarely occurred. In the late 1930s typhus vaccines were developed in both the United States and Russia that were very effective in greatly reducing morbidity and mortality of typhus in World War II. There has been no epidemic of typhus in the United States in over 50 years.

Diseases caused by the typhus fever group of rickettsiae include epidemic or louse-borne typhus and endemic or murine typhus. There is serologic crossreactivity between the two organisms because of soluble antigens as well as specific antigens of the rickettsial body.

Epidemic typhus has been of great historical importance and regularly occurs in times of social disruption such as war, famine, or migration. The disease is present most commonly in eastern Europe and areas of Africa and is only infrequently seen in the United States. Man is the primary mammalial reservoir of the etiologic agent, *Rickettsia prowazekii*. The human body louse, *Pediculus humanus*, is the vector. The disease is more common during the winter, when louse infestation is more prevalent and crowding of humans may occur. *R. prowazekii* is able to replicate in the cells of the gut of the louse following ingestion of infectious blood. The organisms are deposited in feces near the site of a louse bite on the skin. Contamination of the bite wound with the infectious feces introduces the agent, with consequent infection. Transfer from person to person is facilitated because lice leave patients with high fever or cadavers.

Epidemic typhus has an incubation period of 10 to 14 days, followed by onset of high fever, headache, generalized rash, and delirium. As with most rickettsial diseases, the pathology is predominantly associated with involvement of the endothelium accompanied by increased capillary permeability, thrombus formation, and hemorrhagic rash. Often the Weil-Felix test shows a high titer to the *Proteus* OX-19 antigen. The mortality rate of untreated cases is variable, with some epidemics reported to cause 90 percent deaths. Control of epidemic typhus has been greatly improved by the use of insecticides and by utilization of vaccines composed of killed organisms. The disease may be treated by prolonged administration of broad spectrum antibiotics such as tetracycline and chloramphenicol.

Some patients harbor rickettsiae for many years and may have a recrudescence of typhus in a mild form known as Brill-Zinsser disease. In such cases the blood contains fully virulent *R. prowazekii* that can be transmitted to susceptible people if there is louse infestation. Such latent infections may serve as the interepidemic reservoir of epidemic typhus. The Weil-Felix reaction is most often negative in cases of Brill-Zinsser disease.

Endemic typhus or murine typhus is caused by *Rickettsia typhi* (formerly *R. mooseri*). It occurs sporadically as a consequence of transmission to humans of *R. typhi* by fleas and the rat louse from the rodent reservoir, particularly the rat. The disease is not transmissible from human to human. The disease has worldwide distribution and is especially prevalent in South America. The clinical course of the disease is similar to that of epidemic typhus but is considered by some to be milder. Natural infection with either *R. prowazekii* or *R. typhi* induces immunity to both epidemic and endemic typhus. The Weil-Felix reaction is also positve to *Proteus* OX-19.

Spotted Fever Group

Rickettsiae of the spotted fever group are serologically related to each other, and the organisms can be found in both cytoplasm and nucleus of infected cells. Most are transmitted by ticks from a variety of mammalian reservoirs. They are also capable of transovarial passage in the tick; thus organisms can be maintained in nature without a requirement for a mammalian host. Antigenically diverse spotted fevers have been found in various parts of the world and are identified by local names, such as Queensland tick fever and Siberian tick typhus. The important member of the group in the United States is Rocky Mountain spotted fever, caused by *Rickettsia rickettsii*.

Rocky Mountain Spotted Fever. The disease was believed to be confined to the Western states but has now become most frequent in the Southeast, particularly in the Atlantic states. In the West the vector is usually the wood tick *Dermacentor andersoni*, while in the East it is principly the dog tick *Dermacentor variabilis*. The populations formerly at the greatest risk were men working in forested areas; presently women and children are more commonly at risk.

Rocky Mountain spotted fever is a very severe disease with high fever and an extensive hemorrhagic rash. Other serious clinical conditions frequently occurring are edema, hepatitis, myocarditis, and brain involvement. The fatality rate of untreated cases varies considerably, reaching 40 percent. Early treatment with tetracyclines or chloramphenicol is quite effective. A vaccine composed of killed cells is available for people at risk but is not entirely satisfactory. People in areas of exposure are advised to check carefully for tick attachment and to wear protective clothing. Attempts to control the tick population in the wild have not been successful.

Rickettsial Pox. This is another disease classified as a spotted fever by antigenic relationships, but it differs in that the agent, *Rickettsia akari*, is harbored by mice and the vector is the mite *Allodermanyssus sanguineus*. The disease was first identified in New York City, but it has been found in other locations in the United States as well as in the U.S.S.R. It is most often associated with urban settings. It is a clinically mild disease with fever and varicelliform rash. It is seldom, if ever, fatal.

Scrub Typhus Group

Scrub typhus or tsutsugamushi disease composes the third group of rickettsial diseases. The etiologic agent, *Rickettsia tsutsugamushi*, is antigenically diverse. The disease is found in the Far East, particularly Japan, Indochina, and the various islands of the Pacific. The organism is harbored by wild rodents, and the arthropod vectors are various species of mites. Control of spread under field conditions is very difficult. The fatality rate varies between 20 and 60 percent in untreated cases. The disease may be treated with broad spectrum antibiotics. Vaccines have been prepared but are not very helpful, since the killed organisms do not produce good immunity and the great antigenic diversity of strains does not permit crossprotection.

Q Fever

Q fever is a distinctive disease because the causative organism, *Coxiella burnetii*, is much more resistant to extracellular conditions than are other rickettsiae and does not require an arthropod vector for dissemination. The disease has worldwide distribution among various mammals. In the United States cattle are an important source of human infection. Ticks feed on the cattle and shed the organism in their feces. Since the organism is resistant to drying, it may persist on hides and be disseminated as dust. *C. burnetii* is also found in milk and in the placenta of infected animals. Humans usually acquire the organism by inhalation and develop respiratory symptoms without rash. The organism can be widely disseminated in the body, sometimes causing hepatitis or subacute endocarditis. Fatalities are infrequent. There are very few secondary cases, indicating infrequent human to human transmission. Laboratory diagnosis is based on the complement fixation test and other specific reactions. The Weil-Felix test is negative. The disease responds well to tetracycline treatment.

Trench Fever

Trench fever is caused by *Rochalimaea quintana*, which is unique in that it may be cultured on artificial medium with blood agar base. Trench fever is confined to humans and is transmitted by the body louse in the same manner as epidemic typhus. The disease was common in World War I but then subsided, with a lesser outbreak occurring during World War II. The disease is characterized by fever and pain in the legs. The fatality rate is low. As in other rickettsial diseases the organism can remain sequestered in the host for many years with subsequent relapse and potential for an infectious focus.

REFERENCES

Brezina, R., Murray, E.S., Tarrizzo, M.L., and Bögel, K.: Rickettsia and rickettsial diseases. Bull. WHO *49*: 433, 1973.
Weiss, E.: Growth and physiology of rickettsiae. Bacteriol. Rev. *37*: 259, 1973.

38

Chlamydia

David T. Mount

The chlamydiae are obligately intracellular bacteria that have a unique replicative cycle and metabolic requirements. Two species have been established on the basis of differences in several biologic properties. *Chlamydia psittaci* includes many members that infect a wide spectrum of mammalian and avian species. The avian strains are those that most frequently affect humans as the causative agents of psittacosis. This infection usually manifests as pneumonia. *Chlamydia trachomatis* is composed of organisms that are almost all restricted to humans and cause trachoma, inclusion conjunctivitis, pneumonia, lymphogranuloma venereum, and other genital tract infections.

GENERAL PROPERTIES OF CHLAMYDIAE

The chlamydiae undergo morphological changes during the growth cycle from a small infectious form to a larger replicative form. The small infectious elementary body is stable outside of host cells and is the form transmitted between cells or individuals. The elementary body is coccoid and about 200 to 250 nm in diameter. In electron micrographs it is electron dense, with a cell wall and an eccentric nucleoid. The DNA content is appreciably less than that of other procaryotic cells. The elementary body has reduced metabolism.

The larger reticulate body or initial body is the replicative form found within the host cell. It is less electron dense and is from 500 to 1000 nm in diameter. The reticulate body is metabolically active and multiplies by binary fission. The reticulate body is quite sensitive to the extracellular environment and is not infectious.

The growth cycle is initiated by phagocytic engulfment of the initial body. Replication takes place within the phagocytic vesicle, which enlarges to enclose a microcolony of bacteria and form the characteristic cytoplasmic inclusion. The elementary body undergoes morphologic changes to the reticulate body, which then undergoes repeated binary fission. The reticulate bodies then condense back to the elementary form, so that a more mature inclusion will contain a mixture of forms. There may be from 500 to 1000 infectious units in the mature inclusion. Dissolution of host membranes releases the chlamydiae.

Chlamydiae are deficient in some enzyme

513

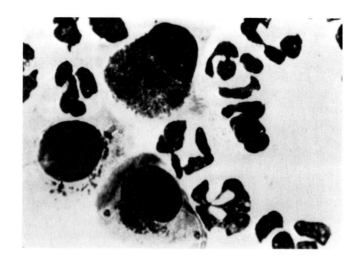

Fig. 38.1. *Chlamydia psittaci* inclusions in three exfoliated cells from an experimental animal infection (×1000). (With permission, Mount, D.T., Bigazzi, P.E., and Barron, A.L.: Infection and Immunity 5: 922, 1972).

systems, particularly those involved in energy generation. One basis of parasitism is dependence on the host cell for ATP. Enzymes for lipid synthesis and isoleucine may also be required.

C. trachomatis strains are identified by the presence of glycogen in the inclusion, a more compact inclusion than that of *C. psittaci*, and sensitivity to sulfadiazine. *C. psittaci* strains do not have glycogen in the inclusion, are insensitive to sulfadiazine, and have a more diffuse inclusion than *C. trachomatis* because the membranes rupture earlier in the developmental cycle (Fig. 38.1).

All chlamydiae can be cultured in the yolk sac of the chick embryo. The yolk sac can be used for serial passage or as a source of antigen for various tests. More conveniently, cell culture techniques have been widely applied. Inoculation onto a nonreplicating cell monolayer is required for greatest efficiency. Inhibition of cellular division may be achieved by irradiation or by the use of metabolic inhibitors. Most importantly, the specimen must be centrifuged onto the monolayer to facilitate adsorption and engulfment of the chlamydiae. The inclusions in nonreplicating cells become larger and are more easily observed. The monolayer may be stained by iodine to observe the glycogen of the *C. trachomatis* inclusion, or by Giemsa stain, or for immunofluorescence. *C. trachomatis* does not readily spread to adjacent cells and may require sonication to disperse the organisms for passage.

The chlamydiae contain a group-specific, heat stable lipopolysaccharide antigen that can be detected by the complement fixation test. *C. psittaci* and *C. trachomatis* cannot be differentiated by this test because they share the common group antigen. Protein-associated, type-specific antigens are also found in the cell wall, but they have not yet been adequately defined. Type specificity may be determined by plaque reduction, mouse toxicity neutralization, or immunofluorescence. By the microimmunofluorescence procedure 15 serotypes of *C. trachomatis* have been defined as A, B, Ba, C through K, L_1, L_2, and L_3. The microimmunofluorescence test can be used to titrate antisera against all serotypes simultaneously or in a simplified procedure against several pools of the various serotypes. The immunofluorescence procedure can also be used to identify isolated strains of *C. trachomatis* by use of monospecific mouse antisera.

CLINICAL MANIFESTATIONS OF CHLAMYDIAL INFECTIONS

Psittacosis

C. psittaci have been found in many mammalian species, including cattle and sheep. The herbivores infected with these agents have abortions and suffer from arthritis. Humans are not readily infected from mammalian sources. *C. psittaci* has been isolated from a wide spectrum of birds, including the psittacine birds, turkeys, ducks, and pigeons. Psittacosis is an occupational hazard to breeders of exotic birds and to growers and processors of domestic fowl, in particular turkeys. The infection in avian species is often called ornithosis. The birds may have obvious disease or may have a prolonged inapparent infection that can be exacerbated by an improper environment. The chlamydiae are shed in the excreta and transmitted to humans by aerosol means. Direct transmission between humans has been documented in situations of close contact, such as nursing care. There have also been a number of cases among laboratory personnel; thus isolation of the organism is best performed in special facilities.

In humans psittacosis may display a varied clinical picture that could include pneumonia, muscle aches, and other signs of toxicity. The disease must be differentiated from influenza, atypical penumonia, and fever of unknown origin. The fatality rate in untreated cases is about 10 percent. Diagnosis may be made by isolation of the microorganism in the chick embryo or in cell culture or serologically by complement fixation. Treatment consists of administration of tetracycline for 3 weeks.

Lymphogranuloma Venereum (LGV)

LGV has long been recognized as a venereal disease restricted to humans. An initial vesicular or ulcerative lesion is generally observed on the external genitalia or on the vaginal wall or cervix. There is then dissemination to the regional lymph nodes and the appearance of an inguinal bubo that can suppurate with prolonged drainage. A systemic phase may occur, with involvement of many tissues, such as the conjunctiva, joints, and central nervous system. In chronic cases elephantiasis of the genitalia and, especially in females, rectal stricture can occur. LGV may be treated with tetracycline and sulfonamides with a prolonged course of therapy.

Diagnosis may be made from the clinical picture, by isolation of the agent in the chick embryo yolk sac or in cell culture, and by serology. There is frequently a high titer in the complement fixation test for the group antigen. The microimmunofluorescence test may also be used. It has been found that LGV is caused by the L_1, L_2, and L_3 serotypes of *C. trachomatis*.

The Frei test has been used in the past for diagnosis but is no longer utilized extensively. It is a skin test using antigen derived from egg yolk sac to detect delayed hypersensitivity. There are crossreactions with other chlamydiae which limit its value, and the sensitivity is less than that of other methods.

Trachoma

Trachoma is an ocular disease of high incidence in the Middle East and some other areas of Africa and Asia. It has been the leading cause of infectious blindness in the world. In the United States the incidence of trachoma is very low; the disease is relatively frequent in the Southwest among Amerindian groups. The agents recovered from areas with endemic trachoma are *C. trachomatis* of the A, B, Ba, and C serotypes. The disease occurs most often in young children. It may become chronic, and reinfection of previously treated persons is common. There is also a problem of latent infection with exacerbation of disease. The agent is spread by direct contact in low socioeconomic groups. The disease develops through stages of conjunctivitis, follicular conjunctivitis, capillary extention into the cornea, scarring of the conjunctiva with dragging of lashes, and, ultimately, corneal opacity. The infection may be treated with antibiotics, including tetracycline, sulfonamides, and rifampin. Because of toxicity of drugs for children and the need for prolonged administration, the optimal treatment regimen has not yet been determined.

Diagnosis of trachoma is based on the clinical picture, demonstration of cytoplasmic inclusions in cells from conjunctival smears, isolation of the agent in the yolk sac or cell culture, and serological examination of the patient. The microimmunofluorescence test is the most useful.

Control of trachoma depends mostly on improving the social conditions of the population so that improved personal hygiene is possible. Mass treatment with antibiotics is difficult to administer. Despite extensive efforts a satisfactory vaccine has not been developed.

Genital Tract Infections

In the last decade it has become apparent that chlamydial infections of the urogenital tract are of great importance in the United States and Europe. The agents recovered are of the C. trachomatis serotypes D through K, which are indistinguishable from those associated with endemic trachoma by other means. Strains isolated from the genital tract are capable of inducing inclusion conjunctivitis and signs of trachoma. Surveys of patients at venereal disease clinics have demonstrated chlamydia recovery rates of 50 percent or more from cases of nongonococcal urethritis and coinfection with chlamydia in about 30 percent of patients with gonorrhea. Treatment for gonorrhea frequently exposes the chlamy-

dial infection, which causes a continued course of post gonococcal chlamydial urethritis. It has also frequently been found that sex partners are infected. The urethritis in males tends to diminish without treatment; however, latent infections may occur with later exacerbations of urethritis. In females the most common clinical condition is cervical erosion. The exact role of chlamydial infection in this process is difficult to assess in view of the complex microbial flora. By extension from the cervix the chlamydial infection may also cause salpingitis or more generalized pelvic inflammatory disease.

Urethritis may be treated with sulfisoxazole, tetracyclines, and other antibiotics. A 14- to 21-day course of treatment is required, and sexual partners should be treated simultaneously to avoid reinfection.

Diagnosis depends largely on isolation of the microorganism in cell culture from endourethral samples or cervical swabs. The rate of recovery of organisms depends on the quality of laboratory procedures employed. Cultures can be observed for inclusions in about 48 hours. Serology is less useful, since many people already have antibodies and rises of titers may be difficult to determine.

Adult Inclusion Conjunctivitis

The eye may become infected from a primary genital infection in the adult. The infection commonly occurs in sexually active young adults but has occasionally been observed in medical personnel. The serotypes of C. trachomatis are usually the same as those found in genital tract infections. The disease appears as an acute follicular conjunctivitis and may progress to corneal involvement. The serious consequences of trachoma, including blinding, do not occur. Diagnosis may be made by cytologic examination of conjunctival smears and isolation in cell culture. Serology may provide additional supportive information.

The disease is treated by systemic administration of antibiotics, particularly tetracycline.

Neonatal Infections

A serious consequence of genital tract infection in pregnant women is the possibility of transmission of the agent to the infant at birth.

Inclusion Conjunctivitis. Eye infection with a purulent exudate may develop in newborns about 1 week post partum. Scrapings from the conjunctiva provide good diagnostic material for cytologic examination. The conjunctivitis is usually limited, without major damage to the eye, but more serious sequelae do occur occasionally. The silver nitrate prophylaxis for gonococcal infection has no effect on chlamydial infections. Treatment generally consists of topical application of tetracycline.

Pneumonia. Recent evidence has shown that infants are also subject to development of pneumonia as a consequence of maternal genital tract infection. It is necessary to obtain nasopharyngeal or tracheobronchial aspirates as the sample for isolation in cell culture. The infant may also show conjunctivitis earlier than pneumonia. This is a condition that presents may clinical problems and that will receive considerable future attention.

REFERENCES

Hobson, D. and Holmes, K.K.: Nongonococcal Urethritis and Related Infections. American Society for Microbiology, Washington, D.C., 1977.

Schachter, J. and Dawson, C.R.: Human Chlamydial Infections. PSG Publishing, Littleton, 1978.

Storz, J. and Spears, P.: Chlamydiales: Properties, cycle of development and effect on eukaryotic host cells. Curr. Top. Microbiol. Immunol. *76*: 168, 1977.

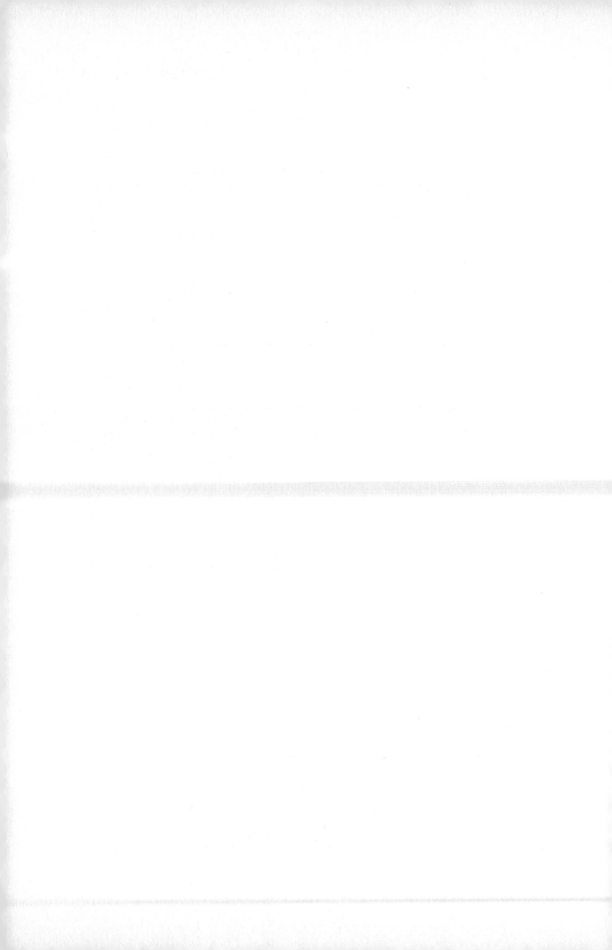

39

Introduction to Virology

Thomas D. Flanagan

Viruses are microorganisms characterized by a unique form of intracellular parasitism. They accomplish their reproduction by superimposing their own genetic information on the synthetic apparatus of the host cell. Since host mechanisms are used for production of viruses, most antibiotic drugs are not active in viral infections. Only certain drugs active against specific virus-encoded enzymes can be clinically useful.

In many cases, viral replication leads to the death of the host cell; however, there are other situations wherein the cell continues to live or even undergoes proliferation after infection. Viruses parasitize many biologic forms, including animals, plants, and bacteria. An important aspect of this parasitism is host specificity. The range of suitable hosts may be broad and include a large number of animal species, as in the case of rabies virus. Alternatively, the range may be narrow, as in the case of poliovirus, which infects only humans and a few other primates. The specificity may be exquisitely restricted, as with some bacterial viruses that can discriminate among strains of a bacterial species.

STRUCTURE AND COMPOSITION OF VIRUSES

Viruses exist in three forms — an extracellular form called a *virion* and two intracellular forms. One intracellular form is referred to as a *vegetative virus* and is present during active replication; the other is the *provirus* form, present as a segment of nucleic acid integrated into the host genome.

The virion is a noncellular particle organized in a regular and specific manner and appearing as a recognizable morphological form when observed by electron microscopy. Virions are small, varying in size from forms that have diameters of 20 nm to particles larger than 300 nm. The size and structure of virions are stable characteristics and are properties used in the classifications of viruses. Virions are composed of protein and one type of nucleic acid, either DNA or RNA. Some viruses have virions that in addition contain lipids present in membranelike structures called *envelopes*. The structures of virions have been determined by electron microscope studies. Virions occur as spherical, ovoid, or rod shaped particles and as complex entities that have a head-and-tail type of structure. The latter forms are found among viruses that parasitize some bacteria and are called *bacteriophages*. Spherical virions may or may not possess envelopes.

Analysis of the structure of virions has shown organization of subvirion elements in regular and symmetrical relationships. Three forms of symmetry have been recognized in virions — cubical, helical, and radial. Particles with cubical symmetry occur as *icosahedrons* (20 sided polyhedrons). Special terms for describing the anatomy of virions have been developed (Table 39.1).

In many cases it has been possible to determine the number of capsomers in virions with icosahedral capsids. This number is constant for various viruses and therefore is property used in classification. Examples of virions found in various genera are given in Figure 39.1.

Analysis of the nucleic acid found in virions has shown much diversity among viruses. As noted above, the nucleic acid is either DNA or RNA. The molecular weight of the nucleic acid is a constant characteristic of a given virus and varies

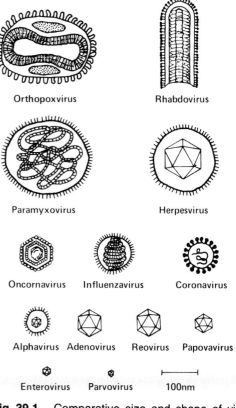

Fig. 39.1. Comparative size and shape of virions representing some virus genera. (With permission, Acton, J.D., Kucera, L.S., Myrvik, Q.N., and Weiser, R.N.: Fundamentals of Medical Virology. Lea & Febiger, Philadelphia, 1974.)

over a wide range among different viruses. The molecular form in which the nucleic acid occurs in the virion can be one of several. DNA can be present as a double-stranded molecule in either linear or circular configuration or as a single-stranded linear molecule. RNA occurs as a single-stranded molecule of either messenger or antimessenger polarity or as double-stranded molecules. In addition, the genome of some RNA viruses occurs in distinct fragments within the virion.

It is important to note the significance of the diversity in the size of viral genomes, since this is directly related to the amount of genetic information. The smallest viruses

Table 39.1.   Anatomic and Structural Terms of Viruses

Virion — the infectious virus particle

Nucleocapsid — the structural unit comprising the capsid and the nucleic acid

Capsid — the protein structure of the virion that surrounds the nucleic acid

Capsomer — the repeating morphological unit that makes up the capsid

Core — the morphological unit comprising the nucleic acid and associated proteins when the latter are present

Envelope — the lipid-containing membrane surrounding the capsid of some virions

Peplomer — the protein subunit of the envelope

---

can code for only a few proteins and are dependent on the host for many functions. In contrast, the large viruses can code for many proteins. They are less dependent on specific host factors, and their virions contain many structural and functional proteins.

A limited complement of enzymes is found in the virions of some viruses. The most frequently encountered enzymes are transcriptases, which mediate the transcription of the genomic nucleic acid into mRNA. This enzyme activity is found in virions of both DNA and RNA virus groups but is more common among RNA viruses. The virion transcriptase of one RNA virus family, the *Retroviridae*, is unique in that it transcribes from RNA to DNA. It is thus called reverse transcriptase. Some viruses also contain neuraminidase activity. Neuraminidase is an enzyme that cleaves *N*-acetylneuraminic acid residues from a variety of carrier molecules.

All of these physical and chemical characteristics are used in modern classification of viruses.

VIRUS CLASSIFICATION

Table 39.2 shows the recognized virus families, genera, and some viruses in those taxa of importance to man. The present official classification of viruses, developed by the International Committee on Virus Nomenclature, recognizes 16 families among viruses that are of primary interest to students of vertebrate virology. There are no recognized species names; however, type species have been designated for each genus. The *Retroviridae* are currently divided into three genera; however, there is a suggestion to classify these as subfamilies. This suggestion has been adopted in Chapter 48.

Most older schemes of classification have fallen into disuse; however, the designation *arbovirus* is still used quite widely. The term is applied to a large and medically significant group of viruses that share a common mode of spread among humans and other animals. All of these agents are disseminated by arthropod vectors, principally mosquitos. Some *Togaviridae, Bunyaviridae, Arenaviridae, Reoviridae*, and *Rhabdoviridae* are arboviruses. Another commonly encountered system of informal virus taxonomy is the use of virus groups. The concept of virus groups was a device used to meet the needs of communication during the development of an official taxonomy. Many of the present genus designations and some family designations are roughly equivalent to the old virus groups. Group names are most often used colloquially when one is discussing viruses in general terms.

BACTERIOPHAGES

Much of our current knowledge of molecular biology and genetics stems from the study of the interaction between bacterial viruses and bacteria. These viruses were first described by Twort in 1915, and many of their basic characteristics were documented by D'Herelle in studies from 1917 through the 1930s.

Many workers have contributed to the bacteriophage literature. The group at the Cold Spring Harbor Laboratory headed by Delbrück has concentrated on elucidating the interactions between *Escherichia coli* strain B and a group of bacteriophages referred to as the T phages. The results of these investigations have yielded a detailed understanding of the molecular and genetic events occurring during the replication of bacteriophages. The descriptions of the interactions of these bacteriophages and bacteria have become important models for other virus–cell systems.

The Lytic Cycle

The interaction of a bacteriophage with a host bacterium in which the virus is repli-

Table 39.2.   Classification of Animal Viruses

Family	Genus	Viruses Important to Man
	RNA Viruses	
Picornaviridae	Enterovirus	Poliovirus (3 serotypes), echoviruses (33 serotypes), coxsackievirus A and B (24 serotypes)
	Rhinovirus	Human rhinovirus (80 serotypes)
	Calcivirus	
Togaviridae	Alphavirus	Viruses of Eastern and Western equine encephalitis, others
	Flavivirus	Yellow fever virus, St. Louis encephalitis virus
	Rubivirus	Rubella virus
Arenaviridae	Arenavirus	Lassa fever virus
Rhabdoviridae	Rhabdovirus	Rabies virus, Marburg virus
Coronaviridae	Coronavirus	Human coronavirus (3 serotypes)
Orthomyxoviridae	Influenzavirus	Influenza viruses A, B, C
Paramyxoviridae	Paramyxovirus	Parainfluenza virus, mumps virus
	Morbillivirus	Measles virus
	Pneumovirus	Respiratory syncytial virus
Bunyaviridae	Bunyavirus	89 serologically related viruses (type species — Bunyamwera virus) including California encephalitis virus
Retroviridae	Oncornavirus	
	Spumavirus	
	Lentivirus	
Reoviridae	Reovirus	Reoviruses (3 serotypes)
	Orbivirus	Colorado tick fever virus
	Rotavirus	Virus of infantile diarrhea
	DNA Viruses	
Parvoviridae	Parvovirus	Nowalk agent of viral diarrhea
	Adenosatellovirus	
	Densovirus	
Papovaviridae	Polyomavirus	SV40, JC virus, PML virus
	Papillomavirus	Human papilloma virus
Adenoviridae	Mastadenovirus	Human adenoviruses (31 serotypes)
Herpetoviridae	Herpesvirus	Herpes simplex virus types 1 and 2, cytomegalovirus, Epstein-Barr virus, varicella-zoster virus
Poxviridae	Orthopoxvirus	Vaccinia virus, variola virus
Iridoviridae	Iridovirus	

cated, that terminates in lysis and death of the bacterium, is called a *lytic cycle*. It is an alternative to another interaction, called the *lysogenic cycle*, in which the infected bacterial cell survives and proliferates. The lytic infection of *E. coli* B with bacter-iophage T-4 is an extensively investigated system that will serve as a model for discussion.

Structure.   The virion of T-4 is illustrated in Figure 39.2. The *head* is a polyhedral structure 95 nm by 65 nm. It is

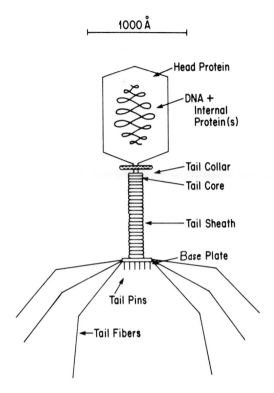

Fig. 39.2. Schematic drawing of bacteriophage T-4.

composed of eleven different proteins and contains the viral genome. The *genome* consists of a single DNA molecule of 106 × 10⁶ daltons. It is a double-stranded molecule and is found in a linear configuration in the virion. There are polypeptides associated with the DNA present within the head. The *tail* is a complex structure attached to one of the vertices of the head; it measures 110 nm by 25 nm. The tail is composed of 17 different proteins and is organized into a number of distinct components. The *collar* is a ringlike structure close to the point where the tail inserts into the head; it is apparently attached to a covering of the shaft of the tail, called the *sheath*. The sheath is composed of an actin-like contractile protein. The inner part of the tail shaft is called the *tube* or *needle*. At the distal end of the tail is a complex structure known as the *base plate*. The base

plate is hexagonal and has short spikelike appendages at each vertex, the *tail pins*. Attached to the base plate are six 140-nm *tail fibers*.

Replication. The kinetics of the lytic replication cycle of T-4 were studied by Delbrück and Ellis in the one-step growth-curve experiment. The experiment was performed by the addition of a known number of bacteriophage particles to an excess of susceptible bacteria, allowing a short time for the viruses to attach to the cells and then diluting the suspension about 100-fold. This was to ensure that viruses once attached to bacteria could not detach and initiate infection of another cell at a later time. It was important that all infections were started at the same time. The investigators then removed a given volume of the suspension of inoculated cells and assayed for infectious centers. The assay system they used was a plaque assay, a method

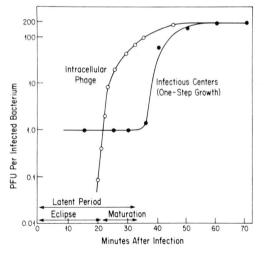

Fig. 39.3 One-step growth curve of bacteriophage T-4 in *E coli* cells. ●, number of infectious centers per bacterium in cultures inoculated with bacteriophage and sampled at various times after infection. ○, number of infectious centers per bacterium in cultures inoculated with bacteriophage and sampled after artificial lysis of cells at various times after infection.

that permits counting of infectious virus particles or, as in this case, virus-infected cells.

The results of an experiment similar to theirs are shown in Figure 39.3. The data showed that there was no increase in the number of virus-infected cells for 35 minutes and then over a short period of 3 to 4 minutes there was about a 100-fold increase in the number of infectious centers. These results indicated that the mode of bacteriophage replication was different from the binary fission characteristic of bacteria. The period of time from the initiation of the infection to the beginning of the rise of the curve was termed the latent period. Artificial lysis of infected cells during the latent period reduced the time required to demonstrate an increase in infectivity, but there remained a significant period wherein no infectivity could be demonstrated. The essential one-step characteristic also remained when cells were lysed.

The constant period in which infectivity is not detected was called *eclipse*, and the time from the end of the eclipse to the end of the latent period was interpreted as a maturation stage. The onset of increase to the leveling of the curve was called the *burst*. The magnitude of increase was called the *burst size* and indicated the number of new infectious virions released from each infected cell. The various events in this cycle have been termed *adsorption, penetration, eclipse* (or, more accurately, *synthesis*), *maturation* or *assembly*, and, finally, *release*.

These events have been studied in fine detail; the following account deals with the process in a somewhat superficial manner.

Adsorption. The attachement of the virion to the cell is accomplished by the contact between the tail fibers of the phage and receptors on or in the cell surface. The interaction is specific in that mutant cells lacking the specific receptor cannot be infected and in that antiserum to tail fibers is capable of inhibiting attachment. Adsorp-

tion of T-4 to *E. coli* B cells is independent of temperature but can be inhibited by extremes of pH or high molar concentration of salts. This suggests the formation of ionic bonds between sites on the tail fibers and the receptors. Morphological studies of phage attachment have shown virions oriented perpendicularly to surface of the bacterium, with the tail fibers attached to the cell wall. The base plate of the tail as about 100 nm from the surface.

The attachment of bacteriophages to bacterial cells has a profound effect on the cells. Under conditions of low multiplicity of infection (MOI) (few viruses per cell) there are detectable changes in the membrane function of the cell. These changes are reversible, and cells recover. When conditions of high MOI are used, cells actually undergo lysis. This phenomenon has been termed *lysis from without*. These effects are due solely to the attachment of phage; the same results can be obtained by using purified phage tails rather than whole virions.

Penetration. The second event in the cycle is the entry of the viral genome into the host cell. Early investigators were puzzled by the consistent finding of phage particles attached to the surface of bacteria and the absence of virions within cells. The suggestion was that entry of the entire virion was not necessary to cause infection. The issue was resolved by the classic experiment of Hershey and Chase in 1952. These investigators differentially labeled the bacteriophage to be used as inoculum by tagging the protein with ^{35}S and the DNA with ^{32}P. After adding the labeled virus to the bacteria and allowing attachment, they submitted the whole suspension to high shearing force to remove adherent virions from the bacterial cell surface. The bacteria were then sedimented, and radioactivity was determined. All of the ^{32}P label of the phage DNA was found in the sedimented cells; over 80 percent of the ^{35}S label of the phage protein was in the supernatant fluid, having been removed from the cell surface. Cells infected in this manner went on to yield virus progeny even after removal of the viral protein coats from the cells. The results demonstrated conclusively that only DNA entered the cell and that the phage DNA contained all of the information necessary for the replication of virus.

The process by which phage DNA is introduced into bacterial cells has been compared to injection by a syringe. Morphologically, the virion appears to contact the surface of the cell at the points of the tail pins. The sheath contracts or shortens, and the tube is thrust through the cell wall. Viral DNA is ejected through the tube and deposited on the cytoplasmic membrane of the bacterial cell. The DNA spontaneously crosses the membrane into the cell by unknown mechanisms.

It should be emphasized at this point that injection involving a contractile sheath is unique to T-"even" phages and that other phages, even those with tails, may use other mechanisms.

Eclipse.   The entry of viral genome into the bacterial cell causes, within a short time, a shutdown of host macromolecular synthesis. All cellular DNA, RNA, and protein synthesis ceases. Cellular DNA undergoes degradation to be incorporated later into viral DNA. These changes are the direct result of virus gene products; that is, they are effected by proteins specified in the viral DNA code and synthesized in the cell during the first minutes of infection. Three classes of viral proteins responsible for changes in the host cell are nucleases which degrade DNA, proteins that modify host RNA polymerase, causing inhibition of cellular RNA synthesis, and proteins that directly interfere with host protein synthesis by modifying tRNA, enzymes, or initiation factors.

Genes of the virus have been classified into three categories according to the time and conditions of their transcription. The first class consists of the immediate early genes, which are transcribed by resident host RNA polymerase; the mRNA can be synthesized in the presence of chloramphenicol. Translation products of these mRNA are involved in the shutdown processes described above. The termination of immediate early transcription is effected by host termination factor ρ. Two immediate early gene products are involved in the progression to the second class of viral genes to be transcribed, the delayed early genes. The first of these products is an anti-ρ protein that inhibits termination, and the second is a σ-like factor that modifies the host polymerase, permitting the transcription of another set of viral genes.

The products of delayed early genes are involved in further shutdown activities, the mechanism of viral DNA synthesis, and the initiation of the transcription of the final set of genes, the late genes. The latter activity is accomplished by the synthesis of another viral σ-like factor. The synthesis of late gene products occurs only after viral DNA synthesis has progressed to a stage where certain single-strand discontinuities are present in newly synthesized strands. This condition is apparently necessary for transcription of the late genes. These late sequences code for the structural proteins of the virion and the enzymes that lyse the host cell.

DNA Synthesis.   The synthesis of viral DNA is initiated during the period of delayed early synthesis and is a function of virus-specified enzymes with the participation of some resident host enzymes. Precursors for viral DNA synthesis are derived from degraded bacterial DNA and from the medium in which the cells are growing. T-even phages are characterized by a unique base, 5-hydroxymethylcytosine, which substitutes for cytosine in viral DNA. In addition, this residue is glucosylated to different degrees among the T-even phages. T-4 phages have all 5-hydroxymethylcytosine residues glucosylated; T-2 and T-6 have about 25 percent unglucosylated residues.

These modifications in the chemical structure of viral DNA are significant factors in the ability of these viruses to complete replication. For example, phage mutants that lack glucosyl residues are unable to replicate in bacteria that normally support the replication of wild-type (glucosylated DNA) virus. The reason for this inability to replicate is that mutant phage DNA, lacking glucosyl residues, is susceptible to the action of nucleases resident in the bacterial cells. The mutant is fully capable of replication in cells that lack these enzymes. This modification of viral DNA, which protects against "restriction" by endonucleases, is further discussed in Chapter 3.

The site of viral DNA replication varies among phages. T4 replication occurs initially at specific plasma membrane sites and later in the cytoplasm of the cell. In the first replicative intermediate, synthesis is unidirectional and involves a circularized molecule. Later replicative intermediates are long linear forms that replicate bidirectionally. These forms, called *concatemers*, contain several genome equivalents each. The T-4 concatemers are packaged in the empty head structures during maturation. The length, and hence the amount of genetic information, of the DNA packaged is determined by the capacity of the head. DNA that has deleted sequences will incorporate repetitions of molecule ends, while small heads will package permuted genomes.

Maturation. The maturation of T-4 occurs by integrating the products of three independent assembly lines. The process is illustrated in Figure 39.4. The head structure is composed of a single major protein and a number of minor proteins. It forms first as an empty structure, after which DNA is packaged. The process of packaging involves the cleavage of polypeptides and removal of a scaffolding protein, an event that probably accounts for the positioning of the DNA in relation to the protein superstructure. The internal proteins are basic proteins and probably function to allow the close packing of the acidic DNA. The amount of DNA is determined by the capacity of the empty head. Therefore "a headful" of DNA constitutes the end of the packaging process; the DNA strand is cut by nucleases, and subsequent to packaging the collar attaches to the head.

Tail construction begins with formation of the base plate, including the tail pins. The entire structure contains 11 different proteins. The tube, sheath, and connecting structure are added in sequence to complete the tail, which attaches to the completed head.

Tail fibers are synthesized in the third component of the process and attach to the assembled head and tail. Each step of the process requires the participation of one or more functional viral gene products with the exception of the joining of head and the tail, which is apparently a spontaneous event.

Release. T-4 phage is released from infected bacteria by lysis of the host cells. This is effected by phage gene products that alter the permeability of the host cell cytoplasmic membrane, allowing the leakage of another phage product, lysozyme.

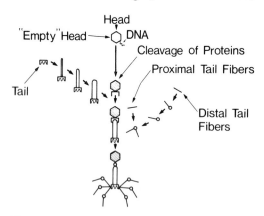

Fig. 39.4. Assembly of bacteriophage T-4. (With permission, modified from Wood, W.B., Edgar, R.S., King, J., Lielausis, I., and Henninger, M.: Bacteriophage assembly. Reprinted from Federation Proceedings *27*: 1160, 1968.)

This enzyme carries out destruction of the bacterial cell wall, leading to the rupture of the cell and subsequent release of the progeny phage virions.

Summary. T-4 phage infects *E. coli* B by attaching to the cell surface, its tail fibers interacting with specific receptors in the cell wall. Viral DNA is introduced into the host cell by an injection mechanism that involves the intrusion of the tail tube through the bacterial cell wall. This is accomplished by contraction of the tail sheath and extrusion of viral DNA onto the plasma membrane of the cell. During the eclipse phase, virus gene products shutdown host macromolecular synthesis and initiate and control synthesis of viral proteins and DNA. The structural elements of the progeny are assembled by three distinct processes, and the new virus particles are released by rupture of the host cell.

Lysogeny

An alternative to the lytic cycle exemplified by T-4 infection can exist between a bacteriophage and its host. This alternative is a state in which the virus genetic information exists within the host cell yet is only partially expressed. Further, the maintenance of this state of partial expression is under the control of virus genes. This relationship is called *lysogeny*. Bacteriophages that characteristically enter into this kind of relationship with a given bacterium are called *temperate*. In the lysogenic state, replication of the virus genome usually occurs simultaneously with host cell replication because the viral DNA is often integrated into the host chromosome. This process accounts for the presence of the viral genome in all cells of a given bacterial strain. Such strains are referred to as lysogenic strains.

The presence of viral DNA, called the prophage in a bacterium, has a number of consequences that profoundly affect the biologic characteristics of the bacterium. Characteristics such as toxogenicity or specific cell surface antigens of bacteria can be a result of the presence of a prophage. These acquired characteristics are usually virus gene products, and their acquisition is referred to as *lysogenic conversion*. Lysogenic strains have a number of other important properties. They exhibit spontaneous phage production — that is, a small fraction of cells in a population of lysogenic bacteria undergoes lysis as a result of the prophage entering into a vegetative state. When this occurs the viral DNA is excised from its integrated site, undergoes replication independent of the host, directs the synthesis of phage structural elements, and assembles progeny virions. Lysis of the host cell ensues, and the progeny virions are released. Their infectivity can be detected on suitable indicator cells (bacteria for which the phage is virulent rather than temperate). In addition, it should be noted that temperate phages often bring about lysis of significant numbers of cells in cultures that can be lysogenized. In this case, plaque assays for phages can be done. These plaques have a characteristic turbid appearance owing to the presence of lysogenic cells. Spontaneous phage production occurs at a given rate in a lysogenic bacterial population. The rate is usually of the order of one cell per 10^6 cells. This rate of phage production can be

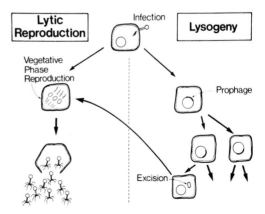

Fig. 39.5. Comparison of lytic reproduction and lysogeny of bacteriophages.

dramatically changed by treatment of the lysogenic bacteria with a variety of physical or chemical agents such as ultraviolet light or nitrogen mustard. These treatments cause almost every cell in the population to enter into phage production. The process is called *induction*.

Another consequence of lysogeny is a state of refractoriness or resistance of bacteria to superinfection by closely related phages. This is called *immunity* (an unfortunate choice of word). The mechanism responsible for this refractory state is related to the control of the lysogenic state itself. Both maintenance of lysogeny and immunity are due to a virus gene product, a repressor, the concentration of which controls the ability of the virus genome to be transcribed.

Temperate bacteriophages are of importance in studies of the genetics of bacteria because they can serve as genetic markers and as vehicles for the transmission of genetic information. Their role in the genetic studies is discussed in Chapter 3.

ANIMAL VIRUSES

Virus–Cell Interactions

Viruses that infect animal cells have a number of specific tasks to accomplish in order to complete their replication. They must recognize and attach to the cell to be infected. They must gain access to the interior of the cell. They must have the capacity to produce mRNA molecules that can be translated on ribosomes of the host cell. They must have the capacity to replicate their genomes in some manner. Finally, they must have a mechanism to transfer their genomes to other host cells.

The stages of animal virus replication can be recognized, as with bacteriophages, as *adsorption, penetration, synthesis, maturation*, and *release*. While the lytic cycle of bacteriophage inevitably leads to the death of the host cell, infections with animal viruses may have a number of variations in outcome. These variations include frankly cytocidal infections in which the virus infects the host cell, brings about a shutdown of host macromolecular synthesis, replicates, and is released from the cell, which undergoes lysis. However, some virus–cell interactions are characterized by a more commensal relationship in which the virus infects the cell, replicates, and is released from the cell without lysis. This type of infection has been termed *moderate* or *steady state*. In some cases this type of infection continues for a short time, ending in the death of the cell, but in other cases the production of virus particles may persist over the entire normal lifetime of the cell.

Another variation encountered among animal virus infections is the *latent infection*. In this situation the animal virus genome is introduced into the cell by the normal infectious process or by acquisition from an ancestral cell; however, the entire genetic potential for viral replication is not expressed. It remains sequestered in a latent form within the host cell. The analogy to lysogeny is appropriate in that there is apparent integration of the viral genome into the chromosomes of the cell and the potential for full expression upon release from whatever control mechanism is present. With some viruses, such as the *Herpetoviridae*, this release may trigger entry into a cytocidal expression of the virus infection. In other cases release may be expressed as a moderate infection resulting in the production of virions by a cell that retains its own potential for function and proliferation; the *Retroviridae* enter into interactions characteristic of this latter situation.

Methods of Study

The methods used to study animal viruses have evolved over the past 80 years to the present state of extreme precision and sophistication. They have contributed to our knowledge of molecular biology and genetics as well as to our understanding of pathogenesis. Since viruses are intracellular parasites, a suitable population of cells must be available to infect in order to study the replication of the agent. Early studies were conducted in adult animals. Studies in suckling and embryonic animals were more successful for some viruses, but whole animal hosts proved to be inadequate and simpler systems were sought. Rapid progress began with the development of modern cell culture techniques.

Cell Culture. *In vitro* cultures of cells from animal sources are the basic tool in studies of animal viruses. There are several types of cell cultures, each of which may present unique advantages to fulfill a particular need or requirement.

Primary cell cultures are those established directly from tissue sources. The procedure used involves the mechanical reduction of solid tissues into small pieces and the separation of cells by enzymatic breakdown of the pieces. The monodisperse cells are suspended in a medium of appropriate osmolarity and requisite nutritional constitution. The cultures are placed in glass or plastic containers. They are incubated under optimal conditions of temperature, humidity, and pH. The cells settle to the substrate, attach, and proliferate. The population of attached cells increases until all of the substrate available is covered. Cells usually do not grow over one another; therefore cultures of this type are referred to as monolayer cultures. Primary cell cultures are characteristically of short duration *in vitro*. They can be rarely subcultured or passaged more than a few times before degeneration and death of the cells.

Cells established in primary culture do not usually retain the differentiated characteristics of the tissue from which they were derived; however, they do retain some species markers such as surface antigens and chromosomal constitution.

Another type of culture is the continuous cell culture. Cultures of this type were, of course, originally established as primary cultures. They differ from primary cultures in that they are capable of maintaining their replicative potential for many generations. Two kinds of continuous cultures have been recognized, continuous cell lines and continuous cell strains.

Continuous cell lines are characterized by an apparently unlimited potential for subcultivation. The cells retain species identity such as cell surface markers and isoenzymes; however, they are karyologically abnormal. Cells of continuous lines grow rapidly, often spreading over one another, displaying a loss of contact inhibition such as is seen in primary cell cultures. Continuous lines are also frequently capable of growth in suspension, not requiring a surface for attachment. This is another characteristic quite distinct from primary cultures.

Continuous cell strains are cultures of cells that are capable of multiple passages *in vitro*; however, they have a finite potential for propagation. The cells retain their species markers and remain diploid during cultivation. Like primary cells, they lose the differentiating characteristics of their original tissue.

Quantitation of Viral Infectivity. An important aspect of all studies of viruses is quantitation. Infectivity is the most significant biologic property of a virus; therefore accurate measurement of infectivity is a basic requirement for valid data.

There are three types of infectivity assays commonly used in virologic investigations: *quantal assays, graded response assays*, and *enumerative assays*. Quantal assays are based on an all-or-none response of a host to viral infection. The responses used may be development of cytopathic effect (CPE) in a cell culture, death of an inoculated animal, or development of hemagglutinin (see below) in an inoculated chicken embryo. The assays are usually carried out by serial 10-fold dilutions of the preparation being measured and inoculation of several replicate hosts with each dilution. For example, poliovirus stock would be diluted serially 10^{-1} to 10^{-9} and 0.1 ml of each dilution (or at least the four or five highest dilutions) inoculated into tubes with cultures of primary monkey kidney cells. The tubes would be observed daily for the development of CPE. The titer of virus infectivity would be calculated from the number of cultures showing CPE for each dilution and estimating the 50 percent end point by interpolation. The results of most quantal assays are expressed as a number of infectious doses (50 percent) per unit volume. These may be tissue culture infectious doses ($TCID_{50}$), mouse lethal doses (LD_{50}), or other appropriate values.

Graded response assays are based upon measurement of some response to virus that may occur on a continuous scale. These assays may relate such measurement as tumor size or organ weight to virus dose.

Enumerative assays are the most satisfactory from the perspective of accuracy and statistical evaluation. These assays are based on the observation of a single response for each infectious unit. The most frequently used assays of this type are plaque assays and focus-forming assays. The plaque assay depends upon the formation of a visible area of lysis in a monolayer culture of cells. The method assumes that one plaque results from initial infection with one virus particle. Experimental data bear out this assumption, conforming to characteristics predicted by the Poisson distribution. Technically, the method must ensure that progeny virus particles from infected cells are confined to the immediate locus and cannot initiate infections at distant sites. This is usually accomplished by overlaying the inoculated cell monolayer with medium in agarose or methyl cellulose. Titers are usually expressed as plaque-forming units (PFU) per unit volume.

Measurement of Other Biologic Properties of Virions. There are important methods used in studying viruses that involve properties other than infectivity. The virion particles of many viruses have properties that lend themselves to quantitation. Often the assay of these properties is more quickly and economically carried out than infectivity assays; therefore these methods are frequently employed.

The surface of virions of a variety of viruses interacts with receptors on the surface of erythrocytes of some species. This interaction brings about the visible aggregation of the erythrocytes. The penonomenon is called viral hemagglutination (HA) and is the basis of assays for virus and antiviral antibodies. HA titrations are carried out by serially diluting the preparation to be assayed in a row of glass tubes or wells in plastic plates and addition of a dilute suspension of erythrocytes. The test is incubated, and the cell–virus aggregates sediment to the bottom of the tube or well. Agglutinated red cells form a characteristic shield on the bottom, whereas unagglutinated cells form a tight button. End points are recognized by the transition from the shield of agglutinated red cells to the unagglutinated cells on the bottom of the tube. Titers are expressed as HA units per unit volume. Antiviral antibodies reacting with the virion surface can inhibit the HA reaction and therefore can be detected and measured by hemagglutination-inhibition (HAI) tests.

Some viruses possess the ability to modify the functions of biologic membranes, bringing about fusion of membranes or lysis of cells. *In vitro* tests with red cells can take advantage of these activities. Viral hemolysis results from the interaction of some viruses with erythrocytes and can be used as a measurement of virus. The lysis results from the interaction of specific glycoproteins of the virion surface with the red cell membrane. Antibodies specific for the glycoprotein inhibit the reaction; therefore inhibition of hemolysis can be used to detect antibodies.

Enzyme activities that reside in or on virions can be used to detect and quantitate viruses. For example, the neuraminidase activity of influenza virus that splits *N*-acetylneuraminic acid from carrier molecules can be measured. The magnitude of this activity can be related to the quantity of virus. Reverse transcriptase can be used to detect and quantitate members of the *Retroviridae*.

The antigenic nature of virions and their components can be used for identification and quantitation. A variety of serologic and immunochemical techniques have been implemented in virology, bringing an exquisite degree of sensitivity and specificity to many studies. The diagnosis of viral infections depends heavily on serologic techniques. Later chapters will point out the relevent diagnostic procedures for the various viral diseases.

Genetics

Viruses as living organisms retain and transmit their characteristics through their genomes. The genetic message is carried in the DNA or RNA found in the virion. As do other biologic forms, viruses display constancy in transmission of properties from one generation to the next by faithful reproduction of the base sequence of their nucleic acid. They also have the capacity to vary genetically through the modification of their genetic endowment. This variation may occur by alteration of their intrinsic genetic material or by acquisition of new genetic material from exogenous sources. The first process is *mutation*; the second, *recombination*.

Genetic studies of viruses, as of other organisms, require markers for recognition of genetic variation and methods to isolate genetically differentiated clones. Two types of conditionally lethal mutants have provided recognizable genetic variation and with plaquing techniques have allowed precise genetic investigations. The temperature-sensitive (ts) class of conditional lethal mutants has been of great utility in these studies. These mutants result from nucleic acid base substitutions in the genome that give rise to amino acid changes in the primary structure of the protein gene product. Such changes are usually detected by loss of function of the protein at higher temperatures. For example, a virus carrying such a ts mutation replicates well at 31°C, the permissive temperature, and fails to replicate at 39°C, the restrictive temperature. The wild-type virus would be capable of replication at both temperatures. Combined with a plaque technique that allows isolation of viral clones, use of ts mutants has permitted precise genetic analysis of many viruses. The other type of conditionally lethal mutants, the host-range mutants, has not found wide application in animal virology as yet.

There are a number of other types of mutants that have been used in genetic studies. Plaque-forming mutants were important tools in early investigations; they were particularly useful in vaccine development and other processes in which markers of viral attenuation were sought. There are viral mutants that are resistant to antiviral compounds as well as mutants that are drug dependent. Certain highly virulent mutants have the capacity to replicate better at temperatures over 40°C than at 37°C. They are frequently referred to as "hot mutants."

Interaction Among Viral Genes and Gene Products. When more than one type of virus infects a single host cell, interactions between the viral genes or gene products may occur. The probability of interaction is greater between closely related viruses. Several different types of interaction have been described.

Recombination between different strains of related viruses occurs with variable frequency. With the exceptions of poliovirus and foot-and-mouth-disease virus, single-stranded RNA viruses have not been found

532   Medical Microbiology

to take part in recombination. Double-stranded DNA viruses readily undergo recombination, and viruses with segmented genomes engage in recombination at high frequencies. The mechanism by which recombinants are generated is the classical breakage and reformation of nucleic acid strands in the case of the double-stranded DNA viruses (and the retroviruses). Recombination among viruses with segmented genomes occurs by reassortment of segments.

Another interaction of considerable importance is that of complementation. When a defective virus that cannot complete its replication because of a genetic defect coinfects a cell with another related virus that has intact function at the defective site of the first virus, both viruses can replicate. The intact virus supplies the required function to allow replication. Complementation analysis using large numbers of ts mutants has permitted the determination of the number of genes in various viruses. It has also provided a powerful method for analysis of the replicative cycle itself.

Phenotypic mixing can occur when two different but related viruses coinfect a cell. In this case the progeny virions carry structural elements of both parental strains, yet the genome is of either one or the other parental type. For example, if poliovirus type 1 and type 3 coinfect a cell, any given progeny virion bears serotypic antigens of both types 1 and 3 as demonstrable by neutralization with antisera to type 1 or type 3. When such a virion infects a cell, progeny of this infection bear only a single type-specific determinant, that of the particular parental genotype carried by the infecting particle.

A similar phenomenon can be observed when cells are submitted to mixed infection with viruses that mature by budding. In this situation the nucleocapsid of one virus may be enveloped with membrane containing peplomers of the second virus. The resulting virion may have all peplomers of the second parental-type virus, or may be mixed. Virions carrying the surface glycoproteins of a virus different from that specified by their genome are called pseudotypes. RNA tumor viruses and vesicular stomatitis virus form pseudotypes quite readily.

PATHOGENESIS AND RESPONSE TO INFECTION

Viruses replicate within the cells of the infected individual; therefore cellular response and pathology must be recognized. However, viral infections have effects that can be understood only by a consideration of the complex response mechanisms of the entire body as well as the nature of the virus–cell interaction. Therefore we will discuss the elements of response and pathology of viral infections on a cellular level and on the level of the entire animal.

Cellular Response

Even at the basic level of cell–virus interaction there are several variations of outcome possible that depend upon the nature both of the virus and of the cell. Some of these variations have been described above as cytocidal, moderate, and latent infections. Cell death as a response to virus infection is perhaps so obvious it is often overlooked. Death of virus-infected cells after the production of virus progeny is of little consequence to the virus. However, should a cell die before the completion of viral replication, the infectious process would not progress and the infection would be aborted. This mechanism may well function as one of the bases for nonsusceptibility to virus infections.

Another set of phenomena related to virus infection are those termed interference responses. A number of these interactions have been described, and they are divided into two categories, *homologous in-*

terference and *heterologous interference.* Homologous interference is observed when a given virus interferes with the growth of itself (*autointerference*) or another closely related virus. Heterologous interference is observed when the growth of one virus interferes with the growth of another unrelated virus.

The best explored systems of homologous interference are those in which defective interfering (DI) particles are active. DI particles are defective virions that contain some of the genome of the "standard" virus but are not able to complete their own replication. Standard virus is required to replicate DI particles, yet these DI particles interfere with the replication of that standard virus. Cell culture studies of DI particle interference suggest that this phenomenon may have a role in the pathogenesis of *in vivo* infections.

Among the examples of heterologous interference, the interferon system is the best known. Isaacs and Lindenmann described experiments in 1957 that suggested the existence of a soluble factor, *interferon*, capable of protecting cells from virus infection. Since the publication of this report, interferon has been the subject of a great deal of research.

Interferons are proteins produced by cells upon appropriate stimulation. They have the ability to evoke a state of refractoriness to viral replication in other cells. Among the stimuli that induce interferon production is virus infection. There are a number of other agents that induce interferon. Among these are ultraviolet-inactivated virus, naturally occurring double-stranded ribonucleic acids, and synthetic polyribonucleotides like polyriboinosinic:polyribocytidylic acid (poly I:poly C).

Three types of human interferon have described: α, β and γ. The first two, α and β interferons, are produced by stimulating leukocytes and fibroblasts, respectively, *in vitro* with viruses or other inducers. These two interferons resemble one another in many physicochemical properties such as heat resistance and acid resistance, but they differ antigenically. The third, γ interferon, is produced by sentitized lymphocytes upon antigenic stimulation. It is sensitive to extremes of pH (pH 2.0 or pH 9.0) which the other interferons normally resist.

Interferons are species specific in that interferon produced by cells of one species is active only in cells of that species or of very closely related species. Thus murine interferon will not protect human cells, nor will human interferon protect murine cells. Exceptions to this rule have been observed; for example, human α interferon is active on some bovine cell lines. There is no specificity regarding the viruses involved. Interferon induced by any given virus is protective to cells challenged with a variety of DNA or RNA viruses.

The mechanism by which interferon protects cells against viruses is not completely understood. It is clear that interferon does not directly inactivate the virus, nor does it inhibit adsorption or penetration of virus. Interferon itself must be taken up by cells by means of a receptor to induce the antiviral state. Cellular RNA and protein synthesis must ensue to produce refractoriness. These processes give rise to products that inhibit transcription of viral genomic nucleic acids or translation of viral mRNA.

There are properties of interferon that have implications in human medicine other than its antiviral action. Evidence is accumulating that interferon may possess antitumor activity as well as activity against a variety of intracellular bacteria and protozoa. It plays an important regulatory role in immune response. It is also a powerful potentiator of the natural killer cell system active against a variety of tumors and virus-infected cells.

Systemic Responses

The pathogenesis of a viral infection is determined by a number of factors, some of which are viral and others of which are related to the host. Two general categories, local and systemic are used to classify infections. However, not all viral infections fall clearly into these categories, and infection by a given virus does not always manifest itself in the same way in different patients. The determinants of pathogenesis include routes of entry, tissue tropisms of the virus, the temperature preference of the virus, and viral susceptibility to the variety of nonspecific and specific mechanisms of protection. Pathogenesis may be further modified by the immunologic status of the host. Reinfection with viruses usually produces a highly modified course of infection; in many cases there is no clinical manifestation at all.

Immune response to viral infection is also a result of a complex set of factors, as is pathogenesis. Local infections of the respiratory and gastroenteric mucosa stimulate a vigorous local immune response characterized by production of secretory IgA antibodies and, to a variable degree, a systemic response consisting of IgM and IgG antibodies. The immunologic memory of local secretory immunity is not long lived, and anemnestic responses are not apparent. However, local infections do engender memory in the peripheral elements of the immune system, and vigorous systemic responses occur with reinfections.

Systemic viral infections are characterized by an initial period of viral replication that occurs at local sites near the portal of entry of the agent. These may be the respiratory or alimentary mucosa in cases where the virus is acquired by inhalation or ingestion. Some viruses are introduced directly into the blood circulatory system by injection. The arboviruses constitute a group of agents that are examples of this mode of entry. In these cases the initial sites of replication are lymph nodes, spleen cells, or Kupffer cells of the liver. Virus spreads from the sites of initial replication by way of the vascular system to secondary sites of replication. This primary viremia may be accompanied by clinical symptoms of infection such as fever, but often no signs are present. Secondary sites of replication are usually the spleen and liver. Virus again enters the blood in a secondary viremic phase. This period of viremia is usually accompanied by frank symptoms of infection. In many systemic viral infections the secondary viremia is coincident with the prodromal stage of disease and is followed by the onset of rash in those infections in which exanthem occurs. Tissues other than skin can function as the final target; for example, the central nervous system is the target in viral encephalitides.

Immune response to systemic infection involves the production of IgM and IgG antibodies and the mobilization of cell-mediated responses as well. The antibodies to virion surface antigens serve to protect cells from infection by abolishing the infectivity of the particle. The in vitro test used to detect such antibodies is called the neutralization test. Among the various tests used in the study of viruses the neutralization test is the most specific, and it is often used to define serotypes.

Cell-mediated immunity in virus infections is frequently directed against virus-infected cells rather than virions. Moderate infections alter the surface of the infected cell by the insertion of viral glycoproteins in the plasma membrane. This antigenically altered cell then becomes the target of the cellular response. Specific cytotoxic T lymphocytes are generated that react with the virally modified cell. Antibody dependent cellular cytotoxicity and complement-mediated cytolysis are other mechanisms that may be operative in eradicating virus-infected cells. For many virus diseases the cell-mediated response is the major specific mechanism of recovery and the antibody component of response the major mechanism for immunity to reinfection.

Another aspect of response to virus infection is the existence of extensive nonspecific mechanisms of protection. The physical and chemical barriers described in Chapter 6 are fully operative against viruses. In addition, the role of macrophages has been recognized as a critical determinant in the outcome of many virus infections. It has been demonstrated, for example, that the apparent nonsusceptibility of certain strains of mice to specific viral infections resides in the antiviral activity of their macrophages. Other strains of mice whose macrophages are themselves infected by the virus succumb to the infection.

There is a natural population of lymphoid cells cytotoxic for virus-infected cells. These natural killer cells undoubtedly play a role in resistance to viral disease.

MODELS OF VIRUS REPLICATION

In order to complete their replication all viruses must accomplish a common series of events. They must have their genome transcribed to mRNA, which can be translated by host cell ribosomes, they must replicate their genomes, and they must generate the virions that are to be released from the cell. Different viruses accomplish these tasks in different ways.

The genomes of viruses occur in six distinct forms: they may be double-stranded (ds) DNA, single-stranded (ss) DNA, double-stranded RNA, single-stranded RNA of messenger sense and function (+RNA), single-stranded RNA of antimessenger sense (−RNA), and finally a +RNA form that requires transcription to DNA. Messenger RNA is transcribed from the ds DNA molecules by action of DNA dependent RNA polymerases. The ss DNA genomes must produce a ds DNA form before mRNA production can ensue. The +RNA virus genomes can associate directly with host cell ribosomes, acting directly as messenger molecules. Negative-stranded (−RNA) genomes must be transcribed by an RNA dependent RNA polymerase to

the messenger form. These viruses that have −RNA carry the necessary transcriptase within the virion. RNA genomes of the *Retroviridae* are transcribed by RNA dependent DNA polymerase to DNA intermediates that are integrated into host DNA and from that site are transcribed into mRNA. These viruses carry the required reverse transcriptase in the virion. Double-stranded RNA viral genomes are asymmetrically transcribed by RNA dependent RNA polymerase in the virion. We will present a series of models to illustrate how some of the major human viruses replicate.

Poliovirus

Polioviruses are a group of human viruses that belong to the genus *Enterovirus* in the family *Picornaviridae*. They are the etiologic agents of poliomyelitis in man. The virion of poliovirus is a spherical particle 27 nm in diameter. There is no envelope around the capsid, which is icosahedral in shape. There are 32 capsomers. There are four major proteins present in the virion, designated VP1, VP2, VP3, and VP4. The genome is a single-stranded RNA molecule of 2.6×10^6 daltons. It is polyadenylated at the 3′ end, and it has a small polypeptide, VPg, attached to the 5′ end. It can be directly translated on cell ribosomes after removal of VPg.

Infection of the host cell is inititated by the contact of the virion with specific receptors on the surface of the plasma membrane. The adsorption of the virion requires divalent cations and is temperature independent. The virion is dissociable at this stage. The second stage is temperature dependent and involves a reorientation of the capsid proteins. VP4 is lost from the capsid, and the virus is no longer neutralizable by antibody. The penetration of the virion into the cytoplasm of the cell is apparently by direct transverse of the plasma membrane. Once it is in the cytoplasm,

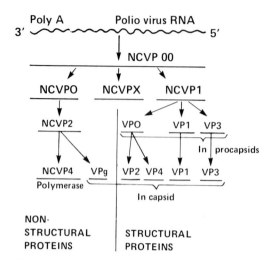

Fig. 39.6. Cleavage of poliovirus polypeptides.

an uncoating step occurs that releases the viral genomic RNA from the capsid. This is accomplished by proteolytic enzymes of the host cell. This step is detected experimentally by the susceptibility of the viral RNA to degradation by ribonuclease.

Viral protein synthesis can be accomplished by the direct translation of the virion RNA after the removal of the VPg polypeptide. The entire genome is read on the host ribosome to yield a single polypeptide of 2.5×10^5 daltons. This polypeptide chain is cleaved by host enzyme and viral-encoded activities into a series of products as illustrated in Figure 39.6. The noncapsid viral proteins (NCVP) are apparently functional proteins involved in viral nucleic acid metabolism. The capsid proteins are cleaved to the stages, VP0, VP1, and VP3. These are the elements that associate in the morphogenesis of the particle. This process will be detailed below. Viral protein synthesis is associated with cell fractions that sediment with rough endoplasmic reticulum.

Viral RNA synthesis takes place in association with fractions sedimenting with smooth endoplasmic reticulum. Analysis of poliovirus-infected cells shows that three species of RNA are present. As illustrated

in Figure 39.7 there are increasing amounts of single-stranded RNA found in the period after infection. Also present are low levels of a completely double-stranded molecule. This entity was originally thought to be functional in the replication of viral RNA; hence it was called the replicative form (RF). The third entity found in infected cells is a multistranded form that is found in large amounts early in the replicative cycle and that later decreases. This form, called the replicative intermediate (RI), is the functional entity in viral RNA replication. It is conceptualized as a single RNA strand of antimessenger polarity that functions as a template from which multiple messenger-sense strands are copied. The polymerase activity that mediated the synthesis of the +RNA has been attributed to the NCVP2 polypeptide. Progeny +RNA strands can be copied by mechanisms not yet understood to form another −RNA that will be functional in another replicative intermediate. Thus the amplification of RNA syn-

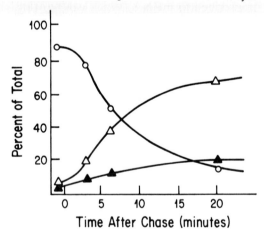

Fig. 39.7. RNA species in poliovirus-infected cells. The percentage of radiolabeled RNA found in a multistranded replicative intermediate form (RI, O), a single-stranded virion form (△), and a double-stranded form (RF, ▲) in relation to the time after addition of the radiolabel. (With permission, modified from Girard, J.: *In vitro* synthesis of poliovirus ribonucleic acid: Role of the replicative intermediate. Journal of Virology 3(4): 382, 1969.)

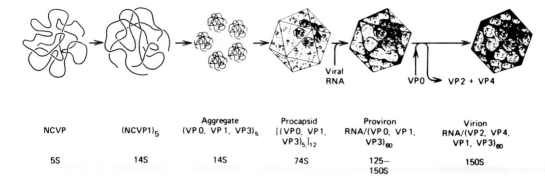

NCVP	(NCVP1)₅	Aggregate (VP0, VP1, VP3)₅	Procapsid [(VP0, VP1, VP3)₅]₁₂	Proviron RNA/(VP0, VP1, VP3)₆₀	Virion RNA/(VP2, VP4, VP1, VP3)₆₀
5S	14S	14S	74S	125–150S	150S

Fig. 39.8. Species of aggregated viral polypeptides that have characteristic sedimentation rates, correlated with morphological appearance of those forms. (With permission, Luria, S.E., Darnell, J.E., Baltimore, D., and Campbell, A.: General Virology. 3rd Ed. Reprinted by permission of John Wiley & Sons, Inc., New York, 1978.)

thesis is accomplished. Progney +RNA may also be incorporated into progeny virions. This process is apparently a result of the 5′ end of the RNA molecule associating with the VPg polypeptide that may mediate the encapsidization process.

The morphogenesis of viral progeny proceeds through a series of aggregation steps as illustrated in Figure 39.8. The 14 S, 70 S, and 125 S particles represent increasingly larger forms made up of VP0, VP1, and VP3. The 125 S form is identifiable by electron microscopy and resembles the mature virion. It is called the *procapsid*. The final events in morphogenesis are the incorporation of the progeny +RNA molecules into the capsid and cleavage of VP0 to VP2 and VP4.

The poliovirus replicative cycle is relatively rapid. It is completed in about 6 hours and culminates with the release of several hundred progeny virions from the dead host cell. Cellular macromolecular synthesis is rapidly shut down early in the viral replicative cycle, sometime after the entry and uncoating of the infecting virus. The viral products responsible for this shutdown have not yet been identified.

Cytopathology of poliovirus-infected cultures includes characteristic rounding and lysis of the cells. The monolayer is rapidly destroyed and the cells lose adhesion, falling off the substrate.

Adenovirus

Adenoviruses are a group of viruses infecting man and a number of other species. They are classified in the genus *Mastadenovirus* in the family *Adenoviridae*. The human viruses occur in 31 serotypes. They cause a variety of diseases mostly of the respiratory tract. The adenovirion is icosahedral, with 252 capsomers. There are 240 hexomeric units (*hexons*) and 12 pentomeric units (*pentons*) to which are attached fibers (*penton fibers*). The virion is 80 mm in diameter, and there is no envelope. There are ten polypeptides found in the virions and a linear double-stranded DNA molecule of 20 to 25 million daltons that has a 55,000 dalton protein attached to each 5′ end. The general scheme of adenovirus replication to be described below has been derived from studies of human adenovirus types 2 and 5. Figure 39.9 shows the replicative cycle.

Adsorption of the adenovirion is accomplished by the interaction of the penton fiber with an undefined host cell receptor. The process is considerably slower than the adsorption of many other viruses, often re-

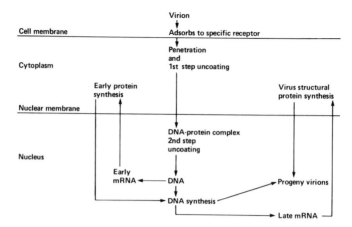

Fig. 39.9. Model of biosynthetic events in an adenovirus-infected cell.

quiring several hours. Penetration occurs by direct traverse of the plasma membrane or by an engulfing movement of the membrane termed *viriopexis*.

Uncoating of the adenovirion takes place in two stages. First-stage uncoating occurs in the cytoplasm of the cell soon after entry of the virion. Morphologic studies of cells early after infection show virions that are devoid of pentons and that have distinctly reoriented hexons. This is followed by complete loss of the hexon coat leaving, the viral core free in the cytoplasm. This structure consists of the viral DNA and associated proteins. The core enters the nucleus of the cell by pores in the nuclear membrane. The associated proteins of the core are removed in the second stage of uncoating in this site.

The synthesis of adenovirus proteins takes place in two phases demarcated by viral DNA synthesis. Early synthesis is directed by mRNA transcribed from 15 percent of the viral DNA. This is carried out by host RNA polymerase, and segments of both strands are transcribed. The products of translation of these early mRNA molecules are proteins functional in viral DNA synthesis. Various enzymatic activities are increased in infected cells. Among these are aspartate transcarbamylase, thymidine kinase, deoxycytidylate

deaminase, and DNA polymerase. Some of these activities are carried out by virus-encoded proteins, while others represent increased levels of host proteins. Early protein synthesis proceeds 5 to 6 hours before viral DNA synthesis begins. During this time host DNA synthesis ceases.

Viral DNA synthesis begins about 8 to 10 hours after infection and proceeds for the next 12 hours. The process involves unidirectional synthesis of a single strand, 5' to 3', with displacement of one of the parental strands. The displaced strand forms a "panhandle" structure because of inverted terminal repeated base sequences. Synthesis of a second progeny strand takes place on this form. DNA synthesis is therefore semiconservative.

Late viral genes begin to be transcribed soon after the onset of viral DNA synthesis, and late proteins, structural elements of the progeny viruses, are produced. It should be noted that transcription and translation of the early mRNA molecules continues well into the period of late synthesis. Late transcription results in 13 species of mRNA molecules that are produced by a process of excision and splicing. All molecules have a common initiation site and leader sequences but differ from each other by the amount of spacer sequence that is excised between the leader and the coding sequence. In addition, there are five different termination sites among the 13 molecules.

Viral protein synthesis takes place in the cytoplasm of the infected cell even though the site of viral DNA synthesis and of virion assembly is the nucleus. Both viral DNA and proteins are produced in large amounts, more than can be incorporated into virions. These products, along with the progeny virions, accumulate in the nucleus to form a characteristic inclusion body. The release of adenovirions from the nuclear site of maturation is poor. For example, less than 1 percent of infectious virus synthesized in infected cell cultures can be found in the culture fluid. The cells must be disrupted mechanically to allow detection of the full yield.

The entire adenovirus replicative cycle is prolonged, requiring up to 24 hours. Cellular macromolecular synthesis gradually subsides during this period, although the integrity of the cell is maintained. Cytopathic effects seen in cultures of cells infected with adenoviruses include rounding of the cells and development of intranuclear inclusions. Despite these changes the cells are adher-

ent to the substrate and are metabolically active.

Influenza Virus

The influenza viruses are members of the genus *Influenzavirus* in the family *Orthomyxoviridae*. There are three serotypes within the genus: influenza A, influenza B, and influenza C. The biology of these agents and their significance as pathogens is discussed in Chapter 40. At this point we will use the events in the replication of influenza A virus as a model to illustrate a number of generalities concerning the biology of some negative-stranded RNA viruses. Figure 39.10 is a schematic representation of influenza virus replication.

The influenza virion is spherical, although filamentous forms can be produced. The spherical particle averages 100 to 120 nm in diameter. There is an envelope composed of a lipid bilayer membrane that surrounds the nucleocapsid. It has two kinds of virus-encoded peplomers protruding from the exterior surface of the envelope and another virus-encoded protein lining the interior aspect of the structure. The surface peplomers are

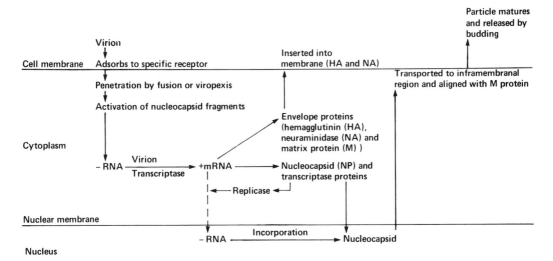

Fig. 39.10. Model of biosynthetic events in an influenzavirus-infected cell.

called hemagglutinin (H) and neuraminidase (N). The H peplomer is a trimeric
structure that contains three H polypeptide
chains. Each chain has a hydrophilic tail
embedded in the lipid bilayer, and the distal segment carries carbohydrate residues.
This peplomer interacts with sialic acid receptors on cell membranes and hence functions in infection and host selection. The N
peplomer is composed of four identical subunits arranged at the distal end of a
polypeptide chain embedded in the lipid
bilayer. The tetrameric units are the site of
neuraminidase activity, which splits *N*-
acetylneuraminic acid from a variety of carrier molecules, including the sialic acid receptors that bind to the H peplomer.

The interior surface of the lipid bilayer is
coated with another polypeptide, the M or
matrix protein. This protein functions to
give stability to the particle and also may
play a role in the maturation process. The
nucleocapsid segments are composed of
genomic RNA and associated proteins. The
NP polypeptide is the predominant species,
forming a helical structure enclosing or
wrapping the RNA molecule. Three other
proteins form the transcriptase complex
that is associated with each segment of the
genome.

The genome of influenza A virus occurs
in eight segments of RNA with a total mass
of 4.8×10^6 daltons. The RNA is in an
antimessenger configuration. The transcriptase activity serves to transcribe complementary RNA molecules from the
genome segment and to participate in the
replication of progeny RNA.

Influenza A virus attaches to the host by
interaction of the H peplomer with sialic
acid receptors on the cell surface. Entry of
virus is accomplished by fusion of the envelope with the plasma membrane of the
cell or by viropexis. The genome segments
do not undergo uncoating, although some
alteration of the structural properties of the
nucleocapsid may occur. Viral mRNA is
produced by the transcriptase associated

with each segment. Each segment is a single gene and gives rise to a messenger molecule that when translated forms the primary
polypeptide product. Seven of the eight
segments code for polypeptides that are
found in the virion. There is a single product found in infected cells but not in virions. At least one of the products, the H
polypeptide, is processed by cleavage and
secondary bonding before being incorporated into the virion.

Viral RNA synthesis in infected cells
yields three classes of molecules. Two types
of complementary RNA (cRNA) are
found: one is polyadenylated and presumably serves as mRNA and the other form is
not polyadenylated and is thought to serve
as a template for the replication of viral
genomic RNA. This later form is the third
type of molecule. The mRNA molecules
have been separated and identified with
specific polypeptide products.

The transcriptive process producing
cRNA can be separated into primary and
secondary stages. Primary transcription can
take place in absence of protein synthesis
(cycloheximide treatment); secondary
transcription cannot. This is generally
taken to indicate that the primary process
involves transcription from the parental
genome and that the secondary process involves transcription of the progeny genomic
molecules. The process is apparently under
the regulatory influence of the cell and of
the viral proteins themselves. Primary
transcription yields equal concentrations of
polyadenylated and nonpolyadenylated
cRNA; however, secondary transcription
produces considerably more of the
polyadenylated species, which, of course,
functions as mRNA. Further aspects of
control are suggested by differences in the
concentrations of different mRNA molecules leading to differences in the amounts
of the different proteins.

Production of progeny -RNA is accomplished by transcription of the nonpolyadenylated cRNA. This is a function of all

three P polypeptides and a nonstructural (NS) viral polypeptide found in infected cells but not in the virion. This polypeptide is the product of the eighth gene segment.

Most viral RNA is found in the cytoplasm of the infected cell, but synthesis is closely associated with the cell nucleus. In addition, accumulation of progeny nucleocapsids takes place in the nucleus.

Viral protein synthesis takes place in the cytoplasm. Viral mRNA is translated on host polysomes. The H and N polypeptides are glycosylated by host transferases within cytoplasmic vesicles and emerge on the cell surface in circumscribed patches. The inner aspect of these converted membranes is lined with the M polypeptide. The membrane-associated M polypeptide probably functions as a site for the alignment of progney nucleocapsid structures. The modified membrane, which now bears the H and N polypeptides, pinches off from the cell surface, enveloping the nucleocapsid structures in the process. The neuraminidase activity of the N polypeptide serves to release the particle from the cell surface by hydrolyzing sialic acid receptors that would hold the virion. It also serves to disaggregate virus particles.

The infection of cells with influenza virus does not cause a rapid shutdown of host function. Cells retain their integrity for variable periods, which allows for the production of thousands of virions. Eventual cell death is the usual outcome, however.

REFERENCES

Fenner, F., McAuslan, B.R., Mims, C.A., Sambrook, J., and White, D.O.: The Biology of Animal Viruses. 2nd Ed. Academic Press, New York, 1974.

Joklik, W.K., Willett, H.P., and Amos, D.B., Eds.: Zinsser Microbiology. 17th Ed. Appleton-Century-Crofts, New York, 1980.

Luria, S.E., Darnell, J.E., Jr., Baltimore, D., and Campbell, A.: General Virology. 3rd Ed. John Wiley and Sons, New York, 1978.

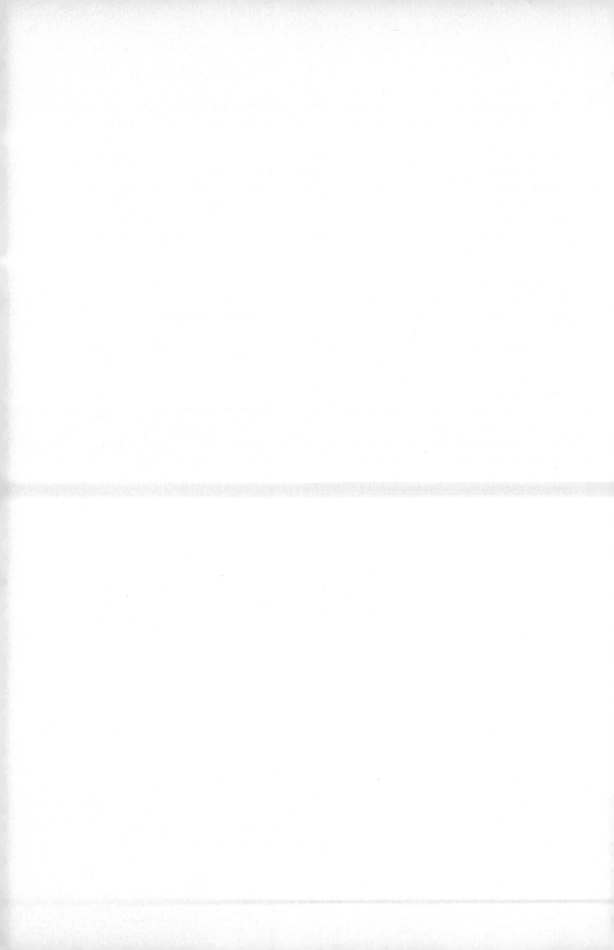

40

Orthomyxoviruses and Paramyxoviruses

Arlene R. Collins

Orthomyxoviruses and paramyxoviruses are enveloped RNA viruses and share several properties, including a single-stranded RNA genome complementary to mRNA, a helical nucleocapsid, and a virion transcriptase. In modern classification the two groups are designated as families. The family *Orthomyxoviridae* contains influenza virus and the *Paramyxoviridae* contain measles virus, mumps virus, respiratory syncytial virus, and the parainfluenza viruses. The differences between orthomyxoviruses and paramyxoviruses are in size of virion, mode of replication, diameter of inner helix, and genome configuration. The basic difference in replication is the nuclear site of certain steps in growth of the orthomyxoviruses. The diameter of the inner helix is 9 nm for the orthomyxoviruses and 18 nm for the paramyxoviruses. The genome of the orthomyxoviruses is segmented, whereas the genome of paramyxoviruses is a single linear molecule. In this chapter the two families will be discussed separately.

ORTHOMYXOVIRUSES

The family *Orthomyxoviridae* has one genus, *Influenzavirus*, in which are two serotypes, A and B, and a provisional separate genus for influenza C. The influenza A viruses are the agents of one of the few remaining epidemic diseases that has not yet been successfully controlled. Influenza A has continued to cause worldwide epidemics, probably because of its ability to radically alter its antigenic character. The influenza B viruses are generally involved in epidemics of lesser magnitude because influenza B viruses undergo only minor antigenic changes at a slower rate. The influenza C viruses are involved in only occasional sporadic outbreaks, yet serologic studies indicate widespread infection.

In recognition of the epidemic potential of influenza A and B viruses, the World Health Organization organized a virus surveillance network that has serotyped and cataloged strains of influenza since 1947. Laboratories in more than 50 different

543

countries are equipped to detect emerging antigenic variants and determine patterns of virus spread. This surveillance system has provided much information about the antigenic variation of influenza A and B viruses. Evidence of recycling of antigenic variants has been derived from this surveillance.

There is also a great deal known about the physical, biologic and genetic properties of influenzavirus. In this chapter the properties of the virus will be discussed and an attempt will be made to interpret the epidemiology of influenza.

Structure and Composition

Preparations of influenza virions contain a mixture of spherical and pleomorphic elongated particles (Fig. 40.1). The spherical particles are 80 to 120 nm in diameter and contain inner helical nucleocapsids surrounded by envelopes covered with two types of surface projections or peplomers.

A model of the influenza virion with its structural components is shown in Figure 40.2. The function of virion components is given in Table 40.1. According to the model the core of the virion contains eight segments of helical ribonucleoprotein. Most segments carry genetic information for a single polypeptide and behave as a cistron or gene, but at least one segment is transcoded to mRNA that can be read in two frames to produce two polypeptides. The segments replicate independently. During maturation the individual segments are assembled and become enveloped.

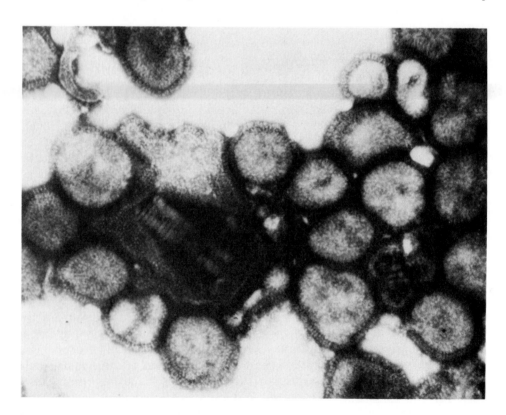

Fig. 40.1. Influenza A/HK/1/68 strain, showing viral peplomers projecting from the envelope and internal helical ribonucleoprotein (× 180,000). (Reprinted with permission from Oxford, J.S. Chemoprophylaxis and Virus Infections of the Respiratory Tract, CRC Press, Boca Raton, 1977. Copyright The Chemical Rubber Co., CRC Press, Inc.)

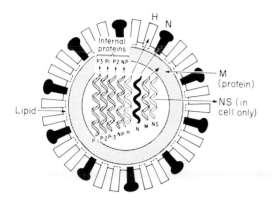

Fig. 40.2 Structure of influenza virus. The structural proteins include H (hemagglutinin) and N (neuraminidase) peplomers, M (matrix) protein, P_1, P_2, and P_3 polymerase proteins, and NP (nucleoprotein). NS (a nonstructural protein) is found only in infected cells. (With permission, Austen, K.B., Bearn, A.G., Brown, M.S., Goldstein, J.L., Kandel, E.R., Kilbourne, E.D., Peart, W.S., Snyder, S.H. and Wood, W.B. The Harvey Lecture Series 73, 1977–1978, Academic Press, New York, 1979.)

Maturation is an inefficient process under certain conditions, and not all mature virions receive the full complement of eight functional gene segments. Virions that lack one or more functional gene segments are called incomplete or defective virions. Incomplete virions are produced more frequently when cells are infected at high multiplicities of infection. The protein component of the ribonucleoprotein is antigenic and contains the serotype-specific antigen that identifies the strain as A, B, or C. The virion core is surrounded by the matrix protein, which is arranged along the inner surface of the virion envelope. The M proteins of influenza A and B have type specificity.

The virion envelope is composed of a lipid bilayer derived from host plasma membrane. Embedded in the lipid bilayer are two types of peplomers, the hemagglutinin and the neuraminidase. Both peplomers have hydrophobic ends embedded in the lipid bilayer and hydrophilic ends projecting out from the virion surface. The hemagglutinin peplomer is a trimer composed of three identical polypeptides, each chain of which may be cleaved by reduction with dithiothreitol into two subunits. The hemagglutinin peplomer is responsible for attachment to a specific receptor on the surface of a cell. The cell may be an erythrocyte or a cell of the respiratory epithelium. The receptor for influenza virus

Table 40.1.   Functions of the Influenza Proteins

Symbol	Structure	Function
H	Hemagglutinin polypeptide	Attachment to a receptor on the cell membrane or erythrocyte; the receptor contains N-acetylneuraminic acid as terminal sugar
N	Neuraminidase polypeptide	Enzymatic cleavage of the α-ketosidic linkage between the terminal N-acetylneuraminic acid and the adjacent sugars of (soluble or) cell membrane glycoproteins; results in destruction of receptor binding site
M	Matrix protein	Stabilization of the core providing structural rigidity; it is the recognition site for nucleocapsid alignment prior to budding
NP	Ribonucleoprotein	Binds to viral nucleic acid
P	Polymerase proteins	Transcription of viral genetic information to messenger RNA and cRNA; RNA replication
NS	Nonstructural protein	Involved in replication; found only in infected cells

contains N-acetylneuraminic acid as a terminal sugar on a glycoprotein or glycolipid side chain.

The neuraminidase peplomer has a head composed of four subunits or tetramers and a stalk that projects into the lipid bilayer. The neuraminidase peplomer has enzymatic activity and specifically cleaves N-acetylneuraminic acid from the side chains at the surface of the cell membrane. The cleavage results in destruction of the receptor for the hemagglutinin.

The Influenza Virus Genome. The genome of influenza virus is composed of eight distinct pieces, each of which acts as a separate gene (or genes) being individually transcribed by the virion associated polymerase into a monocistronic messenger RNA. This situation has several implications in the study of emergence of new antigenic variants. Antigenic variation is the result of molecular alterations of the surface glycoproteins and reflects changes in the constituent genes. Changes in the genome can be brought about by mutation or by gene reassortment (during the course of dual infection) between viruses of the same serotype. The segmented nature of the influenza genome allows gene reassortment to occur at high frequency in dual infections.

The phenomenon of genetic reassortment occurs only among viruses with segmented genomes, such as influenza and reoviruses. Reassortment of segments occurs under conditions of dual infection of an individual cell with two strains of the same virus type. Replication of both strains ensues, and during maturation some of the progeny acquire by reassortment gene segments from both strains. In this way a new genotype can be derived. If the new genotype has a different antigenicity of the hemagglutinin or the neuraminidase peplomer, a variant with potential for causing a pandemic may arise. However, other effects of reassortment may include changes in virulence or host specificity. These also might contribute to or reduce the pandemic potential of recombinants.

Genetic mutations during interepidemic periods are generally believed to contribute to the survival of influenza. A selective influence in the survival of influenza mutants is the presence of antibody to previous strains in the population. If a mutation occurs in the antigenicity of the hemagglutinin, the mutant may react poorly with antibody to previous strains. The mutant would then have a survival advantage and spread more readily in an immune population. However, many antigenic variants do not spread.

Both genetic reassortment and mutation apparently play an important role in the emergence of antigenic variants of influenza.

Antigenic Composition and Classification. Influenza viruses fall into three antigenic types, designated A, B, and C. The types are determined on the basis of the internal ribonucleoprotein antigen and/ or matrix protein antigen. Type-specific antigens are demonstrable by the complement fixation test or immunoprecipitation in agar. Antibody to the type-specific antigen is formed during infection but does not confer protection from reinfection.

Classification of strains of influenza into subtypes is based on the specificity of the hemagglutinin and neuraminidase antigens of the viral envelope. Differences among hemagglutinin antigens are determined by the hemagglutination inhibition or immunoprecipitation tests. Antibody to the hemagglutinin is formed after infection and protects against reinfection with the same strain. The hemagglutinin molecule has many antigenic sites capable of being recognized by specific antibodies. Within a subtype, the H peplomer shares many determinants among strains. On first infection of an individual with influenza, antibodies to the unique and shared determinants are made. On reinfection with a related strain, antibody to the shared determinants of the first invader is stimulated. The recall of antibody to the first influenza strain by infection with a related virus strain has been called "original antigenic sin." In addition to the ability to inhibit hemagglutination, some antibodies to the influenza hemagglutinin are active in the neutralization of infectivity. Antibody to the influenza hemagglutinin as measured by the hemagglutination inhibition test is the principal laboratory index of immunity.

The other specific envelope glycoprotein to which antibody is formed during infection is the neuraminidase peplomer. Antigenic differences in this glycoprotein are determined by the neuraminidase inhibition test. The basis of this test is the release of free *N*-acetylneuraminic acid from a substrate such as fetuin, a reaction that can be measured colorimetrically. The neuraminidase inhibition test is not performed routinely on clinical material. The protective role of neuraminidase antibody seems to lie in its ability to prevent release of virus from infected cells. Presence of antibody to the neuraminidase peplomer has been shown to correlate with decreased shedding of virus by infected individuals.

Table 40.2. Reference Strains of Human Influenza A

Year of Pandemic	Strain Designation
1946	A/FM/1/47 (H1N1)
1957	A/Japan/305/57 (H2N2)
1968	A/Hong Kong/1/68 (H3N2)
1977	A/USSR/90/77(H1N1)

B and C strains no indication is made of hemagglutinin and neuraminidase antigenicity, since subtypes cannot be identified.

A revision of this system has recently been completed (1980) in which the hemagglutinin and neuraminidase antigens of all strains, human and animal, are classified. Hemagglutinins are divided into 12 subtypes and neuraminidases into 9 subtypes based upon reactivity in immunoprecipitation tests in agar. The nomenclature to be applied to this new system will require a simple sequential numbering of the two antigens. All human strain antigens (H1, H2, H3, N1, N2) have retained their previous designations with the exception of H0, which is now included in the H1 subtype.

Classification

In order to adequately describe influenza strains a system of nomenclature was devised by the World Health Organization in 1971. According to this system the designation for influenza A strains should indicate the serotype, the animal host (if other than human), the geographic origin, the strain number, the year of isolation, and, for influenza A strains, in parentheses the antigenic identity of the hemagglutinin and neuraminidase antigens. Table 40.2 gives examples of this nomenclature system for several reference strains of influenza A representing different subtypes. For influenza

Clinical Features

Influenza is transmitted to susceptible persons by inhalation of virus-containing droplets. The virus replicates primarily in the ciliated respiratory epithelial cells. Infection and destruction of cells lining the upper respiratory tract, trachea, and bronchi ensue. There may be a transient viremia and dissemination of virus to nonrespiratory tissue. Symptoms include fever, chills, muscle aches, and respiratory distress lasting for 4 to 7 days. Systemic symptoms may be caused in part by the toxic effects of viral components. In infants influenza A and B may cause obstructive laryngotracheobronchitis or croup, although this syndrome is most commonly caused by parainfluenza viruses. Also in children, tracheobronchitis is a common manifestation of influenza infections. In children and adults primary viral pneumonia is less frequent, and complications of this pneumonia are seen most often in individuals with predisposing cardiac or pulmonary insufficiency. Secondary bacterial pneumonia is a frequent complication. Staphylococci, pneumococci, streptococci, and *Haemophilus influenzae* are the organisms most frequently involved.

A number of nonrespiratory sequelae may follow influenza infections, including myalgia, myocarditis, and pericarditis. Neurologic disorders such as polyneuritis and Guillain-Barré syndrome have also been reported. Guillain-Barré syndrome is characterized by a usually reversible and self-limiting ascending paralysis and has been associated with influenza vaccination and other infections. Cases of Reye's syndrome, a noninflammatory encephalopathy with fatty metamorphosis of the liver, have been seen following influenza infection. Reye's syndrome may also follow after other virus infections such as varicella. The pathogenesis of this syndrome is not well understood.

Epidemiology

In the northern hemisphere the influenza season most frequently occurs in the winter months (November to May). The impact of an influenza epidemic in a community can sometimes be identified epidemiologically by increased school and industrial absenteeism, increased visits to hospital emergency rooms for respiratory problems, and increased or excess mortality due to respiratory disease. The severity and extent of epidemics of influenza have been recorded, using excess mortality as the indicator. Two types of epidemiology of influenza have been described: epidemic influenza and pandemic influenza.

Epidemic Influenza. Influenzas A and B are associated with epidemics of influenza occurring at 1- to 3-year intervals for influenza A (e.g., 1975, 1977, 1978) and every 2 to 4 years for influenza B. The recurrence of epidemic influenza is related to the ability of these viruses to undergo antigenic variation. The nature of the variation is one of gradual minor change in antigenicity and is attributed to mutations in the hemagglutinin peplomer. The process of gradual antigenic change is referred to as *antigenic drift.* Antibody to previously prevalent strains provides only low levels of immunity to newer antigenic variants and allows the antigenic variant to survive and spread.

Pandemic Influenza. On occasion, abrupt changes in the antigenicity of influenza A viruses occur. An antigenically distinct variant arises that has an H peplomer of a different subtype from contemporary strains. This major antigenic change is called *antigenic shift.* It occurs only with influenza A viruses. It is suggested that it might sometimes be due to the emergence of a recombinant strain of virus. One source proposed for the new H is an animal reservoir. Influenza A viruses have been isolated from pigs, horses, ducks, chickens, and other species. All human strains of influenza have antigenically related counterparts among animal strains. The phenomenon of recombination involves dual infection with two related strains of virus and the reassortment of genome segments so that some progeny viruses receive genetic segments from both parents. The exchange of a hemagglutinin gene or a neuraminidase gene can occur by this process, and a new pandemic strain of influenza can emerge as a result. Three (1957, 1968, 1977) major pandemics of influenza have occurred since 1918 in which a major antigenic shift in hemagglutinin has occurred. In the 1957 pandemic a major shift in both hemagglutinin and neuraminidase antigenicity occurred. There appears to be a recycling of antigens in an as yet unpredictable pattern. The problem of influenza pandemics is still not completely understood.

Laboratory Diagnosis

Influenza virus is readily recovered from throat washings or nasal swabs by inoculation of the specimen into embryonated eggs by the amniotic route. The amniotic fluid is harvested 2 to 4 days later and tested for the presence of hemagglutinins. Inoculation of primary rhesus monkey kidney cells is also recommended for virus isolation because influenza B strains are recovered more readily in monkey kidney cells than from eggs. Cell cultures should be tested for hemadsorption. Chicken, guinea pig, or human erythrocytes may be used. Influenza isolates may be identified by the hemagglutination inhibition test using antisera to prototype strains.

Serodiagnosis of influenza is also useful, particularly in epidemiologic studies. Paired sera taken 2 to 4 weeks apart are used in hemagglutination inhibition or complement fixation tests using reference strains of influenza A and B that can be obtained commercially from the Center for Disease Control.

Prevention

Active Immunization. Vaccination by subcutaneous inoculation of inactivated influenza virus vaccine is the current method of prophylaxis. Because of the emergence of new antigenic variants the composition of the vaccine is constantly being revised. Those individuals who should receive vaccine include all persons over 65 years of age and persons of any age with chronic cardiac or pulmonary disease that affects respiratory function. Pregnancy is neither an indication nor a contraindication. Immunity induced by vaccination is of limited duration, and annual revaccination is recommended.

Vaccine preparations include purified whole virus suspensions inactivated by formalin or preparations of chemically extracted virus antigens prepared by disruption of intact virions with ether, sodium deoxycholate, and/or other surfactant. Reactogenicity of vaccine is low in adults and is further reduced in children when disrupted or "split" virus vaccine is administered.

Chemoprophylaxis. Amantadine hydrochloride, a drug that acts by blocking the penetration of influenza A virus into cells thereby preventing replication, has been shown to reduce the frequency of infection. Maximum effectiveness of the drug is achieved when it is given before exposure to the virus and throughout the entire duration of potential exposure. Amantadine is ineffective against influenza B infections. A modest reduction in the severity of illness and duration of fever can be achieved if amantadine therapy is started within the first 2 days of illness.

PARAMYXOVIRUSES

The family *Paramyxoviridae* has three genera; the genus *Paramyxovirus*, in which mumps and parainfluenza viruses are found; the genus *Morbillivirus*, in which measles virus is found; and the genus *Pneumovirus*, in which respiratory syncytial virus is found. Members of this family cause a wide variety of clinical illnesses ranging from upper respiratory diseases to generalized systemic illness to acute and chronic neurologic diseases.

Structure and Composition

Paramyxoviruses are large, plemorphic, enveloped viruses that range from 90 to 300 nm in size. The genome of 7×10^6 daltons is in the form of a single linear RNA molecule that is complementary to messenger RNA. The genome exists in the virion core as a helical nucleocapsid. The envelope of paramyxovirions may contain one or two kinds of peplomers that are associated with several biologic activities. The larger glycoprotein peplomer is responsible for hemagglutination and, when present, neuraminidase activities. The smaller glycoprotein peplomer is responsible for hemolysis and the ability to cause fusion of cells to form syncytia. Not all paramyxoviruses possess all four biologic activities. The distribution of these properties among the various paramyxoviridae is shown in Table 40.3.

The Paramyxovirus Genome. The unsegmented nature of the paramyxovirus genome clearly differentiates these viruses from the orthomyxoviruses and presumably confers upon them a greater degree of genetic stability. The principal method of genetic exchange among paramyxoviruses is the formation of heteroploid particles. This phenomenon involves the envelopment of two complete nucleocapsids within a single particle as a result of mixed infection with two unrelated enveloped viruses. Another related genetic phenomenon is the formation of polyploid particles; this involves the envelopment of multiple copies of the same genome into a very large enveloped particle.

Antigenic Composition. The biologic properties of paramyxoviruses, which include hemagglutination, cell fusion or hemolysis, and neuraminidase activities, are each associated with specific viral polypeptides that are antigenic. A proportion of antibodies directed against these viral polypeptides will inhibit their biologic functions. This interaction forms the basis for a number of serologic reactions that measure inhibition of biologic function. The hemagglutination inhibition test and its counterpart in cell culture, the hemadsorption inhibition test, are the most frequently used serologic tests for identification of paramyxoviruses. Hemolysis inhibition and neuraminidase inhibition tests are less frequently performed, although these antibodies are present in patient's serum. A nucleoprotein antigen associated with the viral nucleocapsid can be detected by the complement fixation test. The parainfluenza viruses occur as four distinct serotypes, designated 1 to 4, as determined by the hemagglutination inhibition and serum neutralization tests. All other paramyxoviruses appear to exist as only single serotypes.

Clinical Features

In this chapter the paramyxoviruses associated with respiratory syndromes will be discussed. Those paramyxoviruses causing systemic infections, measles and mumps, will be discussed in a separate chapter (Ch. 41).

Parainfluenza Virus Infections. Parainfluenza viruses are respiratory pathogens spread by infectious airborne droplets. The extent of respiratory involvement may vary from mild afebrile respiratory illness, such as the common cold, to severe lower re-

Table 40.3. Biologic Properties of *Paramyxoviridae*

Property	Paramyxovirus	Morbillivirus	Pneumovirus
Hemagglutination	+	+	−
Neuraminidase	+	−	−
Hemolysis	+	+	−
Cell fusion	+	+	+

spiratory disease. Serious illness is seen most often in infants and preschool children undergoing primary infection with parainfluenza virus. The most characteristic and clinically important respiratory syndrome in this age group is croup (laryngotracheobronchitis). Parainfluenza virus types 1, 2 and 3 are the principal serotypes involved. Hoarseness, spasmodic coughing, and difficulty in respiration characterize the symptoms of croup. Croup is most serious when it occurs in children under 1 year of age, and such children frequently require hospitalization. Parainfluenza viruses, primarily type 3, are major causes of pneumonia and bronchiolitis in young children, although respiratory syncytial virus is the agent most frequently involved. The incidence of bronchiolitis and pneumonia caused by parainfluenza is highest in children 6 to 18 months of age, while peak incidence for respiratory syncytial virus occurs at 2 months of age. Reinfection in older children and adults occurs frequently with parainfluenza virus but is seldom accompanied by severe respiratory illness; usually only mild afebrile respiratory illness or asymptomatic infection occurs. Immunity is related to the presence of secretory antibody in the respiratory mucosa and to circulating antibodies that develop as a result of infection.

Laboratory Diagnosis of Parainfluenza Virus Infections. Parainfluenza virus infections tend to occur as outbreaks in a community in fall and winter months. A knowledge of the presence of the virus in a community can frequently aid in diagnosis. Throat washings and nasal swabs should be submitted to the laboratory for virus isolation. The most susceptible laboratory host is primary monkey kidney cell culture. Established human or simian cell lines can be used for parainfluenza types 2 and 3 but are decidedly less satisfactory. The growth of parainfluenza viruses in cell culture is often not accompanied by an identifiable cytopathic effect; thus the technique of hemadsorption is applied to identify virus-infected cultures. The viral isolate may be typed serologically using the hemagglutination inhibition or hemadsorption inhibition, serum neutralization, or FA tests. Serologic diagnosis may also be performed and is particularly useful during outbreaks in a community. Paired serum samples taken at the onset of illness and 2 to 3 weeks later can be tested for antibody to known parainfluenza serotypes using the hemagglutination inhibition or complement fixation tests.

Respiratory Syncytial Virus Infections

Respiratory syncytial virus is the major cause of bronchiolitis and pneumonia in infants and young children. In a 13-year surveillance in Children's Hospital of Washington (D.C.) 43 percent of patients admitted with bronchiolitis and 25 percent of patients admitted with pneumonia had evidence of respiratory syncytial virus infection. The peak incidence of bronchiolitis and pneumonia occurs in children 2 months of age. The incidence declines rapidly with age for bronchiolitis but more slowly for pneumonia. Respiratory syncytial virus infection is unique among viral diseases in that it has its maximum impact during the first few months of life. The occurrence of bronchiolitis in this age group is unique among human disease, and the pathogenesis of the disease is not well understood. Maternal serum antibody has no protective effect. In fact, experience with vaccination using inactive respiratory syncytial virus vaccine indicates that serum antibody can predispose to severe bronchiolitis on subsequent natural infection. There is some evidence that maternally derived serum antibody may participate in an immunopathologic reaction and thereby contribute to the severity of bronchiolitis in infants. The presence of maternal antibody may also delay or decrease the immune response of the infant to the virus.

552   Medical Microbiology

Reinfections with respiratory syncytial virus are common, and sizable epidemics occur every year in urban communities. Children and adults undergo only mild respiratory illness upon reinfection but provide a source of virus for the highly susceptible infant. Reinfection does not evoke a strong immune response, although serum and secretory antibodies as well as cell-mediated immunity are stimulated. The immune response offers little protection against reinfection; however, secretory antibody in nasal secretions seems to decrease the level of virus shedding.

Laboratory Diagnosis of Respiratory Syncytial Virus Infections. The diagnosis of respiratory syncytial virus can be made by immunofluorescence, by virus isolation, or by demonstration of a rise in serum antibody. The most efficient diagnostic procedure is the examination of exfoliated cells from the respiratory tract for virus antigens by immunofluorescence. Specimens should be simultaneously examined for parainfluenza antigens, another possible agent causing disease in the same age group. Virus isolation can be performed by inoculation of throat washings or nasal secretions onto human heteroploid cell cultures. Recovery of virus is inefficient unless specimens are immediately inoculated onto cell cultures because of the extreme thermolability of the virus. Virus growth in cell culture can be identified by formation of characteristic multinucleate cells or syncytia. Serologic identification of viral isolates or the demonstration of antibody in patient's serum can be accomplished by the tissue culture neutralization test or by the complement fixation test. Young infants seldom develop antibodies following infection; thus demonstration of viral antigen in exfoliated cells by the immunofluorescence procedure should be applied to diagnose infections in this age group.

REFERENCES

Evans, A.S.: Viral Infections of Humans. 1st Ed. Plenum Medical Book Company, New York, 1976.

Kurstak, E. and Kurstak, C.: Comparative Diagnosis of Viral Diseases. 1st Ed. Vol. 1. Academic Press, New York, 1977.

McIntosh, K. and Fishaut, M.J.: Immunopathological mechanisms in lower respiratory tract disease of infants due to respiratory syncytial virus. Prog. Med. Virol. 26: 94, 1980.

Schild, G.C.: Influenza. Br. Med. Bull. 35: 1, 1979.

41

Measles Virus, Mumps Virus, and Rubella Virus

Harshad R. Thacore

Viruses causing disease primarily in children have been the target of extensive study, especially in the last quarter century. Many if not all have been brought under control in most parts of the world by immunization. The childhood diseases most commonly associated with RNA viruses are measles, mumps, and rubella. Taxonomically measles and mumps viruses are members of the *Paramyxoviridae*, whereas rubella virus is a member of the *Togaviridae*. The viruses causing these diseases are somewhat similar not only in chemical, physical, and many biologic properties but particularly with respect to the epidemiology and the pathogenesis of the disease. There are a few noteworthy differences among them. For example, the virion associated enzyme neuraminidase is readily demonstrable in mumps virus but has not been shown to be present in measles virus. Furthermore, measles and rubella viruses both cause a generalized rash in most cases at one stage during the disease, whereas mumps virus causes a systemic type of disease and lacks the generalized exanthematous stage. During the past several years the incidence of these viral diseases in the United States has declined mainly because of immunization programs implemented throughout the country.

MEASLES (RUBEOLA)

Measles is one of the most infectious diseases that are spread by respiratory secretions. The disease is usually acquired in childhood, and in the United States the highest incidence was in children between the ages of 5 and 10 years before general use of measles vaccine. Currently the 10- to 14-year-old age group shows highest incidence. The disease is most prevalent in the winter and spring months. In developed countries the fatality from measles virus infection is about 1 death per 10,000 cases. In countries with less developed health care services the fatality rate from measles infection can reach 10 percent or even higher. The natural host for measles virus is man. The virus is of one antigenic type, and it is fortunate that immunity following infection is permanent.

Special note should be made of the fact that research on measles virus has received much attention in the past several years primarily because evidence has accumulated that links measles, or a virus very similar to measles, to subacute sclerosing panencephalitis (SSPE). Multiple sclerosis and systemic lupus erythematosus have also been associated with measles, but the evidence is much less convincing than in SSPE.

Measles virus belongs to the family *Paramyxoviridae*. The virus is enveloped, and the genome consists of a single-stranded RNA molecule of the negative configuration (Fig. 41.1). The estimated molecular weight of the genomic RNA is 6.2×10^6 as determined by acrylamide-agarose gel electrophoresis, and it has a sedimentation coefficient of about 52 S in sucrose density gradients. The RNA is surrounded by the nucleocapsid, which is composed of a single protein of about 60,000 daltons that may be a part of the transcriptase complex. The nucleocapsid containing the virus genome is surrounded by the outer lipoprotein envelope derived from the host cell membrane. The spiked envelope contains the viral glycoproteins, a nonglycosylated membrane protein, and the lipids. It should be noted that a number of specific host proteins are intimately associated with the envelope of measles virus particles.

A number of important biologic properties are associated with measles virus. The hemagglutination by measles virus of red blood cells of primates has been extensively studied. This activity is most likely associated with the larger glycoprotein in the virion particle. Hemolysis of rhesus red blood cells by measles virus has also been reported. This hemolytic activity is antigenically distinct from the hemagglutinating activity. The fusion activity mediated by the virus particle — that is, the ability to fuse and form giant cells *in vitro* — is a measure of cytopathic effect. The fusion effect demonstrable by measles virus is more

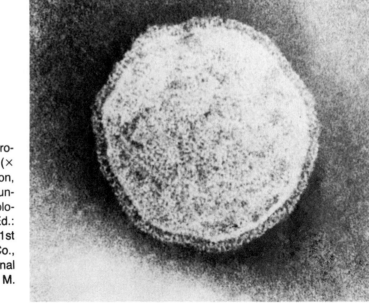

Fig. 41.1. Electronmicrograph of measles virion (× 200,000). (With permission, Dorsett, P.H.: Fundamentals of Animal Virology. In Freeman, B.A., Ed.: Burrows' Microbiology. 21st Ed. W.B. Saunders Co., Philadelphia, 1979. Original photograph courtesy of M. Dubois-Dalcq.)

resistant to heat inactivation than the hemolysis activity. The hemolysis and cell fusion activities have been shown to require both glycoproteins and membrane lipids. The exact role of various envelope proteins in the biologic activity elicited by the measles virus still remains to be determined.

Pathogenesis

Measles is an acute febrile exanthematous disease resembling smallpox and mumps in many respects. The virus is transmitted by respiratory secretions and enters the host via the upper respiratory tract. There is a rather long incubation period of about 10 to 14 days prior to the replication of the virus in the epithelium and the regional lymphatic tissue. During the prodromal stages of the disease the patient often experiences cough, sore throat, and a low grade fever. It is during this period that small red spots with bluish white specks appear on the buccal mucous membrane opposite the molars; these are known as Koplik spots. At about the same time one finds in the nasal secretions large multinuclear cells called Warthin-Finkeldey cells. These giant cells are characteristic of measles pathology.

During the prodromal stages of measles virus infection, viremia occurs allowing the spread of the virus into the capillaries of the corium. At this time the typical red maculopapular rash appears, first on the head and face and then on the body, spreading to the extremities. This rash usually lasts for 3 or 4 days. During this time and for a few days after the rash the virus is excreted in the secretions of the respiratory tract. This promotes the rapid spread of the virus to susceptible individuals.

Complications

During the course of measles virus infection some patients may develop signs of neurologic and central nervous system involvement. The exact time at which central nervous system is invaded by measles virus during the course of infection is not known.

The most common and serious central nervous system complication of measles is encephalomyelitis. This occurs 5 to 7 days after the appearance of rash. The incidence of encephalomyelitis is relatively low (about 0.1 percent), but the fatality is high (about 10 to 30 percent). The onset of encephalomyelitis is sudden and is marked by seizures, confusion, and coma. This condition is due to the direct invasion of the central nervous system by the virus, resulting in perivascular demyelination (predominantly in the white matter) and hemorrhage. About 50 percent of survivors are left with some sequelae involving impaired intellectual, sensory, and motor development.

Other common complications due to measles virus infection include upper respiratory and secondary bacterial infections such as bronchiolitis, keratoconjunctivitis, otitis media, and bronchopneumonia.

Subacute Sclerosing Panencephalitis (SSPE) and Measles Virus. SSPE is a rare and fatal progressive degenerative neurologic disease of children and young adults. The disease manifests as a diffuse encephalitis of the white and gray matter characterized by demyelination and infiltration by lymphocytes and plasma cells. Measles virus has been detected in organs of SSPE patients other than brain, such as lung, kidney, spleen, and lymph nodes. Available data from virologic, serologic, and eletron microscopic studies on brain tissue from SSPE patients all point to the fact that SSPE may be a result of a latent infection by either measles virus, a variant of measles virus, or a virus closely related to measles virus.

The exact nature of association between virus isolated from SSPE brain tissue and the pathologic state is not known. However, there are several data that implicate measles virus or a virus very closely related to measles as the etiologic agent of SSPE: almost all patients have had measles virus infection several years prior to onset of SSPE or have been immunized with live measles virus vaccine; some SSPE isolates appear to be antigenically identical to measles virus; SSPE patients usually have measles antibodies that increase to high titers during the course of the disease; measles virus has been isolated by cocultivation of brain cells with susceptible cells. Recent studies have shown that RNA from some strains of SSPE virus particles have a 100 percent homology with the 50 S RNA of the Edmonston strain of measles virus. While further studies will have to be conducted before a conclusive relationship between SSPE and measles virus can be established, the evidence to date is quite convincing. Not the least significant is the observation that the incidence of SSPE has fallen rapidly since measles vaccination has been practiced.

Immune Response

All measles virus strains belong to a single antigenic type. Measles virus antibodies can be detected first during the appearance of rash, and they rise to high titers during the next 30 to 60 days. The antibodies persist for life. The reason for the lifelong duration of measles-specific antibodies is not known, but one can speculate that reinfection by the same or an antigenically related virus or persistent infection by the virus may account for the antigenic stimulation needed for the antibodies.

Measles virus has been shown to temporarily affect cell-mediated immunity. Individuals infected with measles or vaccinated with live virus show transient loss of delayed hypersensitivity to tuberculin and other antigens. *In vitro* studies have shown that measles virus can cause either a lytic or a persistent infection in lymphocytes, thus impairing their activity. Infected lymphocytes *in vivo* may be responsible for dis-

semination of virus during infection. The survival of infected lymphocytes and other cells persistently infected with measles virus in the presence of specific antibodies is implicated in chronic diseases such as SSPE.

Laboratory Diagnosis

Clinical features of measles infection are so characteristic that isolation of the virus is not necessary. However, virus can be isolated from the nasal and pharyngeal secretions. Serologic diagnosis can be performed by comparing the acute and convalescent sera of the patient for measles-specific antibodies using hemagglutination inhibition, virus neutralization, or complement fixation tests.

Prevention and Control

The primary disease cannot be controlled by chemotherapeutic treatment; however, the disease can be effectively prevented by the use of vaccines prepared in primary chicken embryo cell cultures. A live attenuated measles virus vaccine or a combined live measles/mumps/rubella virus vaccine are commercially available. Both vaccines are effective and have been shown to seroconvert at a rate of 97 to 100 percent. Protective antibodies from monovalent or combined vaccine last for more than 15 years. Reinfection of immunized subjects produces a booster in antibody production, thus prolonging or perpetuating immunity.

Vaccination is recommended for all healthy children after they reach the age of 15 months. The vaccine is not recommended for children with neurologic problems. Measles vaccine is also not recommended for women known to be pregnant or who might become pregnant within 2 to 3 months after vaccination.

MUMPS

Mumps is predominantly a childhood disease with a high rate of subclinical infection. Mumps is clearly not as contagious as other childhood viral diseases such as measles and chickenpox. In the United States mumps is most common during the winter and early spring months. Man is the only natural host, but mumps virus can infect monkeys. Virus can be propagated in embryonated hen eggs; after several passages in eggs the virus loses its virulence for man and monkeys. There is only one antigenic type of mumps virus, and the immunity following infection is lifelong.

Mumps virus belongs to the family *Paramyxoviridae*. The virus genome consists of a single-stranded RNA molecule with a molecular weight of 5 to 6×10^6. The genome is of negative configuration. Surrounding the genome is the nucleocapsid of helical symmetry, and surrounding the nucleocapsid is the viral envelope derived from the host cell membrane, incorporating virus glycoproteins and a nonglycosylated virus protein. A number of enzymes are associated with the virus: RNA dependent RNA polymerase, neuraminidase, polyadenylate transferase, and messenger RNA methyl transferase. Hemagglutinin and neuraminidase activities reside in a single glycoprotein. Another glycoprotein is responsible for cell fusion and hemolysis activities.

Pathogenesis

Mumps virus is transmitted via saliva or respiratory secretions and enters the host via the upper respiratory tract. After an incubation period of 12 to 21 days the virus replicates in the upper respiratory tract and the local lymph nodes. Viremia occurs several days prior to the onset of clinical symptoms which are quite characteristic for mumps. The symptoms begin with an acute onset of pain and swelling in one or both parotid glands, which reaches a maximum in 2 or 3 days and then subsides within 7 to 14 days. Occasionally other organs, such as the thyroid glands, may be involved. Orchitis occurs in 20 to 30 percent

of male adults but rarely in children. Sterility due to mumps infection is rare. In some cases the organ of Corti may also be affected during parotid swelling, resulting in irreversible deafness. Meningoencephalitis is probably the most common extraparotid infection. Death from mumps is rare.

Mumps infection of children less than 3 years old usually presents as an undifferentiated upper respiratory tract infection.

Immune Response

Protective antibodies appear between 2 and 3 weeks after the onset of illness, reaching maximum titers by 4 to 6 weeks. These protective antibodies (IgG) against the viral surface antigens persist for a lifetime. Mumps infection also induces delayed hypersensitivity which can be detected by a skin test using inactivated virus.

Laboratory Diagnosis

Diagnosis of mumps is based solely on clinical observation. However, laboratory diagnosis can be made by isolation of the virus from saliva secretions or from the parotid ducts by inoculation of susceptible cell cultures. In cases of meningoencephalitis, cerebrospinal fluid and urine are the best specimens. Viral antigens in infected cultures can be detected by immunofluorescence. Serologic diagnosis can be made by comparing virus-specific antibody titers of acute and convalescent sera by complement fixation or hemagglutination inhibition tests.

Prevention and Control

There is no specific chemotherapy available for mumps infection. Mumps infection can be effectively prevented by immunization. Childhood vaccination is highly recommended. Immunity due to vaccination or subclinical or clinical infection is lifelong; there is no documentation of two clinical attacks of mumps virus infection in a single individual. For immunization a live attenuated vaccine and the combined live measles/mumps/rubella virus vaccine are commercially available and highly effective. The monovalent or the combined vaccine do not offer protection against mumps infection if one has already become exposed to a natural mumps infection and is in the incubation period of illness. Hyperimmune globulin has been administered to persons exposed to mumps without conclusive results; however, hyperimmune globulin has been found to reduce the incidence and the severity of orchitis.

RUBELLA (GERMAN MEASLES)

Rubella is a highly contagious disease spread by nasal secretions from patients or persons with asymptomatic infection. In the United States outbreaks of rubella are generally reported in high schools, colleges, and — most notably — in hospitals. In urban areas minor outbreaks occur in winter and spring months every 1 or 2 years and major outbreaks occur every 6 to 9 years. In recent years a majority of the cases have ocurred among people 15 years of age or older. Unlike measles, rubella infection is often subclinical, thus fostering virus dissemination and rendering isolation of patients virtually useless. The ratio of subclinical to clinical infections is as low as 1:1 in children but as high as 9:1 in adults.

Rubella virus belongs to the family *Togaviridae*. This family includes viruses that are transmitted via insects; rubella virus is the single known exception to this general means of spread. Man is the only reservoir for rubella virus. The only serious pathology produced is in the fetus when infection occurs during the first trimester of pregnancy.

The rubella virus genome consists of a single-stranded linear RNA of the positive configuration. The RNA from partially purified rubella virus is infectious, sedi-

ments at 38 S in sucrose density gradients, and has an estimated molecular weight of 3.2×10^6. Two distinct complement-fixing antigens have been demonstrated for rubella virus, a "large-particle" antigen, which elutes from gel filtration columns together with infectious virus and hemagglutinating activity, and a "small-particle" antigen, which elutes later. No hemagglutinating activity is associated with the "small-particle" antigen; however, it will react in the complement fixation test.

Pathogenesis

The pathogenesis of rubella is very much like that of measles, except that rubella is milder, is shorter in duration, and has fewer complications. Rubella virus has a prolonged incubation period of 14 to 25 days. During this incubation period the virus replicates and disseminates in the body very much like measles virus. The disease is initiated by 1 or 2 days of fever and malaise. Rash appears 2 or 3 weeks after infection, during which time the virus can be isolated from the blood. The virus can also be isolated from the nasopharyngeal secretions and occasionally from feces and urine as early as 7 days before and as late as 7 days after the appearance of the rash.

No characteristic pathologic lesions have been described for rubella virus infection except for the serious damage induced in infected fetuses. When a fetus is infected transplacentally, rubella virus initiates a persistent infection that results in congenital malformation. When a woman experiences clinical rubella infection during the first trimester of pregnancy, the chance that the infant at birth will have a structural abnormality is about 30 percent. Infection with rubella in the first month of pregnancy may result in abnormality in about 80 percent of the cases. The fetus infected during the first trimester may be stillborn; if it survives it may have deafness, cardiovascular abnormalities, motor deficits, anemia, and low birthweight. This condition of the infant is termed the *congenital rubella syndrome* (CRS). In the United States the number of CRS cases has decreased steadily during the past decade primarily because of successful rubella immunization programs.

The shedding of virus in congenital rubella infection after birth occurs for variable periods of time. Most infants born 6 to 8 months after intrauterine infection shed virus particles in the nasopharyngeal secretions for 6 months to 1 year, even in the presence of high titers of neutralizing IgM and IgG antibodies. Virus has been recovered as late as 3 years after birth. The factors that determine the duration of persistence of the virus in the infected infant are not known. The damage in the fetus seems to involve tissue of all germ layers; it includes frequent chromosomal aberrations that result in reduced cell division.

Laboratory Diagnosis

Diagnosis of rubella virus infection can be made by infection of susceptible tissue culture cells with nasopharyngeal secretions from the patient. Rubella antigens in infected cells can be detected by immunofluorescence techniques. Serologic diagnosis can also be accomplished by hemagglutination inhibition tests.

Prevention and Control

An epidemic of rubella in the United States in 1964 resulted in the disability of nearly 20,000 infants. To avoid such morbidity, prevention of maternal infection is of utmost importance. Monovalent live attenuated rubella vaccine and the live attenuated combined measles/mumps/rubella vaccine are both commercially available and are very effective. It is highly recommended that all health related personnel likely to be in close contact with pregnant women be screened for rubella antibodies, and susceptible persons should be vaccinated. It is also imperative that all women of childbearing age should know their immune status and, if it is negative for hemagglutination inhibiting antibodies, should be immunized with the understanding that they not become pregnant for at least 3 months after the vaccination.

REFERENCES

Evans, A.S.: Viral Infections of Humans, Plenum Medical Book Company, New York, 1976.

Fraser, K.B. and Martin, S.J.: Measles Virus and Its Biology. Academic Press, New York, 1978.

Joklik, W.K., Willett, H.P., and Amos, B., Eds.: Zinsser Microbiology. 17th Ed. Appleton-Century-Crofts, New York, 1980.

42

Coronaviruses, Reoviruses, and Rotaviruses

Harshad R. Thacore

In recent years various groups of RNA viruses have been implicated in a number of illnesses in various animals, including humans. For example, coronaviruses have been shown to be associated with human respiratory tract illness, whereas rotaviruses have been implicated as the cause of infantile diarrhea. It should be emphasized that members of each group of viruses not only are markedly different from members of the other groups in their morphological and biochemical characteristics but differ also in the type of illness caused in their host. For this reason these groups of viruses will be dealt with separately.

CORONAVIRUSES

Coronaviruses are a group of unique viruses capable of causing a broad spectrum of illness, ranging from an upper respiratory tract illness in humans, to diarrheal disease in pigs, calves, dogs, and possibly in humans. In recent years it has become apparent that coronaviruses are important etiologic agents of human respiratory dis-

ease. These viruses are classified into a separate family, *Coronaviridae*, because the surface projections on the envelope of these viruses resemble the solar corona.

Coronaviruses were first isolated in 1965 by Tyrell and Bynoe from a boy with a common cold. This isolate, designated B814, was propagated only in human embryonic tracheal organ cultures and was able to induce common-cold-like illness in volunteers. Since this initial report a significant number of these agents have been isolated in tracheal organ cultures from adults with common-cold-like illnesses. These agents were related serologically to the prototype strain B814. At present there are three known serotypes of human coronavirus. Serologic studies indicate that human coronavirus infections are much more common than is indicated by virus isolations.

The coronavirus genome consists of a single-stranded RNA molecule with a sedimentation coefficient of 50 S and a molecular weight of 9.0×10^6. Human coronaviruses have been reported to contain six to

561

eight polypeptides with molecular weights ranging from 13,000 to 210,000. In the prototype strain OC43 four viral polypeptides contain carbohydrate and one polypeptide contains lipid. Coronaviruses are sensitive to ether and other lipid solvents, suggesting that these viruses are enveloped. Electron miscrocopic studies show the viruses possess a moderately pleomorphic envelope that is acquired during the budding of the virus from infected cells. The envelope contains uniformly spaced club or pear shaped projections 20 nm in length that are narrow at the base and about 10 nm across at the outer edge. The shape and distribution of these projections readily distinguish these viruses from the myxovirus group and are used for tentative classification as coronavirus (Fig. 42.1).

Clinical Aspects

The symptoms of respiratory tract illness caused by coronaviruses are very similar to

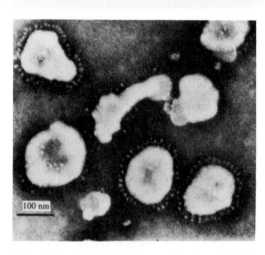

Fig. 42.1. Electron micrograph of negatively stained coronavirus particles. Note the peripheral peplomers that give the group its name. (With permission, Lanser, J.A. and Howard, C.R.: The polypeptides of infectious bronchitis virus (IBN-41 strain). J. Gen. Virol. *46*: 349, 1980. © Cambridge University Press.)

those of the common cold. About 50 percent of volunteers inoculated intranasally with a coronavirus develop symptoms after an incubation period of 2 to 5 days. The illness lasts for an average of 7 days and is characterized by malaise, headache, sore throat, and rhinitis. These characteristics are very similiar to those produced by rhinoviruses. Even though the ability of coronaviruses to cause disease in adults is well documented, the importance of coronavirus as a causative agent of respiratory tract illness in infants and young children is not well established.

Serologic studies conducted with coronavirus strains 229E and OC43 indicate that coronaviruses are second only to the rhinoviruses as the etiologic agent of common-cold-like illnesses in adults.

Laboratory Diagnosis

Isolation and characterization of coronaviruses is not routinely practiced. However there are a number of procedures for diagnosis that are carried out in specialized laboratories.

Coronaviruses are isolated in human embryonic tracheal cultures. The majority of these viruses have not yet been adapted to any tissue culture cell system. Detection of virus growth in organ culture is either by electron microscopic examination of concentrated culture fluid or by comparison of the ciliary action in infected organ cultures to those of control cultures. However, it should be emphasized that the ciliary immobilizing effect is not a very reliable test. Electron miscroscopic examination using negative-staining techniques or immune electron microscopy of culture fluid from infected organ cultures are the most reliable tests.

REOVIRUSES

In 1963 Gomatos and Tamm were the first to recognize reoviruses as having a genome consisting of double-stranded (ds) RNA. Reoviruses were originally isolated from man, but since then viruses possessing ds RNA genomes have been found in vertebrates, invertebrates, bacteria, higher plants, and fungi. Although the pathogenicity of mammalian reoviruses has not yet been established, these viruses have stimulated considerable interest because of their biochemical characteristics and the problems posed by the ds genomic RNA in virus replication.

The morphological features of reoviruses have been studied by electron microscopy using the negative-staining technique. Mammalian reoviruses consist of a nucleic acid core surrounded by two distinct protein shells or capsids. This unique double capsid has an outer layer composed of 80 hexagonal and 12 pentagonal elongated hollow capsomers arranged in icosahedral symmetry. The electron-dense inner capsid is composed of 42 capsomers. The nucleic acid core surrounded by this inner capsid layer is called the *subviral particle* (*SVP*).

Reoviruses are relatively resistant to inactivation by heat, ether, chloroform, and sodium dodecyl sulfate (SDS). Chemical analysis of purified virions indicates that the particles consist of 14 percent RNA and 86 percent protein. The genome has an estimated molecular mass of 10 to 20 $\times$ 10^6 daltons. Gomatos and Tamm (1963) provided the first unequivocal evidence that the reovirus genome was a ds RNA molecule by demonstrating the relative resistance of the RNA to degradation by ribonuclease and by thermal denaturation studies. It has not been possible to isolate infectious RNA. The reovirus ds RNA genome has been shown by various techniques, especially polyacrylamide gel electrophoresis, to exist as ten segments ranging in molecular mass from 2.5 million to 0.61 million daltons. Under suitable conditions the ten segments can be resolved into three size groups. There are three RNA segments in both the large (L) and the medium (M) size groups and four in the small (S) group.

There is a direct relationship between the genomic RNA segments and the virus proteins. Each ds RNA segment has been shown to be a single gene, and from each segment is transcribed a single messenger (m) RNA molecule by a transcriptase enzyme closely associated with the ds RNA. It is active in the SVP only following removal of the outer capsid. *In vitro* studies have shown that the enzyme synthesizes a single-stranded product in a conservative manner and that only one strand of each ds RNA segment is copied. The single-stranded RNA produced hybridizes specifically with the virion RNA. Furthermore, the *in vitro* product is identical to the *in vivo* mRNA isolated from infected cells.

Aside from the ds genomic RNA, the reovirus particles also contain heterogeneous single-stranded RNA with high adenine content. This adenine-rich RNA constitutes about 25 percent of the total encapsulated nucleic acid but is not required for infectivity. Its significance in virus replication is not known.

All mammalian reoviruses have been grouped by hemagglutination inhibition or by neutralization tests into three serotypes, designated types 1, 2, and 3. All strains of reovirus types 1, 2, and 3 possess the ability to agglutinate human erythrocytes.

Owing to the wide host range of reoviruses it is not surprising to find that human infection with reoviruses is common. Reoviruses have been recovered from healthy persons and from persons with upper respiratory illness, diarrhea, or hepatitis. Reoviruses have also been associated with other clinical disorders, such as Burkitt's lymphoma. In all these cases the presence of reovirus was found to be without any etiologic significance, and it was not possible to assess the role of the virus in pathogenesis. No vaccine is currently available for the prevention of reovirus infection.

Laboratory Diagnosis

Diagnosis can be made by the recovery of the virus with tissue culture techniques and demonstration of the presence of the virus by a number of virologic and serologic methods. These include electron microscopy, immunofluorescence, and the hemagglutination inhibition test.

ROTAVIRUSES

In the past decade many studies on acute diarrheal disease in infants have implicated reoviruslike agents as a major causative factor. Reports from many countries showed viruslike particles that resembled reoviruses in duodenal mucosa from children with gastroenteritis. These reoviruslike particles were also observed in partially purified fecal suspensions from infants with diarrhea. It should also be noted that in the past several years reoviruslike particles have also been detected in association with diarrheal disease in other animals, including lambs, piglets, and young rabbits and deer. These reoviruslike agents causing diarrheal disease in humans and other animals have been assigned various names such as orbivirus, rotavirus, duovirus, and infan-

tile gastroenteritis virus. The most widely used term is *rotavirus*, as suggested by Flewett in 1974.

Rotaviruses are approximately 66 nm in diameter and have a double capsid structure. The spokelike capsomers, 32 in number, are characteristic of rotaviruses (Fig. 42.2). The genome consists of double-stranded RNA with a molecular mass of 11 to 12×10^6 daltons. The RNA genome of human rotavirus has been studied by polyacrylamide gel electrophoresis and shown to have 11 segments in four size classes. Five polypeptides have been identified in rotaviruses, four of which are associated with the core of the particle.

Epidemiologic and Clinical Characteristics

It is now well established that human rotaviruses play a major role in infantile diarrheal disease. However, more epidemiologic studies must be conducted to determine what proportion of total diarrheal illness is caused by rotaviruses. Studies conducted to date are based largely on techniques such as electron microscopy for virus detection and complement fixation

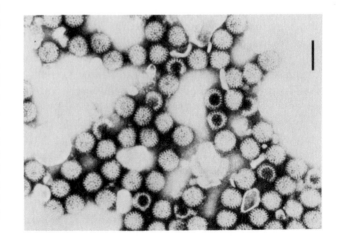

Fig. 42.2. Reoviruslike particles observed in a stool filtrate of a patient after incubation of the stool filtrate with phosphate buffered saline and further preparation for electron microscopy. Particles with double-shelled capsid and "empty" particles are present. The bar represents 100 nm. (With permission, Kapikian, A.E., et al.: Reoviruslike agent in stools: Associated with infantile diarrhea and development of serologic tests. Science *185*: 1049, 1974. Copyright 1974 by the American Association for the Advancement of Science.)

and immunofluorescent antibody techniques. In most of these studies the populations examined for rotavirus infection have been infants and young children hospitalized with acute diarrheal disease. In one of the largest studies, conducted in Australia in 1975, 378 children with acute diarrhea were studied, and 52 percent were shown to shed rotavirus in the feces. In contrast, all of the 116 control children were devoid of detectable rotaviruses. Epidemiologic studies have also shown that rotaviruses are most prevalent during the winter months and are absent during the summer months.

It should be noted that several important questions regarding rotavirus infection still remain to be answered. For example, the frequency of asymptomatic infection or reinfection in the general population is not known. The immunologic response of the host to rotavirus infection also remains to be studied; this is of special importance if one is to determine the duration and nature of immunity, if any, conferred on the host.

Laboratory Diagnosis

Rotaviruses are detected by electron microscopy in the stools of patients with diarrheal illness. Human rotaviruses have been passaged successfully in cultures of bovine or human embryonic kidney cells; however, the efficiency of replication of the virus is rather poor. The presence of the virus in infected cultures can be detected by immunofluorescence, electron microscopic examination, or radioimmunoassay techniques.

REFERENCES

Holmes, I.H.: Viral gastroenteritis. Prog. Med. Virol. 25: 1, 1979.

Oxford, J.S.: Chemoprophylaxis and Virus Infections of the Respiratory Tract. Vol. II. CRC Press, Cincinnati, 1977.

Wyatt, R.G., Kalica, A.R., Mebus, C.A., Kim, H.W., London, W.T., Chanock, R.M., and Kapikian, A.Z.: Reovirus-like agents (rotaviruses) associated with diarrheal illness in animal and man. Perspect. Virol. 10: 121, 1978.

43

Togaviruses, Bunyaviruses, and Rhabdoviruses

Thomas D. Flanagan

Among viruses causing human disease, there are many that require a vector to introduce the infectious particle into the host. Most of these viruses use arthropods as vectors; however, rabies virus is spread to man by vertebrates.

There is a large group of viruses using arthropod vectors whose members have been classified as arboviruses. This is a grouping based on biologic and ecologic criteria. It crosses through the taxonomy based on structural and chemical criteria. Therefore we find members of the *Togaviridae, Bunyaviridae, Arenaviridae, Reoviridae,* and *Rhabdoviridae* families classified as arboviruses. With the exception of rubella virus all *Togaviridae* and, without known exception, all *Bunyaviridae* are arboviruses. Only certain members of the other families are arthropod borne.

Arboviruses persist in nature by serial passage through nonimmune host animals and their vector species. Vectors are hemophagous arthropods, most frequently mosquitoes and ticks. The vector acquires the virus through feeding on a viremic host, becomes infected, and subsequently intro-duces the virus into the nonimmune host during another blood meal. The various arboviruses have defined reservoir hosts and vectors; the reservoir host is the vertebrate species in which the virus is maintained by vector passage. Arbovirus infections in reservoir hosts are usually inapparent and have significantly long periods of viremia. Long viremia is required to provide the opportunity to infect another individual of the vector species and thus propagate the chain of infection. Viruses can be spread to animals other than the reservoir species by vectors, and humans can serve as these occasional hosts. With the exceptions of the urban form of yellow fever and dengue fever, man is a dead-end host, not functioning as a source of virus for further spread of arboviruses.

TOGAVIRUSES

Togaviruses are enveloped RNA viruses that have cubic capsid symmetry. Infectious RNA can be prepared from virions. There are two genera to consider. *Alphavirus* and *Flavivirus*. These groups differ by size, Alphaviruses are larger, measuring 50 to 60 nm in diameter; flaviviruses measure 40 to 50 nm. They also differ in the mode of release from infected cells. Flaviviruses are produced in cytoplasmic vacuoles, and alphaviruses are shed from the plasma membrane. The original differentiation of the groups was based on serologic crossreactivity. Alphaviruses share to variable degrees common antigens not found among flaviviruses. The latter also exhibit variable crossreactivity among members but do not crossreact with alphaviruses. These crossreactivity patterns are detected by hemagglutination inhibition (HAI) tests. Serologic grouping within each genus is determined by the degree of crossreactivity. The individual types of viruses ("species") are determined by virus neutralization reactions. The antibody response early in infection of a host animal is characterized by highly specific reactivity detected by neutralization tests. Later in convalescence, antibodies in serum have a broader spectrum of reactivity when tested by HAI procedures. This spectrum of reactivity can be detected against other members of the genus.

As suggested, the togaviruses agglutinate red cells and thereby provide a convenient method for virus detection and antibody assay. The source of hemagglutinin is usually brain tissue of infected suckling mice, but hemagglutinin also may be prepared from a variety of cell cultures. Togaviruses agglutinate goose and newborn chick red blood cells under conditions of strict pH control. Alphaviruses require pH 5.0 to 6.0, and flaviviruses are best detected at pH 6.0 to 6.6.

Alphaviruses

One group of alphaviruses has significance in the Western Hemisphere. The viruses of Eastern equine encephalitis (EEE), Western equine encephalitis (WEE), and Venezuelan equine encephalitis (VEE) are spread by mosquito vectors and persist in a variety of avian or rodent host species. As the names suggest, infections of horses are usually detected when these viruses are present in a given geographic area. Severe disease of horses can occur.

Human Infection with EEE, WEE, and VEE. Virus is inoculated into the person by the bite of an infected mosquito. There is local replication of the agent in the vascular endothelium and local lymph nodes. A viremic phase ensues, accompanied by constitutional symptoms of fever, headache, nausea, myalgia, and malaise. The encephalitic phase follows, with virus replication occurring in the parenchyma of the CNS. The patient suffers continued headache, lethargy, ataxia, tremors, convulsions, and possibly coma. The severity of infection varies with the viruses. EEE characteristically is the most severe, with 15 to 40 percent fatality in various outbreaks. Infants and elderly persons are most frequently affected, with 70 percent affected with residual neurologic dysfunction. There are about 25 inapparent infections for each clinically manifest case during outbreaks.

WEE is usually less severe clinically, and outbreaks have lower fatality. However, because of larger outbreaks this virus causes more prevalent disease. There are a larger number of inapparent infections, perhaps as high as 300 for each apparent case.

Human infection with VEE rarely causes encephalitis but usually manifests with constitutional signs. There is evidence that horses may participate in the propagation of VEE, since vaccination of this species is effective in controlling outbreaks.

Diagnosis, Treatment, and Control. Etiologic diagnosis of disease caused by the encephalitis viruses is usually accomplished by serologic examination. Both HAI and complement fixation (CF) tests are employed. Demonstration of a significant increase in antibody titer is confirmatory. Single-serum specimens of high titer are also useful in reaching a diagnosis, particularly when supporting epidemiologic data are available.

Treatment of patients with arbovirus encephalitis is palliative. Control of the virus is exercised by controlling the vector populations. Mosquito eradication programs have proved effective in controlling outbreaks and apparently in interdicting potential outbreaks.

Epidemiology. The epidemiologic nature of arbovirus disease is related to the ecology of the reservoir species and the vector. Factors such as host preference of the vector, temperature, rainfall, and available habitat are operative in determining the incidence of human disease. In general, conditions conducive to high mosquito populations and those providing significant numbers of newborns in the reservoir species contribute to an increased probability of human infection. Several gaps remain in our understanding of these viruses, the most significant being how the viruses survive winter in temperate climates.

EEE is distributed in areas adjacent to the East Coast of the United States. The virus also occurs in the Caribbean and in parts of Central and South America. WEE is more widespread in the United States, occuring in many Eastern as well as Western states. VEE has been found in South and Central America as well as in Texas and Florida.

Flaviviruses

St. Louis Encephalitis (SLE). The most significant of the flaviviruses in North America is the virus of SLE. Outbreaks of SLE infection have been responsible for the largest numbers of cases of arbovirus encephalitis in epidemic years. The clinical disease resembles that caused by WEE,

with similar fatality and incidence of inapparent infection. There is a greater morbidity in older persons, and the infection presents as a more severe disease in this age group. The reservoir is wild birds, and a number of mosquito species, especially *Culex tarsalis*, can serve as vectors.

Outbreaks of SLE have occurred in many states and in recent years in such urban centers as Chicago and Detroit.

Yellow Fever and Dengue. The viruses that cause yellow fever and dengue are flaviviruses. Yellow fever as a defined clinical entity was described in the 17th century. The disease was widely distributed in the Americas during the 18th and 19th centuries. Epidemics occurred in Philadelphia and Baltimore as well as cities of the Gulf Coast. Walter Reed and the Yellow Fever Commission conducted investigations in Havana into the problem in 1900. They confirmed the hypothesis of the Cuban physician Carlos Finlay concerning the role of the mosquito vector in dissemination of the disease. The control of mosquito reproduction led to control of yellow fever.

The pathogenesis of yellow fever begins with inoculation of the virus by an infected mosquito. There is local replication in the vascular endothelium and regional nodes. Viremia ensues, and secondary sites of viral replication, particularly the liver and hematopoietic tissues, are initiated. The disease is clinically biphasic, with an initial constitutional phase of fever and malaise followed by an icteric phase in which liver dysfunction, jaundice, and tendency to hemorrhage are manifested. Fatality is about 5 percent of frank cases, but many inapparent infections occur. In the urban form of the disease man is the reservoir as well as the target species. The vector is *Aedes aegypti.*

Another epidemiologic form exists, called sylvan or jungle yellow fever. Various simian species function as the reservoir, and many species of mosquitos serve as vectors. Mosquito control measures have eliminated the urban form of the disease; however, the jungle form remains a potential threat, since the classical man–mosquito–man cycle can be reinitiated from this source.

Dengue fever is caused by a group of related flaviviruses, dengue virus types 1 through 4. Infection with these agents is manifested by symptoms of fever, headache, severe backache, and muscle pain. Certain outbreaks have been characterized by hemorrhagic phenomena leading to a shock syndrome. Dengue fever occurs in tropical and subtropical areas. Among mosquito species, *A. aegypti* is most important; however, other species may act as vectors. Man is infective for mosquitos, and man–mosquito–man transmission is possible. A number of mammalian species can function as reservoir.

Diagnosis, Treatment, and Control. Diagnosis of SLE is carried out by serologic means. HAI and CF tests are most frequently used. Yellow fever is usually diagnosed clinically; however, serologic tests may be helpful. The HAI procedure is preferred. Type-specific antibody response can be detected to dengue virus infection by neutralization or HAI procedures.

There is no specific treatment for the infections caused by these viruses. Palliative treatments are used, with particular attention to liver function disturbances and shock.

Control measures are directed toward vector eradication, particularly in urban environments. Two vaccines for yellow fever have been developed; both are live attenuated virus preparations. The 17D strain is a chick embryo propagated agent, while the Dakar strain is grown in suckling mouse brain. Both agents have proven efficacy.

BUNYAVIRUSES

The bunyaviruses are a large group of viruses with worldwide distribution. They are spherical enveloped viruses that have helical nucleocapsids. The RNA is in three segments. The virions are approximately 100 nm in diameter. Seven serologic types of the viruses are found in North America, but California encephalitis (CE) virus and the closely related LaCross encephalitis (LAC) virus are recognized as the principal human pathogens. The viruses hemagglutinate newborn chick and goose erythrocytes; CF and HAI procedures are used to detect antibodies.

Human Infection with CE and LAC

Encephalitis caused by these viruses is usually relatively mild. However, symptoms can include headache, fever, focal neurologic signs, and convulsions. The typical course is 7 to 10 days. Death in un-

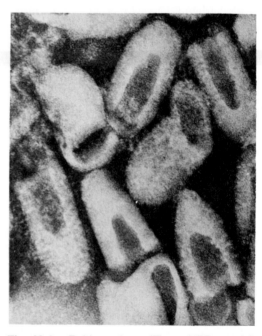

Fig. 43.1. Rabies virus (Flury HEP strain) propagated in BHK 21 cells, purified and stained with sodium phosphotungstate (× 180,000). (Photograph courtesy of Drs. F.A. Murphy, J. Crick, C.J. Smale, and F. Brown, College of Veterinary Medicine and Biological Sciences, Colorado State University.)

complicated cases is rare. There are a number of residual defects that have been described, including seizure disorders, hemiparesis, and auditory and visual perception problems. The frequency and seriousness of these sequelae have varied widely in reported studies.

Epidemiology

Viruses of the CE complex infect a number of mosquito species, particularly members of the genus *Aedes*. Infected mosquitos can function as the reservoir; the virus is passed through the egg to progeny. The viruses also infect a number of small forest rodents in which the viremic stage is sufficiently long to permit infection of mosquitos. These animals can serve as a reservoir.

CE is the most widely distributed of the arthropod-borne viruses in the United States and, except in epidemic years of SLE, is the most frequent cause of viral encephalitis. There is a high rate of inapparent infection.

Diagnosis, Treatment, and Control

Serologic diagnosis is carried out by CF and HAI methods. Treatment is directed to physiologic support of the patient. Mosquito eradication measures are the principal methods of control.

RHABDOVIRUSES

The rhabdoviruses are negative-stranded RNA viruses that mature by budding from the plasma membranes of infected cells. The virions have a unique bullet-shaped form measuring 50 nm by 120 nm. Vesicular stomatitis virus, a pathogen of significance in veterinary medicine, has served as a useful model in studies of the molecular events in replication of negative-stranded viruses. Rabies virus, the best known virus of this family, is illustrated in Figure 43.1.

Rabies

The clinical manifestations of rabies in man and animals have been recognized since antiquity, as have the sources of infection. The virus of rabies is morphologically similar to other rhabdoviruses. It has worldwide distribution, with the exception of certain islands. It is serologically related to five viruses found in Africa, two of which cause human CNS disease.

Rabies Infection in Humans. The virus is usually acquired by direct inoculation of infectious saliva through bite wounds or other trauma. Other modes of spread do occur, such as inhalation of airborne droplets in both natural and laboratory settings. There is a prolonged incubation period that can extend more than a year. The length of incubation is apparently a function of the amount of virus inoculated and the site of entry. Short incubation periods are associated with wounds of the head, face, neck, and fingers. The onset of clinical illness is signaled by fever, headache, malaise, and frequently pain or paresthesia at the site of the initiating wound. The disease progresses rapidly, with agitation, anxiety, convulsions, and coma. Death, which occurs in almost all cases, usually results from cardiac or respiratory failure. Two cases of survival of rabies have been documented in the United States. At death the virus is present in many tissues of the infected individual, including the salivary glands, buccal epithelium, corneal epithelium, and CNS. Postmortem examination of the brain reveals the presence of pathognomonic intracytoplasmic inclusions — Negri bodies — in neurons. These are found most frequently in Ammon's horn. The inclusion is composed of viral antigens and can be demonstrated by immunofluorescence.

Diagnosis, Treatment, and Control. The diagnosis of rabies is really a predictive problem. Since the infection is almost uniformly fatal in humans, the diagnosis is usually made in the animal suspected as a potential source of human infection. With the exception of the bat, all mammalian species succumb to rabies infection. Therefore capture and observation of the biting animal is essential. In dogs, death occurs in 10 to 14 days after onset of rabies. They shed virus during the acute phase of disease, while symptoms are manifested. Pathologic examination of tissues from sick animals or those killed after attacking is a necessary part of diagnosis. Examination of suspected animal tissues, particularly the brain, for rabies virus antigen by immunofluorescence and infectivity studies in mice comprise accepted practice.

Rabies in the absence of a history of exposure is rarely considered as an alternative in the differential diagnosis in cases of encephalitis in humans. However, recent evidence suggests that the infection may occur more often than expected. There has been, for example, the documented transmission of rabies by corneal transplant. Human rabies infections can be diagnosed by demonstration of viral antigen in cells of buccal biopsy or corneal scrapings and by detection of antibody in the serum by indirect immunofluorescence.

Treatment of clinical cases of rabies is supportive, with particular attention given to problems of pain, spasm, and respiratory sufficiency. Postexposure prophylaxis, first practiced by Pasteur, is the method used to prevent development of clinical disease in persons exposed to rabies. The original vaccine developed by Pasteur was a heated suspension of spinal cord from rabies-infected rabbits. The virus passaged in rabbits was somewhat attenuated in virulence and referred to as "fixed." The fully virulent wild strains were called "street virus." Subsequently, formalin-killed virus grown in duck embryo was used. At present, in the United States postexposure prophylaxis consists of active immunization using virus grown in human diploid cell cultures and inactivated with tri-*n*-butyl phosphate. The

usual course is five daily injections given intramuscularly with a single dose of rabies immune globulin on the first day. The current procedure is relatively free of adverse reactions compared to the older vaccines. The long incubation period for rabies permits the effective use of this strategy. The specific measures recommended by the Center for Disease Control for the management of persons possibly exposed to rabies are based upon the type of exposure. Persons bitten by animals that cannot be captured or observed must be regarded as at risk to rabies infection. The treatment consists of rabies immune globulin and a full course of human diploid cell rabies vaccine. If the attacking animal can be captured and observed, treatment can be withheld. If the suspected animal develops symptoms during the holding period of 10 days, the rabies immune globulin and human diploid cell rabies vaccine should be administered. In cases in which the attacking animal is killed, rabies immune globulin and vaccine treatment may be withheld or discontinued on the basis of negative immunofluorescence tests carried out on the brain of the attacking animal. Each potential exposure should be evaluated in light of the specific situation. Such factors as vaccination history of the attacking animal, presence of rabies in a geographic area, or provocation of the attack must be considered in making decisions regarding treatment.

Control of rabies is effected by vaccination of dogs and cats. In countries of North America human exposure to rabies has historically been from dogs and, to a lesser extent, cats. Vaccination and control laws regarding these species have drastically reduced the number of human exposures. Currently, in the United States more exposures result from wild animal bites than from bites by domesticated animals.

Epidemiology. Rabies virus infects all mammalian species, but there is differential susceptibility among the species. In different areas, different animal species act as the principal reservoirs. For example, in the eastern United States foxes and skunks are the principal reservoirs, while in the West coyotes are important.

The role of rabies infection of bats in the maintenance of the virus in nature is at present not completely understood; however, the infection of this species differs from infections of other species in two important ways — it may be inapparent and it may persist. These observations suggest a criti-cal role for bats in the epidemiology and ecology of the virus.

REFERENCES

Baer, G.: The Natural History of Rabies. Academic Press, New York, 1975.
Evans, A.S.: Viral Infections of Humans — Epidemiology and Control. Plenum Press, New York, 1976.

44

Picornaviruses

Arlene R. Collins

The *Picornaviridae* are a family of small RNA viruses. The human viruses in this family are found in two genera, *Enterovirus* and *Rhinovirus*. The enteroviruses infect primarily the human gastrointestinal tract but may cause a variety of clinical manifestations such as meningitis, paralytic poliomyelitis, myocarditis, and febrile illness with skin rash. The rhinoviruses infect primarily the upper respiratory tract; they are the most important viruses causing the common cold. Poliovirus, the causative agent of paralytic poliomyelitis, was the first member of the family to be described when it was reported in 1908 by Landsteiner and Popper. In the 1940s viruses of similar physical properties that were pathogenic for newborn mice were isolated. These viruses, designated coxsackieviruses, were divided into two groups, A and B, based on differing pathology in newborn mice. A number of physically similar viruses not pathogenic for newborn mice were discovered with the widespread use of cell culture. These were called "enteric cytopathogenic human orphan" viruses or echoviruses. Together, poliovirus, coxsackievirus, and echovirus form the *Enterovirus* genus. New serotypes (see below) of this genus have been called enteroviruses and given a serotype number without differentiation as poliovirus, coxsackievirus, or echovirus.

In 1956 viruses that appeared similar in many respects to the enteroviruses were isolated from patients with common colds. When it became apparent that these viruses were distinctly respiratory pathogens, they were classified as a separate genus, *Rhinovirus*.

A number of animal viruses are also found in the *Picornaviridae*. The *Calicivirus* genus contains viruses that infect cats and swine. Human caliciviruses have been isolated from the feces of infants with gastroenteritis and from an outbreak of winter vomitting disease in school children. The foot-and-mouth-disease virus of cattle is found in the *Aphthovirus* genus. The genus *Cardiovirus* contains rodent viruses, such as encephalomyocarditis virus, Columbia virus, and SK virus, that occasionally are transmitted to humans.

MORPHOLOGY AND PHYSICAL CHARACTERISTICS

Picornavirions are nonenveloped icosahedral particles 20 to 30 nm in diameter, possessing a single-stranded RNA genome of 2.7×10^6 daltons. The genome is in the messenger configuration and is enclosed in an outer capsid composed of 32 capsomers. The RNA is infectious after removal of capsid protein.

Within the *Picornaviridae* the enteroviruses are readily distinguished from rhinoviruses by their acid stability and density. Enteroviruses are stable to pH 3 for 1 to 3 hours, whereas rhinoviruses are acid labile. Enteroviruses have a density of 1.34 g/cm^3, whereas rhinoviruses have a density of 1.40 g/cm^3.

ANTIGENIC PROPERTIES

There is no picornavirus group antigen. Individual picornaviruses are identified by the presence of a type-specific antigen. Serotype-specific antigens are found in two antigenic forms on the virion. The D antigenic form is found on complete infectious virions and is the form that reacts with neutralizing antibody. The C antigenic form is associated with noninfectious, heated virions or empty capsids. Heating picornavirions results in a loss of a virion polypeptide VP4, which may form or contribute to the D antigenic determinant.

There are numerous serologic types of

Table 44.1 Picornaviruses of Humans

Picornaviruses	Serologic Types
Enteroviruses	
Poliovirus	1, 2, 3
Coxsackieviruses	
Group A	A1 through A24; A23 is the same as echovirus 9
Group B	B1 through B6
Echoviruses	1 through 33 (10 and 28 have been reclassified)
Enteroviruses	68 through 71
Rhinoviruses	1 through 89, plus 20 or more undefined

enteroviruses and rhinoviruses, each with a distinct serotype antigen. The various distinct serotypes of picornaviruses important to man are shown in Table 44.1. Identification of the serotype of picornavirus isolates from human infections is usually performed in the laboratory using the neutralization test. The complement fixation test may also be employed. It is important to note that immunity to picornavirus infection is serotype specific; for this reason repeated infections with enteroviruses and rhinoviruses are encountered in humans.

CULTIVATION

Human picornaviruses replicate in cell cultures of human or monkey origin. However, there are some distinct host preferences among the various members of the family. Polioviruses are the only enteroviruses that are pathogenic for monkeys and chimpanzees. Direct inoculation into the brain or spinal cord causes paralytic disease. Polioviruses grow well in monkey kidney cell cultures and in various human cell lines. The details of replication are discussed in Chapter 39.

Coxsackieviruses in general do not grow well in cell culture, although all but a few serotypes can be isolated in human cell lines. The coxsackieviruses are pathogenic for newborn mice. The type of pathology produced in infected mice has been used to divide coxsackieviruses into two groups. Coxsackie group A viruses produce widespread myositis in the skeletal muscle, resulting in flaccid paralysis. Coxsackie group B viruses produce a more focal myositis and also cause necrotizing lesions of the maturing fat lobules. Mice infected with coxsackie group B viruses develop paralysis of the spastic type.

Echoviruses, with the exception of echovirus 6, fail to produce disease in newborn mice but grow readily in human or monkey cells. Multiplication of enteroviruses in cell culture is detected by the development of characteristic cytopathic changes in infected cells. Infected cells round up, undergo shrinkage and nuclear pyknosis, and eventually fall off the glass. Rhinoviruses replicate well in human embryonic lung fibroblast cells at lower than normal body temperature and produce a cytopathic effect resembling that of the enteroviruses. Certain strains of rhinoviruses (M strains) will grow in monkey kidney cells. An important characteristic that differentiates rhinoviruses from enteroviruses is the optimal temperature for growth; rhinoviruses grow best at 33 or 34°C, whereas enteroviruses grow best at 37°C.

CLINICAL MANIFESTATIONS

Rhinoviruses and enteroviruses have entirely different modes of pathogenesis and clinical manifestations. Rhinovirus infections are transmitted via respiratory secretions and are limited to the nasopharynx and upper respiratory tract. Rates of infection with rhinoviruses are highest in early fall and late winter. The predominant symptoms are those characteristic of a common cold and include rhinitis, malaise, and cough. There is no viremia and usually no invasion of the lower respiratory tract, although rhinovirus infection may predispose to secondary bacterial invasion. Of importance in resistance to reinfection is the production of neutralizing antibody in the serum and nasal secretions. Repeated infections with rhinoviruses of different serotypes are common, since immunity is primarily associated with the presence of nasal secretory antibody, which is serotype specific.

Enterovirus infections are predominantly associated with the gastrointestinal mucosa. The portal of entry is the alimentary tract via the mouth. Initial multiplication takes place in the oropharynx and the gut. It has been observed that two or more enteroviruses may propagate simultaneously in the alimentary tract, but the multiplication of

one may interfere with the growth of the heterologous type. Interference of this type can result in failure of live polio vaccine to establish infection in the alimentary tract. Viremia may occur following alimentary infection and lead to dissemination of virus to other parts of the body, including the spinal cord and brain, meninges, myocardium, and skin. A wide variety of clinical manifestations are caused by enteroviruses, the most serious manifestation being paralytic poliomyelitis. However, the vast majority of enteroviral infections are subclinical or associated with mild undifferentiated febrile illness. Infections with enteroviruses tend to occur as seasonal outbreaks in late summer and early fall. Immunity to clinical illness with enteroviruses is associated with the production of serum-neutralizing antibody, which is serotype specific.

Poliovirus Infections

The three serotypes of poliovirus are the causative agents of poliomyelitis. Only very rarely have other enteroviruses been implicated. The majority of poliovirus infections are subclinical. Only 1 or 2 percent of infected individuals demonstrate involvement of the central nervous system, which may be paralytic or nonparalytic. In the paralytic disease infection begins by ingestion of poliovirus in contaminated material. Fecal contamination of food, table utensils, or fingers is the usual source of infections. Droplets or aerosols can also be a source. During a 2-week incubation period the virus multiplies in the oropharynx and the mucosa of the small intestine. There is spread to the cervical and mesenteric lymph nodes, followed by viremia and invasion of the central nervous system. The mode of spread from the blood to the central nervous system may be direct or the virus may travel along the axons of the peripheral nerves to the central nervous system. The main sites of invasion are the nerve cells of the spinal cord, most prominently the anterior horn cells. Lesions may also occur in the medulla, brainstem, and motor cortex. Paralysis results from destruction of motor neurons. The destruction of neurons is due entirely to the process of intracellular replication and lysis of infected cells by the virus. The host immunologic response does not seem to play a role. Inflammation occurs following destruction of nerve cells. The lesions consist of diffuse mononuclear infiltration and perivascular cuffing. In its non-paralytic form, poliovirus infection of the central nervous system does not result in infection of neurons; in such cases there may be acute meningitis, but recovery is complete.

Laboratory Diagnosis. Poliovirus is most readily recovered from feces or rectal swabs by inoculation of cultures of human or monkey kidney cells. Virus replication is detected by microscopic examination for characteristic cytopathic changes. Spinal fluid frequently does not yield virus when it is submitted as a specimen for diagnosis. Throat culture may yield virus during the incubation period of illness.

For serologic diagnosis neutralizing antibody levels in sera obtained during the acute phase of illness and sera taken 2 to 3 weeks later are compared.

Epidemiology. Poliovirus infections occur worldwide, but the pattern of infection varies under different environmental conditions. In underdeveloped countries, chiefly in the tropics, primary infection usually occurs in young children (under 4 years of age). Most infections are inapparent, but occasional cases of "infantile paralysis" are seen. In developed countries, in the prevaccine era, because of higher standards of hygiene, infections were occurring in late childhood and adult life. Infections in these age groups were more likely to take a paralytic form. Currently, in the postvaccine era, infection with virulent poliovirus is a rare occurrence and is seen in unimmunized or underimmunized

communities, usually stemming from importation of virulent viruses. In communities where high levels of vaccination exist, vaccine viruses are abundantly excreted by those who have been vaccinated and can be transmitted to unvaccinated persons. In this way the establishment of a virulent poliovirus is precluded. It is therefore important to maintain high levels of vaccination in a community. Current potential sites for outbreaks of polio infection are urban and rural disadvantaged areas, where the importance of vaccination is not emphasized.

Prevention. The method recommended in the United States for prevention of poliomyelitis is the administration of oral vaccine (Sabin vaccine) containing live attenuated poliovirus of all three serotypes. There are several advantages to the use of live oral polio vaccine. Ingestion of live virus simulates natural infection by establishment of viral replication in the alimentary tract, which results in a state of resistance in the gut to colonization by virulent poliovirus strains. Resistance is in part mediated by the production of secretory antibody in the gut and in part by heterologous interference. In addition, the production of circulating antibody regularly follows a brief period of viremia after vaccination. The most persistent form of immunity is due to the presence of neutralizing antibody in the circulation.

Immunization with oral polio vaccine is recommended for infants at 2 months of age with two boosters at 2-month intervals and a fourth dose at 1½ years of age. Persons with immune deficiency diseases, particularly hypogammaglobulinemia or agammaglobulinemia, should be given inactivated polio vaccine (Salk vaccine). Inactivated polio vaccine continues to be used for routine immunization in a few European countries. A schedule of four doses of vaccine at 1-month intervals with a booster every 2 to 3 years is recommended.

Clinical Manifestations of Other Enteroviral Infections

Enteroviruses other than poliovirus are associated with a wide variety of clinical manifestations in all age groups. A summary of enteroviral syndromes is given in Table 44.2. The great majority of coxsackievirus and echovirus infections occur in children less than 5 years old. In this age group the majority of coxsackie group A viruses are identified in cases of skin eruptions, aseptic meningitis, and respiratory illness. Coxsackie B viruses are most commonly found in association with central nervous system involvement and respiratory illness. Echoviruses are identified mainly with cases of aseptic meningitis. In older children (ages 5 to 14 years) central nervous system illness accounts for the largest number of clinical illnesses due to echoviruses. There is some evidence of epidemic periodicity of particular enteroviruses; some enterovirus serotypes show a tendency to recur at regular intervals.

The neurologic syndromes associated with enterovirus infections include meningitis, encephalitis, and other neurologic sequelae. Aseptic meningitis is the most common clinical manifestation of enterovirus infection. Aseptic meningitis may result from infection with other viruses such as mumps virus, herpesviruses and arboviruses, but enteroviruses are the most frequently isolated viral agents. Symptoms include headache, stiff neck, nausea, and lethargy. Most enteroviruses are capable of producing this syndrome. Enteroviruses are less frequent causes of encephalitis. In addition to showing signs of meningitis, patients with encephalitis may have disorientation, alteration in consciousness, tremors, and convulsions arising from the process of inflammation of the brain. Temporary neurologic sequelae occasionally may be seen in young children. Clinical symptoms may involve loss of muscular coordination or ataxia due to damage of the cerebellum.

Table 44.2.   Clinical Syndromes Associated With Coxsackieviruses and Echoviruses

	Coxsackieviruses		Echoviruses
	Group A	Group B	
Aseptic meningitis	+	+	+
Encephalitis	+	+	+
Cerebellar ataxia	+	+	+
Muscle weakness and paralysis	+	+	+
Exanthemata (vesicular, maculopapular)	+	+	+
Epidemic pleurodynia	−	+	−
Pericarditis, myocarditis	−	+	−
Orchitis, parotitis, epididymitis	−	+	−
Generalized disease in early infancy (myocarditis, encephalitis, hepatitis)	−	+	−
Respiratory (acute upper respiratory disease, summer grippe, pneumonia)	+	+	+
Herpangina	+	−	−
Hand, foot, and mouth disease	+	−	−

Febrile illnesses with exanthema occur with both coxsackievirus and echovirus infections. The rash may be maculopapular or vesicular in appearance and may resemble the rashes of rubella or chicken pox. A specific enanthem associated with coxsackie group A viruses is herpangina. This disease is characterized by the presence of small vesicular lesions on the anterior pillars of the tonsillar fauces and the soft palate, and the disease may resemble herpes gingivostomatitis. Hand, foot, and mouth disease is another characteristic clinical syndrome caused by coxsackie group A viruses. It is characterized by simultaneous vesicular lesions of the mouth and the hands and feet. Usually coxsackie virus A16 is involved. Acute myocarditis and pericarditis are serious forms of infection with coxsackie group B viruses. Less frequently, other enteroviruses are involved. In newborns, severe, often fatal cases of myocarditis have been associated with outbreaks of coxsackie group B virus infection in hospital nurseries. In the most severe cases infants may also show symptoms of encephalitis and hepatitis. Coxsackie myocarditis and pericarditis also occur in older children and adults. Some cases in adults may resemble acute myocardial infarction. Recent evidence suggests that coxsackieviruses may persist in cardiac tissue, causing degenerative cardiac disease. Deposition of fibrin and gamma globulin in the late phase of cardiac illness suggests an immunologic basis for pathogenesis. Coxsackie group B viruses have been associated with infection of skeletal muscle. Epidemic pleurodynia or Bornholm's disease is associated with pleural infection characterized by severe abdominal and chest pain in adults and children.

A common manifestation of enterovirus infection seen most often in young children is mild upper respiratory illness. Fever and pharyngitis are the main symptoms of the illness often referred to as "summer grippe."

Recently, a new enterovirus, enterovirus 70, was recovered from Asian, African, and European epidemics of acute hemorrhagic conjuctivitis. Subconjunctival hemorrhage with little or no corneal involvement and complete recovery within 2 weeks are the most prominent features of the illness. Conjunctivitis may accompany other symptoms of enterovirus infection.

Coxsackie group B viruses have been associated with parotitis, epididymitis, and orchitis. Enteroviruses also may occasionally cause renal damage.

LABORATORY DIAGNOSIS

Isolation of enteroviruses is the method of choice for making the diagnosis of infection. Specimens to be submitted may include feces, throat washings, vesicle fluid, and cerebrospinal fluid. The laboratory hosts include primary monkey kidney cells and human fibroblast cells. Cell cultures are examined for evidence of a cytopathic effect, which is characterized by rounding up and shrinking of the infected cells and nuclear pyknosis. Enteroviral isolates are identified serologically using the neutralization test.

Patient's sera collected at the onset of illness and 2 to 4 weeks later may be tested for type-specific neutralizing antibody. Because of the large number of individual serotypes, serologic diagnosis becomes feasible only when a virus isolate from the patient is available or when an epidemic clearly implicates one serologic type. A fourfold or greater rise in antibody titer is considered significant in making a diagnosis.

REFERENCES

Grist, N.R., Bell, E.J., and Assaad, F.: Enterovirus in human disease. Prog. Med. Virol. *24*: 114, 1978.

Gwaltney, E.M., Jr.: Rhinoviruses. Yale J. Biol. Med. *48*: 17, 1975.

Herrmann, E.C., Jr.: New concepts and developments in applied diagnostic virology. Prog. Med. Virol. *17*: 221, 1974.

Jackson, G.G. and Muldoon, R.L.: Viruses causing common respiratory infections in man. J. Infect. Dis. *127*: 328, 1973.

Kurstak, E. and Kurstak C.: Comparative Diagnosis of Viral Diseases. 1st Ed. Vol. 1. Academic Press, New York, 1977.

45

Hepatitis Viruses

Harshad R. Thacore

Viral hepatitis is defined as an acute inflammation of the liver caused by either of the two agents — hepatitis A virus (HAV) or hepatitis B virus (HBV) — excluding by common usage hepatitis caused by well recognized viruses like yellow fever virus, cytomegalovirus, Epstein-Barr virus, and herpes simplex virus. Another entity has been designated non-A, non-B hepatitis to distinguish disease not attributable to any of the known agents.

Viral hepatitis was first observed several centuries ago, but the recognition of the characteristic lesion on histologic examination did not come until the middle 1920s. It was the epidemiologic studies conducted among the troops of World War II that first showed the importance of fecal contamination for dissemination of HAV as opposed to airborne spread of the disease. Outbreaks of the disease have since been prevalent during the various wars in the past several decades, including the Vietnam War. Among the United States troops in the Korean War the number of hepatitis cases rose as high as 36 per 1000 troops per year. Even during peacetime viral hepatitis remains an important cause of disability and a tremendous drain on personal and public finances. In the United States between 1969 and 1973 an average of 62,606 cases of viral hepatitis per year were reported. Furthermore, it should be emphasized that only about 20 percent of cases are reported.

Viral hepatitis is a "high risk" occupational hazard among health care personnel, especially dentists and persons working in renal dialysis units and in institutions for mentally handicapped persons. High rates of HBV infection also occur in drug addicts, prostitutes, patients with immune deficiency, and individuals requiring repeated transfusion of blood or blood products. The chance of transmission of hepatitis in blood transfusions is not definitely known, and the incidence of transfusion-associated disease varies from community to community. The risk factor is significantly higher when blood from commercial sources is used for transfusion as compared to blood obtained from volunteer donors. When fibrinogen is used for transfusion the chance of viral hepatitis is 85 to 95 percent. For these reasons careful evaluation of the beneficial effects versus the risk of transmitting hepatitis must be made prior to ordering a blood transfusion.

Clinical studies in human volunteers clearly established the presence of two epidemiologically and immunologically distinct forms of viral hepatitis. Infectious hepatitis, caused by HAV, is characterized by a short incubation period and is mainly transmitted through the fecal–oral route. In contrast, serum hepatitis, caused by HBV, is characterized by a longer incubation period and is mainly transmitted by infected blood or blood products. However, it should be noted that these modes of transmission of the two agents of viral hepatitis are not absolute. It has been shown that HAV can be transmitted parentally, and antigens of HBV have been shown to be present in many secretions, suggesting the possibility of other routes of transmission.

The nature of the etiologic agents and the pathogenesis of viral hepatitis began to unfold in 1964 with the discovery by Blumberg of an antigen in the serum of Australian aborigines, which was termed Australia antigen. This antigen is now designated hepatitis B surface antigen (HB$_s$Ag). Sub-sequent studies clearly demonstrated a direct relationship between the presence of this antigen and serum hepatitis. This not only allowed the diagnosis of HBV but also provided evidence that the etiologic agent associated with hepatitis B is distinct from that of hepatitis A. This was further substantiated by studies that showed that no crossimmunity existed between HAV and HBV.

CLINICAL ASPECTS OF VIRAL HEPATITIS

Viral hepatitis A is widespread throughout the world. Recent serologic studies show that hepatitis A antibody occurs in about 40 percent of adults in the United States. The incubation period of the disease is 3 to 5 weeks, with an average incubation period of 28 days. A high proportion of infections in children are subclinical and without jaundice. In adults most cases present with jaundice. Some of the important clinical and epidemiologic features of hepatitis A

Table 45.1.   Epidemiologic and Clinical Characteristics of Viral Hepatitis

Characteristics	Viral Hepatitis A	Viral Hepatitis B
Causative agent	Hepatitis A virus	Hepatitis B virus
Virion associated nucleic acid	Single-stranded RNA	Double-stranded DNA
Virion associated enzyme	None	DNA polymerase
Incubation period	15–50 days	43–180 days
Type of onset	Acute	Insidious
Route of infection	Predominantly by the fecal–oral route	Predominantly by the parenteral route
Duration of virus specific antigen in the blood	Days	Months to years
Carrier state	None demonstrable	Present
Duration of transaminase activity	1–3 weeks	1–6 months or more
Increase in IgM levels	Significant	Normal to slight elevation
HB$_s$Ag in serum	Absent	Present
Homologous immunity	Yes	Yes
Heterologous immunity	None	None
Duration of immunity	Probably lifelong	Probably lifelong

are presented in Table 45.1. It should be noted that there is no evidence to date to indicate that HAV infection can progress to produce a carrier state or chronic liver disease.

Hepatitis A virus is spread mainly by the fecal–oral route and under conditions of poor sanitation. Although the most common source of infection is fecal contamination of water, many food-borne outbreaks have been reported. These are frequently due to the contamination of food by infected food handlers in whom the disease is in its incubation period. Ingestion of uncooked foods that have been cultivated in contaminated water can also be a source of hepatitis A infection.

Hepatitis A virus produces clinical symptoms indistinguishable from those produced by HBV (Table 45.1). The major differences between hepatitis A and B are as follows:

1. Viral hepatitis A has a shorter incubation period (15 to 50 days) in contrast to 43 to 180 days for hepatitis B.

2. Hepatitis A spreads predominantly by the oral–fecal route, whereas hepatitis B spreads predominantly by the parenteral route.

3. The most important difference is the presence of HB$_s$Ag in the sera of hepatitis B patients and its absence in patients with hepatitis A.

Apart from these and a few other minor differences, both HAV and HBV produce indistinguishable histopathologic lesions in the liver. Clinical symptoms in both cases can range from asymptomatic infection to fulminant hepatitis resulting in death.

Acute infection with HBV is relatively common, and it is fortunate that a majority of patients recover completely. There is less than 1 percent fatality except in patients with malignancies, in whom the fatality rate is about 2 to 3 percent.

The initial stage of acute hepatitis B is frequently characterized by fatigue, general malaise, symptoms of upper respiratory infection, fever, nausea, vomiting, and an aversion to smoking. This is followed by jaundice. HB$_s$Ag is present in sera of patients for periods up to 6 months after onset of illness. The feces and blood of patients are infectious during the late incubation period and throughout the period of acute illness.

One of the least common complications of acute viral hepatitis is known as fulminant viral hepatitis wherein liver failure occurs very abruptly (less than 4 weeks from the onset of illness). If the liver failure occurs later in the course of the disease — that is, at 1 to 3 months of illness — the condition is known as subacute hepatitis.

Carrier States and Sequelae

One of the most common long-term sequelae of acute hepatitis B is persistent viral hepatitis or chronic persistent hepatitis. This form of hepatitis is further classified into two categories: chronic persistent hepatitis, a benign form of hepatitis characterized by minor inflammatory changes in the liver, and chronic active hepatitis (CAH), a more serious form of hepatitis in which lesions develop in the liver that may lead to cirrhosis, terminating in hepatic failure. In cases of CAH the prognosis is generally poor.

Many clinical studies have shown that a large number of patients with CAH have had no history of an acute icteric illness, suggesting that a mild form of acute hepatitis may provide an unusually good background or may predispose the patient for the development of severe CAH.

Two types of persistent HBV carrier populations are recognized: those classified as healthy carriers, who are spotted during the screening of blood donor populations, and those persons with an immunologic deficiency, who are predisposed to the HBV carrier state.

In North America, 1 out of every 1000 persons is a healthy carrier. This rate is much greater in less developed countries, especially in Africa and Asia. The majority of carriers have been shown to have asymptomatic liver disease.

The relationship between immunodeficiency and the increased frequency of the HBV carrier state has been well documented. It has been described in Down's syndrome and lepromatous leprosy and in patients receiving immunosuppressive therapy. These carriers, in contrast to the healthy carriers, have a much greater incidence of liver damage.

It is not known why some persistent HBV carriers show no evidence of liver damage whereas others develop liver disease. It is conceivable that in carriers with liver damage tolerance may be incomplete and the immunologic response may be inadequate to eliminate the HB_sAg but may be enough to produce varying amounts of immunologically mediated damage to the liver cells. Studies of carriers with normal liver function have been limited; however, they suggest that such carriers lack cell-mediated immunity.

On the basis of information acquired from clinical and epidemiologic studies the following conclusions have been drawn regarding viral hepatitis B and the HB_sAg:

1. A confirmed positive test for HB_sAg is indicative of acute hepatitis, chronic hepatitis, or an asymptomatic carrier state.

2. The presence of HB_sAg in the blood of a patient with acute viral hepatitis B is usually transient, but if it persists for 6 months after the onset of illness, the person becomes a chronic carrier of the antigen.

3. A chronic carrier of HB_sAg may or may not have evidence of related liver damage.

4. The occurrence of acute hepatitis B or the asymptomatic carrier state during pregnancy, or even during the first 2 months postpartum, is frequently associated with infection of the newborn infant. The child should be tested for HB_sAg at monthly intervals for at least 6 months. Many infants who acquire HBV infection in the perinatal period become chronic carriers.

Several methods have been described for the detection of HB_sAg. One of the most sensitive, currently used in many blood banks, is the radioimmunoassay (RIA). In this procedure serum to be tested for HB_sAg is mixed with latex particles coated with antibodies against HB_sAg (anti-HB_sAg). After a period of incubation and washing, anti-HB_sAg labeled with ^{125}I is added. Then the amount of radioactivity adsorbed to the latex particles is determined and compared with an appropriate negative control serum. This procedure is rapid, taking about 3 or 4 hours, but it is relatively expensive owing to the use of radioisotopes.

Another technique for the detection of HB_sAg is the passive hemagglutination (PHA) assay. The PHA technique is as sensitive as RIA and is significantly less expensive and more rapid. In this procedure human red blood cells coated with anti-HB_sAg are used instead of the latex particles. In short, the patient's serum is mixed with human blood cells coated with anti-HB_sAg, and the resulting hemagglutination is compared with appropriate control serum.

CAUSATIVE AGENTS OF VIRAL HEPATITIS

The recognition and partial characterization of specific antigenic markers associated with HAV and HBV not only have led to the development of laboratory diagnostic tests and an insight into the epidemiology and pathology of these agents but also have increased our knowledge regarding identification and nature of the etiologic agents themselves.

Hepatitis A Virus

Very recent advancements have led to an agreement on a prototype virus and a good

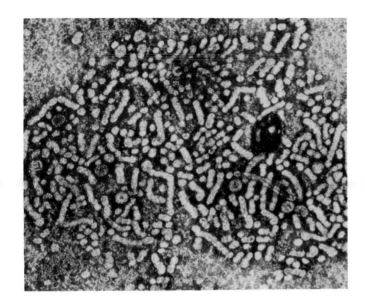

Fig. 45.1. Electron micrograph of the various morphologic forms found in human plasma containing hepatitis B surface antigen (HB$_s$Ag). Unfractionated plasma (diluted 1 : 10) containing 22 nm spheres, filaments, and Dane particles (× 77,000). (Reprinted from Approaching the control of viral hepatitis type B, by Melnick, J.L., Dreesman, G.R., and Hollinger, F.B. Journal of Infectious Diseases *133*: 210, 1976, by permission of The University of Chicago Press. © 1976 by The University of Chicago.)

antigenic marker for HAV. Only one serotype has been identified in patients from several different outbreaks of hepatitis A in different regions of the world.

The biochemical nature of HAV has not yet been studied as extensively as that of HBV. In 1973 Feinstone and co-workers reported the presence of a small, 27 nm icosahedral viruslike particle in feces during the acute phase of illness in adult volunteers infected orally or parenterally with HAV. These findings were later confirmed in other laboratories, providing further evidence for the identification of this virus as the etiologic agent in viral hepatitis A. It should be stressed that these 27 nm viruslike particles were not detected in patients with hepatitis B and furthermore that antibody to these virus particles was detected in serum of patients in the convalescent stage of illness.

Recent studies dealing with the biochemical and biophysical characterization of HAV indicate that the virus shares many properties with enteroviruses. HAV isolated from stools of patients during outbreaks of the disease in Alaska and Georgia has been shown to contain low density (1.34 g/cm^3) and high density (1.45 g/cm^3)

particles that have identical sedimentation coefficients of approximately 157 S in neutral sucrose density gradients. Both of these particles have been shown by immunoelectron microscopy and RIA to be specific for hepatitis A. The particles are indistinguishable in morphology and possess similar diameters of 27 to 30 nm. Alkaline degradation of the particles renders them susceptible to ribonuclease but not to deoxyribonuclease, indicating that the virus particles contain RNA. Analysis of proteins of highly purified preparations of HAV by sodium dodecyl sulfate (SDS) – polyacrylamide gel electrophoresis has shown the presence of four major polypeptides with molecular weights closely resembling those characteristic of the family *Picornaviridae*. These and other findings support the notion that HAV is an enterovirus.

Hepatitis B Virus

Three distinct morphological entities all sharing a common surface antigen (HB$_s$Ag) have been observed in sera from patients with HBV infection (Fig. 45.1). A 22 nm viruslike spherical particle, present in large amounts in the blood of patients with hepatitis B, may represent an incomplete particle devoid of nucleic acid. A filamentous form, 22 nm in cross section and of varying lengths, has also been observed in sera of patients with hepatitis B. The third form, present in very low concentration as compared to the other two forms, is a 42 nm viruslike particle, and appreciation of its significance has grown rapidly since its discovery by Dane and associates in 1970. More and more evidence points to its identity as the infectious form of HBV. This 42 nm particle, called the Dane particle, has a complex internal structure consisting of a 27 nm diameter core and an outer coat containing the group-specific surface antigen (HB$_s$Ag). Treatment of Dane particles with detergent results in the disruption of the coat and release of the internal core-specific antigen (HB$_c$Ag). Cores of similar morphology have been observed in homogenates of liver tissue from fatal cases of hepatitis B. It is postulated that the cores of Dane particles are synthesized in the nucleus of infected liver cells and then transferred to the cytoplasm, where they acquire the coat and are released from infected cells.

Dane particles and cores of Dane particles purified from infected hepatocytes have been shown to contain a double-stranded DNA with a molecular mass of approximately 1.6×10^6 daltons. The viral DNA is circular, approximately 3600 nucleotides long, and contains single-stranded gaps of 600 to 2100 nucleotides. The significance of these gaps in the DNA molecule and the actual mode of replication of the DNA is not known. In 1973 Kaplan and associates provided evidence for the presence of a DNA polymerase associated with the cores of the Dane particles. This enzyme synthesizes DNA using the genomic double-stranded DNA as its template. An exogenous template is not required for the enzyme activity.

HEPATITIS B VIRUS ANTIGENS

The antigenic heterogeneity of the virus particle surpasses its morphological complexity. There are two major antigens associated with the hepatitis B virus particle, the surface and core antigens, designated HB$_s$Ag and HB$_c$Ag, respectively.

HB$_s$Ag is composed predominantly of protein, with small amounts of phospholipids and carbohydrates. The protein is responsible for the antigenicity. The protein fraction of HB$_s$Ag has been resolved by polyacrylamide gel electrophoresis into six or seven polypeptides with molecular weights ranging from 26,000 to 95,000. Individual peptides appear to contain both the group- and type-specific determinants.

The HB$_c$Ag released from the Dane particles is antigenically distinct from HB$_s$Ag. Twelve polypeptides have been resolved by polyacrylamide gel electrophoresis from cores purified from Dane particles. Three of these polypeptides (molecular weights 88,000, 79,000, and 59,000) have also been found to be present in liver-derived HB$_c$Ag, suggesting that these polypeptides are specific for HB$_c$Ag.

A third antigen designated e or HB$_e$Ag, is also present in the Dane particle. This antigen seems to be associated with some but not all particles present in HB$_s$Ag positive sera. The presence of this antigen has been correlated with the development of chronic liver disease and with the potential infectivity of serum. It is also postulated that the antigen may represent the DNA-dependent DNA polymerase associated with HB$_c$Ag.

Careful serologic analysis of HB$_s$Ag indicates that it contains a group-specific a antigen and mutually exclusive determinants d or y and w or r antigen pairs. On the basis of these determinants four different subtypes of hepatitis B virus can be found: adw, adr, ayw, and ayr. Another newly found determinant, δ, distinct from previously identified determinants, has also been described. A host-derived antigenic determinant associated with HB_sAg has been described but owing to its extreme lability has been poorly characterized.

From the epidemiologic point of view the ability to identify type-specific determinants on HB_sAg is of utmost importance. Epidemiologic studies have shown that the d determinant is found most commonly among populations in North and South America, whereas the y determinant predominates in the Middle East, northern Africa, and some parts of Asia.

IMMUNE RESPONSE IN HEPATITIS B INFECTION

The immune response to HBV infection can be detected by sensitive immunologic techniques against the three main antigens — HB_sAg, HB_cAg, and the e antigen.

In patients with acute hepatitis HB_sAg appears in the serum during the incubation period and several weeks before biochemical evidence of liver damage or the onset of jaundice. This antigen persists during the acute phase of the illness and is usually cleared during the convalescent phase. HB_cAg has not been observed in a free state in the sera of patients with hepatitis B. The e antigen appears to be correlated with the rise in the transaminase activity (1 to 6 months or more) in the serum.

Antibody response to HB_sAg in patients with acute hepatitis is detected during the convalescent stage of illness and persists even after the disappearance of the antigen from the serum. Antibody response to HB_cAg in patients with acute hepatitis is seen 2 weeks after the appearance of HB_sAg and sometimes can be found at low levels after recovery from the illness.

In chronic HBV carriers HB_sAg persists for more than 6 months, and antibodies to HB_sAg are not detected. However, antibodies to HB_cAg appear in the sera of such patients shortly after the appearance of HB_sAg, and the antibodies to HB_cAg persist in high titers.

Patients with chronic active hepatitis and cirrhosis of the liver have been shown to produce autoantibodies against mitochondria, smooth muscle, and nuclear components. The presence of these antibodies correlates well with liver damage, suggesting that they are produced in response to antigens released from the damaged hepatocytes. It should be noted, however, that such autoantibodies have been found in patients with acute hepatitis also, although they disappear on recovery.

ROLE OF IMMUNE RESPONSE IN LIVER DAMAGE

There is no unifying hypothesis regarding the mechanism involved in the liver damage caused by viral hepatitis. The possibility that the cytopathic effect in the hepatocytes is a result of replication of HBV is ruled out because large quantities of HB_sAg persist in liver cells and in serum of apparently healthy carriers of hepatitis B virus. However, there is evidence for the hypothesis that inappropriate immunologic response by the host may be responsible for the hepatocellular damage seen in both acute and chronic hepatitis. Three main types of immune reactions could be involved in the cytopathology seen in livers of patients.

Antibody Mediated Cytoxicity

This kind of an immune reaction occurs when viral antigens appear on the surface of infected hepatocytes and the virus-specific antibodies become bound to such cells, resulting in complement-dependent cell lysis. The scattered foci of necrosis observed throughout the liver in acute hepatitis patients could represent such an antigen–antibody cytotoxic reaction.

Antigen–Antibody Immune Complex

The role of immune complexes is being recognized more and more in diseases with an unknown etiology. Immune complexes are produced by the interaction of antigens and specific antibodies. The pathology as a result of these complexes depends not only on the ratio of antibody and antigen but also on the size of the complex. In the early viremia phase of hepatitis, antigen–antibody complexes that may be produced in the presence of excess antigen remain in circulation and may be deposited in certain sites, such as the walls of small vessels, resulting in intravascular coagulation. This type of histopathology has been noted in acute hepatic necrosis. It is also proposed that production of antibodies in excess may cause a severe Arthus-like reaction in the sinusoids of the liver that could contribute to the development of fulminant hepatic necrosis. Both kinds of immune complexes have been shown to be present in the cytoplasm, plasma membrane, and/or on the nuclei of infected hepatocytes of patients with HBV infection.

Cell-Mediated Reaction

Cellular immune responses are known to be of utmost importance in determining the outcome of many viral infections in man. Immunologic responses are capable of producing cell damage, as seen in neurologic lesions of experimental lymphocytic choriomeningitis in mice. A cell-mediated response has been demonstrated during the acute phase of hepatitis B infection and also in some patients with chronic active hepatitis. With imperfect cell-mediated immune response, as may occur with therapeutic immunosuppression, ill health, or malnutrition or because of a genetic fault, the HBV may persist and induce liver damage varying from none to progressive destruction. It is conceivable that HBV may alter the antigenic determinants of infected cells, resulting in sensitization. This would evoke an autoimmune reaction directed by T lymphocytes, which release locally active mediators responsible for the damage of the hepatocyte membrane. It is also possible that the mediators in turn would recruit and activate other lymphocytes and macrophages, thus initiating a nonspecific cytotoxic reaction. This process would result in the cirrhosis of the liver. It should be emphasized that in a majority of the cases where a balanced immune response is elicited, the infected hepatocytes are destroyed, releasing the intracellular virus, which is neutralized by the specific antibodies; the complex is cleared by the reticuloendothelial system.

HEPATITIS B VIRUS AND HEPATOCELLULAR CARCINOMA

Hepatocellular carcinoma (HCC) is one of the most common cancers in humans. HCC is most prevalent in tropical Africa and the Far East and less common in Europe and North America. Immunologic and epidemiologic studies suggest a relatively high prevalence of chronic carriers of HB_sAg in areas of the world where HCC is most common, and a causal relationship between HBV and HCC. More recently, attempts have been made using hybridization techniques to understand the association between HBV and HCC. Preliminary experiments show the presence of HBV DNA sequences in the DNA from liver tissue of patients with HCC. More extensive studies are required to fully understand the relationship between HBV and HCC.

NON-A, NON-B VIRAL HEPATITIS

With the use of more sensitive serologic techniques in epidemiologic studies using hepatitis A and B specific diagnostic methods, it has become apparent that a previously unrecognized form of hepatitis exists in human populations. This new form of hepatitis is definitely unrelated to either hepatitis A or B. In 1974 in the United States it was observed that an agent other than hepatitis B was responsible for approximately 90 percent of the cases in a prospective serologic study of posttransfusion hepatitis. The incubation period was relatively long, and the clinical and epidemiologic characteristics of the infection were not similar to hepatitis A. Other studies provided evidence of the existence of an additional hepatitis virus or viruses transmitted by blood that had an incubation period intermediate between those of hepatitis A and B and that was serologically unrelated to HAV or HBV, cytomegalovirus, or Epstein-Barr virus.

From the evidence available to date it is clear that there is an additional form of viral hepatitis (non-A, non-B; NANB) that is clinically similar to but etiologically unrelated to either hepatitis A or B. Viruslike particles associated with NANB hepatitis in humans have been recovered from experimentally infected chimpanzees. These viruslike particles, 27 nm in diameter, were visualized by immunoelectron microscopy (IEM) in a homogenate from a liver-wedge biopsy from these animals. These virus particles were negative for HAV antigens by IEM and also negative for the HB_cAg of HBV. The accumulated serologic and biophysical evidence suggest that these viruslike particles may represent an etiologic agent of human NANB hepatitis. Needless to say, further identification and characterization of this virus is of utmost importance.

PASSIVE IMMUNIZATION AGAINST VIRAL HEPATITIS

Most studies regarding immunization against viral hepatitis have been conducted with hepatitis B. The availability of laboratory tests for HBV surface antibody has allowed the selection of plasma for the preparation of hepatitis B immunoglobulin (HBIG). There have been many clinical trials to evaluate the efficacy of passive immunization against HBV infection, but the results have been less than conclusive. A number of recent studies carried out to evaluate the protective effects of standard immune serum globulin (ISG) have shown a minimal protective effect against illness was achieved by ISG, whereas a greater reduction in illness by prophylaxis with HBIG has been achieved. Both ISG and HBIG have been used successfully to reduce the incidence of hepatitis B infection in several high risk situations; however, the protection is not complete. Primarily, the products are administered intramuscularly to persons intensively exposed to hepatitis B virus, such as those accidently inoculated with HB_sAg-positive blood or those having intimate contact with HB_sAg-positive patients. ISG has not been demonstrated to have any value in treatment of HB_sAg carriers. In the development and evaluation of passive immunization procedures with HBIG, one has to keep in mind that for every hepatitis B virus particle there may be over a million noninfectious particles. This could greatly diminish the effectiveness of the HBIG in neutralizing the Dane particles, hepatitis B virus.

ACTIVE IMMUNIZATION

No vaccine is currently available for viral hepatitis. The failure to propagate and repeatedly passage HAV or HBV in cultured cells has hampered the progress toward the development of a conventional vaccine. Attempts have been made to actively immunize children with heated (98°C for 1 minute) serum containing HBV; however, the results are inconclusive. Recently a formalin treated hepatitis B vaccine in the form of purified HB_sAg has been prepared from serum of asymptomatic human HB$_s$Ag carriers. This vaccine has been found to be protective against hepatitis B infection in high risk hemodialysis settings.

Attempts are also being made to prepare vaccine from the polypeptide of the 22 nm spherical particles of HB$_s$Ag. A number of these polypeptides are immunogenic in experimental animals and have been shown to stimulate group-specific antibodies. At present the major problem with polypeptide vaccine is the difficulty in obtaining large quantities of pure polypeptides. If this technical problem can be overcome, polypeptide preparations may become useful hepatitis B vaccines.

REFERENCES

Blumberg, B.S.: Polymorphisms of the serum proteins and the development of isoprecipitins in transfused patients. Bull. N.Y. Acad. Med. *40*: 377, 1964.

Evans, A.S.: Viral Infections of Humans. Plenum Medical Book Company, New York, 1976.

Joklik, W.K., Willett, H.P., and Amos, B., Eds.: Zinsser Microbiology. 17th Ed. Appleton-Century-Crofts, New York, 1980.

46

Poxviruses and Adenoviruses

Arlene R. Collins

POXVIRUSES

The *Poxviridae* family is composed of viruses that are the largest in size and structurally the most complex of all viruses. Members of this family cause diseases associated with skin lesions in a variety of animal species. Poxviruses of vertebrates are divided into six genera based on antigenic, morphological, and biologic relatedness. Except for the orthopoxviruses, members of each genus share a common host range. Two important human poxviruses are the variola virus, which is the cause of smallpox, and the vaccinia virus, which is a derivative of smallpox and is used to immunize against smallpox. Both of these viruses are in the *Orthopoxvirus* genus, which also includes cowpox, rabbit pox, monkey pox, and ectromelia viruses.

Other genera include *Avipoxvirus*, which infects birds as a natural host, *Capripoxvirus*, which infects ungulates, *Leporipoxvirus*, which infects rodents, *Entomopoxvirus*, which infects insects, and *Parapoxvirus*. These last agents are of diverse origin and are distinctly different in morphology from the other poxviruses.

Several poxviruses in the *Orthopoxvirus* genus occasionally are associated with human disease. Cowpox, the orf virus of sheep, the virus of milker's nodules (pseudocowpox), and the yaba monkey tumor virus occasionally infect persons who come in contact with diseased animals. In humans these viruses cause only benign lesions of the skin. There is some concern over the occasional occurrence of monkeypox infection in humans now that smallpox immunization has been discontinued. Human monkeypox infections may resemble smallpox cases clinically; however, transmission to secondary contacts has not been documented, and smallpox vaccination protects against monkeypox. Another human poxvirus of lesser importance is the molluscum contagiosum virus, which causes small papillomatous lesions of the skin.

Morphology

Poxviruses are large in size and have a complex structure. The best studied virus of this family is vaccinia virus (Fig. 46.1). Vaccinia is an oval or brick shaped particle 230 nm by 300 nm, containing a DNA genome of 150×10^6 daltons in the form of a linear double-stranded helical molecule. An unusual feature of the poxvirus DNA is the

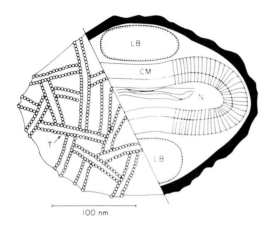

Fig. 46.1. Structure of vaccinia virus: N, nucleoid core containing viral DNA; CM, complex membrane of the core; LB, lateral bodies. The virion is enclosed in an outer membrane covered with tubules (T) composed of globular protein subunits. (With permission, Fenner, F., McAuslan, B.R., Mims, C.A., Sambrook, J., and White, D.O.: The Biology of Animal Viruses. 2nd Ed. Academic Press, New York, 1974.)

presence of a short polynucleotide at or near each terminus which covalently cross-links the strands. The DNA is found in the virion within a central biconcave core. Two oval structures called lateral bodies fit into concavities on either side of the core. The function of the lateral bodies has not been established. Surrounding these structures is the virion envelope. The outer surface of the envelope contains an array of parallel ridges composed of tubular proteins. The unique size, shape, and surface topography of the poxviruses make them readily identifiable when clinical material is examined under the electron microscope. Poxviruses contain eight or more enzymes in the core, including a DNA dependent RNA polymerase (virion transcriptase), which enables the cores to synthesize messenger RNA molecules. Thirty different virion proteins have been resolved by polyacrylamide gel electrophoresis. Although they possess an outer envelope, some poxvi-

ruses, including variola and vaccinia, are partially resistant to ether. These viruses are also stable under drying conditions and can survive for over a year in dried crusts at room temperature. They are inactivated by ultraviolet light (sunlight) or treatment with acid (pH 3) or formaldehyde.

Antigens

Poxviruses share many antigens in common; and thus there is a considerable degree of cross reactivity among the various members. One antigen in particular, the nucleoprotein (NP) antigen, is common to all poxviruses. Approximately 20 antigens have been observed by immunoprecipitation. Variola and vaccinia viruses are very similar antigenically, differing by only one antigen. During infection, poxviruses also produce several soluble (virion-unassociated) antigens and a soluble hemagglutinin. A heat-labile (L) antigen (destroyed at 60°C) and a heat-stable (S) antigen (stable at 100°C) are liberated into the supernatant fluid of infected cell cultures. Antibody to various poxvirus antigens may be demonstrated by immunodiffusion, neutralization, hemagglutination inhibition, and complement fixation tests. The immunodiffusion test is also used with antiviral serum to show the presence of antigens in tissue or fluid material collected from skin lesions.

Cultivation

Vaccinia and variola viruses grow well in many different types of cultured cells, including several human and monkey cell lines. Another convenient host is the chicken embryo. Inoculation of virus onto the chorioallantoic membrane of the chicken embryo leads to the development of characteristic dense white lesions called pocks. The pock morphology is a characteristic property that can be used to distinguish variola from vaccinia and monkeypox. The cytoplasmic sites of viral biosynthesis are visible microscopically in fixed and stained cells as eosinophilic inclusion bodies, termed *Guarnieri bodies.*

Multiplication

Poxviruses multiply exclusively in the cytoplasm of infected cells. After the initial stages of adsorption and penetration a two-stage uncoating process takes place. The first stage is accomplished by host enzymes and results in liberation of the cores. The second stage involves disruption of the cores and requires synthesis of virion encoded enzymes. When the DNA is still in the core a DNA-dependent RNA polymerase present in the core transcribes a segment of the genome. The transcript is processed within the core, and messenger RNA molecules are released that code for several proteins, including a protease that completes the uncoating process. Synthesis of specific enzymes for DNA replication and some structural proteins preceeds viral DNA replication. Biosynthesis of viral DNA, virus-directed messenger RNA and proteins, and virion assembly take place in cytoplasmic sites called *factories.* Maturation involves the virus directed synthesis of viral membranes within which elements of a DNA core condense to form mature particles. Morphogenesis requires the posttranslational cleavage of three major viral proteins as well as glycosylation and phosphorylation of other virion proteins.

Clinical Course

The disease smallpox is initiated as the variola virus enters the body through the respiratory tract and undergoes limited multiplication in the respiratory mucosa. During the next 10 to 12 days the virus spreads via the lymphatics and blood and multiplies in internal organs. A secondary viremia then occurs after which the virus localizes in the skin and mucous membranes of the mouth and upper respiratory tract. The skin lesions evolve through characteristic stages from macule and papule to vesicle and then to pustule. The pustule dries with a thick crust and healing is incomplete, leaving a permanent scar. Secondary bacterial infection may occur.

Smallpox occurs in two forms that may be distinguished by the severity of the skin rash and the fatality rate. *Variola major* is the more severe form and has a fatality rate as high as 25 percent. *Variola minor* or *alastrim* is associated with less extensive skin lesions and has a fatality rate less than 1 percent. There are no apparent biologic or immunologic differences between the viruses causing the two forms of smallpox. Immunity following infection persists for years.

Laboratory Diagnosis

The need for diagnosis of a case of smallpox has become extremely remote. However, in the event of a laboratory accident or a biologic warfare threat there is need for rapid identification of the virus. The use of the electron microscope for examination of vesicle fluid allows rapid identification based on morphology. This procedure should be combined with immunodiffusion using known positive antisera to confirm the electron microscopic observations.

There may be a need, particularly in cases of atypical manifestations, for identification of vaccinia virus. The same procedures as outlined above for variola may be used. In addition, isolation from vesicle fluid may be attempted using primary rhesus monkey kidney cells or human fibroblast cells or by inoculation onto the chorioallantoic membrane of the developing chicken embryo. Serologic diagnosis may be performed by complement fixation, neutralization, or hemagglutination inhibition tests.

Epidemiology

Smallpox is a very serious human disease with a high fatality rate. It was endemic in a number of geographic areas until the past decade. In the recent past smallpox was a serious threat not only in those endemic areas but, by importation of cases, in other parts of the world. However, several features of the disease made it amenable to eradication. First, smallpox is a strictly human disease. It may be spread by direct interpersonal contact or indirectly by infected bed linens or clothes. Airborne spread has also been documented. In 1978 a case of laboratory-associated smallpox occurred in England in which airborne transmission of the virus between floors of a building via the ventilating system was implicated. Second, eradication was possible because there is no known animal reservoir of smallpox. Third, a carrier state does not exist in this disease. Because of these epidemiologic features the World Health Organization in 1967 initiated a global program for the eradication of smallpox. At that time there were probably 10 to 15 million cases per year of smallpox in the world. The eradication campaign involved mass vaccination in countries where smallpox was endemic. In October 1977 the success of the campaign was heralded by the report of the last natural case of smallpox. At the end of a 2-year waiting period, during which an extensive search for cases continued, the last focus of smallpox was certified as free of the disease. The only remaining threat of disease may be in association with the limited number of laboratories that are keeping frozen stocks of variola virus or in the dreadful event of utilization of smallpox as an agent of biologic warfare.

With the success of the eradication program, vaccination is no longer essential. In the event of an unforseen future crisis vaccinia virus anti-smallpox vaccine, which is stable indefinitely in lyophilized form, is being stockpiled by the World Health Organization. Currently, smallpox vaccination may still be required for travelers to developing countries of Asia and Africa. It is anticipated that this requirement will be dropped in the future.

Prevention

Smallpox was the first disease for which prophylaxis by active immunization was widely practiced. Protection against smallpox by live cowpox virus as a vaccine was introduced by Edward Jenner in 1796. The vaccinia virus used today is distinctly different from cowpox and is believed to be an attenuated strain of smallpox that had inadvertently replaced Jenner's original strain. The modern vaccine for use in man contains live attenuated vaccinia virus prepared from vesicular lesions produced in the skin of calves or in the choriallantoic membrane of the chicken embryo. The vaccine may be kept in lyophilized form for long periods. It is administered intradermally into the abraded skin. Successful vaccination results in the formation of a localized lesion or pock.

Three distinguishable responses to vaccination may occur: primary, major, and equivocal. The primary response occurs in individuals with no effective immunity. A papule develops on the fourth day and evolves through the characteristic stages from macule to scab. The entire sequence of evolution may take 3 to 4 weeks and leaves a permanent scar. The major response is seen in individuals with some residual immunity. The severity of the lesion is less pronounced than is seen in the primary response, and the progression of the lesion through its characteristic stages is more rapid, the entire sequence being completed in 7 to 9 days. The equivocal response is usually seen in 8 to 24 hours and is characterized by a red papule which does not progress beyond the vesicle stage. This equivocal reaction is difficult to interpret and may be indicative of a high level of immunity. It is in part a delayed hypersensitivity response to viral proteins. It is considered to indicate adequate immunity only if the vaccine is known to contain fully infectious virus.

Failure to elicit a dermal response to smallpox vaccination is occasionally seen. This usually indicates an inadequate vaccine or improper administration.

Complications of Smallpox Vaccination. Vaccination against smallpox, while usually a safe procedure, may have serious complications affecting the skin or the central nervous system. Eczema vaccinatum is a complication occasionally seen in infants and arises from secondary implantation of virus on eczematous skin. Generalized vaccinia is a progressive and often fatal complication resulting from systemic spread of the virus. It occurs in individuals who are agammaglobulinemic. Progressive vaccinia or vaccinia gangrenosa is a complication in which progressive spread of virus from the initial site of inoculation occurs and in which there is extensive necrosis; this manifestation is seen in individuals with defective cell-mediated immunity. Postvaccinial encephalitis is a central nervous system complication thought to be a form of allergic encephalopathy. Serious residual mental deficiency often follows postvaccinial encephalitis.

The United States Public Health Service has recognized that the risk of contracting smallpox no longer warrants the risks associated with vaccine complications. Statistics indicate that there was one serious complication for every 1000 vaccinations and one death for every million vaccinations. At present, vaccination for smallpox is no longer recommended and is administered only to satisfy requirements for travelers to countries where smallpox was endemic.

ADENOVIRUSES

The adenoviruses are a group of DNA viruses commonly considered among the viral respiratory pathogens in humans. Respiratory infections with adenoviruses are characterized by development of prolonged latency of the virus in tonsillar and adenoidal tissue. The adenoviruses were first described in the early 1950s by Rowe and colleagues, who recovered these viruses from cultures of human adenoids that had undergone cytopathic changes. At about the same time Hilleman and Werner isolated adenoviruses from U.S. Army recruits with acute respiratory disease. The agents were called adenoviruses because of their original isolation from adenoidal tissue.

Adenoviruses are widespread in nature, infecting many mammalian and avian species. All mammalian members possess a common family antigen. Individual adenoviruses are distinguished by several type-specific antigens. There are 33 serotypes that have been isolated from humans. Adenoviruses induce latent infections in tonsils, adenoids, and other lymphoid tissue. They were the first group of human viruses shown to be oncogenic in lower animals under laboratory conditions, and they have served as models for tumorigenesis.

Morphology

Adenoviruses are nonenveloped icosahedral viruses 70 to 90 nm in diameter and containing a double-stranded DNA genome of 20 to 25 million daltons. The capsid is composed of 252 capsomers; 240 capsomers have six sides and are designated *hexons*, and 12 capsomers are five-sided structures called *pentons* located on the vertices of the icosahedron. The pentons are structurally complex, consisting of a base embedded in the capsid and a fiber projecting from it. The penton fiber is the site at which the virus attaches to the host cell.

Antigens

All mammalian adenoviruses possess a common group-specific antigen associated with the hexons and demonstrated by the complement fixation test. Type-specific antigens are associated with the penton fiber and a type-specific determinant of the hexons. Type-specific antigens can be demonstrated by hemagglutination inhibition, immunodiffusion, and neutralization tests. Immunity to reinfection is type specific. Serologic tests for measurement of antibody in patient's sera are based usually on demonstration of type-specific antibodies.

Agglutination of erythrocytes by adenoviruses is complex and varied. Individual serotypes agglutinate monkey or rat erythrocytes to varying degrees. A toxin activity for cultured cells is associated with the penton base.

Cultivation

Some serotypes of adenoviruses grow well in cell cultures of human origin, whereas others are isolated with difficulty. Adenovirus growth causes distinct cytopathic effects consisting of marked rounding and aggregation of infected cells into grapelike clusters. Viral synthesis takes place in the cytoplasm and nucleus. Infected cells show prominent nuclear inclusions. The details of adenovirus replication are discussed in Chapter 39.

Clinical Manifestations

Adenoviruses show considerable variability in the diseases they produce. They are frequently isolated from healthy individuals, but certain types are associated with defined illness. Most adenoviruses are associated with respiratory infections. Infections of the gastrointestinal tract also seem to occur, with virus being demonstrable in the feces for prolonged periods. Primary infection in young children usually manifests as acute febrile pharyngitis. This may be accompanied by conjuctivitis, giving rise to the syndrome pharyngoconjunctival fever. The conjunctivitis is generally follicular in nature without corneal involvement. The same symptoms can also occur in adults. Type 3 is most commonly involved, but occasionally types 7 and 14 are implicated. Among infants and young children hospitalized with acute respiratory disease 8 percent of pneumonia cases and 5 percent of bronchitis cases have been associated with adenoviruses.

Adenoviruses types 4 and 7 are the major cause of acute respiratory tract infections in military recruits. Rhinitis, laryngitis, and conjunctivitis are the most common symptoms. Adenovirus type 8 is generally associated with epidemic keratoconjunctivitis, which is a severe ocular infection initiating as conjunctivitis but later involving infiltration of the cornea. Severe infections may occur in adults in association with eye irritation and may result in impairment of vision. Adenoviruses are also associated with urinary tract infections. Acute hemorrhagic cystitis is a self-limiting disease of some significance in boys 6 to 15 years of age; it is characterized by polyuria, dysuria, and hematuria. Adenovirus type 11 was recovered from urine in 70 percent of patients with acute hemorrhagic cystitis in Japan.

Laboratory Diagnosis

Adenoviruses are isolated in cell cultures of human origin, in which they produce a characteristic cytopathic effect described as grapelike clusters of infected cells. Serologic diagnosis of viral infection is generally performed by testing acute and convalescent patient's serum samples for type-specific antibody by the neutralization test or by demonstration of group-specific antibody by complement fixation. A fourfold rise in serum antibody titer in the convalescent serum is indicative of current infection. The complement fixation procedure is applicable to seroepidemiologic studies because only a single antigenic reagent is required in this situation.

Epidemiology

The contribution of adenoviruses to febrile illness is 7 to 8 percent in the general population and 10 to 11 percent in children. Most infections are asymptomatic. Infections tend to be endemic or to occur as community outbreaks with a single serotype, and they seem to be favored by close living conditions such as military camps and dormitories. The fecal–oral route is the major mode of transmission of certain serotypes. Other serotypes are spread by respiratory transmission.

In military recruits epidemics of respiratory infections due to adenoviruses tend to occur during winter and early spring. Adenoviral conjunctivitis and pharyngitis usually occur during the summer months and are often associated with contaminated swimming pools or small lakes. Keratoconjuctivitis may be seen as outbreaks in industry in connection with eye irritants or as an iatrogenic disease spread by ophthalmic instrumentation.

Prevention

Vaccination of military recruits has been practiced since 1971. The vaccine is an oral preparation containing attenuated adenovirus types 4 and 7. It is given as a gelatin capsule, and it produces a mild intestinal infection accompanied by production of protective neutralizing antibodies in the circulation.

REFERENCES

Baxby, D.: Identification and interrelationships of the variola/vaccinia subgroup of poxviruses. Prog. Med. Virol. *19*: 215, 1975.

Fenner, F.: The eradication of smallpox. Prog. Med. Virol. *223*: 1, 1977.

Jackson, G.G. and Muldoon, R.L.: Viruses causing common respiratory infection in man. IV. Reoviruses and adenoviruses. J. Infect. Dis. *128*: 811, 1973.

Kurstak, E. and Kurstak, C.: Comparative Diagnosis of Viral Diseases. 1st Ed. Vol. 1, Academic Press, New York, 1977.

Moss, B.: Reproduction of Poxvirus. In Fraenkel-Conrat, H. and Wagner, R.R., Eds.: Comprehensive Virology. Vol. 3. Plenum Press, New York, 1975.

Smith, A.S.: Viral Infections in Humans. 1st Ed. Plenum, New York, 1976.

Herpesviruses

Thomas D. Flanagan

Herpesviruses are a group of ubiquitous agents that infect a variety of vertebrate species. They bear structural and compositional resemblance to one another yet display well ordered host preferences and serologic distinctions (Fig. 47.1). An important characteristic of many herpesviruses is the ability to enter into a latent state in the infected host. After primary infection of the individual, during which there is frank evidence of viral replication and host immune response, the virus becomes sequestered. This latency persists, and the infection is in many cases manifested by recrudescence of active replication at later times. While the exact mechanisms by which latency is maintained are presently unknown, the analogy with bacterial lysogeny appears likely.

There are five herpesviruses that frequently infect humans: herpes simplex virus type 1, (HSV-1), herpes simplex virus type 2 (HSV-2), varicella-zoster virus (VZV), human cytomegalovirus (CMV), and Epstein-Barr virus (EBV). In addition, humans can acquire infection with a number of herpesviruses of other primates.

HERPES SIMPLEX VIRUS

HSV-1 and HSV-2 are serologically related and the best characterized variants of human herpesviruses. They cause vesicular eruptions in the skin and mucous membranes as well as other clinical forms of disease.

Morphology and Composition

HSV-1 and HSV-2 are large DNA-containing viruses. The virions are indistinguishable. They have envelopes, and their average diameter is about 180 nm. The nucleocapsids are icosahedral in shape and are constructed of 160 hollow pentagonal capsomers. The genome is a linear double-stranded molecule of DNA with a molecular mass of about 100×10^6 daltons. The genome therefore can code for approximately 50 polypeptides. There is about 50 percent homology between HSV-1 and HSV-2 DNA. The DNA molecules of the two viruses have a unique structure. They consist of two regions of unique sequence DNA bracketed by repeated sequences. Two regions of repeated sequences are

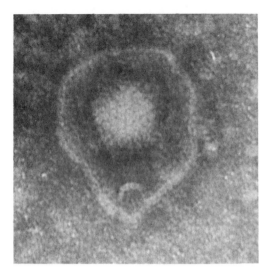

Fig. 47.1. Herpes simplex virus type 1 from vesicular fluid. Negative staining (× 30,000). (Electron photomicrograph courtesy of Dr. M.R. Talty.)

found near the ends of the molecules, with additional inverted repeat sequences separated from the termini by the segments of unique-sequence DNA. This structure allows rearrangement of the unique sequences relative to one another. By such rearrangement four isomeric forms of the genome are generated.

Infectious DNA can be prepared from virions. The virions are complex, revealing several layers on electron microscopic examination. Analysis of the proteins in the virions indicates 23 or 24 different entities, of which four are glycoproteins.

Virus Replication

The HSV envelope attaches to the surface of the cell and fuses with the plasma membrane. This action frees the nucleocapsid of the virus in the cytoplasm of the cell. The core of the virus migrates to the nuclear compartment and from that site directs viral replication. The usual separation of viral protein synthesis into early and late stages with the requirement for viral DNA synthesis to enter late synthesis does not occur

in herpesvirus replication. However, there is a well ordered sequence of viral protein synthesis, giving rise to products classified as α, β, and γ. The α product induces the synthesis of β, which in turn inhibits the synthesis of α and induces γ. The γ product inhibits the synthesis of β. Initiation of the sequence takes place as a function of host factors. Viral DNA synthesis takes place in the nucleus and requires virus-encoded proteins. Assembly of progeny virions begins in the nucleoplasm. Maturation occurs by the budding of the capsid through the inner lamella of the nuclear membrane. This step imparts the envelope to the virion. Further budding events may occur through cytoplasmic membranes or the plasma membrane of the cell. Viral glycoproteins are found in all membranes of the infected cell.

The replication cycle is quite rapid — the first progeny are detected at 6 hours — and continues a variable length of time. Depending on the particular cell system, as many as 10^5 particles may be released from an infected cell. Many of these particles will be noninfectious, however.

The herpesvirus-infected cell dies as a result of infection. The process is accompanied by characteristic changes. The development of an intranuclear inclusion is a hallmark of HSV infection; some strains also cause formation of polykaryons.

Infections Caused by HSV-1

HSV-1 is a ubiquitous human virus. More than 80 percent of all adults have antibodies against this agent. Primary infection occurs early, usually in the first 18 months of life. Expression of primary infection may range from clinically inapparent to serious systemic disease. However, most primary infections are benign, with 10 to 15 percent presenting as gingivostomatitis. The resolution of primary HSV-1 infection is accompanied by the appearance of humoral antibodies and demonstrable cell-mediated immunity. The virus apparently is not completely removed from the body but enters into a latent state. One site at which the virus is sequestered is the trigeminal nerve ganglion. Recrudescent lesion formation occurs later in life in a significant proportion of people. The episodes of recrudescence are variable in number but can average two or three per year. The recrudescent disease is characterized by the eruption of vesicles ("cold sores") in the same area as previously affected. The areas most frequently involved are the mucocutaneous junctions of the lip and the nose. Exacerbations occur in the presence of demonstrable serum antibody and are associated with a variety of physical, pathologic, and physiologic stimuli, such as sunlight, fever, and menstruation.

Infections Caused by HSV-2

HSV-2 is associated with genital infections. Primary infection is usually acquired at the onset of sexual activity. The infection is characterized by vesicular lesions on the mucosa or skin of the genitalia. Anal lesions also are frequently seen. As in the case of HSV-1, the virus can be sequestered in a latent state, and recurring disease can take place. The sites of viral latency are sacral nerve ganglia, and the lesions usually appear on mucosal or skin surfaces of the genitalia or perineum.

The immune response to HSV-2 is similar to that to HSV-1, but most persons infected with HSV-2 have had previous experience with HSV-1 virus. There is considerable antigenic crossreactivity between the two serotypes; nonetheless, infection can be readily acquired in spite of antibody.

Severe Infections With HSV-1 and HSV-2

Usual infections with herpes simplex have been described above, but there are a number of special situations in which infections with these agents occur with increased frequency or enhanced severity.

Encephalitis is the most severe of HSV infections. It can be caused by either type 1 or type 2. HSV-2 is the usual cause when the infection occurs in the newborn. The infection is usually acquired at birth from the mother, who sheds virus into the genital tract. In older children and in adults HSV-1 is the more frequent cause of encephalitis. The infection is focal in nature, often in the temporal lobe of the brain. The fatality rate of untreated herpes encephalitis is greater than 70 percent. Interestingly, in adults HSV-2 causes aseptic meningitis more frequently than encephalitis, while HSV-1 is rarely associated with meningitis. HSV also causes infection of the eye. Both primary and recurrent disease can involve the cornea and produce keratitis. This condition can lead to scarring and formation of opaque plaques, impairing vision.

Certain states and conditions predisposing to HSV infections have been recognized. Newborn infants are particularly vulnerable, often manifesting severe generalized infection as well as encephalitis. Malnutrition contributes to the severity of infection, particularly in children. HSV readily infects eczematous skin, causing eczema herpeticum, which is characterized by vesicular eruptions and fever. Burned skin is similarly vulnerable to infection with HSV.

Increased exposure to the viruses results in a particular pattern of infection among persons with certain occupations. Dentists and physicians are likely to acquire infection of the hands during examination of the oral cavity or genitals of patients. The infection often occurs as a vesicular eruption on the finger near the nail bed. High school and college wrestlers acquire infection through abraded skin; the condition is called herpes gladiatorum. Prostitutes have a high incidence of HSV-2 infection, and some studies have found antibodies to HSV-2 in more than 95 percent of prostitutes.

Diagnosis, Treatment, and Control

Diagnosis of herpes simplex infections can be accomplished by isolation of the agents from clinical specimens. The virus is present in the vesicular fluid and is readily grown out in a variety of cell cultures. Cytopathic effects (CPE) of the herpesviruses are quite characteristic, and usually observation of CPE is sufficient to give a presumptive diagnosis. Confirmation and serotype identification are carried out by serologic tests using type-specific antisera. Immunofluorescence techniques are becoming the most frequently used methods.

Rapid diagnosis can be obtained by the demonstration of viral antigens in exfoliated cells or biopsies by immunofluorescence. This technique is of great importance in the early diagnosis of encephalitis, since specific therapy is available.

Serologic diagnosis of herpes simplex infections is useful only in diagnosis of primary infections in children. Recrudescent infections or acquired infections in serologically positive individuals do not always result in detectable anamnestic responses.

Treatment of serious infections with herpes simplex viruses is possible by employing iododeoxyuridine (IUdR) or adenine arabinoside (ara-A). Herpes keratitis has been treated by topical application of IUdR. The drug has demonstrated efficacy, but drug resistance is frequently encountered. Ara-A has been shown to be of significant benefit when employed in cases of herpes encephalitis. The earlier after onset the drug is used, the better is the prognosis. Acyclovir [9-(2-hydroxyethoxymethyl) guanine], an acyclic substituted nucleoside, has potent antiherpesvirus activity. *In vitro* studies have demonstrated 10- to 100-fold greater activity than ara-A. Clinical tests of the drug have demonstrated its efficacy; however, extensive experience with the drug has not yet accumulated.

Vaccination against herpes simplex viruses is presently a controversial topic. There is evidence that HSV DNA can transform cells, and there is an epidemiologic association between HSV-2 infection and carcinoma *in situ* of the cervix uteri. Any vaccine to be developed will probably be composed of antigenic subunits of the viruses and devoid of DNA.

VARICELLA-ZOSTER

The causative agent of varicella or chicken pox is VZV. The primary infection with this agent usually occurs in children and manifests as a generalized infection with crops of vesicular lesions on the skin and mucosa. The recrudescent disease is known as zoster or shingles and is characterized by painful vesicular eruptions on the skin. Lesions are confined to areas innervated by particular spinal or cranial nerves. The disease usually occurs in adults.

Morphology and Composition

VZV is a typical herpesvirus with an enveloped virion and icosahedral capsid. The virus appears to be similar to other members of the group in composition. The DNA genome is somewhat smaller than that of HSV, having a mass of 80×10^6 daltons. It does not have any homology with the other herpesviruses.

Virus Replication

The details of VZV replication have not been elaborated as yet. The virus grows in a limited number of cell lines and does not replicate with great efficiency in many of them. Like other herpesviruses, the nucleus of the infected cell is the site of viral DNA synthesis and assembly of the virions. Release of viral progeny is not efficient in most cell cultures; however, in the infected child, high titers of infectious virus are found in vesicular fluids and secretions of the oropharynx.

Infected cells develop a typical intranuclear inclusion made up of viral capsid materials. These are demonstrable in cells from lesions as well as from infected cell cultures.

Infections with VZV

Primary infection with VZV results in the disease chicken pox. This is a benign, self-limiting disease in children. The typical case in a normal child is initiated by acquisition of the virus by airborne droplets. The virus implants in the respiratory tract and multiplies locally and in regional lymph nodes. This is followed by a period of viremia, wherein the virus disseminates to skin and various internal organs. Virus replication ensues and fever occurs, signaling the onset of the rash. The typical incubation period is 14 to 16 days.

The exanthem of varicella consists of successive crops of rapidly evolving lesions on the skin and mucous membranes. Lesions first manifest as macules 2 to 4 mm in diameter that quickly develop into vesicles, deflate, and are covered with crusts. The evolution of the lesion takes place over 6 to 8 hours. The period of the exanthem is about 5 to 6 days, with the crusted lesions disappearing by the tenth day. There is fever throughout the time when new lesions are appearing, but it resolves about the sixth day.

Primary VZV infection is more severe in adults. The incubation period is longer, the prodromal stage more protracted, and the fever higher than in children. Significant complications, including diffuse pneumonitis and encephalitis, occur more frequently.

Children and adults with leukemia and patients on immunosuppressive or corticosteroid therapy are at greater risk of severe infections with VZV. The normal immune response to infection consists of antibodies and CMI. The role of CMI in recovery appears to be critical. Patients with compromised cellular responses suffer severe and prolonged infections.

The recurrent infection with VZV is zoster or shingles. The disease occurs in older persons with increasing frequency through the sixth decade of life. It is characterized by vesicular eruptions of the skin in areas innervated by a single dorsal root sensory ganglion. The eruption is preceded by localized pain at the site of eruption, which continues during the active stage and may persist long after resolution of the lesions. The clinical course of zoster is 2 to 4 weeks. There is usually only one episode of recurrence. The disease is frequently associated with trauma, including surgical trauma, certain therapies, cancer, and tuberculosis. Dissemination may occur in patients receiving immunosuppressive therapy.

Diagnosis, Treatment, and Control

The diagnosis of varicella is made on the basis of clinical evaluation. Diagnosis of rare cases presenting with unusual symptoms may be aided by isolation of the virus or serologic tests. The usual procedure is the complement fixation test. A fourfold rise in antibody titer is significant. The test is useful in primary infections and in zoster. Isolation of the agent is rarely attempted but can be done. Methods of direct demonstration of viral antigens in vesicular cells by immunofluorescence or of virions by electron microscopy are becoming widely available for rapid diagnosis of VZV infections.

Treatment of severe VZV infections can be by administration of varicella immune globulin or with ara-A. The efficacy of these agents is dependent upon when treatment is instituted and upon the immune competence of the patient. Human α interferon preparations have been used to treat zoster patients; studies of this therapeutic modality have demonstrated reduction of the duration of lesions, more rapid crusting, and more rapid viral clearance.

Vaccination against VZV infection is currently in development. Experimental live virus vaccines have been reported to be effective in inducing protection in normal and — significantly — in immunocompromised children. Passive immunization of high risk children who have been exposed to the virus can be carried out using varicella immune globulin.

CYTOMEGALOVIRUS

The cytomegaloviruses are a group of herpesviruses that share common biologic properties. They infect animals of many species and cause a variety of diseases. In general, they are highly species restricted, manifest latency, and cause the production of pathognomonic cytomegalic inclusion bodies. Human cytomegalovirus (CMV) has been implicated in a number of distinct syndromes of clinical significance.

Morphology and Composition

The virion of CMV is similar to other herpes virions. It has an envelope and an icosahedral capsid with 160 hollow pentagonal capsomers. The double-stranded DNA genome is distinctly larger than the genome of other herpesviruses, having a mass of 150×10^6 daltons. The number of virion polypeptides is about the same as that of HSV, however. There is evidence that there are serologically distinguishable strains of CMV.

Virus Replication

The replicative cycle of CMV is longer than that of other herpesviruses. The biochemical events in the cycle seem to be similar to those of other herpesviruses; however, there is apparently a more specific requirement for host cell functions for CMV replication. Progeny virions are assembled in the nucleus of CMV-infected cells, and they mature by budding through the nuclear membrane. CMV replication is rather inefficient in that noninfectious particles are produced in great excess compared to infectious particles. Nuclear inclusions are the hallmark of CMV-infected cells. These inclusions are aggregates of virions and other products of viral DNA and protein synthesis. Their occurrence in large exfoliated cells found in urine of patients with CMV infection gave rise to the name *cytomegalic inclusion disease.*

Infections With CMV

CMV is a common virus in human populations. More than 80 percent of older adults (>35 years) have antibody to the viruses. Infections are usually benign and are frequently inapparent. However, there are a number of well defined and clinically significant syndromes attributed to CMV infections.

Congenital infection of fetuses leads to cytomegalic inclusion disease (CID). This syndrome manifests in a number of ways. Severe cases are characterized by hepatosplenomegaly, jaundice, hepatitis, microencephaly, and petechiae. Fatality is high in severely infected infants. Survivors suffer from a variety of neurologic and other deficits. CMV has been cited as an important cause of mental retardation; up to 40 percent of CID infants are retarded in later life. It is also an important cause of premature delivery. Premature infants are a significant source of infection. The virus is shed for prolonged periods in the oropharynx and the urine of infected infants.

Postnatally acquired infections of infants can show some of the symptoms of CID; neurologic involvement leading to residual damage does not usually occur. Infections of older children and adults are usually nondescript; however, a mononucleosislike syndrome does occur in a number of cases, presenting as pharyngitis, lymphadenopathy, low grade fever, and malaise. There is a lymphocytosis, but fewer atypical cells are seen than in disease caused by EBV (see below). Most significantly, there are no Paul-Bunnell antibodies formed. The virus can be acquired by airborne droplet and by direct contact, including sexual contact. There are data that strongly suggest that venereal transmission is a major epidemiologic element in CMV infection. Other important sources of CMV infection are blood transfusions and tissue transplants. Patients receiving large volumes of blood, as in cardiac surgery, may develop a mononucleosis-like syndrome as a result of acquiring the virus from donors. Recipients of other tissues, such as kidney, also have shown increased frequency of these CMV infections. The use of donors who are seronegative for CMV has drastically reduced the occurrence of this disease. The transplantation of bone marrow cells in infants with severe combined immunodeficiencies requires CMV-negative donors because these recipients are particularly vulnerable to the virus.

There is also evidence that CMV can be reactivated from a latent state. Patients receiving immunosuppressive therapy can develop symptoms of infection associated with CMV shedding. Likewise, increased CMV shedding in cervical secretions of pregnant women has been observed. This virus excretion may or may not be associated with evidence of disease.

Diagnosis, Treatment, and Control

CMV can be isolated from clinical specimens — particularly urine — in human diploid fibroblasts, but the methods are slow and expensive. Direct demonstration of viral antigen in exfoliated cells by immunofluorescence is a promising technique hampered presently by a lack of high quality antisera. Somewhat better results have been obtained with an anticomplement immunofluorescence test. Electron micro-

scopy can also be used in certain cases. Serologic diagnosis is useful in infections of adults. A fourfold increase in complement-fixing antibody titer is regarded as significant. Diagnosis of congenital infections requires isolation of the agent, demonstration of virus antigen in cells or virions in secretions, or the presence of IgM antibody to CMV in the serum.

Clinical trials with ara-A have shown reduction of virus shedding in patients with severe disseminated CMV infections. Overall efficacy of ara-A remains to be demonstrated.

CMV has been shown to transform cells. This oncogenic potential is a factor in the development of a vaccine. As with HSV, vaccines to be developed will probably be subunit vaccines.

EPSTEIN-BARR VIRUS

Epstein-Barr virus (EBV) is the latest of the human herpesviruses to be characterized. It was discovered fortuitously by studies on cells derived from a lymphoma of African children, Burkitt's lymphoma (BL). Electron microscopic studies on lymphoid cell lines from these tumors revealed the presence of a herpesvirus. (The relationship of the virus to BL is discussed in Chapter 48.) Serologic investigations on the antigen-containing cells suggested that the virus was also associated with infectious mononucleosis (IM). A number of epidemiologic studies have since confirmed an etiologic role for EBV in this disease.

Morphology and Virus Replication

EBV is structurally similar to other herpes viruses.

Studies on the replication of EBV have been hampered by lack of readily available host cells. The virus has a highly restricted cytotropism. It apparently can infect only lymphoid cells of the B cell variety. This restriction is dependent on the presence of specific receptors for the virus. Several stages of viral replication have been established chiefly by studying the evolution of virus-encoded antigens in infected lymphoid cell lines. The first antigen detected is a nuclear antigen (EBNA). This entity is compatible with continued cell viability and proliferation. Indeed, it is the hallmark of lymphoid cells transformed by EBV into continuously replicating cell lines. Synthesis of early antigen (EA) signals entry into a productive stage of viral replication. Cells in which EA occurs do not survive whether or not later stages of viral replication ensue. Production of viral capsid antigen (VCA) follows EA synthesis. This stage immediately precedes appearance of virion-like structures in the infected cell. The detection of infectious virus produced by cells in culture is a rare event even when there is morphological evidence of virion production. There are a few established cell lines that routinely produce cell-free infectious virus. Cells that enter into stages of viral production later than the EBNA stage die and undergo lysis. In any culture of EBV-infected cells the proportion of cells producing viral antigens (other than EBNA) or virions is always very low, usually 0.5 to 5 percent.

Infections With EBV

The most frequently recognized expression of EBV infection is infectious mononucleosis (IM), which is defined by a triad of findings. Clinically, the patient manifests low grade fever, lymphadenopathy, pharyngitis, and malaise. Other manifestations occur in more severe cases; these may include rash and hepatitis. The second significant finding is an absolute lymphocytosis, with more than 15 percent of lymphocytes appearing atypical. Finally, the patient develops Paul-Bunnell (PB) anti-

bodies in the serum. These antibodies react with antigenic determinants found on the surface of erythrocytes of sheep and of certain other animal species. They belong to a class of antibodies that react with antigens distributed widely in nature. These antibodies, referred to as heterophile antibodies, are discussed in Chapter 8.

The virus is present in saliva of infected persons. It is acquired directly (hence the name "kissing disease"). The clinical course of IM is characterized by an insidious onset, a variable acute phase, variable severity of symptoms and duration, and a prolonged convalescent phase. The period of lymhocytosis occurs frequently very early in the acute phase; PB antibodies are usually detected later in the acute phase and may persist through convalescence. The nature of the immune stimulus for the production of these antibodies is not known; however, it has been established that they do not react with EBV itself. An immune response is made to the various viral antigens. Anti-VCA antibodies are usually present in the acute phase of infection and persist throughout life. Anti-EA antibodies are transient, while anti-EBNA antibodies appear several months after infection and persist. EBV infection of younger children frequently does not take the course of IM but appears in a more protean form. The occurrence of PB antibodies in childhood infection is controversial. Newer, more sensitive methods for detecting these antibodies are yielding data that suggest the response also occurs in children while previously it was held that the antibodies were absent in childhood infections. Other bizarre antibodies may also be found transiently in the serum of IM patients. These include antinuclear antibodies, Wassermann antibodies, antibodies to blood group antigen i, antimuscle antibodies, rheumatoid factor, and antibodies that react with erythrocytes modified by treatment with Newcastle disease virus.

Diagnosis, Treatment, and Control

Diagnosis of IM depends upon demonstration of PB antibodies in serum from a patient with the clinical and hematologic signs of the disease. Anti-VCA antibodies are invariably present during the acute phase; therefore only the demonstration that IgM antibodies of this specificity are present is of diagnostic value. Treatment of the infection is palliative, and at present there is no vaccine. The potential role of EBV in malignant disease such as BL and nasopharyngeal carcinoma places constraints on the development of vaccines.

REFERENCES

Brock, C. and King, D.W.: Herpes Virus: Epidemiology, Molecular Events, Oncogenicity and Therapy. Stratton, New York, 1975.

Juel-Jensen, B.E. and MacCallum, F.O.: Herpes Simplex, Varicella and Zoster. Lippincott, Philadelphia, 1972.

Kaplan, A.S.: The Herpesviruses. Academic Press, New York, 1973.

48

Oncogenic Viruses

*Thomas D. Flanagan and
Kenneth F. Manly*

The origins of tumor virology reach back to the beginning of this century. In 1908 Ellerman and Bang reported that the erythromyeloblastic form of chicken leukemia could be transmitted by filtered extracts of leukemia cells, but the neoplastic nature of the disease was not recognized at the time. The first link between viruses and cancer was subsequently established when Peyton Rous reported in 1911 that a chicken sarcoma could be transmitted by cell-free filtrates of tumor extracts. Twenty years passed before additional evidence for tumor viruses was reported. Between 1933 and 1950 several additional virally induced tumors were described, including rabbit papilloma, mouse mammary carcinoma, frog kidney carcinoma, and chicken lymphomatosis.

The current period of rapid expansion in our knowledge of tumor viruses probably began with the description by Ludwik Gross in 1951 of a mouse leukemia virus. Since then several more virus-induced tumors have been described. In some cases it is possible to regard these tumor viruses as unnatural organisms that would

not exist outside the laboratory conditions under which they were isolated; however, there is evidence that other viruses, such as the leukemia viruses of domestic chickens, cats, and cattle, cause disease and are transmitted among natural populations of these animals.

The development of the field of tumor virology was hampered for many years by problems of inadequate methods and an inadequate understanding of the basic biology of these viruses. For example, even the criteria for defining a viral etiology for a tumor are somewhat vague because the Henle-Koch postulates cannot apply to an obligate parasite such as a virus. In addition, many tumor viruses can persist in an organism in a latent form that is not well understood. Finally, the study of some tumor viruses has been stalled by the simple fact that they cannot as yet be grown or assayed in cell culture.

There are two models for the mechanism by which a tumor virus may cause neoplastic change in a cell. In the first model, the virus is essentially a mutagen, causing random genetic changes in infected cells, some

611

of which make the cell malignant. According to this model the resulting tumor need not carry the virus in any form. In the other model it is the expression of a viral gene that causes a physiologic change in the cell, leading to malignancy. This model requires that a viral gene be associated with the resulting tumor and still be active. The two mechanisms are not mutually exclusive, of course, and in addition viral tumorigenesis may be a multistage process in which both mechanisms operate.

Four major groups of tumor viruses will be described below. Three of these contain DNA as the genetic material: the small papovaviruses, the medium sized adenoviruses, and the large herpesviruses. (The life cycles of the latter two groups are described in Chapters 46 and 47.) The fourth group, the oncornaviruses or RNA tumor viruses, use both RNA and DNA as genetic material; RNA is the genetic material carried in virions, but a DNA provirus is found integrated into chromosomal DNA of infected cells.

One major difference between the DNA tumor virus groups and the RNA tumor viruses is worth mentioning here. The DNA tumor viruses are generally cytocidal for cultured cells of the species of origin. Since a cell must survive in order to become transformed, they are therefore not gen-erally transforming for such cells. They are recognized as tumor viruses by their ability to transform cells of other species in which they do not grow well or by their ability to transform cells of the species of origin under special circumstances that prevent cell killing. The RNA tumor viruses, on the other hand, are generally not cytocidal. Infected cells grow and divide normally, releasing virus continuously, and all the descendants of an infected cell are themselves infected.

TRANSFORMATION OF CELLS IN CULTURE

Tumor virology has depended heavily upon the study of changes that tumor viruses cause in cultured animal cells. These changes are collectively called transformation, and they are interpreted as being analogous to changes that occur during tumorigenesis in an animal. Transformation involves a wide variety of changes in the morphological, biochemical, and social properties of cells. Accordingly, there are several criteria that can be used to define transformed cells. Cells that are transformed according to one set of criteria are often but not always transformed according to other criteria.

The cells normally used for the study of transformation in culture are either secon-

Table 48.1. Properties of Cells Transformed by Viruses

Property	Normal Cell	Transformed Cell
Response to contact with another cell	Inhibition of movement	No inhibition of movement
Requirement for anchorage	Requires solid substrate	Grows in suspension
Growth in agar	Fails to replicate	Replicates to form colonies
Pattern of growth on solid substrate	Ordered monolayer	Disordered, multiple cell layers
Comparative requirement for serum in medium	High	Low
Agglutinability by lectins	Low	High

dary cultures of embryo cells or established cell lines. Such cultures are considered normal cells for the purposes of studying transformation. Some of the properties that change when these cells are transformed by viruses are listed in Table 48.1. In addition to the changes listed, there are numerous biochemical changes, especially in the proteins and carbohydrates of the cell surface. The significance of these changes is not currently understood.

PAPOVAVIRUSES

The family *Papovaviridae* is divided into two genera, *Polyomavirus* and *Papillomavirus*.

Polyomaviruses

The two best studied members of this family are polyoma virus, which was isolated as an oncogenic virus in mice, and simian virus 40 (SV40), which was isolated as a contaminant in rhesus monkey kidney cultures (hence the term simian virus, or SV) used for the production of poliovirus vaccine. Although SV40 will transform human cells in culture, it does not seem to be highly oncogenic *in vivo*. Of the many epidemiologic studies on people who were inadvertently exposed in the late 1950s to SV40 in poliovirus vaccine, only one has reported a possible correlation between SV40 and an increased incidence of cancer.

The virions of polyomaviruses consist of a circular DNA molecule of about 3×10^6 daltons contained in an icosahedral protein capsid 45 nm in diameter. The nucleotide sequences of the DNA of three polyomaviruses, SV40, BK (see below), and polyoma itself, are entirely known (Fig. 48.1). The polyomaviruses replicate in the nuclei of infected cells. During the early stage of the replicative cycle, before DNA synthesis begins, about half of the genome is transcribed into RNA. This early RNA is processed by two (SV40) or three

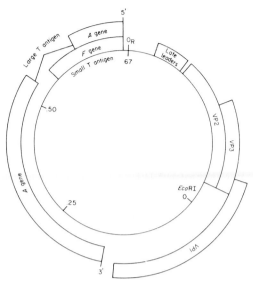

Fig. 48.1. Map of the SV40 genome. (With permission, Tooze, J., Ed.: Molecular Biology of Tumor Viruses, DNA Tumor Viruses, Part 2. 2nd Ed. Cold Spring Harbor Laboratory, Cold Spring Harbor, 1980. © 1980 by Cold Spring Harbor Laboratory.)

(polyoma) alternative pathways to produce messenger RNA, which code for the early proteins. These early proteins are known as T antigens, since they were first described as antigens present in transformed cells. In polyoma virus the T antigens have molecular weights of 22,000, 55,000, and 100,000. During infection of permissive cells (cells in which lytic replication occurs) DNA synthesis begins after the expression of the early proteins. DNA synthesis begins at a specific point on the circular polyoma virus genome and proceeds in both directions around the circle. After DNA synthesis begins, transcription of the late region of the chromosome also begins. Transcripts of this region are processed into three messenger RNA coding for the three capsid proteins. Progeny virions are assembled in the nucleus of the infected cell and released after the death and lysis of the cell.

To demonstrate the transforming ability of polyoma or SV40, nonpermissive cells are infected with a high MOI (Ch. 39) of either virus. Although early antigens are express-ed, viral DNA does not replicate efficient-ly, and most cells survive the infection. A few of these cells become stably trans-formed. These are cells in which part or all of the viral genome has become integrated into the host DNA. This integrated DNA is replicated and inherited as if it were a cellular gene, and at least the early regions are transcribed by the host RNA polymerase II. This transcription gives rise to the characteristic T antigens in the nuclei of infected cells. As mentioned above, there are three T antigens for polyoma virus. Recent evidence suggests that the middle sized protein is the most crucial for transformation of cultured cells. In SV40 the large T antigen seems to be required for both initiation and maintenance of the transformed state. Both polyoma middle T and SV40 large T have associated ATPase and protein kinase activities; these may be activities of associated proteins, or they may be intrinsic activities of the T antigen proteins.

Two viruses of the *Polyomavirus* genus have been isolated from humans. These viruses, JC virus and BK virus, were iso-lated from the brain of a patient with pro-gressive multifocal leukoencephalopathy and from the urine of immunosuppressed pa-tients, respectively. They are immunologi-cally distinct from SV40 and mouse polyoma virus. Antibodies to both viruses are commonly found in many human populations, and the age distribution of seropositive individuals suggests that most people are inapparently infected by these viruses as children. Both of these viruses will induce tumors in newborn hamsters, and BK virus will transform rodent cells in cul-ture. The possibility that these viruses may be involved in human tumors is currently under investigation.

Papillomaviruses

Papillomaviruses constitute the second genus in the *Papovaviridae*. Virions of papillomaviruses are somewhat larger (55 nm) than those of the polyoma group. They carry a closed circular DNA genome of about 5×10^6 daltons. They have been isolated from several species, including man; in the species of origin they normally cause benign skin papillomas or warts. These benign tumors can occasionally be-come malignant.

Rabbit papilloma virus was one of the first oncogenic viruses recognized (it was described by Shope in 1933), and human wart virus is the only human virus whose tumorigenicity is unquestioned. Unfortu-nately, there are no cell culture systems that allow the replication and assay of papillomaviruses, which has greatly re-stricted the study of their properties. In natural warts, replication of papillomavirus has been detected only in terminally differ-entiated cells in the keratinizing layer of the skin. Recent evidence suggests that in humans serologically distinct strains of wart virus are associated with warts at different anatomic locations.

ADENOVIRUSES

The adenoviruses include two genera, *Mas-tadenovirus*, derived from mammalian species, and *Aviadenovirus*, derived from avian species. The life cycles of these viruses are described in Chapter 46. The most relevant to tumor virology are the 31 serotypes of human adenoviruses. These are associated with pharyngitis in young children and with respiratory dis-eases in children and adults. They can per-sist in a latent form in lymphoid tissues. Most humans have been infected by one or more of these viruses.

The human adenoviruses have been di-vided into three groups on the basis of their oncogenicity in rodents or rodent cells. Three serotypes of the highly oncogenic group A viruses rapidly cause tumors when they are injected into newborn ham-sters. Six serotypes of the weakly onco-genic group B viruses occasionally induce tumors when injected into newborn hamsters. The remaining serotypes are nononcogenic in hamsters, but they, like the more oncogenic groups, transform rodent cells in culture.

Transformation by adenoviruses involves the integration of part of the adenovirus DNA into DNA of the transformed cell. Integration of the entire viral DNA occurs rarely if ever. This integrated DNA is at least partially expressed, since virus-specific messenger RNA can be detected in transformed cells. This messenger RNA corresponds to genes that are expressed early during lytic infection by adenoviruses. Late gene expression is not detected in transformed cells.

Cells can also be transformed by treatment with fragments of adenovirus DNA. Attempts to transform cells using different specific fragments of adenovirus DNA have shown that 7 percent of the DNA from one end of the genome is both necessary and sufficient for transformation.

Since adenoviruses are widespread in human populations and since they can be oncogenic in rodents, they could be involved in some types of human cancer. This hypothesis has been tested by attempts to find adenovirus DNA in human tumors with sensitive nucleic acid hybridization techniques. So far these attempts have proved negative.

HERPESVIRUSES

Herpesviruses of several species have been associated with tumors. Marek's disease, a form of lymphomatosis in chickens, is now known to be caused by a herpesvirus. A herpesvirus of frogs causes a form of renal carcinoma that was described in 1938 by Lucké. More recently, two oncogenic herpesviruses of nonhuman primates have been described, Herpesvirus saimiri and Herpesvirus ateles, isolated from squirrel monkeys and spider monkeys, respectively. They are widely distributed among natural populations of these hosts and are not associated with any known disease. When injected into marmosets, however, they cause a rapid T cell lymphoma. Tumors contain viral DNA but no virus particles or viral proteins.

Marek's disease is unique in that it is a naturally occurring lymphoproliferative disease that causes economically significant losses of chickens. The disease can be controlled by vaccination. The vaccine currently used is an antigenically related herpesvirus of turkeys. The fact that vaccination is effective provides the best evidence possi-

Table 48.2. EBV Antigens in Continuous Lymphoid Lines

Antigen	Location	Proportion of Population Displaying Antigen	Classification of Infected Cell
EBNA (Epstein-Barr nuclear antigen)	Nucleus	100%	Restringently infected
MA (membrane antigen)	Cell surface	100%	Restringently infected
EA (early antigen)	Cytoplasm	<5%	Abortively infected
VCA (viral capsid antigen)	Cytoplasm, nucleus	<10%	Productively infected

Restringently infected cells often have acquired an unlimited growth potential in cell culture; cellular macromolecular synthesis is not inhibited. Cellular synthesis is inhibited in abortively and productively infected cells.

ble that the disease is virus induced, and it provides some hope that other tumors might similarly be prevented.

The human herpesviruses that are most interesting to tumor virology are Epstein-Barr virus (EBV) and herpes simplex virus (HSV) types 1 and 2. EBV was discovered fortuitously during investigation of Burkitt's lymphoma, a tumor of African children. Cell lines established from Burkitt's lymphoma tumors were found to be persistently infected with a herpesvirus. Subsequent research defined a number of different viral antigens in these cell lines; the antigens and their occurrence are shown in Table 48.2.

EBV infects B lymphocytes of human origin and lymphocytes of some nonhuman primates. When EBV infects lymphocytes, viral functions are often not completely expressed. Infected cells have been classified according to the degree of viral expression, as shown in Table 48.2.

About one-third of the adult human population in the United States carries antibodies to EBV. Such antibodies appear in a seronegative individual during the acute phase of infectious mononucleosis. EBV is therefore presumed to be the cause of infectious mononucleosis in the United States.

In equatorial Africa EBV is strongly associated with Burkitt's lymphoma. Tumor biopsies and cultured tumor cells contain multiple copies of viral DNA, and tumor biopsies contain EBNA, the virus-specific nuclear antigen. Patients with Burkitt's lymphoma carry antibodies to a wide variety of EBV antigens. Finally, EBV can transform human lymphocytes *in vitro*, and some strains can induce lymphoproliferative diseases in New World marmosets or monkeys. However, some additional factor must be postulated to explain the fact that Burkitt's lymphoma is rare outside of equatorial Africa. Either the African strains of EBV are different from others, or Burkitt's lymphoma appears only when EBV interacts with some other factor, such as malaria.

Similar evidence links EBV with nasopharyngeal carcinoma that occurs most commonly among middle-aged males of Southeast Asia. This association is especially interesting because the tumor cells are epithelial rather than lymphoid.

Both HSV types 1 and 2 have been shown to be able to transform cells in culture. Since these are lytic viruses, transformation can be demonstrated only if the viruses are partially inactivated or if the infection is performed under conditions that do not allow complete expression of the viral functions. Under such conditions HSV can transform embryo cells in primary cultures to give them altered growth properties, including the ability to grow indefinitely in culture. Such transformed cells often, but not always, contain detectable HSV DNA. It is still not clear whether or not HSV DNA must be present to maintain transformation. Since a few percent of the HSV genome could contain enough information to transform cells and since current techniques might not detect that amount, all HSV-transformed cells could contain some HSV DNA. A variety of HSV-specific antigens or proteins have been detected in HSV-transformed cells, including viral membrane glycoproteins and the viral thymidine kinase. None of these is currently a candidate for the protein that causes transformation.

Epidemiologic studies of the occurrence of antiherpes antibodies have suggested connections between HSV type 1 and squamous cell carcinomas of the head and neck and between HSV type 2 and squamous cell carcinomas of the cervix. Attempts to find viral DNA or antigens in cervical carcinoma had given results that were equivocal; however, most recent publications report positive findings. Since herpes simplex viruses are ubiquitous in human populations and since they tend to persist in latent forms, it is extremely difficult to produce solid evidence for their oncogenicity.

RNA TUMOR VIRUSES

The RNA tumor viruses, or oncornaviruses, are the principal subfamily of the *Retroviridae*. The other subfamilies are the lentiviruses, associated with neurologic diseases, and spumaviruses, not associated with any diseases. Retroviruses are characterized by enveloped virions about 100 nm in diameter that contain an RNA genome of two identical subunits and an RNA directed DNA polymerase called reverse transcriptase.

The RNA tumor viruses are divided into three genera, oncornavirus types B, C, and D, on the basis of antigenicity and detailed virion morphology. Type C viruses have cores that are centrally located in the virions; type B cores are eccentrically located. Furthermore, cores of type C virions are assembled at the plasma membrane during budding, while type B cores are preassembled in the cytoplasm (where they are known as type A particles). The cores of type D virions are preassembled in the cytoplasm, but they are centrally located in mature virions; in this respect type D viruses are intermediate between types B and C. Type B oncornaviruses cause mammary tumors in mice, and they have also been isolated from other mammals. Type C oncornaviruses cause leukemias and sarcomas in chickens, mice, cats, cattle, and subhuman primates; they are by far the most completely studied genus, and most of the discussion below concerns type C viruses. Type D viruses have been isolated from primate (including human) cells.

Classification of RNA Tumor Viruses

Exogenous and Endogenous Viruses. As mentioned earlier, RNA tumor viruses are generally noncytocidal. Their genetic material exists in two forms: the RNA form is found in free virions, and the DNA form, or provirus, is found integrated into the cellular DNA of infected cells.

The provirus is inherited like a cellular gene. This property allows RNA tumor viruses to be further classified into exogenous and endogenous viruses. Exogenous viruses are transmitted horizontally (like other viruses) among animals in a population. These viruses infect somatic cells of each infected animal, but they do not infect germ line cells. Progeny of infected animals therefore will not be infected if they are protected from contact with their parents. Endogenous viruses, on the other hand, are transmitted vertically to subsequent generations in an animal population as if they were cellular genes. Endogenous viruses are common in avian and mammalian species studied so far, but often the proviral DNA is expressed only under special circumstances.

Species of Origin. RNA tumor viruses are also often classified on the basis of the species from which they were isolated. This classification usually correlates well with classification based upon antigenic similarities (described below). However, the exogenous viruses and endogenous viruses of a single species are not always closely related antigenically. In addition, certain viruses of different mammalian species have shown an unexpectedly close relationship as judged by antigenic similarity or nucleic acid sequence homology. These relationships are taken as evidence for interspecies transfer of the virus during evolution. For example, an endogenous virus of the domestic cat and of some other members of the cat family is related to an endogenous virus found in Old World primates. This fact and what is known about the evolution of the cat family suggest that an ancestor of the domestic cat may have acquired this virus from a primate in Africa or the Mediterranean region between 3 and 10 million years ago. This event, if it occurred, was not normal horizontal transmission because the virus became established in the germ line of the cat.

Antigenic Similarity. RNA tumor viruses show varying degrees of antigenic similarity, and these similarities have been used as a basis for classification. The most specific determinants, those characteristic of a single isolate of virus, are called *type-specific antigens*. Those determinants that are shared among viruses isolated from a single species are called *group-specific antigens*; those determinants that are shared among viruses isolated from different species are called *interspecies antigens*. Most of the proteins of an RNA tumor virus can be shown to have all three types of antigenic determinants if a sensitive assay, such as competitive radioimmunoassay, is used. However, the proportions of different types of antigens vary greatly for the different proteins. For example, the major glycoprotein found in the envelope of the virion contains predominantly type-specific antigens, while the major internal capsid protein contains predominantly group-specific antigens.

Host Range. The host range of RNA tumor viruses also serves as a classification scheme. Among avian RNA tumor viruses, host range is determined primarily by the interaction of the major envelope glycoprotein of the virion and a specific cell surface receptor. This interaction allows the adsorption and penetration of the virus. Avian RNA tumor viruses are classified into subgroups according to the specificity of their envelope glycoproteins. Similarly, chicken cells are classified according to the specificity of their cell surface receptor. Murine RNA tumor viruses can be classified not only by the interaction of virions and the cell surface receptors but also by additional factors that may restrict the growth of the virus even after successful adsorption and penetration. Murine RNA tumor viruses are thus classified broadly into *ecotropic, xenotropic*, and *amphotropic* groups.

Ecotropic viruses are those that efficiently infect cultured cells of the species of origin; for example, this group includes mouse viruses, which efficiently infect cultured mouse cells. Xenotropic viruses typically infect a wide range of cultured cells except those of the species of origin. Many endogenous viruses are xenotropic in nature. Amphotropic viruses infect cultured cells both of the species of origin and of other species

More detailed host range classifications have also been described for murine viruses. The best described of these is the NB classification for ecotropic viruses. Inbred laboratory mouse strains are classified as N or B type depending upon their genotype at a single Mendelian locus, the *Fv-1* gene. The ecotropic murine leukemia viruses are classified as N-tropic or B-tropic depending upon the efficiency with which they infect each of these types of mice. The NB host range is determined by some event after adsorption and penetration of the virus but before integration of proviral DNA. It has been associated with a specific change in a limited region of the major capsid protein but is otherwise unexplained.

Oncogenicity. RNA tumor viruses may also be classified according to their oncogenic potential. Sarcoma viruses cause solid tumors in connective tissue of susceptible animals and transform fibroblastic cells in cell culture. Mammary tumor viruses cause mammary adenocarcinomas in mice. Acute leukemia viruses cause rapidly developing lymphoproliferative disease in susceptible animals and transformation of fibroblastic or lymphoid cells in cell culture. This group includes avian myeloblastosis, erythroblastosis, and myelocytomatosis viruses as well as murine viruses that cause erythroid leukemia (Friend and Rauscher viruses) and B cell lymphomas (Abelson virus). Lymphatic leukemia viruses, in contrast, cause leukemias or lymphomas, which develop more slowly than the diseases of the preceding group.

Important genetic differences in these groups of viruses, which correlate with the biologic differences, are described below.

Life Cycle of a Nondefective RNA Tumor Virus

The explanation of the life cycle of RNA tumor viruses, called the *provirus hypothesis*, was first proposed by Temin in 1964. This thesis was not widely accepted, however, until the simultaneous discovery 6 years later by Temin and Baltimore of reverse transcriptase. According to this model, when a virus infects a cell the reverse transcriptase carried in a virion makes a DNA copy of the viral RNA in the cytoplasm of the infected cell. The DNA copy is transported to the nucleus of the cell, where it becomes integrated into the host cell DNA. The steps up to this point, called the *establishment stage* of infection, occupy the first 24 hours after infection. The integrated DNA or provirus is then transcribed by the host cell RNA polymerase to produce virus-specific RNA, which is transported to the cytoplasm. This RNA includes both messenger RNA and RNA that will be incorporated into progeny virions. The cycle is illustrated in Figure 48.2.

The biochemistry of provirus formation has been studied in some detail during the past few years. The enzyme responsible, reverse transcriptase, is biochemically similar to cellular DNA polymerases except that it is much more efficient at copying RNA templates. When an infecting RNA tumor virus enters the cytoplasm of a cell, reverse transcriptase begins copying viral RNA at a specific point near one end of the RNA. It copies toward that end, reaches it, and then transfers to the opposite end of the viral RNA molecule and copies the entire molecule. Finally, it transfers again to the opposite end of an RNA molecule and copies a short section near the end. The resulting DNA molecule is longer than the viral RNA and contains a large terminal sequence redundancy. Synthesis of the complementary DNA strand presumably begins after most of the first strand is complete. The resulting linear double-stranded viral DNA molecules are found in the cytoplasm a few hours after infection. These forms are gradually transported to the nucleus, where some of them become circular double-stranded molecules. Finally, one or more of these viral molecules is integrated into the host cell DNA, but it is not known whether the linear or the circular form is precursor to the integrated form.

Integrated proviral DNA is copied by

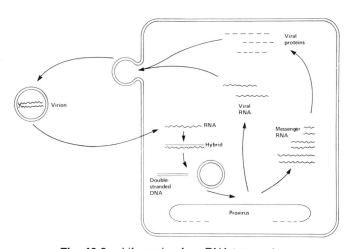

Fig. 48.2.   Life cycle of an RNA tumor virus.

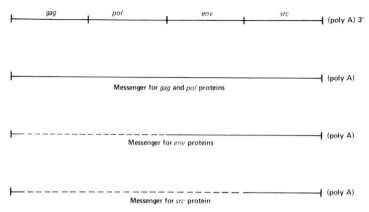

Fig. 48.3. Size classes of messenger RNA molecules transcribed from proviral DNA. Top, virion RNA; second, messenger for *gag* and *pol* proteins; third, messenger for *env* proteins; bottom, messenger for *src* proteins. Dotted lines represent genetic regions missing from that messenger RNA.

host cell RNA polymerase II to produce virus-specific progeny RNA and virus-specific messenger RNA. Three size classes of virus-specific RNA have been identified in the cytoplasm of cells infected with a nondefective sarcoma virus. These size classes are illustrated in Figure 48.3. In the largest size class RNA is of the same size as the large RNA found in virions. This class presumably includes RNA that will be packaged into progeny virions. The same size class also includes messenger RNA for proteins encoded by the *gag* and *pol* genes of the virus. In the second size class messenger RNA does not contain the *gag* and *pol* sequences; it codes for the envelope proteins derived from the *env* gene. In the third class messenger RNA is smaller yet and lacks sequences of the *gag*, *pol*, and *env* genes; it codes for the protein of the *src* gene, and, as would be expected, it is missing in cells infected with leukemia viruses or nontransforming variants of sarcoma viruses.

Specific proteolytic processing plays an important role in the synthesis of viral proteins of RNA tumor viruses. The *gag* region is initially translated as a single polypeptide chain. This primary translation product, sometimes called a *polyprotein precursor*, is cleaved by proteolytic enzymes to produce the four internal virion proteins described below. Occasionally, translation of the same messenger RNA continues from the *gag* region through the *pol* region. This produces a very large polyprotein precursor that is thought to be cleaved by proteases to produce the RNA-directed DNA polymerase. Similarly, the middle size class of messenger RNA is translated to produce a polyprotein precursor of the envelope proteins. This precursor is glycosylated and then cleaved by proteolytic enzymes to produce the envelope glycoproteins. Translation of the smallest class of messenger RNA to produce the *src* protein has not been characterized well enough to determine whether or not proteolytic cleavage is important.

Progeny virions assemble at the cell surface. Viral envelope glycoproteins can be detected in the plasma membrane of the infected cells, and internal proteins of the virion presumably interact with these and with the viral RNA to cause assembly of the virion. Most host cell membrane proteins are excluded from the developing virion, although small amounts of some membrane proteins such as H-2 antigens can be detected by sensitive techniques. The proteolytic processing of the *gag* proteins described above may begin while the virion is being assembled at the cell surface. This processing is not complete when the virion is released from the cell surface, and it continues in the newly released virion. Changes in the genomic RNA also occur during assembly of the nascent virion or shortly thereafter in the newly released virion. Viral RNA in the cytoplasm of infected cells has an apparent molecular weight of about 3×10^6. In purified virions, however, this RNA is found in a complex that contains two subunits of 3×10^6 daltons each and several molecules of host cell transfer RNA. The formation of this complex occurs during or shortly after the assembly of the virion.

Table 48.3 describes the finished proteins found in purified stocks of avian or murine type C RNA tumor viruses. The proteins are named according to their approximate molecular mass in kilodaltons with prefixes gp to denote glycoproteins, pp to denote phosphoproteins, and p to denote unmodified proteins. A homologous set of proteins can be identified in other strains of RNA tumor viruses, although the molecular weights of each protein may differ slightly. In addition to the proteins listed, purified virus contains reverse transcrip-

Table 48.3. Major Virion Proteins of Type C Oncornaviruses

Avian Viral Protein	Murine Viral Protein	Comments
gp85	gp70	Major envelope protein
gp37	p15(E)	Minor envelope protein
p27	p30	Major capsid protein
pp19	pp12	Internal phosphoprotein
p15	p15	Internal hydrophobic protein
pp12	p10	Ribonucleoprotein
p10	—	Not well characterized

tase. In avian viruses this enzyme consists of two subunits of 95,000 and 65,000 daltons; in murine viruses it is a monomeric enzyme of 70,000 daltons.

Genetics of RNA Tumor Viruses

The genome of RNA tumor viruses consists of three or four genes. The *gag* gene codes for four proteins that associate with the viral RNA and form the capsid and the virion. The *pol* gene codes for the RNA-directed DNA polymerase or reverse transcriptase. The *env* gene codes for two glycoproteins that are found in the envelope of the virion. In addition, sarcoma viruses carry the *src* gene that codes for a protein responsible for the maintenance of the transformed state in infected cells. In some sarcoma viruses the *src* gene replaces one or more of the other three genes; the resulting virus is then defective and grows only in the presence of another nondefective virus. In other sarcoma viruses the *src* gene is carried in addition to the other three genes; the resulting virus is therefore nondefective.

The major types of genetic interaction between RNA tumor viruses, as in other viruses, are complementation and recombination. Complementation occupies a special prominence in discussions of RNA tumor viruses because (as mentioned above) many sarcoma viruses are defective. Virus particles of these sarcoma viruses are produced only if the cell is also infected with a nondefective leukemia virus. Many sarcoma viruses are defective in the ability to synthesize envelope glycoproteins. When a leukemia virus complements this defect, the sarcoma virus genomes are packaged in virions that have the host range and type-specific antigenicity of the leukemia virus. They are therefore said to be *pseudotypes* of the leukemia virus.

Recombination between RNA tumor viruses occurs with a surprisingly high frequency. Progeny from a cell infected with two RNA tumor viruses may contain 10 to 40 percent recombinants. Although this high frequency of recombination is reminiscent of the reassortment of genomic subunits as in influenza virus, such a mechanism does not operate for RNA tumor viruses. The genome of RNA tumor viruses is not composed of subunits, and recombination has been shown to occur by crossing over — that is, by exchange of homologous segments of the genome. Recombination may occur between an exogenous virus and an endogenous virus as well as between two exogenous viruses. As discussed below, this phenomenon may be important in viral leukemogenesis in mice, where it appears that a specific type of recombinant virus appears during the preleukemia period.

In 1969 Huebner and Todaro proposed the *oncogene theory*, which held that tumorigenesis may be explained as the result of inappropriate expression of latent viral information. This hypothesis was founded on the newly discovered evidence for the ubiquity of latent RNA tumor viruses in mammals and birds. It described proviral information in terms of the virogene and the oncogene. The information necessary for infectious virus production was called the virogene and is now known to include *gag*, *pol*, and *env*. The information necessary for tumorigenesis was called the oncogene and is now known to include the *src* gene and a number of other cellular genes. These cellular sequences are apparently incorporated into the viral genome by recombination. Although never rigorously tested, the oncogene theory focused attention on the potential importance of latent viral genes on tumorigenesis.

Transformation by Sarcoma Viruses

Among RNA tumor viruses, the sarcoma viruses are those for which the mechanism of oncogenesis is best defined at the molecular level. As already explained,

these viruses cause easily assayed changes in cultured cells (transformation), and mutants exist in which the transforming gene *src* is deleted or in which its function is temperature sensitive. These mutants have been valuable in correlating the transformation gene with specific proteins or enzymatic activities. In general, transforming genes carried by sarcoma viruses seem to be similar to or identical with certain normal cellular genes. These genes may be expressed, although at low levels, even in nontransformed cells. Related sarcoma viruses carry related but distinct transforming genes, and unrelated viruses carry unrelated transforming genes. There are therefore several genes that can cause transformation in cultured fibroblasts when they are carried by an RNA tumor virus, and these genes may have been derived from normal cellular genes.

The *src* gene in nondefective strains of Rous sarcoma virus was the first such transforming gene to be described. It is defined by the nucleic acid sequences that are missing from transformation-defective deletion mutants of Rous sarcoma virus. These sequences are present in several strains of avian sarcoma viruses but are absent from avian leukosis virus and mammalian RNA tumor viruses. The sequences are expressed at high levels in transformed cells but are expressed at tenfold lower levels in *revertant* cells, which are morphologically untransformed. Sequences related to these viral *src* sequences are present in the DNA of normal chicken cells at frequencies corresponding to those of single copy genes These cellular sequences are expressed at low levels in uninfected cells, but their function there is unknown. Similar sequences are also present in all species of vertebrates tested, including humans.

The *src* sequences in Rous sarcoma viruses code for a phosphoprotein of 60,000 daltons, called p60^{src}. A protein kinase activity is associated with this protein, an activity that adds a phosphate group to certain tyrosine residues in proteins. Protein kinases are known to regulate the activity of enzymes by phosphorylation; therefore it is hypothesized that p60^{src} could cause transformation by phosphorylation of enzymes or other proteins in an infected cell. In uninfected cells the amount of phosphotyrosine is very low, and therefore it has been possible to show that transformation by Rous sarcoma virus causes almost a tenfold increase in the amount of phosphotyrosine in cellular proteins. Most of this additional phosphotyrosine is found in modified host cell proteins. Presumably, the altered behavior of one or more of these modified proteins is responsible for the transformed phenotype.

Uninfected cells of several vertebrates, including man, have small amounts of protein similar to the viral p60^{src}. Since the structure of this protein appears to have been conserved throughout vertebrate evolution, it is presumed to be an important cellular protein. Its function is unknown. Also unknown is whether Rous sarcoma virus transforms cells by simply producing too much of this protein or whether it does so by producing it at the wrong time or at the wrong place within a cell.

Rous sarcoma virus is probably the sarcoma virus that has been most completely characterized. As other RNA tumor viruses have been characterized it has become clear that they may differ from Rous sarcoma virus. Three types of differences are discussed below: the presence of cellular sequences in the viral genome, the presence of a novel protein kinase activity in infected cells, and the location and control of the putative transforming gene.

Cellular sequences are found in all or almost all sarcoma and acute leukemia viruses. With some expectations, different strains of virus carry different cellular sequences; thus it appears that there are several genes that can be tumorigenic when expressed as part of a viral genome. It will be important to determine how many such genes there are and whether or not their function is related to some common biochemical purpose.

Thymus Dependent Lymphatic Leukemia

Lymphatic leukemia induced by avian leukosis viruses or by Gross or Moloney murine leukemia viruses appears to be fundamentally different from the malignancies induced by sarcoma viruses or acute leukemia viruses. In the latter case it is possible to argue that the virus carries a gene whose expression in an infected cell causes, more or less directly, the alteration in growth control. In the case of lymphatic leukemia, however, the situation is more complicated. First, there is a long lag between the establishment of viremia in an animal and the appearance of lymphoma. Second, there is no observable effect of the leukemia virus on growth control of cultured cells. Third, there are well defined preleukemic changes in infected animals, such as the disappearance of lymphocytes from the thymus, that do not seem to have any simple relationship to the development of lymphoma.

These preleukemic changes, studied by gross and histologic examination, were described 10 to 15 years ago for several murine viruses and for the spontaneous leukemia of AKR mice. The most striking change occurs in the thymus. Most of the small lymphocytes forming the cortex of the thymus disappear. The medulla of the thymus enlarges as the cortex becomes thinner; then it too shrinks, so that the thymus contracts. The first signs of lymphoma usually appear after the loss of the cortical lymphocytes.

These changes are presumably important in the development of this type of leukemia because the presence of the thymus is essential for the development of the disease. Virus-infected thymectomized mice do not develop lymphatic leukemia, although virus that grows in such mice retains its ability to cause lymphatic leukemia in other mice. When thymectomized mice are given a subcutaneous thymus graft they become susceptible to lymphatic leukemia once again. In such a thymus graft the epithelial reticulum, which defines the structure of the organ, remains in the grafted organ. The lymphocytes from the donor, however, are gradually replaced by host lymphocytes. When a lymphoma develops in a virus-infected thymectomized thymus-grafted mouse it may be derived from either donor or host lymphocytes. Thus the presence of a thymus graft in such a mouse can make the host lymphocytes susceptible to the leukemogenic action of the virus.

Antigenic changes also occur in the thymocytes of preleukemic mice. Antigens characteristic of latent xenotropic viruses are expressed on the surface of thymocytes shortly before lymphomas develop. Recombinant viruses carrying characteristics of both ecotropic and xenotropic viruses can be isolated from such preleukemic thymuses. These observations have suggested that recombination creates a new type of virus in preleukemic thymuses and that it is this virus that is directly responsible for transformation of lymphocytes.

Transforming Genes

The location and control of putative transforming sequences in currently known viruses can be described by one of four patterns. The first is that already described for Rous sarcoma virus. The cellular sequences carried by the virus are separate from sequences coding for viral proteins; they are transcribed into a separate messenger RNA, which codes for a phosphoprotein with protein kinase activity. This pattern, however, is unusual among sarcoma viruses and acute leukemia viruses. It is more common to find the second variation, one in which cellular sequences have replaced some of the sequences coding for viral proteins in such a way that the cellular sequences are joined to part of the sequences coding for the *gag* proteins. These sequences are transcribed in a single messenger RNA that codes for a protein consisting of some viral polypeptides fused to some novel polypeptides. In one case this fusion polypeptide has an associated protein kinase activity. Since the cellular sequences have replaced viral sequences, these viruses are defective and can be grown only in the presence of nondefective helper virus. A third group of viruses carry novel glycoproteins in place of the normal gp70. These novel proteins may be the result of recombination of a virus either with related cellular proteins or with the glycoprotein gene of endogenous viruses. Novel glycoprotein genes are found in some strains of leukemia virus, but at the moment there is no direct evidence to show whether or not these genes are responsible for the leukemogenicity.

Lymphatic leukemia viruses constitute the fourth class of viruses. Until recently, the only genes identified in this class of viruses were those coding for the structural proteins of the virion and reverse transcriptase. This situation left several possibilities for the leukemogenicity of these viruses: either an unknown gene existed in the virus, or one of the viral structural proteins was in itself leukemogenic, or the virus became leukemogenic only after it was modified by growth in the animal. The last explanation was favored because of the relatively long time lag before induction of disease. Recently, however, parts of a lymphatic leukemia virus have been sequenced by recombinant DNA techniques. These experiments have identified a region of the genome that could code for a hitherto unknown hydrophobic protein of about 11,000 daltons. If such a protein is actually produced in infected cells, it could be the protein responsible for leukemogenicity.

Human RNA Tumor Viruses

There have been relatively few reports of isolation of RNA tumor viruses from human tumors or cells, and there have been even fewer well characterized isolates. This situation is in sharp contrast to the multiple isolations from other vertebrates. RNA tumor viruses may be rare among human populations. Alternatively, there may be special culture requirements that prevent their easy isolation and growth. Characterization of the human viruses that have been isolated will be especially important. Antisera or other reagents for the detection of viral proteins or nucleic acids will allow scientists to search for viral expression in human tumors even in the absence of infectious virus.

REFERENCES

Bishop, J.M.: Retroviruses. Annu. Rev. Biochem. *47*: 35, 1978.

Cold Spring Harbor Symposia on Quantitative Biology. Vol. XLIV. Viral Oncogenes. Cold Spring Harbor Laboratory, Cold Spring Harbor, 1980.

Tooze, J.: DNA Tumor Viruses. Molecular Biology of Tumor Viruses. 2nd Ed. Part 2. Cold Spring Harbor Laboratory, Cold Spring Harbor, 1980.

Vogt, P.K.: Genetics of RNA tumor viruses. In Fraenkel-Conrat, H. and Wagner, R.R. Eds.: Comprehensive Virology. Vol. 9. Regulation and Genetics. Genetics of Animal Viruses. Plenum Press, New York, 1977.

49

Interferon and Chemotherapy of Viral Infections

*Thomas D. Flanagan and
Harshad R. Thacore*

The strategy for development of effective antiviral chemotherapeutic agents has focused on three modes of attack. Agents are sought that directly affect the virion, that prevent attachment or penetration of the virus, or that inhibit some specific function during viral replication. Antiviral drugs must have the same characteristics of safety and efficacy as are demanded for antibacterial drugs. Research and development efforts have so far resulted in a small number of useful antiviral agents. However, the proper use of these agents can result in definite clinical improvements in patients. The effort to find new agents continues, of course.

We will discuss several of the better known agents, those for which there are sufficient data to suggest their clinical usefulness.

INTERFERON

Interferons are a family of cellular proteins or glycosylated proteins that are induced in eukaryotic cells in response to viral or nonviral inducers. Normal uninduced cells do not contain interferon. When treated with or exposed to homologous interferons under appropriate conditions cells become refractory or resistant to a wide variety of viruses. This resistance is the basis for quantitation and detection of interferons. It is important to note that interferons by themselves are not the antiviral substances; they have been shown to have no direct effect on viruses. In recent years an increasing number of nonantiviral activities of interferons have been described. It is becoming more and more evident that these nonantiviral activities may be due not to the contaminating materials present in the interferon preparation but to the interferon molecule itself.

Interferons in general are species specific. In other words, interferons produced in human cells protect human cells against virus replication but do not induce resistance in cells of heterologous species, such as mouse or chicken. However, there is

627

crossreaction observed in cells of closely related species. Although interferons are species specific, they are not virus specific. Cells treated with homologous interferon under appropriate conditions show resistance against both RNA and DNA viruses. However, it should be emphasized that not all viruses are equally sensitive to interferon action in all cell systems.

Until recently all interferons were thought to be resistant to prolonged acid treatment (pH 2.0) at 4°C. However, this changed with the discovery of immune interferon produced by lymphocytes upon stimulation with antigens or mitogens. Such stimulation of interferon production is inhibited by the action of actinomycin D. The interferon produced under such conditions is inactivated at pH 2.0. All interferons resistant to treatment at pH 2.0 are now called α or β interferons, whereas immune interferons characterized by their sensitivity to acid treatment are called γ interferons (Table 49.1).

Apart from the properties of interferons mentioned above, interferons are also known to withstand heating at 56 to 60°C for 30 to 60 minutes, and boiling in the presence of sodium dodecyl sulfate (SDS), 5 M urea, and mercaptoethanol. Workers have used polyacrylamide gel electrophoresis for the purification and characterization of many interferons; however, no interferon has been completely purified. Even the highly purified preparations containing high specific antiviral activity per unit protein are considered relatively impure.

Studies from partially purified interferon preparations indicate that interferons derived from the same or different species vary in molecular weight, biologic activity, physical and chemical properties, and their antigenic structures. For example, human α and β interferons differ in many chemical and biologic properties. Human α interferon is significantly more stable than β interferon to denaturation by SDS. Also, studies have shown that α interferon can be separated into two fractions, one of 20,000 and another of 16,000 daltons, whereas β interferon most probably is a single glycoprotein of 20,000 daltons. The role of glycosylation of interferon proteins is not known; however, the possibility exists that glycosylation may be responsible for the heterogeneity noted in interferon molecules, their biologic characteristics, or their species specificity.

The Interferon System

The interferon system can be divided into two separate components, interferon induction or synthesis and interferon action to produce the antiviral state (Fig. 49.1). Although not all the biochemical events involved in the interferon system are well understood, significant advances have been made in recent years in attempts to elucidate the complex molecular events of the interferon system.

Table 49.1. Nomenclature of Interferons

Type	Properties	Other designations
α	Stable at pH 2.0; antigenically distinct from β and γ	Human type I, leukocyte; murine fast migrating
β	Stable at pH 2.0; antigenically distinct from α and γ	Human type I, fibroblast; murine slow migrating
γ	Inactivated at pH 2.0; antigenically distinct from α and β	Human type II, immune; murine immune

A. INTERFERON INDUCTION

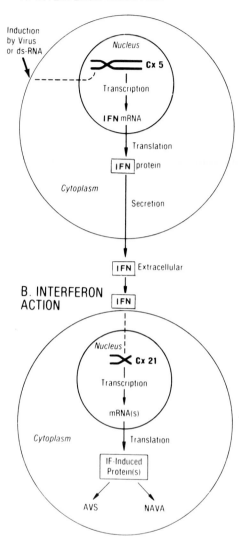

B. INTERFERON ACTION

Fig. 49.1. The interferon system. The example chosen here is for the production and action of human β interferon. The antiviral state (AVS) and nonantiviral activities (NAVA) are indicated as results of response to stimulation by interferon. (With permission, Stewart, W.E., Ed.: Interferons and Their Actions. CRC Press, Inc., Boca Raton, 1977. Copyright The Chemical Rubber Co., CRC Press, Inc.)

Interferon Induction. A wide variety of bacteria and viruses and their products have been shown to induce interferon in cell cultures or in animals. Synthetic substances have also been shown to be good inducers of interferon both *in vitro* and *in vivo*. Studies to date indicate that the double-stranded RNA molecule is the most likely candidate for the agent responsible for the induction of interferon. With viruses the double-stranded RNA molecule has to be synthesized during the viral replicative cycle in the particular host cell. The events involving the recognition of the interferon inducer molecule by the cell and the initiation of transcription of the cellular DNA leading to the synthesis of interferon messenger mRNA are not yet known; however, studies with Chinese hamster–human hybrid cell populations have indicated that only human chromosome 5 is necessary for the production of human β interferon. Furthermore, it is also suggested that interferon structural and regulatory loci are located on the long and short arms, respectively, of this chromosome. It therefore is necessary to transcribe this genetic information into interferon mRNA prior to the synthesis of the interferon molecule.

Messenger RNA molecules for interferons in induced cells have been demonstrated in various *in vitro* protein synthesized systems. The mRNA for human β interferon has been isolated and shown to contain polyadenylic acid sequences at the 3′ terminus of the molecule. The synthesis of this host DNA-directed interferon mRNA is inhibited by actinomycin D when the antimetabolite is added to cell cultures prior to, along with, or immediately after the addition of the interferon inducer. The interferon mRNA is translated into protein. The interferon molecules may or may not be glycosylated prior to their release from the induced cell.

Interferon Action. Studies dealing with the mechanism by which interferon exerts its effect on viral replication point to the fact that interferon itself is not the antiviral substance. Moreover, interferon is known to act by inducing in interferon-treated cells an antiviral protein(s) that in turn is responsible for the antiviral or refractory state of the cell. It is not yet clear whether the interferon molecule itself must enter the cell to exert its effect or whether it acts in some manner at the cell membrane level. It is suggested that in human cells the receptors involved in this process are encoded by chromosome 21; however, it is clear that at least several hours of exposure of cells to homologous interferon at 37°C is necessary for the development of the antiviral state. Studies conducted with metabolic inhibitors have demonstrated that cellular RNA and protein synthesis are required for the development of the antiviral state. These studies indicate that the antiviral state is mediated through the production of an antiviral protein (AVP) encoded by a specific mRNA. This AVP has not yet been isolated from refractory cells. It has been observed that interferon induces the antiviral state in cells with intact nuclei and not in enucleated cells, which suggests that the nucleus is involved in the induction of the antiviral state. Genetic studies conducted in mouse–human hybrid cell populations have shown that in human cells the genes for the antiviral action of interferon are located on chromosome 21. One cannot rule out the possibility that genes on chromosome 21 in human cells may also code for the putative AVP.

Mechanisms of Action of Interferons

The exact mechanism by which interferon exerts its effect on viral replication is not known. However, there are two main hypotheses regarding interferon action: inhibition of viral mRNA transcription, and inhibition of viral mRNA translation.

Interferon treatment has been shown to reduce the accumulation of early viral RNA in cells infected with a number of DNA and RNA viruses. Still to be resolved in many of these studies is whether this represents a direct effect of interferon on primary transcription or an indirect effect from an inhibition of some other process that may be required for viral transcription. More convincing evidence regarding the effect of interferon on primary transcription comes from studies conducted with negative-strand RNA viruses. These viruses contain a virion-associated RNA polymerase (transcriptase). This enzyme directs the synthesis of virus-specific mRNA using the virion genome as a template. This transcriptase activity was first shown by Marcus and co-workers to be inhibited in interferon-treated chicken embryo cell cultures infected with vesicular stomatitis virus (VSV). However, more recent results from other laboratories working with VSV in mouse, chicken, human, and monkey cell cultures contradict the previous results, and those researchers conclude that interferon acts as an intermediate step between primary and secondary transcription, such as viral protein synthesis. Effects of interferon on primary transcription have also been demonstrated with DNA viruses, vaccinia virus, and simian virus 40 (SV 40); however, these studies remain controversial.

The theory of interferon's effect on translation of virus-specific mRNA is very attractive because it involves a step common to the replication of both RNA and DNA viruses and the suggestion that interferon may inhibit these viruses by a common mechanism. Studies with vaccinia virus in L cells have shown that interferon affects the synthesis of early enzymes rather than the transcription of early viral mRNA. Similar results have also been observed with reoviruses. In these studies 75 units of interferon inhibited the transcription of viral mRNA species by only 20 percent, whereas the translation was inhibited by 30 to 72 percent.

Inhibition of viral mRNA translation has been demonstrated most convincingly in several cell-free protein-synthesizing systems. However, the cell-free system may or may not represent the events occurring in interferon-treated cells *in vivo*. In general, the studies conducted in cell-free systems suggest that an early event in the initiation of viral protein synthesis is affected by interferon through a mechanism not yet understood.

One should look at the studies dealing with the mechanism of action of interferon with the understanding that the synthesis of viral RNA and viral proteins are interdependent processes. With many viruses these two processes are difficult to separate; therefore conclusions regarding interferon action are not final. Furthermore, recent evidence suggests that the host cell may play an important role in whether interferon exerts its effect on viral transcription and/or on viral translation.

Clinical Use of Interferon

Two decades of research on interferon and its potential use as an effective antiviral drug produced no great cause for optimism until very recently. Progress has been hampered by difficulties in obtaining sufficient amounts of purified interferon for trials. Human α interferon has been the most useful source; however, recent advances in recombinant DNA technology have provided an unlimited bacterial source of human interferon.

Prophylaxis and Therapy of Localized Infections. Attempts to protect human populations against upper respiratory infections have met with mixed success. Early studies were not able to demonstrate efficacy, but more recent studies using higher interferon dosages demonstrated reduced duration of symptoms and virus shedding in volunteers.

Therapeutic application of interferon by means of drops or ointments has been used on localized viral lesions such as herpetic or vaccinial keratitis, genital herpes and condylomata acuminata (genital warts). These

treatments were effective when high concentrations of interferon were used.

Therapy of Systemic Infections. Interferon has been used in many attempts to treat systemic viral infections. The principal problem associated with this stategy is the difficulty of achieving and maintaining high concentrations of interferon at sites of viral replication. Nonetheless, efficacy has been noted in some studies. Several groups have reported encouraging results of interferon therapy of disseminated herpesvirus infections. In particular, immunosuppressed patients with herpes zoster and cytomegalovirus (CMV) infections have responded to therapy. Encouraging results have also been reported in treatment of chronic hepatitis caused by hepatitis B virus. These reports document reduction of HB_s and HB_c antigenemia and restoration of liver function. Limited experience with congenital rubella and congenital CMV infection suggests some reduction of virus shedding in these cases.

Anticancer Therapy. Some of the most encouraging developments in the clinical use of interferon have been in the areas of cancer therapy. While a detailed discussion is beyond the scope of this chapter, it should be acknowledged that a number of groups have reported positive results in cancer patients. Interferon has caused remission in several studies of Hodgkin's disease and other lymphomas and leukemias. Some solid tissue tumors, such as osteosarcomas, have responded to interferon therapy. Considering the problems and expense of current chemotherapy, interferon therapy promises to have significant impact.

CHEMOTHERAPY

Amantadine Hydrochloride. Amantadine hydrochloride has been used principally in prophylaxis and treatment of influenza caused by A strains (H2N2) of the virus.

The mode of action has been attributed to inhibition of virus penetration of the plasma membrane of the cell. While *in vitro* activity has been demonstrated against a variety of viruses, including rubella and several other influenza A strains, the compound is generally ineffective as a clinical drug for viruses other than influenza A2.

Adenine Arabinoside. This drug (Ara-A) inhibits DNA replication in a variety of DNA viruses. The drug has demonstrated efficacy in serious infections caused by herpesviruses and poxviruses. The most important use of ara-A is in the treatment of herpes simplex encephalitis or disseminated herpetic infection of neonates. Several studies have demonstrated the usefulness of the agent in these infections. In a recent study prompt treatment of patients with herpetic encephalitis reduced the fatality rate from 70 percent to less than 30 percent. The drug also has been shown to be as effective as iododeoxyuridine (see below) in the treatment of herpetic keratitis and vaccinial infections of the eye.

Trials have been conducted that suggest that ara-A has some effect in modifying herpes zoster, varicella, and cytomegalovirus infections. The drug has no clinically significant effect on adenovirus infections. It is relatively nontoxic in doses up to 20 mg/kg/day, and problems of viral resistence or allergic reactions in patients have not emerged.

Cytosine Arabinoside. This drug (Ara-C) is active against DNA viruses. Its mode of action is to inhibit viral DNA replication. The drug has a spectrum of activity similar to that of ara-A, but it is more toxic.

Iododeoxyuridine. This compound (5-iodo-2'-deoxyuridine; IUdR) is one of a series of halogen-substituted deoxynucleosides with *in vitro* activity against DNA virus replication. All of the compounds interfere with DNA metabolism and thereby exert their antiviral effects. IUdR is the most significant of the group from a clinical perspective. It is used topically for the treatment of herpetic and vaccinial keratitis. In this application it has been shown to be an effective therapeutic agent and is the basic drug of choice. IUdR has been tested in other infections and found to be of little use. The principal problems associated with its ophthalmic use are the emergence of drug resistant strains of virus and the development of allergic responses in patients.

Isatin-β-Thiosemicarbazone. This drug and its methylated derivative, methisazone, are effective inhibitors of poxvirus replication. They prevent the maturation of pox virions by inhibiting the synthesis of essential viral proteins. The drugs have demonstrated efficacy in prophylaxis of smallpox and alastrim. Their effectiveness as therapeutic agents is in question.

REFERENCES

Baron, S. and Dianzani, F.: The Interferon System: A Current Review to 1978. Tex. Rep. Biol. Med. *35*: 1977.

Stewart, W.E., II: Interferons and Their Actions. CRC Press, Boca Raton, 1977.

Stewart, W.E., II: The Interferon System. Springer-Verlag, New York, 1979.

50

Introduction to Medical Parasitology

Roger K. Cunningham and
Marek Zaleski

In less well developed societies, particularly those of the tropics, the seriousness of the struggle that humans undertake with their parasites is a daily fact of life. Parasitic infections remain the largest single source of human disease, misery, and suffering on earth.

Parasites are — or rather the parasitic way of life is — very successful. Parasitic forms have evolved independently in nearly every phylum from protozoans to vertebrates. It is very rare to find an organism that is not parasitized. Those that are not parasites are hosts; in some cases parasites themselves can have parasites (termed hyperparasitism). In fact, the parasitic way of life is so successful that there are far more parasitic than nonparasitic (free-living) organisms in the world.

Medical parasitology is the study of interrelationships of two different organisms — humans and their parasites — within their environment. There are many kinds of associations or relationships known to exist between individuals of different species.

Most of these associations have developed from chance meetings and may offer certain advantages to one of the partners. The first, described in 1879, was for a species of algae and fungi that lived together to form lichens. This was termed *symbiosis* by the German botanist Heinrich Anton de Bary. He defined symbiosis as the living together of two heterospecific organisms without implying any type of mutual or unilateral dependency. Thus we talk about *symbionts* (or a *symbiote*) as any animal or plant that spends a portion or all of its life cycle intimately associated with another organism of a different species. For this reason we consider symbiosis a "superset" term; the subset terms *phoresy*, *commensalism*, *mutualism*, and *parasitism* imply some sort of dependency, physical and/or physiologic.

If one examines with some care the large array of organisms in nature that are temporarily or permanently associated in a more or less intimate manner with other organisms of different species, it soon becomes apparent that there are subtle differ-

633

ences not only in physical aspects but also in physiologic nature. For example, the transport of bacteria on the legs of flies is an association in which the flies and bacteria are not dependant on each other, especially physiologically; the relationship is purely accidental and nonobligatory. This is an example of *phoresis*, which means "to carry." During this type of relationship, usually the smaller of the two species, the *phorant*, is carried mechanically in or on the larger species, the *host*, and no metabolic interaction or dependency occurs.

A second type of symbiosis is exemplified by the relationship between the pilot fish and the shark. The pilot fish accompanies the shark in a free-swimming manner, eating fragments of food as the shark tears apart its prey. In fact, the two partners are "eating at the same table," a relationship termed *commensalism*. The spatial proximity of the two partners permits the *commensal* (pilot fish) to feed on substances captured by the host (shark). The shark is neither benefited nor harmed in any way.

A third type of symbiosis exists in which two organisms are mutually dependent on each other. A classic example of this relationship, called *mutualism*, involves certain species of flagellated protozoans that line the gut of woodroaches and termites. The flagellates, which depend almost entirely on a carbohydrate diet, acquire their nutrients in the form of wood chips ingested by their hosts. In return, they synthesize and secrete cellulases, the cellulose-digesting enzymes that are used by the woodroaches and termites in their digestion. The woodroaches, although active wood ingesters, are incapable of synthesizing their own cellulases and thus are dependent on their *mutualists*. Experimentally one can defaunate a woodroach by placing the woodroach in a chamber containing a high concentration of oxygen, which is toxic to flagellates but not the woodroach; the defaunated woodroaches will continue to ingest woodchips but will starve to death.

Parasitism, the fourth category of symbiosis, is defined as an intimate and obligatory relationship between two heterospecific organisms during which the parasite, usually the smaller of the two partners, is metabolically dependent on the other, the host, in some way. This definition implies damage to the host, although it may not be apparent. The simplest definition is that a parasite is dependent on one gene product of its host. The parasite relationship may be permanent, as in the case of tapeworms found in the intestines of mammals, or very temporary, as in the feeding of female mosquitos, ticks, or bedbugs on their host's blood.

Parasitologists often distinguish between parasites that reside on the outer surface of the host's body (*ectoparasites*) and those that reside within it (*endoparasites*). It is conventional to refer to parasitization by ectoparasites as *infestation* and to that by endoparasites as *infection*. An organism that does not absolutely depend on the parasitic way of life but is capable of adapting to it if placed in such a relationship is known as a *facultative parasite*. If an organism is completely dependent on the host during a segment or all of its life cycle in order to survive, it is an *obligatory parasite*. Many obligatory parasites have free-living stages outside the host.

The chapters that follow are concerned primarily with the frankly damaging and disease-producing interactions of those parasites that are pathogenic to humans. However, it must be noted that not all parasites are pathogenic (disease-producing).

A parasite by definition must have a host. The parasite is dependent on the ability of another animal to supply food and shelter. It must also have the ability to reproduce. It is not the "intention" of a parasite to produce disease or to kill the host. Since to survive the parasite needs a living host, in a real sense a parasite casts its lot with the host, and destruction of the host would be suicidal on the part of a parasite.

The ideal state of parasitism, an inconspicuous and noncompromising residence within the host, is achieved only after long periods during the evolutionary process. Parasitic relationship most likely was initiated early in evolution, perhaps by sheer accident. It is not difficult to imagine how a free-living organism taken in with food by some larger animals could happen to survive in the intestinal tract and eventually come to be selected for survival there and, in the process, lose its capacity for free life. It is equally easy to imagine that at early stages countless trials of this lifestyle were unsuccessful. However, given the enormous time available, certain of these associations would have become fixed. The ultimate state for the successful parasite must result from a careful adaptation to the host in such a way that the host is seldom destroyed or debilitated while harboring the parasite.

To put it differently, successful parasites adapt themselves exquisitely to the habits and physiology of their hosts. During this process the parasite must balance its needs for nourishment with those of the host. Furthermore, to ensure continuation of the species the parasites' reproductive forms must be compatible with the habits of the hosts. It is not surprising, then, that the host range of most parasites is extremely narrow and that there is remarkable integration between the lifestyles of a given host and its parasite. The accidental introduction of a parasite into an inappropriate host usually leads to inability of the parasite to survive or a violent host reaction that threatens the survival of both. A violent parasitic relationship that is often fatal for the host may, in general, be viewed as an attempt by a parasitic species to take up a new host species. In the process the host attempts to kill or expel the parasite and when successful eliminates that particular parasite. On the other hand, the host may die during such a reaction; since the parasite is unable to leave, it dies as well. In these cases the parasite should be seen not so much as using the host as a means and site for continued existence but rather as a means of surviving long enough to reproduce.

Parasites in adapting to their host have evolved many patterns of life cycles. Some species are parasitic during only one phase of their life cycle. Others, however, have adapted to more than one host during the phases of their life cycle. Usually this means that one species is the host where the parasite achieves sexual maturity and one or more other species harbor different stages (nonsexually-reproducing) of the life cycle. As a matter of convention, the host species in which sexual reproduction of the parasite occurs is termed the *definitive host*. The species in which the other stages occur are called *intermediate hosts*. If there is no sexual reproduction in the life cycle of the parasite, such as in trypanosomes, we arbitrarily designate the vertebrate (human) host as definitive.

As one begins to consider individual parasites it is important to note that in adapting to their hosts most have lost many of the biologic essentials for independent life. Parasites usually have little in the way of sensory organs; they go through exquisite host-finding behavior or migration through various host tissues to reach their final niche in the host. Eyes, feelers, and similar devices are rare among parasites. Legs, fins, and other locomotive means are usually gone. The alimentary tract of many parasites is primitive compared to those of free-living animals. In fact, some worms have no gastrointestinal tract at all. On the other hand, parasites have replaced the now useless equipment for free life with specialized organs essential for their lifestyle. In place of sense organs and organs of locomotion some parasites have developed a fascinating array of hooks, barbs, suckers, and other attachment devices to hold them in place within the host. Others have developed appendages for boring or enzymatic capacities that are needed to reach their preferred site within a host.

Some parasites, however, are facultative and can be free living or parasitic as needed. The mosquito, for example, visits hosts only long enough to obtain a blood meal. Ectoparasites such as fleas and lice are happy to transfer from one person to another, as a short ride on a crowded bus in many parts of the world will readily prove. Such episodes seem hardly as serious as an intestinal worm, but when one recalls that bacterial, rickettsial, and viral diseases can be transferred by this means, annoyance is not always the best way to characterize ectoparasitic infestation or the bites of certain insects.

The most striking morphological feature of most parasites is their highly developed reproductive systems. When an adult parasite is committed to the host, reproduction becomes of paramount importance to carry on the species. Since the ova or offspring often must find a new host of a particular species, the capacity to produce enormous numbers of progeny is critical. This need is reflected in the incredibly elaborate and extensive gonads present in most parasites. Many parasites appear simply to be gonads in which other minimum functions have been retained. The complexity and redundancy can go so far that certain tapeworms not only possess both male and female gonads within every segment but sometimes possess double sets of each. Furthermore, many worms have developed highly active gonads that often produce millions of eggs over their lifespan.

In spite of their prodigious capacity to reproduce, the life of parasitic animals would be precarious indeed if it were not for their adaptation to the habits of their host species, particularly with respect to their food habits. Since the search for food as a source of energy is the preoccupation of animal existence, parasites have adapted to take advantage of particular food chains. For example, flukes and tapeworms lay eggs that develop into larvae within an intermediate host species that is normally a prey or food source of the definitive host species. The predator–prey chain may even involve more than one species; the developmental form of the parasite that enters the last (definitive) species in a chain may be required to reside in several intermediate hosts before reaching maturity in a species that is a customary prey of the definitive host.

The close association of species in a parasitic relationship leads eventually to a remarkably restricted host range for the parasite; as the particular host–parasite adaptations occur the potential for the parasite to infect a different species becomes sharply reduced. Another way of viewing this is to consider the state referred to as natural host resistance. Members of a given species are said to be naturally resistant to parasites of other species if the parasite is never found to infect the animal in question after proper exposure. This is simply to say that a given species cannot provide a needed environment for the parasite. Often this is no more than possession of a mechanical barrier that cannot be passed by the parasite or, for example, an inappropriate pH or body temperature. Other, more subtle metabolic differences no doubt have roles to play, but these are largely unknown. To some extent the host range for parasites may vary. Some parasites may inhabit several, usually closely related host species. Others must find but one host species; still others may be obliged to find more than one intermediate host, each of which must in some cases be a single species or in others, be several related species. In short, all manner of arrangements can be found.

Other factors bear heavily on the epidemiology of parasitic disease. For example, young animals are often more susceptible to parasitic disease than older animals. In humans, "accidental" infection with parasites of other species occurs most often in children. It may be that age-related resistance simply reflects increasing probability of unintentional immunization. Alternatively, immature animals may be unable to respond effectively or may perhaps possess an immature general physiologic resistance.

There is no question that the nutritional state of the host bears directly on the gravity of ensuing disease. On one hand, it may be said that a well nourished host can support more of a burden of parasites than a host that is malnourished. To an otherwise healthy host the parasite represents a small additional energy demand. However, if the burden of such parasites increases, there is a point at which even the healthiest of hosts will manifest symptoms of disease. When humans are considered, another important element emerges. Most parasitized humans will not die from their infections but do become debilitated to some extent. In poorer areas of the world, where most individuals are marginally nourished and where the risk of infection is high, sick individuals constitute a tremendous drain on the available nutritional resources, since they continue to consume food although they cannot help in its production. For some areas of the world this drain can amount to one-third of the food supply going largely to support parasites resident in humans.

An apparently important but poorly understood element in the host–parasite interaction is the role played by acquired resistance. Both humoral and cellular immunity can often be demonstrated to various antigens of parasites. Specifically, sensitized T and B cells arise during infection, but their exact role in combating and resolving the infection is uncertain. The fact that some individuals when immunosuppressed suffer devastating eruptions of normally innocuous parasites supports the notion that the immune state is important in withstanding parasites. Furthermore, there is a large body of data indicating that genetic mechanisms similar to those affecting an immune response to conventional antigens also influence the host–parasite

relationship. Elegant experiments using genetically defined animals have demonstrated that susceptibility or resistance to certain parasites is under complex genetic control in a fashion strikingly similar to the Ir phenomenon (Ch. 14).

IgE antibodies are said by some to represent an antiparasite class of antibodies, since they arise commonly, if not invariably, during infection. IgG and IgM antibodies can often be found as well and may be directed to a wide variety of parasite antigens, usually soluble. Whether or not antibody can produce a "cure," the humoral response is useful in serodiagnosis of parasitic infection. A wide variety of techniques are available for specific parasites.

More recently, efforts have been made to examine the role of cell-mediated immunity in recovery from parasitic infections and to detect specifically sensitized T cells as a means of diagnosis. The early efforts in this direction seem promising, but much additional work remains.

The impact of parasites on human life is staggering. While precise figures are difficult to acquire, it has been estimated that there are some 3 billion human worm infections existing in the world. These are concentrated largely in the tropical belts; hence inhabitants of other areas of the earth are largely ignorant of the size of this problem. Another problem of the tropical areas that is seldom considered is the impact that parasitism of domestic animals has on the economy of these regions. There are approximately 4.4 billion acres of potentially arable land that cannot be developed because of diseases like malaria, trypanosomiasis, schistosomiasis, and filariasis. For example, there are immense areas in Africa, south of the Sahara, in which domestic cattle cannot be raised because of nagana disease caused by trypanosomes that normally parasitize wild animals. Wild animals tolerate them, but domestic animals quietly succumb to infection. Until some means can be found to control either the trypanosomes or, more likely, their insect vectors, an area larger than the United States cannot be used efficiently for domestic animals.

Why is it that parasitic infections are so devastating in some parts of the world and yet seemingly trivial in others? In attempts to form an answer to this question, several factors should be considered.

The most obvious problems with parasites occur in tropical regions. The mild weather and the richness of animal life surely play roles in transmission of parasites from one host to another. These areas of the world are also economically the poorest, with poor control of human wastes, inadequate protection of food, and inadequate hygienic practices. Those who live what could be termed a European or North American lifestyle in the tropics, in fact, run a much smaller risk of infection. The lesson here is that elements of behavior can and do play a role in perpetuating parasitism. The richer areas of the world do not feel the full impact of parasitism because they are wealthy enough to practice a lifestyle that prevents the spread of parasites. Sewer systems, control of insects, good nutrition, swamp drainage, and similar practices have done far more to eliminate parasites from wealthy areas than medical intervention. Good hygiene, proper nutrition, and education are of primary importance in solving the problems of human parasitic disease.

Although the developed nations are largely free of the serious parasite problems of the tropics, medical parasitology must be part of medical microbiologic training. At least a million children in the United States bear worm infections. The availability of cheap and rapid transportation together with the habit of travel means that more and more parasitic infections are being imported into countries normally free of such infections. For example, a certain form of malaria was reintroduced into the United States in the blood of military personnel who because of the speed of modern travel were transported from the Far East to the United States while the disease was still in the incubation period. Unlike most imported parasites or microorganisms, which usually cannot find an appropriate intermediate host or the means to escape our sewer systems, the malaria protozoa found an appropriate mosquito in the southern United States that allowed the resurgence of a form of malaria that had been eliminated many years before.

The effectiveness of treatment for parasitic diseases varies widely and depends on the parasite involved. Often all that is required is to prevent further infection or reinfection. In many cases the healthy host is fully capable of expelling the parasite but remains afflicted because he or she is continually reinfected. Drugs are available for treatment, but their use is complicated by the fact that most of the drugs used to eradicate parasites are more or less toxic to the host as well. A balanced approach to the patient is therefore essential to her or his overall welfare. Several factors must be considered: The efficacy of the drug must be weighed against its side effects and the necessity of treating a given patient. Patients with few symptoms who are tolerating their parasite well may be better off without drug treatment. Unfortunately, some parasitic infections are essentially untreatable. In some instances there simply are no drugs known to be effective. In others the explosive nature of the disease makes its recognition as a parasitic infection problematic — by the time the disease is accurately diagnosed the patient will have recovered by his or her own resources or succumbed. Drugs used in treatment of parasitic diseases are listed in Table 50.1.

Hand in glove with treatment, of course, is the need to recognize that a given patient's symptoms could be a manifestation of parasitic infection. In affluent societies the possibility of parasitic disease is often considered only when other causes have

Table 50.1.   Drugs for Parasitic Diseases

Drugs	Indications
Available from the CDC	
Pentamidine isethionate (Lomidine)	Pneumocystosis, African trypanosomiasis
Niclosamide (Yomesan)	Cestodiasis
Sodium antimony gluconate (Pentostam)	Leishmaniasis
Suramin (Bayer 205)	African trypanosomiasis, onchocerciasis
Melarsoprol (Mel B)	African trypanosomiasis
Bayer 2502 (Lampit)	American trypanosomiasis
Diloxanide furoate (Furamidel)	Amebiasis
Dehydroemetine	Amebiasis, liver flukes
Bithionol, N.F.	Paragonimiasis
Sodium antimony dimercaptosuccinate (Astiban)	Schistosomiasis
Metrifonate (Bilarcil)	Schistosomiasis
Quinine dihydrochloride	Pernicious malaria
Chloroquine hydrochloride	Pernicious malaria
Commonly available	
Pyrantel pamoate (Antiminth)	Hookworms, ascariasis, enterobiasis
Bephenium hydroxynaphthoate (Alcopara)	Hookworms
Piperazine citrate (Antepor)	Ascariasis
Mebendazole (Vermox)	Trichuriasis
Pyrvinium pamoate (Povan)	Enterobiasis

(Adapted from MMRW *29(11)*: 130, 1980, Center for Disease Control.)

been rendered unlikely. A careful history will often be required to suggest the true basis for a patient's condition. Persistent eosinophilia can be a clue, but generally specific pathognomonic signs are not present; hence an important element in proper diagnosis is an awareness that parasitic disease should be considered among the possibilities.

Almost inevitably, definite diagnosis depends upon the clinical laboratory. Usually this will consist of finding larvae, eggs, or mature parasites in an appropriate specimen. In recent years serologic and skin tests have become available as aids. The key to diagnosis, however, remains not so much in sophisticated laboratory analysis but in an awareness that parasitic diseases can and do afflict large numbers of humans in spite of the degree of their wealth, their social status, or the level of their education.

REFERENCES

Beck, J.W. and Davies, J.E.: Medical Parasitology. 2nd Ed. C.V. Mosby, St. Louis, 1976.

Chandler, A.C.: Introduction to Parasitology. 9th Ed. John Wiley and Sons, New York, 1955.

Faust, E.C., Russell, P.F., and Jung, R.C.: Craig and Faust's Clinical Parasitology. 8th Ed. Lea and Febiger, Philadelphia, 1970.

Gear, J.H.S.: Medicine in a Tropical Environment. A.A. Balkeena, Cape Town, 1977.

Schneierson, S.S.: Atlas of Diagnostic Microbiology. Abbott Laboratories, N. Chicago, 1971.

51

Protozoa

Marek Zaleski and
Roger K. Cunningham

The taxonomy of parasitic protozoa still remains the subject of dispute and occasionally undergoes significant changes as new facts come to light and new concepts are recognized. Table 51.1, which summarizes the presently accepted taxonomy, should be considered not as final but only as a framework for the discussion to be presented in this chapter. In the table only pathogenic species have been included, although some nonpathogenic protozoa will be discussed because sometimes they must be differentiated from those causing human diseases. A brief general description of basic features of protozoa should greatly facilitate subsequent discussion of individual species.

All members of the phylum *Protozoa* are single-cell organisms, each consisting of a nucleus and cytoplasm. The nucleus may be single or multiple depending on either the organism or a particular developmental stage. The cytoplasm enclosed within a cell membrane usually — although not always — contains typical organelles such as mitochondria, Golgi apparatus, endoplasmic reticulum, and various intracellular

vesicles. In addition to the ordinary structures, many organisms have highly specialized organelles or structures associated with strictly defined functions. This class of organelles or structures includes pseudopodia, flagella, cilia, kinetoplasts, undulating membranes, conoids, cytostomes (cellular alimentary openings), cytopyges (cellular excretory openings), and excretory and contractile vacuoles. Finally, many protozoa contain more or less characteristic inclusions, such as phagocytized particles, residues of nutrient material, or volutin granules.

The environmental requirements and metabolic features of protozoa are often poorly understood, but in many instances they appear unexpectedly complex.

The life history of protozoa in many instances consists of several stages forming a cycle composed of two distinct phases, asexual and sexual. Figure 51.1 represents a composite life cycle consisting of all basic stages. In reality, in some organisms some stages either do not exist or remain undescribed. The vegetative forms, usually called *trophozoites*, multiply asexually by

Table 51.1. Taxonomy of the Major Pathogenic Protozoa

Subphylum	Class	Order	Family	Genus	Species	Disease
Sarcomastigophora	Mastigophora (Zoomastigophora)[a]	Protomastigida	Trypanosomatidae	Trypanosoma	gambiense	Trypanosomiasis (sleeping sickness)
					rhodesiense	Sleeping sickness
					cruzi	Chagas' disease
				Leishmania	tropica	Cutaneous leishmaniasis (Oriental sore)
					brasiliensis	Mucocutaneous leishmaniasis (espundia)
					(pifanoi)	Cutaneous leishmaniasis
					(peruana)	Uta
					(mexicana)	Chiclero disease (buba, forest yaws)
					(guyanensis)	?
					donovani	Kala-azar
		Polymastigida	Hexamitidae	Giardia	lamblia	Giardiasis
		Trichomonadida	Trichomonadidae	Trichomonas	vaginalis	Trichomoniasis (vaginitis)
					hominis	Diarrhea (?)
	Sarcodina	Rhizopoda	Dimastigamoebidae	Acanthamoeba		Amebiasis (meningoencephalitis)
				Naegleria	fowleri	Primary amebic meningoencephalitis
			Entamoebidae	Entamoeba	histolytica	Amebiasis
				Dientamoeba	fragilis	Diarrhea (?)
Apicomplexa	Sporozoa	Eucoccidia (Eimerina)		Isospora	hominis	Isosporosis
				Sarcocystis	lindemanni[b]	Sarcocystosis
				Toxoplasma	gondii	Toxoplasmosis
				Pneumocystis	carinii	Interstitial atypical pneumonia
		Haemosporina		Plasmodium (Plasmodium)	vivax	Malaria (tertian)
					ovale	Malaria (tertian)
					malariae	Malaria (quartan)
				(Laverania)	falciparum	Malaria (malignant)
	Piroplasmea	Piroplasmida	Babesiidae	Babesia	bovis	Babesiosis
					divergens	Babesiosis
Ciliophora	Ciliatea	Spirotrichida	Bursaridae	Balantidium	coli	Balantidiasis (colitis)

[a] Subunits are given in parentheses.
[b] *Sarcocystis lindemanni* is sometimes considered a developmental stage of *Isospora hominis*.

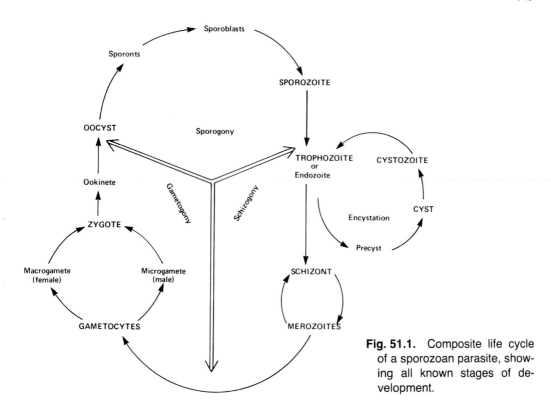

Fig. 51.1. Composite life cycle of a sporozoan parasite, showing all known stages of development.

binary fission or by multiple nuclear divisions followed by cytoplasmic segmentation. This asexual process, which in some instances is called *schizogony*, results in the production of new organisms sometimes called *merozoites*. In other life cycles, such as those of *Leishmania*, *Trypanosoma*, and *Trichomonas*, only asexual reproduction is known, although the former two genera undergo distinct morphological changes during multiplication. In some instances at a certain point dividing trophozoites become encapsulated and form a thick walled *cyst* containing either single or several organisms. Organisms enclosed in cysts are resistant to unfavorable external conditions; in this form they can be transferred from one host to another. A cystic stage is part of the life cycle of the genera *Giardia*, *Entamoeba*, *Isospora*, *Toxoplasma*, *Balantidium*, and *Pneumocystis*. Finally, in some protozoa merozoites differentiate into two sexually distinct cells (*gametocytes*) that

multiply and eventually fuse with each other, forming a single cell, a *zygote*. The process is called *gametogony* and results in formation of an *oocyst*. The cell inside a cyst undergoes several consecutive divisions, which is called *sporogony*, leading to formation of *sporozoites*. The life cycle of organisms belonging to genera *Isospora*, *Toxoplasma*, and *Plasmodium* contains gametogony and sporogony stages.

PARASITIC PROTOZOA OF THE CLASS ZOOMASTIGOPHORA

Members of three families, *Trypanosomatidae*, *Hexamitidae* and *Trichomonaidae*, are pathogenic for humans and will be discussed here in greater detail.

Pathogenic genera of the family *Trypanosomatidae*, *Trypanosoma* and *Leishmania*, may occur in four morphologically distinct stages representing consecu-

644   Medical Microbiology

Table 51.2. Site of the Various Morphological Forms of *Trypanosoma* and *Leishmania* spp. in Their Hosts

Genus	Species	Forms			
		Amastigote	Promastigote	Epimastigote	Trypomastigote
Trypanosoma	*gambiense*	—	Tsetse fly (salivary glands)	Tsetse fly (salivary glands)	Tsetse fly (proboscis); man (blood, lymph nodes)
	rhodesiense	—	Tsetse fly (salivary glands)	Tsetse fly (salivary glands)	Tsetse fly (proboscis); man (blood, lymph nodes, CNS)
	cruzi	Triatomid bug (gut) Man (skin, liver, spleen, myocardium, CNS)	Triatomid bug (hindgut)	Triatomid bug (midgut)	Triatomid bug (feces); man (blood after infection)
Leishmania	*tropica*	Man (skin)	Sandfly (midgut)	—	—
	brasiliense	Man (skin, mucosa)	Sandfly (midgut)	—	—
	donovani	Man (liver, spleen, lymph nodes)	Sandfly (midgut)	—	—

tive developmental forms (Table 51.2). The amastigote stage is an intracellular form that appears as a small round cell without a flagellum but with a distinct basal body. The promastigote is an elongated cell with a terminal flagellum, and the epimastigote has a flagellum beginning in the midportion of the cell. The trypomastigote stage represents the most mature form, with a flagellum that begins in the caudal portion of the cell and forms a well developed undulating membrane. These four forms were formerly referred to as leishmanial, leptomonad, crithidial, and trypanosome stages.

Besides the morphological stages, both genera display striking similarities in the life cycle in that they have two hosts, one being man or some other mammal and the other being an insect vector.

Trypanosoma gambiense

Morphology. When observed in peripheral blood, *T. gambiense* is a slender organism. In stained preparations (Fig. 51.2) it measures 14 to 33 μm by 1.5 to

3.5 μm and has pale blue cytoplasm with azurophilic granules of volutin. A large nucleus is located near the posterior end.

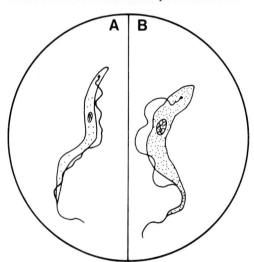

Fig. 51.2. (A) *Trypanosoma gambiense* and (B) *Trypanosoma rhodesiense* as seen in peripheral blood (× 1800). Note that *T. gambiense* is more slender and less curved and has less granular cytoplasm, but the differences are too subtle to be used for differential diagnosis.

Life Cycle and Epidemiology. *T. gambiense* is found in West and Central African waterfront woodlands within a broad belt covering the territory between Senegal, Uganda, and the Republic of Congo. In this area tsetse flies, *Glossina palpalis*, acquire parasites by biting infected humans. Trypanosomes reach the mid- and posterior gut of the fly, where they multiply and then migrate through the esophagus and labial cavity to the salivary glands. The process requires about 20 days and consists of transformation from trypomastigote through the promastigote and epimastigote stages to metacyclic trypomastigote. The last is transmitted back to humans by the bite of a tsetse fly. Since man is the only known source, the infection occurs in relatively densely populated areas and occasionally results in epidemics. After being introduced to man, the parasites live extracellularly in the blood, lymph nodes, and central nervous system.

Clinical Symptoms. Infection with *T. gambiense*, after 20 to 23 days of incubation, results in a chronic generalized disease called African sleeping sickness. The most characteristic course of this disease consists of an initial chancre at the site of bite, followed by the dissemination of parasites and a protracted lymphadenitis accompanied by hepatosplenomegaly, which, after several years, leads to leptomeningitis followed by encephalitis and death. In a few instances, however, a spontaneous recovery at earlier stages may occur.

Diagnosis is relatively easy on the basis of history and clinical symptoms, such as irregular fever in the form of periodic attacks, lymphadenitis characteristically affecting postcervical lymph nodes (Winterbottom's sign), and neurologic signs including muscular weakness, cramps, tremor, incoordination, chorea, paralysis, apathy, excitability, delusions, and coma. The diagnosis should be confirmed by demonstration of parasites in the blood, lymph node biopsy material, or cerebrospinal fluid although in later stages this may be difficult, with repeated examinations often needed to find parasites in blood. Serologic tests consisting of precipitation, complement fixation, or indirect fluorescence using whole organisms or extracts as antigens are helpful but not always reliable. Animal inoculation may also be used for demonstration of parasites.

Pathology. The lymph nodes are originally enlarged and soft, displaying hyperplasia and plasmacytosis, but at later stages they become smaller and harder, with histiocytosis and fibrosis.

In the central nervous system the soft meninges are congested and infiltrated, especially around vessels. In the nervous tissue itself, perivascular and diffuse infiltrates composed of lymphocytes and plasma cells are a striking feature together with proliferation of glial cells and degeneration of neurons and fibers. In the late stages of disease parasites are seldom if ever found in peripheral blood.

Trypanosoma rhodesiense

Morphology. This organism is indistinguishable from *T. gambiense* (Fig. 51.2). In fact, it is suggested that both organisms represent evolutionary variants of a common ancestral genus, *T. brucei*, which causes nagana (or n'gana) disease of cattle.

Life Cycle and Epidemiology. *T. rhodesiense* is found in wooded tracts of savannah in rather sparsely populated areas of Rwanda, Burundi, Uganda, Tanzania, Sudan, Kenya, Mozambique, Zimbabwe, and Botswana. Wild game constitute a natural reservoir from which tsetse flies, *Glossina morsitans*, acquire parasites. During its sojourn in insects, *T. rhodesiense* undergoes transformations similar to those of *T. gambiense* and as a metacyclic trypomastigote is transferred to humans. Because of epidemiologic factors infection with *T. rhodesiense* occurs rather sporadically.

Clinical Symptoms. Ordinarily, infection results in an acute disease that leads to death within weeks. Alternatively a more protracted fatal course of 6 to 9 months may take place during which pronounced nervous system involvement occurs. Clinically, the disease is characterized by frequent and irregular bouts of fever, moderate lymphadenopathy, and progressive pancarditis. Neurologic symptoms are found only in some cases.

Tentative clinical diagnosis should be confirmed by demonstration of parasites either directly or by biologic tests in which material from suspected cases is inoculated into rats.

Pathology. While morphological changes in lymphoid tissue are not different from those caused by *T. gambiense*, changes in nerve tissue are negligible. On the other hand, serous cavity effusions consisting of lymphocytes and mesothelial cells and diffuse or focal infiltrates in the myocardium are typical. Edema, focal necrosis, and fibrosis of the myocardium with general hypertrophy of the heart are common findings in this form of trypanosomiasis. Hyperplasia of the reticuloendothelial system in liver and spleen commonly results in hepatosplenomegaly.

Trypanosoma cruzi

Morphology. *T. cruzi* in humans is found in two distinct forms (Fig. 51.3). The trypomastigote stage found in blood is a slender (20 μm) organism shaped like the letter C with a distinct undulating membrane. After invading various cells (reticuloendothelial, muscle, or glial), they transform into the amastigote stage. These are small (3 μm) round bodies strikingly similar to *L. donovani* (see below).

Life Cycle and Epidemiology. *T. cruzi* is found in semiarid areas of South America and Central America and occasionally in the South and West of the United States. Wild foxes, rats, raccoons, monkeys, ante-

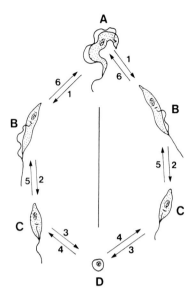

Fig. 51.3. Different morphological forms of *Trypanosoma cruzi*: (A) trypomastigote, (B) epimastigote, (C) promastigote, and (D) amastigote (× 1600). Similar transformation takes place in humans (right) and the vector insect (left), following the sequence indicated by numbers close to arrows.

lopes, and armadillos as well as domestic dogs and cats constitute a reservoir from which 37 to 50 percent of nocturnal insects belonging to a group called triatomid bugs (*Triatoma infestans, Triatoma sordita, Triatoma braziliensis, Triatoma sanguisuga, Panstrongylus megistrus*, and *Rhodnius prolixus*) become infected. Upon entry into an insect, the parasite undergoes transformation over 8 to 10 days from trypomastigote through the epimastigote and promastigote stages, after which it returns to the trypomastigote stage. The latter are expelled with the feces of the insect when it feeds, thus effecting entry into a human through insect feces contaminating the site of an insect bite. A less common means of transmission is directly among humans via coitus, ingestion of maternal milk, blood transfusion, or transplacentally. Ocular inoculation may occur by rubbing of insect feces into the conjunctiva. Trypanosomes that enter blood vessels invade various cells, where they transform into the amastigote stage, multiply by binary fission, filling the cytoplasm, and then transform through promastigote and epimastigote stages to trypomastigotes. During this 3- or 4-day transformation process parasites are released from the cell and reinvade other cells, where the process is repeated. Infections predominate in economically poor communities due to infestation of dwellings with vector insects.

Clinical Symptoms.   Infection with *T. cruzi*, after 7 to 21 days of incubation, results in a generalized illness known as Chagas' disease. The initial sign resulting from an insect bite is an inflammatory reaction consisting of infiltration with lymphocytes, histiocytes, plasmacytes, and neutrophils. It forms an encapsulated focus or ulceration called a *chagoma* and usually is accompanied by localized edema. Since a common site of the insect bite is the border between skin and conjunctiva, a unilateral swelling of eyelids (Romaña's sign) due to blockage of lymphatics is a characteristic early sign of infection. From the primary sites parasites are disseminated via blood vessels to various tissues and organs. Parasites usually invade macrophages, fat cells, muscle cells, and neurons. Some authors, on the basis of cellular tropism, distinguish two strains of *T. cruzi*, a myotropic Colombian strain and a reticuloendotheliotropic Y strain.

At least five distinct clinical forms of Chagas' disease — acute, latent, cardiac, digestive, and congenital — are recognized. The acute form usually affects small children and is characterized by fever, lymphadenopathy, and hepatosplenomegaly. In 90 percent of cases symptoms subside spontaneously within 2 to 3 months, with the acute form becoming the latent form. The latter may be symptomless for indefinite periods, with the person continuing to carry parasites. In 10 percent of acute cases, however, symptoms persist and signs of involvement of meninges and brain develop, followed by death in 2 to 4 weeks. Either latent or acute forms may evolve into heart disease in which parasitic invasion of cardiac muscle leads to carditis, either acute in children or chronic in adults, with subsequent typical signs of cardiac failure within a year. Similarly, invasion and destruction of ganglionic cells of the Auerbach plexus of the esophagus or colon results in the digestive form of Chagas' disease, characterized by disturbances in motility and dilation of corresponding segments of digestive tract. This form occurs endemically in some regions of Brazil. Parasites may also invade the placenta, causing its dysfunction and infection or damage to the fetus (premature birth or stillbirth).

Diagnosis established on the basis of the clinical course and symptoms should be confirmed directly by demonstration of parasites in the blood or lymph node biopsy material or indirectly by infecting guinea pigs or insects fed on the patient's blood. The complement fixation (Marchado-Guerreiro) test with trypanosomal antigen is useful especially in the latent, cardiac, and digestive forms.

Pathology.   Macroscopically, the heart usually is enlarged with apical thrombosis. Microscopically, one sees interfibrillar edema and hyaline necrosis characterized by appearance of dense transverse bands (Magannos-Toures sign). In fully developed carditis there is diffused lymphoplasmacytic infiltration and varying degrees of necrosis and fibrosis. In the nervous system focal and diffuse infiltration is accompanied by glial proliferation and neuronophagia. In the digestive form infiltration and necrosis of neurons in the muscular layer of the intestinal tract are typically seen. The infiltrates observed in chronic stages of Chagas' disease are sometimes considered to be a result of hypersensitivity, since they are found also after inoculation of killed parasites.

Leishmania tropica

Morphology. In humans the parasites found in the macrophages and endothelial cells of skin occur exclusively as amastigotes in the form of small (2 to 3 μm) round intracellular organisms (Fig. 51.4) with pale basophilic cytoplasm and a distinct parabasal body. However, when cultured *in vitro* the organisms assume the promastigote form, appearing as fusiform cells (15 to 25 μm by 1.5 to 3.5 μm) with a terminal flagellum.

Life Cycle and Epidemiology. *L. tropica* is encountered along the West and North coasts of Africa, in Central Asia from Turkey to India, and in the Mediterranean region of Europe. The natural reservoir consists of wild rodents, dogs, and humans, whereas females of different species of the sandfly (*Phlebotomus*) serve as vectors. On rare occasions, the stable fly (*Stomoxys calcitrans*) may mechanically transfer the parasite from one host to another. Upon infecting the sandfly, the parasite undergoes transformation from amastigote to promastigote in the gut and then gains entrance to the salivary glands, from whence it is inoculated into humans when the sandfly feeds. The promastigotes inoculated into skin of man invade macrophages, where they transform into the amastigote form and multiply, spreading to other cells in the vicinity. There are two types of *L. tropica*, major and minor, distinguishable by epidemiologic, serologic, and clinical features (Table 51.3).

Clinical Symptoms. After the incubation period of a few days to several months *L. tropica* causes a characteristic skin disease known as Oriental sore. In uncomplicated cases the site of the bite becomes raised and indurated and forms a reddish papule that after some time becomes covered with whitish scales and eventually ulcerates with relatively little reaction. Regional lymph nodes may occasionally be enlarged. Several months to a year later the sore heals spontaneously, leaving an inconspicuous depigmented scar. In some instances, especially in the Middle East, a single nodule or sore spreads centrifugally, with healing in the center and appearance of new lesions in the periphery. This process may last many years; since clinically it resembles skin tuberculosis, it is called leishmania lupoid or leishmaniasis recidiva. Interestingly, the lesions that may represent a hypersensitivity reaction to the parasite contain very few organisms, if any.

Diagnosis is confirmed by the demonstration of the typical parasites in material from the lesion. In case of diagnostic difficulties one may resort to the Montenegro skin test, in which a standardized suspension of killed leishmania is injected intradermally. Induration larger than 5 mm after 48 to 72 hours, sometimes accompanied by edema or blistering, indicates sensitivity. The posi-

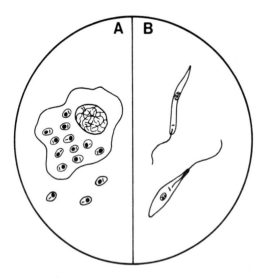

Fig. 51.4. (A) *Leishmania tropica* in biopsy material from an Oriental sore and (B) promastigote forms of this parasite found in the vector insect ($\times$ 1600). Note presence of intracellular, in macrophage, and extracellular parasites in human material.

Table 51.3 Comparison of *Leishmania tropica* major and minor

	L. tropica major	*L. tropica* minor
Natural reservoir	Wild rodents (gerbils) Dogs	Dogs Man
Vectors	Outdoor-living sandflies *Phlebotomus papatasii* *Ph. caucasicus*	Indoor-living sandflies *Ph. sergenti* *Ph. papatasii* *Ph. perfilevi* *Ph. perniciosus*
Geographic distribution	Middle East and Asia	Mediterranean region and Africa
Disease	Moist or rural sore	Dry or urban sore
Victims	Children and visitors to endemic areas	Adults
Prevention	Extermination of reservoir, active immunzation[a]	Extermination of vector

[a] Subcutaneous injection of live culture of *L. tropica.*

tive reaction develops early in the course of disease and remains for life.

Pathology. Histologic changes are limited to the skin and lymph nodes and consist of focal necrosis, lymphoplasmacytic infiltration, and granulation and hyperplasia of the epidermis that resembles epithelioma. Often secondary bacterial infection is encountered.

Leishmania brasiliensis

Morphology. Morphologically, *L. brasiliensis* is identical with *L. tropica*. However, at least five serologically distinct variants are recognized: *L. pifanoi, L. brasiliensis, L. guyanensis, L. peruana,* and *L. mexicana.*

Life Cycle and Epidemiology. The life cycle of *L. brasiliensis* is grossly similar to that of *L. tropica*. A natural reservoir consisting of dogs, cats, some rodents, and monkeys provides the source of parasites for sandflies (genus *Luzomyia*), which serve as the vectors. The parasite occurs usually endemically, but occasional epidemics are reported.

Clinical Symptoms. Infection with *L. brasiliensis* results in a disease summarily

known as leishmaniasis. However, on the basis of geographical distribution and clinical features four discrete forms (Table 51.4) are distinguished.

In all instances, the clinical diagnosis should be confirmed by demonstrating parasites in biopsy material as well as with immunologic tests such as the Montenegro skin test.

Pathology. Skin and mucous membrane lesions consist of infiltrates composed of lymphocytes, plasma cells, and histiocytes. Subsequently, necrosis and ulceration of the epidermis with an accumulation of neutrophils and epithelial hyperplasia develop. Invariably, numerous parasites are detectable in histiocytes of the dermis. In some instances microgranulomata (tubercles) composed of polykaryocytes and epithelioid cells may be found. Their presence usually indicates a relatively high degree of resistance to the parasite. In the later stages fibrous scars that do not contain parasites can be demonstrated.

Leishmania donovani

Morphology. In humans *L. donovani* is found exclusively as the amastigote form

Table 51.4.   Different Clinical Forms of Mucocutaneous Leishmaniasis

	Chiclero Ulcer (Buba, Forest Yaws, Bay Sore)	Espundia	Uta	Diffuse Cutaneous Leishmaniasis (Leproid, Cheloid)
Causative agent	*Leishmania mexicana*	*L. brasiliensis*	*L. peruana*	?
Geographic distribution	Central America (rain forest)	Central and South America	Peru	Venezuela, Ethiopia, Sudan
Natural reservoir	Rodents (mice, rats)	Rodents (paca, pacarana, spotted cavy)	Dogs	Unidentified
Vector	Outdoor-living sand flies *Phlebotomus paraensis* *Ph. cruciatus* *Ph. flaviscutellata*	Indoor- and outdoor-living sandflies	Indoor-living sandflies *Ph. peruensis*	?
Victims	Adult males (collectors of chicle or gum)	Adult men and women (new settlers)	Adult men and women	Adult men and women
Clinical picture and course	Small nodule on exposed skin, self-healing within 6 months; lesion located on earlobe heals with considerable destruction of tissue	Small ulcerating nodule on exposed skin, self-healing within 6–24 months. After 2 years hematogenous metastases in mucocutaneous junctions (nose, mouth, anus, vagina), with destruction and granulation resulting in serious deformations	Single self-limiting and self-healing lesion	Single lesions developing into lepromalike granulomas, resulting in extensive destruction of extremities (fingers); Montenegro skin test remains negative during disease
Prevention	Fly repellants, active immunization	Extermination of reservoir (rodents), extermination of vector (flies), fly repellants	Extermination of vector (flies)	None

called L-D bodies. These are small (4 to 5 μm) organisms with basophilic cytoplasm, a distinct nucleus and parabasal body. The parasites are found intracellularly in both free and tissue histiocytes. In flies promastigote forms, fusiform (15 to 25 μm by 1.5 to 3.5 μm) or rounded with flagellum, are commonly encountered.

Life Cycle and Epidemiology. The parasite is found in endemic foci in South America (Brazil, Guyana, and Paraguay), East Africa (Sudan, Ethiopia, Somalia, and

Kenya), Asia (India and China) and the Mediterranean region (Maghreb and the Middle East). The natural reservoir, vectors, and the mode of transmission vary depending on geographical region (see below). However, the basic life cycle is essentially the same and consists of acquisition by sandflies of amastigote forms from an infected human or animal. The amastigotes transform in the gut of sandflies to promastigotes, which multiply for 5 days before the insect becomes able to infect. In addition to the most common transmission by flies, oral and direct contact infections are known. The promastigote introduced to a human during a fly bite invades local macrophages, where it transforms into an amastigote and multiplies slowly for several weeks or months. Ultimately, infected macrophages or free parasites from the primary lesion are disseminated via lymphatics and blood vessels to various organs, where parasites invade numerous macrophages in which they rapidly multiply.

Clinical Symptoms. Infection with *L. donovani* results is a generalized reticulo-endotheliosis known as kala-azar. The disease, if untreated, is in 90 percent of cases fatal within 6 to 24 months, but if treated properly it has a good prognosis in the vast majority of cases. Table 51.5 summarizes the epidemiologic features of four discrete forms of kala-azar that clinically are quite similar.

After 3 to 5 months of parasite incubation the developing general malaise in the host is accompanied by an irregular undulant fever, progressive emaciation, anemia, neutropenia, hepatosplenomegaly, lymphadenopathy, and often skin hyperpigmentation, papular rash, diarrhea, intestinal bleeding, jaundice, and occasionally hypersplenism. The most common complication, occurring in 2 to 20 percent of untreated or incorrectly treated Indian and African forms, is dermal leishmanoid, which is characterized by disseminated papular depigmented eruptions. Other complications include agranulocytosis, cancrum (necrosis of the mouth wall due to leukopenia), and amyloidosis.

Clinical diagnosis is supported by a for-

Table 51.5.   Different Clinical Forms of Kala-Azar

	Indian	Mediterranean	African	American
Geographic distribution	India Kenya Sudan	Southern Europe China Mideast	South of Sahara Somalia	Brazil Paraguay Central America
Natural reservoir	Man	Dogs, jackals, foxes	Rodents (gerbils)	Dogs
Vector[a]	Indoor-living sandflies *Phlebotomus argentipes*	Indoor-living sandflies *Ph. perniciosus* *Ph. chinensis* *Ph. perfilevi* *Ph. papatasii*	Outdoor-living sandflies *Ph. orientalis* *Ph. martini* *Ph. sergenti*	Indoor-living sandflies *Ph. longipalpis* *Ph. intermedius* *Ph. panamensis*
Victims	Older children	Infants	Adolescents	Young children
Prevention	Extermination of vector, protection from fly bites	Screening and extermination of reservoir, extermination of vector, protection from fly bites	Screening and treating people, protection from fly bites	Screening and extermination of reservoir, extermination of vector, protection from fly bites

[a] Only most common species are listed.

malin-gel reaction in which because of hyperglobulinemia the serum of patients coagulates after it is treated with 40 percent formaldehyde. A more specific indication of kala-azar is a complement fixation test employing the Kedrovsky strain of *Mycobacterium leprae* as an antigen. The test becomes positive early in a course of disease and stays so until 6 to 8 weeks after complete cure. Definitive diagnosis is accomplished by demonstration of parasites in biopsy material of lymph node or spleen.

Pathology. Macroscopically, the spleen and liver are extremely enlarged. In both organs pronounced hyperplasia of the reticuloendothelial system with many cells containing intracellular parasites is found. Similar changes are observed in the heart, lymph nodes, bone marrow, kidneys, and lungs but not in skeletal muscles or nervous tissue. Erythroid hyperplasia and myeloid hypoplasia are seen in bone marrow.

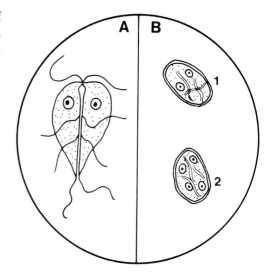

Fig. 51.5. (A) *Giardia lamblia* trophozoite in the duodenal content and (B) cysts found in stools (× 1600). (1) Immature cyst contains two nuclei; (2) in the mature cyst four nuclei are visible.

Giardia lamblia

Morphology. The organism occurs in two forms, trophozoite and cyst (Fig. 51.5). The binucleated trophozoite, measuring 9 to 21 μm by 5 to 15 μm by 5 μm has a heart shape divided by an *axostyle*, with four pairs of flagella emerging at different locations. Viewed from the side, the trophozoite has a crescent shape with a sucking plate or disc located on the concave ventral surface. While the trophozoites are found in the lumen of small intestine, often attached to epithelium, the cysts are present in the large intestine and in formed stools. The oval shaped cyst measures 8 to 12 μm by 7 to 10 μm and, when mature, contains four nuclei and intracytoplasmic fibrils.

Life Cycle and Epidemiology. *G. lamblia* is a cosmopolitan parasite found predominantly in children. The rate of infection ranges from 2 to 47 percent in children depending on socioeconomic conditions. It is more frequently encountered in

warm climates and in poor hygienic conditions. The frequency of infection decreases at puberty, perhaps as the result of development of specific immunity to the parasite. The parasite has a simple life cycle consisting of two alternate stages, trophozoite and cyst. The latter is excreted in normal stools and can infect directly or by contaminated food either the same host or different individuals. There is no apparent animal reservoir, although dogs have been implicated. The ingested cyst, after reaching the small intestine, releases two trophozoites, which are noninvasive and remain in the intestinal lumen.

Clinical Symptoms. It is not entirely clear whether development of overt disease (giardiasis) is triggered by some specific factors or merely reflects extraordinarily heavy infection. The clinical picture is not typical and consists of irregular, dull, epigastric pains or colic, variable intensity chronic diarrhea or steatorrhea, poor appetite, weight loss, and, in severe cases, jaundice or celiac syndrome. One should consider giardiasis in any recurring stomachaches in children.

Diagnosis can be achieved only by demonstration of parasites in duodenal content (trophozoites) or stools (cysts and, during diarrhea, trophozoites).

Pathology. The histologic picture of giardiasis is far from typical. Short and thick villi, focal infiltrates composed of neutrophils and eosinophils, hypervacuolization of epithelium, and often increased mitotic activity in crypts are consistent with giardiasis.

Trichomonas vaginalis

Morphology. Thus far only a single form, the trophozoite, is known (Fig. 51.6). It is oval or pear shaped (7 to 30 μm by 5 to 12 μm) with five flagella, of which four emerge from the anterior pole, with the fifth connected to the cell by an undulating membrane. The lightly basophilic cytoplasm contains siderophilic granules but no mitochondria. A rigid structure, the axostyle, runs through the whole body and pierces the cell membrane at the caudal end. The single nucleus lies eccentrically in the vicinity of the cystostome. *In vivo* trichomonads may ingest bacteria and the host's erythrocytes.

Life Cycle and Epidemiology. *T. vaginalis* has no discernible life cycle; the trophozoite proliferates by binary fission and is sensitive to temperatures above 40°C, dessication, light, and water. The organism lives in the relatively acid (pH 5.5) environment of the vagina, the prostate, and the urethra. It is transferred from one individual to another during coitus, with the male partner being a vector from one female to another. However, since trichomonads are also found often in newborn girls and girls before puberty, nonsexual transmission by direct or indirect contact is apparently possible.

Clinical Symptoms. The infection is most frequent (about 25 percent) in women

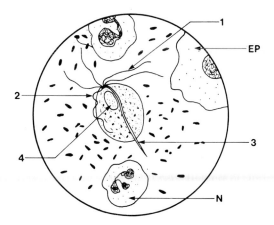

Fig. 51.6. *Trichomonas vaginalis* in vaginal discharge (× 1600). (1) Free flagella, (2) undulating membrane, (3) axostyle, and (4) light vesicular nucleus of parasite are visible. Also, neutrophils (N), epithelial cells (EP), and numerous bacteria (black rods and granules) can be seen.

of 30 to 50 years of age, especially those with poor hygienic habits. In males the frequency is much lower (4 to 9 percent). Overt clinical symptoms occur only in some infected people, while others (about 20 percent) are symptomless carriers. The most common syndrome is acute vaginitis, but bartholinitis, cystitis, urethritis, or prostatovesiculitis have also been reported. At present it is debatable whether the parasite causes inflammation directly or whether its growth and expansion is facilitated by inflammation caused by other factors. Clinically, trichomonal vaginitis is characterized by irregular periods of inflammation, green-yellowish discharge, and coexistence of infection with gram-negative rods or gram-positive cocci. The association with veneral disease, such as gonorrhea, is only incidental. Diagnosis is confirmed by finding the parasites in a vaginal discharge or cervical smears. The parasites must be distinguished from other cells on smears by the appearance of the nucleus.

Pathology. Histologic changes in the early stages are limited to the vaginal epithelium, with intracellular edema, vacuolization, perinuclear halo, hyperchromia, and hyperkeratosis. In the advanced stages intercellular edema, desquamation, and erosions of the epithelium are accompanied by diffuse infiltration composed of lymphocytes, plasma cells, and neutrophils. The epithelial changes (atypia, metaplasia, hyperkeratosis, enlarged nuclei) may mimic early neoplastic changes. Also, the changes associated with trichomoniasis obscure those related to cytohormonal cycles sometimes resembling hyperestrogenism due to an increased number of squamous cells.

Trichomonas hominis

Morphology. Morphologically, this organism is quite similar to *T. vaginalis* except for smaller size (4 to 15 μm by 7 to 10 μm), a fifth flagellum extending beyond the cell body as a free fibril, and occasional formation of pseudopodia.

Life Cycle and Epidemiology. This cosmopolitan parasite is most frequently found in children in warm climates. It occurs only as a trophozoite found in stools with which it is excreted. The stool trophozoite may be mechanically transmitted by flies and ingested with contaminated food. Provided that the stomach acids are neutralized, the trophozoite may survive passage through stomach and populate the intestines.

Clinical symptoms. Pathogenicity of *T. hominis* is still doubtful, although it can be found in stools during relatively mild diarrhea. The importance of diagnosis lies in differentiating commensals such as this from pathogens as well as indicating contact with material contaminated with feces.

PARASITES OF THE CLASS SARCODINA

This large class of protozoa consists of many orders, of which only *Rhizopoda* contains proven pathogenic organisms. These organisms belong to two families, *Dimasti-*

gamoebidae and *Entamoebidae*. Characteristically, members of the order *Rhizopoda* form pseudopodia when they are in trophozoite stage; thus they have no defined shape. They have a simple life cycle (trophozoite and cyst) and multiply asexually by binary fission.

Dimastigamoebidae

Morphology. Pathogenic organisms belong to two ill-distinguished genera, *Hartmannella* and *Acanthamoeba*. They may live freely in damp soil in association with fungi that parasitize clover. They are easily grown *in vitro* in the presence of bacteria (aerobacter). The sluggish trophozoites, 9 to 30 μm in size, have characteristic spiky pseudopodia and granular cytoplasm with a contractile vacuole. The large round nucleus has a distinct karyosome and is surrounded by a halo. *In vivo* the organisms must be distinguished from macrophages. The cysts are small with a refractile double membrane and characteristic pores. Little is known about the life cycle or epidemiology of these parasites.

Clinical Symptoms. Until 1965 only eight cases of infection with *Dimastigamoebidae* had been reported. All of them corresponded to an acute meningitis or meningoencephalitis accompanied by dissemination of parasites in all organs and formation of microabscesses. The atypical symptoms and the fulminating course (4 to 14 days) of the disease makes timely parasitologic diagnosis virtually impossible. The mode of transmission is unknown, although it appears that saliva and tears promote mobility of parasites which together with pronounced involvement of the olfactory areas of the brain suggests possible invasion via the nostrils.

Naegleria fowleri

Morphology. Characteristically, trophozoites may occur in two distinct forms, amebas or flagellates.

Clinical Symptoms. Until the early 1970s 39 cases, all fatal, had been reported, of which 17 occurred in the United States (Virginia, Florida, and Texas). Most of the patients had had contact with water (swimming) and probably became infected by a nasal route. After a short prodromal period (sore throat, nasal discharge) meningoencephalitis rapidly evolved, leading to death within 4 to 7 days. Diagnosis is difficult because symptoms are not typical and cerebrospinal fluid presents an uncharacteristic picture (low pleocytosis, high concentration of protein and sugar, few and difficult-to-see trophozoites).

Pathology. Autopsy reveals generalized meningoencephalitis with focal necrosis in olfactory bulbs and temporal lobes and groups of extracellular parasites in the gray matter.

Entamoeba histolytica

Morphology. *E. histolytica* (Fig. 51.7) has two forms, a trophozoite, found either in unformed stools or in tissues, and a cyst, found in formed stools. The trophozoite (6 to 40 μm) has blunt pseudopodia and moves actively without any linear direction. The cytoplasm is distinctly divided into homogeneous ectoplasm and granular endoplasm. The latter contains vacuoles with ingested erythrocytes, nucleated cells, and bacteria. Neither mitochondria nor Golgi apparatus can be demonstrated. The nucleus is quite large, with regular beadlike peripheral chromatin and a central karyosome. The trophozoite, after several divisions by binary fission, becomes rounded, expels vacuoles, and aggregates glycogen. In this stage, called the *precyst*, it becomes surrounded by a thick wall, and in the cytoplasm large chromatoid bodies appear. Ultimately, both glycogen and the chromatoid bodies disappear and the nucleus divides twice. The resulting mature cyst, containing four nuclei, is infective.

The sizes of both trophozoites and cysts vary within a wide range. It is speculated

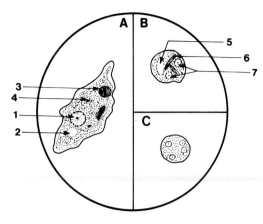

Fig. 51.7. *Entamoeba histolytica*: (A) trophozoite, (B) immature cyst, and (C) mature cyst (× 1000). Note in trophozoite (1) nucleus, hyaline ectoplasm and granular endoplasm that contains (2) vacuoles and (3 and 4) ingested erythrocytes in various stages of decomposition. Immature cysts contain (5) a glycogen mass, (6) chromatoid bodies, and (7) two nuclei, whereas mature cysts contain four nuclei but no other structures.

that *E. histolytica* represents several species or subspecies differing in size, pathogenicity, and probably antigenic structure. Commonly, two subspecies are distinguished. One, *E. hartmanni*, has a small trophozoite (less than 12 μm) and small cyst (less than 10 μm). The other, *E. histolytica*, has a large trophozoite (17 to 40 μm) and cyst (larger than 10 μm) and is found in patients with severe disease. There are medium sized forms isolated from cases of mild and chronic disease. The complexity of *E. histolytica* causes a great deal of dispute regarding its relationship to other entamoebae and necessitates differentiation from nonpathogenic amebas (see below).

Life Cycle and Epidemiology. *E. histolytica* has cosmopolitan distribution, although it is more frequently found in warm climates or the tropics. Dogs, pigs, and monkeys serve as natural reservoirs. The organism has a simple life cycle that consists of trophozoite, precyst, cyst, and metacystic trophozoites. It takes place in the lumen of the intestines. The cyst expelled with feces is quite resistant and survives up to 12 days. It is transmitted by water, food, cockroaches, and flies or by direct contact with objects contaminated with feces. The so-called metacystic organism, containing four nuclei, is released from cysts in the small intestine and divides into single-nucleus trophozoites that migrate to the cecum. Colonization of the cecum and subsequent invasion of mucosa is accomplished by still unknown mechanisms, although participation of lytic enzymes produced by amebas is often discussed. Both colonization and invasion are facilitated by several factors such as malnutrition (excess of carbohydrates, deficiency of vitamin C), mechanical or chemical injury of intestinal mucosa, stress, and bacterial infections (streptococci, *Escherichia coli*, *Salmonella enteriditis*, *Enterobacter aerogenes*). In addition, various strains of amebas have various degrees of genetically determined pathogenicity that, depending on environmental conditions, influence the virulence of the organism.

The frequency of infection with *E. histolytica* varies in different geographic regions, being as low as 0.1 percent in the United States and as high as 98 percent in some regions of Egypt. Not all persons infected with the entamoebae develop overt disease. Those persons who develop disease are more frequently males 25 to 40 years old in warm climates and in poor hygienic conditions. The symptomless (healthy) carriers may be considered as either totally resistant or as having subclinical disease with only microscopically detectable lesions. Epidemiologically, a state of harboring the parasites, regardless of clinical symptoms, is classified as amebiasis.

Clinical Symptoms. The basic clinical syndrome caused by infection with pathogenic *E. histolytica* is that of amebic dysentery (amebic colitis) usually developing after about 1 to 4 months of incubation. The symptoms appear gradually as episodes of diarrhea, cramps, nausea, vomiting, malaise, and so on, but in some instances sudden onset with acute diarrhea and pain may dominate the picture. This primary disease may be and often is complicated by dissemination of parasites either by continuity or by a hematogenous route. The most common complications of amebic colitis are intestinal perforation, localized or generalized peritonitis (1.5 to 21 percent), amebic hepatitis (7 to 50 percent), empyema, pericarditis, and abscesses in such organs as lungs (18 percent), brain (8 percent), or skin (occasionally).

The clinical diagnosis of fully developed disease is relatively easy on the basis of typical symptoms. Nevertheless, it should be confirmed by demonstration of parasites in the intestines (stools or enteroscopic biopsy), liver lesions, pleural cavity, or skin. Depending on the source of material, either trophozoites (in unformed stools, biopsy specimens, and sputum) or cysts (in formed stools) can be found. The latter appear cyclically; thus repeated examinations must be made with both direct films and concentrated samples. In making a microscopic diagnosis one must be aware of the possibility of the presence of different nonpathogenic organisms belonging to the family *Entamoebidae*. Figure 51.8 summarizes the most characteristic features of *E. histolytica* and those of nonpathogenic organisms encountered in stool. Immunologic tests such as complement fixation, passive hemagglutination, precipitation, or immunofluorescence may be employed but are not considered routine. ELISA tests on stool specimens have been developed and are available.

Pathology. Changes observed in intestines represent an evolution of lesions from microscopic damage of epithelium to extensive ulceration seen macroscopically. The primary ulcers occur predominantly in the cecum. The parasites penetrate the epithelium and mucous membrane via narrow channels, and then lytic necrosis spreads in

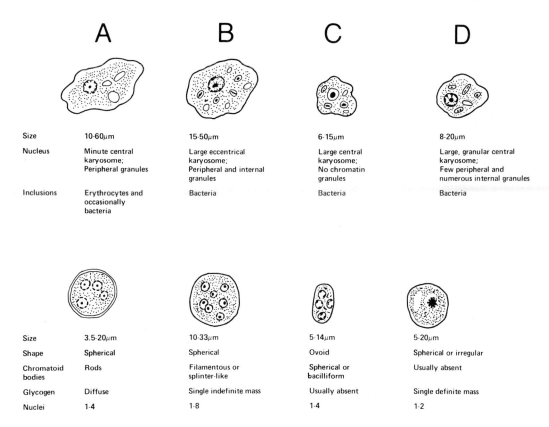

Fig. 51.8. Morphology of hematoxylin stained trophozoites (upper row) and mature cysts (lower row) of most common enteric *Entamoebidae*: (A) *Entamoeba histolytica*, (B) *Entamoeba coli*, (C) *Endolimax nana*, and (D) *Iodamoeba buetschlii* (× 1000). In the description cystic features of those immature (chromatoid bodies and glycogen) and mature (maximal number of nuclei) forms are listed.

the submucosal tissue, resulting in a large ulcer with a pinhead outlet. Parasitic lesions become infected with bacteria, developing into open ulcers with pronounced infiltration. Usually because of spreading of parasites from the site of a primary ulcer in the cecum, new lesions occur along the colon and sigmoid colon. On rare occasions localized ulceration and necrosis of the sigmoid colon or rectum is followed by excessive formation of granular tissue, resulting in a large mass called an ameboma. In typical ulcers or in ameboma one can easily identify nests of trophozoites.

During the early stages of hepatic complication of an amebic colitis, multiple foci of trophozoites and neutrophils, in portal spaces, especially in the right lobe of the liver, suggest hematogenous dissemination via the portal system. In later stages the small foci merge to form a few medium sized or a single large abscess filled with whitish or anchovy-colored gelatinous contents that microscopically appear granular and strongly eosinophilic. The abcess contains remnants of cell nuclei and numerous parasites in the outer zone of the lesion. It is not certain whether direct parasitic activity or toxin is responsible for necrosis. Fifty percent of untreated liver abscesses rupture into the pleural cavity, resulting in empyema. From such an abscess parasites may invade either the thoracic wall or the lung, resulting in skin or lung abscesses, respectively. In treated cases the liver abscess cavity gradually decreases, leaving ultimately a small stellate scar. Skin amebiasis is characterized by edema, induration, a dark red color, and irregular ulcers with necrotic content and fetid odor.

As a result of hematogenous dissemination, amebic abscesses may develop in various organs, but clinically the most important site is the brain. Such abscesses may be either single or multiple, have no preferential localization, and contain a yellowish necrotic mass. Development of a brain abscess leads to the death of the patient within a week. Except for intestinal and skin ulcers, amebic lesions usually do not contain bacteria, thus only limited infiltration due to necrosis is seen.

Dientamoeba fragilis

Morphology. Only the trophozoite form of this parasite has been described

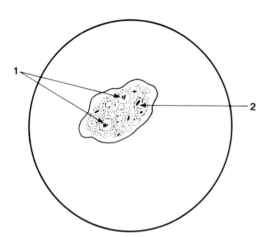

Fig. 51.9. Trophozoite of *Dietamoeba fragilis* (× 1000). Note (1) two nuclei with typical granular karyosome and (2) numerous vacuoles, some containing phagocytized bacteria.

(Fig. 51.9). The cell is small (3 to 22 μm) and often binuclear with very distinct karyosomes forming eight granules. The cytoplasm is distinctly separated into ecto- and endoplasm, with the latter containing multiple vacuoles that often have phagocytized bacteria within them. The parasite moves actively by means of broad pseudopodia.

Life Cycle and Epidemiology. The parasite has a ubiquitous geographic distribution and inhabits the large intestine. Since no cyst form has been demonstrated, it has been suggested that the trophozoite is transmitted either by direct fecal contamination or within ingested eggs of *Enterobius vermicularis*, the pinworm. Infection is rather uncommon (5 percent) in the normal population, but it may be quite frequent (50 percent) in closed populations such as institutions for the retarded.

Clinical Symptoms. Infection with *D. fragilis* may cause relatively mild mucous diarrhea with no typical symptoms. Thus diagnosis is based entirely on demonstration of the trophozoites. This is quite difficult and requires considerable experience.

PARASITES OF THE CLASS SPOROZOA

This large class is further subdivided into subclasses; three of them, *Coccidia*, *Haemosporidia*, and *Piroplasmea*, contain medically important parasites.

Isospora hominis

Morphology. Three species, *I. hominis*, *Isospora belli*, and *Isospora natalensis*, are distinguished, although some authors consider them either variants or actually developmental stages of the same organism. Thus far only sporogony — development of sporozoites in an oocyst — is known, and schizogony and gametogony are only inferred. The *I. belli* cyst is oval (20 to 33 μm by 10 to 19 μm) with a characteristic bottleneck extension on one pole. The cell enclosed, the sporont, is not attached to the two-layered wall. After being evacuated with stools, the cell divides, forming two sporoblasts (also called sporocysts or spores). Each of these, by two consecutive divisions, forms four elongated sporozoites; thus the mature cyst contains eight sporozoites. *I. hominis* is also oval but lacks the extension seen on the cyst of *I. belli*. The maturation process is similar, although often two sporocysts, each containing four sporozoites, separate before stools are passed. *I. natalensis* has rather round cysts (25 to 30 μm) that mature within 24 hours after evacuation with stool.

Life Cycle and Epidemiology. All three parasites are relatively uncommon and are usually found in the Southwest Pacific, South America, and South Africa and occasionally are found in the Mediterranean region, the United States, and other countries. The frequency of infection varies from 0.2 to 2 percent in warm climates. Dogs are considered a natural reservoir, although this has not been proved. The infection occurs orally by consumption of food contaminated with feces containing sporocysts. Ingested sporocysts liberate sporozoites in the small intestine (ileum) and cecum, where they invade the epithelium. Presumably, once in the epithelium and cells of the mucosa, sporozoites multiply (schizogony) and produce merozoites. Some of the latter differentiate into gametocytes (gametogony), which leave the host's cells and the zygotes form oocysts in the lumen of the intestine. Gametogony lasts 10 to 28 days.

Clinical Symptoms. The disease caused by isosporae is characterized by relatively mild diarrhea accompanied by fever, nausea, and anorexia. The disease is self-limiting, and cysts appearing at day 3 or 4 of disease disappear spontaneously. Diagnosis is made exclusively by finding cysts in stools, but it is quite difficult.

Pathology. Pathologic changes are limited to superficial erosions of mucous membrane of the ileum and cecum.

Sarcocystis lindemanni

Morphology. The trophozoite (Rainey's corpuscle or "spore") of *S. lindemanni* is a small (5 μm by 8 μm) curved cell with mitochondria and a distinct nucleus. One end of the cell is slightly pointed and possesses a conoid from which dense streaks called *sarconemes* extend toward the nucleus. The functions of the conoid and the sarconemes, which are seen only with the electron microscope, remain unknown. Numerous trophozoites fill the muscle fiber of the host, forming a cyst called a *Miescher tube*. The latter may be as long as 5 cm, appearing macroscopically as whitish streaks in the muscle. It contains multiple compartments, each filled with closely packed trophozoites.

Life Cycle and Epidemiology. It appears that infection occurs orally by in-

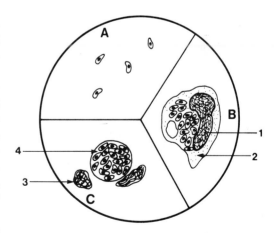

Fig. 51.10 Trophozoites (endozoites) of *Toxoplasma gondii* ($\times$ 1000): (A) free and (B) rapidly multiplying tachyzoites forming a group (pseudocysts) inside the (2) cytoplasm of the (1) host cell, and (C) slowly multiplying bradyzoites forming a true cyst with (4) distinct membrane and surrounded by (3) remnants of host's cells.

estion of oocysts or meat contaminated with parasites. The organisms invade the intestinal epithelium and then are transported in the bloodstream to skeletal and cardiac muscles. At present some authors consider *S. lindemanni* a trophozoitic stage of isosporae. If this were true, geographical distribution and frequency of both genera would be identical. Present data do not yet permit a conclusion.

Clinical Symptoms. In humans sarcocystosis rarely causes symptoms except mild diarrhea and is usually diagnosed incidentally at autopsy. The damage to muscles is negligible, but in a few instances a toxic effect of sarcocystin, a toxin, may cause damage to nervous system, heart, and adrenals. In animals such a toxicosis may produce a fatal disease.

Toxoplasma gondii

Morphology. *T. gondii* in humans and many other animals (rodents, sheep, dogs) that are intermediate hosts may be present in two distinct morphological forms (Fig. 51.10). An individual trophozoite (endozoite), either free or inside the host cell, is a pear-shaped and slightly curved cell (4 to 7 μm by 2 to 4 μm) with basophilic cytoplasm and a distinct nucleus. The pointed end contains a conoid from which toxonemes extend toward the nucleus. The trophozoite inside the host's cells (macrophages, neurons, or muscle cells) are usually smaller than those found extracellularly. They (tachyzoites) multiply rapidly by binary fission or internal budding, filling the cell and forming a group (pseudocyst) enclosed by the host cell membrane. The second morphological form, called a cyst, is formed when originally intracellular trophozoites become enclosed within a thick walled but porous capsule produced by the parasites. Such enclosed trophozoites multiply slowly (bradyzoites), filling the spherical cyst. The organisms in the cyst (cystozoites) may remain for an indefinite period of time without further multiplication.

Life Cycle and Epidemiology. When cysts present in the tissues of small rodents are ingested by cats, the definitive host, the cytozoites are released and they invade the intestinal epithelium. Such invading cystozoites develop into schizonts. This form is a multinuclear cell that then divides into numerous merozoites that invade neighboring epithelial cells to become new schizonts and produce new generations of merozoites.

After one or more such schizogonic cycles, some merozoites differentiate into gametocytes, which in turn during gametogony become either numerous macrogametocytes or relatively few microgametocytes. Both types of gametocytes are released from cells and merge with each other to form a zygote, which becomes surrounded by a capsule to form an oocyst. The oocyst is expelled from the intestines of the cat and matures to form two sporocysts, each containing four sporozoites. Schizogony and gametogony last 3 to 5 days and take place only in intestines of members of the family *Felidae*. Hence *T. gondii* may be considered a coccidian of cats, with humans and other animals being only intermediate hosts. In cats the parasites cause enteritis.

The parasite is cosmopolitan in distribution, as judged by the presence of specific antibodies against *T. gondii*. Infection is quite common, reaching in some countries (Tahiti for example) 100 percent frequency. In the United States the frequency of people who have encountered the parasite varies from 14 to 35 percent and is higher in the Northeast, which may reflect the frequency of cats kept as pets or regional eating habits. The parasites are usually transmitted to man orally either as cyst (with meat of domestic animals containing parasites) or oocyst (with food or objects contaminated with cat feces). In either case the parasites — cystozoites or sporozoites, respectively — are released into the intestinal tract, from whence they invade tissues via the bloodstream. Infected women in the second or third trimester of pregnancy transfer the parasite across the placenta to the fetus in 34 to 44 percent of cases. In 13 percent of these cases such a transfer results in serious disease of the fetus, but in nearly all cases some degree of damage can be seen. Accidental infections in diagnostic laboratories and during transfusion or organ transplantation also have been reported.

Clinical Symptoms. Infection with *T. gondii* produces a generalized acute or chronic disease, toxoplasmosis.

The acute disease occurs as one of five syndromes: afebrile lymphadenitis, febrile lymphadenitis, enteritis or typhuslike syndrome, myocarditis and myositis, or meningoencephalitis. These forms reflect the preference of the parasite to invade reticuloendothelial, muscle, or nerve cells.

The chronic phase of the disease begins with the development of specific immunity leading to the disappearance of clinical symptoms, although cysts containing live parasites may be present in various tissues or organs. During this stage cysts may rupture occasionally, causing local necrosis, infiltration, and scar formation. Parasites released from ruptured cysts are usually promptly eliminated by humoral and cellular immune mechanisms. Thus such an event does not lead to true relapse; however, the local reaction, if it occurs in the brain or eye, may have serious consequences. Retinochoroiditis, although not a frequent complication of toxoplasmosis (1 to 6 percent), accounts for one-third of the cases of this ocular disease in the United States. The ocular changes consist of focal necrosis, inflammation, glial proliferation, granulomatosis, detachment of the retina, and pigmented scars.

In some instances, because of impairment of immune responsiveness, such as drug induced immunosuppression in treatment of neoplasia or tissue transplantation, true relapse of toxoplasmosis with secondary dissemination of parasites may occur.

Transplacental transmission of *T. gondii* results in congenital toxoplasmosis (0.6 percent of newborns), which may be either acute, leading to death of the fetus or newborn with symptoms of hepatosplenomegaly, purpura, and jaundice, or subacute, in which symptoms of encephalitis and retinochoroiditis dominate. If the subacute form subsides, the child may display a characteristic tetrade of symptoms: psychomotor abnormalities, bilateral retinochoroiditis (75 to 85 percent), intracranial calcifications (32 percent) and hydrocephalus (26 percent).

Clinical diagnosis is rather difficult and must be confirmed by laboratory tests. The latter consist of demonstration of parasites in tissue biopsy material or cerebrospinal fluid either directly or by inoculation into mice. Furthermore, serologic tests aimed at the demonstration of immunity to toxoplasma may be employed. In the most commonly used dye test of Sabin and Feldman, the laboratory strain of *T. gondii* is treated with patient serum and then stained with methylene blue. If the serum contains specific antibodies, the organisms are damaged and resist staining. In evaluation of the results of the test a titer over 64, its rise, and a switch from IgM to IgG antibodies are considered indicative of an active infection. In congenital toxoplasmosis the presence of specific IgM antibodies in the cord blood is pathognomic. Other immunologic tests include passive hemagglutination, indirect immunofluorescence, complement fixation, and a skin test with toxoplasmin that detects delayed hypersensitivity. The last, however, develops several months after the onset of the disease; hence it has value as a screening test rather than as a diagnostic procedure for acute disease.

Pathology. Pathologic changes correspond to the intracellular growth of parasites, the destruction of infected cells, and

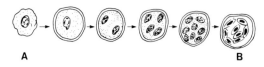

A   **B**

Fig. 51.11. (A) Transformation of single trophozoite of *Pneumocystis carinii* to the (B) cyst containing eight sporozoites surrounded by a thick capsule (× 1500). Note the intermediary forms containing increasing numbers of nuclei and unsegmented cytoplasm.

the release of parasites which in general results in focal necrosis, infiltration with mononulear and neutrophilic cells, and subsequent scar formation. These changes are most strikingly visible in nerve tissue and retina, where necrosis of infected neurons is followed by formation of microglial and astroglial nodules and subsequently fibrous scars. In congenital toxoplasmosis the pathologic changes in the brain are rather diffuse in the periventricular areas and consist of infiltration, vascular thrombosis, necrosis, and scar formation. These lesions, according to some investigators, result from specific antigen–antibody reactions in the vicinity of the cerebral ventricles. The scar formation often obstructs the aqueduct, thus resulting in hydrocephalus.

Pneumocystis carinii

The taxonomic position of this organism is still uncertain, although morphologically it has several features common with toxoplasmas; in the past it was classified as part of the same family, *Toxoplasmatidae*.

Morphology. *P. carinii* (Fig. 51.11) occurs in two distinct forms, a trophozoite and a sporozoite. The trophozoite appears as a small (1.5 to 5 μm) cell with a central nucleus. The cytoplasm contains mitochondria, and occasionally the cell has an irregular ameboid shape. The free trophozoites invade the host's, endothelial cells, where they multiply, producing new organisms that upon being released invade other cells. At some point an intracellular trophozoite surrounds itself by a thick wall and undergoes three consecutive divisions with production of eight nuclei and segmentation of the cytoplasm to produce eight fusiform sporozoites enclosed in a cyst. The cyst has a diameter of 3.5 to 12 μm and a wall that stains with the periodic acid–Schiff reagent.

Life Cycle and Epidemiology. Except for schizogony and asexual cyst formation, no stages of the life cycle are

Table 51.6. Reciprocal Relationship Between Pneumocytosis and Some Predisposing Clinical Conditions

Predisposing Condition	Frequency of Predisposing Condition in Diagnosed Cases of Pneumocytosis	Frequency of Diagnosed Pneumocytosis Among Subjects With a Given Predisposing Condition
Prolonged corticotherapy	82%	Unknown
Malignancy		
Acute lymphocytic leukemia	} 48%	18%
Chronic lymphocytic leukemia		6%
Hodgkin's disease	11%	7%
Lymphomas	7%	4%
Hypoglobulinemia (immunodeficiencies)	21%	Unknown
Recipients of organ grafts	11%	7%
None	Very low	< 0.1%

presently known. The parasite appears to have cosmopolitan distribution, and some animals — dogs, cats, rabbits, mice, rats, and sheep — are suspected of constituting the natural reservoir. Transmission probably takes place via the upper respiratory tract (droplets), although transplacental infection has been also suggested. Some authors hold that *P. carinii* is a common saprophyte that becomes pathogenic under certain conditions. Indeed, pneumocytosis occurs predominantly in individuals with impaired defense mechanisms (premature birth, debilitating disease, immunodeficiencies). Table 51.6 shows the frequency of predisposing conditions among victims of pneumocystosis as well as frequency of pneumocystosis among individuals with predisposing conditions.

Clinical Symptoms. The common clinical expression of pneumocystosis is an atypical interstitial pneumonia, although in very rare occasions generalized extrapulmonary pneumocystosis with involvement of liver, spleen, kidney, heart, or lymph nodes occurs. The onset of pneumonia is insidious, but diagnosis of the fully developed disease is relatively easy on the basis of a typical triad: predisposing disease and its symptoms, discrepancy between minimal physical findings and severe respiratory difficulties, and typical radiologic picture. Untreated disease is fatal in more than one-half of cases, while proper treatment reduces the fatality rate to about 2 percent. Definitive diagnosis is based on demonstration of parasites either in sputum or, more often, in biopsy material. The complement fixation test is of limited value, since antibodies appear relatively late, reaching a peak on days 20 to 30. One must show an increase of titer in successive tests to consider results of serologic tests diagnostic.

Pathology. A characteristic autopsy picture consists of distended lungs with areas of firm and airless, but not edematous, tissue and areas of bullous

emphysema. Microscopic examination reveals intraalveolar exudate containing macrophages, monocytes, alveolar cells, and often parasites. The alveolar septa are thickened and infiltrated with numerous plasmacytes and many parasites, both intracellular and in cysts.

Babesia bovis

Morphology. The parasite in the host is found as a very small (1.5 to 5 μm) round-, ellipsoid-, ring-, or rod-shaped intracellular organism (Fig. 51.11). In severe infections up to 60 percent of erythrocytes and also many white cells contain the parasites. These multiply and rupture the host cells, releasing parasites that reinfect new cells. There are many species of babesiae — *B. bovis*, *B. ovis*, *B. caballi*, *B. equi*, *B. gibsoni*, *B. suis*, *B. trautmanni*, *B. bigemina*, and *B. divergens* — infecting various animals.

Life Cycle and Epidemiology. The babesiae have both asexual and sexual phases of the life cycle. The former takes place in various domestic and wild animals, causing severe and often fatal disease (cattle malaria, Texas fever). Either sick or symptomless carrier animals are the source of parasites for female ticks (such as *Ixodes ricinus*), where the sexual phase of the parasite's life cycle takes place. The gametocytes form an ookinete, which reaches the ovaries of the female tick and is eventually transferred to her progeny. Sporoblasts and sporozoites are formed in the salivary glands of the tick's larvae. The parasite and animal disease caused by it is cosmopolitan (United States, South Africa, Algeria, Soviet Union); however, only a few cases of human disease are documented. It appears that under normal circumstances humans are resistant to babesiae but can become sensitive after splenectomy. This is indicated by the finding that all human cases of babesiosis have occurred in splenectomized subjects and that in controlled experiments subhuman primates become susceptible after splenectomy.

Clinical Symptoms. Clinically, human infection with *B. bovis* produces a disease characterized by fever, progressive anemia, hemaglobulinuria, and chocolate discoloration of skin. As a result of extensive hemaglobulinuria, renal failure usually follows and results in death within a few days. The diagnosis may be confirmed by careful history (splenectomy, contact with animals and animal epidemics) and demonstration of parasites in peripheral blood erythrocytes. Serologic tests may be helpful if considered early enough in the course of disease.

THE GENUS PLASMODIUM

The genus *Plasmodium* consists of several subgenera (even though most textbooks ignore this distinction into subgenera, the present authors consider it justified). *P. plasmodium* and *P. laverania* are of medical significance. Among the members of the subgenus *P. plasmodium*, three species, *vivax*, *ovale*, and *malariae*, are of import-

Table 51.7. Morphological Features of Three Species of Subgenus *Plasmodium plasmodium*

	vivax	*ovale*	*malariae*
Trophozoite	Usually one per RBC; several stages (marginal, ring, ameboid); contains pigment	Usually one per RBC; several stages (ring, irregular); contains pigment darker than *P. vivax*	Usually one per RBC; several stages (ring, band, ameboid); deep basophilic cytoplasm; contains pigment
Erythrocytes	Large, pale, or polychromatic; orange dots (Schüffner granules)	Large, pale, oval, or irregular; Schüffner granules	Normal size, occasionally reticulocytes; no Schüffner granules; after staining with fluorescein-labeled antibodies, Ziemann's dots are visible
Schizont	Single irregular mass with multiple nuclei (8–24) and pigment; segmentation into individual cells and rupturing the erythrocyte	Single large round mass filling entire erythrocyte, usually eight nuclei; segmentation into eight individual merozoites	Single, large mass filling entire erythrocyte; usually eight nuclei arranged concentrically with pigment in the center (daisy head)
Merozoite	Usually 16 (8–24) small organisms released from one erythrocyte and invading other erythrocyte	Usually 8 (4–17) relatively large organisms	Usually 8 (6–12)
Gametocytes	Microgametocyte: large, light spindle nucleus and pigment / Macrogametocyte: basophilic cytoplasm and dense eccentric nucleus	Microgametocyte: large, light nucleus / Macrogametocyte: small, eccentric and dense nucleus	Microgametocyte: large, light central nucleus and pigment / Macrogametocyte: small, eccentric and dense nucleus

ance to humans, and their basic morphological, epidemiologic, and clinical features will be summarized here. There are about 50 other species of plasmodia parasitizing animals, but only those infecting primates may occasionally be transferred to humans. The only species of another subgenus, *P. laverania falciparum*, will be discussed separately.

Plasmodium plasmodium Species

Morphology. All three species occur in a variety of morphological forms depending on the stage of life cycle. Recognition of the morphology of trophozoites,

Fig. 51.12. Erythrocytic schizogony of (A) *P. plasmodium vivax*, (B) *P. plasmodium ovale*, (C) *P. plasmodium malariae*, and (D) *P. laverania falciparum* (× 1000). Major stages depicted are (1) ring trophozoite, (2) ameboid trophozoite, (3) presegmenting schizont, (4) segmented schizont or intracellular merozoites, (5) microgametocyte, and (6) macrogametocyte. Note the difference in size of erythrocytes, appearance of merozoites, and distinct differences between two types of gametocytes.

schizonts, merozoites, and gametocytes is the basis of parasitologic diagnosis. Table 51.7 and Figure 51.12 summarize the basic features of the three plasmodia as seen in the peripheral blood of a subject suffering from malaria. While recognition of infection — trophozoites, pigment, and Schüffner granules — is relatively simple, distinction of the three species is quite difficult, especially for inexperienced examiners.

Life Cycle and Epidemiology. All three plasmodia undergo quite a complex life cycle involving two hosts; the asexual phase (schizogony) takes place in humans, and the sexual phase (gametogony and sporogony) begins in humans but is completed in female anophelian mosquitoes.

Macrogametocytes and microgametocytes are ingested by the mosquito with the blood of a malaria victim. They transform in the gut into corresponding macrogametes and microgametes. The latter merge to form a zygote, which transforms into a motile ookinete. The ookinete migrates through the intestine wall and matures into an oocyst within 2 weeks, depending on external temperature. The mature oocyst contains several elongated sporozoites that are subsequently released and migrate to the salivary gland of the mosquito. When the mosquito bites, the sporozoites are injected into the bloodstream of a mammalian host, from where, within a few minutes, they reach the liver sinusoids and invade the endothelial cells, beginning the phase of extraerythrocytic (EE) schizogony. The invading sporozoite is transformed intracellularly into a schizont, a large (40 μm) ovoid cell with originally a single nucleus but after subsequent division with up to 10^4 nuclei. The schizont segments into numerous small (1.2 μm) spherical cells called merozoites or cryptozoites. Upon rupture of the cell these are released into the bloodstream and either invade erythrocytes or reinvade hepatic endothelial cells, repeating the sequence. Cryptozoites in the reinfection

Table 51.8   Epidemiologic Features of Different Species of Subgenus *Plasmodium plasmodium*

	plasmodium vivax	*plasmodium ovale*	*plasmodium malariae*
Synonyms	*Haemamoeba vivax* *Plasmodium tertianae* *Haemosporidium tertianae*	*P. vivax minutum*	*Haemamoeba laverana* var. *quartanae* *Plasmodium quartanae* *Plasmodium rodhainie*
Geographic distribution	Between 20°C summer isotherms except West Africa, between Mauritania and the Republic of Congo	West Africa and Ethiopia	Tropical Africa, Burma, Sri Lanka, Indonesia, and occasionally South America and the United States
Time of development in mosquito (at 20°C)	16 days	?	35 days
Time of EE schizogony	7–8 days	9 days	3–16 days
Incubation[a]	12 (10–15) days	17 (11–18) days	24 (18–37) days
Time of E schizogony	48 hours	49–56 hours	68–72 hours
Attacks	Every third day	Every third day	Every fourth day
Time of appearance of gametocytes (after first EE cycle)	3–5 days	5–6 days	10–14 days
Frequency of gametocytes per number of leukocytes in peripheral blood	10^{-3}	—	3×10^{-2}

[a] Time between infection and first clinical symptoms.

of hepatic cells are sometimes referred to as metacryptozoites. Ultimately, either cryptozoites or metacryptozoites invade erythrocytes, where they transform into trophozoites, schizonts, and new trophozoites, which are released periodically to reinvade new erythrocytes. This phase is called erythrocytic (E) schizogony and induces the appearance of specific antibodies that help to destroy released merozoites. Some erythrocytic trophozoites differentiate into gametocytes, which may be ingested by mosquitoes.

The plasmodia are quite cosmopolitan, although they are more common in warm climates. Table 51.8 summarizes the major epidemiologc characteristics of different plasmodia.

Malaria was well known to ancient man,

but only recent decades have brought significant progress in is worldwide control and eradication. This becomes obvious when one realizes that only 65 years ago in the United States alone there were 4,000,000 victims of malaria, whereas in 1964 only 171 cases were reported. Still, in the same year close to one-third of the world population was exposed to malaria.

The attempts to eradicate malaria are made in several phases. During the attack phase tests determine the presence and frequency of disease in a given area. The eradication phase consists of active treatment of sick individuals and carriers as well as the removal of vectors (mosquitoes). In the consolidation phase treatment of all new cases must be continued to eliminate a disease, and in the maintenance phase an active search for any possible new cases is made. At present almost one billion people in about 40 countries are subject to the final phases of preventive measures, consisting of search for and treatment of all new cases in the attempt to eliminate the disease. However, there are still highly malarious areas, such as Southern Africa, where the earlier phases of eradication procedures are necessary.

The distribution of plasmodia and frequency of malaria is influenced by several factors. One of these is the natural reservoir. Man is practically the only reservoir, since the species that parasitize other animals, with a few exceptions, are not pathogenic for human beings and since human plasmodia do not parasitize animals (except *P. plasmodium malariae*, which may infect chimpanzees). The plasmodia that infect primates and that may occasionally infect man are *P. schwetzi* (gorilla), *P. eylesi* (gibbon), *P. cynomolgi* (macaque), *P. simium, P. inni, P. brazilianum, P. shortii,* and *P. knowlesi.* To act as a reservoir humans must carry gametocytes with a frequency sufficient to infect mosquitoes. Also, the individual must be exposed to mosquito bites.

Another factor is the nature of the vector. There are about 65 species of the genus *Anopheles* of which a few are capable of acting as a vector as long as they have access to humans that carry a sufficient number of gametocytes. Once gametocytes are acquired by the mosquito, they undergo sporogony, depending on the external temperature (within the range 15 to 39°C), resulting in production of up to 2 × 10^6 sporozoites per mosquito. About 3000 sporozoites are transferred during each biting of a human victim. It is quite clear that the frequency of new cases is directly related to the density of the vector population and the density of gametocyte carriers. A decrease of either one leads to a decrease of disease frequency.

The other critical factor is the availability of susceptible hosts. The exposure to mosquito bites is a prerequisite of being infected, and such exposure is more likely to occur under poor socioeconomic conditions. Even exposed individuals may be partially resistant owing to several factors of genetic or immunologic nature. The former consist of a glucose-6-phosphate dehydrogenase defect, which limits metabolic pathways needed by parasites, or sickle cell anemia, in which a defective hemoglobin of the host is poorly utilized by the parasites. Both defects, as well as some other genetic defects of hemoglobin, partially prevent infection with plasmodia, especially in blacks who otherwise are often victims of these defects. Interestingly, the presence of Duffy blood group substances a or b facilitates invasion of erythrocytes, whereas lack of such substances prevents invasion. The immunologic mechanism counteracting the infection with plasmodia consists of both production of species-specific antibodies and cellular immunity. The antibodies may be acquired by a fetus from the mother or may be actively produced by stimulation by erythrocytic trophozoites but not hepatic merozoites or gametocytes. The antibodies belong to the IgG class and have lytic, agglutinating, opsonizing, and complement-fixing properties. They have protective and therapeutic properties, especially in children, but since they disappear soon after the elimination of parasites their effectiveness is of limited value in adults. The cellular mechanism consists of activating macrophages, thus facilitating phagocytosis and removal of parasites, but with progress of the disease macrophages have a tendency to phagocytize normal erythrocytes; by doing so they compound anemia.

Clinical Symptoms. The major clinical symptom of malaria, periodic attacks of fever, is due to periodic rupture of erythrocytes and release of merozoites, pigment, and possibly toxins. The time intervals between episodes of fever correspond to the time of erythrocytic schizogony. Fever attacks occur every third day with *P. vivax* and *P. ovale* (tertian malaria) or every fourth day with *P. malariae* (quartan malaria) infections. The disease begins suddenly, with high fever, chills, headache, muscular pains, tachycardia, and tachypnea. The symptoms last for several hours and end in a sudden fever crisis, accompanied by profuse sweating in *P. vivax* infections. Such an attack may occur several times, but subsequently the developing humoral immunity destroys some of the released merozoites, preventing the reinvasion of some erythrocytes and therefore contributing to prevention of successive attacks. The symptomless period, lasting for several weeks or even months, may be interrupted by recurrence of disease due to the increased survival of parasites overriding the immunity. The recrudescence (relapse) of symptoms may also be due to additional schizogony providing new parasites for invasion of erythrocytes. The symptomless periods are part of latent disease (or the carrier state), in which parasites can be found in blood and recurrence or exacerbations may occur. Although malaria is a protracted disease, it is rarely fatal.

Malaria in children is often atypical, with a variety of symptoms such as hyperpyrexia, cerebral or cardiac signs, rupture of spleen, nephrotic syndrome, or renal failure. It may be fatal if not treated early.

Diagnosis, although relatively easy on the basis of history and symptoms, must be confirmed by demonstration of parasites in blood. The blood film, either thin or thick, is prepared between attacks and stained with hematologic stains. In all forms of malaria discussed above, all developmental forms of parasites are detectable.

Pathology. Tertian and quartan malaria usually do not produce extensive pathologic changes. However, after prolonged infection, accumulation of malarial pigment (hemozoin) negative for iron and deposited in various organs may be quite obvious.

P. laverania falciparum

Morphology. *P. laverania falciparum* in its life cycle has various morphological forms corresponding to the usual developmental stages of plasmodia (Fig. 51.12). Medically the most important are those found in the peripheral blood of infected persons. Contrary to other plasmodia, only the early forms of trophozoites, often located marginally, appear in an exceptionally large fraction of erythrocytes. The erythrocytes, after they are infected, disappear from the peripheral blood and accumulate in visceral capillaries. The developing trophozoites mature through ring and irregular forms to schizonts. During maturation a few granules of pigment appear, and often distinct stippling of erythrocytes (Maurer's spots) is discernible. The mature schizonts, found only in visceral capillaries, usually have 16 (8 to 32) nuclei arranged as rosettes with centrally located pigment. The early gametocytes have a typical ovoid shape, becoming crescent shaped macrogametocytes or kidney shaped microgametocytes.

Life Cycle and Epidemiology. The life cycle of *P. laverania falciparum* begins with gametogony and fertilization, which take place in the gastrointestinal tract of the mosquito. The resulting ookinete, after leaving the intestines, forms an oocyst, which matures over 9 to 23 days and which contains sporozoites that are released to colonize the salivary glands. Sporozoites introduced to a human during a mosquito bite invade hepatic reticuloendothelial cells, where in a single EE schizogony they produce schizonts dividing into about 3×10^4 merozoites that invade as many as 50 percent of the peripheral erythrocytes, which then accumulate in visceral capillaries. This species of *Plasmodium* is common in the tropics near the equator, but cases do occur in the United States and also in other countries, especially in the Mediterranean region. The transmission and incidence of infection is influenced by factors analogous to those discussed for other species of plasmodia.

Clinical Symptoms. Infection with *P. falciparum* results in malignant forms of malaria sometimes called estivoautumnal or subtertian. The attacks are less regular than in other malarias and occur approximately every 2 days. The attack of fever is prolonged and ends in one of two phases, pseudocrisis or crisis. Because of the large number of erythrocytes being destroyed and their particular anatomic localization, the attack may be quite severe and may take several clinical forms, such as algid (shock, bradycardia, cardiac failure, loss of consciousness, and coma), cerebral (excitement, delirium, convulsions, muscular paroxysms, tetany, paralysis, and coma), hemorrhagic (bleeding, glomerulonephritis, and renal failure), or gastrointestinal (nausea, vomiting, stomachache, diarrhea, and jaundice). Any form may be fatal in the first few days, but the disease may last for several months, with recrudescence. If untreated, this form of malaria is often fatal; treated improperly it results in a special form of malaria known as black water fever. This form is characterized by extensive hemolysis of peripheral erythrocytes due not only to damage by parasites but also to antibodies directed to both infected as well as apparently normal cells. This suggests an involvement of autoimmune phenomena in the pathogenesis of this form of malaria. The hemolysis contributes to the often observed anoxia precipitated by shock, hemostasis, and toxicosis elicited by a hypothetical malarial toxin blocking both respiration and oxidative phosphorylation in the cells. Anemia and hepatosplenomegaly may dominate the clinical picture in protracted cases.

Diagnosis is based on the clinical picture and demonstration of parasites in the blood, which typically appear only as early trophozoites.

Pathology. Pathologic findings vary within broad limits, depending on the clinical form and duration of disease. Macroscopically, the lymph nodes, spleen, and liver are enlarged, with typical discoloration (grayish or grayish-blue) due to accumulation of pigment. Both visceral organs are relatively soft with rounded edges. The kidneys are enlarged, congested, and discolored. The lungs are congested and edematous with foci of inflammation. The brain and meninges are congested with edema, small hemorrhages, and grayish discoloration. Microscopically, in lymph nodes and spleen the follicles are small, and sinuses are engorged and contain cells with parasites and pigment. The liver has congested capillaries, granules of pigment in Kupffer's cells, and scattered infiltrates in portal spaces. In the kidney distinct aggregates of pigment appear in the glomeruli, and often protein and hemoglobin casts can be seen. In extreme cases tubular necrosis may be encountered. Typically, the renal medullary veins contain pigmented mononuclear cells. In the brain capillaries are often blocked with parasitized erythrocytes containing late trophozoites and schizonts. Such cells in larger vessels are distributed close to walls. Occasional perivascular infiltrates, focal necrosis, glial microgranulomas (Durek's granulomas), and foci of demyelinization complete the picture.

PARASITES FROM THE CLASS CILIATEA

Only one member of this class appears to be a proven pathogen and will be discussed below.

Balantidium coli

Morphology. Two distinct forms of this parasite are recognized (Fig. 51.13). The trophozoite is a large (30 to 300 μm by 40 to 70 μm), pear shaped cell covered with tiny cilia, each originating from a separate basal body. At the narrower end of the cell

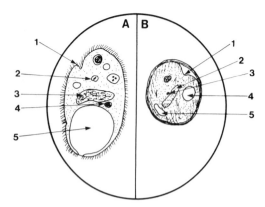

Fig. 51.13. (A) Trophozoite of *Balantidium coli* found in stools (× 750). Note indentation corresponding to (1) cytostome, (2) numerous food vacuoles, (3) macronucleus, and (4) micronucleus as well as (5) contractile vacuole. (B) Cyst of *B. coli* in stools (× 750). Note same structures as seen in trophozoite.

there is distinct cytostome, whereas at the opposite end a cytopyge connects the intracellular contractile vacuole with the surrounding milieu. The central portion of the cell is occupied by two chromatid structures, a large bean-shaped macronucleus and a small compact micronucleus. The cytoplasm contains ingested erythrocytes, starch granules, and inert inclusions.

The round cyst (40 to 60 μm) contains a single organism deprived of cilia but still containing all typical cellular structures, including food inclusions. It is surrounded by a thick membrane.

Life Cycle and Epidemiology. The known life cycle of the parasite consists of two stages, trophozoite and cyst, both extracellular. The cysts are formed in the lower intestine and excreted with stools. The distribution of this organism is cosmopolitan, although it is more common in warm climates. The natural reservoir consists of humans, swine, and rats, but some other animals may also play a role (cockroaches, fowl, rodents, monkeys). The frequency of infections varies from 0.02 to 29 percent and depend on several factors such as hygienic habits. Transmission is via food

contaminated with cysts or meat that contains parasites. Upon reaching the small intestine the cyst liberates a trophozoite, which migrates to the large intestine where it burrows into mucous membrane.

Clinical Symptoms. Many infections are virtually asymptomatic, since humans usually are resistant, but a massive invasion of a compromised individual, especially on a starch-rich diet, results in an overt disease, colitis. Most commonly, victims are elderly, alcoholics, or those suffering from achlorhydria. The clinical picture may be chronic or, less frequently, acute, with diarrhea, either periodic or continuous (dysentery). In rare instances a fulminating form leads to death in a matter of days. Extraintestinal balantidiasis may affect the peritoneum, urinary tract, or vagina. Diagnosis must be confirmed by the demonstration of parasites in stools, usually in the form of cysts and, occasionally, trophozoites. Examination should be made as soon as possible after securing the sample, since trophozoites of this parasite easily disintegrate.

Pathology. Invasion of parasites into the walls of the cecum, appendix, or colon results in multiple ulcers, each with a wide inlet. An accompanying bacterial infection contributes to the infiltration (lymphocytes, neutrophils, eosinophils, and plasma cells). The parasites spread along lymphatics, causing necrosis of mucosa, but they seldom pass beyond the regional lymph nodes. The parasites in tissues are quite typical and easily recognizable.

THERAPEUTIC CONSIDERATIONS

The philosophy underlying the treatment of parasitic diseases was discussed in Chapter 50. Generally, it applies to protozoal diseases, although certain aspects must be considered with special reference to the unique nature of these diseases. The rapidity of proliferation of protozoan parasites makes it advisable that specific treatment be instituted as early as possible. This requirement makes the earliest possible diagnosis an imperative factor in management of the patient. In fact, some of the discussed diseases (e.g., naegleriasis or babesiosis) are often fatal because timely diagnosis is difficult or essentially impossible.

The second important consideration in the treatment of protozoan disease is administration of drugs for a sufficiently long time to assure complete removal of parasites so that recurrence of the disease is avoided. Unfortunately, many of the drugs

employed are potent cytoplasmic poisons that often may severely affect the host's cells; therefore application of these drugs should be prudent. The treatment of protozoal diseases in some instances poses a very specific problem — accessibility of intracellular parasites to the chemical agent.

In addition to the specific antiprotozoan agents, symptomatic treatment must be taken into consideration, depending on the course of the disease and its complications.

The description of specific regimens and specific drugs is beyond the scope of this chapter. Table 51.9 summarizes a general

Table 51.9. Treatment of Protozoan Diseases

Disease	Agent	Effectiveness of Treatment	Fatality Rate if Not Treated
Sleeping sickness	T. gambiense	100% in early stages, 70–100% in later stages	100%
Trypanosomiasis	T. rhodesiense	Good	100%
Chagas' disease	T. cruzi	Good	High
Oriental sore	L. tropica	Good	None
Leishmaniasis	L. brasiliense	Good	None
Kala-azar	L. donovani	85–95%	75–95%
Giardiasis	G. lamblia	Very good	None
Trichomoniasis	T. vaginalis	Very good	None
Acanthamebiasis	Acanthamoeba sp.	—	100%
Negleriasis	Naegleria fowleri	—	100%
Amebiasis	E. histolytica	90%	High
Isosporosis	Isospora hominis or I. belli	?	None (self-cure)
Sarcocystosis	S. lindemanni	—	None
Toxoplasmosis	T. gondii	Good	High among children
Pneumocystosis	P. carinii	80%	80%
Babesiosis	B. bovis	—	100%
Tertian malaria	P. vivax and P. ovale	Good	None
Quartan malaria	P. malariae	Good	None
Malignant malaria	P. falciparum	Good	Some
Balantidiasis (colitis)	B. coli	Good	Low

Duration, dosage, and type of medicine depends on the purpose of treatment (curative or prophylactic) and possible parasite resistance.

outline and effectiveness of the proper therapies, if available. The most important point to be drawn from these data is that with few exceptions protozoan diseases of humans can be successfully treated if one makes an early diagnosis.

REFERENCES

Beck, J.W. and Davies, J.E.: Medical Parasitology. 2nd Ed. C.V. Mosby, St. Louis, 1976.

Chandler, A.C.: Introduction to Parasitology. 9th Ed. John Wiley and Sons, New York, 1955.

Faust, E.C., Russell, P.F., and Jung, R.C.: Craig and Faust's Clinical Parasitology. 8th Ed. Lea and Febiger, Philadelphia, 1970.

Gear, J.H.S., Ed.: Medicine in a Tropical Environment. A.A. Balkeena, Cape Town, 1977.

Maegraith, B.G. and Gilles, H.M.: Management and Treatment of Tropical Diseases. Blackwell Scientific Publications, Oxford and Edinburgh, 1971.

Marcial-Rojas, R.A., Ed.: Pathology of Protozoal and Helminthic Diseases with Clinical Correlation. Williams & Wilkins, Baltimore, 1971.

Padilla y Padilla, C.A., and Padilla, G.M., Eds.: Amebiasis in Man. Charles C Thomas, Springfield, 1974.

Schneierson, S.S.: Atlas of Diagnostic Microbiology. Abbott Laboratories, N. Chicago, 1971.

52

Metazoa

Roger K. Cunningham and
Marek Zaleski

Metazoan parasites of humans are found principally in the phyla *Platyhelminthes* and *Nemathelminthes* and a few in the phylum *Arthropoda*. Helminths are, of course, worms. Unlike the protozoa, worms are multicellular and are large enough to be seen without a microscope at some point in their life cycle. The word worm usually brings to mind a long crawling creature that has little in the way of appendages. Animals of this general appearance can be found in virtually every phylum, but the terms *worms* and *helminths* will be used here to describe members of certain phyla that are parasites of vertebrate hosts. It should be remembered that all of these phyla also contain free-living members. The organization of the taxonomy of helminths is largely based on morphology and, to say the least, is complex enough to be a matter for experts. A minimum of taxonomy will be presented here.

The helminths of medical importance are members of two phyla. The *Platyhelminthes*, or flatworms, are very primitive, dorsally flattened, soft-bodied animals.

Flatworms have no body cavity, and their organs are held in place by means of a parenchyma. When a simple intestinal tract is present, it is a channel or sac that employs one orifice for ingestion and excretion. Most flatworms are hermaphroditic. The *Nemathelminthes*, or roundworms, are long and cylindrical. Members of this phylum possess a body cavity and a complete digestive tract and usually are divided into males and females.

For completeness, it should be noted that there are two other phyla of worms. The phylum *Acanthocephala* includes spiny-headed worms that possess a large body cavity, no digestive tract, and a retractile head (proboscis); they appear as male and female worms. The phylum *Annelida*, the segmented worms, includes the leeches and a few other worms that can occasionally parasitize humans. Neither *Acanthocephala* nor the *Annelida* will be discussed further, since their parasitic members have no significance in human medicine. *Arthropoda* are discussed below.

It is useful to think of the parasites in the

673

context of their preferred site in the human host and to employ such terms as blood flukes, liver flukes, and the like.

PLATYHELMINTHES

The flatworms of medical importance are members of two classes: *Trematoda* (trematodes or flukes) and *Cestoidea* (tapeworms).

All trematodes are parasitic. The life cycle of the medically important species usually involves two host species. All, except blood flukes, are hermaphroditic, and

a very large proportion of their body is occupied by gonads. Some flukes produce as many as 25,000 eggs per day (Fig. 52.1). These escape the host's body with feces, urine, or sputum, depending on the species of fluke. The expelled eggs develop into ciliated embryos called *miracidia*, which hatch in water for some species or, for other species, in the gut of specific snails, which serve as intermediate hosts. The miracidia that hatch in water cannot feed and would die in a few hours unless they find the appropriate snail host. Those that do so, attach to it and either bore or digest their way into its tissues. The eggs of some

Flukes

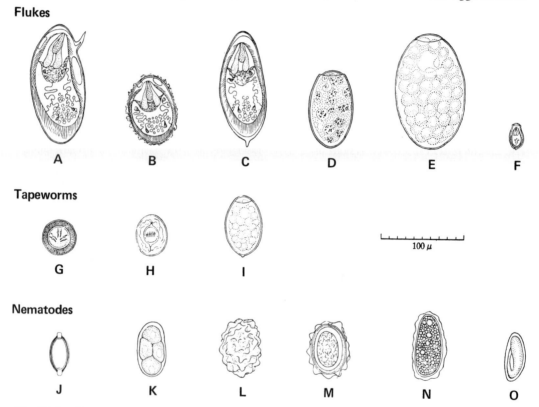

Fig. 52.1. Eggs of some medically important helminths (drawn to scale): (A) *Schistosoma mansoni.* (B) *Schistosoma japonicum.* (C) *Schistosoma haematobium.* (D) *Paragonimus westernmanni.* (E) *Fasciolopsis buski.* (F) *Clonorchis sinensis.* (G)*Taenia* sp. and *Echinococcus.* (H) *Hymenolepis nana.* (I) *Dibothriocephalus latus* (J) *Trichuris trichiura.* (K) *Necator americanus* and *Ancylostoma duodenale.* (L) *Ascaris lumbricoides* (surface view). (M) *A. lumbricoides*, optical section. (N) *A. lumbricoides*, unfertilized. (O) *Enterobius vermicularis.* (With permission, Chandler, A.C. Introduction to Parasitology. 9th Ed. John Wiley & Sons, New York, 1955. Reprinted by permission of John Wiley & Sons, Inc.)

flukes must be eaten by the proper snail before the miracidia can hatch.

The miracidia migrate to various tissues of the snail, depending on the species. Having reached their preferred site, the miracidia shed their coats and become saclike forms called *mother sporocysts* that contain germ cells multiplying either as individual cells or in clusters. In some species of flukes the clusters of multiplying germ cells bud off sacs that resemble the mother sporocyst; these are called *daughter sporocysts*. Sometimes the mother sporocyst internally elaborates a more developed form called a *redia* that has a sucker and gut. Rediae emerge from a birth pore in the mother sporocyst and migrate to the digestive tract of the snail, where they begin to produce masses of cells that develop into embryonal forms eventually shed from the snail. Some flukes form several generations of rediae. The embryonic form that emerges is a morphologically distinct larval state called a *cercaria*. Thus a single egg can lead to the production of thousands of cercariae throughout the life of the snail.

Cercariae must reach the appropriate vertebrate host to develop, mature, and reproduce sexually. All but a few cercariae have tails. Depending on the particular species of fluke, tails may be long, short, forked, or finned. The strategy that a given parasite employs to reach the next host may fall into one of three general patterns. Cercariae may encyst within the snail, which in turn must be eaten by a vertebrate host for the life cycle of the worm to be completed. Alternatively, cercariae may leave the snail, swim to nearby vegetation, encyst, and await ingestion by a new host feeding on such vegetation. Still other cercariae escape from the snail and swim free to either find the new host within a short time or die. In some cases the cercariae in the process of penetrating or encystment shed their tails; the tailless cercariae are called *metacercariae*.

The strict requirement for a particular or narrow range of snail intermediate hosts is the pivot upon which control of flukes rests. In those areas of the world where fluke diseases are prevalent, snail control programs are the most practical means of breaking the chain of infection. Such efforts are most effective, however, when the human population has access to safe water supplies and is also educated to avoid pollution of waters with feces and urine.

BLOOD FLUKES

Although there are many blood flukes of other vertebrates, humans are parasitized by three species: *Schistosoma mansoni*, *S. japonicum*, and *S. hematobium*. (The genus *Schistosoma* is sometimes called *Bilharzia*.) These are unusual human flukes in that they occur as morphologically quite different males and females. The males have the appearance of a flattened cylinder that has been rolled up on its sides for most of its length to form a groove termed the gynecophoric canal. The female, longer but more slender than the male, lies within this groove with its free ends projecting at each end (Fig. 52.2A). Female worms do not become sexually mature until association with males occurs. In most schistosomes this union is permanent.

The life cycle begins with the passing of feces or urine from an infected human into fresh water. In undiluted feces or urine the eggs may survive for several months, especially in cold weather. However, the eggs begin to hatch within minutes to a few hours once the feces or urine are diluted. When the eggs hatch, miracidia (Fig. 52.2C) emerge that must find the appropriate snail host within hours or die. The miracidia find their snail host by more than sheer random chance, for when placed near the appropriate snail they become highly active and seek the hosts directly. Those that strike the soft parts of the snail penetrate and in doing so shed their ciliated out-

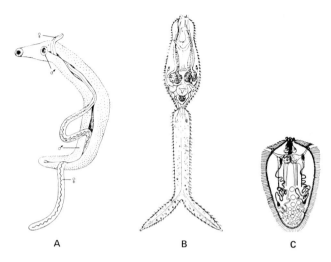

Fig. 52.2. Examples of stages of life cycle of schistosomes. (A) Adult pair, *Schistosoma haematobium*. Male (♂) carrying female (♀) in gynecophoric canal (×8). (B) Cercaria of *Schistosoma japonicum* (×250). (C) Miracidium of *Schistosoma haematobium* (×300). (With permission, Chandler, A.C. Introduction to Parasitology. 9th Ed. John Wiley & Sons, New York, 1955. Reprinted by permission of John Wiley & Sons, Inc.)

A   B   C

er coat and enlongate. There the miracidia develop into mother sporocysts, which begin to produce daughter sporocysts that migrate into the digestive gland and there start to form forktailed cercariae (about 200 μm long). The time required to begin cercarial production varies with the species of schistosome. The yield of cercariae from a single miracidium has been estimated by some to be about 2500 per day over a long period of time.

The cercariae escape in bursts from the snail and begin the search for their human hosts. For 8 or 12 hours the cercariae swim actively with periodic rests. When they find a human host in the water, the cercariae penetrate the skin directly, and in doing so shed their tails. Penetration requires but a few minutes and may be accompanied by itching and a subsequent dermatitis. If ingested, they penetrate the mucous membranes of the mouth. The tailless cercariae, called schistosomula, reach the circulation and eventually the liver, where they grow and mature. When sufficient maturity has been reached, the adult worms couple and migrate into the mesenteric veins and venules of both the large and small intestine or the urinary bladder. Here the pair, each female clasped in the gynecophoral groove of the male partner, remains for

years, continuously producing eggs that are deposited steadily along the vessel. These eggs, by both mechanical and enzymatic processes, break through the vessel wall and eventually enter the surrounding tissue. Most eggs are walled off by the host defenses, but some work their way into the lumen of the intestines or urinary bladder to pass from the host.

S. mansoni and *S. japonicum* prefer the mesenteric vessels; hence their eggs are found in feces, whereas *S. haematobium* adults are found more often in the venules associated with the urinary bladder and their eggs are found in the urine. Schistosomiasis (or bilharziasis) remains as one of the world's most important human parasitic diseases. A recent estimate placed the number of active cases at 500 million, although this must be considered rather more an educated estimate than a firm number. In any case, schistosomiasis is second only to malaria as a scourge of tropical areas.

Schistosoma mansoni

S. mansoni is found in Africa, South and Central America, and the West Indies, including Puerto Rico.

Morphology and Life Cycle. The male

worm is about 1 cm long and about 1.5 mm wide, and the female is longer and more slender. Females produce oval, brownish eggs that have a lateral spine (Fig. 52.1A), a diagnostically important property that distinguishes *S. mansoni* eggs from those of other schistosomes. The eggs require some days to develop a miracidium.

The intermediate hosts of *S. mansoni* in Africa are snails of the genus *Biomphalaria*; while the single species *Biomphalaria glabrata* predominates in the West Indies. One North American snail, *Tropicorbis havanensis*, which is found primarily in the southern United States, can serve as a host for *S. mansoni*, but the capacity for the miracidia to invade is, fortunately, low.

Pathology and Clinical Symptoms. The initial symptoms of infection with *S. mansoni* depend on the number of cercariae; usually a mild, tingling sensation on the skin is followed by dermatitis. The stage of the disease that produces serious symptoms is that in which the adults begin to produce eggs in the inferior mesenteric venules, 4 to 6 weeks after skin penetration. The onset of symptoms is sudden; fever, chills, and severe gastrointestinal disease are common features. Eosinophilia is common, as is urticaria. Apparently, the host tissue becomes sensitized to the eggs as they penetrate; hence inflammation and possibly allergic reactions ensue in the walls of the intestine. Episodic dysentery and increasingly painful abdominal cramps then follow together with liver and spleen enlargement. The liver enlargement eventually subsides, but enlargement of the spleen persists, bloating the body. The abatement of liver enlargement is a reflection of this organ becoming cirrhotic and granulomatous, however. The liver damage can lead to secondary anemia and nutritional impairment. If sufficient numbers of eggs reach the lungs or the central nervous system, pulmonary and neurologic complications can arise.

Effective drugs are available, but their use is contraindicated in patients with liver damage.

Measures to prevent schistosomiasis center on efforts to eradicate the snail intermediate host, or to at least reduce their numbers.

Schistosoma japonicum

Morphology and Life Cycle. This fluke is confined to the Far East, where it is endemic in many areas. The intermediate hosts are snails of the genus *Oncomelania*. *S. japonicum* utilizes a wide range of vertebrate hosts, infecting domestic animals and some rodents. The adult worms live mainly in branches of the superior mesenteric veins, and hence the eggs largely appear in the small intestine and feces. The ova are the smallest of those of schistosomes and have a poorly developed spine (Fig. 52.1B).

Pathology and Clinical Symptoms. Although the symptoms produced by *S. japonicum* are similar to those described for *S. mansoni*, there are some distinct features. *S. japonicum* is a prolific egg layer, and the large number of eggs is probably responsible for more frequent severe cirrhosis and an accompanying high fatality rate. Trapping of eggs in lung arterioles often interferes sufficiently with blood flow to produce cyanosis. Eggs may be deposited in heart vessels as well, leading to an accompanying congestive heart failure. Cardiopulmonary schistosomiasis can evoke the combination of cyanosis and cardiac complications known as *cor pulmonale*. Finally, infection by *S. japonicum* is more frequently associated with central nervous system complications than infection by the other schistosomes.

A particular difficulty in controlling the spread of *S. japonicum* is due to the fact that it is very hard to control the snail intermediate host, which is amphibious and which, furthermore, can hibernate over winter to shed cercariae the following spring.

Schistosoma haematobium

Morphology and Life Cycle. This schistosome is coextensive in Africa with *S. mansoni* but covers a wider geographical area. The parasite also occurs in the Near East and southwestern Asia. It is especially prevalent in Egypt and the Nile valley and has continued to spread to adjacent areas as the practice of irrigation has spread and provided a suitable environment for the intermediate hosts, planrobid snails, which are classified within the subfamily *Bulininae.* Although various snails can serve as intermediate hosts for *S. haematobium*, the parasite is essentially restricted to humans as a vertebrate host. The adult parasites (Fig. 52.2A) migrate predominantly to the pelvic veins of the vesical plexus draining the urinary bladder; hence eggs are passed primarily in urine, although some can be found in feces. The eggs possess a terminal rather than a lateral spine (Fig. 52.1A).

Pathology and Clinical Symptoms. Disease produced by infection with this parasite is in general less severe than with the other blood flukes. The principal early symptom is a painless hematuria often restricted to the last few milliliters of urine. Problems and complications are associated with the reaction of the bladder wall and associated structures against eggs that fail to traverse completely. Urinary passages may become constricted. Fistulas may develop. In all affected urogenital structures fibrosis and calcification may occur.

Diagnosis of Schistosomiasis

Clinical symptoms, though characteristic, are insufficient for definite diagnosis, which must be supported by laboratory findings. Most important is examination of stools or urine, as appropriate, for the presence of eggs (Figs. 52.1A, 52.1B, 52.1C). When the egg count is low it is possible to dilute the feces or urine and examine for released miracidia. Repeat examinations are often required to demonstrate the eggs. Rectal biopsy is also used and is very effective for detecting eggs in suspicious cases when they cannot be found in stools.

A large number of serologic tests for patient antibody are available to aid diagnosis of schistosomiasis; these include complement fixation, indirect hemagglutination, flocculation, and double diffusion. Antigens are derived usually from cercariae but sometimes from adult worms. A complement fixation test using adult worm antigens correlates well with active infection. The most sensitive test is immunofluorescence using frozen section of adult worms as the source of antigen. Effective drugs are available, but their use is complicated by accompanying, sometimes severe, side effects (Table 50.1).

It must be mentioned that cercariae of many schistosomes of birds and other animals can penetrate the skin of humans without going further. This can cause a severe dermatitis called *swimmer's itch*. It may occur in persons who have been repeatedly exposed to either fresh or salt water in the United States. The condition begins with a local itchy feeling, followed by eruption of extremely itchy papules or pustules. Severe swelling can occur, the degree of which is probably related to the degree of previous sensitization. The reaction is allergic in nature and represents both immediate and delayed hypersensitivities that blend together. The condition subsides in about a week.

LUNG FLUKES

The lungs of many mammals — humans, rats, pigs and other carnivores — can be infected with flukes of the genus *Paragonimus*. Substantial differences of opinion exist over what constitutes species within this genus and whether or not particular species infect certain hosts. The story began with the exotic discovery of what was called *P. westermani* in Bengal tigers. Later, *Para-*

gonimus found in human specimens were given the species name *P. ringeri*, while a parasite of mink became known as *P. kellicotti*. In this discussion the name *P. westermanni* will be used, and we will ignore the taxonomic controversy.

Paragonimus westermanni

Morphology of Life Cycle. The hermaphroditic adults live in the lungs, where clusters of them become encysted by host reaction. The cysts, however, rupture occasionally, and eggs are released into the bronchioles to be expelled in sputum. If the sputum is swallowed, the eggs can be found in the feces. After the eggs leave the body they slowly mature into miracidia which penetrate certain snails as the first intermediate hosts. In the snail the miracidia develop into rediae for several generations, the last of which produces cercariae. The cercariae escape the snail and creep (they do not swim) or drift to the second intermediate host, a crayfish or a freshwater crab, where they develop into metacercariae and encyst. When the infected shellfish is eaten raw, the young flukes are released from their cysts by the host's digestive processes and bore through the intestinal wall into the abdominal cavity. Often the larvae seem to simply wander about, aimlessly ending up in the spleen, liver, brain, or locations other than the lung. Such wanderings always suggest a recently acquired parasitic relationship or infection of an unusual host. Normally, the juvenile flukes will migrate to the lungs, where they encyst in the bronchioles. They can persist in this location for at least several years.

Pathology and Clinical Symptoms. *P. westermanni* causes a lung disease called endemic hemoptysis or paragonimiasis. This disease is related to the habit of eating raw crayfish or crabs and thus is found largely in the Far East. The disease does sporadically appear in other areas, however, including the United States.

The symptoms of infection with *P. westermanni* are usually not serious but sometimes are suggestive of tuberculosis. A slow onset of a cough with eventual blood-stained sputum, mild anemia, and slight fever are typical of the disease. Eosinophilia is common. Early diagnosis depends on establishing that the patient ate raw crabs or crayfish or had been in an endemic area. Infections have occurred by transmission from an unwashed chopping block used to clean raw crayfish that was later used to prepare other uncooked food.

Laboratory diagnosis is best made by examining the bloody spots in sputum for the presence of ova (Fig. 52.1D). Eggs may also be recovered from feces. Control measures, where undertaken in endemic areas, consist of controlling the snail intermediate host and education of the population about the hazards of exposure to raw crabs or crayfish or their juices.

INTESTINAL FLUKES

There are no intestinal flukes that can be considered primarily parasites of humans. The host capacity is shared by humans with other animals, chiefly pigs. Of the large number of species that occasionally infect humans, only one will be considered here.

Fasciolopsis buski

Morphology and Life Cycle. This organism, the largest fluke found in humans (7 to 8 cm long), is primarily a parasite of swine. A large proportion of pigs in the Far East carry this parasite. The eggs of this organism appear in the feces of infected humans and pigs and require several weeks to develop into miracidia, which then infect certain small, flat snails as intermediate hosts in which cercariae are produced. The practice of using human wastes (night soil) as fertilizer in endemic areas vastly increases the efficiency of this process. The cercariae escape the host snail and swim to nearby vegetation, where they encyst and await ingestion as metacercariae. In endemic areas the water chestnut, watercress, and, in particular, a water plant known as red ling are the primary food taken in by humans upon which metacercariae can be found. Once ingested, the metacercariae attach to the intestinal mucosa after leaving the cyst.

Pathology and Clinical Symptoms. Symptoms appear several months after ingestion of cysts. A severe diarrhea is accompanied by an appreciable anemia and usually abdominal pain. The severity of symptoms is related to the worm burden present, and massive infections can lead to pronounced anemia, edema of the face and legs, and a distended abdomen. The accompanying physiologic stress may lead to prostration or even death, especially in the case of children.

Diagnosis. Laboratory diagnosis is made by examining stools for the presence of typical eggs of *F. buski*, which possess a marked operculum (Fig. 52.1E).

Control measures in endemic areas focus on elimination of the snail intermediate host and education of the population about the hazards of eating uncooked freshwater plants. It is not practical in these areas to eliminate the practice of fertilizing crops with human wastes, since these materials constitute a substantial part of the available fertilizer supply.

Liver Flukes

The liver and bile ducts of man and domestic animals are inhabited by a large variety of flukes, but only the two most important human parasites of this group will be discussed.

Fasciola hepatica

Morphology and Life Cycle. The adult fluke is 2.5 to 3.0 cm long, has a leaf shape (Fig. 52.3A), and is found in cattle, sheep, goats, pigs, horses, primates, and rabbits, the last being an important reservoir of infection. The parasite can be found worldwide. In domestic animals *F. hepatica* is responsible for considerable damage and consequently represents an expensive problem in agriculture. *F. hepatica*, since it is found in the domestic animals of the United States, is responsible for human infection, especially in those areas where cattle raising is extensive.

The infective cycle begins with the passing of eggs in the feces of an infected sheep or cow into water. The miracidia develop in snails of several related genera and go through a sporocyst stage and two redia stages before cercariae are produced. The cercariae escape the snail and encyst on water vegetation, where they await ingestion by the next host. A common source of human infection is watercress, although other water plants can also serve as an infection source. Ingested metacercariae nor-

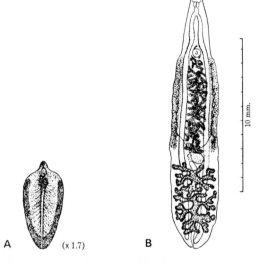

Fig. 52.3. Adult flukes. (A) *Fasciola hepatica* (×1.7). (B) *Clonorchis sinensis*. (With permission, Chandler, A.C. Introduction to Parasitology. 9th Ed. John Wiley & Sons, New York, 1955. Reprinted by permission of John Wiley & Sons, Inc.)

mally bore through the intestinal wall into the peritoneal cavity and finally reach the liver, where they come to rest in the biliary ducts. After a period of growth, adult worms produce eggs that stream through the bile ducts into the intestine, eventually reaching the outside when feces are passed.

Pathology and Clinical Symptoms. The symptoms of disease depend on the degree of infection. In the early stage a peritonitis may occur; fever, abdominal pain, and gastrointestinal complaints occur often with an accompanying eosinophilia. Eggs trapped in small branches of the bile ducts become centers of inflammation, which may lead to hepatitis, jaundice, and pronounced liver enlargement. If sufficient damage is produced, cirrhosis may follow. Massive infections are often fatal.

Laboratory diagnosis depends upon the finding of ova in feces. These must be examined carefully, since they are difficult to distinguish from eggs of *F. buski*. Serologic tests are also available.

Drugs are available for treatment, but they have pronounced side effects. Control of the snail intermediate host and careful washing of food are recommended as preventative measures.

Clonorchis sinensis

Morphology and Life Cycle. The Chinese liver fluke, *C. sinensis* (or *Opisthorchis sinensis*), is but one member of the family *Opisthorchiidae* that contains a large number of flukes that occur in fish-eating animals. Snails are the first intermediate host of these parasites, with fish or crayfish being a second intermediate host. Human infection follows ingestion of raw fish or, rarely, crayfish.

The Chinese liver fluke is widely distributed in the Far East (Japan to India) where it occurs in humans, cats, and dogs. The number of human infections reaches into the millions.

The adult flukes, 1 to 2.5 cm in length,

live in the biliary ducts of the liver, often in groups of hundreds or even thousands (Fig. 52.3B). Eggs are passed with the feces but do not hatch until they are eaten by certain snails. After development of sporocysts and a redia generation, cercariae are produced that escape the snail and encyst as metacercariae in the flesh of freshwater minnows and carp. In contrast to other liver flukes, the metacercariae of *C. sinensis* enter the bile ducts directly from the intestine.

Pathology and Clinical Symptoms. The flukes damage the biliary ducts and clog them. Inflammation of the liver can eventually lead to fibrotic changes and even to cirrhosis. The symptoms are related to the degree of infection and range from none at all to severe diarrhea, even dysentery, edema, hepatomegaly, and abdominal pain. Fatal cases are usually due to secondary complications such as infection or malnutrition. Heavy infections are not treated with any degree of success.

Laboratory diagnosis is made by recovering and identifying eggs in the feces (Fig. 52.1F).

Control measures depend on breaking the habit of eating raw fish and control of the snail intermediate hosts.

TAPEWORMS

The *Cestoidea*, or tapeworms, derive their name from the appearance of the adult worm (Fig. 52.4). A head, called a *scolex*, is used for attachment of the worm to the intestinal wall and is followed by a "neck" that grows continuously, forming regular segments that extend down the host's intestinal tract. Each new segment is actually a new individual that remains attached to the parent scolex. The resulting chain of segments is called a *strobilia*, and each segment is termed a *proglottid*. The youngest descendant is at the neck of the scolex; the oldest is at the distal end of the ribbon or tape, which may be meters away. The youngest proglottids acquire sexual maturity (about midworm) and thereafter continue to produce and shed eggs for a prolonged time.

The scolex is primarily an attachment organ and is customarily equipped with a gripping device of some kind. Suckers, hooks, and spines are found in various species.

Tapeworms do not have a digestive tract. The sole function of the proglottid is reproduction, and nutrients are taken directly from the host's intestinal contents. The reproductive function of the proglottids is assured by each possessing both male and female organs, sometimes doubled. In each individual worm the sexual organs (in the proglottids) range from immature to mature to gravid, the last being packed with eggs. Eggs are released by some species through rupture of gravid proglottids within the host. In other species gravid proglottids separate from the strobilia and pass out intact, and in still others, free eggs are released without rupture into the host's intestinal lumen.

The important tapeworms that infect humans are hermaphroditic and produce a hexacanth embryo or *onchosphere* that possesses six hooks and is enclosed within a shell membrane. In the appropriate intermediate host the onchosphere bores into the gut wall and develops into a larval stage. Depending on the species, the larval stage may exhibit one of several patterns.

The simplest larval form is a small bladder filled with fluid and possessed of a single scolex attached to the inner wall, pointing inward; this form is called a *cysticerus*. If the lumen of the bladder is filled with solid tissue rather than fluid, it is called a *cysticercoid*. A larva that resembles a cysticerus but that contains many inverted scolices is a *cenurus*. The most elaborate larval form is the *hydatid cyst*, which is a large bladder (up to grapefruit size) containing a germinal layer that gives off daughter cysts called *brood capsules*, each of which contains numerous invaginated

scolices (Fig. 52.5). A hydatid cyst may contain millions of scolices, and some species produce secondary cysts within daughter cysts.

Taenia solium

The pork tapeworm, *T. solium*, is acquired by eating infected pork that has been insufficiently cooked. The worm occurs throughout the world, but human infections are often surprisingly infrequent, considering the frequency of infected swine in the same area. This is true in the United States, and why humans are so rarely infected is unclear. It is tempting to conclude that the education directed toward elimination of trichinosis has produced a secondary effect because the population has been well instructed to cook pork thoroughly.

Morphology and Life Cycle. The adult pork tapeworm can attain lengths of 2 m. The scolex is tiny, about 1 mm in diameter, but it produces up to 800 proglot-

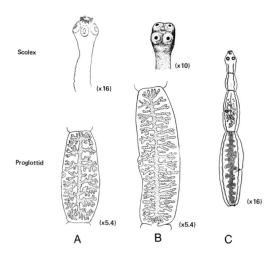

Fig. 52.4 Scoleces and ripe proglottids of some tapeworms. (A) *Taenia solium*. (B) *Taenia saginata*. (C) *Echinococcus granulosus*. (With permission, Chandler, A.C. Introduction to Parasitology. 9th Ed. John Wiley & Sons, New York, 1955. Reprinted by permission of John Wiley & Sons, Inc.)

tids. The solex is equipped with four suckers and 25 to 30 hooks (Fig. 52.4A), short and long, alternating on a projection called a rostellum. Behind the scolex is a thin neck joined to the immature proglottids, which are broader than they are long. About midway in the worm the proglottids are square, but when they are mature they are longer than they are broad and are shaped like a pumpkin seed (Fig. 52.4A).

Humans infected with a *T. solium* regularly expel proglottids. The shed proglottids are flabby and inactive and are found in feces. They infect pigs or dogs when these animals ingest such feces.

After reaching a suitable host the proglottids release the oncospheres; these bore through the gut wall and migrate via lymph channels or the bloodstream to the muscles and other organs. In the muscles the oncospheres develop into cysticerci, small oval white bodies 5 to 15 mm long. The pork tapeworm cysticerci are often called bladderworms or "measles" as well as the more scientific name *Cysticercus cellulosae*. These can be very numerous in a heavily infected animal, and they are readily seen. When such pork, termed "measly," is eaten by humans, the outer layers of the cysticerci are digested away, leaving the bare scolex, which everts and attaches to the intestinal wall to begin growth. Humans seem to be the sole final host and also can replace the pig as an intermediate host.

Pathology and Clinical Symptoms.
The symptoms of disease vary widely. Some humans carry their worms with no obvious symptoms. When symptoms are present they are generally vague — abdominal pain, weakness, and nausea, and others less common. Mechanical obstruction of the intestine can occur in extreme cases.

The most serious form of pork tapeworm infection, cysticercosis, occurs following ingestion of oncospheres by humans who then become intermediate hosts. Autoinfection is seen in humans that carry an adult worm and subsequently infect

themselves by hand to mouth transmission of eggs (Fig. 52.1G). Some feel that those eggs that hatch in the intestine can be digested sufficiently to permit oncospheres to begin boring before being expelled from the host. Cysticerci in muscles are usually not serious but may cause mechanical problems. However, some may come to reside in the eye, spinal cord, brain, or myocardium. These are much more serious.

Diagnosis.
Diagnosis is based on finding proglottids in feces (Fig. 52.4A). These are speciated by counting the uterine branches on one side, which range from 7 to 13, many fewer than found in the beef tapeworm.

Drugs are available and are efficient, in general, for adult parasites (Table 50.1). For cysticercosis there is no effective therapy aside from surgical removal.

Taenia saginata

The beef tapeworm, *T. saginata*, exists worldwide and is the most commonly found large tapeworm of humans. It is passed to humans through raw or incompletely cooked beef. Infections do occur in the United States, where the taste for rare beef is commonplace.

Morphology and Life Cycle.
T. saginata can reach lengths of 4 or 5 m; even longer worms have been recorded. The scolex is 1 to 2 mm in diameter and contains no hooks but possesses four suckers (Fig. 52.4B). A mature worm contains about 1000 proglottids. When detached, the proglottids are very active and are able to crawl; they can crawl out of the host's anus and deposit eggs nearby. The expelled eggs (Fig. 52.1G) are capable of surviving for months under favorable environmental conditions.

The life cycle of the beef tapeworm is very close to that of *T. solium* except that the intermediate hosts are cattle or related animals. In the tropics, water buffalo are commonly involved. The cysticerci of measly beef are easily seen and most often can be found in the jaw muscles and heart, which are usually examined during meat inspection. Low numbers, however, are easily overlooked, and when the meat is eaten raw the scolex is unrobed, whereupon it everts, attaches, and elaborates a strobila.

Humans harbor only adult *T. saginata*. Since humans are not an appropriate intermediate host, cysticercosis does not occur.

Pathology and Clinical Symptoms. In general, the beef tapeworm does little to damage its host. Infections usually involve a single worm and may go unnoticed for years. Rarely, they may cause mechanical obstruction. Such symptoms as do appear are most often abdominal pain, weight loss, and loss of appetite (not an increase, as the stories would have it). Anemia can result occasionally.

Laboratory diagnosis is centered on finding proglottids (Fig. 52.4B) and differentiating them from those of *T. solium* by counting the uterine branching. The branchings in proglottids of *T. saginata* range from 15 to 35 on one side. The search for eggs is not worthwhile, since few are to be found and even when found are indistinguishable from eggs of the pork tapeworm. However, eggs may sometimes be found perianally, where they can be obtained by lifting with transparent tape, as is done for the pinworm (see below).

Effective drugs are available (Table 50.1). A cure requires explusion of the scolex, since if it is not expelled, it will rebuild the strobila. Since it is difficult to find the tiny scolex, the usual practice is to treat and examine for return of proglottids after some months.

Hymenolepsis nana

Tapeworms of other species also can infect humans, usually accidentally. Such infections are sporadic and infrequent. The most common of these is the dwarf tapeworm, *Hymenolepsis nana* which is primarily a parasite of rodents. In the Southern United States infection of children with this parasite is common. Eggs are released from the bowel of rodents that carry adult worms. These eggs are ingested by the larvae of rat and mice fleas, adult grain beetles, or cockroaches. In any case the cystercoid larvae are accidentally ingested with food contaminated by the intermediate host and develop into adult tapeworms. Humans can also serve as intermediate hosts. Fortunately, infections are usually mild. Treatment is effective with appropriate drugs, but autoinfection is sometimes a problem. Diagnosis is made by finding the characteristic eggs in feces (Fig. 52.1A).

Echinococcus granulosus

Echinococcus granulosus is one species of a group of minute tapeworms that as adults live in dogs and wild canines. The larvae, however, form enormous cysts, called hydatid cysts (Fig. 52.5), in their intermediate hosts, including humans. *E. granulosus* infection is most commonly passed back and forth between dogs and sheep or cattle, the so-called pastoral epidemiology. A sylvatic form of this disease occurs in northern areas, where wolves and moose or deer are largely involved. In both forms humans may, with more or less ease, become involved. For completeness, it should be acknowledged that *E. multilocularis*, another minute tapeworm, can rarely cause human infection. However, our discussion will treat only *E. granulosus*.

Morphology and Life Cycle. The adult worm is tiny, 2 to 10 mm, and has a scolex armed with a double row of 30 to 50 hooks. Behind the scolex one immature and two mature and one ripe proglottid are usually present. The eggs (Fig. 52.1G) are passed with feces and left in water or on forage, where they are available for ingestion by cattle, sheep, horses, or other herbivores. Human infection is probably more often caused by too close an association with dogs than by eating or drinking contaminated food. Considering the habits of dogs, it is not difficult to imagine that the "kiss" of a dog may convey more than affection, especially in children. Infected dogs, furthermore, may carry eggs on their fur that are readily transferred to human hands and from there to human mouths.

When ingested by an appropriate host, the egg liberates an onchospore that penetrates the intestinal wall and is carried to the liver or lungs. It becomes trapped and matures into a hydatid cyst. In some animals (deer, moose) cysts are predominantly formed in the lungs; in domestic animals the liver is the preferential site. In humans cysts appear most frequently in the liver, but some appear in the lungs as well. The cysts develop slowly as the larvae turn first into a hollow bladder that then becomes filled with brood capsules that contain many scolices (Fig. 52.5). Eventually, the cysts may reach the size of an apple and contain enormous numbers of brood capsules, each lined with numerous scolices.

Pathology and Clinical Symptoms.
The symptoms of the disease, which is analogous to cysticercosis, are related to the growth of the cyst. Host reaction to parasitic antigens may also elicit a marked allergic inflammation. As the cyst grows, normal tissue may be destroyed. The most serious symptoms result when the cyst develops in the kidneys, spleen, brain, or eyes. When cysts rupture, scolices may be scattered widely, especially if rupture occurs into a blood vessel.

Diagnosis may be difficult, and the growing mass, although it can be seen on x-ray, may be confused with a tumor. Serologic tests are available, but results are sometimes difficult to interpret.

Surgery is the only available therapy. It is important to remove the cyst without

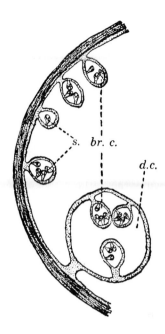

Fig. 52.5. Diagram of a hydatid cyst of *Echinococcus granulosus* showing daughter cyst (d.c.), brood capsules (br.c.), and scoleces (s.). Stippled inner wall of cyst is part of parasite; outer fibrous wall is capsule laid down by host (× 10). (With permission, Chandler, A.C. Introduction to Parasitology. 9th Ed. John Wiley & Sons, New York, 1955. Reprinted by permission of John Wiley & Sons, Inc.)

rupture. As a rule, the cyst is injected with chemicals to kill the germinal tissue *in situ* before removal is attempted.

Control measures in endemic areas center around limiting the amount or intensity of contact with dogs. Dogs should not be allowed to feed on carrion or uncooked meat. Iceland, which once had a high infection rate, has been made almost free of echinococci by treatment of all dogs with drugs to eliminate the parasite, which in addition to the killing of stray dogs greatly reduced the rate of infection. Such a strategy however, clearly works best in isolated areas such as islands.

Dibothriocephalus latus

Morphology and Life Cycle. It is convenient to discuss the fish or broad tapeworm with the other tapeworms even though this is taxonomically inappropriate because this tapeworm is a member of a different order, *Pseudophyllidea*. Formerly called *Diphyllobothrium latum*, *D. latus* is a name applied to what is probably a group of closely related species. *D. latus* is the largest tapeworm of humans; it is found in those temperate regions where the eating of raw or poorly cooked freshwater fish is common. Scandinavia and other Baltic countries of Europe are affected. In the United States and Canada the parasite occurs near the Great Lakes. The range extends through central and western Canada and north to Alaska.

D. latus is a potentially serious threat to the United States and Canadian fishing industry. In the lake regions of both countries many pike and walleyes carry the larvae of the fish tapeworm. This seems to stem largely from the "fish camp" practice of pouring sewage directly into lakes. Many towns in the North simply run a sewer line into a lake. Such outlets, of course, are extremely attractive for fish, since their prey are more abundant in these places. The reader can surmise the result when residents of such places discover the local fishing "hot spot."

The southern parts of South America are also involved with *D. latus*. Both domestic and wild animals, such as dogs, cats, or bears, may harbor adult worms.

D. latus can reach incredible size. Lengths to 10 m have been recorded. Three or four thousand proglottids may be present. However, when multiple worms are present each is correspondingly smaller.

The adult worm lives in the intestine held in place by long suckers that run almost the length of the scolex. Eggs (Fig. 52.1I) are released from ripe proglottids and pass from the host. They are characterized by an operculum at one end that is a "hatch" that opens to release the embryo. In fresh water the eggs undergo transformation into a ciliated embryo, a *coracidium*, which escapes the egg through the hatch and swims or creeps. They must be then eaten by certain species of copepods within 24 hours. If eaten by an appropriate copepod, the coracidum forms a naked oncosphere and develops further into an elongated form. When the copepod is ingested by any one of a number of freshwater fishes or even a predatory chain of fishes, these forms migrate into the flesh of the fish and develop into larvae, which may be several centimeters in length. Infection of the final host occurs when raw or improperly cooked fish is ingested. The larvae will attach to the intestine of the host and grow to adulthood. Egg production can begin in as little as 3 weeks.

Pathology and Clinical Symptoms. Common symptoms of *D. latus* infection are weakness, abdominal pain, weight loss, and, in some patients, a severe anemia thought to result from vitamin B_{12} deprivation caused by the worm, which absorbs the vitamin at high rates.

Laboratory diagnosis is easily made by recovery of the operculated eggs from feces (Fig. 52.1I). Treatment with drugs is effective.

NEMATHELMINTHES

The majority of the estimated half million species of nematodes, or roundworms are free living, and only few are parasitic for humans. However, even those species that do not parasitize humans often have great impact on human life when they parasitize the birds, animals, and even plants that we produce for our sustenance. In fact, some of these are responsible for severe annual agricultural losses.

The nematodes are typically enlongated cylinders with both ends tapered. Their body is surrounded by a tough cuticle that is usually striated and sometimes equipped with spines, ridges, or bristles. These worms have a complete digestive tube with mouth and anus, and a body cavity. Most species are composed of male and female worms. Life cycles are usually quite simple. Two large parasitic groups can be distinguished: those that infect the alimentary tract, and those that invade other tissues.

Trichuris trichura

Morphology and Life Cycle. *Trichuris* means "hair tail," a name that was given to a worm that often inhabits the cecum and colon of many mammals, including man, before it was realized that the narrow end of the worm was actually the head. As the common name, whipworm, implies, the organism is a whip-shaped worm. The thick "handle" of the whip is the rear of the worm and contains the reproductive organs. The thin "whip end" contains the mouth and esophagous.

The worm is about 4.5 cm long; the attenuated oral end represents about two-thirds of the length. Females are slightly larger than males. Males are recognized because they have a curled tail (Fig. 52.6A).

The life cycle is simple. The typically football shaped eggs (Fig. 52.1J) are passed from the host with feces and if left warm and moist they develop into embryos in 3 to 6 weeks, although when conditions are less favorable more time may be required. Infection results from ingestion of contaminated food or water polluted by human or animal feces containing eggs. The eggs contain embryos that hatch and burrow into the wall of the small intestine by means of a spearlike projection. After a period of maturation within the intestinal wall, the young parasites migrate into the cecum, where they take residence. The adult worms may live for years and continuously produce eggs.

T. trichura is found worldwide but is especially prevalent in the tropics and subtropics. It occurs in the United States in the Southeast. In endemic areas large infections can be built up slowly.

Pathology and Clinical Symptoms. Children are much more likely to be infected than adults. Infections with a few worms produce negligible symptoms, if any. When infection is heavy the worms begin to spread from the cecum to the lower colon and rectum, where eventually they may form a lawn that covers the mucous membrane. The symptoms, which can be confused with hookworm infection, include weakness, bloody stools, diarrhea, weight loss, anemia, eosinophilia, and often fever. Prolapse of the rectum is common in chron-

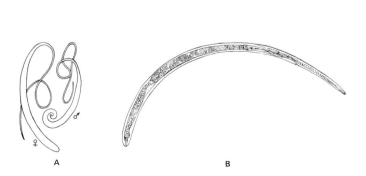

Fig. 52.6. Some adult nematode parasites. (A) Male and female *Trichuris trichiura* (×4). (B) Female of *Trichinella spiralis* (entire worm ×40 in length, width ×80). (With permission, Chandler, A.C. Introduction to Parasitology. 9th Ed., John Wiley & Sons, New York, 1955. Reprinted by permission of John Wiley & Sons, Inc.)

ic cases. The state of the host is an important element in symptom production; malnourished children show symptoms more readily than those with an adequate diet.

Laboratory diagnosis is made by the finding of the typical football or barrel shaped eggs that have polar swellings and double membranes (Fig. 52.1J). Effective drugs are available (Table 50.1), but the disease is difficult to treat because the cecum provides a refuge isolated from the drugs. Light infections may require no treatment.

Control measures depend on sanitary practices — proper disposal of human feces and education of children in habits that will break hand-to-mouth transmission.

Trichinella spiralis

Morphology and Life Cycle. Adult females are 3 to 4 mm long; males are about half this length (Fig. 52.6B). Both sexes are white and taper toward the anterior end. The anal ends of both sexes are blunt. The adult worms live in the intestines, where mating takes place for 2 to 3 weeks after they reach maturity. The number of young produced by a single adult female has been estimated at 1500. Males often pass out of the host directly after mating. The gravid female burrows deep into the intestinal mucosa, so that the young embryos that develop in the uterus are deposited in the tissue of the intestinal wall. The larvae, after leaving the uterus, enter lymph or blood vessels of the gut wall and are disseminated throughout the host's body, lodging in almost any site. Striated muscles are favored by the parasite, in particular those of the eye, diaphragm, larynx, tongue and limbs.

The larvae after reaching their destination in striated muscle, bore through the sarcolemma, undergo encystation, and begin to develop. Cysts are formed around the larvae by host reaction. The larvae grow from approximately 0.1 mm to about

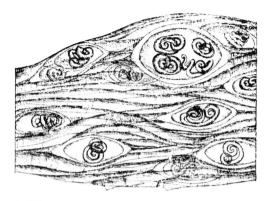

(×75)

Fig. 52.7.   Encysted larvae of *Trichinella. spiralis* in striated muscle fibers in pork (×75). (With permission, Chandler, A.C. Introduction to Parasitology. 9th Ed. John Wiley & Sons, New York, 1955. Reprinted by permission of John Wiley & Sons, Inc.)

1 mm within the muscle fibers in about 15 days, and they curl into a spiral in the process becoming sexually mature (Fig. 52.7). These are about 0.5 mm long and usually contain one or two larvae, but more may be present.

Some cysts remain infective for years in spite of their progressive calcification. Most cysts, however, become inactive within a shorter time. The larvae can infect many animals, but the most important species for human infection is the pig, although bears, whales, and seals sometimes are sources.

Pathology and Clinical Symptoms. Humans are infected by eating raw or partially cooked meat that contains encysted larvae of *T. spiralis*. Digestion frees the larvae, which penetrate into the mucosa of the small intestine, where, after a series of molts, the adult worms develop.

Trichinosis is seldom a tropical disease but is rather a disease of Europe, North America, and the Arctic regions. Trichinosis is an unusual nematode disease because the often serious and sometimes fatal infection is due to the offspring of the adult worms but not to the adults themselves.

As a disease, trichinosis has no definite

set of symptoms. Initially, diarrhea, nausea, gastrointestinal disturbances, and sometimes fever accompany development of parasites in the intestines. As the new larvae begin to disseminate, an eosinophilia develops, often accompanied by weakness and muscle pain, especially in the eyes. The stage in which the larvae migrate is the most serious and can be fatal. Sweating and fever together with puffiness of the eyes commonly occur at this time, accompanied by extreme muscle pain. Invasion of diaphragmatic muscle and intercostal muscles may lead to extreme difficulty in breathing. The route of each larva is marked by an acute inflammatory reaction.

These symptoms become even more pronounced during the encystment stage. The entire face becomes puffed, the limbs are swollen, and the abdomen is distended. The myocardium may become invaded, leading to severe myocarditis. In addition, pulmonary hemorrhaging may develop.

The intensity and combination of symptoms vary from case to case and, in general, are related to the number of cysts ingested and the status of the host. Since ingestion of infected meat will commonly expose a person to 100,000 or more encysted larvae, the number of adult parasites and their offspring can be enormous. It is thought that five larvae per gram of body weight is fatal for humans. Recovery is always slow and may require months.

Diagnosis of trichinosis is often a matter of exhausting other possibilities. Periorbital edema, eye pain, and eosinophilia are highly suggestive findings. Often the disease appears in clusters of cases. A history of ingesting home slaughtered pork or home prepared sausage is helpful in making a diagnosis. Commercially available pork is usually safe because it originates from animals that are most often grain fed.

Laboratory demonstration of cysts is difficult. The specimen of choice is biopsy material from the deltoid, biceps, or gastrocnemius muscle. Available serologic tests are useful as guides; titers become diagnostic about a month after infection. Indirect fluorescent antibody and passive agglutination tests are the most sensitive, although other tests, including a skin test, are also available.

There is no specific and effective treatment for trichinosis. Treatment is directed largely toward relief of symptoms and general supportive measures. Corticosteroids are advocated by some in treatment of severe cases.

Control of trichinosis takes two forms in the United States: the population is educated to cook pork thoroughly, and pig farmers are prohibited from feeding uncooked garbage or scraps left from slaughtering to pigs. In some European countries pork is examined for trichinosis, but such is not the case in the United States, where the incidence of trichinosis is much higher.

There is some evidence that effective immunity is acquired during exposure to small numbers of larvae. The protection is not solid but is rather an enhanced resistance to both larval and adult forms upon reinfection. The larvae are retarded in development, and the adults are inhibited in their reproduction. The mechanisms by which the resistance operates are unknown. Attempts to develop vaccines have been unsuccessful.

Necator americanus and Ancylostoma duodenale

Morphology and Life Cycle. Two species of hookworms are the principal causes of human infection: *N. americanus* and *A. duodenale*. These worms are remarkably similar in morphology and life cycle. *N. americanus* is often called the New World or American hookworm, since it was discovered in the United States. It causes the bulk of hookworm infections in the United States, but it is not restricted to the New World at all. Similarly, *A. duodenale* is called the Old World hookworm, although

A   B

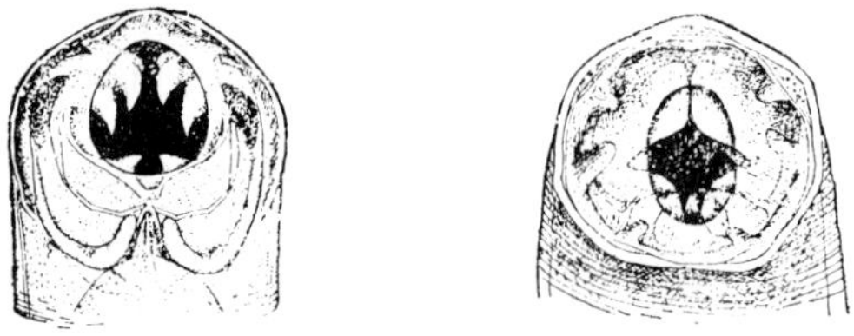

Fig. 52.8 Mouth and buccal cavity of hookworms (A) *Ancylostoma duodenale* (×100) and (B) *Necator americanus* (×230), showing teeth in former and cutting ridges in latter. Dorsal view. (With permission, Chandler A.C. Introduction to Parasitology. 9th Ed. John Wiley & Sons, New York, 1955. Reprinted by permission of John Wiley & Sons, Inc.)

it is not restricted to the Old World but rather predominates there. Hookworm infections flourish, when uncontrolled, in most tropical or subtropical areas of the world. In the United States they occur in the South and in Puerto Rico. Hookworms are found in Central and South America and in West and Central Africa as well as in parts of Asia and the Middle East.

Females of *N. americanus* are about 1 cm long; the males somewhat smaller and possess a characteristic set of rays at the tail. The mouth of *Necator* possesses sharp cutting plates for gripping (Fig. 52.8B).

The female *A. duodenale* is about 1.2 cm long; the males are about 1 cm. The tail of the female is armed with a single spine; the tail of the male is equipped with projections, or rays. The mouth of *A. duodenale* is equipped with six large, strong teeth used to grip the host intestine (Fig. 52.8A). The head part is broader than that of *Necator*.

As adults, both hookworms reside in the small intestine. They fasten tightly in place by gripping a fold of intestinal mucosa drawn into their mouths. The worms then feed themselves by sucking blood and tissue fluids from the intestinal wall. Members of both genera produce copious numbers of eggs; 10,000 eggs per day per female is not unusual. The eggs of the two

hookworms differ in size but are very difficult to distinguish on that basis.

Until expelled from the host, the eggs are in the four cell stage. Embryonic development begins and larvae may be produced in less than a day when eggs are exposed to moisture, warmth, and air.

Early or *rhabditiform* larvae of both species possess a constriction behind the anterior esophagus. They are free living and feed on bacteria and other organic matter in the soil. Subsequently, they lose the esophageal constriction, becoming *strongyliform*. These undergo a series of molts and cease to feed. Such larvae are termed *filariform* and are infective. Development is rapid in warm temperatures but is arrested in lower temperatures. Temperatures below 0°C or above 31°C kill the larvae.

The filariform larvae climb to the highest point that has sufficient moisture and stretch themselves in the air in which position they may make contact with the bare skin of an appropriate host. Hands, feet, ankles, and other skin sites that come into contact with feces or contaminated objects can easily be infected. The discovery that the larvae of hookworms directly penetrate the skin of the host was made after an accidental laboratory spill of a larval culture on the hands of an investigator resulted in an infection.

Once the larvae penetrate the skin, they reach lymph or blood vessels and are carried via the bloodstream through the right heart into the lungs, where most of them are trapped in the capillaries. From the capillaries the larvae penetrate into the air sacs, from where they are swept to the trachea and either expectorated or swallowed. Those that are swallowed burrow into folds in the intestine, molt, develop their buccal teeth or plates, and then fasten themselves in place. An additional molt occurs before they mature and start producing eggs, which appear in the feces about 6 weeks after infection. The adult worms live for several years.

Pathology and Clinical Symptoms.
The symptoms of hookworm infection usually begin with a skin that itches and becomes inflamed although the skin reaction may be overlooked. There seems to be an allergic component to this reaction. In fact, hookworms of cats or dogs may fail to penetrate deeply into inappropriate (human) host skin and may wander close to the surface, also producing a severe skin allergy called *creeping eruption* or *cutaneous larval migrans* in sensitive individuals.

The migration of larvae through the lungs often produces few or no symptoms unless the number of larvae is large. In the latter case, in addition to such signs as fever, headache, cough, and eosinophilia, a pneumonia develops that can be complicated by a secondary bacterial infection. During this phase many larvae are immobilized by the host immune response and are eventually encapsulated. Antibody against larval enzymes is produced.

When worms begin to infect the intestine, new symptoms develop. The intestinal disturbances include nausea, abdominal pain, and diarrhea. The hallmark of this disease, however, is anemia caused by the sucking of blood from the intestinal mucosa. Initially, the host may compensate for the blood loss, but, depending on the host's size, state of health, and diet, as well as on the number of worms, when the drain outstrips the host's compensatory ability more or less severe anemia develops. The typical symptoms at this point are weakness, pallor, breathlessness, and languor. When chronic, these symptoms progress to include failure to grow (in children), flabby heart muscles and palpitations of the heart, edema, and abdominal distention. In addition to loss of red blood cells and iron deficiency, a severe depletion of serum protein can often occur, especially when diet is marginal.

Laboratory diagnosis centers on finding eggs in the feces (Fig 52.1K). At times rhabditiform larvae may be found. These must be differentiated from larvae of *Strongyloides stercoralis* (see below), which are always present as larvae in feces. Persons with light infections and who compensate well generally need no treatment. In heavier infections the primary concern is management of the anemia, which may be life threatening. Once the anemia is under control, drugs to eliminate the worms can be given and are highly effective (Table 50.1). An essential element of treatment is the prevention of reinfection.

Historically, hookworms have been a serious — perhaps the most serious — helminthic threat to humans. With control measures that involve treatment of cases, the wearing of shoes, proper feces disposal, and prevention of soil pollution, hookworms lost their preeminent place. An adequate diet is helpful but often is less easy to provide. In general, well fed and well educated populations that can afford sewage treatment and shoes are at minimum risk of hookworm transmission.

Strongyloides stercoralis

Morphology and Life Cycle.
The life cycle of *S. stercoralis* is in question. Only the tiny (2 mm) female is found in the human intestines, where it burrows into the wall. The eggs resemble hookworm eggs but are smaller and develop much more rapidly. The rhabditiform larvae develop in the intestine and then pass in the feces. They can be distinguished from hookworm rhabditiform larvae by differences in their buccal structure and genital primordium. Some of the larvae can mature into filariform larvae directly within the host and penetrate the colon or perianal area, causing repeated autoinfection. Those filariform larvae that are expelled penetrate the skin of the next host similar to the hookworms and migrate via the lungs to the intestine, where they attach.

Rhabditiform larvae that reach the soil

can develop into free-living adult forms that produce more larvae, some of which may be rhabditiform and repeat the cycle; others may develop into filariform larvae and penetrate the skin of a new host.

S. stercoralis occurs worldwide, and its distribution is similar to that of hookworms. Its range is sometimes limited by a stricter requirement for warmth and moisture. *S. stercoralis* is much more fragile than the hookworms, and its larvae are easily killed by slight variations in environmental temperatures or moisture. Survival for long periods occurs by means of host autoinfection, but not by surviving in soil.

Pathology and Clinical Symptoms. The initial symptom of invasion by *S. stercoralis* is a skin reaction, which can be pronounced in individuals previously sensitized. A spreading eruption may appear in the skin as the larvae migrate. Migration through the lungs can give the same picture as that from the other hookworms. Eosinophilia can be either marked or entirely absent. In the next stage, abdominal pain, nausea, and diarrhea may appear. In heavy infections uncontrollable diarrhea may begin, often with blood in the discharge owing to severe erosion of the intestinal wall. In fatal cases the larvae can be found widely disseminated in the host's organs, and adult worms appear in large numbers through the small intestines. Repeated autoinfection accompanied by allergic symptoms and inflammation of increasing severity is the principal problem.

Since eggs are rarely found, laboratory diagnosis depends upon finding the larvae of *S. stercoralis* in the stools of patients. Often stool samples must be allowed to stand in water for some time to allow larvae to emerge. The problem is to recover larvae, which once obtained can be readily distinguished from other hookworm larvae by comparison of the buccal cavities. In cases of autoinfection the stools often contain no larvae, and larvae must be recovered from the duodenum.

Drugs are available, but several courses of treatment may be required to eliminate the parasite. Since the threat of autoinfection is the main problem of therapy, eradication of *S. stercoralis* must be the aim.

Ascaris lumbricoides

Morphology and Life Cycle. *A. lumbricoides*, or human roundworm, is a large nematode. Females are 25 to 30 cm long and about 2.5 cm in diameter. Males are somewhat shorter and considerably more slender, and they possess a curled tail (in contrast to the blunt tail of the female). The mouth of this worm has three lips, each with small papillae. Both sexes superficially resemble earthworms.

The adult worms live in the small intestine, where they may grip the mucous membrane and suck nutrients from time to time, but they generally live unattached and feed on the semidigested intestinal contents. The egg-laying capacity of ascarids is prodigious; estimates go as high as 200,000 per day. The eggs have a thick, clear inner membrane covered by a bumpy protein coat that is pigmented yellow by bile. Many eggs are infertile; these may be more difficult to identify, since their form tends to be less distinct than that of fertile eggs.

The eggs are passed from the host in feces and must undergo an incubation period at temperatures lower than 37°C with adequate moisture in order to develop further; the eggs are killed by temperatures greater than 37°C. They can remain for years in soil provided that moisture is present. Under optimum conditions eggs develop into embryos in about a week. The embryos become infective in another week, after having molted once within the egg shell.

When mature eggs are swallowed by a new host, the larvae hatch in the small intestine, penetrate through the wall, and reach the bloodstream, which carries them through the right side of the heart, and finally to the lungs. In the lung the larvae bore through to the air channels and finally are brought to the trachea, from where they eventually become swallowed to reside finally as adults in the small intestine. Maturity is achieved in about 2 months. The adults live about 9 months to 1 year.

Ascaris infections have probably been known since humans began domesticating swine. It is believed that humans acquired *A. lumbricoides* from pigs and that some strains of this worm have come to restrict themselves to humans. Pigs, indeed, have *A. lumbricoides*, and a few minutes at any slaughterhouse will provide one with a handful of specimens. Interestingly, this subspecies, *A. lumbricoides suum*, does not infect humans.

Ascaris infection abounds where shade and moisture are present and where human feces are disposed of improperly. This parasite is found worldwide in tropical and subtropical regions, including the United States, where it occurs mostly in the Southeast, with infections appearing elsewhere from time to time. Food and water can carry eggs, but transfer with soil-covered fingers is probably the most common mode of infection.

Pathology and Clinical Symptoms. Symptoms due to the larvae migration are largely pulmonary: coughing, sometimes production of bloody sputum, a pneumonitis, and fever. Eosinophilia may emerge. These symptoms vary according to the size of the larval population.

A few adult ascarids may cause no symptoms whatever. Mild symptoms, such as abdominal discomfort, vomiting, and diarrhea, may appear. Heavy infections are more serious. Large balls of entangled worms may obstruct the intestine, requiring surgical intervention. Malnutrition accompanies heavy infections, especially in those individuals who are on an inadequate diet in the first place. The habit of ascarids to "explore" ducts and cavities can lead to serious complications. They often invade bile or pancreatic ducts, and they may enter the gall bladder or even travel on to the liver. Rarely, the worms manage to enter the peritoneal cavity and cause peritonitis. Adult ascarids sometimes wander forward through the stomach and are vomited up or may continue to emerge in the mouth or out the nose. Deaths have occurred from aspiration of an adult worm into the airway, which then becomes blocked. Invasion of urogenital passages is also possible.

Laboratory diagnosis depends upon recovery of eggs (Figs. 52.1L, 52.1M, 52.1N), which with this parasite is favored by the enormous egg production. However, infection with a male (or males) only will yield no eggs. Infection with a single female will produce infertile eggs, which may be difficult for the inexperienced examiner to identify.

An important precaution must be observed when treatment for other worms is undertaken in the presence of ascarids: treatment with chemicals that do not kill the ascarids can initiate their wandering about. It is important in treatment of a recognized hookworm infection, for example, that careful examination of the stool is carried out to minimize the possibility of a simultaneous ascarids infection, which could be rendered much more threatening by treatment for the hookworm.

Control of ascarids is technically simple but can be difficult in certain populations because of their socioeconomic conditions or even customs. Proper care of feces and simple hygienic measures are all that is required.

Enterobius vermicularis

The chances are very good that all who read this have had, have at present, or will have *E. vermicularis*, otherwise known as the *pinworm*, *seatworm*, *threadworm*, or *oxyuria*. This worm has no respect for status or wealth and is truly cosmopolitan in its distribution, although unlike most parasitic worms it is found primarily in temperate zones. This parasite is restricted to humans; whites are more likely to be infected than blacks.

Morphology and Life Cycle. Adult pinworms live in the cecum and lower intestinal tract, from where the females migrate into the rectum. Both males and females are small white semi-transparent worms and have a head equipped with three small lips and lateral extensions called *alae*. The females are about 1 cm long, and males, which are rarely found, are about one-third as long. Females may often be found wriggling in freshly passed feces. Mature females migrate during the night out from the anus and deposit their eggs on the perianal skin, thereafter retreating back to the rectum. The movement of the female is accompanied by itching around the anus. Freshly laid eggs contain partially developed embryos, called *tadpoles*. These become fully infective in as short a time as 6 hours. The eggs are transparent, are flattened on one side, and contain an easily recognized tadpole larva. Pinworms produce numerous eggs, many of which can be carried on scratching fingers back to the mouth of the same host. Simultaneously, many of the eggs become widely distributed through the host's environment, contaminating food, bedclothes, and dust in the home. Eggs survive for 6 days under optimum conditions. Pinworm infections are easily spread from one person to an entire household. Infections in institutions and schools are a particular problem, since the eggs from a single individual can be disseminated readily through the entire environment. The adult worms live only for 1 or 2 months; hence if reinfection is controlled, outbreaks will die out of themselves.

Pathology and Clinical Symptoms. Symptoms appear in about one-third of pinworm cases; the others are asymptomatic. The itching can be intense and may cause restlessness, nervousness, and inattention. Secondary infection of lesions caused by scratching can be a problem. In girls the worms may invade the vagina and even travel as far as the Fallopian tubes and peritoneum. Immature worms that are developing from ingested eggs may burrow into the cecal region and cause inflammation accompanied by digestive complaints or abdominal pain. Mature worms are sometimes found in an inflamed appendix, but there is some doubt as to whether or not they cause appendicitis.

Examination of feces for eggs is hopeless; very few eggs will be found except in heavy infections. Better results are obtained by seeking eggs (and often female worms) in the perianal skin. A common method employs a piece of transparent tape wrapped over the end of a flat wooden blade or a microscope slide, sticky side out. The tape is pressed against the anal folds, and eggs picked up can be seen easily under the microscope (Fig. 52.1O). This specimen is best taken at night, when female worms are usually active and may even be seen. Several specimens may be required. Six or seven negative specimens should be obtained before concluding that pinworms are not present.

Effective drugs are available (Table 50.1), but treatment is difficult because the widespread contamination of the environment with eggs makes reinfection common. Often entire families must be treated together with the patient, and in institutions mass treatment must also be used. Sometimes two courses of treatment are required.

Control of pinworms depends on hygiene and prevention of autoinfection. If the cycle can be broken, the parasite will die away naturally because of its short lifespan.

ARTHROPODA

Very few arthropods are "true" parasites (i.e., they invade human tissue and live there for a prolonged time). Those few that deserve special attention are discussed briefly.

The mite of *scabies*, *Sarcoptes scabiei*, is a very small animal; males reach 200 to 250 μm and females 300 to 450 μm. Pregnant females burrow into the epidermis, making long tunnels in which they deposit eggs. New generations of the parasite hatch inside the tunnels; after full development is achieved, they continue making tunnels. Although the invasion of parasites is initially symptomless, with time two complications occur: sensitization and secondary infections produced by severe itching and subsequent scratching. The local symptoms are limited to certain areas, such as between the fingers, groin, genitals, and armpits. Infection is quite common among individuals living in large crowded groups and not adhering to proper hygienic habits.

The hair follicle mite, *Demodex folliculorum*, lives in hair follicles, blackheads, acne erruptions, and localized skin infections. This small parasite produces no significant symptoms.

Red bugs, or *chiggers*, *Eutrombicula alfreddugesi*, are the larval stages of free-living mites. The larvae usually parasitize various animals but often attach to humans, especially in the southern United States. Actually, they do not invade tissue but rather attach to the skin surface by a *stylostome*. Larval saliva is secreted through this specialized organ, and it dissolves the tissues, thus providing necessary nourishment for the parasite. Closely related mites from the Far East, *Trombicula akamushi*, not only parasitize but also transfer various rickettsiae. In addition, various mites living in food stores, mills, granaries, or dairies may induce allergic responses in human who come into contact with them or their fragments.

An already discussed tick, *Dermacentor andersoni* (Chs. 7 and 37), may be considered a parasite, since it lives attached to the skin of its victim and derives its nourishment from its victims.

The tongue worm, *Linguatula serrata*, is a parasite of the upper respiratory tract of the dog. This elongated flat or cylindrical organism is deprived of legs and remains attached to the mucous membranes of its host. The eggs, which are normally swallowed by the dog and passed with feces, may be consumed by humans in contaminated drinking water, vegetables, or other food products. The larvae can hatch in the digestive tract of man and migrate through the intestinal walls to invade various visceral organs. Once in such organs, the larvae become encapsulated and remain dormant for many years. In most instances the infection, quite common in certain areas, produces no clinical symptoms and usually is detected incidently during autopsies. However, a few cases of infection in humans with adult organisms have been described. A similar parasite (*Porocephalus* spp.) of snakes may also infect humans.

The larval stages of many species of flies are able to attack humans. Infection with fly maggots is called *myiasis*. The species that do this belong to two groups: the muscoidae and botflies. The former group includes the bloodflies or fleshflies that normally consume dead tissue. Some members, however, enter wounds and feed on living flesh, as, for example, the screwworm of cattle. Botflies belong to several species and have a compulsory parasitic larval stage that is often of long duration. The adult flies often do not feed and have a lifespan just long enough to produce eggs. The eggs are laid on the skin of mammals. When they hatch, the larvae penetrate the skin of the host and develop. Myiasis is usually limited to the skin but may be found in the intestine, urinary tract, or elsewhere. One species, *Dermatobia hominis*, fastens its eggs to large mosquitoes, which then carry the larvae to mammalian hosts. The normal hosts of botfly larvae are domestic and wild animals. Humans are more rarely hosts, but human infections do occur. Botfly infection is largely a problem in the tropics but can be found elsewhere, including the United States. Occasionally death occurs, particularly in children. Fatalities are usually due to secondary infection of the boillike cysts that contain the larvae. In humans the myiasis produced by some species of maggots reflects the fact that humans are unusual hosts in that the larvae and the lump or boil that they produce migrate about under the skin. Cattle, horse, and deer botflies all, on occasion, cause human myiasis, usually limited to one or two larvae. The larvae must be surgically removed in cutaneous myiasis.

REFERENCES

Beck, J.W. and Davies, J.E.: Medical Parasitology, 2nd Ed. C.V. Mosby, St. Louis, 1976.

Chandler, A.C.: Introduction to Parasitology, 9th Ed. John Wiley and Sons, New York, 1955.

Faust, E.C., Russell, P.F., and Jung, R.C.: Craig and Faust's Clinical Parasitology, 8th Ed. Lea and Febiger, Philadelphia, 1970.

Gear, J.H.S., Ed.: Medicine in a Tropical Environment. A.A. Balkeena, Cape Town, 1977.

Schneierson, S.S.: Atlas of Diagnostic Microbiology. Abott Laboratories, N. Chicago, 1971.

53

Microbiology in the Practice of Medicine

Cornelius J. O'Connell

The diagnosis of infectious disease rests on the triad of clinical observations, epidemiologic evidence, and microbiologic tests. Clinical diagnosis ranges from simple recognition of common childhood diseases by observation of their characteristic rashes to complicated procedures employing laboratory tests, biopsies, and the application of x-ray or radionuclear imaging to extend the examination of the patient. An example of the latter forms of clinical detection includes the diagnosis of tuberculosis by observing the changes characteristic of the disease on chest x-ray together with the demonstration of characteristic lesions (caseating granulomas) on biopsy of a mediastinal lymph node. Another example would be the diagnosis of hepatitis on the basis of chemical changes in the blood showing elevated hepatocellular enzymes supplemented perhaps by a needle biopsy of the liver showing pathologic changes characteristic of viral hepatitis.

Epidemiologic criteria may be used to exclude or support a diagnosis of infectious disease. Examples would be the exclusion of a diagnosis of coccidioidomycosis as the cause of a patient's lung lesion because of a lack of history of travel to an area in which the infection may be contracted and the support of a diagnosis of influenza in a patient with a grippelike syndrome by the observation that virologically proven influenza is epidemic in the community at the time.

The third part of the triad, the use of microbiologic tests, concerns the student of microbiology. These tests are specific and fall within the sphere of microbiology, in contrast to the first two parts, which are more properly considered in courses in pathology, laboratory medicine, clinical medicine, or epidemiology. The specific tests rely on seeing the organism either with or without special stains, on growing the organism and appropriately identifying it. Diagnosis is also based on demonstrating an immunologic response to an infecting organism by a serologic test (e.g., salmonella agglutinins in typhoid fever), on demonstrating some unusual but characteristic serologic reactivity (e.g., a rise in cold agglutinins in mycoplasmal pneumonia), or on the employment of tests depending on delayed hypersensitivity to microbial anti-

697

gens (e.g., positive skin tests in tuberculosis). Whatever tests are available, informed and intelligent employment and interpretation of their results is necessary to ensure correct diagnosis.

BLOODSTREAM INFECTIONS

Some infections regularly produce bacteremia as an integral feature (e.g., endocarditis and typhoid fever), while other infections result in occasional or irregular invasion of the bloodstream by microorganisms, as seen in pneumonia or meningitis. Even in the latter cases culture of the blood is helpful in diagnosis, since the infecting organism may sometimes be easier to demonstrate in the blood than in material from the infected area. Also, a positive blood culture for one organism helps the clinician decide which of two or more potential pathogens grown from the primary site of the disease is the one most likely responsible for producing the illness.

If bacteremia is present, it is demonstrated by one blood culture in about 85 percent of cases, by two blood cultures about 95 percent of the time, and by three cultures about 98 percent of the time. Further cultures are subject to the law of diminishing returns, with each additional test adding progressively fewer cases found for the cost expended. For this reason most clinicians avoid ordering more than three blood cultures for any patient.

The practice of ordering cultures related to the patient's temperature, such as "blood culture for temperature over 102°F," is mentioned only to be condemned. There is no regular relationship between positive blood cultures and the height of fever. Since endotoxin causes leukocytes to produce pyrogen after about a 2-hour delay, there is reason to believe that many bacteremias occur hours before the rises in temperature. Further, it is not unusual to see patients who should have had their blood cultured but this has

not been done because their temperatures failed to rise after an order of this type was written. Therefore it is good practice to ask simply for one to three blood cultures to be done at some reasonable interval, such as ½ to 1 hour apart, without relating them to the degree of fever.

All blood cultures require skin penetration by a needle and therefore involve the possibility of contamination of the cultures by skin organisms. This occurs from time to time even with the best precautions, although the frequency of contamination falls as skin preparation for the culture is done with increasing thoroughness. The most common skin organisms to be seen as contaminants are diphtheroids (nonpathogenic corynebacteria) and *Staphylococcus epidermidis*. Their presence as contaminants is strongly suggested when they are seen in only one of several blood cultures and also when they are seen only in low numbers. A laboratory report such as "growth in one liquid medium only" generally indicates extremely small numbers of the organism in question, since a greater concentration of microbes in the blood drawn should have resulted in growth in all fluid media inoculated and even on the solid media used.

In special situations the laboratory may be consulted before one orders blood cultures to ensure that the appropriate media are inoculated. For example, if brucellosis is suspected, special media suitable for the growth of species of *Brucella* and prolonged incubation are needed before the cultures may be reported as negative. Another example would be a case of clinically suspected endocarditis in which routine cultures have been negative; here consideration should be given.to the use of hypertonic or thiol-containing media, which have some value in revealing organisms that fail to grow under routine conditions.

Plastic intravenous catheters may become infected with *Staphylococcus aureus* or candidae, particularly if they have been in place for longer than 48 hours or if they are used for the administration of hyperalimentation solutions. In this situation the significance of positive blood cultures for staphylococci or candidae can be evaluated by withdrawing the suspect intravenous lines, culturing their tips, and then reculturing the patient's blood after 24 hours. Finding the organism on the catheter tip and proving its disappearance from the blood after withdrawal of the catheter establishes the source of the organism.

The finding of multiple species of organisms in a single blood culture was once regarded as definite evidence of contamination of the culture by poor technique in drawing the specimen. It is now known that polymicrobial bacteremia does occur, particularly in debilitated patients with poor defenses or those who are immunosuppressed. In these situations the finding of several species of microbes cannot be dismissed lightly.

In some cases of chronic low grade bacteremia, such as brucellosis or endocarditis, the bone marrow may be positive for the organism even though three blood cultures have been negative. In evaluating culture reports one should remember that contamination by *Staphylococcus epidermidis* and diphtheroids is even more frequent in marrow specimens than it is in blood specimens.

Recent advances in blood culture technique use automated apparatus to detect the release of radioactive carbon dioxide from sugars contained in the media and in some cases allow detection of bacteremia in as little as 2 to 4 hours. In heavy bacteremia, usually due to clostridia or *Staphylococcus aureus*, organisms may sometimes be seen in Gram-stained smears of the blood or, better, of the buffy coat of centrifuged blood, thus giving diagnostic information almost immediately.

A serologic test is available in some medical centers for antibodies against staphylococcal teichoic acid, a cell wall material of the organism extractable by chemical means. The test for antibodies against this substance uses counterelectrophoresis to produce a band of precipitate. Teichoic acid antibodies may be found in staphylococcal endocarditis even in cases where culture of the blood is negative. Other staphylococcal septic conditions may also be indicated by positive tests for the antibody, especially if they are infections that liberate a fair amount of staphylococcal material into the circulation; closed staphylococcal infections, such as osteomyelitis, give negative results by this procedure.

Bloodstream infection should be suspected in the newborn even in the absence of classic clinical indications. The infant may have a subnormal rather than elevated temperature and may simply look ill without specific signs. Bacteria to be expected in such cases include β-hemolytic streptococci of group B, encapsulated mucoid *Escherichia coli, Staphylococcus aureus,* and *Listeria monocytogenes*. In high risk infants such as the premature, those born following prolonged and difficult labor, or those born after the membranes have been ruptured for hours, as well as infants showing fetal distress, culture from the mother's vagina and smear and culture of the newborn infant's first stool (meconium) may reveal one of the above-mentioned organisms. This allows more rapid diagnosis if the infant later appears septic while in the nursery.

INFECTIONS OF THE RESPIRATORY TRACT

A wide variety of microbial agents can infect the respiratory tract, and tests needed for diagnosis depend on the site of the infection in the respiratory tract and the age of the patient, among other factors. A number of syndromes are produced by viruses. Exact virologic diagnosis using cultures or serologic procedures may be carried out in seriously ill individuals and in selected cases during an outbreak of respiratory disease in order to establish the etiology of the epidemic. In the average case, however, laboratory confirmation of the diagnosis of viral respiratory disease is usually not sought.

Mycoplasma pneumoniae causes a variety of respiratory syndromes ranging from pharyngitis in the young to a patchy interstitial pneumonitis in adult patients. Culture is an inefficient method of demonstrating the organism; it is also slow and expensive, and diagnosis is usually made serologically. The inexpensive and easily performed test for cold agglutinins is usually employed. Titers tend to rise after the first week of illness and may be expected to be diagnostic in at least two-thirds of provable cases of mycoplasmal pneumonitis. In the remaining cases the diagnosis is made either clinically or, if considerable importance is attached to making an exact etiologic diagnosis, by sending acute and convalescent sera to a regional laboratory for the determination of *Mycoplasma pneumoniae* antibodies. These antibodies are found in over 90 percent of cases. Occasionally, cases of infectious mononucleosis or other disease cause cold agglutinins to form; if necessary, the laboratory can distinguish between the two types of cold agglutinins, since those of mycoplasmal infection give higher titers with adult group O cells and mononucleosis cold agglutinins give higher titers with O cells obtained from the umbilical cords of newborns.

Bacterial infections may involve any portion of the respiratory tree or its associated structures. Beginning with the sinuses and middle ears, the most common bacteria seen are hemolytic streptococci, pneumococci, and, in young children, encapsulated *Haemophilus influenzae* type b. In chronic otitis media with perforation of the eardrum, the organisms to be expected are *Proteus, Pseudomonas,* and anaerobes.

Appropriate cultures of the drainage from the ear canal may be used to demonstrate these organisms.

Whereas most pharyngitis is due to viral infection, bacterial infection does occur and usually is due to β-hemolytic streptococci of group A, although other groups may be involved in up to 10 percent of cases. The growth of β-hemolytic streptococci in large numbers from a throat swab supports the diagnosis, but diagnosis is somewhat doubtful if only a few streptococci are seen. If confirmation is desired, acute and convalescent antistreptolysin O titers may be measured to demonstrate a fourfold rise in titer or a single titer of 160 or greater. Commercially produced kits are available in most hospital laboratories for carrying out a similar test for antibodies against a variety of streptococcal exoenzymes, and an occasional case may show a convincing rise in titer of these antibodies when results of antistreptolysin O tests are negative or doubtful. In the rare case where clinical findings indicate diphtheria as a possible cause of pharyngitis, the laboratory should be consulted so that specific media may be used for demonstrating *Corynebacterium diphtheriae*, which does not grow well on ordinary media.

A syndrome of great importance in pediatric medicine is that of acute epiglottitis, in which the organ becomes acutely red and swollen and may be seen protruding above the depressed base of the tongue as a cherrylike object, sometimes with impending respiratory obstruction. The disease is almost invariably due to *Haemophilus influenzae*, which may be cultured from the pharynx and often from the blood.

In considering bacterial infections of the lower respiratory tree, including the trachea, the bronchial tree, and the alveolar spaces themselves, the problem of obtaining proper sputum for culture arises. The specimen obtained should represent true sputum from the respiratory tree rather than saliva. The observation has been made that if inspection of the Gram-stained smear fails to reveal a ratio of neutrophils to squamous epithelial cells of at least 4:1, the specimen is probably heavily contaminated with saliva and culture is unlikely to reveal information useful for diagnosis. When the patient is unable to raise a proper sputum specimen for culture, sputum may be induced by nebulization with a 10 percent glycerol solution in 10 percent saline. As a last resort, transtracheal aspiration using a plastic intravenous catheter and 0.5 ml of sterile saline followed by aspiration will give material appropriate for culture. Some centers employ diagnostic lung aspiration using a small-gauge needle thrust through the chest wall into the involved area of pneumonic lung to obtain material for culture; obviously, such a procedure is used only in cases where other methods of obtaining a good specimen are unavailing and the microbiologic diagnosis is critical to the care of the patient.

Once respiratory secretions have been obtained, they are examined using a Gram stain and cultured. A few words about the Gram-stain examination are in order, since this is often carried out by the student physician or house officer.

One should not confuse α-hemolytic streptococci of the normal mouth flora with pneumococci. If they are growing in short chains these streptococci may resemble pneumococci, but they can be recognized by the absence of a capsule and by their tendency to be free in the smear or associated with epithelial cells. A mixed polymicrobial flora showing all sorts of forms, both gram-positive and gram-negative cocci and rods of every shape, should be suspected as being due to a mixed fusospirochetal infection, possibly a lung abscess. In this case further search should be made for pale, lavendar-colored bacilli with pointed ends, often stained in a beaded or banded manner, thus appearing superficially like a chain of streptococci. If present in large numbers, they support an impression of fusospirochetal infection.

Streptococcus pneumoniae is often difficult to recognize with accuracy on the Gram stain. A swelling reaction on fresh sputum using polyvalent antipneumococcal serum is probably more accurate than inspection of the Gram stain. The test is performed by mixing a bit of the sputum with a drop of serum, waiting a few minutes, and then observing the preparation microscopically for the swollen refractile capsules about pneumococci.

It is not unusual to see a fair number of yeasts in stained sputum smears in patients treated with antimicrobials. This is quite ordinary and does not suggest fungal pneumonitis unless the organisms are in considerable numbers and with many pseudohyphae formed by tubular structures projecting out a distance of at least four cell diameters. In the absence of these findings the appearance of yeasts may be taken to indicate simple surface overgrowth due to antibiotic therapy.

The presence of many gram-negative rods in the sputum may indicate either gram-negative colonization of the respiratory tree, which is a common occurrence in antibiotic-treated and very sick individuals, or it may indicate an actual gram-negative pneumonia. Table 53.1 lists some of the common gram-negative bacteria causing pneumonias together with the typical clinical syndromes seen when they present as disease acquired outside the hospital. At least as many gram-negative pneumonias occur as nosocomial infections and will not follow the classic clinical patterns listed in Table 53.1.

One or two blood cultures are advisable in any newly admitted patient with signs of bacterial pneumonia; the organism may be present in the blood but not in the sputum sample submitted for culture. Also, if a doubt exists as to the microbial cause of the pneumonia and pleural fluid forms, culture of the fluid may reveal the offending species. Other studies on the fluid should include a cell count and differential, since a

Table 53.1. Pneumonias Due to Gram-Negative Bacilli

Agent	Clinical Picture
Klebsiella pneumoniae	Lobar pneumonia; may develop multiple cavities, often associated with alcoholism
Proteus spp.	Similar to *Klebsiella pneumoniae*; delirium tremens may be precipitated; empyema frequent
Pseudomonas aeruginosa	Lobar pneumonia; multilocular cavities, severe toxicity, impaired hepatic and renal function, reversal of diurnal temperature with fever in morning, normal temperature in afternoon
Escherichia coli	Bibasilar bronchopneumonia; metastatic from GI or GU focus; blood cultures positive
Serratia spp.	Hospital-related pneumonia; may be associated with nebulizers, other respiratory apparatus

neutrophilic exudate implies pyogenic disease, while the predominance of mononuclear cells suggests granulomatous disease. Appropriate steps to uncover tuberculosis or fungal disease are required in the latter case.

When the clinical pattern suggests tuberculosis, the diagnostic approach is by examination of the sputum for tubercle bacilli by smear and culture, as well as skin testing. A direct smear for acid-fast bacilli may be requested when there is an urgent need to know if the sputum is positive — for example when the question arises of whether or not to isolate immediately a patient whose chest x-ray suggests tuberculosis. Otherwise, the collection of an adequate sputum specimen and its concentration by

alkaline digestion is preferable. Such concentrates are likely to show bacilli, while a direct smear would be positive only in the patient expectorating large numbers of bacilli. Too great reliance should not be put on a negative skin test in excluding tuberculosis. Some quite ill patients give negative reactions to intermediate strength purified protein derivative (PPD) for a variety of reasons but become positive on retesting during convalescence from the acute phase of their illness.

At present there is no satisfactory rapid test for the diagnosis of Legionnaires' disease. Immunofluorescent and passive hemagglutination tests are available through state laboratories and the Center for Disease Control for the demonstration of an antibody rise against *Legionella pneumophila*. Unfortunately, the rise is slow, and the disease can be proven in the majority of patients only after several weeks, making the test useful only in retrospective diagnosis. The organisms are not present in great numbers in the sputum, and even when demonstrated in lung tissue they stain poorly with routine bacteriologic stains such as the Gram stain. If lung biopsy material is available, staining with silver impregnation stains or rickettsial stains, such as the Jiminez stain, may reveal numerous bacilli with some long threadlike forms, suggesting the disease. Immunofluorescent tests are also now available for demonstration of the bacilli.

CENTRAL NERVOUS SYSTEM INFECTIONS

There is great urgency in diagnosis when purulent meningitis is suspected. Table 53.2 lists the agents commonly seen in meningitis at different ages when the disease occurs spontaneously without obvious predisposing causes. After cranial trauma or in association with head and neck infection, such as sinusitis or otitis, other organisms, including gram-negative rods, β-hemolytic

Table 53.2.   Causes of Spontaneous Pyogenic Meningitis in Different Age Groups

Newborns	Encapsulated *E. coli*, β-hemolytic streptococci of group B, *Staphylococcus aureus, Listeria monocytogenes*
Children under 5 years	*Neisseria meningitidis, Haemophilus influenzae* group b, *Streptococcus pneumoniae*
Adults	*Streptococcus pneumoniae, Neisseria meningitidis*; with chronic cerebrospinal fluid leak, *Str. pneumoniae;* in alcoholism, *Str. pneumoniae, L. monocytogenes*

streptococci, and staphylococci, must be added to those shown in Table 53.2. A prompt stain of the sediment from centrifuged spinal fluid is helpful. For an inexperienced worker methylene blue is preferable to the Gram stain, since it is a cleaner stain and is less likely to leave precipitates that may cause confusion. If methylene blue is used, it must be remembered that the distinction between gram-positive and gram-negative organisms cannot be made with the stain and that the nature of the organism must be deduced from its shape alone, possibly with supplementary evidence from a simultaneous Gram-stained slide. If available, counterimmunoelectrophoresis using antisera to *Haemophilus influenzae* group b, pooled pneumococcal antisera, and meningococcal capsular antisera may be employed. The method is capable of demonstrating specific antigens in the spinal fluid in less than 2 hours and may give an exact diagnosis of pyogenic meningitis long before culture results are available.

If prompt culture of cerebrospinal fluid (CSF) is not possible (as might be the case in small hospitals during nights or weekends), the CSF should be placed in an incubator or in a 37°C water bath. Many agents of pyogenic meningitis will die if the specimen is refrigerated and most will multiply in infected spinal fluid if it is kept warm overnight. In fact they may reproduce to such numbers that a Gram stain the next morning will easily demonstrate them.

In cases of suspected tuberculous or fungal infection, the more CSF submitted to the laboratory for inoculation of media, the better. Pathogenic fungi capable of causing meningitis grow on the ordinary chocolate and blood-agar media inoculated with CSF if these are held for a week or two. Therefore it is unnecessary to ask for specific fungal cultures. Cycloheximide-containing media for routine fungal cultures can yield misleading negative results because most pathogenic fungi capable of causing disseminated disease are inhibited by cycloheximide.

In suspected viral meningitis or encephalitis, specimens submitted for virologic studies should include throat swab and stool in addition to CSF, since many common agents of viral meningitis are demonstrated more easily in these specimens. During the arbovirus season (late summer and early fall) clotted blood should also be submitted for viral isolation and antibody studies.

The diagnosis of herpes simplex encephalitis is difficult at present. The virus is not often grown from the CSF of proven cases. Searching for antibodies to the virus in the CSF may be more productive; these are not seen in the absence of nervous system infection due to the virus. At present the most definitive method of diagnosing herpetic encephalitis is by the rather formidable procedure of brain biopsy. One part of the specimen should be submitted for viral culture and immunofluorescent staining for viral antigen. Another part should be examined histologically for the characteristic necrotizing encephalitis with intranuclear inclusion bodies. Attempts to demonstrate herpes simplex virus in the throat in suspected encephalitis due to this agent are valueless; there is no correlation between finding the virus in this specimen and the presence or absence of herpetic encephalitis.

In rabies, microbiologic methods are helpful in two ways. First, the brain of the biting animal may be submitted to a health department laboratory for examination for rabies using immunofluorescence. This method is much better than examination for the classic Negri bodies, which can be negative in the presence of the disease, especially in noncanine species. The spinal fluid of the patient also may be examined for rabies antibodies; these may be present in low titers after active immunization against the disease with rabies vaccine, but if present in titers of several hundred or several thousand they generally indicate the disease. Demonstration of rabies virus antigen in exfoliated cells of the cornea is also possible.

INFECTIONS OF THE URINARY TRACT

The basic microbiologic examination of urine is a quantitative culture performed on a so-called midstream, clean-catch specimen. To collect this specimen, the genitalia are cleaned with soap and water or a mild antiseptic, the cleaning agent is washed off with tap water, and voiding is begun. The first 20 to 50 ml of urine are discarded, since they serve to wash the resident flora out of the urethra. Then a sterile container is inserted into the urinary stream to collect a few mililiters of urine for culture. The remainder of the urine is passed without being collected, since the muscular actions connected with completing the emptying of the bladder and shutting off the urinary stream may massage organisms from the periurethral glands, the prostrate, and the trigone of the bladder to contaminate the specimen. The midstream urine collected in this manner is cultured quantitatively. The most elaborate method involves the preparation of serial tenfold dilutions and preparing pour plates, followed by incubation and colony counting. To save time and expense the routine procedure in most laboratories uses a calibrated bacteriologic loop designed to pick up 0.01 ml of urine followed by streaking the surface of an agar plate. This is simpler and less costly than the serial dilution method and gives results almost as reliable, although the colony count may be slightly lower by the calibrated loop method. In any case, the number of colony-forming units (CFU) per milliliter of urine is taken as an index of the presence or absence of bacteria above the internal sphincter (i.e., from the bladder or kidneys). Colony counts greater than 100,000/ml (or 50,000/ml if done by the calibrated loop method) indicate actual infection of the urinary tract; lower counts merely represent contamination of the urine during voiding.

If the patient has taken antimicrobials that inhibit bacterial multiplication in urine, a false negative urine culture may be produced. On the other hand, if urine is not promptly transmitted to the laboratory for culture, contaminating organisms may multiply to numbers in excess of 100,000 bacteria/ml, producing a false positive result. If there is an unavoidable delay before the urine can be cultured, this problem may be obviated by prompt refrigeration of the specimen to prevent multiplication of the organisms. Most organisms that infect the urinary tract survive refrigeration.

In simple uncomplicated acute infections of the urinary tract, *Escherichia coli* is the most common cause. When other gram-negative bacilli or enterococci are found the clinician should suspect a chronic or complicated urinary tract infection. Such a finding may also suggest the presence of a foreign object such as an indwelling catheter. This is often the case when significant numbers of more than one organism are found.

Once having localized the infection to the region above the internal sphincter by a colony count, the clinician may need to pinpoint the source of the bacteriuria, particularly to distinguish simple infection of the bladder alone from infection involving the kidneys. If urologic examination with cystoscopy is contemplated, ureteral catheterization during the procedure and culture of the urine collected in this way will provide information about possible kidney infection. It may also localize the infection to one or the other side. Without cystoscopy a clue to the localization of the infection may be obtained by testing the bacteria in the urine for adherent antibody using immunofluorescence techniques. The test is straightforward and consists of attempting to stain the bacteria with fluoresceinated antiserum against human gamma globulin. Antibody-coated bacteria are shed from infected kidneys, while uncoated bacteria are present in the urine of patients with simple bladder infections. Also, the presence of serum antibodies directed against the patient's own organisms may be demonstrated using passive hemagglutination. These antibodies are present in high titer in cases of actual kidney involvement and are absent or present in low titer in simple bladder infections.

At times organisms other than the gram-negative rods or enterococci usually expected in urinary infection are cultured from the urine (e.g., hemolytic streptococci or staphylococci). This may indicate that there is a bacteremic illness due to these organisms. They appear in the urine because of secondary involvement of the kidneys rather than representing a primary urinary tract infection.

When urinalysis persistently reveals white cells and repeated cultures are sterile, the possibility of renal tuberculosis should be considered. In the past, 24-hour collections of urine were used for cultures of tubercle bacilli. At present it is felt that the first urine voided in the morning serves as well. Several such specimens should be collected at various times, since excretion of the mycobacteria may be intermittent.

In suspected bacterial prostatitis the prostatic fluid expressed after prostatic massage and the first few milliliters of urine voided after such massage may be cultured to identify the causative organism. Urine is rarely cultured for viruses, but on occasion viral culture may be done to diagnose occasional cases of adenovirus or varicella cystitis or to reveal the shedding of cytomegalovirus in congenitally infected infants.

INFECTIONS OF THE DIGESTIVE TRACT

Many episodes of gastroenteritis are apparently due to infections. This is inferred from their tendency to occur in outbreaks, to spread from person to person, and to manifest as an abrupt and relatively brief illness in otherwise healthy persons. Standard microbiologic tests, including routine culture of the stool for enteric pathogens, pinpoint the infective agent in only a few percent of these cases; the overwhelming majority remain undiagnosed for at least four reasons:

1. Standard cultures are best at revealing shigellae and salmonellae and to a lesser extent some of the other causes of acute diarrhea, such as arizonae or pseudomonads, but are likely to miss other bacterial agents, such as campylobacters or cholera vibrios which require special media. Furthermore, many attacks of diarrhea are due to viruses or protozoa, which cannot be demonstrated by routine bacterial cultures.

2. Diarrhea can be due to toxin production by quite ordinary bacteria, such as *Escherichia coli*, that are indistinguishable from their harmless relatives unless special tests for toxin production are available. In the absence of these tests the organisms appear as normal stool flora. Some comfort may be taken from the fact that advances are occurring in tests for enterotoxins suitable for routine hospital work.

3. Some outbreaks of diarrhea are due to food poisoning by preformed bacterial toxins. In these cases the disease is pro-

Table 53.3. Microbial Causes of Gastroenteritis

Infection of Gastrointestinal Tract, With Invasion and/or Formation of Toxins

BACTERIA

Shigellae	Demonstrable on routine culture
Salmonellae	Demonstrable on routine culture
Arizonae	Salmonellalike disease; milk-borne infections
Pseudomonads	Newborn nursery outbreaks
Aeromonads	Occasional cases of diarrhea
Protei	Occasional summer diarrheas, especially *Pr. morganii*, "Providence" organisms
Yersinia enterocolitica	Diarrhea, mesenteric adenitis; sporadic in campers (stream water); outbreaks if water or food contaminated
Campylobacter spp.	Microaerophilic, requires special culture techniques; sporadic cases
Vibrio cholerae	Cholera outbreaks; definitive identification requires reference laboratory
Vibrio spp.	Variety of noncholera vibrios, some salt-requiring; sporadic gastroenteritis, some outbreaks, often shellfish related or seawater related; generally require special methods to identify
Escherichia coli	Enterotoxin-producing strains, requiring special methods to recognize; otherwise appearing as "normal flora" on routine culture; frequent cause of traveler's diarrhea

VIRUSES

Enteroviruses	Poliovirus, coxsackievirus A and B, echovirus; most identifiable by routine virus laboratory tests
Rotaviruses	Epidemic enteritis of young children; serologic tests may be available soon
Parvoviruses	"Norwalk Agent" and similar viruses in stools of adults with brief enteritis seen by electron microscopy; no routine test at present

PROTOZOA

Entamoeba histolytica	Demonstration in fresh stools by experienced parasitologist
Giardia lamblia	Parasites in duodenum, cysts in stools; some cases of traveler's diarrhea; water-borne outbreaks reported

Presence of Preformed Toxin in Stool, Without Infection

Staphylococcus aureus	Both enterotoxin (three serologic types) and α-hemolysin cause diarrhea
Clostridium perfringens	Sausage- or meat-associated enteritis, with bloody stools

Antibiotic-Related Diarrheas

S. aureus	Uncommon now; masses of staphylococci in stool
Clostridia	Production of an enterotoxin by some species, such as *C. difficle* or *C. sordelli*, thought to be etiology of clindamycin-associated colitis and possibly other antibiotic related diseases

duced by the toxin rather than by the growth of the bacteria, and the stool culture is negative.

4. Another reason for not diagnosing many cases of diarrhea with standard tests is that we have not yet discovered all the microbial causes of diarrhea; further agents remain to be identified.

Table 53.3 summarizes the infective agents known to be responsible for diarrhea together with salient points applicable to them. As can be seen, there are several organisms not demonstrable on routine culture of the stools for enteric pathogens; the difficulty of proving etiology in most cases of infective diarrhea is apparent.

As a practical matter, ordering stool cultures in the hospital for patients with diarrhea is associated with a number of pitfalls. First, it is amazing how often stool cultures are not performed after being ordered on patients with diarrhea. This is often due to errors in communication, resulting in stools being discarded by attendants or patients unaware that a culture has been requested. Also, even if stools are passed and sent for culture they may be exposed to residual disinfectants routinely used on bedpans in some hospitals. The drying of stool specimens before culture may also result in loss of pathogenic organisms. For these reasons it is preferable to obtain fecal material directly. This may be done by inserting a sterile culture swab into the anus far enough to stain it with fecal material and sending it in a transport broth to the laboratory. This assures prompt specimen acquisition and avoids the problems mentioned above.

With respect to Table 53.3, a few comments are in order. First, shigellae may not grow well on a number of routine enteric media used in many laboratories, and it is helpful to use one of the newer enteric media (such as Hektoen enteric agar) capable of supporting their growth. Isolation is further enhanced by inoculation of enrichment broth from which subcultures can later be made on enteric agar. The purpose of the broth is to encourage the growth of shigellae and salmonellae while ordinary stool flora grow more slowly. This increases the relative number of pathogens and therefore the chance of finding them.

Infection by salmonellae may be diagnosed not only by stool culture but also on occasion by concomitant blood culture, which should be performed when this infection is suspected. Also, serologic titers in acute and convalescent phases of disease may prove the diagnosis in retrospect. Many laboratories are now using a battery of five different *Salmonella* organisms chosen from Edwards and Ewing's groups A through E. Since each of the five carries several somatic antigens, this group of organisms provides a broad pool of somatic antigen types, and the convalescent sera of most salmonellosis patients would agglutinate one or more of the test antigens used.

Diarrhea caused by *Escherichia coli* is especially difficult to diagnose without resorting to special methods. As mentioned before, there is the possibility that simple serotyping may help reveal the strains associated with enterotoxin production. Another possibility is that simple tests available in the routine laboratory for enterotoxins may be used to demonstrate their production by the strains isolated from the patient. However, two difficulties still exist. Many people carry a mixture of *E. coli* strains, and negative results for toxin production from one colony does not give assurance that another colony would not be positive. Whatever tests are used, multiple colonies on the same plate should be tested for toxin production before one concludes that there are no enterotoxigenic escherichiae in the patient's stool. Also, a number of *E. coli* are capable of causing dysentery by another mechanism, the ability to adhere to and penetrate intestinal mucosa by means of pili. This method of producing enteritis is at least as important in adult diarrhea caused by this species as production of enterotoxins and is not as regularly confined to certain serotypes as is toxin production. The latter problem may be solved in the future by the development of simple tests to reveal pili and hence invasive ability, using adherence of the bacteria to cell cultures or hemagglutination tests in which the red cells are agglutinated by pilated bacteria.

With regard to attempting a virologic diagnosis in the common diarrheas of late summer and early fall produced by enteroviruses, a number of cell lines in routine use do not support the growth of most type A coxsackieviruses. Laboratories using these lines are therefore much more likely to reveal enterovirus infections due to echovirus or coxsackievirus B strains than coxsackievirus A. Winter diarrhea in children is frequently caused by human rotaviruses; these and other viral agents may be detected by electron microscopy.

In protozoal diarrhea the examination of saline-purged stool for fresh trophozoites of *Entamoeba histolytica* is superior to that of an ordinary stool. The best examination is made on material directly swabbed or aspirated from rectal ulcerations through an anoscope. In the late stages of dysentery, trophozoites drop in numbers quickly, and unless the examination is prompt the diagnosis can be missed. In formed stools passed after diarrhea subsides, retrospective diagnosis may be made if cysts are seen. Concentration techniques are available to increase the chance of observing the cysts. In metastatic amebic disease, including amebic abscess of the liver, the parasites have usually died out in the intestinal tract by the time the patient is seen, and demonstration of amebas in the stool is the exception rather than the rule. Fortunately, serodiagnostic tests for amebiasis become positive quite regularly in metastatic disease.

Of even more importance to the practioner in temperate climates is the occurrence of diarrhea due to giardiasis. These protozoa inhabit the duodenum and upper small intestine. The demonstration of their cysts in stools is important in diagnosis; however, more cases may diagnosed if the duodenal aspirate is examined for the tropozoite with its characteristic "falling leaf" motility. The chance of a positive test is even greater if actual biopsy of the duodenum is done using a biopsy capsule or directly through an endoscope. The shred of tissue obtained should be smeared, mucosal side down, on a slide before being put into formalin for fixation. The smear is moistened with saline and examined under a coverslip for motile trophozoites; the biopsy material, after sectioning and staining, should be examined by the pathologist for a layer of adherent *Giardia lamblia* organisms on the mucosa.

When formed stools are examined for *Giardia* cysts, repeated examinations may be necessary since the cysts are shed sporadically. Purgation does not increase dependably the chance of finding the cysts.

In the case of antibiotic related diarrheas, the relatively uncommon *Staphylococcus aureus* diarrhea may be uncovered by inspecting a Gram-stained smear of stool or rectal swab for the characteristic replacement of the normal heterogeneous bowel flora by a monotonous profusion of gram-positive cocci in grapelike clusters.

When food poisoning by preformed toxins is suspected, diagnosis is more easily made by examination of a specimen of suspected food submitted to the public health laboratory than by examination of clinical material from the patient. A number of tests are being devised to make the demonstration of staphylococcal enterotoxin more convenient than in the past, when animal inoculation was necessary. They depend on sensitive methods for the detection of antigens. They may soon be available routinely in public health laboratories.

Although botulism is not, strictly speaking, an intestinal infection, it is a form of food poisoning due to the absorption of the neurotoxin of *Clostridium botulinum* from contaminated food. When the disease is suspected, a large volume of serum should be submitted to the public health laboratory, since tests for the presence of the toxin in serum are available. Presently, they consist of the production of paralysis in small animals by injection of the serum and the prevention of the phenomenon using antisera prepared against the three types of botulinus toxin implicated in human poisoning: A, B, and E. Again, submission of suspected food for examination is helpful.

Aside from infections of the intestines themselves, the other major gastrointestinal infection consists of viral disease of the liver. Viral hepatitis infections are presently classified as type A, type B, or non-A, non-B hepatitis (Ch. 45).

At present serologic tests for hepatitis A are available routinely. Tests for hepatitis B by demonstration of the presence of the surface antigen of the virus (HB_sAg) are available and are useful in diagnosing hepatitis B in its acute stages but are less useful later on in the disease, since the percentage of patients with positive tests decreases steadily during convalescence. The test is also useful in screening donated blood before transfusion for the presence of hepatitis B virus, and its regular use can produce about a 50 percent decrease in cases of hepatitis B transmitted by blood. Other hepatitis B tests now available in special laboratories include tests for antibody to surface antigen (anti-HBs; useful in determining immunity to the disease or documenting previous infection), for antibody to the core antigen of the virus (anti-HBc; useful in demonstrating which apparently healthy chronic carriers of the surface antigen are likely to show changes of chronic active hepatitis on liver biopsy), and for the e antigen of the virus (HBeAg; often positive in chronic carriers of the surface antigen who have chronic active hepatitis).

In tropical practice it must be remembered that a number of the arboviruses produce inflammation of the liver as a feature of their generalized infection of the host. Dengue and yellow fever are examples of arbovirus diseases in which this regularly happens. Appropriate arbovirus studies, including serology and cultures of whole blood for the virus, are useful in investigation of hepatitis in this situation.

INFECTIONS OF THE SKIN AND SUBCUTANEOUS TISSUES

When signs of inflammation of the unbroken skin and subcutaneous tissues are seen, the usual lesion is a simple cellulitis or infection spreading in the skin without other specific pathologic features. Exact microbiologic diagnosis is often quite difficult, but some attempts to isolate the organism may be made. Material obtained by aspiration of the advancing edge of the inflammatory zone, or of a regional lymph node if it is enlarged, may be cultured. First, 0.25 to 0.5 ml sterile saline is aspirated into a syringe and the air expelled. Then, with a fine needle, the edge of the lesion or node is punctured, and by a back-and-forth movement of the plunger the lesion is drawn up until a distinct cloudiness or discoloration of the saline occurs. After withdrawal, a drop may be expelled onto a microscope slide for Gram staining. The material remaining in the syringe can then be submitted for culture. In performing this aspiration, care should be taken to load the syringe with sterile saline free from preservatives or bacteriostatic substances. Saline from bottles labeled "bacteriostatic saline for injection" or those with labels indicating that preservatives have been added must not be used. Aside from culture of the aspirate from advancing edge of the lesion, a few other tests may be employed. Sometimes cellulitis is accompanied by bullae, from which fluid may be aspirated after sterile preparation of the skin. One may also search for the primary entry of infection. In facial cellulitis this is often an inflamed nose; in leg cellulitis this may be a small puncture wound or a crack between the toes due to dermatophytosis. Cultures of pathogenic organisms may grow from these sources and thus suggest the cause of the cellulitis. Blood cultures may be attempted, but usually they are negative in simple cellulitis unless a septic clinical course is occurring. In cellulitis connected with animal bites it is advisable to include a rich complex medium suitable for growing *Pasteurella multocida*. This organism occasionally is a cause of infection in these circumstances. If all cultures are negative and the clinical course suggests hemolytic streptococcal infection, serologic diagnosis may be tried, including the antistreptolysin O titer as well as tests on acute and convalescent sera for antibodies to other streptococcal exoenzymes. The anti-exoenzyme tests are helpful because streptococcal skin infections seem to be poor stimuli in eliciting antistreptolysin O antibodies, but they do elicit antibodies against the other streptococcal products.

Where intense pain aggravated by muscle movement suggests even deeper infection of an extremity, necrotizing fasciitis should be considered. These lesions are often explored surgically, and direct cultures of the infected fascia at the time of surgery as well as blood cultures are in order.

Spreading subcutaneous infection with frank pus formation under the skin is often caused by anaerobic bacteria particularly after human bites, the illegal injection of narcotics, or surgery on the gastrointestinal or urogenital tracts. When caused by clostridia these infections may be diagnosed almost immediately if a Gram stain is used. In examining the slide for these organisms one should remember that many cells appear gram-negative in smears made from fresh clinical specimens and that spores are rare in this material. The presence of large,

blunt-ended bacilli, sometimes in short chains, at least some of which are gram-positive, should suggest the diagnosis. At other times the infection is fusospirochetal in nature, and the abundance of different forms, including rods and cocci of various sizes and shapes both gram-positive and gram-negative suggests this cause. The observation of faint lavender-staining fusiform bacilli in these preparations is a strong diagnostic indicator. In either circumstance, anaerobically collected specimens should be transported and cultured.

Oozing lesions of the skin with scaling encrustation of the exudate is impetigo, which may be due to streptococci or staphylococci. Careful cleansing of the surface and removal of scales with a sterile needle will allow a specimen for culture to be taken from the moist material underneath. It should be kept in mind that streptococcal impetigo in its late stages often acquires additional staphylococcal flora. As in cellulitis, streptococcal antibody tests are helpful in impetigo, especially if tests for antibodies to streptococcal exoenzymes are used.

With ulcerating skin lesions it is necessary to distinguish between superficial flora, which may represent surface contamination, and deep flora, representing organisms actually responsible for the disease. Ulcerations of the skin associated with surgical wounds, especially following abdominal or pelvic surgery, can be caused by both aerobes and anaerobes. Both aerobic and anaerobic cultures should be done, and specimens for these should be taken from the advancing edge of the lesion or underneath the surface of the wound. So-called synergistic gangrene usually shows microaerophilic streptococci and *Proteus* spp., whereas so-called undermining postoperative ulcers and streptococcal gangrene produce growth of aerobic β-hemolytic streptococci.

In ulcerations of the foot and in bedsores of diabetic patients cultures should include methods to detect anaerobic organisms, since these bacteria are often the cause of these infections. When the history and clinical appearance suggest sporotrichosis, attempts should be made to culture the fungus from the lesion rather than searching for it microscopically; the organism generally is not seen in biopsy material. On the other hand, when the history and appearance suggest so-called swimming pool granuloma, caused by *Mycobacterium marinum*, specimens should be taken for culture of acid-fast bacilli. These should be incubated not only at 37°C but also at 30 to 33°C, since this organism grows better at lower temperatures.

Burn wounds often become infected, and the same distinction between superficial and deep infection should be made as in the case of ulcerative lesions of the skin. Cultures for bacteria should be made from material removed from deep tissues at the time of surgical debridement. When fungal infection is suspected, a biopsy of the border of the wound, again best obtained at the time of debridement, should be examined microscopically and cultured for fungi. They may be present only in the depths of the border and absent from the center of the burn.

In assessing recent surgical wounds that appear to be infected or where the clinical course suggests wound infection, the wound should be inspected for an unhealed section. Infection usually causes slow healing of skin in its neighborhood. If necessary, one or two sutures may be removed; this will cause the wound to gape, allowing a sterile swab to be thrust into the depths of the wound in order to obtain the specimen for culture.

INFECTIONS OF THE MUSCULOSKELETAL SYSTEM

Table 53.4 displays organisms commonly expected in cases of osteomyelitis. In acute blood-borne osteomyelitis (the most

Table 53.4.   Organisms Involved in Osteomyelitis

Newborns	β-hemolytic streptococci, *Staphylococcus aureus*, *Escherichia coli*, and other *Enterobacteriaceae*
Children to age 5	*S. aureus, Haemophilus influenzae*
Age 5 to puberty	*S. aureus*, about 95% of cases
Adults without predisposing factors	*S. aureus*, β-hemolytic streptococci
Sickle cell anemia	*Salmonella* spp.
Narcotic addiction	*S. aureus*, gram-negative bacilli (*Pseudomonas* spp. in infections appearing spontaneously), *Candida* spp.
Trauma (compound fractures, orthopedic surgery, etc.)	*S. aureus*, gram-negative bacilli (*Pseudomonas* spp. may appear as secondary organism after antibiotic treatment for other bacteria)

common type in infants and children) blood cultures may reveal the infecting organism. In chronic osteomyelitis culture of draining sinuses may be used to provide a clue to the infecting organism. The cultures should be interpreted in light of the fact that draining sinuses usually acquire a contaminating surface flora of gram-negative organisms. *Proteus* spp. are the most common contaminants in this regard, and their motility and consequent tendency to swarm over the surface of the agar plate may obscure the actual causative agents. Here consultation with the laboratory is helpful because plates containing phenylethanolamine may be used if available. The growth and swarming of *Proteus* bacilli are inhibited on this medium, which permits the recognition of other organisms. Effusion developing in a joint next to osteomyelitic bone should be tapped for culture. Although many of these effusions are sterile, the growth of an organism from the joint fluid would implicate that organism in the osteomyelitic process. At times, bone biopsy may be necessary to establish the infecting agent.

In septic arthritis fluid from the affected joint should be cultured. The most common cause of septic arthritis in adults up to the age of 50 years is gonococcal infection. A considerable number of joints inflamed by *Neisseria gonorrhoeae* sepsis are sterile on culture because joint involvement begins as a periarticulitis and involves the actual joint space only later. Therefore a search for gonococcal infection elsewhere (including cultures of specimens from the cervix, the urethra, the rectum and the throat) may provide confirming evidence of the presence of the organism. If the characteristic peripheral skin lesions of gonococcal septicemia occur, these may be picked open with a sterile needle and prints made on a microscope slides for Gram staining. Slides prepared in this way show the organism more frequently than do cultures, possibly because the organisms in the skin lesions often die. Serologic tests for gonorrhea are also helpful, since they generally are positive to significant titers only in deep or disseminated infection.

In infections of muscles two groups of organisms should be considered. In North American medical practice, muscle infections with gas formation are most commonly due to *Escherichia coli* or other enteric rods in diabetic patients. Clostridial myonecrosis, or gas gangrene, is considerably less common. In light of this, both aerobic and anaerobic cultures should be initiated from material aspirated from infected muscles or from swabs taken at surgery. Even more important, immediate Gram stains should be prepared and inspected for the presence of clostridia. The appearance of clostridia on Gram-stained smears was mentioned in the discussion of skin infections. It should also be noted that

clostridial myonecrosis is not always a pure infection but often involves a variety of different bacteria. The mere presence of gram-positive, large, blunt-ended rods in the material should suggest clostridial myonecrosis even though other organisms are visible.

THE VENEREAL DISEASES

The diagnosis of gonorrhea in males with urethritis is generally made by inspection of a Gram-stained smear of the urethral exudate. Such smears fall into three classes. Definitely positive smears show the characteristic gram-negative coffee bean shaped diplococci in the cytoplasm of neutrophils. Generally their appearance is spotty, and the leukocytes tend to contain either no bacteria or many organisms (up to two dozen). With this finding the diagnosis of gonorrhea is almost certain, and culture need not be done. Definitely negative smears show no forms resembling *Neisseria gonorrhoeae* and for all practical purposes exclude the diagnosis, again without resort to culture. In a few cases, smears of urethral exudate will fall into a doubtful classification, intermediate between definitely positive and definitely negative. These show a few extracellular but no intracellular organisms resembling gonococci. When this happens, culture is necessary to prove or disprove gonococcal infection.

In females the presence of bacteria that look like gonococci, such as *Acinetobacter* spp., makes diagnosis by smear unreliable, and culture should be done. The material taken from the endocervix gives the highest rate of positive cultures. The specimen is obtained with a small swab inserted within the cervical canal to about 1 cm and allowed to remain a few seconds to absorb any secretions present. Rotation of the swab before withdrawal increases the number of positive cultures. The first 10 days of the menstrual cycle give the highest rate of positive culture. Other urogenital areas, including the vagina and the urethra, may be sampled, but as a practical matter most females giving positive cultures from these areas are found positive by a cervical culture also. Once material from the cervix has been cultured, the greatest increase in case findings may be obtained by culturing material from the anus. Cultures should be done on Thayer-Martin medium, which contains inhibitory substances to discourage the growth of competing flora and permits easier detection of gonococci.

In cases of disseminated gonococcemia, search for the source of organisms should include pharyngeal culture, especially if pharyngitis is present. Care should be taken to ensure that meningococci reported as isolated from the pharynx are in fact proved to be meningococci by carbohydrate fermentation patterns, since gonococci cultured from this area might be mistaken for meningococci.

A variety of transport media are available for use in offices and clinics to minimize the loss of gonococci that occurs from drying. Many of these contain carbon dioxide, which is necessary for preservation of gonococci on swabs. Carbon dioxide is heavier than air and will be dumped out of a tube that is not held vertically while it is uncapped for the insertion of the swab.

Serologic tests for antigonococcal antibodies usually involve an immunofluorescence procedure and are available in many university and state laboratories. Immunofluorescence tests tend to become positive in invasive gonorrhea, especially if gonococcemia has occurred. These tests tend to become negative slowly over the several months following an infection.

Chronic pelvic inflammatory disease is generally initiated by gonorrhea but is perpetuated by other microbes after the inciting gonococci have died out or have been eradicated by antibiotic therapy. In fact, most studies of chronic pelvic inflammatory disease implicate mixed microbial flora: chlamydiae, mycoplasmas, and enteric bacteria including anaerobic bacteroides.

The diagnosis of early forms of syphilis may be facilitated by dark field microscopy if an experienced diagnostician is available. If so, the organism may be demonstrated in primary chancres as well as in secondary lesions. Other methods to demonstrate the organism can be applied to pathologic material. For example, cases of syphilitic gastritis during the secondary phase of the disease sometimes are biopsied endoscopically. If plasma cell gastritis is seen, syphilis should be suspected and can be proved by applying silver impregnation stains to reveal the organism in histologic sections.

More cases of syphilis are diagnosed by serologic methods than by demonstration of the microbes. Tests available fall generally into two categories, those that reveal antibodies directed against the cardiolipin antigen and those that reveal actual antitreponemal antibodies. Generally, patients giving positive cardiolipin tests and negative treponemal tests fall into the category of biologic false-positive reactors owing to a number of causes, including recent viral illness and collagen disease. One exception is lupus erythematosus, where some sera not only react in nontreponemal tests but also give positive reactions in the FTA-ABS test, an immunofluorescence test with *T. pallidum*. Workers experienced with this test claim that false positive reactions given by lupus may be distinguished by their tendency to stain the spirochetes in a spotty and irregular fashion, as contrasted to the uniform staining produced by syphilis sera.

When syphilis is of long duration the serologic tests may not become completely negative even after proper antibiotic treatment. This condition was once known as Wassermann fastness. If there was adequately documented effective treatment in the past and the titers of serologic tests are low, further treatment is not necessary in the absence of symptoms or signs of active disease.

Infants born to syphilitic mothers may give positive serologic tests owing to transplacental transmission of IgG antibody. The distinction between *in utero* infection of the infant and passive acquisition of the antibody is made by testing the infant's blood for IgM levels, since an elevated level of IgM in the infant implies *in utero* infection.

In lymphogranuloma venereum the diagnosis not only is made by histopathology but also by testing the serum for group-specific chlamydial antibodies.

In chancroid the organism *Haemophilus ducreyi* is difficult to culture; the usual method of diagnosis is by inspection of Gram-stained smears obtained either by scraping the undermined edge of the lesion or by aspiration of an involved lymph node. The demonstration of gram-negative rods in chains with parallel arrangement (school of fish) substantiates the diagnosis. Recently, two culture methods have been proposed: inoculating material from ulcers into tubes of the patient's own heat inactivated serum to look for the characteristic parallel chains of the organism after 48 hours of incubation, and the inoculation of chocolate agar supplemented with 3 μg/ml of vancomycin to inhibit other organisms.

FEVER OF UNKNOWN ORIGIN

One of the most baffling clinical problems confronting the clinician is fever of unknown origin. This has been variously defined, but most investigators agree that a significantly high fever, about 100°F, should occur daily for at least 2 weeks and that the diagnosis must have eluded in-hospital investigation for at least 1 week. This definition automatically excludes brief fevers due to viral infections. The major catagories of fever of unknown origin are infection, inflammation due to noninfectious causes, tumors, and miscellaneous causes. While one category includes infectious agents, the application of microbiologic methods in the diagnosis of such cases is of minor importance. Generally the competent clinician

employs appropriate microbiologic studies during the first week in hospital. These would include several blood cultures, cultures of the urine to detect ordinary as well as acid-fast organisms, the application of tuberculin skin tests, and search for antibodies against prominent causes of fever of unknown origin, including salmonellae and brucellae. Therefore by the time the first week of hospital investigation has been completed and the case has truly become a fever of unknown origin, the resources of the microbiology laboratory have been exhausted. Further investigation of the case then hinges on other methods guided by the patient's symptoms and signs. These may include biopsy of the liver or exploratory laparotomy. The principal microbiologic tests that may be applied after the first week of investigation of such cases consist in repeating the blood cultures (which may be negative at some stages of diseases such as endocarditis but positive at others) and in making sure that skin testing with tuberculin is carried through the second strength (250 TU) of PPD. Repeating serologic tests that were negative during the first week may be of some value because in a number of diseases titers may rise slowly. Examples are agglutinins in salmonellosis and cold agglutinins in mycoplasmal infection, which tend not to rise until the second or third week of the disease.

USEFULNESS OF THE LABORATORY IN GUIDING ANTIMICROBIAL THERAPY

The most common test done in the routine microbiology laboratory to guide therapy is the determination of sensitivity of isolated organisms to a panel of antimicrobial agents. The classic method, tube dilution, is too expensive and cumbersome for routine use but remains the standard method against which others are compared. It is also the method favored for research studies. When this test is available, it is superior to other methods because it not only is capable of accurately determining the minimum inhibitory concentration (MIC) of antimicrobials, the lowest concentration needed to inhibit visible growth, but also can reveal the minimum concentration required to kill the organism, the minimum bactericidal concentration (MBC). This will distinguish the actions of drugs that actually kill the offending organisms at clinically achievable concentrations from those that merely inhibit them, a distinction that cannot be made by most other methods.

Because of its ease and convenience, the Kirby-Bauer method of sensitivity testing is standard in most laboratories. This modification of a disk method catagorizes isolates as sensitive or resistant. The test cannot display the MBC of the antimicrobials but does give a reasonable estimate of whether the organism tested will be inhibited or not by blood levels of antimicrobials obtainable by ordinary clinical doses. A third category, intermediate (or slightly sensitive or moderately resistant, depending on the laboratory) indicates organisms the sensitivity of which, by the Kirby-Bauer method, lies between definitely sensitive and definitely resistant. These organisms may be inhibited by high levels of the antimicrobials as produced by greater than ordinary doses. Keep in mind that in the treatment of urinary tract infections the Kirby-Bauer method predicts sensitivity or resistance of organism to *blood levels* achievable with ordinary doses. A number of antimicrobials, especially penicillins and cephalosporins, are excreted in high levels in the urine, where they may well inhibit bacteria even if they are reported as resistant by disk sensitivity testing.

In the last analysis the use of sensitivity testing is only a guide to the clinician in devising therapy. The results produced by the laboratory must be combined with experience and with published data on the clinical usefulness of various antibiotics in different infections. For example, typhoid organisms are inhibited by many antibiotics *in vitro*; in practice, however, some of these, such as chloramphenicol and trimethoprim-sulfas, stand above the rest presumably not only because of their ability to inhibit the organism but also to penetrate cells to contact the bacilli. The latter property cannot be predicted by inspection of *in vitro* sensitivity data alone. Another example is the fact that aminoglycosides are often synergistic with penicillin-type drugs against enterococci. Again, this could not be deduced from sensitivity data alone, since most enterococci appear resistant to all aminoglycosides by ordinary Kirby-Bauer sensitivity testing.

A less commonly used test is the determination of bactericidal effect of an antimicrobial in serum from the patient against the isolate. For practical purposes this procedure is confined to monitoring the treatment of endocarditis due to resistant organisms. It has been shown that maintaining a continuously bactericidal effect in serum to a titer of at least 1:4 is necessary to ensure a cure. To guarantee maintenance of this bactericidal activity, the bactericidal effect of the serum is usually tested at the time of lowest concentration, just before the next scheduled administration of the antibiotic. It should be noted that this measure of the bactericidal effect of the serum not only can demonstrate the action of a single antibiotic but also can show the combined or synergistic effect of a combination of antibiotics. When it is likely that a test for the bactericidal effect of serum may be needed in the future, the laboratory must be alerted so that the organism grown from the patient can be saved to be used in the test.

Laboratory data are also useful to the clinician in the measurement of blood levels of antimicrobials produced by therapy. A number of different tests are available, including bioassay, radioimmunoassay, and enzymatic tests. These are useful in avoiding damage by nephrotoxic antimicrobial drugs; therefore most of the available tests are devised for the measurement of aminoglycoside levels. Levels may be tested at various times, but the most useful are peak levels obtained about 30 to 60 minutes after intravenous or intramuscular administration. These are obtained to ensure that the levels produced by therapy are high enough to be effective against the infecting organism. Trough levels, obtained just prior to the next scheduled dose, are useful in guarding against the possibility that the drug is accumulating to toxic levels as therapy proceeds. These determinations are especially useful in checking dosage of antibiotics in newborns, where blood levels may be difficult to predict from published data, and in the treatment of infections in patients with poor renal function, where accumulation of nephrotoxic antibiotics may occur. Simple computer programs are available in many hospitals in which data relative to the patient (age, sex, weight, creatinine clearance, and so forth) and data obtained from several trough levels may be entered to predict whether or not drugs will accumulate to toxic levels and to make recommendations for dosage adjustment.

REFERENCES

Hoeprich, P.D.: Infectious Diseases. 2nd Ed. Harper & Row, Hagerstown, New York, San Francisco, London, 1977.

Knoeman, E.W., Allen, S.D., Dowell, V.R., Jr., and Sommers, H.M.: Color Atlas and Textbook of Diagnostic Microbiology. J.B. Lippincott, Philaelphia and Toronto, 1979.

Mandell, G.L., Douglas, R.G., and Bennett, J.E.: Principles and Practices of Infectious Diseases. John Wiley and Sons, New York, 1979.

O'Connell, C.J.: Laboratory Diagnosis of Infectious Disease. A Guide for Clinicians. 2nd Ed. Medical Examination Publishing, Garden City, 1980.

Top, F.H., Sr., and Wehrle, P.F.: Communicable and Infectious Diseases. 8th Ed. C.V. Mosby, St. Louis, 1976.

Index

"f" following page indicates figure, "t" following page indicates table

Abdominal actinomycosis, 470
A blood group substance, 190–192, 191t
A, B, O alleles, 191t
ABO blood group system, 190–192, 191t, 195
Abortive transduction, 42
Absidia, 476t, 495
Acanthamebiasis, 671t
Acanthamoeba, 642t, 654
Acanthocephala, 673
Acholeplasma, 434
  laidlawii, 435, 435t
Acholeplasmataceae, 435
Acid-fast bacteria (AFB), 95, 445. *See also*
    Mycobacterium; Nocardia
  direct smears for, 455–456
Acid-fast stain, 233
Acquired immunologic tolerance, 121–122, 125
Actinomadura, 505, 506
Actinomyces, 407t, 408t, 465–467, 466t, 473,
    474t, 484, 506. *See also Nocardia*
  bovis, 466, 468
  diseases caused by, 467–470
  israelii, 466, 467f, 468, 469
  naeslundii, 466, 468, 469
  odontolyticus, 466, 468, 469
  viscosus, 466, 468, 469
Actinomycetes. See Actinomyces; Nocardia
Actinomycosis, 468, 469–470
Actinomycotic mycetoma, 505
Active local anaphylaxis, 165
Active systemic anaphylaxis, 164–165, 164f,
    165f
Acute epiglottitis, 700
Acute febrile pharyngitis, 598, 599
Acute hemorrhagic cystitis, 598
Acute lymphocytic leukemia, 209t
Acute poststreptococcal glomerulonephritis,
    268–269
Acute serum sickness, 219–220
Acute uveitis, 209t
ADCC. *See* Antibody-dependent cell-mediated
    cytotoxicity
Addison's disease, 209t
Adenine arabinoside, 632
Adenosine triphosphate (ATP) formation
  inorganic substance oxidation, 32
  oxidative phosphorylation, 31
  photosynthesis, 29–30, 32–33
  substrate level phosphorylation, 29–30

Adenovirus, 520f, 522t, 597–599
  as oncogenic virus, 614–615
  replication, 537–539, 538f
Adhesins, 92
Adjuvants, 217
Aedes, 109t, 112, 571
  aegypti, 570
Aerial mycelium, 478
Aerobic respiration, 30
Aerotolerant anaerobes, 32
African sleeping sickness, 645, 671t
African trypanosomiasis, 639t, 671t
Agar, 6
Agar diffusion disk test for antibiotics,
    238–239
Agar dilution test for antibiotics, 67, 714–715
Agglutination, 116, 150–151, 153
  immunoglobulin M in, 145
  passive agglutination techniques, 237
Aggregate anaphylaxis, 214
Aggresins, 96
Alastrim, 595
Alcohol, bacteriostatic, 79
Alcoholic fermentation, 30, 30f, 31f
Aleuriospores, 479f, 480
Alkylating agents, inactivation and elimination
    by, 76t, 78–79
Alleles, 38, 187, 188. *See also* Gene;
    Haplotype
  A,B,O, 191t
  codominant, 187
  dominant, 187
  expressivity, 187
  H,h, 190, 191t
  Le,le, 191t, 192
  recessive, 187
  Rh system, 192–193, 193t
  Se,se, 190, 191t, 192
Allelic exclusion, 198
Allergy. *See* Hypersensitivity
Alloantigen, 210
Allodermanyssus sanguineus, 510
Allogenic graft, 199, 212
Allograft immunity, 173, 178, 185
Allograft rejection, major histocompatibility
    complex and, 207
Allotype, 144, 197, 198
α chain, 202
α interferon, 628, 628t

Phagosome, 87
Pharyngitis, 266–267, 269–270, 270f
Pharyngoconjunctival fever, 598
Phenol, as disinfectant, 77–78
Phenol coefficient, 77
Phenotype, 37, 187
  frequency, 188
  variation in, 37–38, 38f
Phenotype mixing, in viruses, 532
Phenoxymethyl penicillin (penicillin V), 55
Phenylethyl alcohol, 79
Phialophora, 504
  verrucosa, 503
Phlebotomus, 109t, 112, 112f, 648, 649, 649t
Phlegmonous gastritis, 283
Phorant, 634
Phoresis, 634
Phospholipase A and B, 79
Photoautotrophs, 28
Photoreactivation, 72
Photosynthesis, 32–33
Phthalylsulfathiazole, 63
Phycomycetes, 494
Physicochemical mechanisms, as host defense
  mechanisms, 84
Picornaviridae, 522t, 535, 575–576, 576t. *See
  also Calicivirus; Enterovirus; Rhinovirus*
Piedra, 476t
Piedraia hortai, 476t
Pili, 25, 25f
  sex, 25, 44–46
Pink-eye, 343
Pinworm (*Enterobius vermicularis*), 249, 658,
  674f, 693–694
Piroplasmida, 642t. *See also Babesia.*
Pittsburgh pneumonia agent (PPA), 336–337
Pityriasis versicolor, 476t, 481
Plague, 83t, 316–317
Plaque, dental, 467–468, 469
Plaque assay, 523, 527
Plasma cell, 131, 132f
Plasmid, 35, 36–37
  conjugative, 44–46
  in *Enterobacteriaceae*, 288
Plasmodium, 102t, 642t
  laverania, 642t
    falciparum, 665f, 668–669
    malaria caused by, 669
  plasmodium, 642t, 665 (*see also* Malaria)
    malaria caused by, 83t, 666–668
    malariae, 664t, 665–666, 665f, 666t, 667,
      668
    ovale, 664t, 665–666, 665f, 666t
    vivax, 664t, 665–666, 665f, 666t, 668
Platelet aggregating factor (PAF), 168t, 169
Platelet lytic factor (PLF), 168t, 169
Platyhelminthes, 636, 673, 674–675

blood flukes, 92, 99, 675–676, 676f. *See also
  Schistosoma*
intestinal flukes, 679–680. *See also
  Fasciolopsis*
liver flukes, 680. *See also Clonorchis;
  Fasciola*
lung flukes, 678–679. *See also Paragonimus*
tapeworms, 674f, 681. *See also
  Dibothriocephalus; Echinococcus;
  Hymenolepsis; Taenia*
Pleiotropism, of major histocompatibility
  complex, 206, 210
Plenciz, Marcus Antonius von, 3
Pleurodynia, 580
Pneumococci. *See Streptococcus pneumoniae*
Pneumocystis, 642t, 643
  carinii, 662–663, 662f, 662t
Pneumocystosis, 639t, 671t
Pneumolysin, 279–280
Pneumonia
  aspiration, 409t
  atypical, 277, 663
  bronchopneumonia, 280–281
  gram-negative, 701–702, 702t
  hemolytic streptococci causing, 268
  Legionella spp. causing, 236, 238, 329–337,
    334t, 335f, 702
  lobar, 280
  mycoplasmal, 92–93, 101t, 433, 435,
    436–443, 441f, 700
    immune response in, 438, 441
  in newborn, 517
  parainfluenza viruses causing, 551
  Pseudomonas aeruginosa causing, 326
  respiratory syncytial virus causing, 551
  Streptococcus pneumoniae causing, 280–281
Pneumonic plague, 317
Pneumococcal bacteremia, 281–282
Pneumococcal meningitis, 281
Pneumovirus, 549, 550t
  respiratory syncytial virus infections,
    551–552
Point mutations, 38
pol gene, 620, 622
Poliomyelitis, 575, 576, 576t, 577–578
Poliovirus. *See also Enterovirus*
  classification, 576t
  infections, 577, 578
  replication of, 535, 537
Polyene, 57, 57f
Polymerase protein, of influenza virus, 545t
Polymorphism, 188
  of H-2 complex, 201
  human leukocyte antigen complex system
    and, 204
  of Ia-1 molecules, 202–203
  of major histocompatibility complex, 210

Side-chain theory, of antibody formation, 122t, 123
Silkworm, disease of the, 3, 4
Simian virus, 613
Single diffusion in agar gels, 148–149
Sinusitis, 409t
Site-specific recombination, 40–41, 49f
"606," 7
Sjögren's disease, 209t
Skin
  infections (*see also* specific infections)
    fungal (*see* Fungi)
    hemolytic streptococci causing, 267
    microbiologic tests for, 709–711
  as host defense mechanism, 83, 83t
    parasites overcoming, 92
  lesions, 83t, 258–259
  parasites of, 101t
Skin grafts, 212
Skin reactions
  cell-mediated, 174, 175–176, 175t, 178
  cutaneous basophil hypersensitivity, 173, 176–177, 185
  humoral, 175t, 176
    Arthus reaction, 153, 158, 170–171, 175t, 176, 177, 218–219
Skin tests
  in anaphylaxis, 216
  in delayed hypersensitivity, 185, 223
  dermatophytoses and, 486
  for fungi, 243, 244, 482–483
  for leprosy, 460, 461t
  for tuberculosis, 450–452, 453, 458–459
Sleeping sickness, African, 645, 671t
Slow-reacting substance of anaphylaxis (SRS-A), 168t, 169
slp gene, 203
Smallpox, 2, 8–9, 103, 103t, 593, 595–597, 632
Smoke, disinfection by, 77
Soft chancre, 343
Solid tissue tumors, interferon for, 631
Somatic cell, 188
South American blastomycosis. *See* Paracoccidioidomycosis
Specialized transduction, 49, 50
Specific defense mechanisms, 82, 115. *See also* Host defense mechanisms; Immunology
Specificity
  of antibodies, 126–127, 126f
  of immunologic reactions, 122
  of serodiagnostic tests, 119
Specific macrophage-arming factor (SMAF), 182
Specimens, for microbiologic diagnosis. 229–233, 242–243, 244–246, 245t *See also* specific infections
Spectinomycin, 60, 60f

Spheroplast, 24
Spirillum, 3
Spirochaetaceae, 415–416. *See also Borrelia; Leptospira; Treponema*
Spirochetes, *See Spirochaetaceae*
Spleen, 134–135
  pneumococcal bacteremia and removal of, 281–282
Sporangiospores, 479, 479f
Sporangium, 479, 479f
Spores, 25–26, 26f, 69
  asexual, 478–480, 478f, 479f
Sporogony, 643
Sporothrix, 480
  schenckii, 476t, 479f, 502–503
Sporotrichosis, 476t, 501, 502–503, 711
Sporozoa, 642t. *See also Eimeria; Haemosporina*
Sporozoites, 643
Sporulation, 26, 26f, 69
Spotted fever diseases, 83t, 510
Spumavirus, 617
Sputum, for bacterial infection diagnosis, 230
Squamous cell carcinomas, herpes simplex virus and, 616
src gene, 620, 621, 622
Ss gene, 203
Staining techniques, bacterial infections diagnosis and, 232–233, 240
Staphylococcal enterocolitis, 259
Staphylococcal teichoic acid, test for antibodies against, 699
Staphylococcus, 101t, 251, 260t
  antigens produced by, 252–253, 253t
  A protein, 253
  aureus, 251–258, 253t, 254t, 698–699, 706t, 708
    lysozymes and, 85, 97
    osteomyelitis and, 711t
    peptidoglycan in, 18, 18f, 19f
    toxin produced by, 93t, 94, 253, 254t, 706t
  bacteriophage typing, 256–257
  diseases caused by, 83, 83t, 258–261
  epidemiology, 257–258
  epidermidis, 251–253, 256, 257, 260t, 698, 699
  genetic variation of, 257
  morphology and physiology, 251–252, 252t
  saprophyticus, 260t
    antigens of, 253, 253t
    morphology and physiology, 251, 252
Staphylokinase, 256
Starch hydrolysis, bacterial infection diagnosis with, 235
Stationary growth phase, 27f, 28
Steady state viral infection, 528
Sterilization, 4, 70. *See also* Inactivation and elimination methods

Thermal death point, 76
Thermophilic bacteria, 28, 75
Thom, Charles, 8
Threadworm (*Enterobius vermicularis*), 674f, 693–694
Thrush. *See* Candidiasis
Thymic aplasia (Di George's syndrome), 104, 177–178, 487
Thymus, 134
Thymus dependent lymphatic leukemia, 618, 623–624
Tick, 108t, 110–111, 425–426, 426t
  Dermocentor andersoni, 695
  relapsing fever and, 425–426
  spotted fever diseases transmitted by, 510
  transovarian transmission and, 110
Tick-born relapsing fever, 425–426
Timoni, Emanuel, 8–9
Tinea, 484–486, 485t
  diseases caused by, 83t
Tine tests, 451
Tissue antigen, 217–218
Tissues, damage to in infectious disease, 224–226, 225f (*see also* Immunopathology)
Tissue tropisms, 534
Tobramycin, 59, 60
Todd units, 266
Togaviridae, 521, 522t, 558, 567–568. *See also* *Alphavirus; Flavivirus; Rubivirus*
Toluene, 79
Tong worm, 695
Torulopsis, 483
Torulosis. *See* Cryptococcosis
Toxins. *See also* Hemolysin; Leukocidin; specific organisms
  neutralization of by humoral immunity, 162
  of microorganisms, 93t, 94–95
Toxoids, 95
Toxoplasma, 642t, 643
  gondii, 102t, 659f, 660–662
    cell membrane breakdown by, 93–94
    cysts formed in, 97–98
    fetus infected by, 103t
    neutrophilic granulocytes and, 97
Toxoplasmosis, 661–662, 671t
T phages, 521
TPI test, 423–424
Trachoma, 515–516
Transcriptases, 521
Transduction, 37, 48–50, 49f
  abortive, 42
Transfer factor (TF). 180
Transformation
  bacterial, 42–44, 43f
    in *Streptococcus pneumoniae,* 43, 44
    in *Haemophilus influenzae,* 42
    in *Neisseria* spp., 42

of cells by viruses
  Adenoviruses, 614, 615
  DNA tumor viruses, 604, 607, 613–615
  Herpesviruses, 604, 607, 615–617
  Papovaviruses, 613–615
  RNA tumor viruses, 617–625
  Sarcoma viruses, 622–623
Transitional-phase variants, 444
Translation, interferon and messenger RNA and, 630–631
Translocation, 189
Transovarian transmission, 110
Transpeptidation, 19, 21f
Transplantation immunity, 173, 178, 185
Transport systems, for nutrient transport, 15
Transposons (Tn), 42
Trematodes (flukes). *See Platyhelminthes*
Trench fever, 511
Treponema, 425
  carateum, 424
  pallidum, 83, 83t, 103t, 416–424, 417f, 418f, 419f
  pertenue, 424
  vincentii, 425
Triatomid bug, 108t, 111
Trichinella spiralis, 687f, 688–689, 688f
Trichinosis, 688–689
Trichomonadidae. See Trichomonas
Trichomonal vaginitis, 653–654
Trichomonas, 642t, 643, 671t
  hominis, 654
  vaginalis, 101t, 642t, 653–654, 653f
Trichophyton, 101t, 476t, 485
  mentagrophytes, 475, 476f, 477f, 486
  rubrum, 486
  tonsurans, 486
Trichosporon, 483
  beigelii, 476t
Trichuris trichura, 687–688, 687f
Trimethoprim, 65, 65f
Trombicula akamushi, 695
Trophozoites, 641, 643
Tropical treponematosis, 424
Trypanosoma, 93–94, 102t, 642t, 643, 644t
  cruzi, 111, 646–648, 646f
  gambiense, 644–645, 644f, 644t
  rhodesiense, 644f, 644t, 645–646
Trypanosomatidae, 642t, 643. *See also* *Leishmania; Trypanosoma*
Trypanosomiasis, 639t, 671t
Trypsin, as host defense mechanism, 85
Tsetse fly, *See Glossina*
T strains of cell wall deficient bacteria, 101t
Tsutsugamushi disease, 510
Tubercle bacilli (*Mycobacterium tuberculosis*). *See Mycobacterium*
Tuberculin-type hypersensitivity, 173, 174, 175, 176, 222f

Tuberculoid leprosy, 461, 462
Tuberculosis, 2, 6, 224
  bacilli characteristics, 445–450, 446f, 448t, 449f
  causative agents, 445, 448t
  childhood, 452
  clinical diagnosis, 454–455
  clinical manifestations, 452–454
  epidemiology, 457–458
  extrapulmonary forms, 453, 454
  exudative, 453
  immune response in, 447–448, 452
  laboratory findings, 455–456, 702
  pathogenic mechanisms of, 450–452
  prevention, 458–459
  primary, 453–454
  productive, 453
  pulmonary, 449, 450, 453, 457
  reactivation, 454
  renal, 705
  skin tests for, 120, 450–452, 453, 458–459
  tests for drug susceptibility in, 456
  treatment, 58, 456–457
Tumor immunity, 173, 185
Tumor viruses. See Oncogenic viruses
Tyndallization, 71
Type specific antigens, 618
Typhoidal tularemia, 358
Typhoid fever, 116, 119, 302–305, 303t, 304t
Typhus fever, 83t, 508–509

Ultrasonic waves, cellular disintegration by, 73
Ultraviolet light, inactivation by, 72–73
Ultraviolet spectroscopy, 240
Undecaprenylmonophosphate, 56
Unitarian theory, of antibody formation, 117
Universal blood donor, 195
Ureaplasma, 435, 435t
  urealyticum, 433, 435, 435t, 436, 441, 442
Urinary tract infections, 410t. See also specific infections; Urogenital tract
  adenovirus and, 598
  enterococci and, 272
  Escherichia coli and, 296–297
  microbiologic tests for, 704–705
  Proteus and, 313
Urine
  bacterial infections diagnosed with, 229–230
  fungal infections diagnosed with, 243
  viral infections diagnosed with, 245t
Urogenital tract. See also Urinary tract infections; Venereal diseases
  chlamydial infections of, 516
  host defense mechanisms at, 100t
  pathogens of, 101t

Uterine myonecrosis septicemia, 398
Uterus, 410t
  clostridial infections in, 398

Vaccination, 10. See also Immunizations and vaccination
Vaccinia gangrenosa, 597
Vaccinia virus, 83t, 245t, 593–594, 594f
Valley bumps. See Coccidioidomycosis
Vancomycin, 56–57, 86
Van der Waals-London forces, 146–147
Varicella, 604, 605–606
Varicella-zoster virus (VZV), 245t, 601, 605–606
Variola major, 593, 594, 595–597
Variola minor, 595
Variolation, 8–9
Variola virus, 102t, 593, 594, 595–597. See also Smallpox
VDRL test, 423
Vegetative mycelium, 478
Vegetative virus, 519
  replication, 49
Veillonella, 407t, 408t, 414
Venereal diseases (Sexually transmitted diseases, STD)
  chancroid, 343, 714
  chlamydial infections, 516
  condylomata acuminata, 631
  cytomegalovirus, 607
  disseminated gonococcemia, 713
  gonorrhea, 60, 361, 363t, 367–371, 368f, 369t, 371f, 372, 712
  Haemophilus ducreyi and, 343
  herpes simplex virus 2, 603, 631
  lymphogranuloma venerum, 515, 714
  microbiologic tests for, 712–714
  pelvic inflammatory disease, 713
  syphilis, 1, 2, 7, 83t, 416–424, 417f, 418f, 419f, 713–714
    asymptomatic, 419
    congenital, 416, 420
    early, 418
    endemic, 424
    late, 419–420
    latent, 420
    primary, 418, 419, 419f
    secondary, 418–419, 419f
    tertiary, 419
    tests for, 418, 419, 422–424, 713–714
    Wassermann test, 418, 419, 422–423
Venezuelen equine encephalitis (VEE), 568–569
Verrucous dermatitis. See Chromoblastomycosis
Vertical spread of infection, 102